Climate Change and Stress Management :

Sheep and Goat Production

Climate Change and Stress Management :

SHEEP AND GOAT PRODUCTION

Editors:

S. A. KARIM, ANIL JOSHI, S.K. SANKHYAN
A.K. SHINDE, D.B. SHAKYAWAR, S.M.K. NAQVI
AND B.N. TRIPATHI

SSPH

SATISH SERIAL PUBLISHING HOUSE

403, Express Tower, Commercial Complex, Azadpur, Delhi-110033 (India)
Phone : 011-27672852, Fax : 91-11-27672046
E-mail :info@satishserial.com, hkjain1975@yahoo.com
Website : www.satishserial.com

Published by :

SATISH SERIAL PUBLISHING HOUSE
403, Express Tower, Commercial Complex, Azadpur, Delhi-110033 (INDIA)
Phone : 011-27672852 Fax : 91-11-27672046
E-mail : info@satishserial.com, hkjain1975@yahoo.com

Reprint, 2020

ISBN 81-89304-81-X

Composed, Designed & Printed in India

Foreword

Small ruminants, sheep and goats, play an important role in livelihood and economic sustenance of resource poor farmers in semiarid, arid, hilly and mountainous region of the country. India is bestowed with 62 million sheep and 124 million goats which contribute significantly towards meat, milk and fibre production. These animals survive under low input system depending mostly on seasonal grasses, foliage and crop straw etc.

As goats and sheep are primarily raised on grazing resources under extensive range management, they are exposed to wide range of climatic and nutritional stresses which affect the growth, reproduction, production and health of animals. In prevailing situation of progressive shrinkage of grazing resources, poor nutrition, climate change reflected in erratic precipitation and temperature regime, feed and water scarcity, long distance migration, poor *en route* shelter and early disposal of lambs are a matter of major concern which need to be addressed in a holistic manner. Development of mitigation and adaptation strategies due to impending climate change coupled with appropriate health cover is the need of the hour and has to be addressed on priority.

It is apt that the Indian Society for Sheep and Goat Production and Utilization (ISSGPU) is organizing a National Seminar on Stress Management in Small Ruminant Production and Product Processing in collaboration with Central Sheep and Wool Research Institute (CSWRI), Avikanagar and Central Institute of Research on Goat (CIRG), Makhdoom to discuss some of these issues and develop a road map involving different players to enhance production and productivity of small ruminants to enhance income of resource poor farmers who rear small ruminants.

I am happy that the organizers are bringing out a compendium on this occasion which could be useful for different stake holders. I compliment the organizers and wish the event all success.

Dated the 6th January, 2010
New Delhi

(S. Ayyappan)
Secretary, Department of Agricultural
Research & Education and
Director General, Indian Council of Agricultural Research
Ministry of Agriculture, Krishi Bhavan, New Delhi - 110 114

Preface

Sheep and goats are among the major economically important livestock in the country. There are about 64.26 million sheep and 125.45 million goats in the country, playing an important role in the livelihood of resource-poor farmers. They provide meat, milk, skin, hair, fibre and manure for cash, security, gifts, religious rituals, medicine, etc. Very often, small ruminants are described as the village bank. The contribution of livestock sector to the Gross State Domestic Product is 2.88 % and to the agriculture and allied activities it is 25.70 %. Sheep contribute 234456 tonnes of the meat, 45.90 million kg of the wool and 57960 tons of the skins. Goats, on the other hand, provide 4.00 million kg milk, 543000 tons of meat and 129960 tons of fresh skins. Small ruminants substantially contribute in the national economy to the tune of 30% to GNP.

The demand of meat and fibre is increasing in the country and it would be double by 2050 due to ever increasing population of human beings. Simultaneously livestock population is also increasing where goat population is increasing exponentially in almost all the regions of the country. However the grazing lands, which ensure major source of forage to small ruminants are declining sharply leading land degradation, climate change, water and biodiversity loss. Climate change adversely affecting (i) forage yield and quality from grazing lands (ii) provoking early disposal of lambs for slaughter due to feed and fodder scarcity (iii) declining of flock size and (iv) shifting of traditional people to some other occupations. The problems surrounding small ruminants' production cannot be considered in isolation. Economic, social, health and environmental perspectives will be critical to solving some of these problems. We hope to develop a greater understanding of these complex issues so that we may encourage policies and practices to reduce the adverse effects of livestock production, while ensuring that humans are fed and natural resources are preserved, today and in the future. Small ruminants are exposed to wide range of stresses under field existence namely thermal, walking, and nutritional, predation, frights etc. Earlier feeding, breeding, health and management are considered the major factor responsible for improving production, however in the recent past more attempts are require to look into well being of animals including stress management with changing climate and market.

The organization of National Seminar on Stress Management in Small Ruminant Production and Product Processing to discuss, deliberate and present various issues pertaining to small ruminants production in present scenario of climate and market change and developing suitable strategies for mitigating its adverse effect is need of hours. We take an opportunity to thanks the scientific and technical staffs of the Institute and all others who have contributed reference papers for the book published on the occasion of National Seminar.

We hope the reference book will be useful to students, researchers, educationists, developmental officers and all other who are directly or indirectly related to small ruminants production.

Editors

Contents

❏❏❏

1

Stress Management in Small Ruminants for Sustainable Production

S.A. Karim and M.K. Tripathi
Central Sheep and Wool Research Institute,
Avikanagar (via- Jaipur), Rajasthan, India 304 501

Introduction

Achieving environmental sustainability and social acceptance for small ruminant production system require research and development approaches to harness the beneficial environmental impacts on livestock production addressing community concerns on livestock and livestock products. In order to develop better understanding of key stressors and stress-management in animals and provide the component knowledge needed to design production systems to meet community expectations, technologies are to be developed and disseminated. The need of the day is to develop technologies contributing to resource sustainability in fragile marginal grazing lands/degraded environment or to enhance environmental quality in production. The animal welfare is the key issue during stress which regulates animal productivity.

The stress can be defined, when "minimal total comfort" of the animal is compromised by surrounding biotic or abiotic factors and animal experience discomfort known as stress. The stressors such as environmental, nutritional, physiological, and metabolic or transition create discomfort to the animal system. These factors induce intake controlling signals mediated through central nervous system and, thus 'discomfort' alters the optimal supply of a nutrient and balances that in turn influence animal health, production and well being. The exposure of sheep to elevated ambient temperatures induces an increase in the dissipation of excess body heat to negate the excessive heat load. Dissipation of excess body heat is excluded by evaporation of water from the respiratory tract and skin surface via panting and sweating, respectively. Sweating in woolly sheep is much less effective due to the presence of the wool cover. With the elevation in environmental temperature, a high proportion of heat is also dissipated in conductive heat loss via the ears and legs. Under situation where the physiological mechanisms of the animal fail to negate the excessive heat load, the core/rectal temperature increases. At the same time, such exposure of sheep to heat stress evokes a series of drastic changes in the biological functions, which include decrease in feed intake and utilization, disturbances in water, protein, energy and mineral balances, enzymatic reactions, hormonal secretions and blood metabolites. Recent studies indicate that the supra chiasmatic nucleus (SCN) regulates the circadian and seasonal rhythms of most biological functions, particularly the reproductive functions and behaviour in mammals. The regulation includes the phasic and tonic release of hormones, oestrus and in some cases, gonadal size. This is due to the fact that there is evidence suggesting that the SCN is sensitive to changes in ambient temperature with some cells being more responsive to cold and others more responsive to heat, although photoperiodic changes may also have a strong influence. Therefore, exposure of sheep to elevated ambient temperature negatively affects the biological functions which are reflected in the impairment of their production and reproduction traits (Marai et al., 2007). The over riding facts remain that under stress full environment the priority of the animals is to survive as a result the energy is diverted from production to priority function of thermolysis.

Small ruminants have adaptability to wide range of environmental conditions. On exposure to harsh hot climate, these animals try to avoid the extra heat load activating their metabolic process in order to maintain homeothermy. During heat stress, feed consumption decreases, while drinking increases (Silanikove, 1992) and weight gain slower down, which is parallel to feed consumption and net nutrient balance. Additionally, the animals strive hard while attempting to balance body temperature, which in turn increases their energy need (Rout et al., 2002). Heat stress is caused by a combination of environmental factors, such as air temperature, relative humidity, incident and reflected radiation and wind speed. When exposed to hot ambient temperatures, animals increase their respiration rate and body temperature or adjust their behaviour in an attempt to maintain thermal balance (Regula et al., 2004). Lowered food consumption is a well-known effect of heat stress resulting in sub-optimal production. Lowering and preventing heat stress for increasing performances in the summer requires the protection from incident and radiated heat and raising the loss of heat from body to environment (Rosen, 1992). In hot climates, small ruminants get rid of the extra heat occurring depending on their metabolic activities, in order to maintain their core temperature by activating physiological mechanisms. If the core temperature continues to rise despite these mechanisms, the sheep/goats experience heat stress. Small ruminants inhabiting hot arid and desert environment have acquired various adaptation mechanisms that benefit them in enduring the water deficiency. They have evolved high water economy and utilize their body water more efficiently which results in the maintenance of dry matter intake and production during the terms of water scarcity (Silanikove, 1994). This could be enhanced during heat stress. Small ruminants are considered highly suitable animals for rearing in the stressed areas, as they were the first domesticated in the hot and arid regions of the world. They may encounter periods of lack of water, notably during the dry summer season, and proceed into a state of dehydration for several days. A number of reports have documented the capability of sheep/goat tolerating dehydration (Silanikove, 1994, 2000). During periods of water shortage, sheep/goats activate several water saving mechanisms that would result in minimizing their water losses and therefore increasing their capability to withstand water deficit. They possess a higher capability to alleviate the detrimental effects of limited water availability and therefore, their performance is maintained. Goats has capability to maintain productive performance up to a 50 % water restriction during heat exposure though a mechanism of economizing body water and maintain new water balance with the advance of restriction (Alamer, 2009). However, as a general rule, the negative effects of water deprivation and heat stress override the benefits from increased feed utilization. Goats, having poor insulation capacity, and sheep, with excellent insulation capacity, represent two physiological models. Darcan and Cankaya

The physiological basis of each type of stress is different, however effects of stress on animal welfare and productivity effect is mediated by modification of the food intake. Heat load effect is mediated through elevation of body temperature and secondarily through increase in gut fill, which reduces feed intake. The response to heat stress is more diverse, since heat load affects both the energy and water metabolism, and varies due to differences among ruminants in insulation properties and body size. Water restriction does not disturb plasma tonicity and its effect is mediated by modification of the food-related drinking. Water deprivation effects are mediated through elevation of plasma osmolarity and secondarily through increase in gut fill and ruminal

Na concentration. As water scarcity and high temperatures are characteristic of dry areas, interactions exist between these two factors. The stress induced by infrequent drinking, water restriction, and heat load in ruminants reduce appetite and increase feed utilization. Reduction in rumen motility, rumination activity and saliva secretion reduce passage rate, and hence increase the digestibility of structural carbohydrates. However, contrary to a commonly held view, these digestive responses are directly related to the imposed stress, rather than secondarily related to reduction in feed intake. Although water deprivation, water restriction and heat load similarly affect appetite and digestion, whereas as a general rule, the negative effects of water deprivation and heat stress override the benefits from increased feed utilization. Dehydration due to water restriction or deprivation decreases feed intake with the lengthening of the period of dehydration, increase the apparent digestibility of dry matter, and the consume only the amount of feed which is needed to satisfy their maintenance requirements (Silanikove, 1985). Recovery of displaced core body temperature, is accomplished by utilizing several adjustments in certain thermoregulatory parameters. The increase in respiration rate is believed to mediate an increase in the respiratory evaporative cooling. Furthermore, the increase in heart rate and skin temperature suggests changes in the hemodynamics and blood flow from the splanchnic to peripheral cutaneous regions in order to dissipate the accumulating internal heat load. Under confined environment, in addition to increased water volume and frequency, animals shift their feed intake to night time instead o day time (Al-Tamimi, 2007). To prevent this, some measures which are related to improving the management, such as keeping the animals in shaded areas, ventilation, showering and making them drink coldwater, have to be taken (Yousef, 1987). Beede and Collier (1986) reported that, in order to prevent heat stress, animals which are well adapted to hot climates should be chosen, better feeding conditions should be provided and barn management should be readjusted for hot climate conditions. Knizkova et al. (2002) modified microclimatic factors in the barn by opening and closing sidewall plastic curtains.

Effect of Heat stress

In many parts of the world, small ruminants are the preferred ruminant species over other ruminant livestock, because of better tolerance and performance under harsh environments, especially in predominantly arid and semi-arid ecologies. Excessive heat stress may cause hyperthermia and potentially have several physiological side effects and economical impacts on the animal production systems. These include the aberration of reproductive functions (Roth et al., 2002), oxidative stress and enzymatic dysfunction (David et al., 2001), electrolyte imbalances (Augustinsson et al., 1986; West et al., 1991), reduced meat quality (Kadima et al., 2004), and eventually severe economical losses resulting from increased mortalities and decreased overall animal performance. Animals of dry regions have ability of some extent to heat tolerance, especially to chronic thermal and solar exposure. The tropical sheep breeds rely more on cutaneous evaporation while the temperate breeds depend more on respiratory ventilation for thermolysis. The sheep through centuries of adaptation to under feeding and negative energy balance for most part of the year rely more on cutaneous evaporation as predominant mode of heat dissipation which is known to cost four times less energy than respiratory ventilation (Karim, 1991). To facilitate the process of cutaneous evaporative cooling the tropical sheep breeds have open type coarse wool traits. The goats acquire homeothermy following chronic exposure to solar heat via harmonized thermoregulatory mechanisms, e.g. the adjustment of respiratory evaporative cooling and blood redistribution and a subsequent increase in the peripheral blood flow with a modification in feeding and water intake patterns (Hales, 1971; Al-Tamimi, 2007), and the suppression of thermogenic hormone production (Baccari et al., 1983). In multiple behavioural adaptive mechanisms, the change in posture and reduced muscular activity in addition to changing the pattern of feed and water intake (Brosh et al., 1998; Mitlöhner et al., 2002) play a major role.

The animals chronically exposed to heat manifest a series of adaptive measures viz. longer extremities to maintain distance from the heated ground to avoid long wave radiation and migration in search of food and water, extended body surface area to facilitate heat dissipation, open type of fleece cover to facilitate cutaneous evaporation, lustrous coat cover to reflect incident solar radiation etc. Moreover survival of the sheep in hot critical region has enabled them to evolve highly efficient nutrient selectivity in rangeland. The random pasture samples during summer months has as low as 4 % CP while by intensive selection on plants parts rich in protein, the CP content of mouth grab and oesophageal cannula have as high as 10-11 % CP (Sankhyan et al., 1999). Moreover our experience shows that it is energy which is critical while lower DMI during summer results in both CP and energy deficiency requiring extraneous supplementation. In general the reports emerging from temperate location indicate reduction in nutrient digestibility under heat exposure (Shibata and Mukai,1977) while those from hot region like India indicate that nutrient utilization improved under such situation (Singh et al., 1983; Karim, 1990). The Indian sheep have ability to reabsorb water from GI tract at a faster pace to meet the thermolytic requirement hence the retention time of digesta in GI tract increase under heat exposure with general improvement in nutrient digestibility except fiber fraction which reduces because of faster reticulo-ruminal washout. In this context sheep and goat differ: with lesser total gut length and higher retention time, the goats exhibit better nutrient digestibility than sheep. Moreover the goat diet is predominantly browse species which are succulent and nutritious while sheep subsist on fibrous diets (Devendra, 1990). Moreover the sheep is close grazer and soil ingestion during summer months accounts for 30% of DMI as a result the denture undergoes rapid withering with sloughing of gastro intestinal epithelium resulting in reduced nutrient digestibility and negative protein balance (Shinde et al., 2004).

Energy expenditure of stall fed rams under protection in comfortable weather condition is 70 kcal/kgw$^{0.75}$ while it increases by 43% in field existence due to involved exercise, heat load and solar radiation effects. Energy budgeting of rams in different seasons indicated that during monsoon winter and summer the energy requirement was 78, 15 and 33% higher compared to stall fed sheep (Shinde, 1996). Further the ME intake was deficit by 46 and 26% of the requirement in monsoon and summer where it was 42% higher then the requirement in the winter season. It is also a fact that the core temperature heat stressed animals remain 2-3°C above normal resulting in 20 to 30% increase in energy expenditure due to Vant Hoff effect.

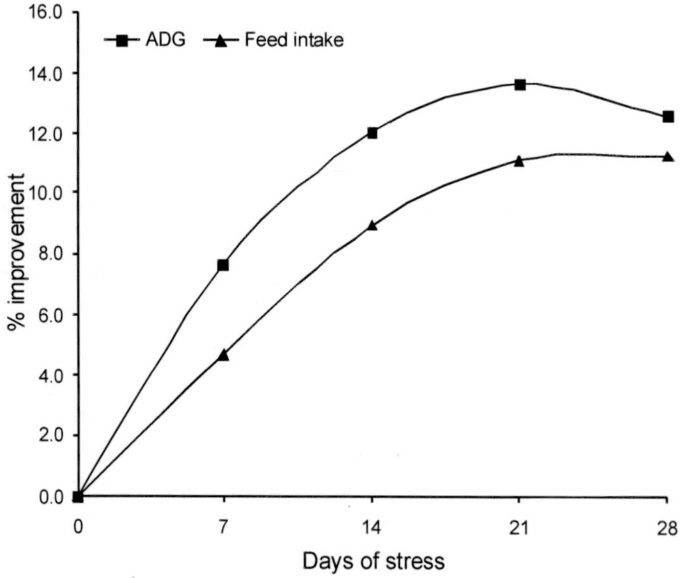

Fig. 1. Effect of added supplementation of organic Zn and Mn on improvement of daily gain (ADG) and feed intake (FI) during stress. Improvement can be predicted using the polynomial equations

Feed intake (% improvement) = -1.634 + (1.049*day of stress) + (-0.021* day of stress^2); R=0.726
Daily gain (% improvement) = 0.514 + (1.214*day of stress) + (-0.028* day of stress^2); R=0.699

The situation in farmers' field is different then what is observed in the protected rangeland. The CPR which is main stay for grazing and survival of farmer animal is grossly over stocked by 5 to 50 times in different locations then the carrying capacity of the land. Hence the animals experience deficit nutritional regimen round the year compelling the farmers to migrate with their stock to the neighbouring state in search of food and water.

Management of physiological stress

The studies on nutrition environment interaction conducted over last 4 decade at the station indicated that native breeds are most adapted to hot conditions while the animals with exotic inheritance were vulnerable and that the response of crossbreds was in between. The studies conducted to assess relative performance of native and crossbred sheep as well as goats under graded nutritional stress during summer and winter months indicated that nutritional stress during winter was a greater stress then summer. Moreover the goats and native sheep with lower body reserves lost more weight and required longer period to regain lost weight on realimentation (Karim and Rawat, 1996).

In arid and semi-arid tropical environment extreme ambient temperature are being experienced, which may be elevate up to 48°C during summer and may drop below 3°C during winter: small ruminant maintained on grazing are therefore exposed to environmental and nutritional stressors (Maurya et al., 2004). Animals exposed to hot environment manifest a significant increase in physiological responses to counter balance heat stress. Increased physiological reactions, decreased voluntary feed intake, fiber digestibility, thyroid function, blood insulin and increase in cortisol etc have been observed during heat stress in small ruminants. The consequences of these changes are the decreased production and reproductive functions of animals under stress. The reproductive functions of the sheep are drastically affected by thermal stress because it has deleterious effect on oestrus incidences, oestrus intensity and embryo production (Naqvi et al., 2004). Thermal stress is known to reduce the circulating estradiol-17â concentration with consistent increase in adrenocorticotropin secretion, which in turn blocks the estradiol induced oestrus behaviour (Doney et al., 1973). The reproductive behaviour of the animals in the environment in which they are kept should be fine-tuned to produce maximum number of offspring most efficiently (Lindsay, 1996). Heat stress is revealed by the inability of animals to cope with its environment, a phenomenon that is often reflected to achieve full genetic potential (Dobson and Smith, 2000). To maintain optimum reproductive performance nutritional stress could be minimized during hot or cold stresses. Heat stress is known to reduce feed intake but increases water intake, while reverse affects are of cold stress. Advanced pregnant animals require greater feed intake to satisfy higher nutrient need to growing foetus, however, during this physiological stage animal reduces feed intake, which imposes reproductive stress. Nutritional stress in pregnant and male animals could be managed through supply of high quality low quantity diets. Similarly, electrolyte balance must be kept with the required normal circulation levels through supplementation during hot or cold stress. Srikandakumar et al. (2003) reported that sheep were able to maintain a normal acid-base balance when heat stress increased their rectal temperature and respiratory rate and that Omani sheep is more heat tolerant than Merino sheep, therefore, different breeds have varying ability to cope with heat stress. An interesting result was noted on analysing performance data of temperate sheep breeds over four decades of their existence in a semiarid environment. Birth weight, a trait relatively protected from environmental variables, of temperate breeds like Dorset, Suffolk, Rambouillet, Merino reduced significantly over the generation intervals and year of rearing indicating that these breeds adapted to the stress full environment on the cost of production (Singh and Karim, 1995).

Management of transit stress

The marketing and transportation systems used for live animal trading of small ruminants results in excessive loss of micronutrient due to environmental and fear stresses, which modifies the hormonal and other body balances. This stress may result a shrink of 9.3 % in live weight within 24 hr of transit because of reduced feed intake by 50 % (Galyean et al., 1995). These stresses impair animal performance during and post transits due to reduced dry matter intake, increased rectal temperature, lower body weight and increased susceptibility toward infections especially respiratory (Chirase et al., 1994). Body balance of Zn and Mn are related to ability of animal to cope with infections and stress. Transportation stress of animals up to 2500 km can be minimized by additional supplementation of methionine-Zn-Mn complex providing added supplement of each Zn and Mn 50 mg/kg diet, improved dry matter intake, rectal temperature and body weight gain, and immunity for bovine respiratory disease (Chirase and Greene, 2001). The improved daily gain and feed intake are predicted, using polynomial estimates. Therefore, dietary organic Zn and Mn combination supplement mitigates transit stress. Supplementation of antioxidant nutrients such as vitamin E, â-carotene, selenium, copper, zinc and manganese are important in protecting an animal's tissues from oxidative destruction, due to an improved immune response which decreases infectious disease incidences arising in stressed animals following shipping (Nockels, 1996).

Management of oxidative stress

Oxidative stress arises when there is an imbalance between radical-generating and radical scavenging activity; it may therefore cause an increase in oxidation products and cell damage. Stress may precede an infectious episode in animals by decreasing antioxidants needed later by an active immune response. Antioxidant nutrients such as vitamin E, â-carotene and the trace elements selenium, copper, zinc and manganese in enzymes are very important in protecting an animal's tissues from oxidative destruction (Nockels, 1996). Lipid peroxidation is a general mechanism whereby free radicals induce toxic products and tissue damage, and is implicated under several diverse pathological conditions (Halliwell and Chirico, 1993). Increased free radical generation and enhanced lipid peroxidation were demonstrated in whole animal and cell culture models of Cu deficiency (Uriu-Adams and Keen, 2005). Lower feed intake and excessive loss of body water may alter micro mineral balance in stressed animals, that may posse oxidative stress due to accumulation of reactive oxygen. Saleh et al. (2008) reported that plasma Cu level of above 9 µmol/l required for counteracting erythrocytic oxidative damage secondary to impaired oxidant defences in grazing sheep. Se-yeast supplementation 0.3 mg/lamb had positive effects on performance lamb meat quality. Selenium contributes to enzymes involved in thyroid hormone metabolism, specifically the conversion of T4 to T3. Also, a protection of biological membranes against oxidation by hydrogen peroxide and other oxidizing agents, *e.g.*, free radicals, superoxide and organic hydroxiperoxide induced by selenium, might be related with the cortisol reduction (Domínguez-Vara et al., 2009).

Thermal stress may disrupt male harmonious interaction of gametogenic and endocrine testicular activity, which are responsible for the production of spermatozoa and seminal plasma, thus effecting spermatogenesis and steroidogenesis to different degrees. The stage of spermatogenesis that is most susceptible to elevated temperature is the primary spermatocytes although damage to B spermatogonia can occur and prolonged exposure to heat can damage dividing spermatocytes and spermatids. Heat stress occurs when the scrotum is not able to reduce the temperature of the testicles below normal body temperature, which also cause oxidative stress. Oxidative stress in semen can be minimised by a tris-based extender containing the antioxidants hypotaurine (5 mM) and cysteamine (5 mM), and an amino acid solution (13 %), increases sperm motility, and decreases total abnormality rates in comparison to the control group. The antioxidants hypotaurine and cysteamine decreased super oxide dismutase activity when compared to an amino acid supplementation (Bucak et al., 2009).

Nutritional management of stress

Nutritional management is one of the practices proposed to alleviate both the extension and severity of stress in animals. Animal under stress modulates mineral balance. Heat stressed animals suffer electrolyte alterations, which can produce negative mineral balance, decreasing serum electrolyte level and voluntary nutrient ingestion; thus, reducing production per food unit (Phillips and Piggins, 1992). Heat stress decreases performance in tropical and subtropical animals.

Management of electrolyte balance during heat stress

At environmental temperatures above 30 °C, additional Na in the diet is necessary because this mineral is lost through sweating (NRC, 2001) and heat stress increased urinary Na excretion (Tsuda et al., 1991), even with the use of amounts above nutritional needs, negative Na and Zn balances occurred indicating that Zn metabolism can also be affected by environmental temperature. In experiments on heat stress, more attention should be devoted to Zn balance because this mineral is important for the integrity of the immune system. Heat-stressed animals decrease feed ingestion (as a means to decrease metabolic heat), and thereby ingest lower amounts of energy. Although mineral levels did not change significantly in the blood, heat stress affected this profile for P, Na, K and Zn. Supplementation of sodium bicarbonate in lambs fed high concentrate diet also reduce stress imposed due to acidosis and improve animal performance (Tripathi et al., 2004). NRC recommended dietary concentration of Na above 0.18 % DM during heat stress because of low dietary Na intake has been attributed to a reduction in DM intake, increased urine Na excretion due to an increase in bicarbonate ion ($HCO3_{-)}$ excretion caused by respiratory alkalosis (West et al., 1991), to compensate for losses due to an increased rate of sweating (Schneider et al., 1986) under heat stress. Therefore, as with other nutrients, a higher dietary Na concentration is required to maintain a recommended minimum daily intake (Sanchez et al., 1994). Granzin and Gaughan (2002) recommended feeding of additional NaCl on grazing during warm humid conditions and suggested a final dietary Na concentration of 0.55 %, feeding additional NaCl can cause a partitioning of energy towards live weight gain. Monensin supplementation modifis Mg and Zn serum levels according to the environmental temperature. Monensin changed the serum levels of Ca, Na and P in beef cattle fed high-concentrate diets (Duff et al., 1994). Monensin supplementation to heat-stressed growing animals decreases the concentration of some minerals in faeces and urine; however, apparent absorption and retention increases in others. These results support the hypothesis of the Darden et al. (1985) that mineral metabolism in young growing animals, probably, is more sensitive to supplementation with ionophores. According to Phillips and Piggins (1992), heat stress increases the total excretion of all minerals. Therefore, monensin saves some minerals from excretion in young heat-stressed ruminants, thus, making them available for metabolism and probably decreases disturbances caused by the deficiency of these minerals. Salles et al. (2008) evaluated influence of monensin on mineral balance, which are modulated by environmental temperature. This study examined the effect of monensin and temperature on macro (Ca, P, Na, K and Mg) and micromineral (Cu and Zn) balance in feedlot animals. Supplementation of monensin alleviates environmental temperature induced mineral balance and metabolism modulation. Supplementation of the monensin (33 mg/ kg diet DM) improved the balance of several minerals in heat stressed animals by increasing apparent retention of P, Na and K, and also by decreasing Ca fecal excretion and urine excretion of P, Na, K, Mg and Zn. This in turn improved animal performance.

Probiotics effect in heat stress

Few studies have examined effects of *S. cerevisiae* culture as nutritional supplements to heat stressed animals. Bruno et al. (2009) determined effects of feeding a culture of *Saccharomyces cerevisiae* on lactation performance during heat stress. Daily temperature, humidity and the THI did not change but reduced rectal temperature of cows in the control and SC treatments differed with days postpartum. Intake of DM was similar between diets, but cows fed SC produced more milk, more milk true protein, solids-not-fat and lactose than that produced by control cows. Feeding SC did not influence plasma metabolites, insulin, or body condition score of cows, but urea N concentrations were reduced. Feeding a yeast culture of *S. cerevisiae* improved yields of milk and milk components in heat-stressed cows. It has been suggested that fungal cultures *Aspergillus oryzae* feeding to animals exposed to high ambient temperatures reduce signs of heat stress, such as rectal temperature and respiration rate, and improve lactation performance (Huber et al., 1994). Recently, feeding a culture of *S. cerevisiae* to mid-lactation dairy cows during summer had no effects on yields of energy-corrected milk (ECM) and on DM intake, but improved efficiency (Schingoethe et al., 2004), which suggests that yeast culture can benefit ruminants subjected to heat stress. Tripathi et al. (2008) and, Tripathi and Karim (2008) also reported improved performance of lambs on supplementation of liquid yeast cultures during pre- and post weaning phase of growth under hot semi-arid climate. Al-Saiady et al. (2004) reported that chaelated-Cr supplementation reduces heat stress and increases feed intake and milk production. Se-yeast combined Cr-yeast supplementation 0.3 mg/lamb, had positive effects on performance and carcass composition of finishing lambs. These Cr and Se sources modified blood hormones and metabolites which could improve lamb meat quality (Domínguez-Vara et al., 2009). Selenium contributes to enzymes involved in thyroid hormone metabolism, specifically the conversion of T4 to T3. The effect of Cr in the immune system is related to cholesterol and its role in the metabolism of protein and lipids.

Others Nutritional approaches

Feeding some fat also reduces the heat stress in sheep and goat as the heat of increment of fat is less than that of carbohydrate and protein in ruminants. As a result of feeding supplementary fat dietary energy density is increased and heat load of the animal is reduced during heat stress. Supplementation of 26 g/kg diet added palmitic acid reduced adverse effects of heat stress (Warntjes et al., 2008). Supplementary feeding of fat have been shown to improved daily gain in heat stressed lamb and have no effect on growth hormone, cortisol, rectal temperature and respiration rate. But feeding hydrolyzed animal fat changes the milk fat composition and increase the calcium requirement.

Providing ascorbic acid to heat stressed lamb lower the respiration rate and rectal temperature than control lamb and prevents the changes in PCV, Hb and serum total protein. It also increases serum thyroxin and decreased cortisol-indicating improvement of heat tolerance in lamb. Use of natural shed and iodine supplementation improved the fertility of tropical Merino ewes and this effect was most pronounced when ambient temperature was higher. Similarly supplementation of iodine for the first 7- 10 days after lambing in shaded ewes have higher pregnancy rate than un-shaded and un supplemented ewes.

Management of water and feed scarcity stress

Water and feed scarcity poses stress on animals because of poor availability of the two cause discomfort and animal losses their productive performance. Drinking water is often a limiting factor for livestock in grazing areas of the semiarid and arid region. During the dry season animals have to tolerate a stress condition due to high temperatures and low food and water availability. The lack of water consumption due to a decreased food intake affects water loss and body weight (Abdelatif et al., 1994; More and Sahni, 1981). Most mammals can die if the body water loss is higher than 15 % instead ruminants and specially sheep can tolerate a water loss greater than 20 % (Jaber et al., 2004) because the fore stomach is able to accumulate water to use it in periods of low water supply. Sheep can tolerate dehydration and restricted feeding during summer (More et al., 1983; Alamer and Al-Hozab, 2004). Water restriction 20 to 40 % in intensively maintained sheep did not affect milk production and growth performance in sheep (Casamassima et al., 2008). Further, water deprivation up to 48 hr does not adversely affect feed intake and nutrient digestibility in non-producing adult goats (Misra and Singh, 2003) under hot semiarid environment.

Above stresses are mainly due to poor precipitation pattern termed as drought. Meteorologically a drought is a situation when the deficiency of rainfall at a meteorological sub-division level is 25 per cent or more of the long-term average (LTA) of that sub-division for a given period. The drought is considered "moderate", if the deficiency is between 26 and 50 per cent, and "severe" if it is more than 50 per cent. The agricultural drought is said to occur when soil moisture and rainfall are inadequate during the crop-growing season to support healthy crop growth to maturity. It occurs when there is severe meteorological drought with a rainfall deficiency of more than 50 per cent. The severity of drought depends by the region's ability to cope. The success of preventive or mitigating strategies depends on the strength and effectiveness of socio-political and economic institutions, as well as the relative reliability of the weather forecasting. Daily water consumption (per head) by sheep and goats ranges between 2 to 8 litres, however, it increases with an increase in size of animals, dry matter intake and temperature. Extremely hot weather could increase 20 to 30 percent water requirement. Unavailability of clean drinking water for animals remains major problem in drought hit areas. During drought condition the pasture vegetation deplete and concurrent higher stocking density results in under feeding and low plane of nutrition. Livestock ordinarily avoid toxic/less nutritious plants, but during a drought, animals are forced to eat them. Such problems may be aggravated by deficiencies of phosphorus or vitamin A in livestock, which greatly alter their grazing behaviour. At times animals consume plants high in anti-nutritional/ toxic principles. There are traditional and modern improved methods for efficient rainwater harvesting, which can be adopted for location-specific environments and needs. Given the increasing scarcity of water and frequency of calamities, rainwater harvesting may prove to be the only feasible solution in the rural areas. Effective watershed development is another strategy for the soil and water conservation measures to regenerate the process of vegetation development in drought prone area. The measures taken are both engineering and vegetative in nature. However, in highly degraded lands, before regeneration programme to stabilize the slopes and create conditions conductive to plant growth by arresting fine soil and improve moisture status needed. Constructing temporary check dams or gabion check dams can do gully stabilisation. The plantation of vegetation, in catchments is simultaneously done. The choice of species should aim not only re-greening of the area but to rehabilitate the site ecology in a way that ensure sustainable utilization of eco-system components. Therefore plant species adapted to local conditions, that provide quick green cover and bind soil, have fast growth, can fix nitrogen and have social and economic value to local population and capable to provide fuel/fodder will be best choice. Plantation of grasses and legume mixtures for quick initial establishment of vegetative cover in problem land is necessary. However, for sustainable water shed development/ management peoples participation is prerequisite. Equitable water shearing mechanism, diversification of agriculture for better utilisation of land and water resources and improving farm income, conservation of feed resources, judicious use of feed resources, and integrated approach are necessary components.

Conclusions and Recommendations

To avoid the effect stressors, of low or high environmental temperature, tolerant breeds of sheep and goat should be selected. Native sheep are more tolerant to heat than exotic or crossbred (Srikandakumar et al., 2003). Small ruminant of tropical origin are more tolerant than breeds of temperate origin. Sheep breeds like Chokla, Malpura and Nali are more heat tolerant than purebred Merino or Rambouillet. Crossbreds are fairly comparable to native or in between native and exotic sheep in their heat tolerance. Similarly goats like Sirohi, Beetal and their crosses with Alpine, Sannen or Toggenberg performs well in farm condition but have not been largely adopted by farmers due to lack of managemental and nutritional support in the tropic. Nutritional stress in pregnant and breeding males could be managed through supply of high quality low quantity diets. Similarly, electrolyte balance must be kept with the required normal circulation levels through supplementation during hot or cold stress. Transportation stress of animals up to 2500 km can be minimized by additional supplementation of methionine-Zn-Mn complex providing added supplement of each Zn and Mn 50 mg/kg die which can improve dry matter intake, rectal temperature and body weight gain, and immunity. Supplementation of antioxidant nutrients such as vitamin E, â-carotene, selenium, copper, zinc and manganese are important in protecting an animal's tissues from oxidative destruction, due to an improved immune response which decreases infectious disease incidences arising in stressed animals following shipping. In grazing small ruminants, plasma Cu level above 9 µmol/l required for counteracting erythrocytic oxidative damage caused due to stress. Combination of Cr-yeast and Se-yeast supplementation each 0.3 mg/lamb, had positive effects on performance lamb meat quality during heat stress. Oxidative stress in semen can be minimised by a tris-based extender containing the antioxidants hypotaurine (5 mM) and cysteamine (5 mM), and an aminoacid solution (13%). Dietary concentration of Na above 0.18 % DM required during heat stress. Under hot humid conditions a final dietary Na concentration of 0.55 % is suggested, for partitioning of energy towards live weight gain. Supplementation of the monensin (33 mg/kg diet DM) can improve the balance of several minerals in heat stressed animals. Supplementation of 26 g/kg diet added palmitic acid reduces adverse effects of heat stress. Feeding fat reduce the heat stress in sheep and goat because the heat of increment of fat is less than that of carbohydrate and protein in ruminants. As a result of feeding supplementary fat dietary energy density is increased and heat load of the animal is reduced during heat stress. Providing ascorbic acid to heat stressed lamb lower the respiration rate and rectal temperature and prevents the changes in PCV, Hb and serum total protein. It also increases serum thyroxin and decreased cortisol-indicating improvement of heat tolerance in lamb. Use of natural shed and iodine supplementation improved the fertility during high ambient temperature.

References

Abdelatif, A.M., Muna, M. And Ahmed, M. 1994. Water restriction,thermoregulation, blood constituents and endocrine responses in Sudanese desert sheep. Journal of Environment 26: 171-180.

Alamer, M. 2009. Effect of water restriction on lactation performance of Aardi goats under heat stress conditions. Small Ruminant Research 84: 76-81.

Alamer, M. and Al-Hozab, A. 2004. Effect ofwater deprivation and season on feed intake, body weight and thermoregulation in Awassi and Najdi sheep breeds in Saudi Arabia. Journal of Arid Environment 59: 71-84.

Al-Tamimi, H.J. 2007. Thermoregulatory response of goat kids subjected to heat stress. Small Ruminant Research 71: 280-285.

Augustinsson, O., Holst, H., Forsgren, M., Andersson, H. and Andersson, B., 1986. Influence of heat exposure on acid/base and fluid balance in hyperhydrated goats. Acta Physiologia Scandavia 126: 499- 503.

Granzin, B.C. and Gaughan, J.B. 2002. The effect of sodium chloride supplementation on the milk production of grazing Holstein Friesian cows during summer and autumn in a humid sub-tropical environment. Animal Feed Science and Technology 96: 147-160.

Baccari Jr., F., Johnson, H.D. and Hahn, G.L., 1983. Environmental heat effects on growth, plasma T3, and post-heat compensatory effects on Holstein calves. Experimental Biology and Medicine 173: 312-318.

Beede, D.K. and Collier, J. 1986. Potential nutritional strategies for intensively managed cattle during thermal stress. Journal of Animal Science 62: 543-548.

Brosh, A., Aharoni,Y.,Degen, A., Wright, D. And Young, B. 1998. Effects of solar radiation, dietary energy and time of feeding on thermoregulatory responses and energy balance in cattle in a hot environment. Journal of Animal Science 76: 2671-2677.

Bruno, R.G.S., Rutigliano, H.M., Cerri, R.L., Robinson, P.H. and Santos, J.E.P. 2009. Effect of feeding *Saccharomyces Cerevisiae* on performance of dairy cows during summer heat stress. Animal Feed Science and Technology 150: 175-186.

Bucak, M.N., Tuncer, P.B., Sarýozkan, S., Ulutas, P.A., Coyan, K., Baspýnar, N. and Ozkalp, B. 2009. Effects of hypotaurine, cysteamine and aminoacids solution on post-thaw microscopic and oxidative stress parameters of Angora goat semen. Research in Veterinary Science 87: 468-472.

Casamassima, D., Pizzo, R., Palazzo, M., D'Alessandro, A.G. and Martemucci, G. 2008. Effect of water restriction on productive performance and blood parameters in comisana sheep reared under intensive condition .Small Ruminant Research 78: 169-175.

Chirase, L.K. and Greene, N.W. 2001. Dietary Zn and Mn sources administered from fetal stage onward affect immune response of stressed and virus infected offspring steer calves. Animal Feed Science and Technology 93: 217-228.

Chirase, L.K., Hutcheson, D.P., Thompson, G.B., Spears, J.W. 1994. Recovery rate and plasma Zn and copper concentration of steer calves fed organic and inorganic Zn and Mn sources with or without injectable copper and challenged with IBRV. Journal Animal Science 72: 212-222.

Darden, D.E., Merchen, N.R., Berger, L.L. and Fahey, G.C. 1985. Effects of avoparcin, lasalocid and monensin on sites of nutrient digestion in beef steers. Nutrition Report International 31: 979-989.

David, M.H., Garry, R.B., Larry,W.O., Linjing, X., Ronald, D.M. and Carl, V.G. 2001. Mechanisms of circulatory and intestinal barrier dysfunction during whole body hyperthermia. American Journal of Physiology of Heart and Circulation 280: H509-H521.

Devendra, C. (1990). Comparative aspects of digestive physiology and nutrition in goats and sheep. ln: Ruminant Nutritiona and Physiology in Asia, Devendra, C. and Imazumi, E. (Eds). pp. 45-60.

Dobson, H. and Smith, R.F. 2000. What is stress and how does it affect fertility. Animal Reproduction Science 60: 743-752.

Dobson, H., Tebble, J.E., Smith, R. F. and Ward, W.R., 2001. Is stress really all that importance. Theriogenology 55: 65-73.

Domínguez-Vara, I.A., González-Mu˜noz, S.S., Pinos-Rodríguez, J.M., Bórquez-Gastelum, J.L., Bárcena-Gama, R., Mendoza-Martínez, G., Zapata, L.E. and Landois-Palencia,

L.L. 2009. Effects of feeding selenium-yeast and chromium-yeast to finishing lambs on growth, carcass characteristics, and blood hormones and metabolites. Animal Feed Science and Technology 152: 42-49.

Duff, G.C., Galyean, M.L., Branine, M.E. and Hallford, D.M. 1994. Effects of lasalocid and monensin plus tylosin on serum metabolic hormones and clinical chemistry profiles of beef steers fed a 90% concentrate diet. Journal Animal Science 72: 1049-1058.

Galyean, M.L., Gunter,S.A. and Malcolm-Callis, K.L. 1995. Effect of medication with tilmocasin phosphate on health and performance of newly received beef cattle. Journal of Animal Science 73: 1212-1222.

Halliwell, B. and Chirico, S. 1993. Lipid peroxidation: its mechanism, measurement, and significance. American journal of Clinical Nutrition 57 (Suppl.): 715S-725S.

Huber, J.T., Higginbotham, G., Gomez-Alarcon, R.A., Taylor, R.B., Chen, K.H., Chan, S.C. and Wu, Z., 1994. Heat stress interactions with protein, supplemental fat, and fungal cultures. Journal of Dairy Science 77: 2080-2090.

Jaber, L.S., Habre, A., Rawda, N., Abi Said, M., Barbour, E.K. and Hamadeh, S. 2004. The effect of water restriction on certain physiological parameters in Awassi sheep. Small Ruminant Research 54:

Kadima, I.T., Mahgouba, O., Al-Ajmia, D.S., Al-Maqbalya, R.S., Al-Mugheiryb, S.M. and Bartolomeb, D.Y., 2004. The influence of season on quality characteristics of hot-boned beef m. longissimus thoracis. Meat Science 66: 831- 836.

Karim S.A. 1990. Relationship of dietary energy and heat tolerance in sheep. PhD thesis submitted to NDRI Karnal.

Karim S.A. and Rawat P.S. 1996. Responses of sheep and goats during summer and winter to graded feed restriction and efficiency of regain on alimentation. World Review of Animal Production 31:93-103.

Knizkova, I., Kunc, P., Koubkova, M., Flusser, J. and Dolezal, O. 2002. Evaluation of naturally ventilated barn management by thermographic method. Livestock Production Science 77: 349-353.

Lindsay, D.R. 1996. Environmental and reproductive behaviour. Animal Reproduction Science 42: 1-12.

Al-Saiady, M.Y., Al-Shaikh, M.A., Al-Mufarrej, S.I., Al-Showeimi, T.A., Mogawer, H.H. and Dirrar, A. 2004. Effect of chelated chromium supplementation on lactation performance and blood parameters of Holstein cows under heat stress. Animal Feed Science and Technology 117: 223-233.

Marai, I.F.M., El-Darawany, A.A., Fadiel, A. and Abdel-Hafez, M.A.M. 2007. Physiological traits as affected by heat stress in sheep-A review. Small Ruminant Research 71: 1-12.

Maurya, V.P., Naqvi, S.M.K. and Mittal, J.P. 2004. Effect of dietary energy level on physiological responses and reproductive performance in Malpura sheep in hot semi-arid region of India. Small ruminant Research 55: 117-122.

Misra, A.K. and Singh, K. 2002. Effect of water deprivation on dry matter intake, nutrient utilization and metabolic water production in goats under semi-arid zone of India. Small Ruminant Research 46: 159-165.

Mitlöhner, F., Galyean, M. and McGlone, J. 2002. Shade effects on performance, carcass traits, physiology and behavior of heat stressed feedlot heifers. Journal of Animal Science 80: 2043-2050.

More, T. And Sahni, K.L. 1978. Effect of water deprivation on growth and body fluid composition in Chokla lambs under semi-arid conditions. Indian Journal of Animal Science 48: 600-604.

More, T. and Sahni, K.L. 1981. Effect ofwater intake on feed digestibility. World Review of Animal Production 17: 33-40.

More, T., Howard, B. and Siebert, B.D. 1983. Effect of level of water intake on water, energy and nitrogen balance and thyroxine secretion in sheep and goats. Australian Journal of Agriculture Research 34: 441-446.

Naqvi, S.M.K. 1987. Physiological adaptation of sheep during energy crisis and thermal stress. Ph.D. thesis, Kurukshetra University, Kurukshetra, India.

Naqvi, S.M.K., Maurya, V.P., Gulyani, R., Joshi, A. and Mittal, J. P. 2004. Effect of thermal stress on superovulatory response and embryo production in Bharat Merino ewes. Small Ruminant Research 55: 57-63.

National Research Council, 2001. Nutrient Requirements of Dairy Cattle, seventh revised ed. National Academy Press, Washington, DC, USA.

Nockels, C.F. 1996. Antioxidants improve cattle immunity following stress. Animal Feed Science and Technology 62: 59-68.

Phillips, C. and Piggins, D. 1992. Farm Animals and the Environment. CABI, pp. 1- 430.

Regula, G., Danuser, J., Spycher, B. and Wechsler, B. 2004. Health and welfare of dairy cows in different husbandry systems in Switzerland. Preventive Veterinary Medicine 66: 247-264.

Rosen, S. 1992. Heat stress management in Israel. Extension Service, Ministry of Agriculture, Extensions, Beit Shean, Israel, pp. 83-90.

Roth, Z., Arav, A., Braw-Tal, R., Bor, A. And Wolfenson, D. 2002. Effect of treatment with follicle-stimulating hormone or bovine somatotropin on the quality of oocytes aspirated in the autumn from previously heat-stressed cows. Journal of Dairy Science 85: 1398-1405.

Rout, P.K., Mandal, A., Singh, L.B. and Roy, R. 2002. Studies on behavioural patterns in Jamnapari goats. Small Ruminant Research 43:185-188.

Saleh, M.A., M. Al-Salahy, M.B. and Sanousi, S.A. 2008. Corpuscular oxidative stress in desert sheep naturally deficient in copper. Small Ruminant Research 80: 33-38.

Salles, M.S.V., Zanetti, M.A. and Salles, F.A. 2008. Effect of monensin on mineral balance in growing ruminants reared under different environmental temperatures. Animal Feed Science and Technology 141: 233-245.

Sanchez, W.K., McGuire, M.A. and Beede, D.K. 1994. Macro-mineral nutrition by heat stress interactions in dairy cattle: review and original research. Journal of Dairy Science 77: 2051-2079.

Sankhyan, S.K.,. Shinde, A.K, Bhatta, R.and Karim, S.A. (1999). Comparison of diet and faecal collection methods for assessment of seasonal variation in dry matter intake by sheep maintained on a Cenchrus pasture. Anim. Feed Sci. and Tech.82,261-269.

Schingoethe, D.J., Linke, K.N., Kalscheur, K.F., Hippen, A.R., Rennich, D.R. and Yoon, I. 2004. Feed efficiency of mid-lactation dairy cows fed yeast culture during summer. Journal of Dairy Science 87; 4178- 4181.

Schneider, P.L., Beede, D.K. and Wilcox, C.J. 1986. Responses of lactating cows to dietary sodium source and quantity and potassium quantity during heat stress. Journal of Dairy Science 69: 99-110.

Shibata, M. and Mukai, A. 1977. The effect of environmental temperature and level of hay intake on heat production and some physiological responses of dry cows. Japanese Journal of Zootechnical Sciences 48: 509-514.

Shinde A.K., 1996. Seasonal changes in energy expenditure of sheep on pasture. PhD thesis submitted to JNKVV Jabalpur.

Shinde A.K., Sankhyan, S.K., Singh, N.P. and Verma, D.L. (2004). Soil ingestion and its effect on dry matter intake and digestibility in sheep grazing on native ranges of semiarid region of Rajasthan. Indian Journal of Small Ruminant. (Accepted)

Silanikove, N. 1985. Effect of dehydration on feed intake and dry matter digestibility in desert (black bedouin) and non-desert (Swiss saanen) goats fed on lucerne hay. Comparative Biochemistry and Physiology Part A: Physiology. 80: 449-452.

Silanikove, N. 1992. Effects of water scarcity and hot environment on appetite and digestion in ruminants: a review. Livestock Production Science 30: 175-194.

Silanikove, N. 1994. The struggle to maintain hydration and osmoregulation in animals experiencing severe dehydration and rapid rehydration: the story of ruminants. Experiential Physiology 79: 281-300.

Silanikove, N. 2000. The physiological basis of adaptation in goats to harsh environments. Small Ruminant Research 35: 181-193.

Singh, M., Rai, A.K. and Karim S.A. 1983. Relative heat tolerance of Indian Nali and Soviet Merino x Nali half-bred sheep to continuous 35° and 40°C temperature conditions. Journal of Animal Physiology and Animal Nutrition.

Singh, G and Karim S.A.1995. Changes in birth weight of temperate sheep breeds under tropical condition. World Review of Animal Production. 30: 55-60.

Srikandakumar, A., Johnson, E.H. and Mahgoub, O. 2003. Effect of heat stress on respiratory rate, rectal temperature and blood chemistry in Omani and Australian Merino sheep. Small Ruminant Research 49: 193-198.

Tripathi, M.K., Karim, S.A., Chaturvedi, O.H. and Verma, D.L. 2008. Effect of different liquid cultures of live yeast strains on performance, rumen fermentation and microbial protein synthesis in lambs. Journal of Animal Physiology and Animal Nutrition 92: 631-639.

Tripathi, M.K., Santra, A., Chaturvedi, O.H. and Karim, S.A. 2004. Effect of dietary sodium bicarbonate supplementation on ruminal fluid pH, feed intake, nutrient utilisation and growth of lambs fed high concentrate diets. Animal Feed Science and Technology 111: 27-39.

Tsuda, T., Sasaki, Y. and Kawashima, R. 1991. Physiological Aspects of Digestion and Metabolism in Ruminants. Academic Press, Inc., San Diego, California, USA.

Uriu-Adams, J.Y. and Keen, C.L. 2005. Copper, oxidative stress, and human health. Molecular Aspects Medicine 26: 268-298.

Warntjes, J.L., Robinson, P.H., Galo, E., DePeters, E.J. and Howes, D. 2008. Effects of feeding supplemental palmitic acid (C16:0) on performance and milk fatty acid profile of lactating dairy cows under summer heat. Animal Feed Science and Technology 140: 241-257.

West, J.W., Mullinix, B.G. and Sandifer, T.G. 1991. Changing dietary electrolyte balance for dairy cows in cool and hot environments. Journal of Dairy Science 74:1662-1674.

Yousef, M.K. 1987. Principles of bioclimatology and adaptation of livestock. Elsevier Publ., Holland, WAS, B5, 17-31.

❑❑❑

2

Global Climate Change and Diseases of Small Ruminants

M.C. Sharma[1*], Puneet Kumar[2] and Rupasi Tiwari[1]
[1]Indian Veterinary Research Institute, Izatnagar, Bareilly-243 122, Uttar Pradesh
[2] Central Institute for Research on Goats, Makhdoom,
Farah, Mathura- 281122, Uttar Pradesh

Introduction

One of the environmental threats our planet faces today is the potential for long-term change in the Earth's climate patterns known as *'global climate change'*. The overall effects of climate change are likely to be harmful. Global climate change could potentially cause sea levels to rise as oceans warm and expand as a result of ice cap and snow cover melting. Sea-level rise, could lead to the loss of many coastal wetlands, and entire island nations could disappear. Changes in the quality and availability of water resources could occur and worsen conflicts over water use. Healthy forests could be greatly reduced. Humans and animals could suffer from increased spread of infectious diseases, heat-related deaths, and air pollution. The Intergovernmental Panel on Climate Change projects a sea level increase of six inches to more than three feet by the year 2100 (Anon., 1994). Because half the U.S. population lives within 50 miles of the coastline, this would be disastrous. Large areas of Florida and Louisiana could be submerged, while many beaches along the

East Coast would disappear. Even worse, many small-island nations with no high ground to retreat could disappear.

The earth's atmosphere and the greenhouse effect

In order to understand why global climate change is occurring, it helps to understand what occurs in the Earth's atmosphere. The Earth's atmosphere consists mainly of nitrogen and oxygen, with small amounts of hydrogen, helium, argon, neon, and other gases. Some of other gases, such as carbon dioxide (CO_2) and methane (CH_4) are major greenhouse gases. A greenhouse gas is a gas that traps *infrared energy* (heat) in the atmosphere. Table 1 lists the natural sources of carbon dioxide and methane.

Table 1. Natural sources of carbon dioxide and methane

Source	Emission	
1.	Volcanic eruptions	Carbon dioxide (CO_2)
2.	Natural fires	
3.	Wetlands	Methane (CH_4)
4.	Termites	
5.	Oceans	
6.	Freshwaters	
7.	Hydrates	

Source: Anthropogenic methane emissions in the U.S: Estimates for 1990.

Even though greenhouse gases represent only a small portion of the gases in the earth's atmosphere, they play an important role in the earth's climate. By trapping heat in the atmosphere instead of letting it escape into space, these gases warm our planet. This natural warming phenomenon is known as the '*greenhouse effect*' and is very beneficial. Without the greenhouse effect, the earth would be colder and unable to support plant and animal life.

During the past century, greenhouse gas concentrations in the atmosphere have been rising sharply. This is largely due to the increased production of these gases from human-related, or '*anthropogenic*', sources such as the burning of fossil fuels like oil and coal. The concentration of CO_2 in the atmosphere remained fairly constant for hundreds of years, until the late 1800s when it began to increase rapidly (Fig. 1). This rapidly increasing concentration of CO_2 in the atmosphere coincides with the beginning of the industrial revolution when humans were expanding their use of fossil fuels. As human activities have increased the concentration of greenhouse gases in the atmosphere, the natural greenhouse effect has been amplified, leading to rising global temperatures and global climate change. The largest sources of anthropogenic greenhouse gases are listed in Table 2.

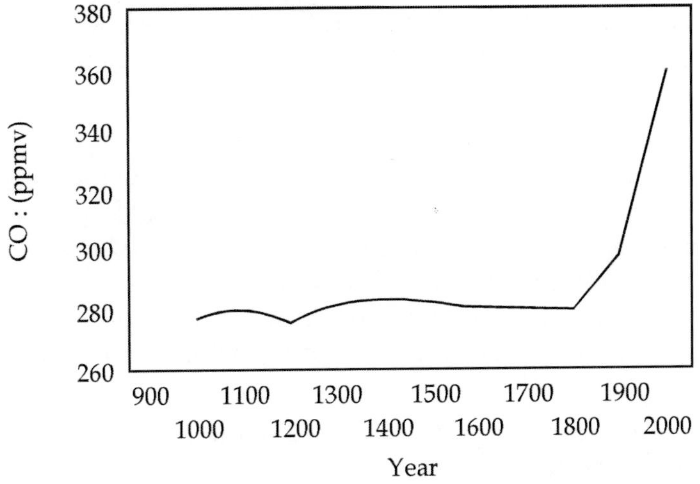

Source : Intergovernmental panel on Climate Change, 1994

Fig 1. CO_2 concentration over time

Table 2. Major anthropogenic sources of greenhouse gases

Sources	Emission (s)
Fossil fuel combustion: coal, natural gas, petroleum	CO_2, CH_4, N_2O
Fuel production and processing: coal mining, oil and natural gas systems	CO_2, CH_4
Transportation	CO_2, CH_4
Industrial processes	CO_2, CH_4, N_2O
Landfills	CH_4
Wastewater treatment	CH_4
Waste incineration	N_2O
Land use change	CO_2
Biomass burning	CO_2, CH_4
Agricultural activities: digestive processes of domesticated ruminant livestock, manure management, rice cultivation, agricultural waste burning, agricultural soil management, fertilizer use	CO_2, CH_4, N_2O

CO_2= Carbon dioxide; CH_4 = Methane; N_2O= Nitrous oxide

They include the burning of coal, oil, and natural gas, and activities such as raising cattle, growing rice, and cutting down trees for agriculture and development. While all of these activities are needed, an effort must be made to minimize the quantity of greenhouse gases emitted from these sources. If action is not taken, scientists believe that the atmospheric level of greenhouse gases could triple by the year 2100 resulting in irreversible global climate change.

Methane is one of the primary greenhouse gases found in the Earth's atmosphere. It is the principal component of natural gas and often serves as an energy source in homes, cars, and power plants. Methane is produced by the decomposition of organic matter in the absence of oxygen. Reducing methane emissions from anthropogenic sources can be a very effective means of lowering the methane concentration in the atmosphere and, in the near term, slowing global climate change. Reducing methane emissions is important because:

- Methane is second only to carbon dioxide in its contribution to the greenhouse effect.
- Methane concentrations in the atmosphere are rising and have more than doubled over the last two centuries.
- Methane is a very potent greenhouse gas, 21 times more effective at trapping heat in the atmosphere than carbon dioxide.
- Methane has a relatively short atmospheric life compared to other greenhouse gases, so reducing methane provides relatively rapid benefits.
- Most anthropogenic methane emissions are controllable through cost-effective reduction technologies that are currently available.

Sources and sinks of methane

Methane is released into the atmosphere from both ***natural and anthropogenic sources***. Methane emissions from natural sources make up approximately 30% of the total global methane emissions. The major natural sources of methane and the estimated amounts released by these sources each year are shown in Table 3.

Table 3. Natural sources of methane emissions

Source	Estimated amount (million metric tons/year)
Wetland	115
Termites	20
Oceans and fresh water	15
Gas hydrates	05
Total	**155**

Source: Anthropogenic Methane Emissions in the U.S.: Estimates for 1990

Methane from anthropogenic sources accounts for the remaining 70% of emissions. Table 4 lists these sources and the estimated amounts they release each year.

Table 4. Anthropogenic sources of methane emissions

Source	Estimated amount (million metric tons/year)
Domesticated livestock	80
Rice farming	60
Natural gas, petroleum processing and use	50
Coal mining	40
Biomass burning	40
Landfills	30
Livestock manure	25
Wastewater treatment	25
TOTAL	**350**

Source: Anthropogenic Methane Emissions in the U.S.: Estimates for 1990

The concentration of methane in the atmosphere is regulated by the balance between sources and sinks. A sink is something that absorbs, destroys, or removes gases from the atmosphere. When sources of greenhouse gases exceed sinks, methane concentration in the atmosphere increases and contributes to an amplified greenhouse effect. In recent years, the concentration of methane in the atmosphere has been increasing at a rate of about one per cent every year. This increase is largely attributed to increased emissions from anthropogenic sources.

The primary sink for methane is the atmosphere itself which contains free hydroxyl (OH) ions. Once released into the atmosphere, methane undergoes a chemical reaction in the troposphere (lower region of the atmosphere), combining with hydroxyl ions to form water vapor and carbon dioxide. A secondary sink is the soil which contains bacteria that absorb methane and oxidize it. Because the emission of methane exceeds its removal by sinks, concentrations are increasing, enhancing the natural greenhouse effect and contributing to global climate change.

Consequences of global climate change

There is also a growing concern regarding climate change taking place insidiously. It is predicted that global warming will be characterized by increase in temperatures and humidity. Droughts, floods and storms could become more severe. The entire agricultural regions could become disrupted as rainfall and temperature patterns will shift. It is unknown whether farmers and governments will be able to adopt new techniques and management approaches that can deal with the negative impacts of climate change. It is also hard to predict how relationships between crops, pests, weeds, and livestock will evolve. The result could be an inability to provide adequate food resources to a growing world population. This could lead not only to higher food prices, but also to increased conflict throughout the world as people compete for resources in a very different global environment. Natural resource based livelihoods will be affected first and most and therefore promotion of sustainable agriculture and livestock rearing will be vital to ensure that the impact of climate change is minimized on the communities. This will involve rearing of animals which are more sturdy, heat tolerant, disease resistant, and relatively adaptable to the adverse conditions. In such a situation some of the indigenous breeds will be able to cope much better than the crossbreds as crosses containing higher exotic inheritance do show problems of survival when compared to indigenous breeds.

Climate change is strongly associated with many emerging and re-emerging animal diseases. Emerging disease is a new infection resulting from the evolution or change of an existing pathogenic agent, a known infection spreading to a new geographic area or population, or a previously unrecognized pathogenic agent or disease diagnosed for the first time and, which has a significant impact on animal or public health. General trend towards intensification and industrialization of animal production is expected to continue and will increase the opportunity for animal disease to emerge and re-emerge. Other factors are: increasing trade and tourism, changing consumer preference, and increasing urbanization,

Climate change and farm animals

At least a billion of the world's poorest people depend on animals for food, fiber, income, social status, security, and companionship. Climate change is expected to cause an increase in weather-related disasters and extreme weather events, such as droughts, heat waves, storms, desertification, and increases in insect infestations. Long-term changes in climate will jeopardize the future of all animals; including those in oceans, on farms, in forests, in wilderness areas, and in our homes. All climate change related hazards and their related disasters have a negative impact on animals. Animal agriculture, the raising of animals for food, clothing, and draught power, is a major contributor to climate change, responsible for 18% of greenhouse gas (GHG) emissions (9% CO_2, 37% methane and 65% N_2O).

The worldwide redistribution of disease vectors - the animals, insects, microorganisms and plants that transmit diseases - which is already upon us could increase due to global climate change. Many tropical diseases such as dengue fever, yellow fever, avian influenza, swine influenza, Japanese encephalitis, leptospirosis, brucellosis, tuberculosis, rabies, and malaria, etc are beginning to be seen at higher latitudes and altitudes as warming occurs. This warming could potentially result in a greater number of people being exposed to these deadly diseases. Many ecosystems could have a difficult time adjusting to the rapid rate of climate change if the world does not reduce greenhouse gas emissions. Animals and plants that are excellent competitors under stable environmental conditions often cannot survive when their habitat is altered by rapid change. Instead, parasite species such as weeds, rodents, insects, bacteria and viruses will quickly reproduce and colonize disturbed environments. The recent population explosion of termites, cockroaches and mosquitoes in New Orleans and rodents in southern Africa are examples of this type of problem. There are also likely to be significant economic and social costs as agriculture is forced to make painful adjustments in response to climate changes. Projected climatic changes are expected to increase the risks of vector-borne and other diseases in humans and animals, such as malaria and cold-water vibriosis in fish. Many of the potential impacts of climatic change will take years or even decades to become obvious.

Increasing temperatures have supported the expansion of vector populations into cooler areas, either into higher altitude systems (for example, malaria and livestock tick-borne diseases i.e. babeiosis, theileriosis anaplasmosis) or into more temperate zones (for example, the current outbreak of bluetongue disease in northern Europe). Changes in rainfall pattern can also influence an expansion of vectors during wetter years. This may lead to large outbreaks of disease, such as those seen in East Africa due to Rift Valley Fever virus, which is transmitted by a wide variety of biting insects. The potential complexity of climate change influences with other factors associated with vector populations is well illustrated by the distribution of tsetse flies in sub-Saharan Africa (McDermott et al., 1999, 2001). Tsetse flies transmit African trypanosomes widely in livestock (ruminants, equids, and pigs). Tsetse are very sensitive to environmental change, either due to climate or direct human impacts on habitat.

Beyond vector-borne diseases, helminth infections like filariasis, fascioliosis etc., particularly of small ruminants will be greatly influenced by changes in temperature and humidity. Climate changes could also influence disease distribution indirectly through changes in the distribution of livestock. Areas becoming more arid would only be suitable for camels and small ruminants.

If these species are forced to aggregate around water points, the incidence of parasitic diseases could increase. The most important adaptive trait of tropical livestock is disease resistance. Two of the most important disease resistance traits have been identified for trypanosome tolerance in African ruminants and helminth resistance, particularly in certain breeds of sheep across tropical and temperate regions. Particularly for trypanosome tolerant breeds, climate change may decrease the importance of this trait in sub-humid zones of West Africa. One potential danger is that if climatic changes lead to selection against trypanosome tolerance in the short to medium term, these adaptive traits that have developed over millennia will be lost if future conditions lead to greater disease risk in the longer-term.

Climate change is bound to have impact on heat-related mortality and morbidity (Patz et al., 2005). While climate change impacts may have few direct impacts on diseases, climate variability impacts on food production and nutrition can affect susceptibility to other diseases (Williams, 2004). Changing disease burdens are bound to add considerably to the development problems caused by successive natural disasters and emergence from conflict, associated with low levels of adaptive capacity (Brooks et al., 2005). Some vector borne diseases (VBDs) are zoonotic diseases and cause serious illness and death in humans. Climate change is likely to increase the prevalence and incidence of such diseases, either geographically or from seasonal to year-round. Global warming and resulting rising sea levels, for example, would displace some human populations, perhaps resulting in migration into wilderness areas where zoonotic infectious agents are being transmitted in silent life cycles.

Climatic factors can have a major effect on the rate of transmission of many infectious diseases. Microbial agents and their vectors are sensitive to factors such as temperature, humidity, precipitation, surface water, wind and changes in vegetation. This applies particularly to vector-borne diseases (VBDs) such as RVF, transmitted by mosquitoes, African horse sickness (AHS) and BT, both transmitted by biting midges (*Culicoides* spp), ASF, East Coast fever, anaplasmosis, babesiosis and Nairobi sheep disease, both transmitted by ticks, and trypanosomosis, transmitted by tsetse flies. Lumpy skin disease has long been suspected of being transmitted by arthropod vectors. In general, increased temperature and moisture will enhance transmission. It is projected, therefore, that climate changes and altered weather patterns will affect the range, intensity, and seasonality of vector-borne and other infectious diseases.

Considerable progress has been made in investigating and defining the climatic and environmental factors that influence vector biology. The data has generally been obtained by a combination of field and laboratory studies.

These approaches, combined with satellite remote sensing, geographical information systems and bio-mathematical modeling, could be used to develop models to predict when and where disease outbreaks are likely to occur and how the situation might alter with climate change. Armed with this information, control strategies, such as the use of prophylactic vaccination and vector control, could be used to protect animals in advance of the spread of a disease and thereby reduce its impact.

In the UK, recent mean temperatures have consistently increased by between 1°C and 4°C compared to the 30-year monthly averages. Furthermore, all available predictive models for the UK indicate that the climate is likely to change further and feature more extreme weather events and a trend towards wetter, milder winters and hotter, drier summers. These changes will alter the prevalence of endemic diseases spatially and/or temporally and impact on animal health and welfare. Most notable among these endemic parasites are the helminths, which have been shown to be very strongly influenced by both the short-term weather and climate through effects on their free-living larval stages on pasture.

The collective geographical location of livestock diseases of major economic importance - FMD, rinderpest, contagious bovine pleuropneumonia (CBPP), CSF, ASF, sheep and goat pox, trypanosomosis, tick-borne diseases, New Castle disease and probably infectious bursal disease (IBD) - extends from Africa across the Near East and into Asia, encompassing many of the poorer countries of the world. Sustained control of these diseases requires:

- Socio-political stability;
- Access to all livestock by veterinary personnel;
- Input of resources to supply and deliver vaccines;
- Maintenance of effective surveillance systems to detect suspected cases at an early stage;
- Provision of trained manpower and resources to implement disease-control strategies in the event of outbreaks.

India- A hot-spot for emerging infectious diseases

Zoological Society of London along with researchers from Georgia and New York analyzed 335 emerging diseases from 1940 to 2004 to study links between emergence of infectious diseases (EID) with resource misallocation. If we look into the global resources pool to fight EIDs, most are focused on rich countries that can afford surveillance, but most hotspots are in developing countries. If we look at the high impact diseases of the future, we're missing the point." Major recommendations of the study include increased focus on conservation efforts to reduce man-wildlife conflict and redistribution of global resources to tackle EIDs.

At least 11 pathogens have emerged or re-emerged in India during 1992-2009, majority of animal origin. Risk factors for emergence reside in multiple sectors. Emergence and spread of H5N1 has clearly demonstrated the vulnerability of the system. The study reiterate need for urgent, targeted and multisectoral preparedness and response to EIDs. Integrated Disease Surveillance Project, National Rural Health Mission, International Health Regulations (2005), networks of veterinary and wildlife institutions are some opportunities at hand. The relationship of climate change to disease has received more attention with regard to human health, but there is growing awareness and documentation that animal health is also affected. Specific information on the relationship of climate change to goat disease is rare, but concrete examples are beginning to emerge.

Climate change and vector-borne diseases

Vector-borne diseases are widespread in Europe and are the best studied diseases associated with climate change. In both human and animal health, it is in the area of vector-borne diseases, that link between climate change and disease has become most apparent. In a number of cases, arthropod vectors such as ticks, midges and mosquitoes that can transmit various viral and protozoal diseases to animals and humans are expanding their ranges into new geographic areas. Furthermore, in temperate regions, warmer winters are allowing these vectors to survive year round thus increasing the likelihood that cycles of infection will be continuous rather than be interrupted by winter freeze.

According to the World Organization for Animal Health (OIE), 66 listed diseases affecting the categories of bovine, swine, caprine, ovine, equine and multi species disease, 22 are considered as vector-borne diseases (Table 5).

The transmission of vector-borne diseases is dependent on three stages involving the infectious agent, the vector and finally the host(s). The diseases which appear on the OIE list have been chosen for two main reasons: the economic impact caused by an outbreak and its consequences, as well as the veterinary health factor. One of these diseases which causes both large financial and social damages to an affected region, as well as being able to provoke serious morbidity and mortality rates is the arboviral disease (arthropod-borne viral disease) called "bluetongue" (BT).

Table 5. List of vector-borne diseases

Vector -borne disease	Occurrence	Vector	Hosts
African horse sickness	Africa, Middle East, Europe	*Culicoides imicola* and *C.bolitinos*	Eqine
African swine fever	Sub-Saharan Africa, Europe	*Ornithodoros* tick species	Swine
Bluetongue	Worldwide	*Culicoides* midges	Ruminants
Crimean Congo-hemorrhagic fever	Africa, Europe, Balkans, South Africa and Asia	*Argasid ixodid* ticks	Wild and domestic animals (zoonosis)
Equine encephalomyelitis (eastern and Western)	Canada, Caribbean, North, South and Central America	Mosquito	Equine, birds (zoonosis)
Equine infecriousanaemia	Worldwide	Biting flies, mosquitoes	Equine
Japanese encephalitis	Asia, Australia, India	*Culex* mosquito	Pigs, birds (zoonosis)
Lumpky skin disease	Africa, South and North Africa, Isreal	Arthopods	Cattle, zebus, giraffe, impala
Nairobi sheep disease	East Africa	*Rhipicephalus* ticks	Sheep and Goats
Rift valley fever	Africa	Mosquito	Multiple species(zoonosis)
Venezuelan eqine encephalomyelitis	North, Central and South America	Mosquito	Equine (zoonosis)
Vesicular stomatitis	United States, Europe, South Africa	Arthropods	Mammals (zoonosis)
West Nile fever	Worldwide	Mosquito	Multiple species (zoonosis)
Bovine anaplamosis	Worldwide	Tick species	Cattle
Bovine babesiosis	Worldwide	Tick species	Cattle
Tularemia	North America, Europe and Asia	Arthropods	Rodents, rabbits, hares

Contd...

Equine piroplasmosis	Worldwide	Ixodid	Equine
Heartwater	Africa, West Indies	*Amblyomma* tick species	Ruminants
Leishmaniosis	Worldwide	*Phlebotomus* and *Lutzomyia* sandflies	Dogs, rodents, opossum (zoonosis)
Surra (Trypanosoma evansi)	Asia, Africa and South America	*Tabanus* spp. (biting flies)	Multiple species
Theileriois	Worldwide	*Ixodid* ticks	Bovidae and ruminants
Trypanosomosis	Africa, South and Central America	*Glossina* spp. *(tse-tse)*	Cattle (Zoonosis)

Blue tongue

The incursion of blue tongue virus (BTV) infection into Europe in the last 10 years has been quite convincingly linked to global warming. Increases in night time temperature and winter temperature along with increases in precipitation in summer and autumn have led to an increased geographical and seasonal incidence of BTV transmission (Purse et al., 2005). The bluetongue incursion into Europe has directly affected goats. In the epizootic in Northern Europe which began in 2006, clinical cases in goats due to BTV-8 were seen in the Netherlands (Dercksen et al., 2007).

Blue tongue is a vector-borne, non-contagious, viral disease which affects domestic and wild ruminants (www.oie.int). The virus, of which there are currently 24 known serotypes, is a member of the *Reoviridae* family and Orbivirus genus. Although distributed worldwide, many serotypes are linked to a specific BT vector, and have been 9 usually restricted to certain geographic regions. For example BTV -1, -3, -9, -15, -16, - 20, -21 and -23 occurring in Northern Australia, BTV -1, -3, -4, -6, -8, -12 and -17 circulating in the Central American-Caribbean Basin, and BTV1–16, -18,-19 and -24 being responsible for African outbreaks (www.iah.bbsrc.ac.uk). Previous to 2006, BT had been circulating in the Mediterranean and Balkan regions since late 1990s on a regular basis (Purse et al., 2005). It had spread into these areas through two main pathways. The first main pathway was the eastern to western movement of BTV -1, -4, - 9 and -16 originally affecting the Greek islands and moving into the Balkan regions as well as the Mediterranean islands of Corsica, Sicily and Sardinia. The second being the southern to northern expansion involving BTV -2,-3 and recently BTV-1 from Algeria, Tunisia into mainland Italy, the

Spanish Balearic islands and finally mainland Spain and Portugal (Purse et al., 2005). Bluetongue virus serotype 8 appeared in northern Europe in 2006, firstly being reported in the Netherlands and Belgium, followed by Germany, Luxembourg, and northern parts of France. During winter of 2006-2007, no further cases were detected, yet in spring of 2007 BTV-8 was discovered again in sentinel animals in Germany. It was consequently reported in the same countries as the precedent year, with the additional spread into south-eastern England, Denmark and was detected in the northern part of Switzerland at the end of October 2007. Bluetongue disease is exclusively related to the presence of the virus in the competent vector: insects of the *Culicoides* species. Depending on the geographic area, BT is spread by different species of *Culicoides* midges. These vectors belong to the order diptera in the ceratopogonidae family, where currently there are 1,340 species known (Mellor, 1998). The threat of BT re-occurring in 2007 was thought decreased due to the effect of the winter season on *Culicoides* activity and survival, since below certain temperatures (circa 12°C), there is virtually no virus replication possible in the midge. Yet as shown early on in this year, BT cases reappeared in previously affected areas. There are no concrete theories on the mechanisms of BT over-wintering yet a few hypothesis have been mentioned: i) the virus in the insect remains dormant in the colder periods, along with prolonged survival of the midge in colder temperatures, ii) the immune system of the host allowing for the virus to remain active until the next vector season or iii) the possibility of transovarial transmission as seen in many arboviruses and their invertebrate vectors.

Along with BT, several other vector-borne diseases have been emerging into areas for the first time or previously eradicated especially in the last half century, including many zoonoses such as malaria, dengue fever, shistosomiasis and plague. This has been attributed to a range of factors either climate driven or associated to changes in industry and urbanization. These can all affect the spread of vector-borne diseases by increasing the ability of the vector to transmit a disease, or in creating suitable habitats for it to establish. In some scenarios, whether accidental or induced by man made phenomenon, diseases which had been related to one type of vector species have also been seen in new vectors which might have different hosts and habitats, as is the case for West Nile disease. Human travel, increased transhumance, deforestation, irrigation projects and the upsizing of farm animal holdings are a few examples of factors associated to vector-borne disease spread created artificially, whilst temperature changes, El Niño activities and general global warming belong to climate driven factors responsible for this occurrence. As described in the World Health Organization work group on climate change (www.who.int/globalchange/climate/), the habitats of certain vectors are indirectly being expanded due to larger areas and altitudes becoming warmer as well as extreme climatic events bringing abnormal quantities of rainwater or heat waves, each affecting the transmission of vector-borne diseases in specific ways.

Outbreak of BT disease in Tamil Nadu

Bluetongue is a viral disease causing morbidity and mortality in sheep, cattle and wild ruminants, including deer, sambar and bluebull. BT is endemic in many parts of India and its outbreak in Tamil Nadu during the monsoon season of 1997–98 caused the death of 300,000 sheep and goats. Current research for controlling BT is confined to the development of vaccines in disease vulnerable states,with which complete success is questionable because of the presence of more than 20 serotypes of the virus. Vector control through integrated intensive management is feasible, but there is little knowledge of the biting midges, *Culicoides latreille* (Diptera: Ceratopogonidae) in southern India. *Culicoides brevitasis, C. keifferi* and *C. imicola* are proven vectors of BT virus, occurring widely in India. There is an urgent need to study *Culicoides* sp. intraspecies variation and genetic variation because of the recent BT disease outbreak. The extent of BT infection in domestic and wild ruminants in South and South East Asia is unknown, but its actual occurrence and potential is a matter of serious concern.

Rift Valley fever (RVF)

According to OIE, the threat of tropical diseases is moving to new areas. One of these is Rift Valley Fever. Other climatic events besides global warming can adversely affect livestock health, including goat health. For example, it is now well documented that Rift Valley fever epizootics in Africa are associated with the El Nino-Southern Oscillation (ENSO) phenomenon. These warm ENSO events are known to increase precipitation in portions of East Africa. Epizootics often follow periods of heavy rainfall when the rain facilitates the hatching of previously laid, dormant, infected mosquito eggs resulting in sudden increases in the infected *Aedes* mosquito populations. These initiate infection which is then amplified markedly by *Culex* and other species of mosquitoes whose population increases lag somewhat behind those of the *Aedes* mosquitoes. Two additional factors that contribute to epizootics are heavy winds that blow infected insects into previously uninfected areas and transport of infected livestock into such areas.

RVF in goats has been reviewed. An RVF epizootic which affected the contiguous areas of the Northeastern province of Kenya, the south of Somalia and southern Ethiopia in 1997-1998 is estimated to have affected over a half million goats and sheep and sickened 89,000 people leading to possibly 450 human deaths in Kenya alone. A similar, severe RVF outbreak occurred in Kenya and Tanzania in late 2006 through early 2007 and spread later in the year into Sudan. The good news is that retrospective studies on data available from 1950 through 1998 demonstrated that an analytical model which included measurements of southern oscillation indices, equatorial sea surface temperatures in the Pacific and Indian oceans and satellite derived vegetation indices in East Africa would have accurately predicted 100% of the RVF epizootics that occurred during that 48 year period (Linthicum et al., 1999). Such predictive epidemiological tools can be extremely useful for instituting effective disease control programs such as vaccination and/or movement of animals away from areas of high risk. This is important because the frequency and severity of ENSO events are thought to be increasing.

RVF was named after the Rift Valley in Kenya, over a century ago, as a cause of severe mortalities in newborn lambs. RVF causes epidemics of abortions in sheep and goats with acute deaths in lambs and kids. It has also been described in wild ruminants, cattle and camels. During an outbreak of RVF in South Africa in the 1950-51 rainy season, 100,000 sheep died and over half a million aborted. Many of those veterinarians and animal health officers who were involved in diagnosing and controlling the outbreaks in 1950/51 and again in 1976-78, in South Africa were, as a direct result, partially blinded by retinal detachment and some died.

In 1977, more than 200,000 Egyptians were infected with RVF and 598 died. Mosquitoes breeding in the large new dam were the main vectors and the disease affected both rural and urban communities along its bank. Between 1997 and 1998, there was a major outbreak in East Africa and in 2000, RVF spread to Saudi Arabia and Yemen, in the Middle East, sparking fears of a possible spread into Asia and Europe.

Between October and December 2006, the rainfall in Kenya was three times the average for that period and 13 times greater than the same period in 2005. Severe flooding resulted and, as the water drained away, leaving muddy pools, mosquitoes multiplied. According to Pub Med, by the 26th of January 2007, 404 human cases of RVF had been reported with 118 deaths. The most important risk factors for transmission to humans were: drinking unpasteurized milk (72%), living within 100 metres of a swamp (70%), being in contact or owning a sick animal (67%), drinking milk from a sick animal (59%), working as a herdsman (50%), being in contact with a dead animal (50%) and slaughtering an animal (42%). Although 9% of those affected said they had been in contact with a sick person, transmission from human to human is thought to be unlikely. Two patients from Nairobi were suspected to have become infected by handling and eating partly raw or undercooked meat.

Symptoms in livestock

Abortion storms and mortality in young animals are considered to be the most common symptoms of RVF. Haemorrhages can sometimes be seen under the skin and in the mucous membranes of the eyes, mouth and vulva and, in the latest cases in South Africa, calves showed a bloody diarrhoea. Blood clotting also appeared to be impaired in dairy cows. On post mortem examination acute deaths can result in bleeding throughout the carcass with bloodstained organs and small haemorrhages in the muscles and organs. The OIE strongly supports vaccination, rather than culling out, as a control measure for RVF in livestock.

Tick-borne diseases

Tick-borne encephalitis (TBE) is caused by an arbovirus of the family *Flaviviridae* and is transmitted by ticks (predominantly *Ixodes ricinus*) that act both as vectors and as reservoirs. Similar to other vector-borne diseases, temperature accelerates the ticks' developmental cycle, egg production, population density, and distribution. It is likely that climate change has already led to changes in the distribution of *I. ricinus* populations in Europe. *I. ricinus* has expanded into higher altitudes in the Czech Republic over the last two decades, which was related to increases in average temperatures. This vector expansion is accompanied by infections with TBE virus. Human granulocytic anaplasmosis is caused by *Anaplasma phagocytophilum*, which is usually transmitted to human beings by *I. ricinus*. In Europe, this disease was known to cause fever in goats, sheep, and cattle until it emerged as a disease in human beings in 1996. It has now shifted to new geographical habitats throughout Europe, and migrating birds have been implicated in its expansion.

Foot and mouth disease

It is a highly contagious virus disease of cloven-hoofed animals. There are seven distinct types of FMD virus. It is the animal disease with the greatest impact on international trade. The OECD countries are normally free from this disease, but it is endemic in less-developed countries (LDCs). The endemic distribution of the seven types of FMD is broadly as follows: Type O: Asia, Africa, the Near East and South America; Type A: Asia, Africa, the Near East and South America; Type C: Asia, Africa, South America (this type occurs rarely and tends to be sporadic); Type Asia 1: Asia; Types SAT 1, SAT 2 and SAT 3: Africa. In recent years, serious epidemics of FMD have occurred outside areas of endemicity, causing major economic losses. Examples are: Type O in Taiwan province of China in 1997 and again in 2000; Type O pan-Asian topotype, which over 10 years spread eastwards from south Asia to China, Japan, South Korea, Vietnam, Cambodia and Taiwan Province of China and westwards to the Near East and south-east Europe; during 2000-2001, it leapt to South Africa, the United Kingdom, France, the Netherlands and Ireland. Type SAT 2 spread to Saudi Arabia in 2000, which is the first time this type has been recorded outside Africa.

Animal movement, trade and disease incidence

In developing countries, movement of livestock is common. Such movements inevitably bring livestock from different groups into contact. Where there are heavy concentrations of wildlife animals, the migrations of wildlife and livestock bring the two groups into contact. Such contacts are a source of disease dissemination. The introduction of CBPP in the early 1990s into Botswana and Tanzania was due to movement of only a few sub clinically infected animals from endemic areas. FMD, rinderpest, sheep pox, PPR, ND, IBD and others have been disseminated through such movements.

The transport of contaminated meat and fodder around the world is a mechanism by which FMD can be spread over long distances and by which exotic strains can be introduced into new territories. Advances in molecular biology, in particular reverse-transcription polymerase chain reaction (RT-PCR) sequencing, have proved to be extremely valuable for characterizing isolates of virus and identifying their probable origin. The application of such techniques to FMD is probably the most advanced. The most dramatic example, however, is the spread of FMD serotype O that is now referred to as type O Pan-Asian topotype, which over a ten-year period has spread through most of Asia and parts of Europe and South Africa. This virus was first identified in northern India in 1990. It spread westwards into Saudi Arabia during 1994 and throughout the Near East and into Europe (Turkish Thrace, Bulgaria and Greece) in 1996. In 1993 it was found in Nepal, in 1996 in Bangladesh and in 1998 in Bhutan. In 1999, it was reported from mainland China (Tibet, Fujian and Hainan) and then detected in Taiwan Province of China. In late 1999 and in 2000 it reached most of South-East Asia. Most recently it has been introduced into the Republic of Korea, Japan, the Primorsky Territory of the Russian Federation and Mongolia, areas free from FMD since 1934, 1908, 1964 and 1973, respectively. The total cost of the outbreaks in Japan alone has been calculated at US$ 77 million. The virus has been isolated from a wide variety of host species - cattle, water buffaloes, pigs, sheep, goats, camels, deer and antelope.

It is often difficult, however, to determine whether the observed change in disease pattern is the result of specific genetic change in virulence, selection of more adaptive disease-causing agent strains, variation in genetic susceptibility of host animals or environmental factors such as changes in farming practices. FMD is a prime example in which asymptomatic carrier animals or subclinically affected animals have set up outbreaks in previously free areas or have disseminated infection widely during the course of an outbreak. During the 1990s, several countries in eastern Asia, including the Philippines, Taiwan Province of China and Viet Nam, experienced outbreaks of FMD by a virus strain that caused disease only in pigs. The FMD outbreak in Argentina early in 2001 is believed to have been introduced by asymptomatic carrier cattle. The dissemination of FMD in February and March 2001 in the United Kingdom and thence to Ireland, France and the Netherlands has been principally by subclinically infected sheep.

Examples of recent epidemics of transboundary small ruminants diseases (TADs)

Peste des petits ruminants (PPR)

PPR also known as goat plague, is a highly contagious disease of small ruminants (SRs) caused by a *Morbillivirus* close to rinderpest virus (RPV). PPR is characterized by classical signs of alimentary tract disorders (ATD's) and respiratory tract disorders (RTD's) exhibited mainly in form of fever, necrotic stomatitis, lacrimation, pneumonia, foetid enteritis and high mortality.

Although goats and sheep are the natural hosts of PPR but goat appears to be more susceptible and suffer a more severe clinical disease than sheep. PPR also occur in other species, particularly in captive wild ungulates. Cattle, buffaloes, camels, and pigs are also susceptible to infection but do not exhibit clinical signs and are unable to transmit the disease to other animals. PPR is not infectious to humans. It was until recently, PPR was considered to be limited to West Africa. It is now, however, the most evolving epidemic of small ruminants and widely prevalent in most of Asian and African countries and has reached to Turkey, which borders Europe. PPR is responsible for heavy losses in small ruminants in Nepal, Pakistan, India and Bangladesh.

Sheep and goat pox

Capripoxviruses are the cause of sheep pox, goat pox and lumpy skin disease (LSD) of cattle. These diseases are of great economic significance to farmers in regions in which they are endemic and are a major constraint to international trade in livestock and their products. Although the distribution of capripoxviruses is considerably reduced from what it was even 50 years ago, they are now expanding their territory, with recent outbreaks of sheep pox or goat pox in Vietnam, Mongolia and Greece, and outbreaks of LSD in Ethiopia, Egypt and Israel. Increased legal and illegal trade in live animals provides the potential for further spread, with, for instance, the possibility of LSD becoming firmly established in Asia. Capripoxviruses have the potential to become emerging disease threats because of global climate change and changes in patterns of trade in animals and animal products. They also could be used as economic bioterrorism agents.

Under natural conditions, goat pox virus (GPV) is highly host specific, infecting only goats but there are strains that may cause disease in both sheep and goats. Kenyan and Yemen isolates as well as an Oman sheep isolate infect sheep and goats equally. Usually, middle-east and Indian isolates of goat pox exhibit host preference. However, it is envisaged that when sufficient isolates have been examined biochemically, no clear distinction will be possible between goat and sheep isolates, but rather a spectrum would emerge in which some strains have clear host preferences while others would be less defined and would naturally infect whichever host they come into contact with. The GPV may also produce lesions in rabbits and reindeer. The status of goat pox virus as zoonotic agent is still debatable.

India's infrastructural development to control small ruminant diseases

A net work of 26,717 Polyclinics/Hospitals/Dispensaries and 28,195 veterinary aid centers (including stockmen centers/mobile dispensaries), which are supported by about 250 disease diagnostic laboratories, are functioning in the states and Union Territories for quick and reliable diagnosis of diseases. Further for control of major livestock and poultry diseases by way of prophylactic vaccination the required quantity of vaccines are produced in the country at 26 veterinary vaccine production units. Of these, 19 are in the public sector and 7 are in private sector. Import of vaccines/diagnostics by private agencies is also permitted as and when required. Strengthening of these institutions is necessary to meet the international requirements.

Trans-boundary animal diseases and emerging, reemerging and exotic animal diseases are assuming a new dimension to the livestock productions systems in various countries. The key intrinsic factors for making these diseases important at a global scale are mainly the mode of survival and spread of the causal agents, variability and the availability of hosts/alternate hosts and vectors (in case of viral diseases).

Infectious diseases do not respect national boundaries. Human epidemic of "plague" in 1994 in India, alarming panic created by SARS and bird flue epidemics in 2003-04 in neighboring countries and the recent outbreak of bird flu in India declaring a Global Alert for the first time in the history of WHO is unparallel. In India, during the last five decades, trans-boundary transmission of animal diseases has inflicted severe losses due to bluetongue, peste des petits ruminants (PPR), swine fever; equine influenza & African horse sickness, canine parvo-virus in livestock and Marek's disease, Gumboro disease, egg drop syndrome, chicken infectious anemia and Lichi heart disease in poultry. Some of other exotic diseases recognized in the country at times included bovine viral diarrhea in cattle / buffaloes, Equine coital exanthema in horses, equine infectious anemia in horses, Aujeszky's disease in swine and non-pathogenic avian influenza (strain H9N2) in poultry.

In animals, the entry of diseases like malignant catarrh fever (MCF), rabbit hemorrhagic syndrome (RHS), avian influenza (AI) has been checked through diagnosis in the imported livestock and poultry at the entry point of quarantining.

Resurgence/emergence of new diseases

There are new diseases emerging at unprecedented rate over the last decade without clear-cut explanation of the reasons for their emergence or recurrence. These diseases now continue to spread over large areas e.g. contagious agalactiae (mycoplasmosis), enzootic abortion (ovine chlamydiosis), caprine arthritis/encephalitis (CAE), equine infectious anaemia (EIA), equine influenza, equine virual rhino-pneumonitis, porcine reproductive and respiratory syndrome (PRRS), infectious bursal disease/Gumboro (IBD/GD), Marek's disease (MD), avian mycoplasmosis, Aujeszky's disease (IBD/GD), Marek's disease (MD), avian mycoplasmosis, Aujeszky's disease (pseudorabies), bovine viral diarrhea (BVD), bovine immunodeficiency virus infection (BIV), Border disease, infectious hydropericardium syndrome, bovine leucosis etc.

Regional diagnostic laboratories

Till 1990, the concept of quality assurance process was not being adopted in India. Recently, the Dept. of Animal Husbandry and Dairying has designated one central and four regional disease diagnostic referral laboratories under the Animal Disease Management and Requlatory Medicine Scheme at Pune, Kolkata, Bangalore and Jalandhar. The Centre for Animal Disease Research & Diagnosis (CADRAD) of the Indian Veterinary Research Institute, Izatnagar has been identified as the referral apex laboratory. There are about

100 district level diagnostic laboratories in country. In addition a large number of State level diagnostic laboratories are also functional in private and public sector to meet out the requirement of the country but these units need to be updated and strengthened to meet the SPS requirements. For exotic animal diseases diagnosis ICAR has established High Security Animal Disease Laboratory (HSADL) at Bhopal with Biosafety Level-4 (BL-4) containment facilities.

Animal quarantine network

In order to regulate the import and export of livestock and livestock products, control of exotic disease and to provide certification as per OIE regulations, Animal Quarantine and Certification Services (AQ&CS) at few international air ports under the control of Department of Animal Husbandry & Dairying is existing and the department is contemplating to set up two more Quarantine Stations. Further, no facilities are available at the seaports, which are very important imports points. The quarantine facilities at land route border also do not exist. These need to be put in place immediately. The Animal Quarantine Certification and Enforcement Authority is being established with necessary autonomy, authority to function as an independent body empowered with legislative authority, so that the movement of animals risking infection/disease could be adequately controlled through important airport, seaport, international land routes and movement within the states. Establishing Diseases Free Zones for selected diseases by zoning and buffer zoning keeping international view of OIE and WTO, with strict enforcement of phyto-sanitary and zoo sanitary requirements is a new initiative.

Rapid and sensitive disease diagnosis and control

With the concerted efforts during recent past many of the conventional diseases are on decline but new diseases are emerging. Therefore, in order to sustain the productivity it is essential to develop research support for diagnostics technologies and immunobiological against various diseases of livestock and poultry using newer technological interventions. Development of protocols and diagnostic kits for existing as well as emerging diseases through newer technologies, up gradation to cost efficient industrial processes for their mass production are necessary.

Development of potent vaccines against most bacterial and viral diseases with testing for their efficacy and safety under field conditions are the pre-requisites of any diagnostics and vaccines. Application of biotechnological tools such as recombinant DNA, hybridoma technology, etc, for novel vaccine needs to be adopted. Control of disease can be achieved only in a phased manner by the application of large-scale immunization of all the susceptible livestock using a potent vaccine. The crux of the problem is therefore, the judicious use of a quality assured vaccine. Research should be continued on the development of new generation vaccine/diagnostics using recombinant DNA technology with synthetic and sub-unit vaccines and built-in adjuvant. Quality and safety for livestock and livestock products are essential, hence the need for the use of GMP, HACCP approach and risk assessment management is essential in formulating the action points in terms of quality control.

The present export and import policy announced by Govt. of India recently have the philosophy to regulate necessary export and import through the tariff mechanism by abolishing the licensing restriction. The basic objective of policy is to encourage the attainment of high and internationally accepted standards of quality and thereby enhance the picture of India as a whole. The capital goods, raw materials, consumable, spares parts, accessories and other goods are allowed to be imported without any restriction except to the extent such imports are regulated by the negative list of imports. Therefore, in clear terms it can be explained that a free import of any veterinary bilologicals except those listed in negative list under Section G can be imported.

Bio-containment facility

The disease causing agents of both humans and animals are broadly classified into risk groups I, II, III, IV and V. The risk group I and II are of low individual and community risk, and moderate individual risk and limited community risk respectively. These disease causing agents (risk group I and II) can be handled in conventional laboratories existing all over the country. Risk group III organisms having high individual and low community risk should be handled in Biosafety level-III laboratories. Risk group IV organisms pose high individual risk and high community risk, while Risk group V organisms are exotic (non-native) to a country. These organisms (risk group IV and V) should be handled in maximum containment laboratories (Biosafety level-IV). The recently established High Security Animal Disease Laboratory (HSADL), IVRI, Bhopal in 1998 has BL-4 facility to safely handle high risk pathogens.

Status of O.I.E. List 'A' and List 'B' diseases in India

Among the List 'A' diseases of cattle and buffaloes, except for foot and mouth disease, India is free from all other diseases namely, rinderpest, vesicular stomatitits, contagious bovine pleuropneumonia, lumpy skin disease and Rift Valley fever.

The OIE was founded in Paris in 1924 as the world organization for animal health, and comprised of 167 Member Countries in the year 2005. The principal aims of the OIE are: to ensure transparency in the global animal disease and zoonosis situation, to collect, analyze and disseminate scientific veterinary information, to provide expertise and encourage international solidarity in the control of animal disease, within its mandate under the Agreement on Sanitary and Phytosanitary Measures (SPS Agreement) of the World Trade Organization (WTO), to safeguard world trade by publishing health standards for international trade in animals and animal products, to improve the legal framework and resources of national veterinary services and to provide a better guarantee of the safety of food of animal origin and to promote animal welfare trough a science-based approach.

The role of the Food and Agriculture Organization (FAO) of the United Nations

FAO, established in 1945, is responsible for agricultural development and food production. The Animal Production and Health Division ('AGA') within the Agriculture Department is concerned with livestock development, and it includes the Animal Health Service ('AGAH'), the main role of which is to assist member countries in the control of animal diseases, with the aim of improving livestock production as an integral component of general social, economic and agricultural development. FAO's involvement in testing veterinary biological is primarily through its technical assistance system to member countries to set up and even execute independent quality control of vaccines and other biologicals. One example is FAO's assistance to the AU (African Union) in setting up a system for continental testing of veterinary vaccines, especially against rinderpest and contagious bovine pleuropneumonia, by the Pan African Veterinary Vaccine Center (PANVAC). FAO also commissions, at the request of member countries, initiatives for either quality assurance of vaccines and other biologicals or expert consultations on this subject, or publication of manuals on the production and quality control of vaccines. Furthermore, two auxiliary services can be asked to intervene on matters concerning these products, namely Codex Alimentarius and the Division of Nuclear Techniques in Food and Agriculture. The latter is operated jointly by FAO and the International Atomic Energy Agency (IAEA) based in Vienna (Austria). It has an Animal Production and Health Section, which assists veterinary services and research institutes in developing countries to establish radio-immunoassay (RIA) and ELISA techniques. Linked to this activity is a quality assurance scheme under which laboratories in receipt of FAO/IAEA ELISA kits are required to routinely monitor internal quality controls and to periodically (once or twice a year) test a batch of unknown samples, and to forward the results to IAEA. The overall aim is to provide assurance to all concerned that the results being generated through the use of such internationally standardized and validated kits can be relied upon as correct.

The developed countries have well organized animal health information management systems through epidemiological surveillance, a priority area of international activity of the FAO. These systems essentially incorporate active monitoring through national random sample surveys; develop computerized national relational data bases and networks; analysis and GIS mapping of national epidemiological disease data and interactive national animal health information system and disease forecasting system for the benefit of end-user, contributors, planner, decision-makers and researchers.

The role of the World Health Organization

Currently WHO in not directly involved in preparing international reference preparations (i.e. antigens or antibodies) for purely veterinary use, but has developed and still retains in the National institute for Biological Standards and Control, Potter's Bar (UK) some materials related to purely veterinary diseases (e.g. Newcastle disease live vaccine, anti-swine fever serum). WHO wishes to retain a role in this area in instances where the veterinary reference preparations and guidance documents have a direct relevance to human health. This involves zoonotic and potentially zoonotic agents and other infectious agents of animal origin that are potential contaminants of biological products, whether these are vaccines produced in cell cultures or organs for xenotransplantation. At the meeting of the Expert Committee on Biological Standardization in October 1998, a review of currently retained international standards and reference preparations for veterinary medicine was carried out and a list of candidates for discontinuation, replacement and revision was suggested. The Expert Committee however decided to defer taking action on preparation of veterinary reference materials pending an evaluation by WHO with its partners in the veterinary field of the need for these various biological products. In addition, the present day topicality of certain preparations, especially veterinary vaccines against known zoonoses (e.g. anthrax, burcellosis) adopted and/or revised in the 1960s and 1970s, also needs to be evaluated.

The role of VICH

VICH is a trilateral (EU-Japan-USA) programme aimed at harmonizing technical requirements for veterinary product registration. Its full title is the

International Cooperation on Harmonization of Technical Requirements for Registration of Veterinary Medicinal Products. VICH was officially launched in April 1996.

Conclusions

Some of the limitations and challenges in small ruminant production system that needs to be addressed are inadequate feed and water resources, low productivity and limited availability of health services, limited hygienic facilities for marketing safe and fresh meat and other value added products and poor management practices. However, the scope of developing the small ruminant sector clearly exists if organized efforts are undertaken to improve the preventive and curative animal health services, and the access and quality of common property resources, which forms a major source of feed and fodder and lastly improvement of the germ-plasm. Diseases like PPR, enterotoxaemia, sheep pox can be prevented by timely vaccinations and losses to farmers be minimized. Poor infrastructural facilities and inadequate health services leads to heavy economic losses to farmers due to high mortality. Therefore, delivery of animal health services to shepherds and marginal farmers need to be strengthened. Since sheep and goats are left to browse on common lands, post harvested cropped areas, road side and limited forest areas with minimal or no supplementary feeding, on an average carcass of sheep and goat weighing 12 kg and 10 kg, respectively, are only obtained. With the introduction of interventions like stall feeding and basic knowledge of primary health care (such as de-worming) can raise the body weight substantially and benefit farmers. Unavailability of sufficient feed and fodder resources due to environmental degradation compels the farmers to migrate to neighboring areas or states. Annual sheep migration is driven by feed, fodder, and water scarcity rather than a voluntary option. Since landless, small and marginal farmers are dependent on common property resources, often they get affected by policies of forest department and watershed programs that deny access to these resources.

Although blamed for negatively impacting environment, small ruminants can improve soil and vegetation cover as well as plant and animal biodiversity, for example by consuming biomass, which otherwise might provide the fuel for bush fires, by controlling shrub growth and by dispersing seeds through their hooves and manure, which can improve plant species composition. In addition, trampling can stimulate grass tilling; improve seed germination and break-up hard soil crusts. Small ruminants are vulnerable to a variety of infectious emerging and non-emerging diseases. In the recent years, a number of emerging and reemerging diseases affecting the small ruminants have been reported causing enormous economic losses. Out of many emerging diseases,

PPR, sheep pox, goat pox, BT, enterotoxaemia and brucellosis are notable ones. So, an in depth knowledge of the emerging and re-emerging diseases including the pathogenesis, clinical symptoms, diagnosis, treatment and control is the need of the hour so that the management of the diseases can be made in a very effective and efficient manner.

References

Anon, 1994. Intergovernmental Panel on Climate Change 1994. Radiative Forcing of Climate Change - Report of the Scientific Assessment Working Group of IPCC - Summary for Policy Makers.

Brooks, N., Adger, W. N. and Kelly, P. M. 2005. The determinants of vulnerability and adaptive capacity at the national level and the implications for adaptation. Global Environmental Change 15: 151-163.

Dercksen, D., Nibbelink, N.C., Paauwe, R., Backx, A., Rijn, P. and van Vellema, P. 2007. First outbreak of bluetongue in goats in the Netherlands. Tijdschr. Diergeneeskd 132(20): 786-790.

Linthicum, J.L., Anyamba, A., Tucker, C.J., Kelley, P.W., Myers, M. and Peters, C.J. 1999. Rift Valley fever and satellite imagery. Science 285: 397-399.

McDermott, J.J., Randolph, T.F. and Staal, S.J. 1999. The economics of optimal health and productivity in smallholder livestock systems in developing countries. Review Scientific Technical Office International Epizootics 18(2): 399-419.

McDermott, J.J., Kristjanson, P.M., Kruska, R.L., Reid, R.S., Robinson, T.P., Coleman, P.G., Jones, P.G., Thornton, P.K. 2001. Effects of climate, human population and socio-economic changes on tsetse-transmitted trypanosomiasis to 2050. In: R. Seed, S. Black (Eds). World Class Parasites – Vol. 1. The African Trypanosomes, Kluwer, Boston, 25-38. ISBN 0-7923-7512-2.

Mellore, P.S. 1998. Climate change and the distribution of vector-borne diseases with special reference to African horsesickness virus. Towards livestock disease diagnosis and control in the 21st century. In: Proceedings of the IAEA/FAO symposium on diagnosis and control of livestock diseases using nuclear and related techniques. Vienna, IAEA.

Patz, J. A., Campbell-Lendrum, D., Holloway, T. and Foley, J. A. 2005. Impact of regional climate change on human health. Nature 438 : 310-317.

Purse, B. V., Mellor, P.S., Rogers, D. J., Samuel, A. R., Martens, P. P. and Baylis, P. S. M. 2005. Climate change and the recent emergence of bluetongue in Europe. Nature Review of Microbiology 3: 171–181.

Willliams, J. 2004. Sustainable development in Africa: is the climate right? IRI Technical Report IRI-TR/05/01. The International Research Institute for Climate Prediction, Palisades, New York. Online at http://iri.columbia.edu

□□□

3

Water-Related Disasters in Asia Context : Risk Management and Environmental Response - Concern to Animal's for Human Sustainability

Anil K. Gupta*, Sreeja S. Nair and Mohammad Yunus[1]
National Institute of Disaster Management, Government of India, New Delhi- 110 002
[1]School for Environmental Sciences, B.B. Ambedkar (Central) University
Lucknow- 226 025, Uttar Pradesh

Introduction

The world is facing an increasing frequency and intensity of disasters - natural and man-made - that has had devastating impacts. As reported by the secretariat of the International Strategy for Disaster Reduction (ISDR, 2004), the last ten years have seen 478,100 people killed, more than 2.5 billion people affected and about US$ 690 billion in economic losses. In 2005 alone, over 150,000 people perished in some 700 disasters that affected 600 million men, women and children, and caused $265 billion in damages. Future trends with regard to natural disasters are expected to be non-linear, featuring critical thresholds caused by abrupt changes in earth system dynamics. Asia and South Asia, in particular, are among the most disaster prone regions in the world. During the last decade 56% of those killed world wide by disasters were in South Asia.

The impact of the disasters on pets and other animals is often far more devastating than on the human population in the disaster area. Animals are not allowed in shelters, and their owners often have no time to make other arrangements for their pet's safety and security before the disaster strikes. After departing from the area of the disaster, the animal owners will often try to re-enter the now secured area of the disaster, only to be stopped by law enforcement personnel whose job it is to prevent people from entering the disaster area. The survival of a beloved pet or valuable livestock then will often depend on the plans that its owner has made in advance. Most prevalent 'disaster science terminology' in recent times is given hereunder:

(i) Disaster

A serious disruption of the functioning of a community or a society causing widespread human, material, economic or environmental losses which exceed the ability of the affected community or society to cope using its own resources. A disaster is a function of the risk process. It results from the combination of hazards, conditions of vulnerability and insufficient capacity or measures to reduce the potential negative consequences of risk.

(ii) Hazard

A potentially damaging physical event, phenomenon or human activity that may cause loss of life or injury, property damage, social and economic disruption, or environmental degradation. Hazards can include latent conditions that may represent future threats and can have different origins: natural (geological, hydrometeorological or biological) or induced by human processes (environmental degradation and technological hazards). Hazards can be single, sequential or combined in their origin and effects. Each hazard is characterised by its location, intensity, frequency and probability.

(iii) Hydrometeorological hazards

Natural processes or phenomena of atmospheric, hydrological or oceanographic nature, which may cause loss of life or injury, property damage, social and economic disruption, or environmental degradation. Hydrometeorological hazards include: floods, debris and mud floods; tropical cyclones, storm surges, thunder/hailstorms, rain and windstorms, blizzards and other severe storms; drought, desertification, wildland fires, temperature extremes, sand or dust storms; permafrost and snow or ice avalanches. Hydrometeorological hazards can be single, sequential or combined in their origin and effects.

(iv) Disaster risk management

The systematic process of using administrative decisions, organization, operational skills and capacities to implement policies, strategies and coping capacities of the society and communities to lessen the impacts of natural hazards and related environmental and technological disasters. This comprises all forms of activities, including structural and non-structural measures to avoid (prevention) or to limit (mitigation and preparedness) adverse effects of hazards.

At least a billion of the world's poorest people depend on animals for food, fibre, income, social status, security, and companionship. Climate change is expected to cause an increase in weather-related disasters and extreme weather events, such as droughts, heat waves, storms, desertification, and increases in insect infestations. Long-term changes in climate will jeopardise the future of all animals—including those in oceans, on farms, in forests, in wilderness areas, and in our homes. All climate change related hazards and their related disasters have a negative impact on animals.

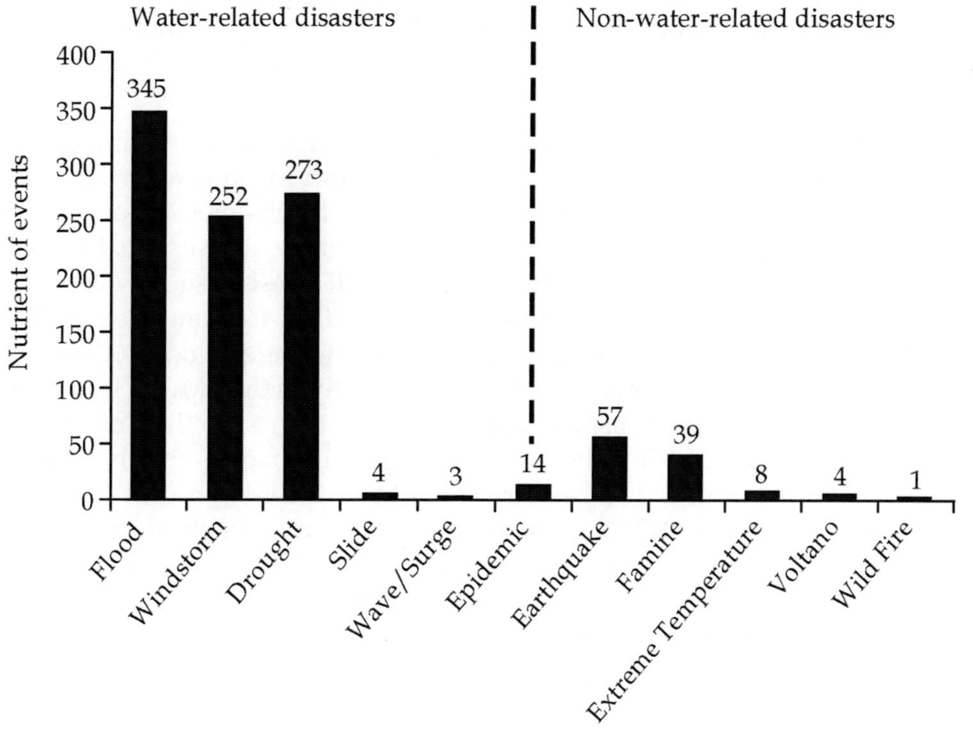

Fig. 1. One thousand most disastrous natural disaster events from 1900 to 2006

As the global temperatures will increase, the effects will be quite complex and vary from region to region. Though the extent of these effects is uncertain, it is known that those communities and regions with the least resources, such as rural agricultural areas, will be the most vulnerable to climate change. Warmer and wetter weather (particularly warmer winters) will increase the risk and occurrence of animal diseases, as certain species who serve as disease vectors, such as biting flies and ticks, are more likely to survive year-round. Certain existing parasitic diseases may also become more prevalent, or their geographical range may spread, if rainfall increases. This may contribute to an increase in disease spread, including zoonotic diseases.

Transportation of animals for personal, entertainment, or agricultural purposes also increases the possibility for the introduction and subsequent presence of diseases and pests, including ticks and parasites, previously considered exotic. The viral infection Bluetongue Disease, for example, was once only a threat in Africa, now affects cattle and sheep in the whole of Europe. Conditions inherent in industrial animal agriculture facilities can increase the emergence of diseases that affect humans and animals alike. Outbreaks of diseases such as Foot & Mouth Disease or Avian Influenza affect very large numbers of animals and contribute to further degradation of the environment and surrounding communities' health and livelihood.

Disasters: Global scenario and trends

Trends in natural disasters show they are continually increasing in most regions of the world. Among all observed natural and anthropogenic adversities, water-related disasters are undoubtedly the most recurrent, and pose major impediments to achieving human security and sustainable socio-economic development, as recently witnessed with disasters such as the Indian Ocean tsunami in 2004, Hurricane Katrina in 2005, Cyclone Sidr in 2007, Cyclone Nargis in 2008 and many others. During the period 2000 to 2006, 2,163 water-related disasters were reported globally in the EM-DAT database, killing more than 290,000 people, afflicting more than 1.5 billion people and inflicting more than US$422 billion in damages. The factors that have led to increased waterrelated disasters are thought to include natural pressures, such as climate variability; management pressures, such as the lack of appropriate organizational systems and inappropriate land management; and social pressures, such as an escalation of population and settlements in high-risk areas (particularly for poor people). The United Nations University Institute for Environment and Human Security (UNU-EHS) warns that unless preventative efforts are stepped up, the number of people vulnerable to flood disasters worldwide is expected to mushroom to two billion by 2050 as a result of climate change, deforestation, rising sea levels and population growth in flood-prone lands (Bogardi, 2004).

Table 1. The frequency of recorded natural disaster occurrences globally between 1900 and 2006.

	1900-2006	Number of Disasters	(%)	Number killed	(%)	Total affected	(%)	Real Damage	(%)
Water-related Disasters	Flood	3,050	29.8	6,899,095	18.5	3,027,693,701	48.3	342,968,287	25.9
	Windstorm	2,758	26.9	10,008,806	3.2	752,843,507	12.0	536,432,227	40.5
	Drought	836	8.2	1,208,806	26.8	2,239,624,826	35.7	61,262,901	4.6
	Slides	508	5.0	55,980	0.2	10,206,768	0.2	3,487,457	0.3
	Wave/Surge	52	0.5	295,813	0.8	2,596,663	0.0	7,850,747	0.6
Non Water-related Disasters	Epidemic	1,035	10.1	9,528,995	25.6	40,156,618	0.6	4,737	0.0
	Wild Fire	312	3.0	2,710	0.0	4,019,267	0.1	29,574,293	2.2
	Extreme Temperature	322	3.1	69,138	0.2	11,466,747	0.2	21,843,847	1.6
	Volcano	193	1.9	95,917	0.3	4,907,517	0.1	3,842,646	0.3
	Insect Infection	83	0.8	0	0.0	2,200	0.0	230,125	0.0
	Famine	76	0.7	7,158,229	19.2	70,996,301	1.1	93,449	0.0
	Earthquake	1,025	10.0	1,963,172	5.3	104,038,367	1.7	317,580,870	24.0
	Total	10,250	100.0	37,286,332	100.0	6,268,551,482	100.0	1,325,171,586	100.0

In general, all water-related disasters events increased between 1980 and the end of the twentieth century. Floods and windstorm events increased drastically from 1997 to 2006, but other types of disaster did not increase significantly in this period. Floods doubled during the period 1997 to 2006 and windstorms increased more than 1.5 times. Drought was severe at the beginning of the 1980s and gained momentum again during the late 1990s and afterwards. The numbers of landslides and water-borne epidemics were at their highest during the period 1998–2000 and then decreased. Waves and surges increased between 1980 and 2006.

Hydro-meteorological disasters in Asia / South-Asia and rest of the world

Records show that Asia had the highest number of people affected by floods during the period from 1980 to 2006, with a steady nine-digit number. Asia is prone to floods, windstorms and slides, among other water-related disasters, and Africa is particularly prone to water-borne epidemics. The ranking according to the number of water-related disasters they experience is Asia, Africa, the Americas, Europe and Oceania, in descending order.

(i) Floods

In general, the number of floods increased between 1980 and 2006 in every world region. The number of floods was recorded as being highest in

Asia and more than trebled during the period. Floods increased more than four-fold in Africa in the 1990s, which overtook the Americas to take the second-worst rank. In Europe floods increased from the early 1980s to 2006. Flood fatalities in Asia ranked worst, followed by the Americas, Africa, Europe and Oceania in that order. Between 1980 and 2006, flood disasters throughout the world claimed more than 182,000 lives, and Asia alone accounted for more than 64% of the global total, followed by the Americas with more than 26%.

(ii) Windstorms

Windstorms increased between 1980 and 2006 in every region, except for a trough during the period from 1995 to 1997 in Asia. It is worth noting that windstorms increased steadily in the Americas throughout the period from 1980 to 2006. Asia is the most windstorm-prone region, closely followed by the Americas. The other regions are also hit by windstorms, but less frequently.

(iii) Slides

Slides (landslides and avalanches, see Glossary) did not show any distinct trends in any region except in Asia, where they increased more than four-fold, with the highest numbers recorded between 1980 and 2006 – although there was a decline between 2003 and 2006 (Figure 3.8). The Americas are second in terms of the number of slides, but have shown nothing likes the increases seen in Asia and there was no significant change in the number of slides during this period. Numerous gigantic slides were recorded between 1980 and 2006 in India and China, followed by Bangladesh, the Philippines and Iran. The number of fatalities caused by slides increased in Asia between 1980 and 2006, with a peak in the period 1995 to 1997, one in the late 1980s and another in the late 1990s. More than 64% of the fatalities between 1980 and 2006 occurred in Asia, 25% occurred in the Americas, and 6.5% occurred in Europe.

(iv) Waves and Surges *(including tsunami)*

Because waves and surges occur only occasionally, it is impossible to analyze the trends between 1980 and 2006. From 1980 until the mid- 1990s, no waves and surges were recorded in any region except in Asia. But since the mid 1990s, waves and surges have been recorded in the Americas, and since 2000, waves and surges have begun to occur in other regions including Africa and Oceania.

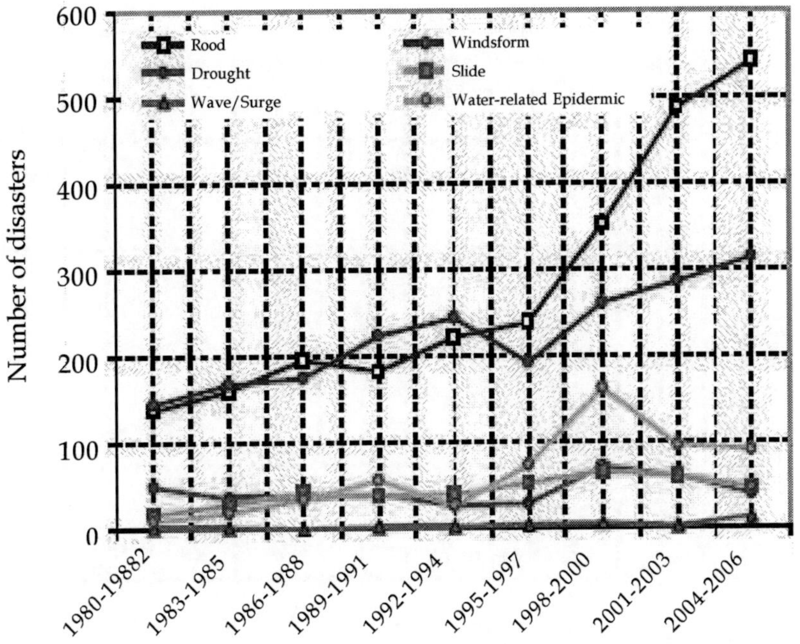

Fig 2. Water-related disaster events recorded globally, 1980 to 2006

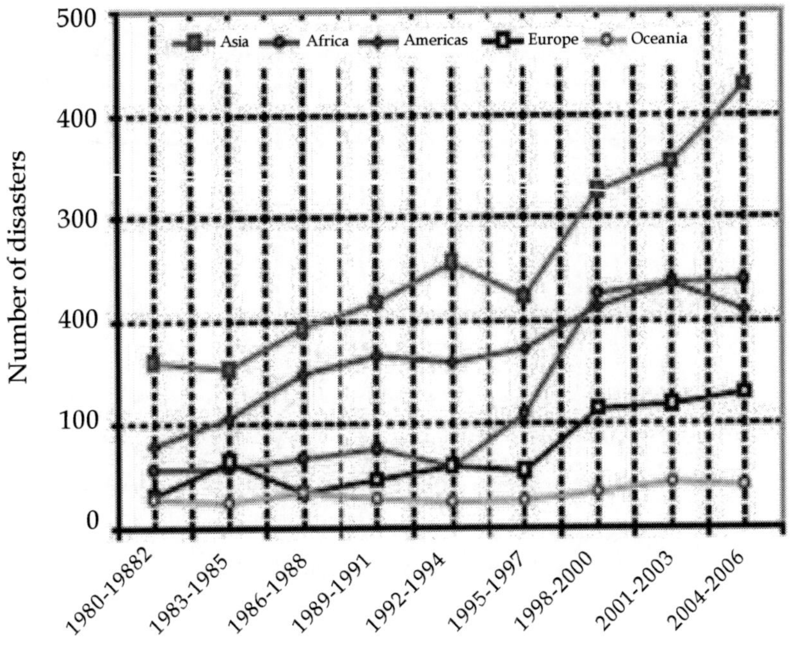

Fig. 3. Recorded water-related disasters by region, 1980 to 2006

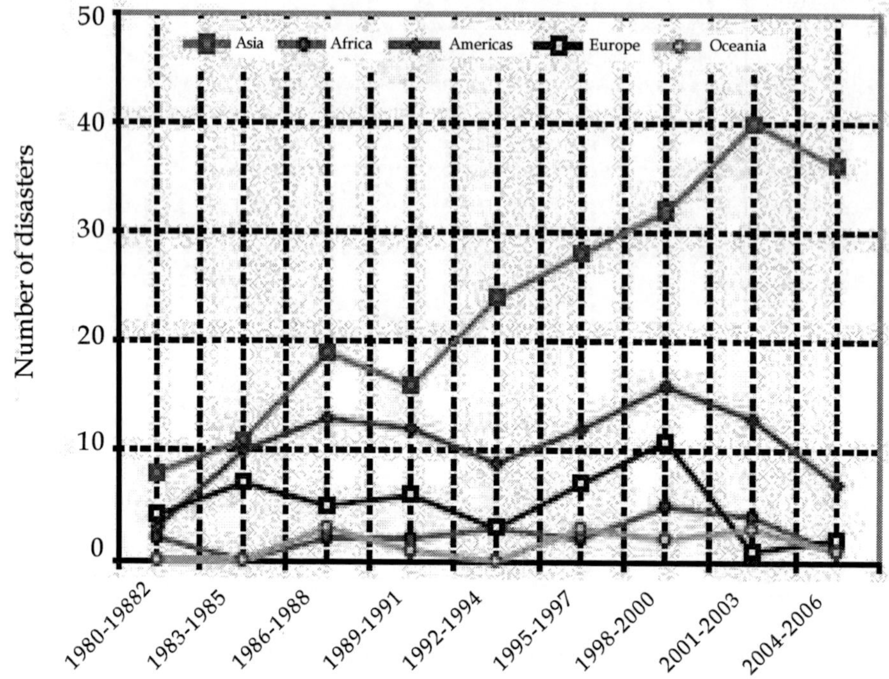

Fig. 4. Recorded numbers of slides by region, 1980 to 2006

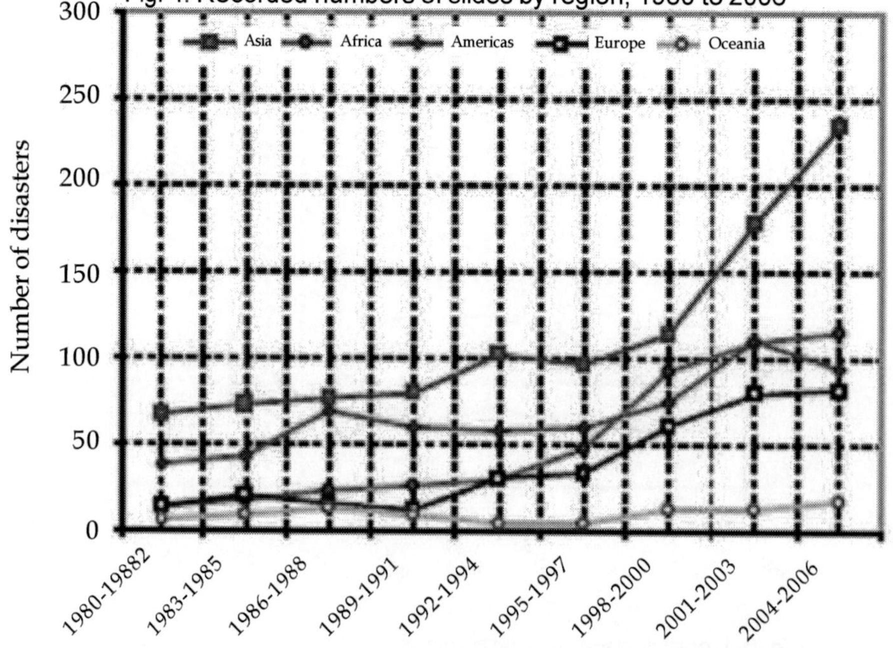

Fig. 5. Recorded numbers of floods by region 1980 to 2006.

(v) Droughts

The numbers of droughts did not show any clear pattern from 1980 to 2006 though droughts are prominent in Africa. In the African region, droughts decreased in the period from 1992 to 1994, then increased again. Asia and the Americas suffered the highest number of droughts between 1998 and 2000. It is interesting to note that droughts in all regions except Africa peaked between 1998 and 2000 and then declined. It has been reported in recent years that droughts have caused huge damage in regions other than Africa, through crop failures in Australia, the Mediterranean region, some parts of Europe such as Spain and Portugal, and parts of Asia such as India and China. Approximately 99% of the total fatalities worldwide between 1980 and 2006 were Asians, which further suggests that the region is the most vulnerable to wave and surge disasters. In Asia, drought fatalities increased until 1991 and then declined suddenly. In general, drought fatalities were recorded more commonly around the world indicating an increase in severity.

(vi) Epidemics

Water-borne epidemic diseases show an increasing trend between 1980 and 2006; especially from the mid 1990s, which is alarming. A drastic increase in epidemics coincides with the increasing number of floods and windstorms, which supports a conclusion that water-borne epidemics are a direct aftermath of these disastrous events. The geographical distribution indicates that Africa is severely affected by epidemics (PWRI, 2008), suffering a total of 334 water-borne epidemics between 1980 and 2006, whereas Asia encountered less than half that number (145 events). Globally, the number of epidemics was at its highest in the period from 1998 to 2000, which is thought to be influenced by the African and Asian regional peaks. It is worth noting that Asia and Africa had similar patterns in term of the number of water-borne epidemics until 2000, after which they declined in Asia but became more vigorous in Africa. In general, fatalities caused by water-borne epidemics decreased in Asia but remained steady in Africa between 1980 and 2006.

Climate-Change Implications

Climate-change, a phenomenon described as resultant global temperature rise, is known to accelerate the melting of glaciers, and thus exacerbated the risks and likely disastrous consequences on the people and their land-uses. Besides this the increase in the incidence of abrupt variability in climate patterns has posed major threats to human environment. It often occurs in the form of heavy precipitation over shorter periods, unexpected lack of rain in certain areas, thus, realizing threats to severe losses of life, property and natural resources which are the main livelihood support systems in the mountains. Populations had adapted to the known threats over the evolutionary periods, but now under the climate-change age, have to learn new adaptations in terms of livelihoods, natural resource management (NRM) practices, and living including disaster responses, health, food, etc. Mountains host the fragile ecosystems and therefore developing the region-specific adaptation strategies for climate-change impacts and related disaster-risks is a basic requirement for sustainable mountain development. Linking community based natural resource management (CBNRM) practices to disaster-risk-management is, thus, has to be an strategy line, and the scientific interpretations based on region-specific environmental risk assessments and hazard & vulnerability mapping may be an approach in practice.

Animals are intrinsically dependent on the environment, and any fluctuations in weather and climate can affect them through water and land changes, such as desertification, and feed and water availability, access, and appropriateness. Climate change will not only impact the health and welfare of animals, but also the more than billion people who depend on them. Desertification and climate change are inextricably linked through feedbacks between land degradation and precipitation: less rain leads to soil compaction and hardening, making the land unable to absorb rainwater. This could have disastrous effects as rain becomes less frequent but heavier. Climate-change as result of complex and cumulative impact globe-wide regional/locale scale environmental degradation (emission plus sink reduction) along unprecedented environmental/anthropogenic stresses/alterations has led to accelerated incidences and intensities of disasters and their impacts (Fig. 6).

The increased use of chemical-based agricultural inputs, including artificial fertilizers, pesticides, and herbicides, and their impact on soil and water quality will likely exacerbate the effects of climate change by further degrading other ecosystems such as coral reefs1 and rivers2, decreasing the land's ability to produce food3. It is much easier for farmers in developed countries to endure a climatic setback than those in poorer nations such as Malawi, where 80% of the population lives in rural areas4 and approximately 40% of the economy is supported by rain-fed agriculture5. For example, as grazing areas dry up in sub-Saharan Africa, pastoralists will be forced to travel farther to find food. Cattle, goats, camels, sheep, and wildlife dependant on access to grazing areas for food will suffer6. This will lead to greater conflict between people and between people and animals. Resources must be made available to educate and prepare for change if the negative impacts of climate change on animals suffering is to be minimized. Following actions are recommended in line concerning emphasis on animal care concern within climate-change adaptation framework:

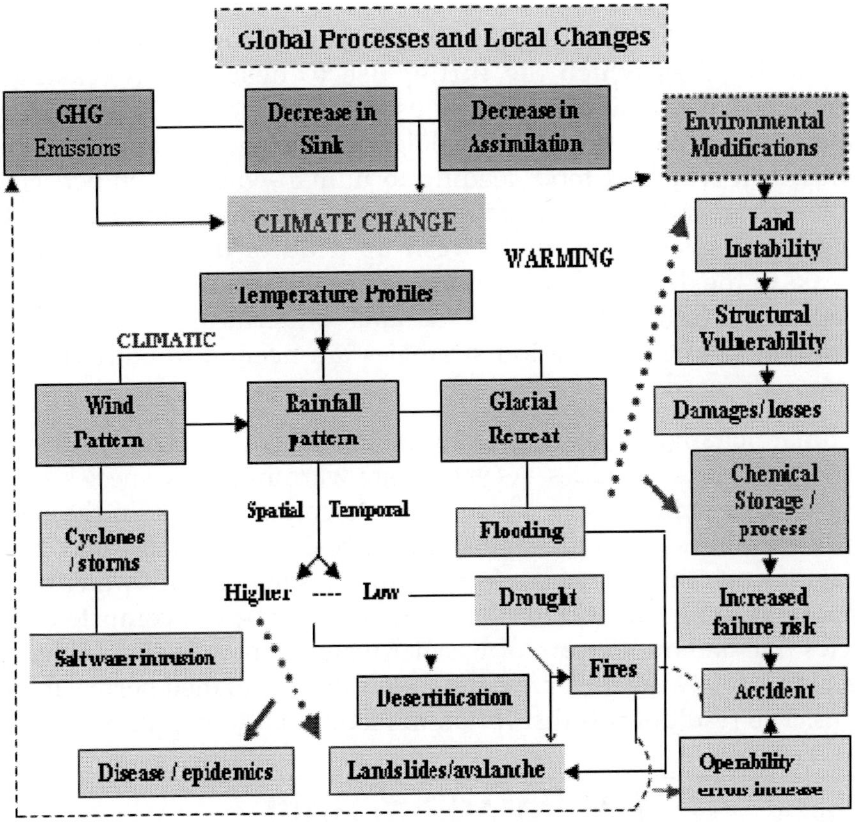

Fig. 6. Environment, climate-change and disasters – Schematic network (conceptualised by authors, Gupta and Nair, 2008).

- Require consultation and guidance from welfare scientists and experts when drafting climate change policy, such as how to reduce green house gases emissions, agriculture management, mitigation strategies, and disaster response;
- Include animal welfare policies in development programmes, compare these programmes to different climate change scenarios and include strategies for minimizing the risk to animals from climate change; and
- Conduct a thorough review of the impact of climate change on farm animals and their welfare, including increased risk of animal disease and starvation due to drought.

Climate change is affecting animals around the world. Not only companion animals stranded after natural disasters, but also livestock and wildlife. Species of sea turtles, some old enough to have seen the dinosaurs come and go, are disappearing before our eyes. Stronger storms are eroding the sandy beaches which the turtles use to nest and increasing sand temperatures have skewed egg sex ratios, producing mostly females. The loss of summer sea ice is causing starving polar bears to move to towns and human settlements in search of food, leading to human-wildlife conflict. Harmful algal blooms are stripping seabird feathers of vital water-proofing properties, causing hundreds of seabirds to wash up dead or dying on our beaches. Outbreaks of the deadly Ebola hemorrhagic fever virus are increasing among great apes. The future migration of monarch butterflies is threatened. Long-term climate change adaptation strategies are needed to address many of these animals' needs.

Climate change is leading to food shortages and changes in feeding patterns of migratory species. As waters are warming, prey species are either not thriving or shifting their range towards colder waters. In the Southern Ocean for example, penguins, albatrosses, seals, and whales may be faced with significant food shortages. As temperatures in bodies of water rise, krill, an important source of food for these species, may be out-competed by *salps*, a species that is more tolerant of warmer waters. There is also evidence that predators are following their prey into waters outside of their normal migratory patterns. The result of this disruption in feeding patterns can be disastrous.

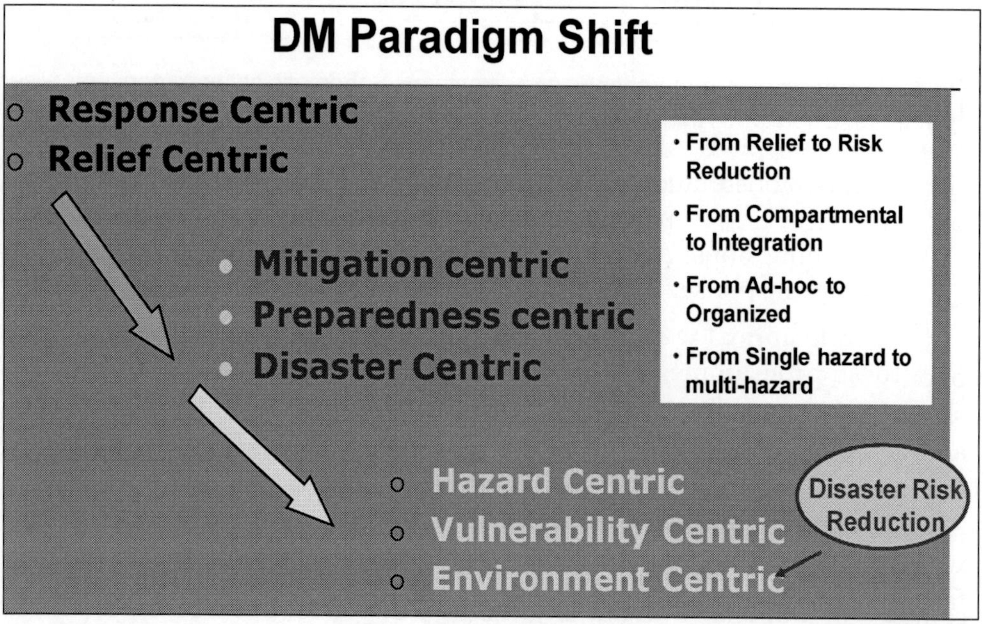

Fig. **7**. Incarnating in-coming 2nd Paradigm shift in Disaster Management (as discipline of environmental science)

Increased risk of oil spills

Another indirect impact of climate change related hazards is an increased risk of large oil spills at sea, resulting in great injury to ecosystems, affected communities and marine wildlife. People are using vast amounts of oil. From the petroleum used to fuel our transportation, heat our homes, and lubricate our machinery, to the asphalt we use to pave our roads, to the myriad of oil-derived products such as plastics, medicines, ink, paints, and fertilizers, oil is literally everywhere. 82 In an increasingly technological era, the world has become and will continue to become more dependent upon oil-based products to help us maintain our high standard of living. 83 In 2007, the United States consumed about 7.5 billion barrels of oil, an increase of almost 30 percent over the last 20 years alone. 84 Currently, global consumption of oil is 3 billion gallons a day. 85 This number is expected to grow as global demand for oil increases. The Organization of the Petroleum Exporting Countries (OPEC) has projected that by 2030 global demand for oil will increase by nearly 34 percent above 2006 levels.

Every step of the transportation equation - from loading, shipping, unloading, piping and storage - presents a chance for oil to escape. 87 During shipping, large unintentional oil spills can be caused by human error, breakdown of equipment, or extreme weather events. 88 Approximately 5.65 million tons of oil was lost as a result of tanker incidents from 1970 to 2008. Oil spills occur all around the world. Large spills (at least 10,000 gallons) have occurred in the waters of 112 nations since 1960. In China, at least 90 percent of the nation's crude oil imports are transported by sea. In 2004, this figure was nearly 110 million tons. Between 1973 and 2003, more than 2,350 oil spills occurred along the nation's coast - one spill every 4.6 days.

Climate change and oil spills

The long-term impacts of climate change are linked to an increased risk of oil spills. Studies have noted that climate change could potentially cause a shift in the Gulf Stream in the North Atlantic, making the Northwest Passage across North America more easily navigable. This, in turn, could lead to increased shipping traffic, possibly increasing the risks of oil spills in a delicate Arctic ecosystem already threatened by melting ice-caps. Short-term extreme weather events are more often the direct cause or one of the contributing factors of large oil spills at sea. This, along with the fact that climate change will likely lead to an increased frequency and intensity of climate change-related storms is likely to increase the risk of future large oil spills.

Impacts of oil spills on animals

Oil spills can be deadly for marine wildlife. When an oil spill occurs in water, it spreads very rapidly, leaving little possibility of escape. Many animals are killed directly after an oil spill. Even a seemingly harmless dime-size drop of oil could kill a bird. In the case of Exxon Valdez, 300 harbor seals, 900 bald eagles, 2,800 sea otters and 250,000 sea birds were killed days after the incident. Three species of cormorant, a type of seabird, the common loon, the harbor seal, the harlequin duck, the pacific herring and the pigeon guillemot still have not fully recovered. The primary immediate effects of oil contamination on animals include hypothermia; dehydration resulting from lack of food; stomach and intestinal disorders and destruction of red blood large oil spills can threaten the livelihoods of those communities that rely on the ocean for food or income.

In the case of Exxon Valdez, over $300 million of economic harm was done to more than 32,000 local people whose livelihoods depended on commercial fishing. Oil spills can also cripple coastal and eco-tourism. Coastal areas provide a variety of recreational activities that are compromised by oil spills, such as boating, scuba diving, fishing, swimming, and whale watching. In the year immediately following the Exxon Valdez disaster, tourism revenue decreased by eight percent in South-Central Alaska and 35 percent in Southwest Alaska. In addition to the direct effects of oil spills mentioned above, public health may also be affected by indirect exposure to oil.

Examples of indirect exposure

Include consumption of contaminated fish or water, or inhalation of evaporated cells resulting from ingestion of oil; pneumonia resulting from inhalation of oil vapors; skin and eye irritation from direct contact with oil; and impaired reproduction. In addition, oil destroys the insulating ability of fur-bearing mammals, such as sea otters, and the water-repelling abilities of a bird's feathers, thus exposing these creatures to hypothermia or possibly freezing to death. Even species that do not come directly in contact with oil can be harmed by a spill. Predators that consume contaminated prey can be exposed to oil through ingestion. In addition, oil can cause incalculable injury to wildlife habitats, making them unsuitable for feeding, nesting, and other services they provide to marine life.

Although marine wildlife may be seriously injured or killed very soon after contact with the oil in a spill, non-lethal toxic effects can be more subtle and often more long-term. In cases where oil does not directly kill an animal, it may compromise its survival. For example, animals with eye damage may be unable to effectively avoid predators. Others may die prematurely due to organ damage. Reproductive success may also be affected by these injuries or by direct damage to reproductive organs or changes in behavior caused by oil exposure. Also, exposure to oil, either directly or via food sources, can have lasting impacts on individuals, populations, and ecosystems.

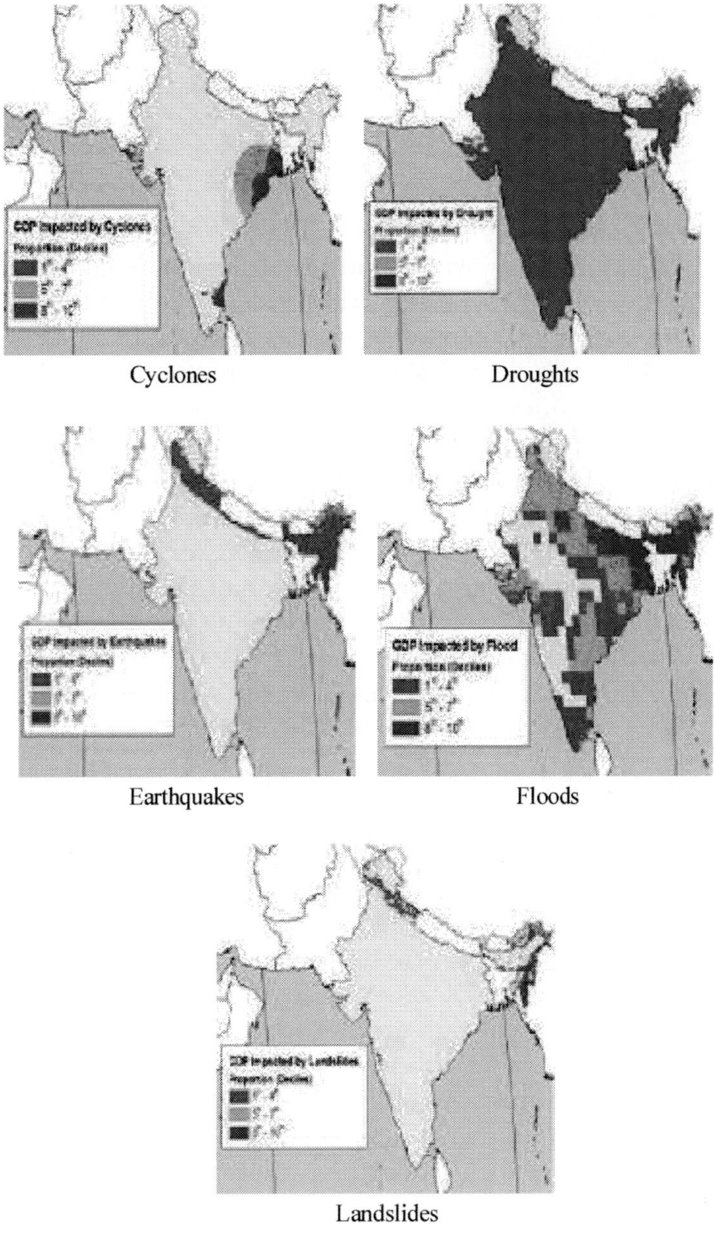

Fig. 8. Natural disaster risk hotspots (Weighted by Proportion of GDP Impacted)

Reduced numbers of prey species due to oil exposure can have a chain reaction, affecting all the species in the food web. It is not clear how long it takes for environments to recover from oil spills. In the case of Exxon Valdez, for example, oil persisted in the environment years after the incident and continues to cause harm to individual animals and some animal populations. In 2006, the Exxon Valdez Oil Spill Trustee Council listed 31 species and resources as still injured by the spill. In the case of the Torrey Canyon, an oil tanker that ran aground off the Isles of Sicily in 1967, spilling 31 million gallons, some scientists believed that the marine environment took over 30 years to fully recover.

Disasters in the Indian context & emerging situations

Due to its unique geo-physical and hydro-climatic conditions, India is vulnerable to almost every type of natural disaster. 85% of the country's area is vulnerable to disasters, wherein 190 districts are accounted to multi-hazard prone areas. About 60% of India's land is prone to earthquakes of various intensities; over 40 million hectares is prone to floods; about 8% of the total area is prone to cyclones and 60-62% of the area is drought prone. India's coastline around 7500 kms is prone to coastal hazards cyclone, flooding and multiple hazards. In the decade 1990-2000, an average of about 4344 people lost their lives and about 30 million people were affected by disasters every year. According a World Bank study, India had been loosing more than 2 percent of its GDP and 15 percent of its revenue every year due to natural disasters whereas equivalent amount could not be invested on health care system. Sub-Himalayan regions and Western Ghats are vulnerable to landslides. (Kanwar 2001: 7, and GOI, 2004:32).

In the decade, 1990-2000, on average, 4,344 people lost their lives and 30 million people were affected by disasters in India every year (GOI 2004:1). Orissa Cyclone (1999) affected almost all the coastal districts of Orissa and a few inland areas also. It is estimated that some 166.69 lakh people were affected by the cyclone. Similarly, in the 2001 Gujarat Earthquake, more than 14,000 lives were lost, 10 lakh houses were damaged and the assets worth Rs. 15,000 crore were damaged / lost (GOI, 2004:33). In droughts, water bodies including tanks and wells dry up, causing acute scarcity of water. Consequently, the problem of drinking water gets accentuated. For example, as a result of drought of the year 2000 in Gujarat, 25 million people in 9500 villages, four metros, and 79 towns were hit by drinking water scarcity (IRMA - UNICEF, 2000). The Orissa Super Cyclone of October 1999 affected around 13 million people, about one third of the state's population and 10,000 people lost their life. It has been estimated that around 4350 persons lost their life every year and 30 million people suffered every year in India due to natural disasters during 1991-2000.

India is facing a serious problem of safer scarcity resulting in droughts of varying scales and nomenclatures, and the increase in drought is attributable to man-made reasons. Socio-economic and environmental vulnerability, both based in regional natural resources & livelihood support system, are the main attributes to the natural hazard related risks to India's people. Poor and marginal people are most vulnerable, often occupying hazard prone areas as well as hazardous land-use practices, besides the populations and sometimes environmental settings under the ill-planned developmental projects and programmes. The trend of so-called natural disasters is towards increase in frequency and intensity due to increase in vulnerability, migration from safer to un-safe places and conditions, population growth, agriculture marginalization, poverty and coupled with aggravating hazards as a possible threat of climate change impacts.

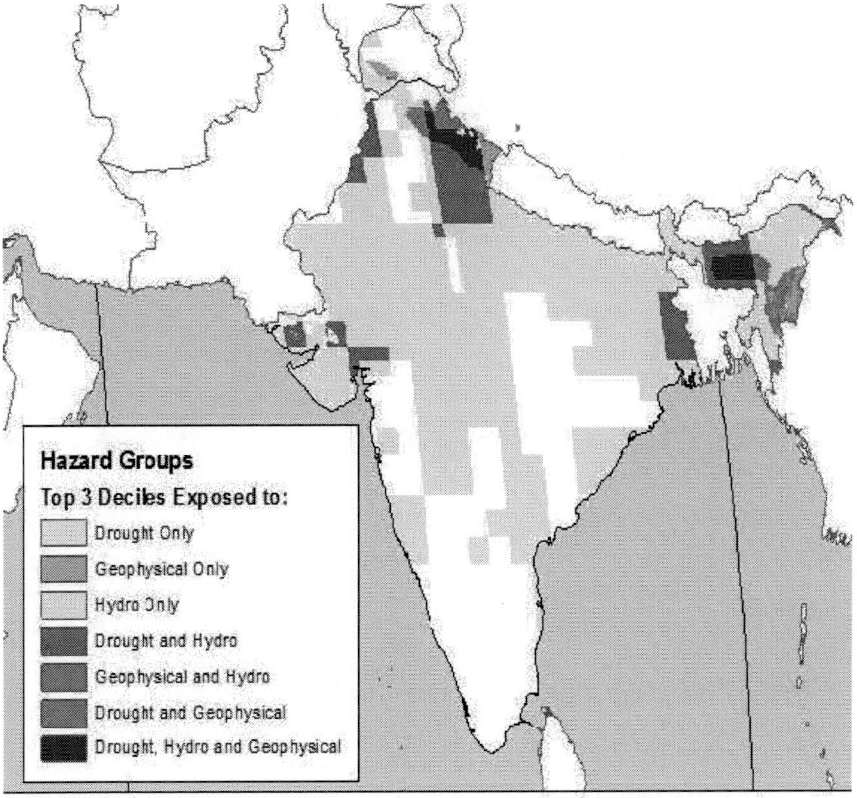

Fig 9. Multi-hazard disaster risk hotspots by hazard groups
(Top Three Deciles) (http://www.ldeo.columbia.edu/chrr/research/profiles/india.html)

Talking of chemical-industrial catastrophes in India, the world's worst ever chemical disaster in Bhopal, was followed by 1985 release of hexacyclopentadiene killed 200 people in Cochin. 1988, fire and explosion in a factory in erstwhile Bombay killed 35 and injured 26 people. 93 were killed and 53 injured when explosion and fire happened in Medhvan Khind in 1991. Same year, 100 more people were exterminated by LNG caused explosion and fire in Bombay Ahmedabad highway. 1993, Sulphuric Acid release from a factory in Kalyan, Maharashtra killed 49 and injured 1123. There have been as many as 119 industrial accidents between 1984 to 1995 involving hazardous chemicals. Year 2000 Hindustan Petroleum Complex - HSD leaked and to more than 100 m of the enclosure wall from A/G tank. More than 60 Kl naptha leaked into river due to overflow in filling operation at Panipat Refinery expansion project: Oil water mixture due to overflow leaked on the ground and got ignited when preparation for hot work on overhead pipeline (4 to 6M high). Recent Industrial/chemical disaster in Jaipur (2009) wherein petroleum fire in oil depot lasted for more than 6 days with reported loss of Rs. 1000 crores, evacuated 5 lac people and in 10 km diameter area, affected livestock and other animals as well who could not get back due to 'no concern' or 'no plan'.

Reported Catastrophe Losses in India, 1965-2001

(Nominal US$ million at then applying exchange rates)

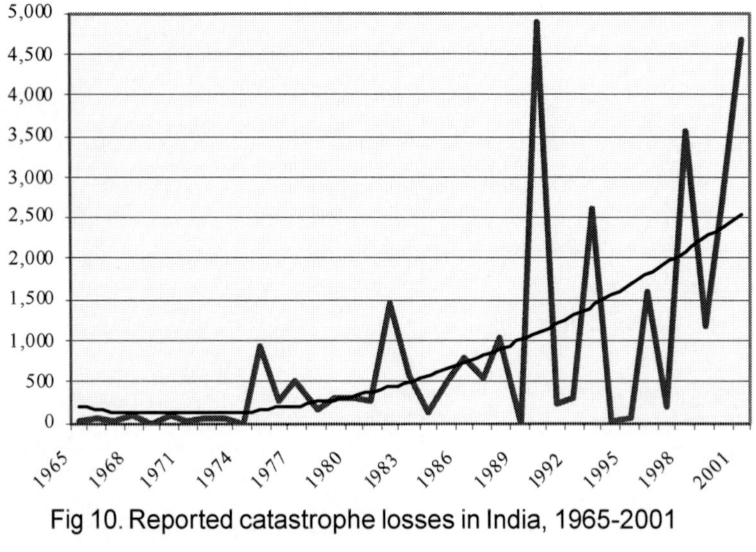

Fig 10. Reported catastrophe losses in India, 1965-2001

Disasters and animals

Every year natural disasters or war wreak havoc on millions of people and their environment. The human tragedy of these incidents is well documented, but less known is the plight of animals: all too often, they are the forgotten victims.

When people's properties are destroyed, animal's homes often disappear too. Wild animals face the prospect of having to flee their home habitat to survive, whilst domesticated animals are at grave risk of remaining trapped and abandoned without food or water on farms, in people's homes, or even at zoos.Flash floods usually occur in areas where the landscape cannot absorb all the water during excessive precipitation events, in steep gradient landscapes, or in zones that have been recently affected by drought or wildfire. Living downstream from a significant precipitation event is a danger zone. Knowing if you are actually downstream may not necessarily be apparent since many flash floods happen in arid regions also. Livestock have a natural *move away* instinct to flash flood waters. They generally seek higher ground if possible. When purchasing or designing your livestock operation, it is important to allow livestock a way to reach high ground in each pasture. Without access, livestock will fight fences and be at a greater risk of drowning. Livestock will initially panic during flash floods. This complicates livestock handling.

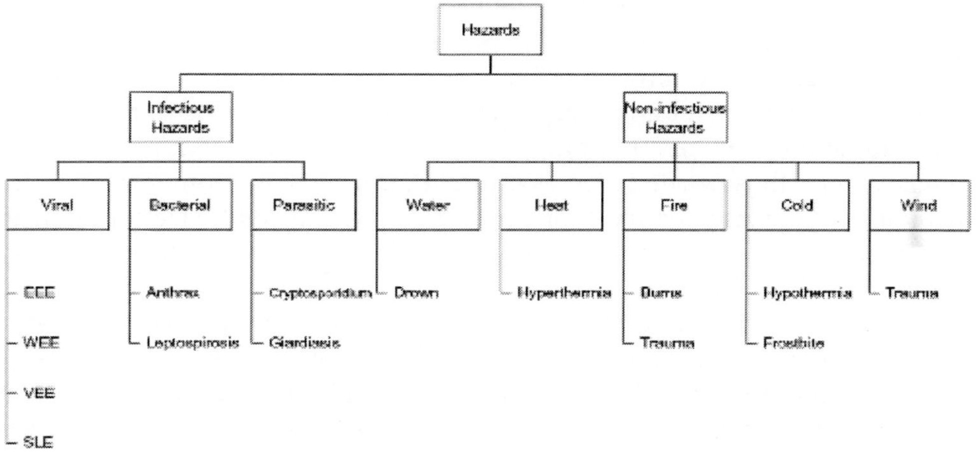

Figure 11. Animal-health hazards of concern and their consequences during natural disasters.

Since large-scale floods are more predictable and usually slower to develop than flash floods, there may have more response time. Livestock will move gradually away from rising floodwaters to higher ground. However, it is a risk; the higher ground may not be high enough to compensate for the final flood level of large-scale floods. Tornadoes have extreme intensity, wind speeds 2 to 3 times that of a hurricane, but they have a very short duration. Livestock hear and sense impending tornadoes. If your family or home is at risk, the livestock will be a non-issue. If your personal safety is not an issue, you may only have time to open routes of escape for your livestock.

Although the surface speeds of wildfires vary from 5 to 40 miles per hour, all wildfires generate smoke, heat and sound. Livestock are very sensitive and responsive to wildfire anywhere within their sensory range. Normal reactions vary from nervousness, to panic, to aggressive and resistive escape attempts. Livestock are often injured or killed by fleeing from a wildfire into fences, barriers and other fire risks. Once the flight syndrome kicks in, it is retained long after the smoke, heat and noise stimuli are removed. Drought is a silent disaster (along with famine and pestilence) because it has a slow onset period that does not encourage monitoring because of its discomfort. The key elements to managing animals in drought disaster are food, water and shelter. The lack of any of these factors, or a scarcity of one or more, can lead to a slow death for livestock. Animal reaction to drought is slow and vague until at critical health levels. Of all the disaster types, drought has the greatest potential to affect the widest area, often impacting multi-state regions at the same time.

Disaster science – Concepts and strategies

Disaster Management is a discipline combine of studies, research and action planning concerning (a) risk management and (b) emergency response. Both, risk management and emergency response - revolving in and around environmental systems/supplies, and environmental/ natural resources management, thus has emerged as a ***specialization*** of environmental science. It requires interdisciplinary coordination of multi-disciplinary inputs from expertise of geology, chemistry, environmental/public-health engineering, ecology, biology/medical, economics/social sciences, medial/veterinary, agriculture/forestry, information systems/geoinformatics, and environmental law. Conceptual schematic of Disaster Management is shown in **Figure 11**. Disaster Science is emerging world-over (especially in developing world) in close proximity with natural resource management and interdisciplinary focus where the combination of hard sciences like biology, physics, geology, mathematics are augmented with soft sciences like human ecology and economics, and thus within the schools of environmental studies or sciences. Government of India, in Ministry of Human Resources Development, has decided to incorporate 'Disaster Management' as a sub-module in 'Environmental Studies' - the compulsory UGC Module for all Undergraduate Studies at College/Universities. Similarly it may be added to the Environmental Studies in the Schools levels as well and can be introduced as an optional subject (additional) at class IX-X levels in the school curriculum.

'Risk management' has to start very early in the disaster management action, as pro-active pre-disaster prevention and mitigation efforts, and therefore has to emphasise on risk assessment and early warning system for the hazards and disaster risks as well. Disaster scenario takes into account the 'vulnerability' that considers exposure factors, susceptibility and weaknesses in the receptors settings. Vulnerability may be understood as the 'qualification' of being affected by a particular risk factor, hazard, incidence or a disastrous phenomenon/impact. Emergency response must begin with assessment of likely emergency situations. Environmental response often being most crucial, after rescue/evacuation - by focussing on water, shelter, sanitation, food, hygiene, etc and thus calls for multidisciplinary approach in an integrated manner. Information system has a significant role in the components - risk management and emergency response - early warning, communication, risk assessment, vulnerability mapping and response planning.

Figure 12. Schematic of Disaster Risk Management and Response (Conceptualised by authors / Gupta and Nair, 2009 – Risk to Resilience/Strategic Tools for DRR, NIDM/ ISET).

Recommendations for the planning in respect of integrated action strategy for climate-change adaptation, disaster risk reduction and emergency management for animals are followings:

- Develop a comprehensive plan (e.g. health, disaster reduction) to deal with the migration of disease due to climate change;

- Develop positive animal welfare contingency plans to control zoonoses caused by climate change;
- Use vaccinations (e.g., rabies vaccines) as a control measure where appropriate in regions where disease is endemic;
- Improve biosecurity at animal production sites that also safeguard animal welfare; and Limit transportation of live animals.

Disaster relief programmes

Protecting farm animals during and after a disaster is more than just preserving local, regional, and national resources. It is also more than just preserving income. It is also about ensuring livelihoods, and regional economic and political stability. As farm animals are generally uninsured, farmers and pastoralists are especially vulnerable to poverty, disease, and conflict when animals perish in disasters. Current sanitation and safety considerations restrict animals from inclusion in most refugee/disaster camps, and evacuation plans often exclude animals. This can inhibit disaster response and effectiveness as people will often refuse to leave behind their animals. With effective planning, early warning systems and appropriate partners such as governmental and humanitarian organisations, the effects of disasters involving animals can be mitigated. Tips for the disaster relief are given hereunder:

- Incorporate humanitarian animal relief bodies to improve response effectiveness and efficiency;
- Incorporate risk reduction plans into poverty reduction policy;
- Include early warning systems (e.g., Hyogo framework based) in the animal relief communities to prepare owners of animal populations;
- Integrate veterinarians and animal protection experts in disaster assessment teams;
- Conduct joint disaster trainings and exercises with humanitarian and animal protection experts;
- Require animal shelters and veterinary clinics to be wind and earthquake resistant and located at an appropriate distance from storm surge areas where possible.

In 2005, after Hurricane Katrina, the International Fund for Animal Welfare dispatched emergency rescue teams to New Orleans. The teams methodically combed the city, door-to-door, rescuing thousands of cats and dogs left behind by evacuees. Most of the residents left their pets thinking they would be allowed to return home in a couple days. Others were rescued by first responders and weren't allowed to bring their pets. Evacuees who made their way to shelters or temporary housing were not allowed to bring pets either.

Information systems for disaster management

The provision of timely and effective information, through identified institutions, that allows individuals exposed to a hazard to take action to avoid or reduce their risk and prepare for effective response. Early warning systems include a chain of concerns, namely: understanding and mapping the hazard; monitoring and forecasting impending events; processing and disseminating understandable warnings to political authorities and the population, and undertaking appropriate and timely actions in response to the warnings.

Disaster record classification

The classification of an event as a disaster varies from database to database, due to large differences in scope, focus and the objectives of organizations engaged in collecting and distributing disaster information. EM-DAT defines and gathers records on a disaster if it falls into at least one of the following categories:

- There have been ten or more fatalities,
- One hundred or more people have been affected,
- A state of emergency has been declared, or
- International assistance has been called for.

Disaster events in the database are classified based on disaster group (e.g., natural disaster), disaster type (e.g., flood) and disaster sub-type (e.g., flash flood). In this report, if a term such as 'flood' is used, the data for all its sub-types as categorized by EM-DAT are added together and analyzed. Different types of natural disasters have the following sub-types:

Floods:	Coastal and lake flood, plain flood, valley flood, and flash flood
Windstorms:	Typhoon, hurricane, cyclone, tornado, tropical storm, winter storm, and storm (non-water-related disasters may be included in this disaster type. However, this report considers all windstorm disasters as water-related disasters).
Waves & surges:	Tidal wave and tsunami
Slides:	Landslide, avalanche, mudflow and rockfall

Droughts: No sub-type

Epidemics: No sub-type (In this report epidemics are divided into two categories, water-borne and non-water-borne, in order for water-borne epidemics to be categorized as water-related disasters. This categorization criterion is adapted from the WHO definition of water-borne epidemics).

EM-DAT definitions for the terms such as region, disaster-category, and disaster-type are used in this report. Some of these definitions are vague, especially those of disaster types. For instance, a flood can be triggered simultaneously by heavy rain caused by a rain front and a typhoon, but is difficult to pinpoint which caused the flood. Worldwide, GIS (geographical information system) is being used to solve problems associated with wildlife management. From calculating existing wildlife densities, assessing sustainability of habitat for wildlife populations, to evaluating human impact on the wildlife and land, GIS can prove to be an invaluable tool.

Environmental management and disaster risk reduction

Land-use planning

Branch of physical and socio-economic planning that determines the means and assesses the values or limitations of various options in which land is to be utilized, with the corresponding effects on different segments of the population or interests of a community taken into account in resulting decisions. Land-use planning involves studies and mapping, analysis of environmental and hazard data, formulation of alternative land-use decisions and design of a long-range plan for different geographical and administrative scales. Land-use planning can help to mitigate disasters and reduce risks by discouraging high-density settlements and construction of key installations in hazard-prone areas, control of population density and expansion, and in the siting of service routes for transport, power, water, sewage and other critical facilities.

Environmental factors

Affect human health in important ways, both positive and negative.

- Positive environmental factors sustain health, and promoting them is preventive medicine. They include:
  - Sources of nutrition (farming: soil quality, water availability, biodiversity/bio-integrity, genetically modified organisms (GMOs); hunting, fishing: wildlife, fish populations.)

- Water (drinking, cooking; cleaning / sanitation);
- Air quality;
- Ozone layer (protection from UV, cancers, etc);
- Space for exercise and recreation;
- Sanitation/waste recycling and disposal.

❒ Negative environmental factors are threats to health, and controlling them is public environmental health. They include:

- Environmental conditions favouring disease vectors (endemic and exotic vectors);
- Invasive biota (viruses, bacteria, etc), their hosts and vectors;
- Environmental disruptions: floods, droughts, storms, fires, earthquakes, volcanoes;
- Air quality: pollen and pollution leading to respiratory diseases or cancers;
- Water quality: biotic and abiotic contaminants; integrity of water transport and treatment infrastructure;
- Monitoring and management of municipal, agricultural, industrial outflows to the environment (gases, liquids, solid wastes);
- Human changes of the environment that
  - create conditions that favour disease;
  - disturb and release noxious levels of previously bound chemicals (e.g. mercury released becomes poison) or biota (e.g. methane released from thawed peat contributes to climate change);
  - create temporary, intense, life-threatening heat islands (e.g. urban heat waves exacerbated by climate change);
  - result from nuclear, biological or chemical warfare or terrorism; disruption caused by other war and violence.

Animals in disasters management: capacity building

Livestock animals are highly valued for their milk, meat, eggs, draft animal power, wool, leather, and dung. Often one of the only economic activities available to poor people in developing countries, livestock rearing can provide a steady stream of food and revenue for families, and does not require formal education, large amounts of capital, or land ownership. 6 Owning livestock also increases the essential consumption of protein and creates employment opportunities beyond the immediate household.

Though disasters of the size and scope of Hurricane Katrina are the exception rather than the rule, the impact of disasters on animals is not. There is an urgent need to ensure that animals are formally considered in disaster preparedness plans. Most consider pets to be part of the family and abandoning them is unthinkable. We need to ensure that policy and planning reflect this sentiment. No one should be forced to leave a pet behind. Whether we rely on them for food, revenue, companionship, or to help balance our ecosystems, animals play an important role in our lives. The Food and Agriculture Organization of the United Nations (FAO), the leader in international efforts to defeat hunger, has recognized the close link between the welfare of humans and the welfare of animals. Currently, roughly one billion people depend directly on animals for income, social status and security as well as food and clothing.

Wildlife

In addition to the emotional, aesthetic, and social benefits that people gain from experiencing wildlife in their natural habitats, wildlife plays a vital role in essential ecological and biological processes on which we depend. Biodiversity, the combination of life forms and their interactions with each other and with the rest of the environment, provides invaluable goods and services that support human survival. Studies show that biodiversity influences the rate, magnitude, direction, and delivery of essential ecosystem processes such as pollination, agricultural pest and disease control, nutrient conservation in soil, and water purification. In order for humans to thrive, we must protect biodiversity. Given that species are disappearing at an alarming rate due to the impacts of climate change and human activity, this need to prevent the further loss of biodiversity is greater than ever.

Livestock

More than 900 million people worldwide are undernourished. Most of those people are in developing countries where secure food supplies often depend on the health and productivity of animals, and these in turn depend on the care and nutrition that animals receive. Climate change is expected to worsen this hunger crisis by negatively affecting crop productivity and loss of livestock. As climate change impacts food availability, livestock animals are becoming increasingly important. In Asia, for example, livestock currently provides the livelihood support for over 35 percent of the poor and is seen as one of the key sectors for poverty alleviation. In addition to the direct consequences of climate change-related disasters, animals lose their lives and suffer from indirect impacts of these natural hazards. These biological disruptions include aggravated disease, disrupted migratory patterns, and increased stranding.

Shift in migratory patterns

Because they require separate breeding, wintering, and migration habitats of suitable locations, migratory species are expected to be at greater risk due to climate change than others. 59 migratory species are already suffering, and are likely to do so even more in the future, from changes in their critical habitats and shifts in their migratory patterns. One major concern is related to food availability.

The conceptual framework of elements considered with the possibilities to minimize vulnerabilities and disaster risks throughout a society, to avoid (prevention) or to limit (mitigation and preparedness) the adverse impacts of hazards, within the broad context of sustainable development. The disaster risk reduction framework is composed of the following fields of action, as described in ISDR's 2002 publication *Living with Risk: A Global Review of Disaster Reduction Initiatives*.

- Risk awareness and assessment: includes hazard analysis and vulnerability/capacity analysis.
- Knowledge development including education, training, research and information.
- Public commitment and institutional frameworks, including organisational, policy, legislation and community action.
- The application of measures including environmental management, land-use and urban planning, protection of critical facilities, the application of science and technology, partnership and networking, and financial instruments.
- Early warning systems including forecasting, dissemination of warnings, preparedness measures and reaction capacities.

Most human emerging infectious diseases originate from a wildlife reservoir. Approximately 80 percent of emerging infectious diseases affecting humans are zoonotic (i.e. transmissible between a wild or domestic animal and humans), and a rising number of these diseases are spread by either direct or indirect (with livestock as an intermediary) contact with wildlife. Therefore, as livestock producers and wildlife shift their distribution in response to changes to water and vegetation caused by climate change, opportunities will arise for more wildlife disease to infect both people and domestic animals. In addition to the health threats that diseases pose to human and animal populations, the pathogens that originate from or move through wildlife populations have already caused significant economic losses. For instance, several livestock diseases that have re-emerged since the mid-1990s (including avian influenza) have caused an estimated $100 billion in losses to the global economy. Climate change will likely influence the incidence and geographic range of vector-borne diseases such as malaria, encephalitis, yellow fever, dengue, and plague. As vectors, or carriers, shift their range as a result of climate change, the distribution of their transmitted diseases will shift as well.

Local level animal care plan (LACP) In Disaster Management

The plan shall address small and large scale emergencies, disasters and evacuations. To ensure successful implementation of these guidelines, effective and timely planning activities are essential. This may include a series of meetings with representatives of groups and with individuals who are legislated and/or qualified to provide resources and expertise for the care of animals in disasters and evacuations. The persons who represent these groups form the Animal Care Committee (ACC) under Disaster Management Authorit (DMA). The goal of the Animal Care Committee should be to develop a program that caters to the needs of animals and their owners in emergencies, disasters, and evacuations.

The committee must include the representative/expertise on (a) animal husbandry (b) wildlife/zoo/ park management (c) environmental-health/ public health engineering (d) information systems / public relations, (e) eco-geologist/natural resource specialist (e) disaster management - interdisciplinary coordinator, and (f) local authority/community representatives, and others (as per need of the case/region basis).

The guidelines may be intended to encourage (pre-disaster) planning for the care of animals during (and post) disasters in communities and to encourage participation and support for these efforts. The guidelines should be implemented whenever there is a need to access resources that can provide care for animals and their owners in emergencies, disasters, and evacuations.

Responsibilities of animal owners

- To provide an appropriate standard of care for their animals at all times, including during emergencies, disasters and evacuations.
- To ensure that their animals are not a threat to public health and environment.
- To ensure that their animals do not harm other persons' property, including animals, and limit the spread of contagious disease to other animals.

- To ensure the standards/procedures/care of animals and human beings during owner evacuating taking their animals with them (Most owners affected by disasters or having to evacuate take their animals stay with friends and family. This self-reliant behavior should be encouraged at all times).

Responsibilities of the local Emergency Management Agency with respect to the care of animals in disasters and evacuations

- To endorse the need for an Animal Care Committee as a resource to Emergency Management for the care of animals in emergencies, disasters and evacuations.
- To advise members of the Animal Care Committee of required and desired training, such as Emergency Operations Planning, Incident Management, Volunteer Resource Management.
- To task the Animal Care Committee with solving problems that arise out of the need to provide care for animals in emergencies, disasters and evacuations.
- To develop with the Animal Care Committee methods for liability protection and cost reimbursement for the Animal Care Committee after it has been activated by the Emergency Management Agency.
- To include a representative from the Animal Care Committee in the Local Disaster Management Authority (DMA), or other appropriate committees.

Responsibilities of Nodal Department

- To ensure that public safety / environmental-health is not endangered by (stray) animals.
- To capture stray animals.
- To provide temporary housing of animals which owner's cannot be identified.
- To offer adoption of animals that has been housed for a statutory limit of time.
- To euthanize and dispose of animals which cannot be adopted for any reason, including injuries, disease, inappropriate behavior, or other undesirable traits.

Responsibilities of the animal care committee with respect to the care of animals in disasters and evacuations

- To be the principal resource to Emergency Management to provide care of animals affected by emergencies, disasters and evacuations.
- To familiarize its members with the local disaster risk mitigation and emergency operations procedures.
- To become trained according to the requirements of the Risk Mitigation (Prevention Plan) and Emergency Response Plan.
- To identify legislated and/or qualified groups or persons who will care for animals in pre-disaster situations and during emergencies, disasters and evacuations.
- To identify resources in the community that are needed to adequately plan and respond to the needs of animals in emergencies, disasters and evacuations, such as housing.
- To coordinate legislated and/or qualified groups and persons to plan for and respond to the care of animals in emergencies, disasters and evacuations.
- To maintain a current list of committee members and community resources that support planning and operations for the care of animals in emergencies, disasters and evacuations.
- To care for animals which are accompanied by their owners in emergencies, disasters and evacuations.
- To refer the care of stray animals, i.e., animals which are not accompanied by their owner at the time the animal is found or help is sought, to the Town or Municipal Department (Public Health) in which the animal was found.
- To develop with Emergency Management methods for liability protection and resource funding.
- To attend Local Disaster Management Authority (DMA) /Crisis Group (DCG/LCG) or other appropriate meetings.

Responsibilities of animal care professionals

- Examples of animal care professionals include: veterinarians, veterinary technicians, breeders, boarders.
- To provide care for injured and diseased animals in a capacity with which the animal care professional is qualified.
- Animal care professionals enter into service contracts with animal owners for the care of animals. These contractual agreements are usually based on a fee for service.

- Often, in disasters, animal care professionals will provide pro bono service, but it should never be assumed that this will be the case.

Responsibilities of the Department of Agriculture/Environment/Wildlife

- To enforce the animal welfare related laws.
- To license commercial animal boarding, grooming, and breeding facilities.
- To ensure that certain reportable diseases are contained and/or eradicated with adequate environmental-health control and conditioning.
- Extension educators provide information on animal husbandry, health care, and nutrition.
- Information technology/mapping professionsal provide information access on space and time basis, about locations, incidences, shelters, care centres, movement routes, etc.

Responsibilities of the veterinarian

- To monitor animal health in the area/locale.
- To ensure that certain reportable diseases are contained and/or eradicated.
- To define the types of livestock for that region/locale
- To fulfill other state functions related to animal health.

Responsibilities of Department of Public-Health/Environmental Engineering

- To ensure that public-health facilities meet local and state health codes. Public facilities include shelters, food, medicines, etc. These public facilities must meet specific guidelines set forth by the Department of Public-Health. These environmental guidelines describe the conditions under which animals are permitted into public facilities.
- Depending on the jurisdiction of the Department of Health it can enforce state, district or municipal regulations.

Responsibilities of the Department of Natural Resources

- To manage all aspects of care of native wildlife (dead and alive).
- To certify and license wildlife rehabilitators.
- To maintain food/fodder and other supplies,
- To assess/report associated environmental issues of resource supplies and maintenance for animals/livestock.

Responsibilities of "other" groups and persons that provide animal care

- Examples of "other" animal care groups include: humane societies, breed (rescue) groups (usually for dogs, cats and horses), producer (livestock, poultry) associations, and (national) emergency animal response programs.
- Many of these "other" groups provide welfare services for animals.
- Because many "other" groups do not have jurisdiction over stray animals, in most cases "other" groups deal with owned animals. Any care provided to stray animals must be provided with prior agreement of Animal Control or the group/person that has the mandate to deal with stray animals.
- The services provided by "other" groups should be specified in advance. Although the services rendered to owners by "other" groups are often without cost to the owner, the arrangement between owners and "other" groups is usually based on verbal or written expectations, equivalent to a contract. Therefore, when owners choose the services of these "other" groups, they should do so with an understanding of these contractual arrangements.

Responsibilities of the red cross/response groups with respect to the care of animals in disasters and evacuations

- To keep a current list of members of the Animal Care Committee who can be called upon to provide care for animals in emergencies, disasters and evacuations.
- To refer all calls and care of animals to the Animal Care Committee.
- The Red Cross/Response Groups does not manage or take on a formal leadership role for the care of animals.

Pre-disaster responsibilities

- Develop an Emergency Operations Plan.
- Assess Response Capability.
- Shelter Capability.
- Training.
- Preparedness Activities with Local Government.
- Preparedness Activities with Local Animal Care Businesses, Associations and Organizations.
- Preparedness Activities with State Government.

Response Activities

A: Scenarios

1. Typical scenarios
2. Deployment areas (Disaster site or evacuation area; Shelter facilities)
3. Local Government Emergency Operations Center (EOC).

B: Concept of Operations

1. Alert notification.
2. Internal Notification Procedures.
   a. During work hours
   b. After normal working hours
3. Initial Response.
4. Specific functional responsibilities
   a. Administration.
   b. Animal care.
   c. Animal Fostering and Adoption.
   d. Contacts between shelter residents and animals.
   e. Liaison.
   f. Public Affairs.
   g. Veterinary care.
   h. Animal Care Volunteers.
   i. Operations Orientation.

Stray animals

Stray animals fall under the jurisdiction of the Town or Municipal Departments in which the animals are found. Although it is illegal to remove animals from that jurisdiction, most members of the public are not familiar with these laws and frequently act independently of them.

If stray animals are brought to a shelter from a different jurisdiction to where they were found, the Department (concerned) where the animal was found should be contacted and consulted on how they would prefer to handle the situation. Arrangements will be easiest if neighboring concerned departments have been contacted as part of the planning process.

Epilogue

Disaster Risk Management and Emergency Response, planning and implementation require a long-term but very objective, written/documented, tested, verified approach in strategies. Concepts like environmental auditing and environmental impact assessment, ecological footprint, life-cycle assessment, has to be further evolved to address disaster management functions. Environmental-health has to be a core component in disaster management and to be facilitated by the support of information and mapping technologies for better and faster management of information on geospatial and temporal grounds. Animal Care during disaster must not be seen as welfare but as a basic need for human's own welfare for maintaining standards in relief, and environmental health conditions for protecting the well being during and after disasters.

Acknowledgements

The article has incorporated a range of information from published and unpublished literature worldwide, internet, journals, books, reports, etc. and has interpreted by the authors. Authors acknowledge their original sources and contributors, known and unknown. Authors acknowledge support from Executive Director, NIDM, for providing academic environmental for growth of knowledge in disaster management in India.

Reference cited

Abramovitz, Janet. 2001. Unnatural Disasters. Ed. Linda Starke, Worldwatch Paper 158. Washington, DC www.worldwatch.org.

American Red Cross Disaster Services Notice #161: Animals in American Red Cross Disaster or Evacuation Shelters.

Animal Management in Disasters. 1999. Sebastian Heath, Mosby, St. Louis.

Animals in Disaster, Independent Study Course, IS-10. Module A, Awareness and Preparedness. Federal Emergency Management Agency. Washington, D.C.

Animals in Disaster, Independent Study Course, IS-11. Module B, Community Planning. Federal Emergency Management Agency. Washington, D.C.

Cannon, T. 1993. A hazard need not a disaster make: Vulnerability and cause of 'natural disaster'. In: P.A. Meniman & C.W.A. Browit, editors. Natural Disaster. London: Thomas Telford : 92-105.

China's Science & Technology Actions on Climate-change. MST et al. 2007. Government of China, Ministry of Science & Technology.

Climate-change Adaptation & Disaster Risk Reduction. 2008. Tidings – NIDM Newsletter, 2(3): 5.

Dhar Chakrabarti, P.G. 2008. Delhi Declaration on Disaster Risk Reduction (Editorial). Tidings, 2(4): 01.

Ecosystem Approaches to Human Health, IDRC. http://web.idrc.ca/en/ev-3314-201-1-DO_TOPIC.html.

EM-DAT. 2005.The OFDA/CRED international disaster database. Brussels, Université Catholique de Louvain, www.EMDAT.be.

Environment and Vulnerability - Emerging Perspectives. 2008. (at http://postconflict.unep.ch/publications/env_vulnerability.pdf).

Faust, E., Hoppe, P., Wirtz, A. and Schmidt, S. Trends in Natural Catestrophes – Potential Role of Climate Change. Geo-Risks Research Department, Munich, Re.

Freemantle, M. 1996. *Ten Years after Chernobyl Consequences Are Still Emerging*, by

Freemantle, Michael, Chemical and Engineering News, April 29.

Garg, N.K. and Hassan, Q. 2007. Alarming scarcity of water in India. Current Sc. 93(7): 932-941.

Global Trends of Water-Related Disasters: An Insight for Policy Makers. 2009. World Water Assessment Programme, International Centre for Water and Hazard Research, International Hydrology Programme, UNSECO, Paris, France.

GOI. 2004. Disaster Management in India: A Status Report, Natural disaster Management Division, Ministry of Home Affairs, Government of India, new Delhi

Gupta, A.K.,. Suresh, I.V., Misra, J. and Yunus, M. 2002. Environmental risk mapping approach: risk minimization tool for development of industrial growth centres in developing countries. Journal of Cleaner Production 10: 271-281.

Gupta, A.K., Yunus, M. and. Misra, J. 1998. Disaster reduction and sustainable development. Enviro-news 4: 06.

Gupta, A.K., Tyagi, P. and Yunus, M. 2007. Disaster-risk Management Concept and Environmental Perspectives: Issues for Integrating Climate-change Risks, Ecological & Land-use Vulnerability and Environmental Resilience in Strategic Planning. Journal of Tropical Ecology.

Gupta, A. K., Inakollu V. S., Misra, J and Yunus, M. 2002. Environmental risk mapping approach: Risk minimization tool for development of industrial growth centres in developing countries. Journal of Cleaner Production 10 (5):271-281.

Gupta, A. K., Nair, Sreeja, S. and Shard.2009. Chemical Disaster Management: Proceeding Volume of the National Workshop (30 Sept.-01 Oct. 2008, New Delhi). Ministry of Environment & Forests (GoI) and National Institute of Disaster Management, New Delhi.

Gupta, A. K., Nair, Sreeja S. and Sehgal, V. K..2009. Hydro-meteorological disasters and climate change: conceptual issues and data needs for integrating adaptation into environment and development framework, Earth Science India Volume-2(I).

IDNDR (1991-2000). International Decade for Natural Disaster Reduction (IDNDR), United Nations, Geneva.

IPCC, Intergovernmental Panel on Climate Change. 2007. Climate Change 2007: Synthesis Report. Working Group contributions to the Fourth Assessment Report, Valencia, Spain, IPCC.

JAVMA 1996;208(12):1988-97. Shomer R.R. Natural castrophes and disasters. JAVMA 190(6):706-8.

Kanwar, R. 2001. Disaster Management. The Administrator Vol. XLIV, December, pp. 96-110,

Kelman, I. 2007. Natural Disasters Do Not Exist. Version 1, 26 July, http://www.ilankelman.org/miscellany/NaturalDisasters.rtf,

Mcmichael A.J., Campbell-Lendrum D.H., Corvalán C.F., Ebi K.L., Githeko A., Scheraga J.D., Woodward A., Climate Change and Human Health - Risks and Responses, WHO 2003, p. 250 http://www.who.int/globalchange/publications/cchhbook/en/.

Mcmichael A.J., Campbell-Lendrum D.H., Corvalán C.F., Ebi K.L., Githeko A., Scheraga J.D. and Woodward A., Climate change and human health - risks and responses, WHO 2003, p. 250 http://www.who.int/globalchange/publications/cchhbook/en/.

Munich Re Topics. 2000, Natural Catastrophes—the current position. (as in Disaster Reduction and Sustainable Development, ISDR 2003, www.isdr.org).

Murphy, H. and Savage, K. 1992. Environmental risk assessment and management programmes. In: Proceedings of the National Conference of Environmental Engineering. June 17-19, Gold Coast, Queensland, pp. 45-52.

Murray, A.M., and Choo, C.W. 2002. Information failure and catastrophes: what can we learn by linking information studies and disaster research? 65th Annual meeting of ASIST, November 18-21, USA.

National Training Workshop on Climate-change & Disaster Management.2007. (a) August 2007, Jaipur and November 27-31, New Delhi.

National Training Workshop on Management of Chemical & Industrial Disasters. 2007. (a) 25-27 May and (b) 03-07 December, New Delhi.

NEPCSC .2006. CChEM- A National Framework for Chemicals Management in Australia-Discussion Paper (www.ephc.gov.au).

No More Bhopals Alliance. 2004. www.opensecrets.org, www.greenpeaceusa.org, www.bhopal.net), June.

Panorama of the environmental impact of the recent natural disasters in Latin America and the Caribbean. An inter-agency Technical Committee of the Forum of Ministers of the of Environment of Latin America and the Caribbean, UNEP/LAC-IGWG.XII/TD.2, Barbados.

Preparedness and response to chemical emergencies. 1996. India Country Report (for World Health Organisation), June.

Preparedness for Chemical Incidents in case of biological and chemical emergencies and warfare agents. 2008. http://www.who.int/EN/Section23/section 1001.

PWRI, The Public Works Research Institute. 2008. Technical report on the trends of global water-related disasters. Technical Note No. 4088, Tsukuba, Japan,PWRI.

Reason, J. 1997. Managing risks of organizational accidents. Brookfield: VT: Ashgate Publishing Company.

Reeves, W.C. 1967. Factors that influence the probability of epidemics of western equine, St. Louis, and California encephalitis in California. California Vector News14: 13-8.

Reeves, W. C. and Milby, M. M. 1989. Changes in transmission patterns of mosquito-borne viruses in the U.S. In: Demography and vector borne diseases. Ed. Michael W., Boca Raton: CRC Press, Inc. pp. 121-42.

Reiter, P. Weather, vector biology, and arboviral recrudescence. 1989. The arboviruses: epidemiology and ecology, Ed. P. Thomas, Vol I. Boca Raton: CRC Press, Inc., pp. 245-55.

Reynard, N.S. 2007. Climate change. In: Coastal Erosion and Management.

Rocha T. 1998. A review of leptospirosis in farm animals in Portugal. Revue Scientifique Et Technique Office International Des Epizooties 17(3):699-712.

Rose, John B.; Lisle, John T.; LeChevallier, Mark. 1997. Waterborne cryptosporidiosis: incidence, outbreaks, and treatment strategies. In: Fayer, Ronald, Editor. Cryptosporidium and Cryptosporidiosis. Boca Raton: CRC Press, Inc., pp. 93-111.

Ross, W.A. and Kaneene, J.B. Evaluation of outbreaks of disease attributable to eastern equine encephalitis virus in horses.

Sigma. 2006. Natural catastrophe and man-made disasters 2005. 2: 2006, Swiss Reinsurance Company, Zurich, Switzerland.

Sreeja S. Nair and Gupta, A.K. 2009. Siting of industries in a multi-hazard environment: Applications of GIS and MIS. In: Chemical and Industrial Disaster Management (Proc. International Conference), FICCI, NDMA, New Delhi 2009.

State-level Regional Multi-stakeholder Consultations on Climate Change Adaptation & Disaster Risk Reduction, at (a) Lucknow, (b) Jaipur, (c) Patna, (d) Ahmedabad, (e) Chennai, in relation to MoEF-UNDP-GEF project, and subsequently following National Steering Committee meetings at MoEF and inter-institutional discussions at NIDM, UNDP, etc.

Steinfeld, H., Gerber, P., Wassenaar, T., Castel, V., Rosales, M. and de Haan, C. 2006. Livestock's long shadow: environmental issues and options. Food and Agriculture Organisation, Rome.

The OFDA/CRED International Disaster Database: www.em-dat.net; Université Catholique de Louvain –Brussels, Belgium.

Turner, B.A. 1978. Man-made disasters. Taylor and Francis. London, UK.

Tzoua, T.L., Hankinson, G., Edwardsa, D. and. Chung, P.2004. Evaluating Safety Information Management Performance – A key to preventing disaster. In: Bhopal and its Effects on Process Safety - International Conference on the 20th Anniversary of the Bhopal Gas Tragedy at Indian Institute of Technology, Kanpur, India December 1 to 3.

Un-natural Disasters. 2009: Impact of Climate-related Emergencies on Livestock, Wildlife and Companion Animals. International Fund for Animal Welfare (IFAW), Yarmouth Port, United States.

UN-WWAP, The United Nations World Water Assessment Programme. 2006. The United Nations World Water Development Report 2: Water, a Shared Responsibility. World Water Assessment Programme (WWAP), Paris, UNESCO Publishing and New York, Berghahn Books

UN-WWAP, The United Nations World Water Assessment Programme. 2003. The United Nations World Water Development Report 1: Water for People, Water for Life. Paris, UNESCO Publishing and New York, Berghahn Books.

Wagner, N.L., Wagner, P.J. and Jayachandran, P. 2005.Distance learning courses in occupational medicine- methods and good practice. Indian Journal of Occupational and Environmental Medicine 9:57-61.

Water and Ethics.2004. Ethics of Water Related Disasters. UNESCO Hydrology Programme, Paris, France.

Water for Health – Taking Charge.2001. Report, WHO. http://www.who.int/water_sanitation_health/takingcharge/en/.

❑❑❑

4

Influence of Climate Change on Mineral Uptake in Plants and its Effect in Livestock

K. T. Sampath*, N. K .S. Gowda and D. T. Pal
National Institute of Animal Nutrition and Physiology
Bangalore - 560 030, Karnataka

Introduction

Global warming and climate change as a result of elevated levels of green house gases (GHG): carbon dioxide, methane, nitrous oxide, ozone and chlorofluorocarbon) in the atmosphere has been expected to bring a shift in the plant and animal habitat and biology. The increase in concentration of GHG is mainly attributed to industrialization, fossil fuel combustion, change in land-use practice, intensive agriculture and livestock farming and more importantly reduction in forest canopy. The global change variables (GCV) that contribute to global warming are water vapour (36-72%), carbon dioxide (9-26%), methane (4-9%) and ozone (3-7%). The climate change resulting from such elevated levels of GCV is expected to modify the productivity of green vegetation and alter species distribution. Elevated levels of CO_2 have been shown to enhance growth rates in plants through photosynthesis representing sequestration of atmospheric carbon into plant biomass. Thus the green vegetation could act as a carbon sink, but the increased photosynthesis and growth rate of plants demands more nutrient availability from soil. This could cause potential stress to plants due to constrained nutrient availability in the soil.

Nutrient stress on plant growth

Nutrient stress often limits plant growth as major nutrients like nitrogen (N) and phosphorus (P) controlling plant growth are rarely available in correct amounts that plants require. Such stresses have been proposed to reduce the potential growth response of plants to elevated atmospheric CO_2 levels. The plants also attempt to adopt for demanding higher growth through expanding root growth, carbon exudation to the soil, modification of nutrient requirement and mycorrhizal colonisations. More rapid vegetative growth (leaf, stem) may decrease the life span of plant and accelerate litter fall and return of nitrogen and minerals to soil. These events could accelerate plant-soil-nutrient cycles, eventually resulting in increased nutrient-use efficiency, in addition to increased plant productivity. On the other hand, it is also likely that nutrient limitations in soil could constrain plant responses to the elevated CO_2 level resulting in homeostatic adjustments.

It is very difficult to predict the plant growth response to climate change because of the large uncertainties of nutrient availability. Increased CO_2 level in environment should stimulate nitrogen fixation by both free-living organisms and symbiotic systems, and improve soil properties for mineral availability as a result of increased organic matter deposition in the soil. On the other hand, increased temperature and altered and / or unseasonable rain fall patterns may offset the above process. Hence there are large complexities and uncertainties in understanding nutrient / mineral availability and plant nutrition as a result of climate change. This is likely to have an influence on mineral intake by livestock; particularly those that depend on grazing and browsing the vegetation.

Natural ecosystems, range lands and pastures in less developed countries are largely characterized by multiple nutrient stresses like sub-optimal availability or toxicity of a nutrient or a non-nutrient mineral like aluminium and heavy metals. Hence, it is very difficult to understand or predict plant response to global change variables. Other stresses for plant growth include poor drainage, poor water retention, soil shallowness, acidity, alkalinity, salinity and metal toxicity. Soil acidity (pH below 5.5) is a feature of soils of the tropics and subtropics. Acid soils are characterized by phosphorus (P) deficiency, aluminium (Al) toxicity and poor availability of calcium (Ca).

Negative effects of climate change on plant system would have disproportionate affects on both human and animal welfare, since the third world agriculture has a poor access to soil fertility amendments. Soil alkalinity (pH above 7.5) is a characteristic of arid and semi–arid regions and does not support dense vegetation. The availability of P and other minerals (Fe, Cu, Mn and Zn) to plants are low in alkaline soils. Salinity is a feature of arid, semi-arid and irrigated agriculture. Salinity stress is an important constraint to world agriculture affecting 50% of irrigated land. Saline soils present an array of problems to plant growth including poor water availability, toxic amounts of Na, Cl with low availability of Ca. Crop irrigation without adequate drainage and poor fertilization policy has created serious salinity problems. The vegetation grown under these soil properties will find it difficult to adapt for the stress induced by climate change.

Plant adaptation to stress

Plants display physiological adaptations to stress through conservative use of nutrients, slow growth, induction of organic exudates to protect root tips exposed to mineral toxicity, alteration of root architecture to explore soil nutrients. Such plant adaptations are only the short term options and would have repercussion on plant longevity in continued scenario of environmental stress. Elevated CO_2 reduces the leaf level transpiration in plants. This is particularly important for Ca and silicon that are especially dependent on transpiration in most plant species. Silicon is an essential element for many plants for maintaining cell integrity and resistance to insect and fungal infestations. The stimulatory effect of elevated CO_2 on legumes has been observed in legume-grass pastures and soybean. Phosphorus availability plays a key role in legume response to CO_2, since legume nodules have a high P requirement. Elevated CO_2 can increase the carbon gain in plants, which can dilute the concentration of other nutrients in plant. Higher CO_2 level is known to reduce the content of Ca, S, Mg and Zn in wheat crop as a result of higher carbon in the form of tissue carbohydrate accumulation combined with transpiration driven reduction in Ca uptake. Reduced nutrient content in plant could trigger plant stress responses and the major negative consequence would be dietary effects on vegetation-feeding insects and herbivores, including humans. Other global climate variables like ozone, high temperature, UV radiation can increase the formation of Reactive Oxygen Species (ROS) in plant chloroplast. Plants grown on alkaline soil with low Mg availability, base imbalances, aluminium toxicity and Mn toxicity will be more sensitive to such stress reactions.

Soil temperature has marked effect on plant root growth, morphology, longevity, respiration and membrane fluidity, which influence the plant nutrient acquisition efficiency. Generally soil warming enhances nutrient uptake but higher temperature does not modulate the nutrient dilution effect of elevated CO_2. Several phenolic compounds in plant leaves are known to decrease in response to higher temperature. Such effects on plant secondary metabolites could negatively influence the plant integrity, stability and thereby increase the decomposition rate.

Genomics as a tool to understand plant stress

Plants continuously evolve multiple mechanisms to maintain nutritional homeostasis in changing environment. Many such phenotypic adaptations are genetically complex. Expression profiling using cDNA and oligonucleotide micro array is a powerful tool to study the plant genomics and its transcriptional response due to climate change. Genomic information can be used to identify molecular markers linked to genes of interest for plant adaptation to nutrient stress. This marker aided selection will be useful in evolving plant varieties which are stress-tolerant, heat–tolerant and efficient in nutrient acquisition from soil. This effort is a much complicated process, since the phenotypic response are the sums of multiple interacting gene products at several levels of regulation (transcription, translation and post-translational modifications). Hence, we need a true integration of functional disciplines of agriculture and livestock to understand the process of plant response to climate change and its ultimate effect on livestock productivity.

References

Lynch J. P. and St. Clair, S. B. 2004. Mineral stress: the missing link in understanding how global climate change will affect plants in real world soils. Field Crops Research 90: 101-115.

Tans, P. P., Fung, I. Y. and Takahashi, T. 1990. Observational constraints on the global atmospheric CO_2 budget. Science 247: 1431.

Kramer, P. J. 1981. Carbon dioxide concentration, photosynthesis and dry matter production. Bioscience 31: 29-33.

Sinclair, T. R. 1992. Mineral nutrition and plant growth response to climate change. Journal of Experimental Botany 43 (8): 1141-1146.

□□□

5

Forage Production and Feeding Plan for Small Ruminants during Scarcity in Drought Prone Region

N. V. Patil* and A.K. Patel
Central Arid Zone Research Institute, Jodhpur-342 003, Rajasthan

Introduction

The hot arid tropical zone of India covers about 12 % of the country's geographical area and occupies over 3.2 lakh sq km of land located in parts of Rajasthan (61%), Gujarat (20%), Andhra Pradesh and Karnataka (10%); and Haryana and Punjab (9%). Both human and livestock population in the region is also very high in comparison to other deserts of world. Rain fed agriculture combined with animal husbandry is the major source of livelihood of desert dwellers. Frequent droughts result in failure of annual crops hence livestock is more important in the region but insufficient availability of fodder is a bottleneck for livestock. The fodder production varies widely depending upon cropping pattern, socio-economic conditions, and type of livestock. The cattle and buffaloes are fed on the fodder available from cultivated areas and supplemented grass and top feed. The three sources of fodder are crop residues, cultivated fodder and fodder from common resources, viz. forests, permanent pastures and grazing lands. The deficiency in feed and fodder is identified as one of the major constraints in achieving desired level of livestock production.

The shortage of dry fodder, green fodder and concentrates are up to 21.8, 61.5 and 47.1 % compared with the requirements of 560, 1006 and 79.4 million tones for the livestock population, respectively (Bhagmal et al. 2006). However, the feed and fodder scenario is worst in the arid region as there is a perennial shortage of 28 million tons of green fodder (40% of the requirement). The requirement increases up to 80-90 % during extreme drought years, requiring large quantity of fodder transportation from the neighboring states. The research outcome of the last five decades of CAZRI for pasture establishment and utilization techniques for various sub-agro-climatic regions showed that pasture grasses like *Cenchrus ciliaris, Cenchrus setigerus, Lasiurus sindicus, Dichanthium annulatum* and *Panicum antidotale* are promising for higher forage production in arid region (Daulay and Bhati, 1989).

Silvipasture Systems in Arid Zone

Traditionally silvipasture is used to grass farming in forest areas, which accommodate millions of livestock for grazing on the herbaceous growth. Extending this principle, silvipasture is the conscious practice of cultivation of forage annuals along with fodder trees and shrubs some what similar to agroforestry. Although the word silvi means tree and is now practice growing trees in the farm fields for fodder in western Rajasthan. Farmers in arid region encourage Khejri (*P. cineraria*) and Bordi (*Z. nummularia*) in crop fields for harvesting in winter for fodder and fuel wood. Silvipasture denotes silvi means tree and pasture means grasses or grass + legumes mixture and trees/shrubs for optimizing land productivity conserving plant, soil and nutrient and producing forage, fuel and wood timber on sustainable basis (Deb Roy and Pathak, 1974). Nair (1993) defined the silvipastoral system as the land use system in which trees and/or shrubs are combined with livestock and pasture for forage and fuel wood production. Silvipastoral system has special significance in deforestation and land degradation areas of arid and semi-arid regions due to low and erratic rainfall. The production of small ruminants is low mainly in arid region due to poor quality and seasonal availability of forage. In such situations, forage based silvipastoral system could be a promising approach for fodder production. Tree fodder in silvipastoral system also provides shade to the grazing animals and serve as fences, hedge and wind breaks.

Suitable silvipastoral models for different land types and rainfall situations

The selection of suitable species of trees/shrubs, grasses and legume for establishment of silvipastoral system depend on agro-climatic condition of the regions. The following trees/shrubs and pasture species for different land types and rainfall zones have been recommended:

(A) Suitable species for silivipastoral system under different land types

Land types	Grasses	Legumes	Trees/shrubs
Desert land and sand dunes	*Lasiurus sindicus Cenchrus ciliaris, Cenchrus setigerus*	*Lab lab purpureus, Clitoria ternatea, Atylosia scarabaeoides*	*Acacia tortilis, Acacia nilotica, Acacia senegal, Prosopis cineraria, Prosopis juliflora, Azadirachta indica, Ziziphus nummularia, Colophospermum mopane Dichrostachys nutan, Colligonum polygonoides*
Ravine lands	*Cenchrus ciliaris, Cenchrus setigerus, Dichanthium annulatum, Pannisetum pedicellatum, Saccharam spontaneum, Chrysopogon fuluus*	*Stylosanthes* spp, *Stizolobium decrigenum Macroptilium atropurpureum, Atylosia* spp	*Acacia tortilis, Acacia nilotica, Acacia catechu, Albizia lebbek, Albizia amara, Dalbergia sissoo Zizyphus spp., Ficus spp., Emblica officinalis, Eugenia jambolana*
Cultivable waste lands	*Cenchrus ciliaris, Cenchrus setigerus, Pennisetum polystachyon, Panicum antidotale, Sehima neruosum, Chrysopogon fuluus, Dischanthium annulatum*	*Macroptilium atropurpureum, Glycine jaranica, Clitoria ternatea*	*Albizia spp, Hardwickia binnata, Leucaena leucocephala, Acacia* spp. *Sesbania* spp., *Dichrostachys nutans, Prosopis cineraria Ziziphus mauritiana*
Salt affected area	*Cynodon dactylon, Paspalium notatum, Chloris gayana, Lasiurus sindicus, Brachiaria mutica, S porolobus marginatus, Urochloa*	*Glycine jauanica, Macroptillum* spp. *Phaseolus junatea, Stylosanthes*	*Acacia tortilis, A.nilotica Prosopis juliflora, Saluadora spp, Ziziphus spp. Sesbania spp., Albizia amara Atriplex spp*

(B) Suitable species of grasses and trees on the basis of rainfall

Rainfall Zone	Grasses	Legumes	Trees/shrubs
150 to 300	*Lasiurus sindicus, Cenchrus ciliaris*	*Lab lab purpureus, Clitoria ternatea*	*Prosopis juliflora, Acacia tortilis, Acacia senegal, Ziziphus nummularia. Colligonum polygonoides, Dichrostachys nutans*
300 to 500 mm	*Lasiurus sindicus, Cenchrus cilaris, Cenchrus setigerus, Panicum antidotale*	*Lab lab purpureus, Clitoria ternatea*	*Acacia. tortilis, A.nilotica, P. cineraria, Tecomella undulata, Colophospermum mopone, Ziziphus spp. Colligonum polygonoides, Azadirachta indica, H. binnata, Ailanthus exelsa, Albizia lebbek*
Above 500 mm	*C. ciliaris, Dichanthium annutatum, Chrysopogon fulvus, Sehima nervosum, Panicum antidotale, Heteropgon contortus*	*Stylosanthes*	*Acacia nilotica, Acacia catechu, Dalbergia sissoo, Leucaena leucocephala, Albizia spp., Alianthus excelsa, Hardwickia binata*

Forage Production of various Silvipastoral models

In traditional silvipastoral system, trees/shrubs are permitted to grow at random in fields on the boundary of the fields or community grazing land with grasses of low productivity and nutritive value. In arid zone of Rajasthan, Kaul and Ganguli (1963) recorded maximum combined yield of grass and Pala (1.0 t/ha) under 14 % of land area covered with Zizyphus spp canopy cover. Similarly, highest grass yield (1.1 to 1.5 t/ha) under Khejri and lowest (0.6 to 0.7 t/ha) under Kumat plantation of 14 to 18 year old with substantial contribution of Cenchrus and Eleusine spp as under storey perennial grasses was recorded. The productivity and carrying capacity of grazing land can be increased through improved silvipastoral system. At IGFRI Jhansi, Pathak et al. (1996) reported that the degraded lands produced hardly 1 t/ha/year biomass, which can be improved up to 10 t/ha through silvipastoral system. A study conducted at NRCAF, Jhansi revealed that an average total biomass yield of 12.62 t/ha/year recorded under silvipastoral system consisting of *A. amara* and *L. leucocephala* as trees, *D. cinerea* as shrub and *C. fulvus* + *S. hamata* as pasture was about 4 time higher than 3.16 t/ha/year obtained under natural grassland (Rai et al., 1999). Silvipastoral studies undertaken at CAZRI, Pali involving four tree species, (*Acacia tortilis, Azadirachta indica, Albizia lebbek and Holoptelia integrifolia*) and four grasses (*C. ciliaris, C. setigerus. D. annlatum and Panicum antidotale*) revealed non significant difference in the dry fodder yield under different tree species, however, the mean dry forage yield was maximum in *Dichanthium annulatum* (2.8t/ha) followed by 2.51 t/ha in *Cenchrus ciliaris* and 2.2 t/ha in *Panicum antidotale* (Muthana and Shankarnarayan,1978). Silvipastoral studies at Jodhpur indicated that sowing of *Cenchrus ciliaris* under *H. integrifolia* did not interfere with normal growth with an additional dry forage yield of 0.7 to 1.2 t/ha. In another study, Harsh et al. (1992) reported that a mixture of *C. fulvus* and *Sehim nervosum* grass produced 3.25 t/ha forage under canopy of five year old *Hardwickia binata*. Similarly Patidar (2006) recorded maximum herbage yield with *L. sindicus* + cowpea (9.0 and 3.1t/ha) green and dry forage yield) followed by sole (8.9 and 3.08 t/ha) green and dry fodder yield and *C. ciliaris* + cowpea system (8.46 and 2.86 t/ha green and dry forage yield grown in association with *C. mopane* and *H. binnata*. The forage yield was not different due to tree species however, application of 40 kg N/ha enhanced fodder yield by 13-14% over control. Yadav and Poonia (2003) recorded maximum biomass yield of grasses and tree from silvipastoral system with *Dichrostachys nutans* followed by *Prosopis cineraria* at farmers' field in arid climatic condition of Rajasthan. In horti-pastoral studies, on sandy rain fed of Rajasthan, Sharma and Diwakar (1989) reported that *Cenchrus ciliaris* in association with *Ziziphus mauritiana* system produced 1.2 t/ha forage yield and did not affect the fruit yield.

Similarly in another study an additional forage yield of 0.47, 1.29 and 3.29 t/ ha in first second and third year, respectively after planting of *Cenchrus ciliaris* in inter-rows of *Ziziphus rotundifolia* was observed.

Leaf fodder production- an additional source of feed in dry areas

Studies on lopping intensity (Bhimya et al., 1964) revealed that heavy intensity of lopping adversely affected the growth of Khejri. Recurrent lopping reduces leaf fodder yield due to successive reduction in overall surface area of new shoots. It suggests rest between two lopping in Khejri. It has been suggested that in arid area lopping of *Acacia* spp., particularly *A. nilotica* (ex. *A arabica)* should be regulated on a cycle of 4 years with restriction on lopping of thicker (diameter of 1.9 cm and above) branches. In Madhya Pradesh and Tamil Nadu lopping of *Hardwickia* spp was permissible only in times of scarcity. Sharma and Gupta (1981) studied the effect of seasonal lopping on the top feed production and growth of *P. cineraria*. They observed that winter is the ideal season for lopping as it improves plant height and bole diameter of the tree as compared to trees lopped during remaining spring, summer and monsoon seasons.

Feed and fodder requirement and availability

Estimates worked out on the requirement of feeds and fodders for livestock vary widely. The fodder demand was estimated to be 28.13 million tones for year 2000 on dry matter basis (Venkateswarlu et al., 1992). According to another estimate, the arid western Rajasthan harbours livestock equivalent to 10.96 ACU requiring 39238 thousand tones dry matter annually. Dry roughages and green forage requirement will be 21849 and 41200 thousand tones, respectively. In addition, about 13 million tones of concentrate will be required annually to feed 23.96 million livestock in arid zone of Rajasthan (Patidar and Saxena, 2007). The availability of dry forages during normal and drought year is estimate to be 14000 and 4390 thousand tones and of green forages 8710 and 2690 thousand tones, respectively, revealing the annual deficiency of 35.9 and 79.9 %, respectively. Similarly, during these conditions, the green forages are deficient by 78.9 and 93.5 %, respectively. The overall deficit of fodder ranges from 76 % in western districts to 81 % in the central districts and 82 % in the eastern part (Narain and Kar, 2005).

Alternate Feed Resources for Arid Livestock

Arid regions have many feed resources in the form of agricultural produce, weeds, byproducts from agro-processing etc. Tumba (*Citrullus colocynthis*) seed cake is a by-product of the oil extraction industry. It is nutritionally rich and contains 16- 22% crude protein. Inclusion of 25% tumba seed cake (TSC) in concentrate feed lowers the cost of feeding by 18-35% without any adverse effect on the production, general health and reproductive performance (Mathur et al., 1989; Mathur et al., 2000). Salty shrub Lani (*Salsola baryosma*) at vegetative stage is a good source of fodder to animals. The acceptability and palatability of fresh cut shoots showed that Lani is palatable (Mathur et al., 2007). Lana (*Haloxylon salicornicum*) seeds having 18.6 % crude protein could replace about 25% of the conventional sesame cake in the concentrate for lactating cows. The powder of *Prosopis juliflora* pods can be used up to 35% in the concentrate of lactating goats without any detrimental effect on health (Mathur et al., 2003). Similarly *P. juliflora* pod husk can be used up to 50% level in the concentrate along with tumba (*Citrullus colocynthis*) seed cake as low cost ration in the sheep without any adverse effect on animal health (Mathur et al., 2002).

Fresh leaves of *Hardwickia binata* are palatable to goats and sole feeding supports the growth of kids (Patil et al., 2009). Feeding fresh leaves of *Colophospermum mopane* is possible in goats but it can be fed at 35-40 % of whole ration (Patil et al., 2007). The palatability of dry *C. mopane* leaves was low and decreased with progress of feeding from 15 to 5 % from 1st to 5th week and *P. cineraria* leaves are better source of supplementation even in the dry form and support milk yield of goats (Mathur et al., 2006). Thorn less cactus *Opuntia ficus indica* introduced in Indian arid region has fodder value as maintenance feed and reduce the water requirement if fed along with the dry roughages in goats, sheep and growing cattle. In addition, its higher mineral contents reduce the mineral requirement, as arid animals often suffer from mineral imbalance (Mathur et al., 2009). The weeds in the rocky and sandy habitat of arid region have a distinct relative preference index for grazing sheep and goats. Patil et al. (2005) studied the preference of these animals to different weeds and found in the order: Kanti (*Tribulus terristris*), Kagio (*Tetrapogon tenellus*), Santo (*Trianthema protulacastrum*), Lolaru (*Digeria muricata*), Bekario (*Indigofera cordifolia*) and Gangan (*Grewia tanax*).

Animal performance on desert top feeds

By and large, the consumption of *Z. nummularia* leaves is more than that of *P. cineraria* leaves, in both sheep and goats, moreover goats consume considerably higher than sheep (Ghosh and Bohra, 1984). The leaves of *A. excelsa, Z. nummularia* and *P. cineraria* are higher in TDN and total digestible nutrients (64, 50 and 41.0%, respectively), while the digestible crude protein (DCP) value of *A. excelsa* leaves is higher (16%) than *P. cineraria* in sheep (3.1%) and goats (5.5%) (Bohra, 1980). The DCP contents of *Z. nummularia* in sheep and goats were 4.1 and 3.6 %, respectively (Bohra, et al., 1999). From the point of nutritive value, *A. excelsa* leaves can be considered as best fodder among all desert tree leaves. However, this tree does not grow as extensively as *P. cineraria* or *Z. nummularia* in the region. The digestibility of cellulose from desert grass *C. ciliaris* (Bohra and Ghosh, 1977) is higher than that of the tree leaves presumably because of the high lignin content of the top feeds.

The nutritive value in terms of digestible crude protein and total digestible nutrients of different feeds differ with animal species. *Z. nummularia* has high nutritive value for camel followed by the sheep and goats, while *P. cineraria* have the highest value for goats, followed by camel and the sheep. The browsing rams and grazing bucks reared under a silvipastoral system having *C. ciliaris* as a dominant grass and supplementaed with loppings of *Zizyphus rotundifolia* exhibited substantial body weight gains (Patil et al., 2009). In the arid zone a substantial area is salt affected, where nothing can come up, except a few halophytic plants like *Salicornia bigelovii,* which can be cultivated under flood irrigation of brackish well water (Bohra et al., 2009).

The desert top feeds, especially, *P. cineraria* and *Z. nummularia* leaves although have appreciable quantities of crude protein but their DCP value is very low because of tannins and lignin (Bohra et al., 1999), which not only reduces the palatability, but also hinders utilization of dietary proteins by the animals as indicated by *in situ* degradability study of *P. cineraria* leaves in sheep rumen (Mathur et al., 1998). Attempts have been made to improve the nutritive value of *Z. nummularia* leaves by treatment with dilute formaldehyde (Ghosh et al., 1971) and *P. cineraria* leaves by treatment with ferric chloride. For this purpose, over night soaking the leaves with 0.5 N aqueous sodium carbonate solution, followed by washing with water, proved to be the best method for reducing tannin contents of *P. cineraria* leaves, it removes about 94% tannins (Bohra and Goyal, 1986). *P. juliflora* leaves are not relished by the animals, but its pods are highly palatable and relished by almost all the species of the livestock. Feeding of1e quantity of micro-minerals also.

Improvement of livestock productivity

Supplementary feed blocks

As the livestock in arid regions are mostly suffer from deficiency of essential nutrients including fermentable energy, protein, minerals as well as carotene. Appropriate formulations of multi-nutrient feed blocks (MNB) using locally available feed resources wheat bran, guar korma, *Bajra* husk and *Ardu* leaves, *Prosopis juliflora* ground pods, sugar cane molasses, urea, vitaminized mineral mixture, dolomite, common salt, deoiled soya bean meal have been developed. Organic product-guar gum powder is being used as a binder. A proto-type solar dryer where the blocks can be dried has also been developed. A briquette machine to process all ingredients and prepare the blocks has been developed at CAZRI. The supplementary feed blocks have been tested in cattle, sheep and goats and found economical source of nutrient supplementation to support the production of milk, body weight gain and wool yield. During 16 weeks feeding trial, the MNB supplemented sheep recorded 3.6 per cent gain over the sheep maintained on roughage diet. The supplementary feed blocks found to improve the nutrient utilization in cattle. In a digestibility trial study on Rathi cows, the digestibility coefficient for DM and crude protein were improved (Mondal and Bohra, 2001). The supplementary feed blocks in the arid areas were found to improve the production performance of lactating animals especially cows, buffaloes and goats. The farmers also reported reduction in pica cases in the animals suffering from mineral deficiency along with increase in feed and water intake. In case of cattle and buffaloes, 2 kg block is sufficient for 7 and 5 days, respectively (Patel et al., 2003). Feed block production units at farmers' places have been established following training to the farmers and rural youth about processing the feed ingredients using locally developed gadgets, providing rural employment.

Supplementary multi-nutrient mixture

For the small grazing ruminants, supplementary multi-nutrient mixture formulations were developed using the same ingredients. Feeding these mixtures to goats and sheep after grazing improve body weights and milk yield appreciably (Rohilla et al., 2009; Patel and Bohra, 2004).

Complete feeds and feed/fodder banks for arid livestock

A low cost balanced diet has been formulated for ruminants, which avoids the sending of animals for grazing in the rangelands. The alternate feeding based on crop residues and locally available agro-industrial products like straws, fallen tree leaves, by-products from other crops like cotton seeds, maize, groundnut, subabul, forest products like dry grass, pods, which can be blended to enable balanced supply of nutrients to the animals has been developed. The complete feed rations have been formulated for different area as per the availability of various agricultural residues. To improve the livestock productivity, total mixed ration (TMR) or complete feed blocks (CFB) have been developed. In an evaluation trial, the lactating Tharparkar cows fed TMR prepared out of local fodder *Cenchrus ciliaris* and concentrates available in the area were found beneficial for producing milk more economically compared to cows fed on local grass and supplemented with pellet cattle feed (Mathur et al., 2006).

The results of trials conducted at Avikanagar under intensive feeding on 50:50 roughage and concentrate ratios of complete feed indicated that the feed efficiency was higher than 20%. In this study, the crossbred weaner lambs maintained on these diets had higher ADG of 180 g compared to 127 ADG in native lambs. In another study, lambs fed intensively on 50:50 RC based complete feed attained 33.5 kg finishing weight with 11% feed efficiency at 6 months of age (Shinde et al., 1995). In a study conducted on Marwari kids, Patil et al. (2006) observed that the kids weaned at 2 months age had comparatively better growth rate than the kids weaned at 3 and 4 months age when they were fed on complete feed containing roughage to concentrate ratio 30:70 utilizing Khejri leaves and Masoor straw. The cost of feeding was economical for kids reared on CFB after weaning at 2 months age (Rs. 65.37 kg^{-1}) as compared to those weaned at 3 months (Rs. 70.40 kg^{-1}) and at 4 months (Rs.71.27 kg^{-1}). Similarly, in the intensive system, Marwari kids fed on CFB along with goat paneer whey gained higher body weight than the kids fed on CFB only. The results of the above studies indicated that goat and sheep can be reared intensively and can achieve the targeted body weights in limited period. It also helps to achieve the expanded use of crop residues and locally available agro-industrial by-products by formulating complete rations. The technology of complete feeds is appropriate for the arid livestock encountering frequent droughts. In such situations advanced planning could be of great help to store complete feeds, which can be easily transported to places of deficiency.

References

Bhimya, C.P. and Kaul, R.N. and Ganguli, B.N. 1964. Studies on lopping intensities of *Procopis cineraria*. Indian Forester 90 (1) : 19-23.

Bhagmal, P.S., Pathak, V.S. Upadhyaya, J.N. Gupta, and G. Suresh 2006. Forage crops and grasses. In: Hand book of Agriculture ICAR, New Delhi, pp 1128-1161.

Bohra, H. C. 1980. Nutrient utilization of *Prosopis cineraria* (Khejri) leaves by desert sheep and goats. Annals of Arid Zone 19:73-81.

Bohra, H. C. and Ghosh, P. K. 1977. Effect of restricted water intake during summer on the digestibility of cell wall constituents, nitrogen retention and water excretion in Marwari sheep. Journal of Agricultural Science (Cambridge) 89:605-608.

Bohra, H. C. and Goyal, S. P. 1986. Chemical de-tanning of *Prosopis cineraria* leaves. In: Proceedings of the V Animal Nutrition Workers Conference, Udaipur, July 14-17.

Bohra, H.C., Ghosh, P. K. and Goyal, S. P. 1999. Nutrient availability from *Zizyphus nummularia* leaves in desert sheep and goats. Journal of Eco-physiology 2:129-134.

Bohra, H.C., Patel, A.K. and Kaushish, S.K. 2009. Palatability, digestibility of various constituents and nitrogen retention in Marwari sheep offered *Salicornia bigelovii* biomass and *Cenchrus ciliaris* straw mixed diet. Indian Journal of Animal Sciences 79: 1050-1053.

Livestock Census 2003. Government of Rajasthan, Jaipur.

Daulay, H.S. and Bhati, T.K. 1989. Crops and pasture production potential of sandy soils. Book on Review of Research on Sandy Soils, CAZRI, Jodhpur, pp. 245-262.

Deb Roy, R. and Pathak, P.S. 1974. Silvipastoral management. Indian Farming 24: 41-42.

Ghosh P. K., Ratan R. and Taneja G.C. 1971. Effect of chemically protecting dietary protein from microbial degradation in the rumen on wool growth. Indian Journal of Experimental Biology 9: 109-110.

Ghosh P.K. and Bohra H.C. 1984. Palatability, digestibility and nutritive value of some important top feeds of arid and semi-arid regions of India. In: Agroforestry in Arid and Semi-arid Zones (Ed. K.A. Shankarnarayan). Jodhpur: Central Arid Zone Research Institute.

Harsh, L.N., Tewari, J.C., Burman, U. and Sharma, S. K. 1992. Agroforestry in arid regions. Indian Farming 40: 32-37.

Kaul , R.N. and Ganguli, B.N. 1963. Fodder production of Zizyphus in the shrubs grazing lands of arid zones. Indian Forester 89: 623-630.

Mathur B. K. 2003. Livestock: Human need for sustainability in arid environment. In: Human Impact on Desert Environment. (Eds. Pratap Narain, S. Kathju, Amal Kar, M. P. Singh and Praveen Kumar). Arid Zone Research Association of India and Scientific Publishers (India), Jodhpur, pp. 506-514.

Mathur, B. K. and Bohra, H.C. 1993. Nutritive value of *Prosopis juliflora* leaves and pods. Workshop on potential of *Prosopis* spp. for arid and semi arid regions of India, Central Arid Zone Research Institute. Jodhpur November 22-23.

Mathur, B. K., Patel, A.K. and Kaushish, S. K. 2000. Utilization of Tumba (*Citrullus colocynthis*) seed cake of desert for goat production. Indian Journal of Animal Sciences. 70: 431-433.

Mathur, B. K, Bhati, T. K and Tewari, J.C. 2006. Comparative palatability of *Prosopis cineraria* v/s *Colophospermum mopane* leaves in lactating Marwari goat in arid region. In: National Symposium on Livelihood Security and Diversified Farming Systems in Arid Region organized by Arid Zone Research Association of India, CAZRI, Jodhpur. January 14-16, pp.51-52.

Mathur B.K., Bohra H.C., Patel A.K. and Kaushish S.K. 1998. *In situ* rumen degradability of Khejri (*Prosopis cineraria*) leaves in Marwari sheep. In: Proceedings of the Golden Jubilee Seminar on. Sheep, Goat and Rabbit Production and Utilization for Maximizing Production Efficiency, Indian Society for Sheep and Goat Production and Utilization. Jaipur: CSWRI pp., 27.

Mathur, B.K., Mittal, J.P. and Prasad, S. 1989. Effect of Tumba cake (*Citrullus colocynthis*) feeding on cattle production in arid region. Indian Journal of Animal Sciences 59: 1464-1465.

Mathur, B. K., Patil, N.V., Mathur, A.C., Bohra, H.C., Bohra, R.C. and Sharma, K.L. 2009. Comparative mineral status of Jodhpur district villagers' cattle v/s institute farm managed Tharparkar cattle in hot arid zone. In: Proceedings of the Animal Nutrition World Conference, 14-17 Feb., New Delhi, India pp. 61.

Mathur, B.K., Patil, N.V., Mathur, A.C., Bohra, H.C., Patel, A.K and Bohra, R.C. 2006. Effect of total mixed ration prepared from local feed resources on feed intake, milk production efficiency and blood profile of Tharparkar cattle in arid region. In: VI Biennial Conference of Animal Nutrition Association on Strengthening Animal Nutrition Research for Food Security, Environment Protection and Poverty Alleviation September 15-17, 2006. Sher-e-Kashmir University of Agricultural Sciences & Technology, Jammu, pp.77.

Mathur, B.K., Singh, J.P., Beniwal, R.K. and Singh, N.P. 2007. Utilization of salty shrub-Lani (*Salsola baryosma*) of arid region as drought feed for goats. In: International Tropical Animal Nutrition Conference, October 4-7, NDRI, Karnal, pp.33.

Mathur, B.K., Siyak, S.R. and Bohra, H.C. 2003. Feeding of vilayati babool (*Prosopis juliflora*) pods powder to Marwari goats in arid region. Current Agriculture. 27(1-2): 57-59.

Mathur, B.K., Siyak, S.R. and Paharia, Shailesh 2002. Incorporation of *Prosipis juliflora* Pod husk as ingredient of low cost ration for sheep in arid region. Current Agriculture 26:95-98.

Mondal, B. C. and Bohra, H. C. 2001. Effect of multi-nutrient feed block supplementation on feed intake and nutrient utilization in Rathi heifers. In: Proceedings of the X Animal Nutrition Conference on Emerging Nutritional Technologies for Sustainable Animal Production and Environment Protection, N.D.R.I., Karnal, November 9-11, pp. 95.

Muthan, K.D. and Shankaranarayan, K.A. 1978. Scope of silvipastral system in arid region. In: Souvenir on Arid Zone Research Silver Jublee, CAZRI, Jodhpur, India.

Nair, P.K.R. 1993. An introduction to Agroforestry. Kulawar. Academic Publisher, The Netherland.

Narain, Pratap and Kar, A. 2005. Drought in western Rajasthan impact, coping mechanism and management strategies, CAZRI, Jodhpur pp 45.

Patel, A. K., Bohra, H. C. and Bhati, T. K. 2003. On farm trial of multi nutrient block on buffaloes in arid region. In: Proceedings of the IV Asian Buffalo Congress on Buffalo for Food Security and Rural Employment, New Delhi, February 25-28, pp 167.

Patel, A. K. and Bohra, H. C. 2004. On-farm trial of nutrient-mixture supplementation in lactating goats under semi-arid conditions. In: Proceedings of the V Biennial Conference of Animal Nutrition Association on New Dimension of Animal Feeding to Sustain Development and Competitiveness held at NIANP, Bangalore, November 24-26, pp 112.

Pathak, P.S., Gupta, S.K. and Singh, P. 1996. IGFRI Approaches: Rehabilitation of degraded lands. IGFRI, Jhansi, pp1-23.

Patidar, M. 2006. Strip cropping of grasses and legume in silvipastoral system. In: National Symposium on Livelihood Security and Diversified Farming System for Arid Region. January 14-17 CAZRI, Jodhpur pp. 33.

Patidar, M. and Sexena, Anurag 2007. Paryavarn sarankshan ke liye chara utpadhan. Kheti 60 (3): 18-22.

Patil, N. V., Mathur, B. K., Patel, A.K., Bohra, H.C. and Khan, M. S. 2006. Growth performance of arid breed kids weaned at different ages and received on complete feed block. In; Proceedings of the Animal Nutrition Workers Association Conference, SKUAT, Jammu, September 15-17pp., 78.

Patil, N.V., Mathur, B.K, Bohra, H.C and Patel, A.K. 2005. Relative preference index for arid forages for goat and sheep. In: Proceedings of the National Seminar on Conservation, Processing and Utilization of Monsoon Herbage for Augmenting Animal Production, ARS, CSWRI, December 17-18, Bikaner, pp.190.

Patil, N.V., Patel, A.K., Khan, M.S. and Bhati, T.K. 2009. Potential assessment of silivipasture system of arid Rajasthan based on its traditional use for rearing growing lambs and kids. In: Proceedings of the World Conference 2009 on Animal Nutrition Preparedness to Combat Challenges, New Delhi, February 14-17, pp 278.

Rai, P., Solanki, K.R. and Rao, G.R. 1999. Silvipasture research in India. A review. Indian Journal of Range Management. 1: 107-120.

Rohilla, P.P., Patil, N.V, Bohra, H.C. and Patel, A.K. 2009. Effect of supplemental feeding of urea molasses mineral block (UMMB) on growth performance of Marwari lambs. In: Proceedings of the National Symposium on Organic Livestock Farming- Global Issues, Trends & Challenges. W B University of Animal & Fishery Sciences, Kolkata, February 26-28, pp 87.

Sharma, S.K. and Diwakar, G.D. 1989. Economic evaluation of horti pastoral system in arid region of west Rajasthan. Indian Journal of Range Management 10: 119-122.

Sharma, S.K. and Gupta, R.K. 1981. Effect of seasonal lopping on the top feed production and growth of *Prosopis cineraria* (Linn.). Indian Journalof Forestry 4 (4): 253-255.

Shinde, A.K., Karim, S.A., Singh, N.P. and Patnayak, B.C. 1995. Growth performance of weaner lambs and kids under intensive and semi intensive feeding management. Indian Journal of Animal Sciences 65: 630-633.

Venkatateswarlu, J., Anantharam, K., Purohit, M. L., Khan, M. S., Bohra, H. C., Singh, K. C. and Mathur, B. K. 1992. Forage 2000 AD. The Scenario for Arid Rajasthan. CAZRI, Jodhpur. 32 pp.

Yadav, G.L. and Poonia, T.C. 2003. Production potential of grasses between existing stocks of trees under silvipastoral system in semi arid watershed area. In: National Symposium on Sustainability Advancement and Future Thrust Area of Research on Forage, March 5-6, CCS, HAU, Hisar pp. 53.

❑❑❑

6

Feeding and Management Strategies for Small Ruminants during Stressful Conditions of Drought

R. C. Jakhmola
Arid Region Campus, Central Sheep and Wool Research Institute
Beechwal Industrial Area, Bikaner- 334 006 (Rajasthan)

Introduction

Droughts, unfortunately, are part of India's rural scene, and their frequency and severity in the future are likely to be increased. Unlike earthquakes, the occurrence of floods, cyclones and droughts is a gradual process with long lasting effects. On an average 28% of geographical area of India is vulnerable to drought. Meteorologically 19% deviation in rainfall from the long term mean is considered normal in India. Deficiency in the range of 20 to 59% represents moderate and more than 60% severe drought (Samra, 2004). From 1871, India has witnessed 22 major droughts and five of them were severe. Although, with time India has developed institutionalized system for monitoring, prevention, mitigation, preparedness, relief and impact analysis, as a result there were hardly any starvation- or drought- related human deaths after 1967. However, livestock causalities are immense, making livestock farming, vulnerable in event of continuous droughts – either directly through the improper supply of feed and water, or indirectly by reduced income both during and after drought. Deterioration of pasture and soil erosion are less obvious costs, but important, particularly in the long-term sustainability of production from ruminants.

Small ruminants (SR) are found in wide variety of climatic zones owing to their ability to produce heat and also to control its dissipation thus maintaining homeothermy. The activity in rumen play important role by converting cellulosic materials into useful biomass and proteins, for this, ruminants also need healthy and procreative micro-organisms in their rumen. The fermentation of feed in the rumen and its subsequent digestion require energy. However, the process is not completely efficient and heat is produced as a by-product (Heat increment). While it is useful in a cold climate, it can be a nuisance and some time danger to health in a sustained hot and humid environment. The SR's move long distances for want of feed and water that leads to various stresses affecting production and reproduction of animals (Jakhmola et al., 2006b).

Drought and small ruminant farmers

Availability of water is the major constraint that affects the animal most during drought. As dry period progresses and water supplies dwindle, the existing water supplies overtaxed and finally dry up. The feed/fodder resources are depleted, as a result animal and farm families begin to migrate in search of better grazing lands for their livestock. If the supplies of feed are not restored, famine can occur, and therefore further acceleration of migration out of the drought stricken areas to less affected zones will occur. The migration may, in itself, contribute to spread the scope of the disaster, especially if grazing animals are moved with the people. If drought is long term, it may result in permanent changes of settlement, social, and living patterns, in that case, its impact on development can be severe. It is more serious in arid/ semi-arid regions because, livestock farmers of this area are relatively poorly resourced.

The drought induces the long-term problem of household viability of small ruminant farmers. Long-term rainfall depletes their essential capital, their flocks, in a manner that can only be rectified over a period of years. Depending on severity and longevity of a drought, flock structure both in number and quality disrupt which will take several years to regain their pre-drought production/ reproduction capacity. The longer is the drought period, the greater is the flock/ herd recovery time. There is now a fairly well recognised sequence that occurs when herders are faced with extended drought conditions. Several farmers leave the animal rearing occupation permanently and try to find alternate jobs. These processes are now largely understood, by academics, aid agencies and NGOs but solutions need to be generated and applied. Long-term structural assistance is more difficult to provide than emergency aid, probably because of compassion fatigue.

Drought: Curse to grazing ruminants

Nutrition influences reproductive efficiency of small ruminants directly by the supply of specific nutrients required for the processes of oocyte and spermatozoa development, ovulation, fertilization, embryo survival and the establishment of pregnancy. It also influences reproductive efficiency indirectly through its impact on the circulating concentrations of the hormones and other nutrient-sensitive metabolites that are required for the success of these processes (Jakhmola et al., 2006a).

Prolonged drought especially extended warm season often put ruminants under thermal stress that at times also affect endocrine system. The exposure of sheep to elevated ambient temperatures induces an increase in the dissipation of excess body heat, in order to negate the excessive heat load. Dissipation of excess body heat is excluded by evaporation of water from the respiratory tract and skin surface via panting and sweating, respectively. Sweating in woolly sheep is much less effective due to the presence of the wool cover. With the elevation in environmental temperature, a high proportion of heat is dissipated via the ears and legs. Increased sweating and evaporative water loss at the lungs are reflected in increased antidiuretic hormone concentrations in plasma. Thermal stress increases turn over of Na and K. Prolectin concentrations are elevated during thermal stress (Collier et al., 1982). The chronic thermal stress resulted in lower metabolic rate. This is reflected in lower concentrations of growth hormone, thyroxin, and glucocorticoids in blood (Mitra et al., 1972; Collier et al., 1982). Likewise, increased electrolyte turnover is also associated with altered aldosterone concentrations. Prolectin concentrations are elevated during thermal stress. The chronic thermal stress results in lower metabolic rate. This is reflected in lower concentrations of growth hormone, thyroxin, and glucocorticoids in blood. Thus, the water remains the most important nutrients for ruminants during drought. Reduction in voluntary feed intake near or above the upper critical temperature of the animal is widely accepted as a major negative influence on productivity.

During calamities like drought animals walk long distances for want of food and water. This leads to stresses that animal often encounter. Detailed information of grazing stress and its effect on production and reproduction in small ruminant are given by Jakhmola et al. (2006a). Dry matter intake begins to decline markedly as temperatures exceed above 25-27°C. However, other environmental factors such as wind velocity, humidity, and radiation also directly affected homeothermy under natural conditions. Apart from selectively grazing feeds with high protein content, sheep and goat has also ability to decrease nitrogen losses particularly in low nitrogen intake due to renal activity and increased urea recycling to the gut. The efficiency of economizing nitrogen metabolism by recycling urea is high on low protein diet. Water deprivation is a common constraint in desert goat which decrease N losses in urine, increased urea recycled into the gut and improve N balance by the animal. During drought, animals do graze on pastures intensively and it leads to elimination/ depletion of nutritious grasses/ forbs, increasing distribution of weeds and toxic plants. Livestock ordinarily avoid toxic/ less nutritious plants, but during drought, animals are forced to eat them. Such problems may be aggravated by deficiencies of phosphorus or vitamin A in livestock, which greatly alter their grazing behaviour. At times animals consume plants high in anti-nutritional/ toxic principles. Drought, followed by a rainfall, allows very high uptake of nitrate in plants. Nitrates found in forages, are converted to nitrite in rumen, and in turn the nitrite is converted to ammonia and then converted to protein by bacteria in the rumen. If animal rapidly ingest large quantities of such plants, nitrite will accumulate in the rumen. Nitrite is then absorbed into red blood cells and combines with haemoglobin to form methaemoglobin, so the animal's heart rate and respiration increases, muscle tremors can develop, staggering occurs and the animal eventually suffocates. Nitrate toxicity may result when animals suddenly consume large amounts of forage containing 2-3 percent or more nitrate ion on a dry matter basis. Even forage with lower levels may adversely affect reproduction or become toxic if animals are nutritionally stressed or metabolically abnormal and suddenly eat a large amount of such forage. Rumen paralysis may occur. Laboured or difficult breathing may be observed. Animals may go down and die suddenly. Likewise there would be adverse effects of ingestion of large amount of tannins and other anti-nutritional factors. Therefore, there is a need to develop habit of preparedness to tackle drought.

Preparedness for drought

Drought planning should be part of the ongoing animal management in arid and semi-arid tropics. It is important so that the financial burden can be spread over the good seasons as well as the bad ones. Important areas that can be considered when planning for drought are: stocking rate, fodder conservation; development of pasture, improve water supply; irrigation; fodder tree plantings and development of feed banks. Drought strategies need to be flexible, continually reassessed and varied according to changing circumstances such as increased cost of feeding, changes to stock prices or a shift in the financial situation of the farmer. Strategies should include: the current value of stock and develop priorities for the sale of sheep; a prediction of the value of stock at the end of the drought although this is somewhat dependent on the length of the drought; the availability and cost of fodder; the cost of feeding; the expected value of production through the drought. In early drought there is often plenty of poor quality pasture. Supplementary feeding should aim to make best use of this feed through the supply of limited nutrients. Principles for efficient use of supplements include: balance the supplement to ensure efficient rumen function, which can make up to 15 per cent crude protein in cereal grain supplements. Young and lactating animals have a greater need for protein; choose feeding techniques which minimize disruption to the digestive system; start feeding animals with the greatest needs (for example, pregnant ewe of low fat score or weaners below critical live weights); monitor feeding levels through fat scoring and weighing sheep. When pasture is no longer capable of supporting 30 per cent of nutritional requirements, or when further grazing is likely to deplete pastures to the point where soil erosion could occur, sheep should be restricted to small paddocks or feedlots. The benefits of restricting sheep from grazing are to: limit overgrazing and pasture degradation; limit the risk of soil erosion; restrict possible weed contamination from purchased fodder; achieve more efficient use of fodder by reducing the energy cost associated with grazing; reduce costs associated with feeding and stock management.

Development of water sources and irrigation systems

Strengthening of water resource both in terms of availability and management is most effective tool to fight drought. The age old water harvesting systems - wells, khadins, tanks, nadi etc. are still important for increasing water use for crop cultivation using minor irrigation system (Venkateswarlu, 2008). The well-planed irrigation systems in Indo-Gangatic plains of northern India have transformed the area with increased crop/ animal productivity. In western Rajasthan, famous Gang Canal command had transformed arid region. In 1927, Sri Ganga Singh Ji, the ruler of the State of Bikaner thought of bringing Sutlej waters to the arid land in the north of the Bikaner state; (now Sriganganagar) and the Gang Canal in the area was constructed with judicious settlement policy. Today, Sriganganagar is agriculturally the most progressive district of Rajasthan. The yield of important crops, like wheat and cotton, are comparable to those of the Punjab. After Independence India has initiated planned irrigation system named Indira Gandhi Nahar Pariyojna (IGNP). Once completed, the project will provide irrigation to 18.7 lakh ha of land. However, abuse of water in arid region can lead to water logging and salinity (Sharma, 2001). The forestation of 3.62 lakh ha along the side of canal was developed to increase bio-drainage .The grass-legume pastures that appear underneath plantation can also be good source of nutrients for livestock. The enhanced availability of crop by-products

– seeds, oilcakes and crop residues from command can play important role in drought mitigation as well as enhancing livestock productivity in western Rajasthan.

Increasing production from common property resources

Rearing small ruminants (SR) on pasture is a global phenomenon. Still SR depends mainly on the common property resources (CPR) – community grazing lands including permanent pasture, uncultivable and cultivable wastelands, fallow lands, village forests etc. Arid and semi-arid region of Rajasthan have large CPR though they are now degraded. Over years the CPR declined not only quantitatively, but also qualitatively (Singh et al., 2005). Jodha (1986) reported that the CPR area had declined by as much as 30 to 50 per cent between 1950 and 1982. Because of this migration to long distant places is now common. The extent of migratory sheep management in the country is estimated to nearly 45 percent (Malhotra, 1982). However, it is as high as 80 per cent in arid regions (Shinde, 2004). The topography of the land, level of aridity, poor socio- economic conditions of the farmers and frequency of drought are the predominant factors leading to the migration of SR's.

The native ranges located in semi-arid region and continuously being grazed by livestock yield 1.5q/ha dry matter (Sankhyan et al., 1999). The biomass content of degraded land was reported to be 4.92 and 1.36 DM q/ ha during monsoon and winter respectively (Shinde, 2004). The protection of rangeland from grazing during plant growth phase increased the yield to 17.9 q/ha (Mann and Singh, 1982). The forage yield of rangelands increased 2-3 times when re-seeded with perennial grasses (Mann and Mehta 1998). Adding legume adds to the nutritional quality of grazed / harvested feed that improved, intake, digestibility of feed and productivity. Developing silvi-pasture systems wherein multi purpose trees that provide feed, fuel and timber, bushes grasses The technical details for rejuvenation techniques for pasture (Sharma and Subhash Chander, 2007) and regeneration of wastelands into silvi-pastures (Dagar and Singh, 2003) are available. Thus, appropriate grassland / pasture land management coupled with appropriate soil, water and range management techniques offer immense possibilities of increasing productivity from CPR. There is an urgent need to provide logistic and financial support through framing regulations as well as providing funds to improve and maintain CPR for effective development and utilization. The key elements of such an approach are deliberate public action to curtail further deterioration of the CPR, restricting the commercial and mining activities in the CPR and technological and economic intervention for conservation and regulation of CPR use (Jodha, 1992). User participation will be as essential element in any CPR conservation activities. Creation of awareness about the importance of the CPR through educating the rural population and demarcation and strict vigilance of CPR land carries important role in the conservation of the CPR.

Forage Conservation for Lean Seasons

The good management of feed and fodder resources in the country need immediate attention. However, the conservation and feeding techniques are not very common as a result in event of feed-crisis situation the losses of animal lives and productivity are immense. The fodder that is produced during rainy season is not properly conserved. Creation of fodder banks and other community feed storage plans are not on ground. The large portion of valuable feed resources (paddy/ wheat straw, sugarcane tops etc.) produced in UP, Haryana, Punjab, Madya Pradesh are either burnt or used for industrial purposes. These resources can be conserved for scarcity period. In event of drought' which is frequently occurring phenomenon in Rajasthan, Gujarat and Andhra Pradesh; animal lives can be saved out of conserved fodder. The techniques for improvement of poor quality roughages and various methods of conservation of surplus vegetation are available (Jakhmola, 2003; Prasad and Jakhmola, 2003; Jakhmola, 2008) for increasing use of these feeds for managing nutritional deficiency in ruminants during scarcity.

Development of feed banks

Feed banks can play important role in drought mitigation. The crop residues based feeding system has limitations. There are two basic limitations with fibrous roughages, one is poor in nutritional value and second is low in bulk density. Offering nutritionally imbalanced feeds to ruminant - a commonly used practice during relief camps, not only affect the production but it also adversely affect important reproductive traits (Robinson et al., 2006). Supplementation of diets with energy, protein, mineral and vitamin sources increases the nutritive value of roughage-based feeds. But in traditional feeding system where roughages and concentrate are fed separately has practical difficulty especially during crisis feeding camps. Another approach where nutritionally balanced roughage based feed mixtures are prepared also has disadvantage because due to variation in bulk density; roughage and concentrate portions are not mixed well and significant amount of mash portion get settled at the bottom in the feeding trays. Even during rescue operations transportation of these mixtures are inconvenient and also at the same time concentrate portion tend to get settled. Due to low bulk density the transportation is highly inconvenient, costly and hazardous. Thus, in an organized system of animal rearing a wholesome complete feed is always desirous.

Under conditions of acute shortage of feed transportation in condensed form is always quick and economic. Complete Feed Blocks (CFB) are prepared by compressing feed mixtures that comprises roughage, concentrate and other supplementary nutrients and non-nutrients compounds in a proportionately balanced form that are desired for optimum animal productivity. CFB feeding synchronises the supply of nutrients to rumen micro organisms, which enhance rumen fermentation. Higher concentration of rumen anaerobic fungi was noticed (Samanta et al., 2003) in goat kids fed CFB over mash diet. Therefore, it seems block feeding promote rumen microbial growth and activity thereby increasing digestion of poor quality roughage. Feeding of CFB increases organic matter and crude protein digestibility of diets (Raghuvansi, 2004). Higher protease activity was noticed in the rumen of CFB fed animals which in turn increased protein digestibility of CFB (Vaithianathan et al., 2003). Consumption of feed block over the day ensures a synergy between nutrient demand of rumen micro organisms to degrade low quality feedstuffs and the provision of adequate level of these nutrient without exceeding the transformation capacity of microbial population. Improved intake, nutrient utilization, nitrogen retention and better animal performance are the bright features of CFB feeding over mash. Results of series of experiments showed that feeding straw based CFB diets improved dry matter and digestible dry matter intake by 20 and 17 % respectively over the mixed mash diets. Under prevailing circumstances, CFB technology has promise as it provide ease in transportation, storage, feeding and supply of nutrient to animals in a proportionate manner, indeed this technology have future for revolutionary change in animals production system of the country (Jakhmola, 2005).

Recommendations

- In arid and semi-arid areas that are most vulnerable, drought planning should be part of the ongoing animal management so that financial burden can be spread over the good seasons as well as the bad ones.
- The water availability and management which is most effective tool to fight drought need to be strengthened by use of both conventional water harvesting system as well as planned irrigation systems. This will increase availability of crop by-products – seeds, oilcakes and crop residues from command area that can play important role in drought mitigation as well as enhancing livestock productivity.

- There is need for good feed and fodder resources management in the country. The conservation of feed for odd times can save both losses of animal lives and productivity.
- To combat the feed scarcity situation during drought, which is regular feature in arid regions of India, the surplus feed and fodders from different parts of country can be processed following block technology and be transported to required places. Since keeping quality of these blocks is quite good hence fodder banks can be developed.

References

Collier, R.J., Beede, D.K., Thatcher, W.W., Isreal, L.A. and Wilcox, C. J. 1982. Influences of environment and its modification on animal health production. Journal of Dairy Science 65:2213-2227.

Dagar, J.C and Singh, G. 2003. Pasture production in degraded and problematic soils. In Sustainable Animal Production. (Eds. R.C. Jakhmola and R. K. Jain). Pointer Publishers, Jaipur. pp94-119.

Jakhmola, R.C. 2003 Forage Conservation. In:Sustainable Animal Production (Eds. R.C.Jakhmola and R.K.Jain) Pointer Publishers, Jaipur, pp 208-224.

Jakhmola, R.C. 2005. Final Report. Evaluation of locally available feed and fodder to improve quality and formulate complete economic rations with high roughage diets. National Agricultural Technology Project, CSWRI, Avikanagar.

Jakhmola, R.C. 2008. Feed quality improvement for managing nutritional deficiency of herbivores. In: Diversification of Arid Farming System. (Eds: Pratap Narain, M.P.Singh, Amal Kar, S. Katju and Praveen Kumar) Scientific Publishers, Jodhpur. Pp.383-394

Jakhmola, R.C., Shinde, A.K. and Bhatta, R. 2006a. Grazing stress - Production and reproduction performance of sheep and goat in desert ranges. In Strategies for Sustainable Livestock Production (Eds. S.K.Kaushish, A.K. Patel, H.C. Bohra, A.C. Mathur and B.K. Mathur). Kalyani Publishers, New Delhi. pp 69-83.

Jakhmola, R.C., Tripathi, M.K. and Ror, D. 2006b. Role of micronutrients for augmenting reproductive efficiency in small nutrients. In: Proceedings of the National Seminar on Innovations and Recent Advances in Reproduction for Augmenting Small Ruminant Production. Central Sheep and Wool Research Institute, Avikanagar. 28-30 December, pp. 168-177.

Jodha, N. S. 1986. Common Property resources and the rural poor in dry regions of India, Economic and Political Weekly, 21 (27): 1169-1181.

Jodha, N.S. 1992. Rural common property resources: The missing dimensions of development strategies, Washington, D.C., World Bank.

Malhotra, S.P. 1982. Livestock management and nomadism in the arid zone of Rajasthan, In: Problems and Prospects of Livestock Development, IDS, Jaipur.

Mann, J. S and Singh, N. P. 1982. A field study on the performance of natural and re-seeded grassland in the semi arid conditions of Rajasthan. Livestock Advisor. 2:23-29.

Mann, J. S. and Mehta, R.S. 1998. Feed and fodder resource development for small ruminant production. In: Proceedings of the Golden Jubilee Seminar on Sheep, Goat and Rabbit Production and Utilisation, Jaipur 24-26 April, pp 89-94.

Mitra, R., Christensen, G. I. and Johnson, H. D. 1972. Effect of prolong thermal exposer on growth hormone (GH) secretions in cattle. Journal of Animal Science 34:776-779.

Prasad, R. and Jakhmola, R.C. 2003. Improvement of low grade roughage and crop residues. In Sustainable Animal Production (Eds. R.C.Jakhmola and R.K.Jain) Pointer Publishers, Jaipur, 298-331.

Raghuvansi, SKS. 2004. Preparation and testing of high roughage based complete feed block in sheep feeding. Ph. D. Thesis, Udai Pratap Autonomus College, Varanasi, UP, India. pp 115.

Robinson, J.J., Ashworth, J.A., Rooke, J.A., Mitchel, L.M. and McEvoy, T.G. 2006. Nutrition and fertility in ruminant livestock. Journal of Animal Feed Science and Technology 126: 259-276.

Samanta, A.K., Singh, K.K., Das, M.M., Maity, S.B. and Kundu, S.S. 2003. Effect of complete feed block on nutrient utilization and rumen fermentation in Barbari goats. Small Ruminant Research. 48: 95-102.

Samra, J.S. 2004. Review and analysis of drought monitoring, declaration and management in India. Working paper 84. International Water Management Institute. Colombo, Sri Lanka.

Sankhyan, S.K., Shinde, A.K. and Karim, S.A. 1999. Seasonal changes in biomass yield, nutrient intake and its utilisation by sheep maintained on public rangelands. Indian Journal of Animal Sciences 69:617-620.

Sharma, K.C. and Subhash Chander. 2007. Effect of different rejuvenation techniques and fertilisation on sewan (*Lasiurus sindicus*) pasture in hot arid region of Rajasthan. Indian Journal of Agronomy 52:335-339.

Sharma, K.D. 2001. IGNP – lessons learnt from past management in the Indian arid zone. In. Regional Management of Water resources (Eds. A.H. Schumann, M.C. Aceman, R. Davis). IAHS Publishing Wallingford, U.K. pp 79-55.

Shinde, A.K. 2004. Nutrition and feeding management of sheep under different production systems, National seminar on Opportunities and Challenges in Nutrition and Feeding Management of Sheep, Goat and Rabbit for Sustainable Production, February 10-12, CSWRI, Avikanagar

Singh, V.K., Suresh, A., Gupta, D.C. and Jakhmola, R.C. 2005. Common property resources rural livelihood and small ruminants in India: a Review. Indian Journal of Animal Science. 75:1027-1036.

Vaithiyanathan, S., Raghuvansi, S.K.S., Mishra, A.S., Tripathi, M.K., Misra, A.K., Prasad, R. and Jakhmola, R.C. 2003. Effect of feeding chemically treated mustard (*Brassica campestris*) straw on rumen fiber degrading enzymes in sheep. Asian-Australasian Journal of Animal Science 16:1610-1613.

Venkateswarlu, J. 2008. Changing paradigms in water development and management systems in arid zone of India. In. Diversification of Arid Farming System. (Eds: Pratap Narain, M.P.Singh, Amal Kar, S. Katju and Praveen Kumar) Scientific Publishers, Jodhpur, 155-178 pp.

❑❑❑

7

Mitigation of Enteric Methane (Greenhouse Gas) Emission for Eco-Friendly and Economic Small Ruminant Production

D.N. Kamra
Centre of Advanced Studies in Animal Nutrition
Indian Veterinary Research Institute, Izatnagar, Bareilly-243 122, Uttar Pradesh

Introduction

Some of the carbon containing gases (carbon dioxide and methane) and the moisture absorb radiant energy of long wavelength and maintain the temperature of the atmosphere. Had these gases, which are also known as green house gases, not been present in the atmosphere, the temperature of earth would have been 40°C lower than the present temperature. The green house effect is similar to the effect in glass houses where glass retains radiations of long wavelength and maintains a temperature suitable for plant growth. This natural green house effect makes the existence of life possible on the earth. But the increasing concentration of these gases in the atmosphere has the following adverse effects on the environment.

- There has been an increase in earth's temperature, which is indicated by increased number of hot days, hot nights and heat waves during the last fifty years and there are less frequent cold days, cold nights and frost. For the next two decades International Panel on Climate Change projects a warming of about 0.20C per decade.

- Due to increased temperature of earth, the ice on the mountains, Arctic and Antarctic areas melts, which results in expansion of water and a rise in global sea level. Global average sea level rose by 1.0 mm per year over 1961-2003 and the rise has been maximum during the last one decade. But in a recent study reported in the Proceedings of the National Academy of Sciences, it has been predicted that the sea level might rise in a range of 75 to 190 cm in the period 1990-2100 (Vermeera and Rahmstorfb, 2009), which is very alarming and needs immediate attention of people concerned with climate change.
- Changes in eco-system due to changed temperature and water availability in a particular area have a significant impact on quality and quantity of vegetation, fruit, cereal grain, aromatic and medicinal plants.
- Changes in pathogenesis of plants, animals and human beings are expected as the insects and pathogens are strongly dependent on atmospheric temperature and humidity.
- Alteration in living style of the people due to above changes.

Greenhouse gases

Six gases are included under the head "greenhouse gases" i.e. carbon dioxide (CO_2), methane (CH_4), nitrous oxide (N_2O), hydrofluorocarbons (HFCs), perfluorocarbons (PFCs) and sulphur hexafluoride (SF_6) (IPCC, 1996). The first three are present in the atmosphere and are also produced as a result of agricultural and livestock activities of the human beings. The Global Warming Potential (GWP) of these gases in comparison to carbon dioxide is several times higher (Table 1) like methane and nitrous oxide have 23 and 296 times higher potential for global warming, respectively (IPCC, 2001). Therefore it is essential that their levels in the atmosphere are kept within safe limits. During the last two centuries the levels of two important green house gases like methane and nitrous oxide have risen by 115% and 15%, respectively (IPCC, 1996) which is not a good indication for the environment. The global warming potential of three industrial gases is several thousand times higher and therefore needs much more attention of the researchers to control or to completely stop the release of these dangerous gases into the atmosphere.

Table 1.Green house effect gases and their source of production

Gas	GWP*	Source
Agricultural activities		
Carbon dioxide	1	Combustion of fossil fuels
Methane	23	Enteric and waste fermentation, emissions from natural gas and oil fields
Nitrous oxide	296	Agricultural and industrial activities
Industrial activities		
Hydrofluorocarbons	12,000	Refrigeration and air conditioning
Perfluorocarbons	2,290	By-product of smelting process
Sulphur hexafluoride	22,200	Insulant in electrical switchgear and transformers

*Global warming potential (IPCC, 2001)

Mitigation strategies

In rumen fermentation, hydrogen generated as a result of carbohydrate fermentation is primarily used for reduction of carbon dioxide to methane by the methanogenic archaea. The other non-methanogenic hydrogenotrophic bacteria present in the rumen are:

- Acetogens convert carbon dioxide and hydrogen to acetate,a good source of nutrients for the ruminants (the process known as reductive acetogenesis), but this group of bacteria is not competitive enough to replace methanogenesis in the rumen.
- Sulphate reducers convert sulphate to hydrogen sulphide by using molecular hydrogen in the rumen (Morvan et al., 1996). The bacteria have a good affinity with hydrogen, but hydrogen sulphide is toxic for the animal and other microbes present in the rumen. Therefore, this group of bacteria cannot be encouraged to grow in the rumen.
- Fumarate reducers reduce fumarate to succinate by using hydrogen (Asanuma and Hino, 2000). Succinate is further metabolized (decarboxylated) to propionate, which again is a good source of energy for the ruminants. But the feeding of fumarate is required at a higher level to inhibit a considerable amount of methane and at that level fumarate lowers the pH of rumen content that adversely affects rumen fermentation.
- Nitrate/nitrite reducers which convert these inorganic electron acceptors to ammonia which can further be incorporated into amino acids and

microbial protein in the rumen (Sar et al., 2005), but the conversion of nitrate to nitrite is faster than conversion of nitrite to ammonia, therefore, it results in an accumulation of nitrite in the rumen which is toxic for the animals due to formation of met-haemoglobin which hampers the transport of oxygen to different tissues of the animal body.

Reductive acetogens

Acetogens are usually less competitive than methagogens for hydrogen utilization. This is also proved by Fonty et al. (2007) who inoculated methaogen free lambs (containing well established acetogens) with a mild inoculum of methanogenic archaea, the latter could establish themselves immediately while acetogens usually have great difficulty in competing with the methanogens in the normal rumen where they are well established. They also demonstrated for the first time that an adult sheep can be reared without methanogenic archaea and this animal could be used as an experimental model to study the exact role of methanogens in rumen fermentation and its effect on the microbial diversity of the rumen. In meroxenic methaogen free lambs, the feed intake and level of VFA in the rumen were lower, which might be due to absence of protozoa and fungi in the rumen. On the basis of results of experiments conducted by Fonty et al. (2007) it can be concluded that the presence of methanogens in the rumen is not mandatory for fermentation and utilization of feed. In the absence of methanogens, the acetogens and other hydrogenotrophic bacteria can establish in the rumen, but hydrogen recovery is not complete in the presence of these alternate hydrogen sinks. This problem can be taken care of by inoculating methane suppressed rumen with acetogens isolated from herbivores or from non-methanogenic anaerobic ecosystems in which acetogens play a vital role in hydrogen consumption (Breznak and Switzer, 1986, Bernalier et al., 1996).

The results of *in vitro* experiments have shown that reductive acetogenesis can serve as an alternate hydrogen sink in rumen fermentation, but *in vivo* experiments have failed so far. One of the major reasons for its failure might be due to poor affinity of the reaction with molecular hydrogen as it requires higher hydrogen threshold level (1.26 *vs* 0.067 mmole/l) as compared to that required for methanogenesis (Weimer, 1998). Efforts are needed to explore the biochemical pathways that determine the direction of hydrogen transfer either for methane generation or for acetate synthesis. If all the reducing power generated during rumen fermentation is diverted towards reductive acetogenesis, 5-10% of the gross energy intake by the animals can be saved and brought back into the energy cycle of the animals, which otherwise would have been lost in methane generation and released by the animals into the atmosphere. In addition to that it will also helps in protecting the environment by reduced release of methane by the animals.

Fumaric acid as a feed additive

Fumaric acid acts as an alternate electron acceptor in rumen fermentation and competes with the process of methanogenesis for the availability of hydrogen and therefore, is capable of decreasing methane emission by the animals (Carro and Ranilla, 2003), but feeding fumaric in high concentration (at which it is active against methanogenesis) might cause lowering of pH. The lower pH in the rumen is detrimental for many useful processes in the rumen like digestion of cellulose and other carbohydrates, feed intake, feed conversion efficiency and finally the productivity of the animals. Therefore Wallace et al. (2006) used fumaric acid in encapsulated form and included fumaric acid at the rate of 10% of diet and reported that there was a significant depression in methane emission (50% on inclusion of fumaric acid and 75% on inclusion of encapsulated fumaric acid). Although this experiment was conducted for a short duration (43 days), there were positive trends for better growth rate in growing lambs and improved feed utilization efficiency on inclusion of encapsulated fumaric acid.

Nitrate/nitrite reducing bacteria

Nitrate and nitrite reducing bacteria in the rumen of goat are: *Selenomonas ruminantium, Veillonella parvula* and *Wollinella succinogenes*. Not all the types of these bacteria are able to reduce NO_3/NO_2, but only a small fraction of the total number of these three genera has been found to be able of reducing NO_3/NO_2 to ammonia. *S. ruminantium* is the most important of these three genera to accomplish this reaction. The mixed ruminal microbes from the rumen of goats fed on high roughage diet reduced nitrate and nitrite to a greater extent than the rumen microbes from an animal fed on high concentrate diet (Iwamoto et al., 2001). These bacteria may act as alternate hydrogen sink in the rumen by converting NO_3/NO_2 to ammonia. The reduction of nitrate to ammonia is accomplished through nitrite as an intermediate. But the reduction of nitrate is 2-3 times faster than that of nitrite, resulting in an accumulation of nitrite in the rumen. Therefore, reduction of nitrite in the rumen should be enhanced to avoid intoxication of other rumen microbes.

Sar et al. (2005) reported that nitrate inhibits methanogenesis significantly in sheep at the rate of 1.3 g $NaNO_3$/kg $W^{0.75}$ of the animals, but it was accompanied with higher levels of plasma nitrite and blood methaemoglobin. These negative effects of nitrate feeding could be reduced or completely removed by feeding *Escherichia coli* culture at the rate of 150 ml (2×10^{10} cells/ml), which has a capability to reduce nitrite with nitrite reductase activity.

Plant secondary metabolites

The chemical composition of plants reveals that in addition to normal constituents like cellulose, hemicellulose, soluble sugars, proteins, fats etc., there are also present some unique molecules. As these molecules are not synthesized as a result of primary metabolism of the plants, such compounds are known as plant secondary metabolites, which are usually meant for providing protection to the plants against predators, pathogens, invaders etc. Several thousands of such metabolites have been identified. Majority of these compounds fall in the category of lignins, tannins, saponins, terpenoids/ volatile essential oils, alkaloids, etc. These plant secondary metabolites have anti-microbial activity, but their mechanism of action and inhibition of microbial growth is very specific and therefore these are active against a specific group of microbes. This specificity of these plant secondary metabolites against microbial groups can be used for selective manipulation of rumen fermentation. The methanogens, which are classified as archaea, has a distinctly different chemical composition of the cell walls from that of the other true bacteria present in the rumen. Therefore, there is a possibility that any one of the plant secondary compounds might act as a selective inhibitor of methanogens and can be used as a feed additive for the manipulation of rumen fermentation.

At Indian Veterinary Research Institute, a project funded by FAO/IAEA Joint Division of United Nations has just been completed in which a large number of plant secondary metabolites and their extracts have been tested for their potential to inhibit methane emission. Ethanol, methanol and water extracts of 41 plants, 23 plant combinations and 3 oils have been tested for their antimethanogenic activity, antiprotozoal activity and their effect on *in vitro* true digestibility of feed consisting of wheat straw and concentrate mixture in equal proportions in *in vitro* gas production technique. The results indicated that *Terminalia belerica, Terminalia chebula, Emblica officinalis, E. Jambolana, Quercus incana, Populus deltoides, Foeniculum vulgare, Syzygium aromaticum, Allium sativum, Psidium guajava, Canabis indica, Trachyspermum ammi, Mangifera indica, Mentha pipperita* and *Eucalyptus globulus* inhibited methane emission significantly (25-100%). A large number of plants were also inhibitory for ciliate protozoa. *Terminalia chebula, Emblica officinalis, E. jambolana, Syzygium aromaticum, Mentha pipperita* and *Eucalyptus globulus* also had an adverse effect on the *in vitro* true digestibility of feed (Kamra et al., 2006, 2008). In this experiment it was observed that only the alcoholic extracts (especially the methanol extracts) of above plants were effective against methanogenesis and ciliate protozoa (Patra et al., 2006a, b, c).

Vaccine against methanogens

Two vaccine formulations have also been tested in sheep and cattle in CSIRO. Extensive publicity has been given to a vaccine against methanogens being developed in Australia that is claimed to reduce CH_4 production per kilogram of food by 11-23%. This approach shows great promise as it might involve "once-in-a-lifetime" injection and be applicable to all classes of ruminants. It is, however, still at the development and testing stage and is unlikely to be available soon, even for evaluation.

A recent study by Williams et al. (2009), it has been a target to identify methanogens present in sheep and develop a vaccine against these prominent methanogens and to study its effect on total methane emission by the animals. They identified five phylotypes of methanogenic archaea, which accounted for more than 52% of total methanogens present. A vaccine generated against these five strains was used for vaccination of sheep, which caused an increase in specific immunoglobulin G titers in plasma, saliva and rumen fluid, but methane emission and methanogen numbers were not different in vaccinated and non-vaccinated groups. The methanogenic diversity was greater in vaccinated animals. One interesting finding was that the methogenic microbes usually take more than 4 weeks to get stabilized and care must be taken to carry on experiments for longer duration to get acceptable and repeatable results. The observations of this experiment indicated a necessity of a broad spectrum vaccine representing majority of methanogens present in the rumen to get positive influence on methane emission by the animals.

In vivo experiments with small ruminants

In an *in vivo* feeding trial with sheep Patra et al. (2009) studied the effect of *Terminalia chebula* and *Allium sativa* individually at the rate of 1% of dry matter intake and a mixture of the two in equal proportion at the same level. There was no effect on dry matter intake due to inclusion of these feed additives. Methane emission (L/kg digested DM) as estimated by open circuit respiration chamber and methane energy loss as percent of digestible energy intake were lower in *T. chebula* (P=0.09) and Mix (P=0.08) groups as compared to control (Table 2). The data indicated that *T. chebula* showed antimethanogenic activity whereas both *T. chebula* and *A. sativum* improved nutrients digestibility. Therefore, these two plants appear to be suitable candidates for use as feed additive to mitigate methane emission and to improve nutrient utilization by sheep.

Sapindus mukorossi (soapnut) is rich in saponins and can be used for manipulation of rumen fermentation in sheep. In an experiment conducted in the author's laboratory, ethanol extract of soapnut at the rate of 20 ml/ animal caused a significant depression in methane emission (26.99 *vs* 8.91

litres/kg DDM, 67% inhibition), but it was accompanied with a depression in digestibility of dry matter (from 0.541 to 0.482, a 11% reduction) and a 25% inhibition of ciliate protozoa. On reduction of ethanol extract to 10 ml/animal/day, the methane inhibition was reduced from 67% to 23%, but there were no adverse effects on dry matter digestibility or ciliate protozoa in the rumen of sheep. The extract of *Sapindus rarak* depressed rumen xylanase and carboxymethylcellulase activities. There was an adaptation of *Ruminococcus albus*, *Ruminococcus flavefaciens* and Chytridiomycetes (fungi) to saponin when fed over a long period. No correlation between the cell wall degrading enzyme activities and the cell wall degrading micro-organisms was observed which suggests that the organisms tracked in this experiment are not the only key players in ruminal cell wall degradation. *Sapindus rarak* saponins partially defaunate the rumen of goat (Wina et al., 2005), which might also affect methane inhibition by the rumen microbes. It appears from these results that if we do not target complete inhibition of methane, there are many plant extracts that can be used for reducing emission of methane by the ruminants without affecting productivity of the animals.

Table 2. Effect of feed additives on *in vivo* methane emission in small ruminants

Animal	Feed/Feed additive	Active principle	Methane production	Reference
Sheep	*Lotus pendunculatus* *Medicago sativa*	Condensed tannins (10%) Absent (<0.02)	25.3 to 17.5 g/kg DDM (33% inhibition)	Waghorn et al., 2002
Sheep	Concentrate + wheat straw (10% fumaric acid)	Fumaric acid	23.9 litres/d to 6.0 l/d (75% inhibition)	Wallace et al., 2006
Sheep	Ethanol extract of soapnut (*Sapindus mukorossi*)	Saponins	26.99 to 8.91 litre/kg DDM (67% inhibition)	Bhar et al., (Unpublished data)
Goat	*Kobe lespedeza*	Condensed tannins	26.2 to 10.9 l/d/head (58.4% inhibition) with inhibition of ciliate protozoa	Animut et al., 2008
Sheep	*Terminalia chebula* (1% of dry matter intake)	Tannins, chebulinic acid (astringent substance), gallic acid and resin	24.0% inhibition	Patra et al., 2009
	Allium sativum (1% of dry matter intake)	allicin, diallyl disulfide and diallyl trisulfide	11.9% inhibition	
	Terminalia chebula and *Allium sativum* (0.5% each of dry matter intake)	Tannins and essential oils listed as above	23.5% inhibition	

The effect of diet containing condensed tannins was studied in goats by Animut et al. (2008) on a ration consisting of a mixture of high condensed tannin (151 g/kg DM) containing forage, *Kobe lespedeza* and a forage containing low level of condensed tannins (0.3 g/kg DM), *Sorghum bicolor*. Methane emission by goats was 26.2, 17.6, 13.8 and 10.9 l/day with increasing level of *Kobe lespedeza* in diet at 0, 33, 67 and 100%, but at higher methane inhibition levels, the protozoal numbers were also inhibited adversely. Therefore to avoid the adverse effects on feed utilization, relatively low dietary levels of condense tannins should be employed to lessen CH_4 emission without a marked detrimental effect on other conditions such as nutrient utilization by the animals.

What needs to be done?

There are a large number of studies in which methane inhibition has been demonstrated in sheep and goat by use of various techniques like diet manipulation, use of chemical feed additives, defaunation, microbial manipulations and use of plant secondary metabolites. Of course there are a few limitations in some of these techniques, but there do exist methods which could be optimized for practical application. Therefore, long duration feeding experiments on growing small ruminants are needed and the quality of livestock products from the animals fed non conventional feed ingredients needs to be assessed, so that the livestock products are safe for consumption and acceptable among the masses.

The second most important aspect which needs immediate attention of researchers is to investigate microbial diversity of the rumen microbes, especially fibre degraders and methanogenic archaea and to identify inter-relationship between these two microbial groups to better understand the eco-system for selective control of microbes/microbial reactions to check methane emission by the animals without adversely affecting other metabolic processes of the animals.

References

Animut, G., Puchala, R., Goetsch, A.L., Patra, A.K., Sahlu, T., Varel, V.H. and Wells, J. 2008. Methane emission by goats consuming diets with different levels of condensed tannins from lespedeza. Animal Feed Science and Technology 144(3-4): 212-227.

Asanuma, N. and Hino, T. 2000. Activity and properties of fumarate reductase in ruminal bacteria. Journal of General and Applied Microbiology 49:119–125.

Bernalier, A., Lelait, M., Rochet, V., Grivet, J.P., Gibson, G.R. and Durand, M.. 1996. Acetogenesis from H2 and CO2 by methane- and non-methane-producing human colonic bacterial communities. FEMS Microbial Ecology 19:193–202.

Breznak, J. A. and Switzer, J.M. 1986. Acetate synthesis from H2-CO2 by termite gut microbes. Applied and Environmental Microbiology 52:623–630.

Carro, M.D. and Ranilla, M.J. 2003. Influence of different concentrations of disodium fumarate on methane production and fermentation of concentrate feeds by rumen micro-organisms *in vitro*. British Journal of Nutrition 90: 617– 623.

Fonty, G., Joblin, K., Chavarot, M., Roux, R., Naylor, G. and Michallon, F. 2007. Establishment and development of ruminal hydrogenotrophs in methanogen-free lambs. Applied and Environmental Microbiology 73: 6391-6403.

IPCC. 1996. *Intergovernmental Panel on Climate Change*. Guidelines for national greenhouse gas inventories – Greenhouse gas inventory reference manual. IPCC WGI Technical Support Unit, Bracknell, UK.

IPCC. 2001. *Intergovernmental Panel on Climate Change*. Climate change 2001: the scientific basis. [Third Assessment Report from Working Group 1. Edited by Houghton, J.T. et al.] Cambridge University Press, UK.

Iwamoto, M., Asanuma, N. and Hino, T. 2001. Effects of pH and electron donors on nitrate and nitrite reduction in ruminal microbiota. Animal Science Journal 72 (2): 117-125.

Kamra, D.N., Agarwal, N. and Chaudhary, L.C. 2006. Inhibition of ruminal methanogenesis by tropical plants containing secondary compounds. International Congress Series 1293, 156-163.

Kamra, D.N., Patra, A.K., Chatterjee, P.N., Kumar, R., Agarwal, N. and Chaudhary, L.C. 2008. Effect of plant extracts on methanogenesis and microbial profile of the rumen of buffalo: a brief overview. Australian Journal of Experimental Agriculture 48: 175-178

Morvan, B., Bonnemoy, F., Fonty, G. and Gouet, P. 1996. Quantitative determination of H_2-utilizing acetogenic and sulfate-reducing bacteria and methanogenic archaea from digestive tract of different mammals. Current Microbiology 32: 129–133.

Patra, A.K., Kamra, D.N. and Agarwal, N. 2006a. Effect of plant extracts on *in vitro* methanogenesis enzyme activities and fermentation of feed in the rumen liquor of buffalo. Animal Feed Science and Technology 128: 276-291.

Patra, A.K., Kamra, D.N. and Agarwal, N. 2006b. Effect of plants containing metabolites on *in vitro* methanogenesis, enzyme profile and fermentation of feed with rumen liquor of buffalo. Animal Nutrition and Feed Technology 6: 203-213.

Patra, A.K., Kamra, D.N. and Agarwal, N. 2006c. Effect of spices on rumen fermentattaion, methanogenesis and protozoa counts in *in vitro* gas production test. International Congress Series 1293: 176-179.

Patra, A.K., Kamra, D.N., Bhar, R., Kumar, R. and Agarwal, N. 2009. Effect of *Terminalia chebula* and *Allium sativum* on *in vivo* methane emission by sheep. Journal of Animal Physiology and Animal Nutrition (*In press*).

Sar, C., Mwenya, B., Pen, B., Takaura, K., Morikawa, R., Tsujimoto, A., Kuwaki, K., Isogai, N., Shinzato, I., Asakura, Y., Toride, Y. and Takahashi, J. 2005. Effect of ruminal administration of *Escherichia coli* wild type or a genetically modified with enhanced nitrite reductase activity on methane emission and nitrate toxicity in nitrate infused sheep. British Journal of Nutrition 94: 691-697

Vermeera, M. and Rahmstorfb, S. 2009. Global sea level linked to global temperature. Proceedings of National Academy of Sciences www.pnas.org cgi doi 10.1073_pnas. 0907765106.

Waghorn, G.C., Tavendale, M.H. and Woodfield, D.R. 2002. Methanogenesis from forages fed to sheep. Proceedings of New Zealand Grasslands Association 64: 167–171.

Wallace, R.J., Wood, T.A., Rowe, A., Price, J., Yanez, D.R., Williams, S.P. and Newbold, C.J. 2006. Encapsulated fumaric acid as a means of decreasing ruminal methane emissions. International Congress Series 1293: 148–151.

Weimer, P.J. 1998. Manipulating ruminal fermentation: A microbial ecological perspective. Journal of Animal Science 76: 3114-3122.

Williams, Y.J., Popovski, S., Rea, S.M., Skillman, L.C., Toovey, A.F., Northwood, K.S. and Wright, A.G. 2009. A vaccine against rumen methanogens can alter the composition of Archaeal populations. Applied and Environmental Microbiology 75:1860-1866.

Wina, E., Muetzel, S. and Becker, K. 2005. The dynamics of major fibrolytic microbes and enzyme activity in the rumen in response to short- and long-term feeding of *Sapindus rarak* saponins. Journal of Applied Microbiology 100: 114–122.

❑❑❑

8

Feeding Management of Small Ruminants in Cold Climates of Temperate Region

A. Sahoo
Division of Animal Nutrition, Central Sheep and Wool Research Institute
Avikanagar, via Jaipur- 304 501, Rajasthan

Introduction

Sheep and goats provide meat, milk and (or) wool/fibre to many people of the world, thus playing a special role in achieving food and economic securities in the developing and underdeveloped countries. Nutrition plays an essential and special role in the systems of sheep and goat farming for the following main reasons. First, it is the production factor that farmers can act on the most easily and rapidly (amounts of feeds, composition of diets, on-pasture management) having the most marked effect on production costs and accordingly on farmer incomes. Furthermore, the management of feeding in flocks depends on vegetal mass production and rangeland, pasture and crop by-product management. Feeding directly impacts the other components of small ruminant production systems as well, such as pathological conditions and the reproductive performance of flocks. Moreover, a nutritional program must always be established by taking into account the genetic characteristics of the breed or genotype used (potential of production, ability for adaptation, *etc.*). The observation from Devendra (2000) that "little attention has been paid to the feeding of small ruminants in the past so that relatively low inputs to improve feeding could produce relatively high gains in productivity" remains true.

In India, the small ruminants are maintained on scrub vegetation available on shrinking wastelands, community grazing lands, crop stubbles and tree lopping with little or no supplementary feeding resulting in low productivity and high morbidity and mortality. The grazing resources fail to meet energy and protein requirements including that of minerals and vitamins throughout the year affecting flock health, growth, production and reproduction. The scenario in temperate high hill regions of India is not that better. The husbandry practised is mostly influenced by the location, topography, and cropping pattern of an area, the availability of waste land, communal grazing land and forest areas, and by market prospects. The cost of transportation of bulky forages due to scarce availability in the region particularly during winter is a major impending problem to sustain the sedentary livestock population.

Within the world's temperate zones, small ruminant production systems are found in two main situations. Firstly, they are the main agricultural land-users in areas where there are combinations of difficult terrain, poor soils and harsher climates. Secondly, small ruminants utilize more intensive pastures. The land available to agriculture is often steep, rocky and has poor soils. The hill livestock husbandry system can be described in two broad categories, sedentary and migratory.

Sedentary system

Animals are kept in one area throughout the year and are penned at the homestead at night time. They may be stall-fed, semi-stall-fed or completely grazed. In cities, towns and peri-urban areas, and in valleys where cropping is very intense and pasture/forest area is limited, small ruminants are raised sparsely under a stall or semi-stall feeding system. Animals are let loose for a certain period of the day, but due to limited availability of grazing land and fodder, these animals are normally supplemented at the stall with roughage (grasses, straw, fodder tree leaves) and in some cases, food grains as concentrate. However, the majority of the sedentary goat and sheep flocks are maintained under an extensive management system, where the animals are driven to the pasture land or forest for grazing during the day, and are not supplemented at the stall. The livestock farmers follow a specific traditional grazing management, in which the available grazing land is utilized in a rotational manner-animals are moved to a new area each day completing the rotation in four to six days. Farmers believe that this system allows adequate regrowth of grasses and vegetation in between grazing. However, availability of grass in a grazing area directly influences this practice, and pasture areas with good grasses are grazed more frequently than those that are less productive. The grazing of animals in a limited area throughout the year leads to the development of a heavy parasitic burden, so that associated parasitic diseases are a major constraint upon the productivity of this system. Moreover, these sheep and goats have to compete for forage with cattle and buffaloes maintained under a similar system. The number of goats and sheep raised by a single family is very variable and is influenced by the availability of free pasture or forest resources, and by the availability of family labour.

Migratory system

This is the usual system of animal keeping that is followed in the high hills. Livestock moves from one vegetation/climatic zone to another. Full scale transhumance, important for mountain regions is less common in foothill systems, but most systems involve movement of livestock from higher land to lower land for winter grazing, or even into housing for part of the winter. Animals are moved to different areas throughout the year, and are maintained entirely under grazing management. The flocks migrate from the lower hills (600–900m msl) up to the high alpine pastures (3600–4800m msl) and back again as the climate determine the availability of fodder and forage. Once arable cultivation begins, animals are forced to move higher up the hill, and they return later in the year after the crops have been harvested. This transhumance system of animal keeping is considered to be one of the oldest forms of livestock husbandry, having evolved at the time when animals were domesticated. A typical migratory flock consists of 200–250 animals, but the flock size can vary within the range of 50–800 animals. Systems in the mountains and hills tend to be dependent upon grasslands, both semi-natural and improved, although in some regions browsing of dwarf shrubs in the winter period is as important as browsing of shrubs in the arid regions.

Free ranging and nutritional adequacy

In free ranging, if the food availability is scarce, the animals are forced to travel long distances in search of food to meet their energy requirements and this extra energy drain can be an important contributor to the ME need for maintenance. Both sheep and goats adapt well to environmental conditions prevailing in arid lands, being able to obtain and adequate diet even when forage is scarce and they can feed over rugged and otherwise inaccessible terrain. Energy requirements in open range may increase several fold over values assessed for restrained animals. The NRC (1981) considers that in goats the increased muscular activity of the animal under grazing conditions accounts for a 25% increment in the case of light activity, a 50% increment on semi-arid rangeland pasture and on slightly hilly land and a 75% increment in case of long-distance travel on sparsely vegetated grassland or on mountainous transhumance pasture. Both the increased energy expenditure of eating and the energy expended in walking would account to this increased maintenance requirement.

Nutritional physiology

Many investigations dealt with the involvement of thyroid hormones in the expression of endogenous seasonal rhythms, such as reproduction and hair growth cycles in fibre-producing (wool, mohair, cashmere) sheep and goats. Many endogenous (breed, age, gender, physiological state) and environmental factors (climate, season, with a primary role of nutrition) are able to affect thyroid activity and hormone (TH) concentrations in blood, acting at the level of hypothalamus, pituitary and/or thyroid gland, as well as on peripheral monodeiodination (Todini, 2007). Variations in hormone bioactivity allow the animals to adapt their metabolic balance to different environmental conditions, changes in nutrient requirements and availability, and to homeorhetic changes during different physiological stages. This is particularly important in the free-ranging and grazing animals, such as traditionally reared small ruminants, whose main physiological functions (feed intake, reproduction, hair growth) are markedly seasonal. T3 directly stimulates feed intake at the hypothalamic level (Kong et al., 2004), while on the other hand, the quantity and quality of food eaten is a major factor determining plasma concentrations of TH (Dauncey, 1990). Similarly, day length is the major environmental variable governing seasonal breeding, and the pineal gland is needed for this response to occur in many photosensitive species. Melatonin has been proposed as the pineal hormone; its timed administration replicate the effect of day length on seasonal breeding in several mammals, including long-day, like the hamster, and short-day breeders, like the sheep (Cardinali, 1984; Mahapatra and Sahoo, 2006). In the true temperate zones, sheep and goats have seasonal breeding and in the hill regions, lambing is linked to seasonal availability of pastures. It is normal for lambing to commence at the beginning of the grass growing season, with lactation occurring through the period of highest grass growth and quality. Mating and pregnancy typically coincide with the period of poorest growth and often the most difficult climatic conditions. There are, thus a number of adaptations that cope with the patterns of production and availability of pastures in hilly regions (El Aich and Waterhouse, 1999).

Standard requirements

Small ruminants require energy, protein, vitamins, minerals, fibre, and water. Many factors affect the nutritional requirements of small ruminants: maintenance, growth, pregnancy, lactation, fibre production, activity, and environment. As a general rule of thumb, sheep and goats will consume 2-4% of their body weight on DM basis. The exact percentage varies according to the size (weight) of the animal, with smaller animals needing a higher intake (percentage-wise) to maintain their live weight. Maintenance requirements increase as the level of the animals' activity increases. For example, migratory sheep or goat that has to travel a farther distance for feed and water will have a higher maintenance requirement than animals in a feedlot/stall. The maintenance requirement becomes higher in environmental stresses like cold and severe weather to maintain body heat. Then, there is added stresses of pregnancy, lactation, and growth, which further increase the nutrient requirements. Paul et al., (2003) collected data from 19 feeding trials conducted on growing sheep from different institutes across India and subjected to regression analysis to derive requirements of TDN, CP and DCP for maintenance and body weight gain. The maintenance requirements for TDN, CP and DCP were 37.0, 6.68 and 4.43 g/kg $W^{0.75}$, respectively for the BW range of 7-15 kg, and the corresponding maintenance requirements for the BW range of 15.1-30 kg were 35.3, 6.98 and 4.49 g. The corresponding requirements for 1 g gain in BW were 0.91, 0.47, and 0.31 g, for 7-15 kg BW and 1.21, 0.43 and 0.30 g, respectively for 15-30 kg BW range. Similarly, Mandal et al. (2005) analysed data from 25 feeding trials conducted on growing goats from different research institutes across India. They found maintenance requirements for TDN, CP and DCP at 30.1, 5.83 and 3.22 g/kg $BW^{0.75}$, respectively. The corresponding requirements for 1 g gain in BW were 1.61, 0.45 and 0.34 g, respectively. NRC (2007) revised many concepts in small ruminant nutrition and came out with guiding principles for formulating rations based on nutritional requirement for different levels of activity (Table 1) and state and type of production.

Nutrient requirements for migratory sheep and goats

Migratory system of animal keeping is ancient and its biblical references to shepherds and their flocks. It is practiced both in plains and high hills. Animals are moved to different areas throughout the year, and are maintained entirely under grazing management. At plains the flocks migrate in search of feeding and grazing resources from one place to other and from the lower hills (800–900m above msl) up to the high alpine pastures (3600–4800m above msl) and back again as the climate determines the availability of fodder and forage. Once arable cultivation begins, animals are forced to move higher up the hill, and they return later in the year after the crops have been harvested.

Nutritional allowance during winter

Cold semi-arid and arid climatic temperate regions have variable degree of rainfall and thus the native vegetation showed typical pattern of growth in response to short period of rainy season followed by long spell of dry winter and vegetation revival after snow. Such seasonal pattern has a great influence on diet composition and intake of grazing sheep and goat in semiarid/arid pastures and ranges. Grazing of sheep on pasture in lower ambient temperature requires more energy for thermoregulation resulting in greater energy expenditure. Sheep in nomadic pastoral ecosystem allocated 47% of a total ME for basal metabolism, 16% for travel, 14% for other activities and 23% for production (Coppock et al., 1986). The maintenance energy requirement of sheep on pasture in different locations was 43-64% (Young and Corbett, 1972), 33% (Sahlu et al., 1989) and 43% (Shinde et al., 1998) more than stall-fed. Estimates of the energy cost of walking were 3.35, 31.7 and -13.2 J kg^{-1} BW^{m-1} for horizontal, ascending and descending movement, respectively (Lachica and Aguilera, 2003). The heat production (HP) attained 401 kJ $kg^{-0.75}$ per day for restrained goats. The increase in HP for unrestrained over restrained goats was 43.1% and daily distance travelled (say 2km) accounted for 9% of the extra HP. AFRC (1998) suggested that energy used in activity (MEa) for stall-fed goats was 10% of fasting heat production (10% of 315 kJ/kgBW$^{0.75}$), with additional costs for grazing based on BW1.0 for horizontal movement (3.5 J/(kgBW × m)), vertical movement (28 J/(kgBW × m)), standing (0.417 kJ/(kgBW × h)) and change in position (0.26 kJ/(kgBW × number of changes)), and then application of the efficiency of ME use for maintenance. Conclusively, forage consumption increased energy expenditure to a greater extent than walking and may lessen effects of walking and walking speed on the grazing activity energy cost (Berhan et al., 2006). In this line there is a strong need to assess the nutrient requirements of migratory flock of sheep and goats which followed an annual cycle of upward (4000-5000 m above msl) and downward migration (plains) and exposed to a variable degree of under-nutrition.

The food requirement of animals can be estimated by calculating the amount of food needed to provide the requisite amount of ME for maintaining its state of production. An estimate of daily food intake depends primarily on data obtained from practical feeding trials. However, the recorded data needs scientific validation based on information from the local people, chemical composition of available pasture/fodder species, *in vitro* and *in sacco* study trials. Nutritional adequacy, on the other hand, needs assessment of the availability of feed and nutrients and sustainability for a particular state of production without affecting the productive life cycle of the animal. The time spent grazing, is dependent on the amount of forage consumed and the relative availability of herbage. Therefore, free ranging animals pay relatively higher costs of foraging for dispersed foods, avoiding or battling predators and parasites, dealing with more extreme climatic conditions, and interacting socially with other species competing for the same pasture or fodder resources (Sahoo, 2005).

Table 1. Nutrient requirements of goats at hilly and mountainous pasture

BW (kg)	Feed Energy				Crude Protein		Minerals		Dry Matter per Animal 1 kg=2.0 Mcal ME		1 kg=2.4 Mcal ME	
	TDN (g)	DE(Mcal)	ME(Mcal)	NE (Mcal)	TP (g)	DP (g)	Ca (g)	P (g)	Total(kg)	% of BW	Total(kg)	%of BW
Maintenance plus medium activity **(=50% increment, semiarid rangeland, slightly hilly pastures, & early pregnancy)**												
10	239	1.05	0.86	0.48	33	23	1	0.7	0.43	4.3	0.36	3.6
20	400	1.77	1.44	0.81	55	38	2	1.4	0.72	3.6	0.60	3.0
30	543	2.38	1.95	1.10	74	52	3	2.1	0.98	3.3	0.81	2.7
40	672	2.97	2.42	1.36	93	64	4	2.8	1.21	3.0	1.01	2.5
50	795	3.51	2.86	1.62	110	76	4	2.8	1.43	2.9	1.19	2.4
60	912	4.02	3.28	1.84	126	87	5	3.5	1.64	2.7	1.37	2.3
70	1023	4.52	3.68	2.07	141	98	6	4.2	1.84	2.6	1.53	2.2
80	1131	4.98	4.06	2.30	156	108	6	4.2	2.03	2.5	1.69	2.1
90	1236	5.44	4.44	2.50	170	118	7	4.9	2.22	2.5	1.85	2.0
100	1336	5.90	4.82	2.72	184	128	7	4.9	2.41	2.4	2.01	2.0
Maintenance plus high activity **(=75% increment, arid rangeland, sparse vegetation, mountainous pastures, & early pregnancy)**												
10	278	1.22	1.00	0.56	38	26	2	1.4	0.50	5.0	0.42	4.2
20	467	2.06	1.68	0.94	64	45	2	1.4	0.84	4.2	0.70	3.5
30	634	2.78	2.28	1.28	87	60	3	2.1	1.14	3.8	0.95	3.2
40	784	3.46	2.82	1.59	108	75	4	2.8	1.41	3.5	1.18	3.0
50	928	4.10	3.34	1.89	128	89	5	3.5	1.67	3.3	1.39	2.7
60	1064	4.69	3.83	2.15	146	102	6	4.2	1.92	3.2	1.60	2.7
70	1194	5.27	4.29	2.42	165	114	6	4.2	2.14	3.0	1.79	2.6
80	1320	5.81	4.74	2.68	182	126	7	4.9	2.37	3.0	1.98	2.5
90	1442	6.35	5.18	2.92	198	138	8	5.6	2.59	2.9	2.16	2.4
100	1559	6.88	5.62	3.17	215	150	8	5.6	2.81	2.8	2.34	2.3

Source: NRC, 1985; 2007

Micronutrient demand and supply

For sheep/goat at pasture, deficiencies and excesses of many, but not all, have been reported. Only a handful of elements are commonly responsible for nutritional problems that affect growth, milk production or fertility performance of sheep and goats and the seven of practical significance (in approximate order of importance) are Se, cobalt (Co) (as vitamin B12), Cu (and its antagonist molybdenum (Mo)), iodine (I), zinc (Zn), iron (Fe) and manganese (Mn). The availability of copper can result in a four-fold difference in the ability of feeds to provide absorbable copper, depending on the concentrations of other mineral elements. Similarly, in case of Se, little is known about its dietary availability and whether its shared absorption pathway with molybdate and sulphate make these anions absorptive antagonists (Underwood and Suttle, 1999). Cobalt is another element in which the availability of its functional entity, vitamin B12, may be impaired by the formation of analogues that disrupt the vitamin's biological activity. Physiological functions are progressively affected by deficiencies. For example, loss of pigmentation occurs with intakes of Cu that are sufficient for pregnancy maintenance and haemoglobin formation. Pregnancy is not maintained by intakes of Cu that prevent anaemia. Furthermore, the disruption to Fe metabolism caused by Cu deficiency does not occur until after most other clinical signs have appeared (Mills, 1987). Deficiencies and imbalances of trace elements can affect productivity of ruminants. Whereas improvement in feed intake can occur quickly in response to Zn or cobalt supplementation, productivity responses to Cu or Se may be slower to become evident by improved health of newborns, greater resistance to mastitis, or increased weaning weights (Kincaid, 1999). Further, macro-minerals (Ca, P, Mg) and trace elements (Cu, Co, Mo, Se, Zn, etc.) can influence host–parasite relationships (Suttle and Jones, 1989).

Vitamins are supplied through diet, synthesized by the animal or produced via microbial activity in the rumen. Given adequate protein, energy and precursors, normal rumen function will produce sufficient B-group vitamins and vitamin K to meet animal needs. Vitamin C is synthesized endogenously from glucose and galactose, while vitamin D is produced in the skin through the interaction of ultra-violet (UV) radiation and precursor sterols. Only vitamin A, its precursor b-carotene and vitamin E are diet-dependent and are therefore of general practical significance. Sporadic outbreaks of thiamine deficiency in sheep at pasture are thought to be due to a marked increase in thiaminase activity in the rumen (McDonald, 1982); thiaminase may be present in ingested plants, such as ferns (more prevalent in sub-Himalayan regions of HP, Uttarakhand), but more often arises from microbial activity in the rumen.

Declining grazing resource and range management

Sedentary flocks of sheep and goats compete with large ruminants throughout the year and poor pasture quality forces animals to utilize forest resources. Overgrazing/browsing is adversely affecting the forest vegetation, and so lack of proper pasture management is leading to forest deterioration. The same is true for pastures grazed by migratory flocks, and thus palatable grasses are being replaced by thorny weeds complicating the situation further. The environmental impact of winter feeding of transhumant herds, however, is often very negative. In systems totally dependent on grazing, overall numbers tend to be kept in check by how many can be over wintered. When concentrates are fed, however, large numbers can be maintained through the lean season. This greatly increases the pressure on the grazing land, especially if the livestock are allowed to graze before the herbage has fully recovered in spring, which is, unfortunately, often the case. To address the problems mentioned above studies were undertaken on the establishment of fodder grass which provides green fodder all the year round. Exotic temperate species like; Rye grass (Lolium perenne), Cocksfoot (*Dactylis glomerata*), White clover *(Trifolium repens* cv. Khumal), Lotononis (*Lotus maku*), Alfalfa (*Medicago sativa*) are under study for their performance. Experimental trials are going on to study the effect of mixed cultivation of Clover with cocksfoot for more biomass production (Singh, 1996). Most of the high altitude rangelands are the public lands used by high altitude livestock herders. To improve the condition of those open ranges and Pasture lands the user's group play a significant role. To motivate the herders to form user's group and jointly work for their better future, trainings are needed in the field of group formation, mobilization, and management of natural resources for optimum use without adverse effects on their eco-system. Positive impacts can be expected from the group approach working in partnership with the Government and non- government agencies for rangeland development and poverty alleviation program. To get maximum benefit from livestock they have to use their feed resources properly and conserve forages for winter season and use the forest lands for cultivation of grasses and legumes under the trees.

The mountain areas exhibit a great diversity in climate, landforms, resource availability and agricultural practices. Remunerative agriculture in the form of double cropping is practiced up to an elevation of 1000 m only, and beyond this altitude, the uncertainty of climate and steep slopes have restricted the agricultural activity, mainly to livestock husbandry. The forage resources are limited to grasslands, cultivable wastelands, fodder trees and crop residues. About 40.0% of the total geographical area is under natural grasslands, which get shrunken in the period of long winter due to snow coverage. The rapid changes in political boundaries and policies that have led to restricted livestock mobility and the marginalization of pastoral people, pointing out that such changes need to be understood in order to identify realistic strategies for livestock and rangeland development. Limbach et al. (2000) studied adaptability of forage grasses at higher altitudes and graded *Poa compressa, Poa pratensis var. alpinum, Dactylis glomerata, Festuca ovina, Agrostis alba, Phleum pratense, Deschampsia caespitosa, Trisetum flavescens, Elymus trachycaulus*, Tibetan Mixture, and two varieties of *Medicago sativa* as best varieties.

Major problems and constraints

(i) Legal and land tenure problems

Land tenure or lack of clarity in grazing rights is identified as a serious problem in most of the Himalayan zone. For land under the jurisdiction of Forest Departments, laws and regulations on access, stock numbers, and timing of grazing and grazing fees were enacted long ago, but regulations have little effect unless there is both political and popular will to enforce them.

(ii) The conflict between the political decisions and the ecological reality of the environment

The failure to understand the functioning of the system leads to deterioration of the production system.

(iii) Impact social change

Conflict of interests between settled farmers and herders is increasing with rising population pressure and intensification of agriculture throughout the Himalayan zone.

(iv) Poor pasture condition

This is widespread and is due to overstocking and poor management techniques. Much of the overstocking is due to increases in human population and a lack of alternative means of earning a livelihood. Mismanagement is exacerbated by lack of defined rights to grazing, by lack of grazing rules to assure proper land use or by lack of will to apply either. Degradation varies from changes in the specific composition, through drop in yield, to invasion by undesirable plants and erosion.

(v) Limited feed storage

Storage of feed limited to harvesting mature forest grass, leaves, ripe vegetable plants and little cultivable fodder plants (bajra, maize, rye, millets, etc.). Hay and silage making is nearly non-existent.

(vi) Socio-economic constraints

Herders were generally poor with low educational levels which limits access to outside employment and, perhaps, to markets. They certainly, have a hard lifestyle and can carry few possessions, but they do have considerable capital in their herds and with a series of good years, they can accumulate wealth to invest in, amongst others, land and other profitable trade.

(vii) Transformation of small ruminant production systems

Dynamics of productions systems under present demographic pressures and economic changes, such as reduction in mobility of herds discussed above, lead to an increase in human settlements, which is associated with more demand for cultivation land. As the population becomes more and more sedentary, the amount of agro-pastoralism increases. All these factors related to the transformation of the pastoral systems make the systems heavily dependent on external feed resources and agricultural by products.

Marketing: Marketing of stock and produce was a problem in many of the areas at high hills. Lack of infrastructure, roads or pavements, absence or breakdown of trekking routes, improper pricing of the livestock produce, and unscrupulous dealers are some of the principal identified problems faced by the herdsmen.

Conclusions

In temperate zones, there are concerns that either too little or too much grazing by small ruminants is leading to environmental degradation. There is a need to more fully understand the role that grazing plays in maintaining habitats and landscapes in favourable condition. Domestic animals continue to make important contributions to global food supply and, as a result, animal feeds have become an increasingly critical component of the integrated food chain. Livestock products account for about 30% of the global value of agriculture and 19% of the value of food production, and provide 34% of protein and 16% of the energy consumed in human diets. Consumption in the developing world including India is determined by purchasing power, and greater consumption of meat and milk will be stimulated by economic growth and more disposable income in the growing, more prosperous middle class. Thus, future increases in small ruminant production are also likely to be boosted by considerable annual increases in agriculture and allied production, considering the agrarian economy of the largest section of people in India. Problems of under- and over-grazing need to be recognized and dealt with so that environmental degradation can be prevented by appreciation that careful management of the small ruminant is the main means by which the chosen environmental state can be achieved and the socio-economic back-bone of such a huge dependent livestock population can be sustained. Some of the futuristic approaches are delineated below. Any development or augmentation in livestock production must be accompanied by adequate marketing facilities if they are to lead to better livelihoods for the producers.

- Strategic supplementation of critical nutrients stimulate feed intake and increase the efficiency of ruminant productivity on low quality & unconventional roughage-based diets.
- The feeding habits based on tree leaves can be put in to advantages due to richness of different plant secondary metabolites, e.g. condensed tannins may be used as organic protectant of protein from rumen degradation thus providing more dietary and microbial protein post-ruminally for production purposes and may also be manipulated against GI parasitism.
- Sheep and goat meat production should concentrate on prolific indigenous breeds under sedentary and stall-fed conditions
- Strategies to increase the proportion of large ruminants maintained under stall feeding regimes should be encouraged, so that production from small ruminants, especially sheep can be increased in the migratory systems most suited to them.
- Envisage on flock productivity and economics of different types of pastures in respect of quantity and quality of meat and wool production per unit land.

References

AFRC. 1998. Agricultural and Food Research Council. *The Nutrition of Goats* CAB International, Wallingford, UK

Berhan T., Puchala R., Goetsch A.L. and Merkel R.C.2006. Effects of walking speed and forage consumption on energy expenditure and heart rate by Alpine does. Small Ruminant Research 63: 119-124.

Cardinali, D.P. 1984. Pineal and melatonin actions in reproductive endocrinology. Archivos de Biología y Medicina Experimentales (Santiago) 17:239-247.

Coppock D.L., Swift, D.M., Ellis, J.E. and Gelvin, K. 1986. Seasonal pattern of energy allocation to basal metabolism, activity and production for livestock in a nomadic pastoral ecosystem. Journal of Agriculture Science (Cambridge) 107: 357-365.

Dauncey M J. 1990. Thyroid hormones and thermogenesis. The Proceedings of the Nutrition Society 49:203-215.

Devendra, C., 2000. Perspectives on research in goats in Asia and the Pacific. In: Proceedings of the 7th International Conference on Goats, vol. 2, Tours, France, 10–15 May 2000, pp. 892–893.

El Aich, A. and Waterhouse, A. 1999. Small ruminants in environmental conservation. Small Ruminant Research 34:271-287

Kincaid R. L. 1999. Assessment of trace mineral status of ruminants: A review. Proceedings of the American Society of Animal Science. Pp 1-10.

Kong, W.M., Martin N.M., Smith K.L., Gardiner J.V., Connoley I.P., Stephens D.A., Dhillo W.S., Ghatei M.A., Small C. J. and Bloom S.R. 2004. Triiodothyronine stimulates food intake via the hypothalamic ventromedial nucleus independent of changes in energy expenditure, Endocrinology 145:5252–5258.

Lachica M. and Aguilera J.F. 2003. Estimation of energy needs in the free-ranging goat with particular reference to the assessment of its energy expenditure by the 13C-bicarbonate method. Small Ruminant Research 49: 303–318.

Limbach, E.W., Liu, Y and Ma, Y. 2000. Grass and Legume Variety Trials in Eastern Tibet. In: Proceedings of the Third International Congress on Yak, 4-9 September, 2000. Zhao X.X. (Ed.). International Veterinary Information Service, Ithaca NY

Mahapatra, R.K. and Sahoo, A. 2006. Hormones of Pineal Gland and role in Clinical Physiology in Small Ruminants. In: Short Course Compendium, CAS in Animal Physiology, IVRI, Izatnagar.

McDonald, J.W. 1982. Mortality and ill thrift associated with thiamine deficiency in lambs. Australian Veterinary Journal 58:212-213.

Mandal, A.B., Paul, S.S., Mandal, G.P., Kannan, A. and Pathak, N.N. 2005. Deriving nutrient requirements of growing Indian goats under tropical condition. Small Ruminant Research 58:201-217.

Mills, C. F. 1987. Biochemical and physiological indicators of mineral status in animals: copper, cobalt and zinc. Journal of Animal Science 65:1702-1711.

NRC, 1981. Nutrient Requirements of Goats, National Research Council, National Academic Press, Washington DC, U.S.A.

NRC, 1985, Nutrient Requirements of Sheep, 6th revised edition, National Research Council, National Academic Press, Washington DC, U.S.A.

NRC, 2007. Nutrient Requirements of small Ruminants, National Research Council, National Academic Press, Washington DC.

Owen, J.B. 1976. Sheep Production. Bailliere Tindall, London, UK.

Paul, S.S., Mandal, A.B., Mandal, G.P., Kannan, A. and Pathak, N.N. 2003. Deriving nutrient requirements of growing Indian sheep under tropical condition using performance and intake data emanated from feeding trials conducted in different research institutes. Small Ruminant Research 50:97-207.

Sahoo, A. 2005. Nutritional requirement of wild mammalian herbivores. In: Proceedings of the National Symposium on Wildlife Health and Husbandry Constraints, 4th Annual Convention of Association of Indian Zoo and Wildlife Veterinarians. 25-26 October, 2005, College of Veterinary Science, AAU, Guwahati, Assam.

Shalu, T., Jung, H.G. and Morris, J.G. 1989. Influence of grazing pressure on energy cost of grazing by sheep on smooth brome grass. Journal of Animal Science 67: 2098-2105.

Shinde, A.K., Karim, S.A., Sankhyan, S.K. and Bhatta, R.1998. Seasonal changes in physiological responses and energy expenditure of sheep maintained on semi-arid pasture. Journal of Agriculture Science (Cambridge) 131: 341-346.

Singh S.B. 1996. Fodder Development initiates and Hill conservation in Nepal. Rangeland and Pastoral Development in the Hindukush Himalayas. Proceedings of a Regional Experts Meeting, Nov. 5-7, 1996 Kathmandu, Nepal. (Eds: Daniel J. Miller and Sienna R. Craig).

Suttle, N. F. and Jones, D. G. 1989 Trace elements, disease resistance and immune responsiveness in ruminants. Journal of Nutrition 119: 1055-1061.3.

Todini, L. 2007. Thyroid hormones in small ruminants: effects of endogenous, environmental and nutritional factors. Animal 1:997–1008

Underwood, E.J. and Suttle, N.F. 1999. The Mineral Nutrition of Livestock, 3rd Edn. CAB International, Wallingford, UK, 614 pp.

Young, B.A. and Corbett, J.L. 1972. Maintenance energy requirement of grazing sheep in relation to herbage availability. I. Calorimetric estimates. Australian Journals of Agricultural Research, 23: 57-76.

❏❏❏

9

Strategies for Enhancing Forage Production in Dry Zones of India

A. K. Misra and K. A. Singh*
Indian Grassland and Fodder Research Institute, Jhansi-284 003, Uttar Pradesh

Introduction

Animal husbandry is an integral part of the Indian farming system and plays an important role in the livelihood security and economic sustenance of people. In the arid and semi-arid zones crop husbandry always remains a gamble due to uncertainties of normal rainfall. In climatic adversity people become solely dependent on livestock. This can be visualized from extreme cold conditions of the arctic region to the Great Sahara desert, where livestock is the only source for the survival of human beings. In dry zones majority of the livestock are reared on rangelands. These rangelands supports full spectrum of production systems from sedentary to traditional nomadic and semi-nomadic systems. In this region, the major challenges to the livestock production include inadequate feed and fodder supplies due to the progressive shrinkage in grazing lands and simultaneous increase in livestock population. This results in over stocking and over grazing by all kind of livestock thereby depleting the grazing resources and leading to soil erosion and ecological degradation. Besides this, the long dry spell (8-9 months) does not allow the proper rejuvenation of the vegetation. Water scarcity during summer months further aggravates these problems. In spite of the harsh climate and feed scarcity, the dry zone is gifted with drought tolerant, dairy and draught breeds of cattle, meat and milch breeds of goat and meat and wool breeds of sheep and well-known draught breeds of camel.

Dry zones

On the basis of atmospheric moisture and its availability, the climatic zones of the country are classified into six types (Humid, Sub-humid, Moist, Sub-Moist, Semi-arid and Arid). Dry zones are semi-arid and arid zones and categorized under water deficit zones. In the semi-arid zone only two-third of the total water requirement is met while only one-third of the total water requirement is met in the arid zones. In both the zones, the rainy season is short and erratic. As per an estimate 10.16 percent of the total geographical area (3.18 lakh km^2) spread over 7 states of the country comes under arid region. The semi-arid zone covers 30.56% of the total geographical area (9.56 lakh km^2) and is spread over 10 states of India (Table 1).

Table 1 Dry zone in India

States	Area under Semi-arid (*Lakh km^2*)		Area under Arid (*Lakh km^2*)	
	Land area	Per cent of land area	Land area	Percent of land area
Rajasthan	1.21	12.64	1.95	61.00
Gujarat	0.90	9.47	0.64	20.00
Maharastra	1.89	19.82	0.01	0.40
Andhra Pradesh	1.38	14.49	0.22	7.00
Tamil Nadu	0.95	9.95	-	-
Karnataka	1.39	14.57	0.09	3.00
Uttar Pradesh	0.64	6.72	-	-
Madhya Pradesh	0.59	6.22	-	-
Punjab	0.32	3.32	0.16	5.00
Haryana	0.27	2.80	0.13	4.00

Livestock resources

The percent distribution of various categories of livestock under different regions has been presented in Table 2. Approximately 55.90 % cattle, 84.24% buffaloes, 85.00% sheep, 58.50% goats and 97.60% camel of total livestock population of the country are present in the arid and semi-arid states. Buffaloes are more concentrated in states under semi-arid regions of the country. Sheep, goats and camels are especially more concentrated in arid regions of the country (Singh and Shinde, 2006). The man to livestock ratio is much higher in arid zones and at present it is 124 livestock per 100 human populations. This ratio may further go up to 200-300 under districts with extreme arid conditions.

Table 2. Livestock population (000) in arid and semi-arid states of India *(17th Indian Livestock Census, 2003)*

States	Cattle	Buffalo	Sheep	Goat	Camel
Rajasthan	10854	10414	10054	16809	498
Gujarat	7424	7140	2062	4541	53
Maharastra	16303	6145	3094	10684	-
Andhra Pradesh	9300	10630	21376	6277	-
Tamil Nadu	9141	1658	5593	8177	-
Karnataka	9538	3991	7256	4484	-
Uttar Pradesh	18551	22914	1437	12941	16
Madhya Pradesh	18912	7575	546	8142	-
Punjab	2039	5995	220	278	-
Haryana	1540	6035	633	460	50
Total	**103602**	**82497**	**52271**	**72793**	**617**

Feed and Fodder Resources

The limited availability of the feed and fodders due to poor herbage yield from rangelands, high stocking density and constant grazing pressure, are the major constraints to animal production in these regions (Patnayak, 1994). Grazing based animal husbandry is the predominant occupation in these regions. The availability of grazing lands from forests, pastures, grassland and uncultivated arable land has been declining mainly due to encroachment of area under forests, pastures and public land by a rapidly growing population, and redistribution of common lands under poverty elevation programs; in part, a reduction in their biomass output due to degradation of forests and other grazing lands. Rao et al., (2004) developed a typology for arid and semi-arid regions (Table 3) in reference to the feed and fodder resources. Rangelands occupy about 45 percent coverage of the total land area. In extreme arid tracts like Jaisalmer in Rajasthan the coverage may reach up to 90 percent of the area. However, in semi-arid regions the rangelands area limited to only 15 to 20 percent of land area. The degraded lands (ravines) and problem soils (saline depression and flats) also provide considerable grazing area (Shankar and Kumar, 1987). In addition to grazing, the cultivated fodders include pearl millet, sorghum and finger millet. Predominant fodder legumes are cluster bean, moth bean, cowpea, *Dolichos,* horse gram, mung bean etc. In areas receiving rainfall over 500 mm, the most common fodder based cropping systems are (i) pearl millet + cowpea, (ii) pearl millet + moth bean (iii) *Cenchrus ciliaris* + moth bean. Besides these there are also pulses and oil seed based production systems prevalent in the region. Crop residues of wheat, barley, oat, bajra, sorghum, pulses, oilseeds and sugarcane tops also contribute to feed and fodder pool. Shrubs and top feeds play an important role in animal feeding. In spite of the variety of feed fodder resources, the arid region suffers from the feed shortage both in terms of quantity the quality. The nutrient availability, requirement and deficiency in the different states of arid and semi-arid zones have been estimated (Singh and Shinde, 2006) and presented in the Table 4. All the states except Maharastra are deficient to fulfill the DM requirement of the livestock. The protein availability is not sufficient in all the states to meet requirement. The total digestible nutrient requirement is also deficient in all the states except Punjab for the livestock.

Table 3. Proportion of total feed and fodders under different typologies of arid and semi arid regions

Typology Zone	Agro ecological region	Total Feed and Fodder* (Tone/LU**)		Proportion to total feed and fodder (1998)			
		1982	1998	Crop Residues	Grasses	Green Fodder	AIBP
Arid and semi arid (LR, LI)							
2	Hot semi-arid	1.84	2.31	46.30	11.02	29.27	13.41
3b	Hot semi-arid	0.85	1.14	63.80	20.32	9.44	6.44
4	Hot semi-arid	1.50	1.70	67.85	25.70	1.35	5.11
7	Hot semi-arid	2.05	2.27	77.61	11.37	5.37	5.65
10	Hot arid & semi-arid	1.50	1.94	62.00	9.43	18.08	10.50
15	Hot semi-arid	1.37	1.76	64.57	22.74	4.95	7.73
	Semi-arid (LR, HI)						
9	Hot semi-arid	3.39	3.67	66. 21	2.41	24.01	7.38

*: Includes crop residues, grasses from grazing lands, green fodder crops and AIBPs on dry matter basis; **: LU Livestock unit

Table 4 Dry matter, digestible crude protein and total digestible nutrient availability, requirement and deficit (000 tones, annually) for livestock of arid and semi-arid states of the country (*Singh and Shinde, 2006*)

		Nutrient Availability			Nutrient Requirement			Nutrient Deficient	
	Dry matter	Digestible crude protein	Total digestible nutrient	Dry matter	Digestible crude protein	Total digestible nutrient	Dry matter	Digestible crude protein	Total digestible nutrient
Rajasthan	31060.21	1530.18	14959.36	43413.32	3460.85	36407.75	-12353.11	-1930.67	-21448.39
Gujarat	19219.65	827.59	9025.12	22923.18	1663.26	19008.66	-3703.53	-835.67	-9983.54
Maharastra	49309.03	1334.79	22127.04	42792.82	3057.95	35948.21	6516.21	-1723.16	-13821.17
Andhra Pradesh	36513.26	1164.99	16657.56	36563.86	2608.91	30072.12	-50.6	-1443.92	-13414.56
Tamil Nadu	21148.92	758.19	9663.54	21372.45	1754.2	18500.92	-223.53	-996.01	-8837.38
Karnataka	36012.53	1023.37	16157.58	32565.03	2412.82	27426.88	3447.5	-1389.45	-11269.3
Uttar Pradesh	94472.34	2209.74	41782.44	82914.21	6234.03	69745.41	11558.13	-4024.29	-27962.97
Madhya Pradesh	51865.89	2406.78	24686.21	62553.9	4813.25	53977.07	-10688.01	-2406.47	-29290.86
Punjab	32849.53	732.77	14547.72	16145.38	1188.89	13306.06	16704.15	-456.12	1241.66
Haryana	19254.42	551.93	8653.26	12572.27	1034.5	10615.37	6682.15	-482.57	-1962.11
Total	**391705.78**	**12540.33**	**178259.83**	**373816.42**	**28228.66**	**315008.45**	**17889.36**	**-361276.09**	**-136748.62**
India	**493031.55**	**15717.35**	**224731.52**	**525326.55**	**40182.84**	**447153.82**	**-32295**	**-24465.49**	**-222422.3**

Augmenting feed and fodder resources

The major fodder resources in the arid and semi-arid regions are forest areas, barren, uncultivable land, land under miscellaneous trees, crops and grooves, cultivable wastelands and fallow lands. Poor herbage yield of rangeland, high stocking density causing serious deterioration of vegetation and constant grazing pressure, are the major limitation to animal production in semi arid and arid tropics (Patnayak, 1994). Grasses and forbs in this environment usually sprout immediately after rain, attain peak growth in September-October, and subsequently wither off with the onset of winter, form major source of forage to grazing animals. Short life cycle and constant grazing pressure does not allow vegetation in the arid and semiarid regions to attain maximum yield (Shinde and Bhatta, 2001). Therefore augmentation of fodder availability in these regions will lead towards the sustainable animal production thus ensuring the livelihood of the farmers.

Soil and water conservation measures

Proper soil and water conservation measures boost the natural recovery leading to many times higher forage yields. Contour bunding / trenching are quite effective in this zone. The main objective of contour bunding is to intercept the overland runoff flowing down the slope, to reduce soil loss and to provide opportunity for increased infiltration of water. Along the contour lines and also along the periphery, bunds are made either manually or by using tractor-mounted implements. The bunds are stabilized by seeding with *Dicanthium annulatum, Cenchrus ciliaris* and *Panicum antidotale*. In extremely arid rangelands with gravelly shallow soils, contour furrows (in between trenches and core wall 400-500 m apart) trap sands on which species like *Lasiurus sindicus* grow well and produce adequate forage (Singh, 1995).

Preference to perennials

The perennials should be preferred for assured continuous fodder supply. Some of the suitable perennials for fodder are listed below:

Shrubs and Trees	*Dichrostachys cinerea, Zizyphus numularia, Leucaena leucephala, Anogeissus latifolia, Anogeissuspendula,, Azadirachta indica, Acacia tortilis, Hardwickia binata, Albizia species, Acacia species, D sisoo, Alianthus excelsa*
Legumes	*Atylosia scarabaeoides, Stylosanthes hamata, S. scabra, S seabrana, Mecroptilum atropurpureum*
Grasses	*Sehima nervosum, Chrysopogon fulvus, Heteropogon contortus, Cenchrus ciliaris, C. setigerus, Panicum antedotale, Dichanthium annulatu, Panicum maximum, Pennistum pedicellatum*

The native ranges species in semiarid region are deteriorating at a very rapid rate; moreover, unpalatable plant species has replaced most of the palatable one. There is an urgent need for rehabilitation of these ranges by perennial grasses to ensure adequate supply of forage to grazing animals in the years to come (Patnayak, 1994). Unwanted thorny plants like *Lycium barbarum, Balanites aegyptiaca, Mimosa hamata*, etc hinder the growth of grass species and are also troublesome to grazing. Heavy infestation of such bushes in the pasture areas reduces the open space available for grasses to grow and produce herbage. Studies have indicated that in arid Rajasthan the desirable shrubs should be in the range of about 14 % of the land area covered by the shrub canopy for optimum forage as well as top feed production.

Introduction of legumes

Perennial grasses are usually low in protein content ranging from 4 (May-June) to 12% (August - September) crude protein. The One of the best methods to overcome to this situation is the introduction of legume (*Clitoria ternetae, Lablab purpurium, Atylosia scarbaeoides, Stylosanthes hamata, Stylosanthes scabra* and *Rhyncosia minima)*, a component that is generally lacking in arid rangelands. The introduced legumes also provide a usefuland cheaper alternative source of nitrogen fixation. It has been found that *Lablab purpurium* sown with cenchrus in l: l ratio by alternate row gave the highest yield than cenchrus alone. *Vigna unguiculate* sown with cenchrus in 1:1 ratio yields 86:115 q/ha. *Cenchrus ciliaris* in combination with *Macroptilium atropurpureum, Clitoris ternatea* and *Lablab purpurium* yields 37.5, 45.0 and 59.0q mature forage per hectare. Cenchrus with moth (*Phaseolus aconitifolins*), guar (*Cyamopsis tetragonoloba*) and cowpea (*Vigna unguiculate*) yields 13.0, 14.9 and 19.2 q DM /ha more fodder than *Cenchrus* alone.

Reseeding

Natural succession of superior perennial species in arid grasslands is a time consuming process. However, reseeding with suitable perennial grass species having high nutritive value and high yield potential has emerged as the best alternative. The reseeding can increase the carrying capacity of ranges by 2 to 3 times (Mann and Mehta, 1998). *Cenchrus ciliaris, Cenchrus setigerus* and *Lasiurus sindicus* are the well-known perennial grasses recommended for rehabilitation of land in the dry zones of the country. Average yield of *Cenchrus ciliaris* ranges between 27-33q DM/ha in September to 7 q/ha in May month. *Cenchrus ciliaris* is most suited in low rainfall of <250 mm and light to medium type of soil. *Lasiurus sindicus* grows well in sandy soil of arid region and can withstand ambient temperature up to 48°C. *Lasiurus sindicus* yields up to 25-30q DM/ha. The recommended grass species for different agro-climatic regions of Rajasthan are mentioned in Table 5.

Table 5 Recommended grass species suitable for reseeding pastures

Soil type	Rainfall	Grass species
Heavy soils	>380 mm	*Dicanthium annulatum*
Well drained soil	Medium- Low	*Cenchrus ciliaris* *Cenchrus setigerus*
Sandy to medium textured soils	250-300 mm	*Lasiurus sindicus* *Panicum antidotale*
Hilly terrain	-	*Sehima nervosum*

Promotion of live hedges

Protection from grazing is well documented for vegetation recovery and thereby improving grassland production. Native ranges located in semiarid region under continuous grazing by all kinds of livestock, produce a biomass of 1.5q DM/ha (Sankhyan et al., 1999). Simply by protecting the grazing area during growth phase, increased the yield to 17.9q DM/ha (Mann and Singh, 1982).Comparison of efficacy and cost effectiveness of various kinds of fencing show that live hedges fencing is the cheapest and practical method of protecting larger areas.

Plantation of fodder trees

The fodder trees supply forage to grazing animals during winter and summer, when ground vegetation depletes drastically. During summer, fodder leaves alone constitutes 80-90% portion of diet of sheep and goats in arid regions. Agro forestry based forage production systems like silvipastoral systems, agri-silvipastoral systems, alley cropping and shelter belts may be promoted based on land capabilities and rural need. Such systems are capable of yielding wood, leaf fodder besides conserving and rehabilitating ecosystem (Singh and Roy, 1991). In dry land areas alley cropping or avenue cropping is an important alternate land use system to stabilize the productivity of crops and serves manifold purposes. Fast growing trees are planted in hedgerows at required spacing and the inter row spaces are utilized for raising food and/or forage crops. The lopping could be utilized either as mulch to conserve moisture under dry land conditions or fed to the animals as feed supplement. Kharif crops like, cowpea, sesame, pigeon pea and peanut could be taken in the inter row space without adversely affecting the yields under the system. The land remains covered with tree canopy after the annual crops are harvested. The trees provide foliage as fodder during lean period and twigs as fuel wood during the period when normally these lands remain barren. The sloppy areas and areas along with the submergence or higher water table or canal or the field boundary or part of the crop field where the profitable agriculture is not possible, need to adopt conservation measures with optimum land productivity. The energy farms put as shelterbelts, serve in turn the purpose of wood/leaf fodder production and environment amelioration. Production from energy farm at short rotation of 5 years could reach upto 74.3 t/ha/yr in case of *Leucaena leucocephala*. In a ravenous wasteland, in two years, *A. nilotica* produced 2.2 t/ha, followed by *P. juliflora* (0.6 t/ha) under very dry situation. In poor soil, water and nutrient situation where cropping is not possible, the establishment of silvipasture comprising of grasses, shrubs and trees can serve these purposes. Fodder trees should be either planted in single row on the bunds or intensive plantation on infertile and uncultivable soil. Simply by planting fodder trees on farm boundaries of 0.09ha land produce 91% more dry fodder during dry season than without trees and reduce soil erosion by 57%. *Prosopis cineraria, Gymnosporia spinosa, Acacia nilotica, Azardirachta indica, Albizia lebbek, Bauhinia racemosa, Morus alba* and *Leucaena leucocephala* trees in combination with grasses like *Cenchrus ciliaris, Cenchrus setigerus, Panicum antidotale* for improving forage yield have been studied at CSWRI Avikanagar. It was found that multi-tier system (*Ailanthus excelsa* + *Dicrostachys nutans* + *Cenchrus ciliaris*) provides maximum dry fodder and green leaves. A plot of 1 ha having 100 *Ailanthus excelsa* trees and *Dicrostachys nutans* bushes and ground cover of *Cenchrus ciliaris* yield 5.29qDM tree leaves plus 2.28qDM Dicrostachys leaves and pods and 23.5 q DM grasses, totaling to 31.00 q DM/ha (Sankhyan et al., 1996). It was found that pearl millet in comparison to combination with cowpea and guar gave highest fodder yield with Babool trees. Sorghum (*Pennisetum typhoids*) in combination with *Ailanthus excelsa* also gave better yield. Certain fruit trees and shrubs like *Zizyphus nummularia*, Anola (*Phylanthus emblica*) in agro-horticulture system in combination with perennial grasses provide fruits, fodder and wood. The suitable trees, shrubs, grasses and legumes are listed in Table 6.

Post harvest processing of crop residues

Crop residues form major part of the livestock feeding systems. However, these are low in energy, protein, calcium and phosphorus and several minerals and also poorly digestible. Some kinds of physical, chemical and biological processing are needed to increase daily intake and enhance rate and/ or extent of digestion for increasing nutrient availability. A considerable amount of these feed resources are wasted due to improper feeding practices. In large area of the country, the green and dry fodders like stover / kadbi are offered to animals without chaffing, resulting in wastage of large portion of these resources. The use of a simple chaff cutter would minimize the wastage to a large extent. The nutritional technologies like urea treatment, mineral supplementation and complete feed are some of the option available for practical adoption to enrich and upgrade the nutritive value. The recent concept of complete feed block or pellet from crop residues, concentrate and other supplements in required proportion is a noble way to increase intake and its utilization. Complete feed block ensure better consumption of feed in desired concentrate to roughage ratio without any selection and prevent refusal of unpalatable portions of plant residues. Many fold increase in bulk density of processed feed in to blocks also reduce the expenditure on transportation (Jakhmola, 2005). After densification fodder could be transported from excess producing areas to deficit areas especially during the natural calamities.

Table 6 Suitable species for silvipasture systems

Trees/Shrubs	Grasses/Legumes
Hot Arid Desert (Western Rajasthan, parts of Gujarat and Haryana	
Acacia nilotica, A.tortilis, Albizzia amara, Azadirachta indica, Dichrostachys cinerea, Eucalyptus tereticornics, E.camaldulensis, Prosopis cinerarea, P. juliflora	Grasses – *Cenchrus ciliaris, C.setigerus, Lasiurus sindicus* Legumes – *Atylosia scarabaeoides, Stylosanthes hamata, Clitoria ternatea*
Semi-arid, Rocky & Gravely (Parts of UP, MP, AP and Karanataka)	
Acacia catechu, Ailanthus excelsa, Albizzia lebbek, Cassia siamea, Dalbergia sissoo, Dendrocalamus strictus, Dichrostachys cinereal, Hardwickia binata, Prosopis juliflora	Grasses – *Cenchrus ciliaris, C.setigerus, Panicum antidotale, Chrysopogan fulvus, Dicanthium annulatum* Legumes – *Macroptelium atropurpureum, Desmodium trifolium, Stylosanthes spp.*
Cold Desert (Laddakh – J&K)	
Hippophae spp., Juniperus communis, J. wallichiana, Populas spp., Salix spp.	Hay species – *Pranges pabularia*
Ravine lands (UP, MP, Rajasthan & Gujarat)	
Acacia nilotica, A.catechu, A.tortilis, Albizzia lebbek, Dalbergia sissoo, Dendrocalamus strictus, Dichrostachys cinerea, Eycalyptus spp., Prosopis juliflora	Grasses – *Cenchrus ciliaris, C.setigerus, Pennisetum pedicellatum, Chrysopogon fulvus* Legumes – *Alysicarpus monilifer, Atylosia scarabaeoides, Stylosanthes gracilis, S. humilis*
Cultivable wastelands	
Acacia spp., Albizzia spp., Hardwickia binata, Leucaena leucocephala, Sesbania spp.	Grasses – *Cenchrus ciliaris, C.setigerus, Chrysopogon fulvus, Dicanthium annulatum, Pennisetum polystachyon, Sehima nervosum* Legumes – *Clitoria ternatea, Glycine javanica, Macroptelium atropupureum, Stylosanthes spp.*

Improved fodder production from arable lands

Use of improved varieties

Many superior varieties of fodder crops and grasses like bajra, cowpea, guar, lablab bean, oat, berseem, lucerne, dinanath grass, guinea grass, anjan grass, dhavalu grass and marvel grass are available for cultivation in arid and semi-arid regions.

Adoption of improved production technologies

Intensive fodder production systems may be adopted under irrigated situation. The conservation of excess fodder as silage or hay during lush green period under this system would provide the solution of many problems associated with feed scarcity under the arid and semi-arid regions. The perennial crop based system like Napier-Bajra hybrid + Guar-Lucerne; Napier-Bajra hybrid + Hedge Lucerne or Sesbania or Leucaena are some of the promising combinations which can be adopted in a variety of situations. Besides the intensive fodder production systems in irrigated conditions several other interventions may be adopted like intercropping with graminae and leguminous fodder crops (Table 7), cultivation of short duration forage crops in the gap period of the prevalent crop sequences, by product utilization of agricultural crops like sugarcane tops, green plants of pea, cauliflowers, turnip and cabbage. Similarly, under rain fed areas and risk prone areas like drought-affected areas, grass and tree-based approaches, viz., ley farming and alley cropping systems hold promise to increase the overall productivity of marginal and sub-marginal lands and strengthen the livestock enterprise and conserve the land-water resources. The productivity of mono-cropped areas could be raised through intercropping of short duration forages with the (long duration) rainy season food crops like grain sorghum and pigeon pea (Lal and Singh, 1993). Ratooning of sorghum and pear millet provide additional forage yield. Pearl millet could profitably be ratooned for fodder and grain production in northern areas. In case of hybrids, which mature early, ratooning should be done after 30-40 days of crop growth and top dressing with 20 kg n/ha be done simultaneously. Ali and Rawat (1986) reported that pearl millet (cv. Bj104) rationed at 5 weeks crop stage, produced 192 q/ha green fodder, followed by 7.4 q/ha grain and 30.5 q/ha stover. Over seeding of *Stylosanthes* in cereal crops also improves the forage yield in grass intercropping and in rotation as the results of experimentation on this crop at IGFRI have indicated that grain yield of cereals improved by 6 to 26 per cent with over seeding of *stylosanthes*. The dry forage yield (cereal + *stylosanthes*) increased up to 16 per cent of the total forage production.

Table 7 Productivity of sorghum and pigeon pea – based food-fodder system

Intercropping System	Grain Yield (T/ha)		Green Forage Yield Of Inter crop (T/ha) With	
	Sorghum	Pigeon pea	Sorghum	Pigeon pea/ Sorghum (sole)
Sorghum (Sole)	2.15	-	-	-
Pigeon pea (Sole)	-	1.14	-	-
Sorghum/Pigeon pea+ Cluster bean	1.77	1.00	4.55	5.16
Sorghum/Pigeon pea + Cowpea	1.58	0.88	9.05	10.58
Sorghum/Pigeon pea + Sun hemp	1.54	0.63	9.07	12.00
Sorghum/Pigeon pea + *Stylo*	1.94	-	2.05	-
Sorghum/Pigeon pea + Rice bean	1.96	-	3.38	-
Sorghum/Pigeon pea + Field bean	1.83	-	3.87	-
Sorghum/Pigeon pea + Sesbania	1.75	-	2.73	-
Sorghum/Pigeon pea + Moth bean	1.70	-	7.22	-
Pigeon pea + Forage Sorghum	-	0.95	-	8.37
Pigeon pea + Sudan Grass	-	0.98	-	7.58
Pigeon pea + *P. Pedicellatum*	-	0.90	-	5.64
Pigeon pea + Teosinte	-	1.08	-	5.59
Pigeon pea + Maize	-	1.00	-	5.69
Pigeon pea + Pearl millet	-	1.02	-	6.40

References

Ali, M. and Rawar, C.R.1986. Production potential of different food fodder cropping system under dry land conditions of Bundelkhand. In: Proceedings of the National Seminar on 'Advances in forage agronomy and future strategies for increasing biomass production', IGFRI, Jhansi, UP, India, 6-7 October, pp 65-68.

Anonymous, 2003. Seventeenth Indian Livestock Census, Government of India, Ministry of Agriculture, Department of Animal Husbandry and Dairying, Krishi Bhawan, New Delhi

Jakhmola, R.C. 2005. Evaluation of locally available feed and fodder to improve quality and formulate complete economic rations with higher roughage diets. Final report, NATP, CSWRI, Avikanagar.

Mann, J. S. and Mehta, R. S. 1998. Feed and fodder resource development for small ruminants production. In: Proceedings of the Golden Jubilee Seminar on Sheep, Goat and Rabbit Production and Utilization. 24-26 April, pp 89-94.

Menhi Lal and Singh, P. 1993. Land use planning for soil conservation and watershed management with special reference to Bundelkhand region. In: Proceeding of the National seminar on 'Role and functions of state land use boards for conservation, management & development of land resources' Yojana Bhawan, Lucknow, 14-16 October, pp. 82-92.

Patnayak, B.C. 1994. Livestock productivity on Indian arid and semiarid pastures. In: Sustainability Development of the Indian Arid Zone (Eds. R. P. Singh and Surendra Singh). Scientific Publisher, Jodhpur.

Rao, P., Parathasarthy, Brithal, P.S., Kar Dharmendra, Wickramaratne, S.H.G. and Shrestha, H.R. 2004. Increasing livestock productivity in mixed crop-livestock systems in South Asia. In: Report of a project, National Centre for Agricultural Economics and Policy Research, New Delhi, ICRISAT, Patancheru, A.P.

Sankhyan, S. K, Shinde, A. K, Karim S. A, Mann, J. S, Singh, N. P. and Patnayak, B. C. 1996. Plane of nutrition and growth performance of lambs and kids maintained on two and three-tier silvipasture. Indian Journal of Animal Sciences 66: 1194-1197.

Sankhyan, S. K, Shinde, A. K. and Karim, S. A 1999. Seasonal changes in biomass yield, nutrient intake and its utilization by sheep maintained on public rangeland. Indian Journal of Animal Sciences 69: 617-620.

Shankar, V., Kumar, S. and Tyagi, R.K. 1987. Grazing resources of semi arid and arid regions. In: Pasture and Forage Crops Research (Ed. Panjab Singh), IGFRI, Jhansi, U.P.

Shinde, A. K. and Bhatta, Raghavendra. 2002. *Nutrition of Sheep and Goat on Pasture*: A Bulletin published by Central Sheep and Wool Research Institute, Avikanagar.

Singh, N.P. and Mann, J.S. 1980. Sheep feeding practices in semi-arid region of Rajasthan. Livestock Advisor 5:19-22.

Singh, P. and Roy, M.M. 1991. Forage production through agro forestry: Constraints and priorities. Range Management and Agro forestry 12:169-178.

Singh, V.K. and Shinde, A.K. 2006. Livestock raising arid and semi-arid zones: A perspective. In: Livestock Feeding Strategies For Dry Regions (Eds. P.S. Pathak and S. S. Kundu). International Book Distributing Company, Lucknow, U.P.

❑❑❑

10

Methane Emission by Sheep and Goats, its Effect on Global Warming and Ameliorative Measures

Raghavendra Bhatta*, C. S. Prasad[1] and K. T. Sampath
National Institute of Animal Nutrition and Physiology, Bangalore-560 030, Karnataka
[1]Indian Council of Agricultural Research, Krishi Bhavan, New Delhi- 110 114

Introduction

Considerable evidence of climate change associated with emissions of greenhouse gases (GHG), mainly carbon dioxide (CO_2), methane (CH_4) and nitrous oxide (N_2O), in the atmosphere has resulted in international efforts to reduce GHG emissions. Greenhouse gases allow solar radiation to pass through the earth's atmosphere. But after the earth absorbs part of that radiation, it reflects the rest back. That's where the problem lies. Particles of greenhouse gas absorb the radiation, heating up, and warming the atmosphere. The increasing levels of greenhouse gases are causing too much energy to be trapped - the so-called 'greenhouse effect' (IPCC, 2001). Methane is the second major GHG after CO_2 and it is 20 times more potent than CO_2 contributing about 15-20% of the total greenhouse gases. Enteric methane emission is produced in sheep and goats as a result of microbial fermentation of feed components. Primary digestive microorganisms (bacteria, protozoa and fungi) hydrolyze proteins, starch and plant cell wall polymers into amino acids and sugars. These simple products are then fermented to volatile fatty acids (VFA), hydrogen (H_2) and CO_2. Acetate, propionate and butyrate, which are the major VFA, are then absorbed and utilized by the host animal. The major producers of H_2 are the organisms which produce acetic acid in the fermentation pathway (Hegarty and Gerdes, 1998). Acetate and butyrate production results in CH_4 production, while propionate formation serves as a competitive pathway for H_2 use in the rumen.

Methane production from livestock

The annual global methane production from livestock is about 80 Tg from enteric fermentation (Chynoweth, 1996). India's contribution is about 11 Tg per year, which corresponds to 14 % of the global influx of methane. The relative contribution of methane is about 18% to atmospheric warming (Fig. 1). Singh (1997) reported that methane production by Indian sheep and goat is about 11.6 and 10.1 g/head/d, respectively. Approximately 700 g/kg of methane production arises from an anthropogenic sources, of which agriculture accounts for about two-thirds with enteric fermentation being responsible for one-third of methane from agriculture (Moss et al., 2000). Assuming 9 kg of ruminal CH_4 emission per sheep annually and the 1057 million sheep and 677 million goats in the world in 1996 (Morand-Fehr and Boyazoglu, 1999), sheep and goats account for about 200 g/kg of CH_4 emission from enteric fermentation. CH_4 from enteric fermentation by ruminants is not only an important greenhouse gas associated with environmental problems, but it also represents a loss of feed energy (20–150 kJ/MJ intake (Johnson and Johnson, 1995).

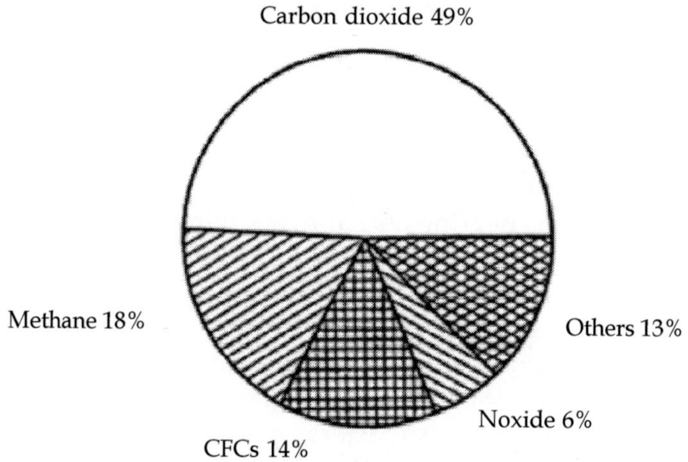

Fig. 1. Relative contribution (%) of greenhouse gases to atmospheric warming (Source: World Resources Institute).

Consequences of global warming

A trend in atmospheric methane accumulation is depicted in Fig. 2. Even given the moderate 0.8°C of global warming measured to date, the impacts can already be felt in every part of the world. For example, the summer extent of the ice mass in the Arctic Ocean has already shrunk by about half since the 1970s (Stroeve et al., 2007). Since the ice is also thinning dramatically at the same time, the volume of ice declines even more rapidly (Kwok et al., 2009). If warming should escalate unabated to 4°C or more, it would fundamentally change the earth system along with all its ecological resources and services. Global temperature differences on such a scale would roughly correspond to the difference between temperature at the peak of the last Ice age 20,000 years of age and temperature today. Global warming has the following consequences:

- The sea level rises due to the thermal expansion of sea water and the influx of melt water into the oceans and the warmer it becomes, the faster the sea level rises. Since, 1880, the global sea level has risen by around 20 cm. It could, however, rise by 50-150 cm by 2100.
- Already, an increase in extreme weather events such as heat waves, droughts, extreme rain-fall events, floods and tropical storms has been observed in many regions (IPCC, 2007). A further rise of extreme weather events in the wake of additional warming is deemed probable to very probable, depending on the type of event.

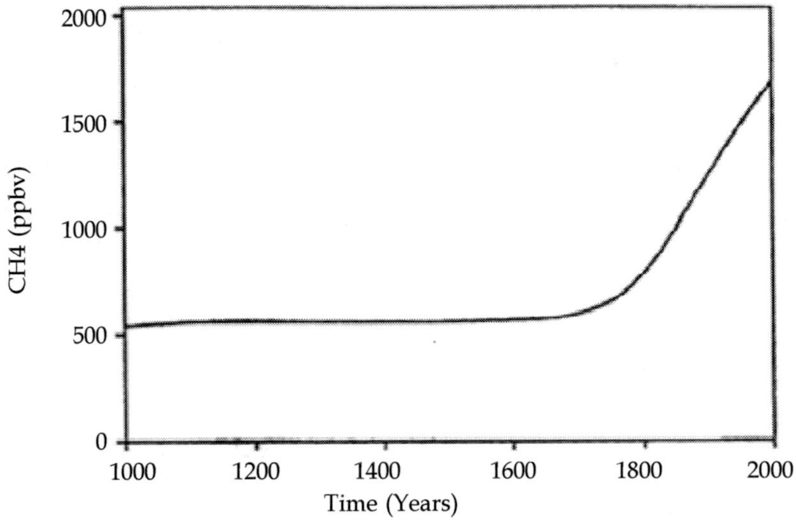

Fig. 2. Trends in atmospheric methane accumulation
(Source: Khalil and Rasmussen, 1986)

- Global warming in excess of 2°C threatens to accelerate the loss of genetic, species and ecosystem diversity, since many regions world will very rapidly enter climatic conditions not experienced for several million years. According to the IPCC (2007), this would place such an intolerable strain on nature's adaptive and regenerative capacity as to risk the irreversible loss of 20-30 % of animal and plant species and associated genetic resources. Ecosystems such as mangrove forests and coral reefs would suffer irreversible damage or destruction. Biodiversity loss would entail loss of ecosystem resources and services – e.g. the availability of clean drinking water and genetic resources which are also crucial functions for society's efforts to adapt to climate change.

A series of tipping elements have been identified within the climatic system (Table 1). Triggering these tipping elements may lead to catastrophic ecological consequences. Among the most significant risks are the abrupt cessations of ocean currents, unpredictable shifts in the monsoon system or irreversible destabilization of large ice masses. One example is the Greenland ice sheet: if it melted completely, it would cause a global sea level rise of 7 m. Even global warming of more than 1.9°C for a prolonged period of time may be sufficient to trigger melting of the entire ice sheet (IPCC, 2007).

Table 1. Impacts of climate change on livestock and livestock systems

Factor	Impacts
Feeds	***Land use and system change***
	As climate changes and becomes more variable, species niches change. May modify animal diets and compromise the ability of stallholders to manage feed deficits
	Changes in the primary productivity of crops, forages and rangeland
	Effects depend significantly on location, system and species. But in C4 species, temperature increases up to 30-35°C may increase productivity of crops, fodders and pastures
	For food-feed crops, harvest indexes will change and so will the quantity of stover and availability of metabolizable energy for dry season feeding
	In the semi-arid rangelands where contractions in the growing season are likely, rangeland productivity will decrease.
	Quality of plant material
	Increased temperatures increase lignifications of plant tissues and thus reduce the digestibility and the rates of degradation of plant species.

Contd...

	Resultant reduction in livestock production may have impact on food security and incomes of smallholders
	Interactions between primary productivity and quality of grasslands will demand modifications in grazing systems management to attain production objectives
Biodiversity	***Changes in ecosystem***
	In places, warming will accelerate the loss of genetic and cultural diversity in agriculture already occurring as a result of globalization, in crops and domestic animals
	A 2.5°C increase in global temperature above pre-industrial levels will see major losses; 20-30 % of all plant and animal species assessed could be at high risk of extinction (IPCC, 2007)
	Ecosystems and species show a wide range of vulnerabilities to climate change, depending on the imminence of exposure to ecosystem-specific, critical threshold, but assessments are fraught with uncertainty related to CO_2 fertilization effects
Livestock	***Consequences***
	Major impacts on vector-borne diseases: expansion of vector populations into cooler areas or into more temperate zones
	Increase in heat-related mortality and morbidity

(Source: Thronton et al., 2007; 2008)

Effect of climate change on livestock

Climate change may have direct or indirect effects on livestock. The quantity and quality of the feed supplied to the animal is a major factor but as well as the direct relationship between the nutrition of the animal and its thermal environment, modifications to the seasonal availability of forage may have implications on animal production systems. For example, altered lambing times may be possible if patterns of spring forage growth change which would have implications for the marketing of finished lamb (Rowlinson, 2008).

Direct effects

Direct effects of climate results from the normal rules of environmental temperature, along with relative humidity, wind speed etc, on the animal's climatic physiology. The responses of animals to changes in environmental temperature and emphasizes the key difference between our ruminant and non-ruminant species in their comfort zones. Ruminants have wide comfort zones and high degree of thermal tolerance so it is likely that climate change resulting in an increase of a few degrees is not going to have a major effect on animal performance. The exceptions would be at the extremes. Areas currently characterized by low temperatures and high rainfall may become more favourable and be associated with a reduction in the mortality of lambs. At the other extreme, high summer temperature may be expected to present the dairy cow/ buffalo with thermal stress and result in reduced intake and performance. Adaptations to management systems such as increased provision of shade and water should be adequate to counter this. By contrast the non-ruminant species have a very narrow comfort zones. This is one of the reasons our pig and poultry enterprises have often been based on intensive housed systems. Dealing with housed livestock we might expect the direct effects of climate to be small- which is true with tow important riders. Higher environmental temperatures in winter may lead to a saving in heating costs for poultry buildings/ extra covering for goats. However, in the summer months our existing housing systems may not be able to cope with the increased thermal load. This may lead to an increased requirement for costly air conditioning/ cooler systems. Additionally, there may be issues associated with the transport of live animals in elevated environmental temperatures. Although the likely direct effects of climate change on the animal are likely to be small, consideration could be given to inclusion of traits associated with temperature tolerance in breeding indices for species/breeds under threat e.g. genetics of heat stress and G*E interactions (Rowlinson, 2008).

Indirect effects: Nutrition and feeding

Climate change can be expected to have several impacts on feed crops and grazing systems (Hopkins and Del Prado, 2007), like:

- Change in herbage growth brought about by change in atmospheric CO_2 concentration and temperature
- Changes in the composition of pastures, such as changes in the ratio of grasses to legumes
- Changes in herbage quality, with changing concentrations of water-soluble carbohydrates and N at given dry matter (DM) yields
- Greater incidences of drought, which may offset any DM yield increases
- Greater intensity of rainfall, which may increase N leaching in certain systems

With regard to supply of feed, central to this consideration is an appreciation of what is currently fed to our farm livestock. Non-ruminant livestock will continue to receive diets consisting of cereals and de-oiled cakes and with least cost ration formulation fairly major changes in ingredient inclusion can be made without altering the nutrient specifications. Many diets already include a lot of high quality by-products and imported ingredients and it is unlikely that climate change would alter the range of ingredients available for ration formulation. A much greater threat is likely to be posed by the food: feed: fuel conflict providing reduced supplies, together with issues to do with 'feed miles'- the miles travelled by so much for our animal feed raw materials. Ruminant diets differ in that there is a major forage component. In the case of extensive system like in sheep and goat, this may make up the entire diet whereas in more intensive dairy cattle or goat rearing systems the forage will be balanced by a more concentrated supplement. It is the source, quality and quantity of the forage component of ruminant's diet which is likely to be affected by climate change. The result may be either effects (advantageous or deleterious) on the existing forage species or a change to forage species not currently grown. With respect to our existing forage species, low environmental temperature, particularly in spring, is one of the major limitations to higher dry matter production. Thus any increase in temperature might be expected to have benefits on early season growth. It is important to note the effect which this might have on the component species of a mixed pasture. If mean rainfall were to decline this would lead to soil moisture deficits which would require expenditure on irrigation unless reductions in DM yield were to be accepted. For existing species the stage of maturity at which the crop is cut is major determinant of quality and in any altered climatic scenario the interplay between increasing quantity and declining quality would continue to be of major importance although the alterations in climate may be favourable to conservation and reduce losses during hay making. In many hill and upland areas which are currently characterized by low temperatures and water logged soils, climate change may be expected to lead to more favourable conditions and result in a shift towards more productive species with accompanying implications to animal production.

The other major possibility is that climate change will lead to a shift in the forage species grown in a country. For example elevated temperature may lead to an increase in the hectarage of maize grown. This might be expected to result in improvements in both the quantity and quality of forage for ruminant livestock and could lead us towards the forage component of rations fed to dairy cattle elsewhere. In semi-arid regions of the country, the palatable species of the plants might get replaced by non-palatable species in the pasture and might result in lower quantity of edible biomass for sheep.

Methane mitigation in sheep and goats

Decreasing the production of CH_4 from small ruminant livestock is desirable both as a strategy to reduce global greenhouse gas emissions and as a means of improving feed conversion efficiency. Decreases in CH_4 production have been obtained using different approaches that induce changes in metabolic pathways, that alter the rumen microbial consortium and/or that influence the animal digestive physiology.

In the anaerobic conditions prevailing in the rumen, the oxidation reactions required to obtain energy in the form of ATP release hydrogen. The amount of hydrogen produced is highly dependent on the diet and type of rumen microbes as the microbial fermentation of feeds produces different end products that are not equivalent in term of hydrogen output. For instance, the formation of propionic acid consumes hydrogen whereas the formation of acetic and butyric acids releases hydrogen. Methanogenesis is the mechanism favored by the rumen to avoid hydrogen accumulation. Free hydrogen inhibits dehydrogenases and affects the fermentation process. The utilization of hydrogen and CO_2 to produce CH_4 is a specificity of methanogenic archea.

The metabolic pathways involved in hydrogen production and utilization and the activity of methanogens are two important factors that should be considered when developing strategies to control methane emissions by ruminants. Reduction of hydrogen production should be achieved without impairing feed fermentation. Reducing methanogens activity and or/ numbers should ideally be done with a concomitant stimulation of pathways that consume hydrogen to avoid negative effect of the partial pressure increase of this gas.

Mitigation through feeding

Increased proportion of concentrates in the diet of the animal

Replacing plant fibre in the diet with starch induces a decrease in ruminal pH and modifications in microbial populations. A shift of VFA production from acetate towards propionate occurs, which results in less hydrogen production (Bhatta et al., 2005). A lower tolerance to low pH by protozoa and cellulolytic bacteria decreases further hydrogen production. A positive correlation between cellulolytic and methanogens in the rumen of different animal species has been shown, except in buffalo. This exception was explained by the fact that *F. succinogens,* a non-hydrogen-producing cellulolytic species, was the major cellulolytic bacteria in buffalo. The relationship between concentrate proportion in the diet and methane production is curvilinear (Sauvant and Giger Reverdin, 2007) with a marked decrease in methane observed when dietary starch is higher than 40%. This has been assessed in young bulls by Martin et al. (2007). As compared to diets containing 30 %

starch, a diet containing starch decreased methane production by 56 % without altering animal growth.

Dietary fat seems a promising nutritional alternative to depress ruminal methanogenesis without decreasing ruminal pH as opposed to concentrates. Medium chain fatty acids are known to affect methanogen numbers (Machmuller et al., 2003) but not long chain FAs such as linoleic acid. Polyunsaturated fatty acids also contribute to methane decrease through toxic effect on cellulolytic bacteria (Nagaraja et al., 1997) and protozoa (Doreau and Ferlay, 1995). This effect, observed with all long chain fatty acids, is probably through an action on the cell membrane particularly of Gram- positive bacteria. Linolenic acid is toxic to cellulolytic bacteria (Maia et al., 1997). These microbial changes favour a shift of ruminal fermentation towards propionate, and thus to increase in hydrogen utilization. These multiple actions may impair digestion of the number and activity of primary microbial fermentors is too affected or if the negative effect on methanogens leads to an accumulation of hydrogen in the rumen. Biohydrogenation of polyunsaturated fatty acids results in an uptake of hydrogen. However, its influence on Methanogenesis is low since the complete hydrogenation of one mol of linolenic acids spares 0.75 mol of methane. As adaptation of the rumen micro-flora to fatty acid supplementation over long term may be possible, the sustainability of methane suppressing by fatty acid should thoroughly investigated (Grainger et al., 2008).

Grazing management practices

Pasture management

Improving pasture quality is often cited as a means of reducing emissions, especially in less developed regions, because of improvements in animal productivity as well as a reduction in the proportion of energy lost as CH_4 due to a reduction in dietary fibre. However, there is evidence that the impact of pasture quality on CH_4 emissions per kg of pasture consumed is small in temperate, well managed pasture. Molano and Clark (2008) reported no difference in CH_4 emissions per kg of grass DMI between lambs fed pasture with OM digestibility of 666 or 766 g/kg. Measurements with beef heifers in Ireland fed zero-grazed pastures with similar range in digestibility showed no impact on CH4 emissions per kg of DMI, although there was a significant increase in DMI of the high quality pasture. So, while it appears that pasture quality in well managed pastures will not have a large effect on emissions per kg of pasture consumed, there could be significant improvements in lifetime emissions or emissions per kg of product which should be examined in a whole system analysis. If pasture improvements leads to increased stocking densities, it could lead to greater emissions per ha. The effect of pasture improvement in Australian sheep farms was recently modeled by Alcock and Hegarty (2006), who reported only a small reduction in CH_4 output per kg live weight. But in their case, the assumed individual sheep productivity was already quite high, and the pasture improvement was calculated to lead mainly to an increase in stock numbers. In addition, the simulation showed little effect on digestibility of the forage, but rather gave an increase in the quantity of forage available. Lovette et al. (2006) modeled diary production systems in contrasting soil types (wet and impermeable vs. dry and free draining) and reported that the drier soils with a substantially longer grazing season supported milk production with significantly lower GHG emissions per kg of milk produced.

Controlled grazing

One of the best ways to improve productivity of their sheep and goat is to implement a well-planned controlled grazing system. This can result in greater production of higher quality forage than with traditional grazing practices. With the development of new fencing and watering technologies, farmers and entrepreneurs can take advantage of the economic benefits associated with this highly productive grazing system while protecting the environment. Continuous stocking is a management system where sheep and goats have uninterrupted use of a unit of grazing land throughout the grazing season. This system of grazing often fails to maximize the productive potential of the land resulting in wasted forage, decreased pasture productivity and lower weight gain per unit of land. Controlled grazing, a more productive grazing systems, requires a pasture to be subdivided into individual grazing units called paddocks. The individual paddocks are alternatively grazed and rested throughout the grazing season. The paddocks are grazed to keep plants in a vegetative stage, the stage just before seed production. The size and number of paddocks depends upon pasture productivity, stocking rate and the desired residency period of the sheep in each paddock. Because it is easier to maintain effective balance between forage demand and supply with controlled grazing, this system can promote higher forage yield, more uniform levels of forage quality and improved harvest efficiencies. Because controlled grazing leads to more productive sheep and grater live weight gains per acre, it can benefit from increased profits while reducing methane emissions per unit of live weight gain. An additional benefit of controlled grazing is the increased ability of the pasture to act as a sink for carbon dioxide, the major greenhouse gas. As pasture quality improves with controlled grazing, carbon builds up in the soil and plant biomass, reducing the total amount of carbon dioxide in the atmosphere. However, in semi-arid region where the growing of the vegetation takes place from July-September and withers off in October –November, this practice has no relevance. Similarly, when majority of the sheep and goats are reared under extensive system of rearing and there is migration during acute summer, this option is not feasible.

Mitigation through feed additives

Ionophores and organic acids

Among the feed additives, ionophore antibiotics such as monensin, typically used to improve efficiency of animal production are known to decrease methane production (Beauchemin et al., 2008). This is due to a shift of fermentation towards propionogenesis. Organic acids (malate, fumerate) have been assayed as diet additives. An exceptional decrease in methane production by 75 % has been shown that with 10 % encapsulated fumeric acid in the diet of sheep, but the hydrogen used to produce propionate from fumerate is not enough to explain such a drop in methane. Further research is needed with such a product. It has been suggested by Martin (1998) that the high malate content in fresh forages at early growth stage, especially Lucerne could lead to significant changes in rumen fermentation. Similar results were also recorded by Bhatta et al. (2008).

Plant extracts

In recent years, there is growing interest in the use of plant secondary compounds (tannins, saponins, essential oils) as a CH_4 mitigation strategy because of their natural origin in opposition to chemical additives (Bhatta et al., 2002, 2006). Two modes of action of tannins on methanogenesis have been proposed by Tavendale et al. (2005): a direct effect on ruminal methanogens and an indirect effect on hydrogen production due to lower feed degradation. Recently, Bhatta et al. (2009) have reported that tannins suppress methanogenesis directly by reducing the number of archea and indirectly by reducing the number of protozoa. The source containing both condensed and hydrolysable tannins is more effective in suppressing methane emission as compared to those containing only hydrolysable tannins. This was further confirmed in feeding trials in goats kept in open circuit respiration chamber. It was observed that at lower level of tannin (2.5 %), methane suppression was primarily due to the reduction in the number of archea/ protozoa, whereas at higher level of tannin (5.0%), increased methane suppression was due to the combined effect of reduced archea coupled with reduction in digestibility of nutrients (Bhatta et al., 2009). The mode of action of saponins seems to be clearly related to their anti-protozoal effect (Newbold et al., 1997). Additional research in vivo is required to determine the optimal dose of the active compounds, to consider the potential adaptation to the microbes, the presence of residues in animal products as well as the potential anti-nutritional side-effects of such molecules.

Mitigation through biotechnologies

Immunization and biological control

Several biotechnological strategies are currently being explored. A vaccine against three selected methanogens decreased methane production by nearly 8 % in Australian sheep. However, vaccination using a different set of methanogen species or in other geographical regions did not elicit a positive response (Wright et al., 2004). The highly diverse methanogenic community present in animals reared under different conditions might account for immunization failure.

Some bacteriocins are known to rescue methane production *in vitro* (Lee et al., 2002). Nisin is thought to act indirectly, affecting hydrogen producing microbes in a similar way to that of the ionophore antibiotic monensin (Callaway et al., 1997). However, there is no published *in vivo* trial of the effects of this bacteriocin on methane. Nisin is widely used in the food industry as a conservative and fears of microbial cross-adaptation might prevent its approval as a feed additive. A bacteriocin obtained from a rumen bacterium, bovicin HC5, decreased methane production *in vitro* up to 50 % without inducing methanogens adaptation.

Probiotics

The use of probiotics or the stimulation of rumen microbial populations capable to decrease methane emissions potentially remains an interesting approach. Diverting hydrogen from methanogenesis towards acetogenesis has been assayed by several authors. The final product of the reaction, acetate, has the additional advantage of being a source of energy for the animal. However, in the rumen environment, acetogens are less efficient than methanogens in the competition for reducing equivalents and attempt to boost their activity had been so far unsuccessful. The recent isolation of new, high-hydrogen utilizing species from diverse gut environments could offer a better alternative than previously tested acetogens (Klieve and Joblin, 2007). Methanotrophy, i.e. the oxidation of methane, was reported to be less than 0.5 % in vitro (Kajikawa et al., 2003).

Can genetic improvement of sheep and goat reduce methane emission?

If heritable traits can be indentified and enhanced to increase the level of production in animals, then overall methane emissions will decrease. Feed conversion efficiency is one example of an inherited trait that can lead to lower methane emissions. Genetic traits can be bred into sheep and goat that allow them to convert grains and roughage into meat, wool and milk more efficiently. Improved genetics combined with good management can also increase reproductive efficiency of sheep and goat. This can result in higher birth rates and weaning weights. Because increased reproductive efficiency decreases the size of the flock needed to produce a given number of lambs, methane emission per unit of meat produced is reduced. Improved genetics can increase biological efficiency and reduce methane emissions per unit of product because fewer but more efficient sheep can satisfy the consumer demand for livestock products. Research on genetic improvements is valuable because it can help producers improve the profitability of their operations while decreasing overall methane emissions.

Is there any animal variation in methane production?

The decrease in emissions through low methane-producing animals is an ongoing debate. It has been established by several researchers groups that within-animal variability is high and that the ranking of animals in CH_4 production differs with changes in diet and or/ physiological stages (Pinares-Patino et al., 2007) or between successive measurements for a same diet and a same feed intake (Munger and Kreuzer, 2008). The latter authors evaluated the repeatability as 47 and 73 % depending on diets. The repeatability may be due either to between-animal differences in microbial ecosystem or to intrinsic animal characteristics such as retention time of particles in the rumen. Until, now there is no evidence for the effect of these factors, although methane and VFA productions are correlated. It can be assumed that for a same intake cows with a low retention time of particles in the rumen produce less methane than cows with a high retention time s suggested by Pinares-Patino et al. (2007); however, there is not enough data to analyze the heritability of methane production and thus to consider a possible selection of animals for this trait. Hegarty et al. (2007) have shown that the selection on feed efficiency and residual intake reduces methane production.

Methane mitigation in ruminants is possible through various strategies. The feeding management is mostly developed in recent years. Other strategies (biotechnologies, additives) are promising but diversity and plasticity of functions of the rumen bacterial and methanogenic communities may be limiting factor for their successful application. Environmental impacts of strategies should take into consideration a global vision of production systems that considers all greenhouse gases emissions from the animal up to the farm scale as well as grassland use. The sustainability of methane suppressing strategies is an important issue.

References

Alcock, D. and Hegarty, R.S. 2006. In Greenhouse Gases and Animal Agriculture: An update. (Ed. Soliva CR, Takahashi J, and Kreuzer M), pp 103-105 (Elsevier International Congress Series 1293, Amsterdam, The Netherlands).

Beauchemin, K.A., Kreuzer, M., O' Mara, F. and McAllister, T.A. 2008. Nutritional management for enteric methane abatement: a review Australian Journal of Experimental Agriculture 48: 21-27

Bhatta, R., Enishi, O., Yabumoto, Y., Takusari, N., Nonaka, I. and Kurihara M. 2009. B Methane suppression in goats fed complete diet containing natural source of tannin. British Journal of Nutrition (In press)

Bhatta, R., O. Enishi, N. Takusari, K. Higuchi, I. Nonaka and M. Kurihara. 2008. Diet effects on methane production by goats and a comparison between measurement methodologies Journal of Agricultural Science (Cambridge) 146: 705-715

Bhatta, R., Shinde A. K., Vaithiyanathan S., Sankhyan S. K. and Verma D. L.. 2002. Effect of Polyethylene glycol-6000 on nutrient intake, digestion and growth of kids browsing Prosopis cineraria Animal Feed Science & Technology, 101 (1-4): 45-54.

Bhatta, R., Tajima, K. Takusari, N., Higuchi, K., Enishi, O. and Kurihara, M.. 2005. Comparison of sulfur hexafluoride tracer technique, rumen simulation technique and in vitro gas production techniques for methane production from ruminant feeds. In: Greenhouse Gases and Animal Agriculture: An update. (Eds. Soliva C.R., Takahashi, J., and Kreuzer, M), pp 419-421 (Elsevier International Congress Series 1293, Amsterdam, the Netherlands)

Bhatta, R., Tajima, K., Uyeno, Y., Enishi, O. and Kurihara, M.. 2006. Effect of plant extracts as natural source of tannins on methane production in vitro. In: International Workshop on Monsoon Asia Agricultural Greenhouse Gas Emissions, March 7-9, Tsukuba, Japan, pp 67

Bhatta, R., Uyeno, Y., Tajima, K., Takenaka, A., Yabumoto, Y., Nonaka, I., Enishi, O. and Kurihara, M. 2009. Difference in the Nature of Tannins on In Vitro Ruminal Methane and Volatile Fatty Acid Production, and Methanoginic Archaea and Protozoal Populations Journal of Dairy Science 92 (11): 5512-5522

Callaway, T.R., Carneiro De Melo, A.M.S., Russell, J.B. 1997. The effect of nisin and monensin on ruminal fermentations in vitro. Current Microbiology 35, 90-96.

Cynoweth, 1996. Environmental impact of biomethanogenesis, monitoring and assessment. 42:3-18, Kluwer Academic Publishers. Printed in the Netherlands.

Doreau, M. and Ferlay, A. 1995. Effect of dietary lipids on nitrogen metabolism in the rumen: a review. Livestock Production Science 43, 97-1 10.

Grainger, C., Clarke, T., Beauchemin, K.A., McGinn, S.M. and Eckard, R.J. 2008. Supplementation with whole cottonseed reduces methane emissions and can profitably increase milk production of dairy cows offered a forage and cereal grain diet. Australian Journal of Experimental Agriculture 48(1-2): 73-76.

Hegarty, R. S. Goopy, J. P. R. Herd M. and McCorkell, B. 2007 Cattle selected for lower residual feed intake have reduced daily methane production. Journal of Animal Science 85:1479-1486

Hegarty, R. S., and R. Gerdes. 1998. Hydrogen production and transfer in the rumen. Recent Advances in Animal Nutrition 12:37-44.

Hopkins, A. and Del Prado, A. 2007. Implications of climate change for grassland in Europe: impacts, adaptations and mitigation options: a review. Grass and Forage Science 62:118 - 126

IPCC (Intergovernmental Panel on Climate Change) 2007. Climate Change 2007: Impacts, Adaptation and Vulnerability. Summary for policy makers. Online at http://www.ipcc.cg/SPM13apr07.pdf

IPCC 2001 Technical Summary: Contribution of Working Group I to the Third Assessment Report.

Johnson, K.A. and Johnson, D.E. 1995. Methane emissions from cattle. Journal of Animal Science. 73: 2483–2492

Kajikawa, H., Valdes. C., Hillman K., Wallace. R. J. and Newbold. C. J. 2003. Methane oxidation and its coupled electron-sink reactions in ruminal fluid Letters in Applied Microbiology 36 (6): 354 - 357

Khalil M. A. K. and Rasmussen R. A., 1986. Inter-annual variability of atmospheric methane: Possible effects of the el niño-southern oscillation, Science 4 April: 56-58.

Klieve, A.V. and Joblin, K. 2007. New Zealand Pastoral Greenhouse Gas. Research Consortium Report. pp 34-35

Kwok, R., Cunningham, G. F., Wensnahan, M., Rigor, I., H Zwally, J. and Yi, D. 2009. Thinning and volume loss of the Arctic Ocean sea ice cover: 2003–2008, Journal of Geophysics Research, 114, C07005, doi:10.1029/2009JC005312.

Lee, S. S., Hsu, J.-T., Mantovani, H. C. and Russell, J. B. 2002. The effect of bovicin HC5, a bacteriocin from Streptococcus bovis HC5, on ruminal methane production in vitro. FEMS Microbiology Letter 217:51–55.

Lovett, D.K., Shalloo, L., Dillon, P. and O'Mara F.P. 2006. A systems approach to quantify greenhouse gas fluxes from pastoral dairy production as affected by management regime. Agricultural Systems 88, Issues 2-3, pp. 156-179.

Machmuller, A., Soliva, C. R. and Kreuzer, M. 2003. Methane suppressing effect of myristic acid in sheep as affected by dietary calcium and forage proportion. British Journal of Nutrition 90: 529–540.

Maia, M.R., Chaudhary, L.C., Figueres, L., Wallace, R.J. 2007. Metabolism of polyunsaturated fatty acids and their toxicity to the microflora of the rumen. Antonie Van Leeuwenhoek, 91 (4), pp. 303-314.

Martin, C., Dubroeucq, H., Micol, D., Agabriel, J. and Doreau, M. 2007. Methane output from beef cattle fed different high-concentrate diets. In: Proceedings of the British Society of Animal Science, pp. 46.

Martin, S. A. 1998. Manipulation of ruminal fermentation with organic acids: a review. Journal of Animal Science. 76: 3123-3132.

Molano, G. and Clark, H. 2008. The effect of level of intake and forage quality on methane production by sheep. Australian Journal of Experimental Agriculture 48:219–222.

Morand-Fehr, P. and Boyazoglu, J. 1999. Present state and future outlook of the small ruminant sector. Small. Ruminant Research 34: 175-188

Moss. A. R., Jouany, J. P. and Newbold, J. 2000. Methane production by ruminants: its contribution to global warming. Annals of Zootechnology 49: 231-253.

Munger, A. and Kreuzer, M. 2008 Absence of persistent methane emission differences in three breeds of dairy cows. Australian Journal of Experimental Agriculture. 48 no.277-82.

Nagaraja, T. G., C. J. Newbold, C. J. Ven Nevel, and D. I. Demeyer. 1997. Manipulation of ruminal fermentation. In: The Rumen Microbial Ecosystem, (Eds. P. N. Hubson and C. S. Stewart) Acad. and Prof., an imprint of Chapman and Hall, London, UK. Pp 523–632

Newbold,C.J., Hassan, S. M. El., Wang, J., Ortega, M. E and Wallace, R. J. 1997. Influence of foliage from African multipurpose trees on activity of rumen protozoa and bacteria British Journal of Nutrition 78 (2): 237-249

Pinares-Patiño, C. S., Waghorn, G. C., Machmüller, A., Vlaming, B., Molano,G., Cavanagh, A. and Clark, H. 2007. Methane emissions and digestive physiology of non-lactating dairy cows fed pasture forage Canadian Journal of Animal Science 87: 601-613

Pinares-Patino, C.S., Waghorn, G.C., Machmuller, A., Vlaming, B., Molano, G., Cavanagh, A. and Clark, H. 2007. Methane emissions and digestive physiology of non-lactating dairy cows fed pasture forage Canadian Journal of Animal Science 87: 601-613

Rowlinson, P. 2008. In: Livestock and Global Climate Change, Cambridge University press. (Editors: P. Rowlinson, M. Steele and A. Nefzaoui) pp 61-63.

Sauvant, D. and Giger-Reverdin, S. 2007. In: Energy and Protein Metabolism and Nutrition. EAAP publication 124, Wageningen Academic Publishers, The Netherlands pp 561,

Singh, G. P. 1997. Effect of greenhouse gases on climate change and Indian ruminant livestock. Current Science 72: 441-446

Stroeve, J., Holland M. M., Meier, W., Scambos, T. and Serreze, M. 2007. Arctic sea ice decline: Faster than forecast, Geophysics Research Letter, 34, L09501, doi:10.1029/ 2007GL029703.

Tavendale, M.H., Meagher, L.P., Pacheco., Walker, N., Attwood., G.T., Sivakumaran, S. 2005. Methane production from in vitro rumen incubation with lotus pendunculatus and Medicago sativa and effects of extractable condensed fraction on methanegenesis. Animal Feed Science and Technology 123/124: 403-419.

Thornton, P. K., Herrero, M., Freeman, H. A., Okeyo, M., Rege, E., Jones, P. G. and McDermott, J. 2007. Vulnerability, climate change and livestock opportunities and challenges for the poor. Journal of Semi-Arid Tropical Agricultural Research 4 (1). (www.icrisat.org/Journal / specialproject. htm)

Thornton, P.K., Notenbaert, A., van der Steeg, J. and Herrero, M. 2008. The livestock-climate-poverty nexus: A discussion paper on ILRI research in relation to climate change. ILRI. Nairobi, Kenya, pp 90

Wright, A. D. G., Kennedy, P., O'neill C. J., Toovey A. F., Popovski S., Rea S. M., Pimm C. L., Klein L., 2004. Reducing methane emissions in sheep by immunization against rumen methanogens Vaccine 22:3976-3985.

❑❑❑

11

Stress Factors for Small Ruminants Under Field Existence and Strategies for their Amelioration

A. K. Shinde
Division of Animal Nutrition, Central Sheep and Wool Research Institute
Avikanagar, via Jaipur- 304 501, Rajasthan

Introduction

Small ruminants are raised under extreme extensive conditions on marginal lands in the country that cannot be cultivated or used for other agricultural purposes. These grazing lands include community, barren, fallow, peripheral forests and roadside lands. In Rajasthan, 84% of the poor villagers depend on common property resources for grazing of animals (Jodha, 1990). These lands bear natural vegetation after rainy season and ensure better nutrition to animals during monsoon, which is thereafter substantially declined due to deterioration of forage yield or quality, maturity or withering of vegetation and constant higher grazing pressure. Forage scarcity from grazing lands and lack of cultivated fodder compels the shepherds to take their animals to neighbouring states where grazing resources are relatively better either due to higher precipitation or lower population density of sheep and goats. Moreover the erratic, poor, delayed or unequal distribution of rainfall in the dry region further aggregates the scarcity of fodder. Under these situations the farmers either go for distress sale of animals or long duration migration. Water salinity and scarcity during long dry period is a common problem in most of the regions of Rajasthan and Gujarat leading to physiological stress and reproductive disorders in small ruminants. Many sheep flocks in the desert do not get drinking water even on alternate days. Research indicates that frequency of water intake twice in a week is sufficient for sheep but its adverse effects in terms of stress and low productivity needs thorough investigation. Goats in comparison to sheep are in advantageous position in dry zones because of their ability to browse on shrubs and tree species when grasses are not available during summer months. This could be one of the reasons for their rapid growth in population and less dependence on migration than sheep breeds of dry regions.

Sheep and goats are primarily maintained in wide ranges of environments from hot, dry arid and semi-arid plains to cold, wet mountainous and hilly regions under sedentary, migratory and transhumance systems in the country. Small ruminants under field conditions are exposed to variable stresses namely, thermal, nutritional and walking. The ambient temperature in the desert environment fluctuates between 10-12^{0}C in winter to 45-46^{0}C in summer. Both sheep and goats in the cold and hot seasons require additional energy for thermoregulation. However, poor grazing resources are unable to support their energy requirements resulting in nutritional stresses causing production and death losses. Sheep and goats also suffer from severe thermal stress in humid and hot climatic conditions during early monsoon because of poor dissipation of heat through cutaneous system against ambient temperature and humidity gradients. Goats are mostly bred during summer months in hot desert region. It has been observed that thermal stress during early monsoon causes early embryonic losses and abortion. The provision of shelter and access to drinking water is one of the options for minimizing heat stress and averting the embryonic losses. Sheep flocks in western parts of Rajasthan are maintained under migratory system ranging from short duration migration of 3-4 months to round the year migration. Long distance walking under hot climate and feed scarcity during migration cause multiple stresses in animals. The management of animals under migratory system is life style of nomads and compulsion for them for mitigating feed scarcity in dry regions. However, grazing animals during cooler hours of day, frequent watering, night grazing and provision of shelter can minimize the adverse effect of stresses during migration. In addition to thermal, nutritional and walking stresses, sheep and goats during migration also suffer from predation, poisoning due to consumption of toxic plants, pesticides or hazardous chemicals, fright of vehicles, accidents and rude behavior of shepherds.

In the present scenario of change in climate, sheep and goats production is being affected in four ways: (a) feed/grain availability and price, (b) pasture/forage crop production and quality, (c) change in distribution of diseases and pests and (d) direct effect on health, growth and reproduction. Recent research findings suggest that the impact of change in climate on pastures and rangelands would deteriorate pasture quality towards poor quality subtropical C_4 grasses in temperate regions as a result of warm temperature. However, there might be potential increase in the yield and possible expansion of area if climate changes are favourable as a result of the increase in CO_2 concentration. As a consequence of such changes the productivity of grazing lands could also be altered. The alteration of precipitation and temperature regimes may lead into spread of diseases and parasites into new regions or enhance the incidence of diseases, which in turn would reduce animal productivity and increase animal mortality.

Grazing stresses

The studies conducted at different locations in the country indicated that comfortable conditions for sheep and goats are: 22-24^{0}C ambient temperature, of 25-30 q DM/ha biomass yield containing 12 % CP, and 4-5 km of daily walking. However, these conditions are not common in tropical climate where the ambient temperature shoots up to 45^{0}C during summer, feed scarcity remains for 8 to 9 months and animals are forced to walk for long distances in search of feed and water. These unfavourable conditions under field existence cause thermal, nutritional and walking stresses in animals that adversely affect their production and reproduction performance.

Nutritional stress

Grazing lands and nutritional stress

Most of grazing lands in the country fall under the category of rangeland occupied by natural vegetation, forbs, shrubs and trees. The herbaceous species sprouts after rain in monsoon season followed by rapid growth and maturity and subsequently gets withered off with the advancement of season within 3-4 months. Sheep and goats get adequate nutrition during rainy season on these rangelands and for the remaining 8-9 months are exposed to poor nutrition (Shinde and Bhatta, 2002). These rangelands are utilized by all kind of animals without any restriction. Constant grazing pressure and high stocking density further deteriorate the carrying capacity of rangelands. The study carried out in semi-arid regions of Rajasthan indicated that the stocking density was about 70 times higher than the carrying capacity of rangelands (Sankhyan et al., 1999). Shrubs and other deciduous tree species are widely found in desert environment and constitute an important source of foliage for the animals. However, the presence of anti- nutritional factors like tannin, saponine, mimosine, etc. adversely affects animal production and health. The use of top feed as feed supplements rather than sole feed has been recommended for improving production and reproduction in sheep and goats in dry zones of the country (Bhatta et al., 2005). Majority of sheep and goat flocks are maintained on community grazing lands in the country. Forage intake of sheep on rangeland fluctuates between seasons. It has been reported that the DM and DCP intake of sheep was declined from 649 and 45.04g in monsoon to 500 and 13.38g in summer on community lands (Sankhyan et al., 1999). Poor nutrient intake in summer causes loss of body weight and production. Supplementary feeding with concentrate mixture or legume roughage is suggested, but the financial constraints and the availability of poor feed resources with farmers restrict them for adopting supplementary feeding resulting in low growth and production.

Soil ingestion and nutritional stress

Sheep has a peculiar habit of close grazing, which provokes the ingestion of soil along with forage on sparse vegetation cover in desert regions. Soil ingestion increases excretion of endogenous nitrogen per unit of feacal organic matter besides causing damage to gut mucous lining, rapid wearing of incisor teeth and brushing of dental pads. Soil ingestion from ground surface sizably increases during drought and famine situation due to poor vegetation cover. The study conducted at CSWRI on community land in semi-arid of Rajasthan during drought year showed that sheep ingested soil by 39.10, 15.62 and 46.41% of total dry matter intake. It severely affected their nutrient digestion and also caused deaths in some cases under prolonged exposure (Shinde et al., 2005). Vaithyanathan and Singh (1984) also reported soil ingestion of 71-163g daily in sheep on arid pasture at Bikaner.

Mineral imbalances and nutritional stress

Mineral imbalance caused by their deficiency or excess amount is a common problem in tropics that affects reproduction, growth and health of animals. Certain minerals are required for the normal physiological functions of animals. Small ruminants depend on natural vegetation from grazing lands for major part of the year. The feed resources are deficient in majority of the essential minerals in tropics. The incidence of pregnancy toxeamia in ewes, fertility and other reproductive problems due to deficiencies of minerals and urinary calculi (kidney stones) due to toxicities are frequently noticed. The study conducted under AICRP on improvement of feed resources and nutrient utilization in raising animal production indicated that deficiency of Ca, P,

Cu, Zn and Mn mineral elements was common in semi-arid region of Rajasthan. However, supplementation in sheep and goats by area specific mineral mixture improved their production and reproduction (Shinde et al., 2006). The major constraint in supplementation with mineral mixture is due to system of rearing sheep and goats on pasture without any kind of concentrate supplementation. Mineral mixtures in form of mineral bricks or briskets are given in organized farm where animals lick the bricks as per their desire. Recently a mineral mixture in the form of pellet has been developed by CSWRI. The pellets are easy to supplement in sheep and goats, bring 60% of sheep into estrus within 15-21days and the remaining after 42 days, increase wool yield by 4-8% and milk yield by 10-15% (Shinde and Sankhyan, 2009). The cases of urinary calculi due to imbalances of calcium and phosphorus are frequently noticed in weaner lambs on high concentrate feed and such cases increase during water scarcity period. The supplementation of ammonium sulphate @1% reduces cases of calculi. Moreover, roughage intake from grazing lands may be encouraged or hay may be supplemented at stall for reducing urinary calculi cases in weaner lambs.

Saline water and nutritional stress

Desert topography is characterized by scarcity of food and water. The situation is further complicated by saline drinking water beyond tolerance levels in major part of western desert. Saline water severely affects health, reproduction and production of sheep and goats. These two species are exposed to saline water for more than 8 months in desert. Sheep and goats can tolerate mild concentration of TSS in water. However, when the concentration is more than 4.5g/litre it affects their reproduction and production besides causing diarrhea, emaciation, depression of estrus cycle and early embryonic losses. Drinking water in desert also contains higher proportion of fluorine and nitrate that adversely affects the production and reproduction in sheep and goats (Mittal and Ghosh, 1984). The provision of safe and clean water from water sources free from contaminants may help in reducing stresses in animals.

Toxic and poisonous plant species and nutritional stress

Sheep and goats are exposed to toxic and poison plant species on rangelands, which causes death and production losses. *Tribulus terrestris* poisoning in sheep on community grazing land of semi-arid region of Rajasthan was reported by Shinde et al. (2004). Major symptoms were swelling in ear and head, skin photosensitization, skin cracking, itching, in-appetite, weakness, ruminal stasis, weight loss, dehydration, rise of temperature, urine discoloration and oozing of blood and fluid from the skin cracks. The grazing of sheep in *T. terrestris* dominated pasture should be discontinued when such symptoms start appearing in the flock. Sheep and goats graze on wide range of grazing lands contaminated with pesticide residues, hazardous chemicals and heavy metals in *en route* to migration. Moreover in some cases, residues of hazardous chemicals appear in animal products and harm human beings. Further chemicals and antibiotics used in the form of drenching, dipping, vaccines are routinely used in rearing sheep and goats. These harmful chemicals appear in meat, wool and milk products and cause detrimental effect on health of human beings. It has been reported that organic farming is the best option for safety and quality assurance of animal produce. Meat and wool produced from sheep in the country is near to organic because they are raised on rangelands free from fertilizer and pesticides application moreover under prevailing rearing practices, least chemicals and antibiotics are used in treatment and prophylaxis of sheep and goats. A study conducted at CSWRI clearly indicated that meat and milk from sheep was free from pesticide residues and safe for human consumption (Shinde and Karim, 2009).

Fibrous forage and nutritional stress

The sheep diet mainly constitutes mature, bulky, fibrous and lignified forage on pasture during major parts of the year in tropics. The bulky and fibrous foods increase the energy cost of prehension, mastication and rumination. The digestion of fibrous food in gut increases the heat increment, which adds to thermal load in animals during hot months. A study at CSWRI indicated that sheep and goats linearly increased rumination (bites/ bolus) and mastication rate (bite/ min) with fibre content of diet (Shinde et al., 1997, Bhatta et al., 2001). In goats, rumination rate was increased from 44.9 in monsoon to 69.0 bites /bolus in summer (Bhatta et al., 2001). It was suggested that fibrous grasses require more energy for prehension and digestion than succulent fodder. The digestibility of DM, CP, EE and energy of diet decrease sizably in sheep when roughage constitute more than 75% of diet. Such deleterious effects can be alleviated by supplementary feeding with concentrate mixture in warm climate.

Strategies for ameliorating nutritional stress

Sheep and goats on community lands of deserts experience sub-optimal nutrition during major part of the year. Sub-optimal nutrition influences onset of puberty, expression of reproductive behaviour, reproductive rates, lamb/ kid growth and post-partum estrus. Optimal level of nutrition is required in animals for expressing their full genetic potential for reproduction and production. The forage yield of community lands in dry region is very low and can hardly sustain one ACU in round the year grazing system. The rehabilitation of community lands with perennial grasses is one of the options for enhancing biomass yield but its implementation is difficult in the present land use pattern. *Cenchrus ciliaris* and *Lasiurus sindicus* are best-suited pasture grasses for semi-arid and arid ecology. The rehabilitation of community lands with perennial grasses increase the forage yield of lands from 4-5q to 25-30q/ha and can sustain 4-5 sheep per hectare. Grazing management is another option of enhancing pasture yield and sustainability. In the present system, all kinds of animals are continuously grazed in the community grazing lands without any kind of rest to land, these results in poor regeneration of grass and subsequent forage yield and quality. The study conducted at CSWRI, Avikanagar and IGFRI, Jhansi indicated that deferred rotational or rotational grazing was beneficial in maintaining stable grazing resource and extending its availability for longer periods. The stocking of lands as per carrying capacity is one of the options but in the present state of gradual shrinkage of grazing lands and exponential increase of livestock, its application in practice seems to be meager.

Perennial grasses poor in protein contents cannot meet the requirement of growing lambs and lactating or pregnant sheep on grazing alone. The inter-cropping of *Dolichus lablab* and *Clitoria ternatea* with perennial grasses increases the protein contents of pasture. The grass pasture ensures nutrient requirement of sheep during monsoon and early winter but not during summer due to deterioration in yield and quality. Tree leaves rich in protein and minerals increase availability of quality foliage to sheep during summer season in dry region. Three tier silvipasture consisting of *Cenchrus ciliaris* grass, *Dicrostachys nutans* as shrub and *Ailanthus excelsa* as fodder tree yields up to 29.25q DM/ha and ensures quality forage to sheep for longer period. Lambs and kids were found to attain body weight of 19.93 and 21.90 kg at six month of age under the silvipasture grazing system (Sankhyan et al., 1996). Mixed grazing of sheep and goats improve utilization of pasture and animal performance as both the species do not compete with each other but rather graze in close harmony. By grazing on cenchrus pasture occupied by bushes, sheep and goats gained 6.17 and 9.37 kg in a year, while the annual yield of wool was 2.4 kg in sheep and milk yield was 714 g in goats. Lambs and kids on mixed grazing along with mother attained 18.17 and 15.2 kg weight at weaning (Shinde et al., 1996). Mix grazing of sheep and goats is recommended for better utilization of grazing resources and harvesting higher return from a single piece of land.

The leaves of *Prosopis cineraria, Acacia nilotica, Albezia lebbek, Ailanthus excelsa, Azadirachta indica and Bauhinia racemosa* are widely used in feeding of sheep and goats in tropics (Bhatta et al., 2005). The presence of tannin adversely affects the palatability, voluntary intake, digestion and nitrogen retention (Silanikove et al., 1996). Small quantity of leaves in avoids the adverse effect caused by anti-nutritional factors on digestion kinetic and nutrient utilization but rather helps in improving nutrient utilization by small ruminants. A study showed that 4% tannin in diet improves digestion and nutrient utilization while reduces methane production and parasitic load. Moreover, it has been reported that tree leaves containing tannin are more beneficial if used as a supplement rather than a sole feed (Bhatta et al., 2005). Fodder tree are valuable source of protein and energy in dry zones and may be supplemented for harvesting maximum nutritional and economic benefits.

Behavioural adjustment of animal to feed scarcity

Sheep and goats adjust their grazing behaviour to ameliorate the nutritional stress and sustain production and reproduction. The rumination rate (bites/bolus) increases in both the species with the progress of season for better utilization of fibrous feed. Rumination rate was found to increase from 44.9 in monsoon (vegetation succulent) to 69.0 in summer (fibrous) (Bhatta et al., 2001). They select quality forage from grazing lands to meet their nutrient requirements. It was found that the goats selected forage containing 13.40% CP in monsoon, 12.78% in winter and 14.48% in summer against 9.94%, 7.19% and 6.61% CP in pasture grasses during the respective seasons (Bhatta et al., 2001). Similarly, sheep diet contained 11.5% CP in monsoon, 10.0% in winter and 7.8% in summer against 10.5%, 8.4% and 4.0% CP on native rangelands of semi-arid Rajasthan during respective seasons (Sankhyan et al., 1999). Moreover, sheep and goats consume succulent plants and parts of plant containing higher proportion of CP to reduce energy cost of mastication, rumination and digestion. Some of the native species rich in protein and relish by sheep and goats in community lands of semiarid region are *Tribulus terrestris, Indigofera cordifolia, Trianthema portolacastrum, Commelina forskalaei, Achyranthus aspera, Phaseolus tribulus and Melilotus indica*. Goats are opportunist browser but also graze on native grasses and forbs during monsoon season when most of the browse species are poor in palatability due to higher concentration of toxic principles and astringent. A study conducted at CSWRI indicated that goat diet consisted of 24% grasses during monsoon while it was almost negligible during winter and summer (Shinde et al., 2000). The flexible and opportunistic behaviour of goats enable them to ameliorate nutrition stress on rangelands and help them to adapt to various range conditions. The characteristic bipedal stance in goats helps in consumption of several tree species and overhead portions of shrub species. Contrary to this, split (bifid) upper lip in sheep partly accounts for their greater ability to graze close to ground and help them to gather food from sparse vegetation cover of rangeland.

Adaptation of animals to feed scarcity

Sheep and goats of desert region have peculiar characteristics of urea recycling and lower nitrogen loss due to efficient renal activity. Bedouin goats of desert recycle up to 90% of nitrogen intake (Silanikove et al., 1980) and efficiency is higher in poor nitrogen containing pastures. Further, these goats are efficient in digesting structural carbohydrate. These animals when dehydrated under exposure to heat, they are able to replenish their body water losses with one watering and able to drink over 40% of their dehydrated body mass. These goats reduce urea excretion through kidney by two ways: (a) reducing glomerular filtration and (b) high tubular re-absorption of urea (Silanikove, 1984). Urinary water excretion in desert animals is relatively lower, which help them to increase urea recycle and decrease nitrogen loss.

Desert sheep and goats by virtue of their exposure to water scarcity for longer period of the year, conserve water by desiccating pellet feaces, concentrate urine, reduce metabolic rate and evaporative losses and reallocate water in rumen. Goats in extreme desert of Rajasthan are provided water once in 4 days and perform without any detrimental effect on body (Khan et al., 1979). Moroccan goats of desert use low water turnover by combining fugal water economy and capacity to endure severe dehydration and rapid re-hydration (Hossali-Hilani et al., 1993). The increase in water turn over was recorded up to 6% in the winter and 7% during summer in sheep of Indian desert. It was reported that watering of sheep once in 2-3 days increase nutrient digestion and urea recycling (More and Sahni, 1978). Sheep in heat exposure induces a marked increase in water turnover in the process of acclimatization to hot condition of desert. Karakul and Awassi are fat tail sheep breeds found in desert. They store fats in their tail region that weighs up to 4-5kg and utilize them as source of energy during feed scarcity period. This peculiar characteristic helps them to sustain and produce during feed scarcity period in desert. Good walking ability, resistant to diseases and heat, and better efficiency of utilization of dried pasture also help them to survive and produce in the desert environment.

Tannin or alkaloids rich foliages having toxic effects (damage to the liver, kidney and epithelium of the digestive tract) are the major constituent of goats and sheep diet in desert especially during scarcity periods. Goats secrete salivary protein, which binds tannin thus reducing the adverse effect of tannin on palatability, feed intake as well as on post-ingestive effect on digestive enzymes. Their use is restricted because palatability, voluntary intake, digestibility, nitrogen retention and energy utilization are inversely related with high tannin levels (Bhatta et al., 2005). Goat rumen has tannase enzymes, which help in better utilization of tannin rich feed than sheep. Moreover, goats have relatively larger liver than sheep, which helps them in detoxifying anti- nutritional factors more efficiently than sheep. Malnutrition, poor management and synergistic diseases under traditional management drastically reduce animal survivability and system productivity. It has been reported that gastro intestinal nematodes reduce nutrient availability to the host through reduced both voluntary feed intake and /or reduced efficiency of nutrient absorption. The study indicated that level of nutrition influences resilience and resistance of the host to parasitic infection. Feed supplementation could be used as an alternative method of parasite control in animals (Coop and Kyriazakis, 1999).

Thermal stress and Animal Adaptation

Sheep and goats are reared under temperate to subtropical and tropical climates in the country. They are exposed to harsh environmental conditions like high ambient temperature, humidity, solar radiation and drought and feed scarcity under extensive management system. They spend considerable amount of energy in seeking food owing to sparse vegetation cover and harsh environmental conditions in tropics. Sheep and goat flocks are exposed to >45 °C ambient temperature in summer in hot desert of Rajasthan and Gujarat and <4°C in winter in Himalayan regions (Shinde and Karim, 2007). Higher ambient temperature above thermo neutral zones of animals increase the energy cost of thermoregulation to maintain homoeothermic condition while lower temperature below thermo-neutral temperature also provoke greater demand of energy for thermoregulation and in both the cases, they spend sizable amount of energy on thermoregulation. The major portion of energy is diverted for thermoregulation and survivability resulting in compromise of growth and production.

The heat input from metabolic heat production and solar radiation, and heat output through evaporative and non-evaporative avenues determine the body temperature of animals. When heat loss does not equate heat gain, heat is stored in the body as a result body temperature of animal's increases. Animals maintained body temperature within fairly narrow limits hence above the upper critical temperature; additional heat is released through pulmonary and cutaneous routes and below the lower critical temperature, metabolic rate increase to produce heat. Lower critical temperature is governed by both insulation and thermo-neutral metabolic rates. Insulation is influenced by body size, body condition and fleece characteristics. Sheep and goats use thermolysis as an adaptive strategy to tolerate heat stress. Respiration rate, heart rate and cutaneous evaporation increased above thermo-neutral zones to dissipate body heat during daytime in field. In well-adapted breeds of desert, little changes were observed in respiration rate with rise of heat production because animals dissipate heat through panting and sweating. The increase demand of energy by respiratory muscles is compensated by a decrease in metabolism of other tissue. There is an increase in blood flow to the respiratory system and decrease to some other tissues during heat stress. In Bedouin goats, VO_2 consumption is higher by 15 % under protection from solar radiation than unprotected one. Bedouin goats under heat load condition reduce heat production (HP) by reducing alimentary activity.

Broadly minimum heat production in sheep occurs between 24-27°C ambient temperature and in goats between 20-26°C under confinement in psychromatic chamber. The estimation of minimum heat production of animals in field is difficult because of influence of other factors of field existence. The rise of body temperature is mainly influenced by ambient temperature. The rectal temperature (RT) was found to increase by 1.0, 2.1 and 2.0 °C with mean of 1.7°C in sheep from 06:00 to 14:00 h and 2.0, 1.5 and 1.5°C with mean of 1.6°C in goats during monsoon, winter and summer in semiarid pastures of Rajasthan (Shinde et al., 1998; 2002). On the other hand, RT of stall-fed sheep was increased by 0.9°C from 06:00 to 14:00 h. At dry bulb temperature (DBT) below the critical temperature goats maintain minimum energy expenditure (EE) by non-evaporative heat loss. At higher DBT, EE increase with increase cost of thermoregulation. The rise of EE with RT suggesting that goats maintain a minimum EE up to 38.5 °C RT by increasing evaporative heat loss and above 38.5 °C increase through respiration resulting in gradual rise of EE (Shinde et al., 2002). Sheep reduce feed intake in hot and dry conditions to minimize heat production by digestive and metabolic processes. Lower feed intake facilitates the adaptation of animals to heat stress but it is detrimental to production. In heat stress, the redistribution of blood from the gastro intestinal tract to body surface and respiratory tract reduced the absorption of the product of digestion.

Morphological character of animal and adaptation to hot climate

Morphological and anatomical characters of breeds play an important role in regulation of body temperature and heat production. Several studies on heat tolerance and adaptability of exotic breeds and their crosses have been conducted at CSWRI, Avikanagar (Singh and Acharya, 1977; Singh et al., 1980, 1982). These studies have shown that Rambouillet has less body surface for heat dissipation in relation to body mass than lighter native breeds. Moreover, heavy wool coats of Rambuillet inhibit heat loss from the skin surface than the lighter open fleeced coats of native breeds. Rambouillet sheep rely on respiratory evaporative cooling which requires almost four times more energy than cutaneous evaporative cooling which is major route of heat dissipation in native sheep. This results in higher energy demand for thermoregulation in Rambouillet than native breeds. Crossbred sheep in comparison to native breeds are more vulnerable during monsoon season of hot semiarid region because ambient temperature often exceeds body temperature and elevated humidity impedes moisture evaporation from respiratory and skin surfaces thus magnify the heat stress. The temperate sheep breeds reduce their feed intake during thermal stress to minimize heat production while Chokla a native sheep breed consumes more feed during thermal stress. This shows their better efficiency of heat dissipating mechanism and relatively better adaptability to thermal stress.

Temperate sheep breeds maintained under organized management over generations at CSWRI clearly indicated that lamb's birth was linearly declined when maintaining their dams for generations in hot semi-arid locations. Such decline was recorded from the 6th to 11th generation in Rambouillet lambs, while the reduction was apparent from 2nd generation in Suffolk lambs (Singh and Karim, 1995). This clearly indicated the adverse effect of heat stress on temperate breeds in hot conditions of tropics and animals managed to survive by compromising on their production. The effects of heat stress on growth performance are the product of a decrease in anabolic activity and the increase in tissue catabolism. The decrease in anabolism is essentially caused by a decrease in voluntary feed intake of essential nutrients. The increase in tissue catabolism occurs mainly in fat depots and/or lean body mass. The letter effect is due to the catabolism of endogenous DNA and RNA purines due to the increase in catacholamines and glucorticoids (Marai and Habeeb, 1998)

Supplementing sheep and goats with low-quality highly fibrous feed may sustain the animals when pastures are meager, but cannot improve their well being. On the other hand, supplementing ruminal escape protein and fat may reduce the heat increment of feed; improve nitrogen utilization thereby animal welfare. The provision of shade from artificial structure or trees is essential for the welfare of sheep and goats where ambient temperature during summer exceeds 40°C and THI 70. To negate the effect of other stressful factors of field existence, provision of supplementation and clean water at least once in a day may be followed. It would be unethical from welfare point of view to grow purebred animals from temperate environment in areas where ambient temperature during summer exceeds 40°C and THI exceeds 70.

Behavioural adjustment to ameliorate thermal stress

Sheep and goats undergo several adjustments in their grazing pattern to ameliorate the effect of heat stress by declining grazing hours with rise of ambient temperature. It was found that grazing hours of goats in hot condition of Rajasthan are negatively correlated with ambient temperature and humidity (Bhatta et al., 2001). Sheep seek shade in hot sunny day for major part of day to protect themselves from solar radiation thereby feed intake is reduced. Sheep during hot weather in tropical conditions lie down and reduce their locomotion. Instead, they tend to graze before sunrise, at dawn and during night. Seeking shade during heat of the day is a conspicuous form of behavioural adaptation in these areas. Sheep tend to crowd, and to stand intimately side-by-side in order to reduce effective areas for heat exchange (Marai et al., 2007). Sheep in hot desert environment are housed in open on sandy soil floor. They provide sufficient opportunity for them to lose all the heat gained from previous day, particularly when night temperature drops below 21°C. However, when night temperature does not drop below 21°C, capacity to completely dissipate heat gained during the preceding day is severely hampered and animals suffer from heat stress.

Migration stress

In earlier days, the migration and sheep rearing were complementary to each other but in recent days, the functional relationship has undergone considerable changes with the socio-cultural and technological transformation. On migration, sheep and goats are exposed to long distance walking, intense solar radiation and vagaries of nutrition. Migratory system is generally considered as long distance migration in dry plains or transhumance in hilly or mountain regions. About 70-80% of sheep flocks in arid regions of the country are managed under migratory system and the number further increase during drought and famine years. In spite of advancement in agriculture and socio-economic condition of farmers, nomadic/migration still exists Moreover condition such as drought is forcing the nomads to leave sheep husbandry and search for wages in urban areas. In fragile ecosystems, nomadic and transhumance sheep production cause less damage to environment. Professor Elinor Ostrom, who awarded Nobel Prize for the year 2009 for economic governance, studied satellite images of Mangolia and neighboring areas of China and Russia, where livestock has been grazing on large grasslands areas for centuries. Historically, the region was dominated by nomads who moved their herds on a seasonal basis. When government imposed state owned agricultural collectives (where most users settled permanently) it resulted in heavy degradation of land. Topography, feed resources and socio-economic conditions of people besides, low and erratic rainfall, frequent drought and low crop production are some of the factors responsible for continuation of migratory system in arid regions. In migration system, sheep graze on barren and marginal lands of dry regions followed by relatively better fallow lands, stubbles, marginal lands etc in neighboring states. In *en route* migration, wide varieties of ground vegetation and top feed, rich in vitamins, minerals and other nutrients help them to meet their requirements. In semi-arid region, sheep flocks migrate within and between the districts for 2-3 months during summer for protection of flocks against vagaries of nutritional stress. Shrinkage of grazing lands, increase in livestock population, reduction of fodder trees and forage beside water scarcity, predators, poachers and loss of lambs and weaker animals due to inclement weather conditions and diseases exaggerate the problem of shepherds under migration system. The provision of *en route* shelter, disease treatment and prophylaxis, wool shearing and marketing, animal insurance etc are some of the options for smooth functioning of system. Sheep on migration are also transported between the places by vehicle, it is also widely recognized that stress starts as animals are being loaded onto the vehicle and take them to other places. Poor nutrition of animals, over crowding, injuries, no stop over and long travel also cause stress in animals that adversely affects their health.

Management options for mitigating migration stress

Three basic managements require for reducing stress during *en route* migration are: (a) physical modification of environment, (b) genetic improvement of resistant breeds and (c) improved nutritional management. The provision of shelter in *en route* migration for protecting animals and shepherds from inclement weather would protect the animals from production, reproduction and death losses. Provision of natural or artificial shade is the simplest method to reduce the impact of solar radiation. The artificial shade structure should simulate the natural trees in term of well being of animals. The rearing of sheep and goats breeds under migratory system should be genetically resistance to diseases like endoparasite, ectoparsite, lamness foot rots etc and well adapted to harsh climatic conditions. The native breeds are well adapted to migration and also climate rather than exotic breeds brought from temperate climate or crossbreds developed from temperate breeds. Breeding sheep for higher genetic resistance to climate and diseases is better alternative. This approach, if appropriately developed, is likely to be more readily accepted and affordable to sheep or goat keepers. Moreover, grazing management techniques should be implemented properly for worm control measures for reducing reliance on anthelmintics treatments. Selection and development of breeds for genetic resistance to gastro intestinal strongyles is more economic and affordable approach for worm control in sheep. In selecting and breeding the animals for rearing under migration system, morphological and physiological characteristics, that can withstand heat and drought stress should be considered. The morphological characteristics such as large skin area to live weight ratio, pigmented skin, light colour or white body coat, walking efficiency to long distance, low water or forage requirements, tolerant to high intake of salts either in water or forage, poor quality food, harsh climate and resistance to GIN and other pests should be considered. Nutritional management of sheep on migration by reducing crowding in grazing lands, use of stubbles, tree leaves, supplementary feeding of growing lambs are some of the options for mitigating migration stress. Grazing of animals during night hours and restraining in protected enclosures during day may be helpful in reducing thermal load and stress on animals.

Walking stress

Energy cost of locomotion of animals varies as per ascends, descends and gradient of the slope or on different surface such as snow or sand. On inclines, the cost is 10 times higher for each unit of elevation gained due to the energy expended to move against gravity whereas during down slope travel, potential energy is recovered as kinetic energy leading to a decrease in energy expenditure (EE) relative to horizontal costs. Under sedentary system, sheep spend 43% more energy on pasture than on stall-feeding due to higher energy cost of thermoregulation, grazing and walking activities (Shinde et al., 2000). In arid region, under permanent migration they spend still higher EE due to long distances traveling and exposure to intense solar radiation. While in transhumance system in temperate region, vertical movement of sheep from foothills of Himalaya and other mountain regions to alpine pastures the EE is still higher in high altitude locations. It has been reported that energy cost of walking in vertical plain is 10 times higher than horizontal plains (ARC, 1980).

In Naveda mountain range, Alberta goats spend 31.6 and 46.6% more energy in autumn and summer seasons than restrained goats. Prieto et al., (1991) reported energy cost of locomotion accounts for an increased energy requirement above maintenance of between 20 to 53% in goats. The energy cost of vertical locomotion lies 37.7 to 23.9 J/kg BW/m corresponding to apparent energetic efficiencies of 26 to 41% (Lachica and Aguilera, 2003). It has been observed leggy, compact body and tall animals have better walking efficiency under migration and the farmers prefer them under migration.

Practical Considerations

Lot of information is available on grazing stress and its adverse effect on production and reproduction in sheep and goats under different climatic conditions. The implementation of knowledge to achieve high level of production and at the same time sustain profitability is the need of hour. The challenge before the researchers is to develop sheep and goat management practices at a pace consistent with the rapidly changing socio-economic status of producers and climate.

- In harsh environment of desert and other mountain regions, sheep and goat breeds well adapted to prevailing climatic conditions may be propagated and improved through selection.
- Forage resource development including fodder trees, pastures and fodder crops resistance to drought should be encouraged to reduce feed and fodder scarcity.
- The grazing resources in the dry region of the country have deteriorated to such an extent that raising of animals on grazing alone under round the grazing system is not possible for sustaining and improving production. Supplementary feeding should be followed for improving production.
- In the present scenario of harsh climatic changes, provision of shelter should be prioritized in sheep and goat rearing to ameliorate thermal stress.
- Sheep and shepherds insurance programme should be implemented in large scale to reduce financial losses to shepherds from casualties caused by accidents, diseases and inclement weather.

References

ARC. 1980. The Nutrient Requirement of Livestock: Commonwealth Agricultural Bureau, UK.

Bhatta R., Vaithyanathan, S., Singh, N.P., Shinde, A. K. and Verma, D.L. 2005. Effect of feeding tree leaves as supplements on the nutrient digestion and rumen fermentation pattern in sheep grazing on semiarid range of India -I. Small Ruminant Research 60:273-280.

Bhatta, Raghavendra, Sankhyan, S. K., Shinde, A. K. and Verma, D. L. 2001. Seasonal changes in diet selectivity and grazing behaviour of goats on semi-arid rangeland. Indian Journal of Animal Sciences 71:62-65.

Bhatta, Raghavendra., Sankhyan, S. K., Shinde, A. K. and Verma, D. L. 2001. Seasonal changes in diet selectivity and grazing behaviour of goats on semi-arid rangeland. Indian Journal of Animal Sciences 71:62-65.

Bhatta, Raghavendra., Vaithyanathan, Subhiah., Shinde, Ajay Kumar and Jakhmola, Ramesh. C. 2005. Effect of feeding complete feed block containing Prosopis cineraria leaves and polyethylene glycol (PEG) - 6000 on nutrient intake, its utilization, rumen fermentation pattern and rumen profile in kids. Journal of the Science of Food and Agriculture 85: 1788-1794.

Coop, R. L. and Kyriazakis, I. 1999. Nutrition - parasite interaction. Veterinary Parasitology 84: 187-204.

Hossali-Hilani, J., Benlamlih, S. and Dahlbo, K. C. 1993. Fluid balance and milk secretion in the fed and food deprived Black Moraccan goats. Small Ruminant Research 12: 271-285.

Jodha, N. S. 1990. Rural common property resources: Contributions and crisis. Economic and Political Weekly 25: A 65-78.

Khan, M. S., Sasidharan, T. U. and Ghosh, P. K. 1979. Water economy of the Barmer goats of Rajasthan. Journal of Arid Environment 1: 351-355.

Lachica, M. and Aguilera, J. F. 2003. Estimation of energy needs in the free - ranging goats with particular reference to the assessment of its energy expenditure by the ^{13}C - bicarbonate method. Small Ruminant Research 49:303-318.

Marai, I. E. M., Darawany-EI, A. A., Fadiel, A. and Abdel-Hafez, M.A.M. 2007. Physiological traits as affected by heat stress in sheep - A review. Small Ruminant Research 71: 1-12.

Marai, I. F. M. and Habeeb, A. A. M. 1998. Adaptation of Bos taurus cattle under hot climate conditions. Annals of Arid Zone 37(3): 253-281.

Mittal, J. P. and Ghosh, B. K. 1984. The tolerance of Indian desert ewes and their lambs for prolongs intake of natural saline water. Animal Production UK 39: 427-432.

More, T and Sahni, K. L.1978. Effect of long-term water deprivation on body weights and water intakes of breeding ewes under semi-arid conditions. Journal of Agricultural Science Cambridge 90: 435-439.

Prieto, C., Reyes, M., Lachica, M., Caballero, E. and Anguilera, J. E. 1991. Application of the labeled ^{13}C bicarbonate method for estimating energy expenditure of the goats under field conditions. In: Proceeding of the International Symposium on Nuclear and Related Techniques in Animal, International Atomic Energy Agency, FAO, Vienna, pp 150.

Sankhyan S. K., Shinde A. K. and Karim S. A. 1999. Seasonal changes in biomass yield, nutrient intake and its utilization by sheep maintained on community grazing land. Indian Journal of Animal Sciences 69:617-620.

Sankhyan, S.K., Shinde, A.K., Karim, S.A., Mann J.S., Singh, N.P. and Patnayak, B.C. 1996. Plane of nutrition and growth response of lambs and kids maintained on two and three tier silvipasture. Indian Journal of Animal Sciences 66:1194-1197.

Shinde A.K., Karim S.A., Patnayak B.C. and Mann J.S. 1997. Dietary preference and grazing behaviour of sheep on Cenchrus ciliaris pasture. Small Ruminant Research 26: 119-122.

Shinde A. K., Karim S. A., Sankhyan S. K. and Bhatta, R. 1998. Seasonal changes in physiological responses and energy expenditure of sheep maintained on semi-arid pasture Journal of Agriculture Science Cambridge 131: 341-346

Shinde A. K., Sankhyan, S. K. Singh N. P. and Verma D. L. 2005. Soil ingestion and its effect on dry matter intake and digestibility in sheep grazing on native ranges of semiarid region of Rajasthan. Indian Journal of Small Ruminants 11: 37-42.

Shinde, A. K, Bhatta Raghavendra, Sankhyan, S. K. and Verma, D. L. 2002. Effect of season on thermoregulatory responses and energy expenditure of goats on semi arid range in India. Journal of Agricultural Science Cambridge 139: 87-93.

Shinde, A. K., Sankhyan S. K., Karim, S. A., Singh, N. P. and Patnayak, B. C.1996. Nutrient intake, its utilization, and preference of sheep and goats on semiarid *Cenchrus ciliaris* pasture. World Review of Animal Production 31:35-40.

Shinde, A. K., Sankhyan, S. K., Bhatta, R. and Verma, D. L. 2000. Seasonal changes in nutrient intake and its utilization by range goats in a semi-arid region of Indian. Journal of Agricultural Science Cambridge 135:429-436.

Shinde, A. K. and Bhatta, Raghavendra 2002. Nutrition of Sheep and Goat on Pasture. Bulletin, Central Sheep and Wool Research Institute, Avikanagar.

Shinde, A. K. and Karim, S. A. 2007. Energy expenditure of sheep and goat at pasture. Indian Journal of Small Ruminants 13:1-18.

Shinde, A. K. and Karim, S. A. 2009. Screening of pesticide residues in meat and milk samples of sheep maintained in institute and field flocks Indian Journal of Small Ruminants 15: 92-94.

Shinde, A. K. and Sankhyan, S. K. 2009. Feed resources and feeding practices in different agro-climatic zone of Rajasthan In: Feed resources and feeding practices in different agro-eco zones of India (Eds N. K. S. Gowda, D.T. Pal, Rajan Gupta, C.S. Prasad and K.T. Sampath), National Institute of Animal Nutrition and Physiology, Bangalore.

Shinde, A. K., Sankhyan, S. K. and Singh, N. P. 2004. *Tribulus terrestris* poisoning in sheep maintained on community grazing land of semiarid region of Rajasthan. In: New Dimensions of Animal Feeding to Sustain Development and Competitiveness. Proceedings of the V Biennial Conference of Animal Nutrition Association, National Institute of Animal Nutrition and Physiology, Bangalore, 24-26 November.

Shinde, A. K., Sankhyan, S. K., Karim, S. A., Kumar, Ravindra and Singh,V. K. 2006. Mineral Limits of Ruminants in Rajasthan. Bulletin, Central Sheep and Wool Research Institute, Avikanagar.

Silanikove, N. 1984. Renal excretion of urea in response to change in nitrogen intake in desert (Black Bedouin) and non-desert (Swiss Saanen) goats. Comparative Biochemistry and Physiology 79: 651-654.

Silanikove, N. Tagari, H. and Shkolnik, A. 1980. Gross energy digestion and urea recycling in desert Black Bedouin goats. Comparative Biochemistry and Physiology 67: 215-218.

Silanikove, N., Giloba, N., Pervolotsky, A. and Nitsan, Z. 1996. Effect of daily supplementation of polyethylene glycol on intake and digestion of tannin containing leaves (*Quercus calliprinos, Pistacia lenticus* and *Ceratonia siliqua*) by goats. Journal of Agricultural Food Chemistry 44:199-205.

Singh, G. and Karim, S. A. 1995. Change in birth weight of temperate sheep breeds under tropical conditions. World Review of Animal Production 30 (3/4): 55-60.

Singh, M and Acharya, R. M. 1977. A note on the mode of heat dissipation in different types of sheep. Indian Journal of Animal Sciences 47:367-368.

Singh, M., More, T., Rai, A.K. and Karim, S.A. 1982. A note on the adoptability of native and crossbred sheep to hot summer conditions of semi-arid and arid areas. Journal of Agricultural Science Cambridge 99: 525-528.

Singh, M., Rai, A. K., More, T. and Dhaliwal, J. S. 1980. Note on comparative physiological responses of sheep and goats to high ambient temperature. Indian Journal of Animal Sciences 50: 202-205.

Vaithiyanathan, S. and Singh, M. 1984. Seasonal influence on soil ingestion by sheep in arid region. Small Ruminant Research 14: 103-106.

❑❑❑

12

Existing Feed Resources & Feeding Practices of Small Ruminants with Reference to Rajasthan

S.K. Sankhyan* and R. S. Bhatt
Central Sheep and Wool Research Institute, Avikanagar, via Jaipur- 304 501, Rajasthan

Introduction

Rajasthan, the largest state of India (3,42, 653 sq km) situated in the north -western part of the Indian Union (23° 30′ and 30°11′ North latitude and 69° 29′ and 78° 17′ East longitude) is largely arid for most of its parts. Presenting an irregular rhomboid shape, the state has a maximum length of 869 km from west to east and 836 km from north to south. Rajasthan is a predominantly agrarian state with agriculture contributing to about 25- 40 % of the *'States Domestic Product'* and about 70 % of the population engaged in agriculture and allied activities. Rajasthan is the largest producer of mustard, pearl millet, cluster bean, cumin, coriander and isabgol and the second largest producer of oilseeds. The state is also ranked second in the production of gram, barley, castor and kharif pulses and third in soybean and garlic production. It has emerged as an important cotton producing state and holds a share of about 25 % in the total national production of non-metallic minerals. Rajasthan's progressive transformation from a desert land to a prosperous agricultural land is largely due to the development of the Indira Gandhi Canal.

Rajasthan State has been divided in to 9 Agro-Climatic Zones on the basis of climatic conditions and agriculture production systems as follows: Aravalli hills climatically divide the State into two distinct parts. The western side of the hill is severally influenced by desertic conditions with an average rainfall of 360 mm. The eastern side is relatively better with semi-arid conditions with an average rain fall of 874 mm. State's 40 % area is arid, 21 % between arid and semi-arid, 20 % semi-arid, 9 % sub-humid and 10 % humid zones. Agro-climatic zones IA, IB, IIA and IIB fall under the arid region. These regions form the *'Great Indian Thar Desert'* comprising 13 districts and covering 58.28 % of the total area and 41.34 % of the total human population of the state. The IIIA, IIIB, IVA, IVB and V Zones fall under the semi-arid region cover 41.72 % of the total area of the state and consists of 19 of the 32 districts in the State viz. Ajmer, Alwar, Banswara, Baran, Bharatpur, Bhilwara, Bundi, Chittaurgarh, Dausa, Dhaulpur, Dungarpur, Jaipur, Jhalawar, Karauli, Kota, Rajsamand, Sawaimadhopur, Tonk and Udaipur.

Livestock sector is an important source of income for small farmers' families who are generally constrained due to non-availability of surplus land for cultivation. This sector also acts as a cushion in substantiating the farmers' livelihood during financial distress. The role of small ruminants is more pronounced in the arid and semi-arid zone of country, where the risk and uncertainty of crop failure is high due to low availability of water and frequent natural vagaries like drought. Sheep is well adapted to arid and semi-arid regions even under scarce water and fodder availability conditions. They act as a means of asset retention with high liquidity and help in absorbing unemployed family labour (Suresh et al., 2007). Low and irregular rainfall and lack of irrigation facilities compels the farmers of arid regions to diversify from crop to livestock production to counter the risk of crop failure. Knowledge about the land holding pattern and its utilization as well as livestock feeding practices is an important prerequisite to motivate the farmers for adopting animal nutrition related technologies for improving the livestock production. It is therefore felt that there is an acute need of documentary evidence of prevalent feeding practices followed in the farmers' field in the different regions of semi arid region. It is also essential to have information on feed resource availability, their chemical composition, mineral composition and feeding pattern and practices of livestock in semi-arid region of Rajasthan. This information will help in alteration or intervention in feeding pattern of different categories of livestock to optimize production as well as harvesting maximum benefit from every penny spent on their maintenance.

Requirement of DM and nutrients of sheep and goats in the country

The small ruminant population in India is 190.million (32 % sheep and 68 % goats). Population data for small ruminants showed a 10% increase during the last 20 years with higher figure in the more arid regions. Almost 2/3 of the Indian sheep and goat population is distributed on 40 % of the total geographical areas, which includes forest, permanent pasture, cultivable and uncultivable waste and follow lands for grazing in the country. These lands are unfit for cultivation and are thus utilized for grazing by all kinds of livestock. It is often defined as extensive area mostly under natural vegetation. There has been 13% decline in grazing areas during the last 20 years because more and more areas have been gradually brought under crop cultivation. On the other hand livestock population has increased which has resulted in overgrazing and deterioration of forage from land (Singh and Ramchandra, (2004). The 9.86 m ACU accounts to about 3 % of total range managed livestock species consuming 10 % DM resources of the country (Table 1). It is established that range managed sheep on an average require 0.4 MT DM/head/year thus the total requirement of the two species will be 19.71 m MT. Ranjhan (1997) calculated the total feed availability of the country to be 387.9 m MT crop residues 573.5 m MT green fodder and 35.7 m MT concentrate ingredients indicating deficit of 40, 25 and 47 %, respectively for these items. Ramachandra et al. (2001), based on the livestock population of the year 2000, calculated that the feed and fodder requirements of the country were 950 m MT of fry fodder and 1135 m MT of green fodder as against the availability of 450 and 320 m MT, indicating a deficit of 53 and 72 %, respectively. Moreover the total concentrate feed production in organized feed manufacturing sector is 5 m MT as against the demand of 42 m MT.

Table 1. Potential availability of coarse straws at the national level over the years ('000 tonnes)

Coarse straw	1985 – 86	1990 – 91	1995 – 96	1999 – 00
Jowar	25492.50	29203.00	23317.80	22156.80
Bajra	9160.00	17232.50	13452.30	14143.50
Maize	16610.00	22404.30	23835.00	28681.80
Barley	2011.82	2134.96	1965.21	1874.31
Small Millets	3042.50	2975.00	1947.00	1603.80
Sugarcane tops	42662.00	60261.40	70274.90	74759.10

Since the livestock population of the country is not only surviving but also providing sustenance level of production for meeting the farmer's requirements, it is apparent that while calculating feed resource availability, the rangeland and top feed resources were not given due weightage. The fact remains that in critical semi-arid and arid region of the country, these two feed resources serve as a backbone for sheep feeding and rearing.

Major feed and fodder available in the semi-arid region of Rajasthan

Major types of feed and fodder in different agro-climatic zones of semi-arid Rajasthan are green and dry fodder, cereal straws, stovers, grazing resources, tree leaves and concentrate mixtures.

Fodder crops

Fodder cultivation in the region is area specific and based on the livestock requirement. Small farmers generally do not cultivate any green fodder due to small landholdings and irrigation facilities. However, large farmers grow lucerne and berseem in Rabi season and sorghum, maize and bajra in Kharif and Zaid seasons. Fodder crops are cultivated in large scale in adjoining areas of Haryana, Punjab and Uttar Pradesh . The green fodder availability from different crops in different agro-climatic zones is given in Table 2.

Table 2. Availability of fodder crops (in tons) in different agro-climatic zones of semi-Rajasthan

Crop	Agro-climatic zone IIIA	Agro-climatic zone IIIB	Agro-climatic zone IVA	Agro-climatic zone IVB	Agro-climatic zone V
Sorghum	487035	1698075	737775	27405	982755
Pearl millet	246605	9990	28046	2997	2109
Maize	6840	630	9540	4260	840
Lucerne	1446955	175270	1051535	64175	639965
Berseem	-	38000	47440	2960	30880
Total	**2187435**	**1921965**	**1874336**	**101797**	**1656549**

Cereal and legume straws

Wheat, mustard, gram, barley, taramira, jeera and linseed straws during Rabi and maize, sorghum, pearl millet, green gram, black gram, sesame, ground nut, cluster bean, moth and cowpea straws during Kharif are the major straws for feeding of livestock. Annual straw production from various cereal and legume crops was worked out by the grain: straw ratio. The total straw production of the Agro-climatic zone IIIA, IIIB, IVA and V during kharif and rabi season was worked out to 12748967, 10301665, 5638401, 1822592 and 7294100 tons (Table 3).

Table 3. Straw production (tons) from major crops grown in different agro-climatic zones of semi-arid Rajasthan

Agro-climatic zone	Agro-climatic zone IIIA	Agro-climatic zone IIIB	Agro-climatic zone IVA	Agro-climatic zone IVB	Agro-climatic zone V
		Kharif			
Maize	304503	41880	3528723	1114146	909045
Sorghum	4465310	262140	282620	6820	657325
Pearl millet	4188456	4035952	21412	1356	814904
Green gram	134485	125	10059	93	1080
Black gram	25268	273	38509	19377	40701
Ground-nut	202522	4806	142134	464	14854
Cluster bean	503850	187590	118176	29130	26004
Paddy	156	19160	23468	131512	88180
Moth	1449	60	15	9	25
Cowpea	33252	306	3468	264	456
Sugar cane	3761	15634	12523	5106	10364
Sesame	54820	14780	71972	4080	68984
Soya bean	73	-	367590	31468	1260212
		Rabi			
Wheat	1836594	3139896	742310	426126	1628736
Barley	167189	50185	29634	4300	8347
Linseed	399	8	875	50	2443
Gram	124433	166937	86837	46737	108789
Mustard	678054	2356533	150195	1407	1649040
Rape seed	24393	5400	7881	147	4611
Total	**12748967**	**10301665**	**5638401**	**1822592**	**7294100**

Source: *Shinde et al. (2006)*

Grazing lands

The availability of dry biomass to grazing animals in Agro-climatic zone IIIA, IIIB, IVA and V during the year was worked out to 3-4qDM/ha.

Concentrate ingredients/ mixtures

For calculation of availability, milling data was used. It was: bran 10% of the grain production, broken grain/ polishing/ chunnies -5% of the 95% grain production, oil cakes -35% of seed yield, whole grain feed -5% of production, the dry matter content of grain being considered as 95%. The total availability of concentrate grains and cakes in the Agro-climatic zone IIIA, IIIB, IVA and V during the year for the livestock species was worked out to 2.44, 0.27, 0.20, 0.13 and 0.33 million tons, respectively.

Important fodder trees

The land less sheep and goat farmers pay Rs40-60 per tree to farmers having fodder trees in their fellow or cultivated land for feeding to animal during scarcity period in semi arid region of Rajasthan. During scarcity months when ground vegetation is all most depleted tree leaves constituted about 90 % of the diet of the sheep and goats. The green fodder yield of common fodder trees found in semi arid region of Rajasthan was worked out to *Acacia nilotica* 35, *Acacia Senegal* 10, *Acacia tortalis* 45, *Albizia lebbek* 45, *Ailanthus execlsa* 60, *Azadirachta indica* 60, *Prosopis cineraria* 36, *Gymnosporia spinosa*15, *Bauhunia recemosa* 28, *Ficus bengalensis* 240 and *Ficus religiosa* 210kg/tree (Karim, 2006).

Actual assessed requirement, availability and deficiency/ excess of feed and fodder in different zones of semiarid region of Rajasthan

The total annual requirement of concentrate for the livestock species in agro-climatic zone IIIA, IIIB, IVA, IVB and V during the year was worked out to 1.24, 0.92, 1.24, 0.53 and 1.02 million tons; green fodder 8.67, 6.49, 8.67, 3.74 and 7.15 million tons and dry fodder 6.19, 4.63, 6.19, 2.67 and 5.11 million tons. However, the availability of concentrate in the agro-climatic zone IIIA, IIIB, IVA, IVB and V was 2.44, 0.27, 0.20, 0.13 and 0.33 million tons; green fodder 2.18, 1.92, 1.87, 0.10 and 1.65 million tons and dry fodder 11.99, 7.92, 5.40, 1.81 and 5.57 million tons. Overall deficiency of concentrate mixture for the livestock species in the agro-climatic zone IIIA, IIIB, IVA and V was -0.99, -0.65, -1.04, -0.40 and -0.69 million tons; green fodder was -6.48, -4.57, -6.80, -3.64 and -5.49. The dry fodder was available in sufficient quantity in agro-climatic zone IIIA, IIIB and V and was found deficient in agro-climatic zone IVA and IVB (Table 4).

Table 4. Requirement, availability and deficiency/ excess of feed and fodder in different agro-climatic zones of semi-arid Rajasthan (In million tons)

	Agro climatic zones IIIA	**Agro climatic zones IIIB**	**Agro climatic zones IVA**	**Agro climatic zones IVB**	**Agro climatic zones V**
Requirement					
Concentrate feed	1.24	0.92	1.24	0.53	1.02
Green fodder	8.67	6.49	8.67	3.74	7.15
Dry fodder	6.19	4.63	6.19	2.67	5.11

Contd...

Available					
Concentrate feed	2.44	0.27	0.20	0.13	0.33
Green fodder	2.18	1.92	1.87	0.10	1.65
Dry fodder	11.99	7.92	5.40	1.81	5.57
Deficient/excess					
Concentrate feed	1.20	-0.65	-1.04	-0.40	-0.69
Green fodder	-6.48	-4.57	-6.80	-3.64	-5.49
Dry fodder	5.79	3.28	-0.79	-0.85	0.46

Livestock Production Systems

Migration and transhumance are the way of sheep rearing in desert and hilly tracts of country. About 70-80% of sheep flocks are managed on migratory system in the country. In spite of advancement of agriculture and shrinkage of fallow land, this system is still in existing as a prime system for sheep rearing. In very few cases nomadic system has changed to settle life. Nomadic and transhumance system offer the best possible productive system for the use of fragile ecosystems of the arid and semiarid region. The topography, feed resources and social compulsion are some of the factor responsible for prevalent of nomadic system. The compulsions are low and erratic rainfall, frequent drought, low crop production and socio-economic condition of people in arid and semiarid regions. Sheep in migration are grazed on uncultivated and marginal land of dry zone followed by fallow land in good rainfall areas of neighboring states. Sheep on migration are exposed to new vegetation as frequent change of place often provide them wide variety of vegetation, rich in vitamins, minerals and other nutrients that help them to meet their requirement and improve the production (Singh and Shinde, 2006).

Migration system in dry areas

Migration is traditional practices to sustain sheep from vagaries of feed scarcity in desert areas. About 70% of sheep population remains on permanent, seasonal or temporary migration in Rajasthan. In temporary migration, sheep begin to move on migration after October and return to their home at the onset of monsoon. Sheep from the border districts of Rajasthan are maintained under permanent migration for the whole year. At the onset of monsoon these animals return to hilly areas and forest areas. Large population of sheep from Rajkot, Kutch, Jamnagar, Bhavnagar, Banaskantha and Surendranagar migrate to middle and south districts of Gujarat after October-November. Allocation of area for grazing is decided by group leader of shepherd and sarpanch to avoid the overcrowding. Animals are allowed for grazing on payment basis. Quite often payment is made in term of kind instead of cash.

Semi-arid eastern plain

The districts fall under agro-climatic zone IIIA are Ajmer, Tonk, Jaipur and Dausa. Total numbers of livestock species in the IIIA zone are: cattle 1.40 million, buffaloes 1.68 million, sheep 1.42 million and goats 1.75 million. Cattle contribute 0.479 million ton of milk in the region. Buffaloes contribute 0.889 million ton of milk and 20.21million kg of meat. Sheep contribute 1.74 million kg of wool and 4.53million kg of meat. Though sheep contributes small quantity of milk but constitute an important portion of dietary requirement of shepherds. Goats contribute 0.132 ton of milk and 6.47 million kg of meat. In addition to milk, cattle bullocks contribute sizably as draught power used in agriculture operation. Sheep and goats on the other hand are maintained on community land alone and fed tree foliage during winter and summer depending upon the availability with the farmers. They are also taken to short distance migration during summer months. The average wool yield of Malpura breed is although low but they are excellent meat producing animals. They are also known for their better milk yield and mothering ability. Kheri on the other hand are preferred for their better wool quality and better migration ability. Most of goat population in the region is Sirohi and their crosses. Sirohi is well known breed of goats yield 800-900g of milk daily. Kids attained body of 12-13 kg at 3 months and 22-24 kg at 6 months of age. Sheep and goats are sold in the local market on per head basis rather than live weight basis. In majority cases, middlemen procure the animals from villages and take them to Dehli market on weekend. The average rate of procurement of animals, if expressed on live weight basis, comes to Rs 35-40/ kg. Wool is sold either on per head basis to the shearer (who includes the cost of shearing at the rate of Rs 4-5 per sheep) or in the Wool Mandi at the rate of Rs 40-50/ kg. The major constraints faced by farmers in the region are scarcity of feed and fodder (due to decline of areas under grazing land) low or erratic rainfall, reproductive disorders in buffaloes, heavy mortality due to PPR in sheep and goat flocks and inadequate price offered by the middlemen for animal produce (Sankhyan et al., 2008).

Flood Prone Eastern Plain

The districts falls under agro-climatic zone IIIB are Alwar, Karoli, Bharatpur and Dholpur. Total numbers of livestock species are: cattle 0.543 million, buffalo 1.88 million, sheep 0.257 million and goats 0.957 million. Cattle contribute 0.148 million ton of milk in the region. Buffaloes contribute 0.785million ton of milk and 22.62 million kg of meat. Sheep contribute 2.27 million kg of wool and 0.821million kg of meat. Sheep contributes small quantity of milk and mostly used in the family. Goats contribute 0.061 ton of milk and 3.53 million kg of meat. Most of sheep in the region are non-descript. The average wool yield although is low but they are excellent meat producing animals. Most of goat population in the region is non-descript and crosses of Jamunapari and Barbari goats. They yield on an average 1 kg of milk daily. Kids attain body of 10-12 kg at 3 and 20-22 kg at 6 months of age. Barbari kids are relatively lower in body weights at 3 and 6 months of age. Jakharana goats, a well known breed found in Jakhrana village of Alwar district of Rajasthan, yield 1.0-1.5 kg milk daily and 10-15% twining in the flocks. Sheep and goats are sold in the local market on per head basis rather than live weight basis. In majority cases, middlemen procure the animals from them villages and take them to Agra market on weekend. However, the average rate of procurement, expressed on live weight basis, comes to Rs 30-40/ kg. Wool produced by the sheep is poor in quality and sold either on per head basis to the shearers (which include the cost of shearing at the rate of Rs 4-5 per sheep) or in the Wool Mandi at the rate of Rs 18-20/ kg. The major constraints faced by farmers in the region are scarcity of feed and fodder during summer period, reproductive disorders (particularly anoestrus and prolapsed of uterus in buffaloes), incidence of PPR and other infectious diseases in sheep and goat flocks and inadequate price offered by the middlemen for animal produce.

Sub-Humid Southern Plain and Aravali Hills

The districts falls under agro-climatic zone IIIB are Udaipur, Chittorgarh, Rajsamund and Bhilwara. Total numbers of livestock species are: cattle 2.65 million, buffaloes 1.45 million, sheep 1.44 million and goats 2.52 million. Cattle contribute 0.227 million ton of milk in the region. Buffaloes contribute 0.388 million ton of milk and 17.43 million kg of meat. Sheep contribute 1.38 million kg of wool and 4.61 million kg of meat. Sheep contributes small quantity of milk. Goats contribute 0.096 ton of milk and 9.32 million kg of meat. Bullock population is negligible and tractors are used in most of the agricultural operations. Sheep population in the region is non-descript type. The average wool yield although is low but they are excellent meat producing animals. Most of goat population in the region is also non- descript. They yield 400-500g of milk daily. Kids attained body weight of 10-12kg at 3 month of age and 18-20kg at 6 months of age. Sheep and goats are sold in the local market on per head basis rather than live weight basis. In majority cases, middleman procures the animals from villages and takes them to Mandi. However the average rate of procurement if expressed on live weight basis, comes to Rs 35-40 a kg. Wool produced by the sheep is of poor quality and sold either on per head basis to Shearer's, which include the cost of shearing at the rate of Rs 4-5 per sheep or sold in the Wool Mandi at the rate of Rs 30-40 a kg. Major constraints faced by farmers in the region are scarcity of feed and fodder during summer period, worm load and other infectious diseases in sheep and goat flocks and scarcity of balanced feed for high yielding crossbred cows.

Humid Southern Plain

The districts falling under the agro-climatic zone IV B are Dungarpur and Banswara. The total numbers of livestock species are: cattle 0.9812 million; buffaloes 0.3033 million; sheep 0.1574 million; and goats 0.7322 million. Cattle contribute 0.055 million ton of milk in the region. Buffaloes contribute 0.115 million tons of milk and 4.83 million tons of meat in the region. Goats contribute 0.16 ton of milk and 2.3 million kg of meat. In addition to milk, cattle bullocks contribute sizably as draught power used in agricultural operations. Most of goat population in the region is non-descript yielding 300-400g of milk daily. Kids attain body of 9-10 kg at 3 month and 13-14 kg at 6 months of age. Sheep and goats are sold in the local market on per head basis rather than live weight basis. In majority of the cases, the middlemen procure the animals from villages and take them to market on weekend. The average rate of procurement, expressed on live weight basis, comes to Rs 25-35/ kg. The major constraint faced by farmers in the region is their poor socio-economic status as most of them belong to tribes and having no access to newer technologies. They maintain their animals on natural resources in forest areas under the traditional system.

Humid southern eastern plain

The districts falling under agro-climatic zone V are Sawai Madhopur, Kota, Bundi, Baran and Jhalawad. The total number of livestock species are: cattle 1.62 million, buffaloes 1.04 million, sheep 0.228 million and goats 1.17 million. Cattle contribute 0.177 million ton of milk in the region. Buffaloes contribute 4.16 million ton of milk and 11.43 million kg million kg of meat. Sheep contributes 2.47million kg of wool and 5.50 million kg meat. Sheep milk is utilized by shepherds for their own use. Goats contribute 0.069 ton of milk and 10.56 million kg of meat. Most common breed of sheep in the region is non-descript and crosses of Marwari and Jaiselmeri. The average wool yield of sheep is 1.4-1.6kg but they are excellent meat producing breed. Most of goat population in the region is non-descript. They yield 500-600g of milk daily. Kids attained body of 12-13kg at 3 month of age and 15-17kg at 6 months of age. Most of milk is sold through dairy cooperatives and also by private vendors. Sheep and goats are sold in the local market on per head basis rather than live weight basis. In majority cases, middleman procures the animals from villages and takes them to market on weakened. However the average rate of procurement if expressed on live weight basis, comes to

Rs 35-40 a kg. Wool is sold either on per head basis to Shearer, which includes the cost of shearing at the rate of Rs 4-5 per sheep or sold in the Wool Mandi at the rate of Rs 20-22 a kg. The major constraints faced by farmers in the region are scarcity of feed and fodder (due to declining area under grazing land and low rainfall) reproductive disorders in buffaloes, heavy tolls of mortality (due to PPR and other related diseases in sheep and goat flocks) and inadequate price offered by the middlemen for animal produce.

Feeding practices for sheep and goats

In the semi-arid region of Rajasthan sheep are exclusively maintained on dry feed resources. No concentrate mixture is supplemented to them in any stage. These animals gather nearly 850 to 1100g dry matter from the community grazing areas and nearly 200 to 250g dry fodder is being supplemented to all categories of ewes depending upon the availability and economic status of the farmer. No concentrate mixture is being supplemented to ewes in any of the critical physiological stage in the semi arid region of Rajasthan (Fig 1).

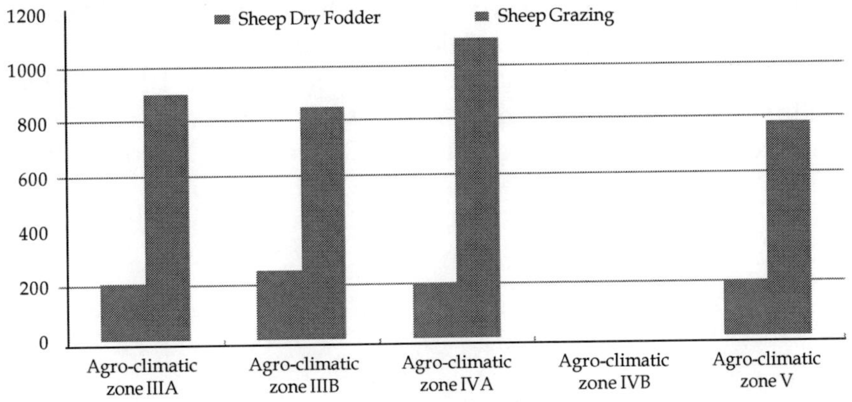

Fig. 1. Feed and fodder fed (g) to sheep in different agro-climatic zones of semiarid region of Rajasthan

As compared to sheep goats are better fed animals during pregnancy and lactation does are supplemented 200 to 250 g concentrate mixture of sole grain after grazing to have better milk production. Dry fodder at the rate of 300 to 400 g is also supplemented and it has been observed that goats generally collect 600 to 900g browsing material from grazing area. Goat kids are also well fed (Fig.2)

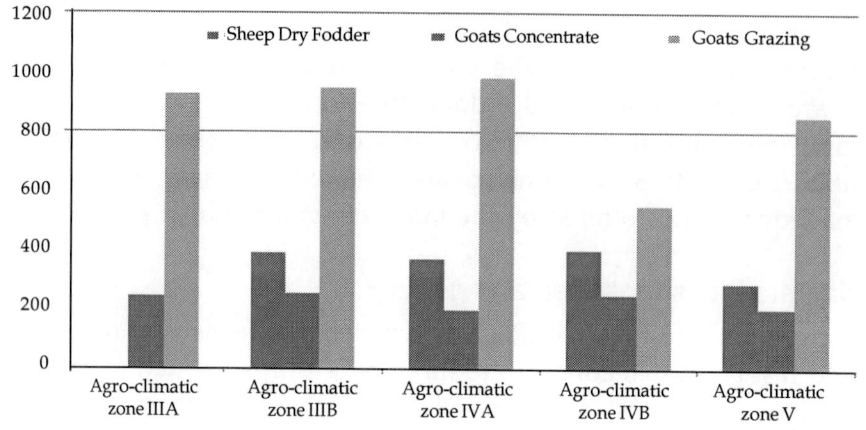

Fig. 2.Feed and fodder fed (g) to goat in different agro-climatic zones of semi-arid region of Rajasthan

Intake of essential nutrients by small ruminants in different zones

Nutrient intake by sheep

Nutrient intake of sheep in different agro-climatic zone of semi-arid region of Rajasthan has also been worked out. It has been found that DM requirement of sheep is generally not met under prevailing conditions. As against to requirement of 1.3kg DM/d they could only get 800g to 1 kg/ day and least availability is in agro-climatic zone V. It has been observed that sheep are not kept in agro-climatic zone IVB. Similarly, DCP and TDN requirement is also not met in any of the climatic zones (Fig. 3 and Table 5).

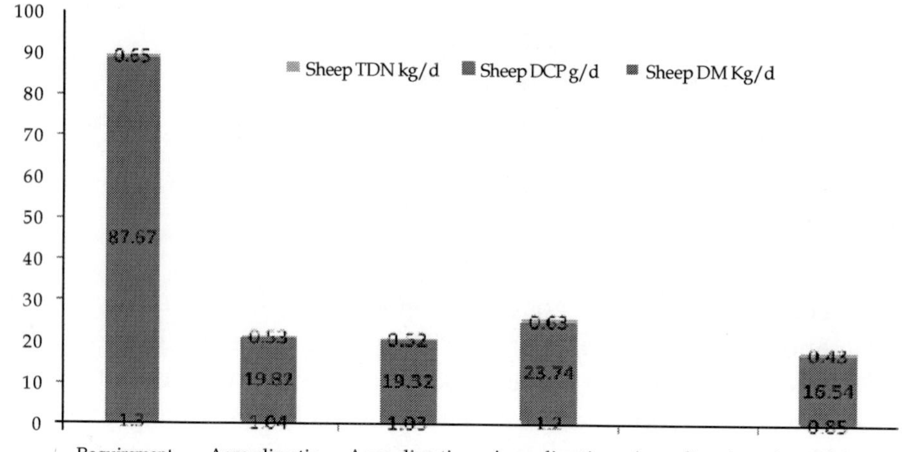

Fig. 3. Nutrient intake by sheep in different agro-climatic zones of semi-arid Rajasthan

Table 5. Nutrient intake of sheep in different agro-climatic zones of semi-arid Rajasthan

	Requirement*	Agro-climatic zone IIIA	Agro-climatic zone IIIB	Agro-climatic zone IVA	Agro-climatic zone IVB	Agro-climatic zone V
Lambs						
DM kg/day	0.340	0.510	0.270	0.240		0.240
DCP g/day	37.00	41.99	30.96	26.24		26.24
TDN kg/day	0.220	0.290	0.170	0.150		0.150
Adult sheep						
DM kg/day	0.775	1.010	0.820	0.700		0.750
DCP g/day	38	18.75	14.22	14.00		15.00
TDN kg/day	0.350	0.510	0.400	0.360		0.390
Pregnant						
DM kg/day	1.440	1.210	1.260	1.400		0.900
DCP g/day	105	22.71	23.75	26.62		16.62
TDN kg/day	0.750	0.610	0.640	0.710		0.450
Lactating						
DM kg/day	1.580	0.900	1.000	1.600		0.900
DCP g/day	120	18.00	20.00	30.62		18.00
TDN kg/day	0.855	0.47	0.52	0.820		0.470

*Kearl, (1982)

Nutrient intake by goats

Although goats are supplemented concentrate and dry roughage in the coral after grazing during evening hours but data revealed that the nutrient requirement of these animals for DM, DCP and TDN are not met in any of the climatic zone. As against the requirement half of the nutrient supply is received by these animals indicating poor production under field condition (Fig.4 and Table 6).

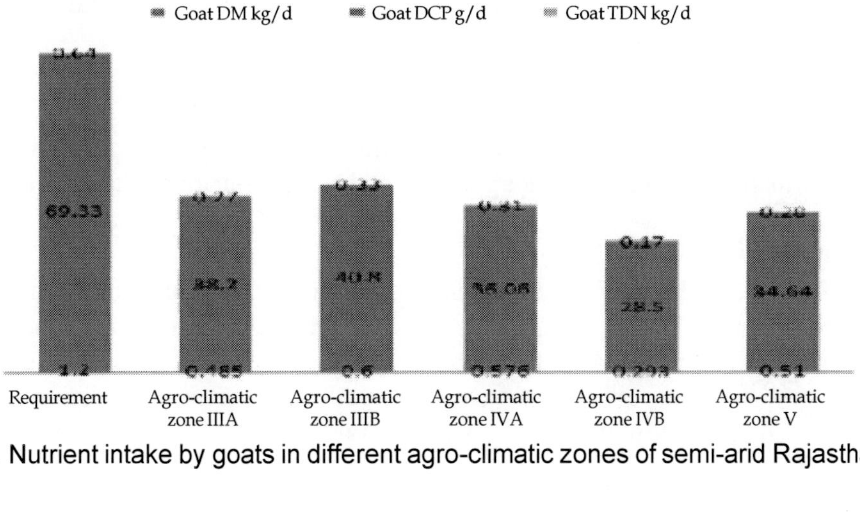

Fig.4. Nutrient intake by goats in different agro-climatic zones of semi-arid Rajasthan

Table 6. Nutrient intake by goats in different agro-climatic zones of semi-arid Rajasthan

	Requirement*	Agro-climatic zone IIIA	Agro-climatic zone IIIB	Agro-climatic zone IVA	Agro-climatic zone IVB	Agro-climatic zone V
Kids						
DM kg/day	0.645	0.370	0.350	0.260	0.192	0.260
DCP g/day	43.00	30.28	16.86	11.61	9.05	11.61
TDN kg/day	0.420	0.210	0.170	0.130	0.120	0.130
Adult						
DM kg/day	0.830	0.390	0.650	0.630	0.300	0.530
DCP g/day	39.00	23.10	23.24	23.02	19.67	20.03
TDN kg/day	0.400	0.200	0.310	0.300	0.175	0.260
Pregnant						
DM kg/day	1.320	0.510	0.650	0.550	0.301	0.530
DCP g/day	80.00	41.99	56.80	40.57	26.76	43.20
TDN kg/day	0.725	0.290	0.380	0.330	0.145	0.300
Lactating						
DM kg/day	1.470	0.550	0.500	0.550	0.280	0.480
DCP g/day	89.00	49.51	42.37	44.61	39.08	40.69
TDN kg/day	0.795	0.320	0.290	0.310	0.189	0.280

*Kearl, (1982)

There is an urgent need to maintain stable grazing resources throughout the year for sustainable small ruminant production. This can be done by two ways: (a) land under grazing should be rehabilitated by perennial greases and trees, and (b) unproductive and low yielding animals should be slowly removed from land to reduce pressure on grazing land and spare available resources for animals to optimize production from them

Productivity improvement strategies for small ruminants

The common strategies for supplementation of limiting nutrients for improving productivity of Sheep and goats in semi-arid of Rajasthan are:

Supplementary feeding

Most of the sheep and goat flocks in the region are maintained on grazing resources alone. The grazing lands in the region are deteriorating at a very rapid rate and also in quality forage. The sheep and goats experienced shortage of forage for most part of the year especially during summer months. The supplementary feeding of concentrate mixture or dried or green leaves or legume straws be followed during this period to avoid any nutrition stress and production losses.

Rehabilitation of grazing lands

Most of barren, uncultivated, wasteland and pasturelands are in the state of severe deterioration. The biomass yield of these lands in round the year basis lies below 3-4qDM/ha and cannot sustain even 1ACU. These grazing lands be rehabilitated by perennial grasses viz., *Cenchrus ciliaris* and *Lasiurus sindicus* to improve forage and also extend its availability for longer periods. These lands be brought under silvi-pasture establishment for enhancing quality vegetation to animals even in lean period and also for eco-conservation.

Fodder banks at Village level

The scarcity of feed and fodder is common feature in the region for animals. Seasonal fluctuation with adequacy during monsoon season and deficiency in summer compels the farmers to sell their animals or to migrate to neighboring states. The situation becomes worst during drought and famine condition. The development of fodder bank where surplus fodder can be conserved and stored for supplying to farmers on nominal price during scarcity period may serve the purpose of bridging the gap between the demand and availability of fodder.

Conservation of monsoon grasses

Native and sown grasses ensure better feed and fodder during monsoon season; these grasses are not properly utilized in feeding of animals and deteriorate in quality with the progress of season. These grasses be conserved in form of hay or silage depending upon the type of grasses and legumes for feeding of animals during scarcity period.

References

Karim, S. A. 2006. Livestock feeding in Rajasthan In: Livestock Feeding Strategies for dry regions. (Eds P.S.Pathak and S.S. Kundu) International Book Distributing Co. Lucknow pp 429-450

Kearl, L.C. 1982. Nutrient Requirement of Ruminants for Developing Counties. International Feedstuffs Institute, Utah Agricultural Station, Logan, U.S.A.

Ranjhan, S. K. 1997. Problems and prospective of animal nutrition research in India in twenty first century. Platinum Jubilee Lectures, Center of Advance Studies, IVRI, Izzatnagar, India.

Ramachandra, K. S., Anandan, S. and Raju, S. S. 2001. Livestock feed resources availability in India and need for national data base. Emerging Nutritional Technologies for

Sustainable Animal Production and Environmental Protection, Proceedings Xth Animal Nutrition Conference, NDRI, Karnal, 9- 11 November, pp. 134- 144.

Sankhyan, S.K., Shinde, A.K. and Karim, S.A. 2008. Existing Feed resources and feeding practices of livestock in semi arid region of Rajasthan. Central Sheep and Wool Research Institute, Avikanagar, pp. 1-85

Shinde, A.K., Sankhyan, S.K., Karim, S.A., Kumar, R. and Singh, V.K. 2006. Mineral Limits of Ruminants in Rajasthan. Central Sheep and Wool Research Institute, Avikanagar, pp. 1-55

Singh, K and Ramachandra, K.S. 2004. Feed and fodder availability, requirement and strategy for meeting the shortage in different regions for small ruminants. In: Proceedings of the National Seminar on Opportunities and Challenges in Nutrition and Feeding Management of Sheep, Goats and Rabbits for Sustainable Production. Central Sheep and Wool Research Institute, Avikanagar, Rajasthan, February 10-12, pp.1-19.

Singh, V. K. and Shinde, A. K. 2006. Livestock raising in arid and semi-arid zones. In: Livestock Feeding Strategies for dry regions. (Eds P. S. Pathak and S.S. Kundu) International Book Distributing Co. Lucknow, pp. 119-139

Suresh, A., Gupta, D. C., Mann, J.S. and Singh, V.K. 2007. *Sheep production in semi arid zones- management and economics* (Research Bulletin). Central Sheep and Wool Research Institute, Avikanagar.

❑❑❑

13

Shelter Management for Sheep and Goats for Mitigating Climatic Stress

R.P. Misra*, S.P. Singh and N. Ramachandran
Physiology, Reproduction and Shelter Management Division
Central Institute for Research on Goats, Makhdoom, Farah, Mathura- 281 122, Uttar Pradesh

Introduction

India, sheep and goat farming is practiced by the people who are socio-economically weak and their level of management is based on traditionalism. Sheep and Goats constitute a very important species of livestock in our country, mainly on account of the short generation intervals, higher rate of prolificacy and the ease with which the goats as well as their products can be marketed. All livestock need protection from climatic extremes even in moderate climatic regions, primarily to insure survival of animals for continued production and reproduction. Housing is considered essential for intensive animal production in both hot and cold environments, but the most suitable structures are largely dependent upon the local situations. For example, shades for dry areas should be high and oriented to take advantage of radiation reflected to the cool sky, whereas; in humid areas, and particularly where cumulus clouds are frequent, shades should be as low as possible. This minimum height must be modified as is required by sanitation considerations. In most situations, locally available materials can be used effectively to reduce construction costs. Layers of straw or thatch can, for instance, prove superior to reflective metal roofs as materials for shades in some situations. In determining the housing requirements best suited to local conditions, diurnal variations in temperature, humidity, velocity, direction of wind and solar radiation should be considered. Various part of our country has a climate with hot and dry summer as well as very cool winter season. Sheep and goat farmers have to deal with high as well as low temperatures and with their effects on animal production. In these regions livestock are commonly exposed to high and low temperatures for long periods. It is necessary to develop strategies for the development of shelter to protect animals from the effects of such conditions.

Present status of shelters for small ruminants

In India, as not much of attention is paid so far to the importance of shelter, we find different types of goat and sheep houses constructed without careful planning and designing. Housing instinct is widely prevalent in the animal kingdom and small ruminants are no exception. Since the species have lived in diverse macro-climates of the Indian subcontinent they have exhibited remarkable ability to adapt varying climatic conditions. This, however, does not necessarily mean that small ruminants will not be benefited from the optimum housing, particularly under intensive system of management (Borut et al., 1979). The cost of construction of small ruminant houses is one of the important economic factors even in time to come. In order to invent or select protective shelters or devices wisely, basic knowledge needed for

- An evaluation of the climatic environments to which an animal may be exposed.
- The relative importance of various climatic factors to the physiological reaction being considered.
- The quantity of heat that an animal must dissipate in order to attain the desired productive or reproductive goals.
- The effectiveness with which an animal can dissipate its heat by each of the avenues of heat transfer- convection, radiation, evaporation and conduction.
- Knowledge of heat transfer processes and the effectiveness of various media of heat transfer.
- Knowledge of material including an appreciation of the costs and complexity of providing and operating them.

The modern housing systems, as well as the development of intensive animal production, have gained the attention of scientists on the effects of microclimate inside the animal houses, the management practices and animal welfare. In specialized dairy sheep flocks, housing systems may offer improved welfare and health of livestock by protecting animals from heat or cold stress and by supplying adequate feeding (Brosh et al., 1998). Many factors, such as the possibility of free access to external areas (Casamassima et al., 2001), the protection from thermal extremes (Sevi et al., 2001) the sufficient space allocation, careful control of indoor climate and hygiene (Hartung, 1994), proper ventilation and light regimes can markedly improve the health and welfare of housed sheep. Goats are sensitive to cold and heat stress and all reasonable steps should be taken to minimize the effects of climatic extremes and other factors that produce either cold stress or heat stress in goats. Goats are vulnerable to cold stress, especially off shears or in low body condition, and require the provision of permanent shelter or good natural shelter.

Importance of shelters for small ruminants

It is generally believed that small ruminants do not require housing. In fact, like other domestic animals, small ruminants also need shelter for protection from inclement weather such as rains (in particular), peak cold days during winter and excessive heat load during summer. Separate housing arrangements for different categories of animals viz. growers, pregnant females, lactating females, breeding males, etc. are to be ensured for feeding them as per requirement. Weather is a constraint on efficient livestock production systems. Evaluation of the degree of constraint is a difficult, but necessary task before selection of appropriate modifications in management or environments can be made. The climatic environment can impair performance of animals susceptible to adverse weather conditions because of such factors as age, genetic makeup or production level. When animals are subjected to extreme cold stress, substantial dietary energy may be diverted from productive functions to the generation of body heat. Failure to produce sufficient heat can result in death. More often, however, cold stress leads to the development of secondary changes and possibly disease. With prolonged exposure to even mildly cold conditions, physiological adaptation occurs in animals resulting in increases in thermal insulation, appetite and basal metabolic intensity, as well as alterations in digestive functions. Much of the reduced productivity, and in particular the reduced nutritional efficiency, observed in ruminant production systems during the colder part of the year, can be accounted for by these adaptive changes. While the provision of shelter during inclement weather may reduce disease, animal losses or loss of productivity, the economic advantages are not always evident or appropriately assigned. The optimum type and extent of animal shelter depends upon climatic conditions, construction and operating costs, and potential direct and indirect influences on the animals. In cold environments the heat from maintenance and productive processes may be of considerable value in maintaining body temperature, thus avoiding shivering or other cold induced thermogenic processes. Conversely, in a hot environment, thermoregulatory mechanisms may be needed to eliminate excess body heat. Heat from the so-called maintenance processes of a producing animal may be elevated relative to that of a non-producing animal because of increased vital functions, activity and overall total requirements (Canas et al., 1982). Provision of shed during intense sunshine to sheep and goat reduces the heat load of these animals (Abdel et al., 1998) and reduces the adverse effect of heat stress. Sheep having access to shed show better growth rate, feed conversion efficiency and improved fertility than control one (Davis et al., 1994). The physiological responses viz., respiration rate and heart rate were lower in shaded and nutritionally restricted or ad lib feeding sheep than exposure in sun. Heat stress during pregnancy also significantly affects the growth rate of the fetus and therefore provision of shed has been recommended during this period (Stephenson et al., 1980).

Goats and sheep can tolerate a wide range of temperatures but should be protected from wind and rain. However, a long period of high ambient temperatures inhibits reproduction. Heat stress also reduces lambing percentage, decreases the incidence of twinning, and decreases the birth weight of lambs. When temperatures are below 7°C at breeding time, ewes show improved reproductive efficiency. Goats and Sheep are affected by temperature, humidity and rain. In hot climates, goats need shelter from intense heat during the day. In humid areas they need protection from prolonged heavy rain. Excessive wetting from rain can cause pneumonia and an increase in parasitic infestation. Sheep and goat housing design is mainly concerned with the physical environment, in particular climatic and mechanical factors, but all other factors should also be considered in order to create a good layout, where healthy, good producing animals can be provided with correct feeding, can be easily handled and can produce without stress or suffering physical harm. All domestic livestock including goats and sheep are homeotherms; that is, they maintain relatively constant internal body temperatures, usually within a 1 to 2° C range (Range of internal body temperatures for sheep is 38.3 - 39.9° C with average 39.1° C and for goats 38.7 - 40.7° C with average 39.3° C). They maintain their body temperatures by balancing internal heat production and heat loss to the environment. Good designed shelters provide better environment, reduce their stress level and help them to maintain the homeothermy of the body. Increased conversion of feed to heat energy is used to counteract low ambient temperatures, while for example increased respiration (rate and volume) and blood circulation in the skin counteracts high ambient temperatures. Varying temperature also results in changed behaviour. The body can tolerate short periods of heat stress, but if the ambient temperature exceeds the body temperature for an extended period, it may have adverse effects on health and prove fatal. In humid climates a simple thatched shelter will provide shade and protection from excessive rain. Sheep and goats do not tolerate mud well; therefore yards and shelters should be built only on well drained ground. Where housing facilities are provided, it will be necessary to have, in addition to water, feed troughs and permanent partitions, provision for temporary panels to divide and handle the flock when necessary to carry out operations like disease treatment, docking, shearing, milking and lambing. In temperate climates and at high altitudes a more substantial structure may be needed. An open front building facing north provides wind protection and a maximum of sunshine. A rammed earth floor with a slope of 1:50 toward the open front is recommended. A concrete apron sloped 1:25 and extending from 1.2m inside to 2.4m outside will help maintain clean conditions in the barn.

Small ruminant housing under different climatic conditions

Housing requirements of small ruminants depend on climate, level of adaptation, breed and production system. The geographical classification of climate is not adequate and the physiologists prefer to classify the climate in consideration of its effect on physiological functions. The climatic conditions in our country vary from temperate type in the Himalayan range, warm, hot and humid in the coastal regions and variable type in North-West plains. The environmental conditions prevailing in cold climate favour intensive goat production system, which may require high standard housing with good insulation, slatted or straw-bedded floors and efficient ventilation. Contrarily, goat houses in hot weather environments with prevailing extensive production system are mere shades that reduce radiant heat load on the animals. A sheltered area and a big open yard available at low cost are most common. Typical goat houses in the humid tropics are characterized by slatted floors raised above the ground and space boarding on the sidewalls to promote good ventilation, easiness of cleaning and better parasitic control. In winters the warmest part of the house should be reserved for young animals. Avoidance of overcrowding and well-drained and clean floors and yards may be very important. In semi-intensive and intensive production systems, decisions concerning the location of the building, the internal lay-out of the various compartments, the feeding, watering and milking facilities to be used, the feed storage space required, the roughage and manure handling system to be adopted etc. are all important factors affecting the success of small ruminant production.

Temperate climate

The climate of Northern Himalayan hilly regions of the country remains cold for most part of the year. The plains in Northern India experience such environment during December to February. In Himalayan regions, the mean minimum temperature varies from 15 °C in May to June to – 40 °C in January to February. The minimum temperature particularly during cool part of the year is of specific concern in planning the housing in this climate. The lower critical temperature i.e. lower limit of the zone of thermoneutrality for goats habitat in temperate climatic zone is expected to be almost similar as in breeds originating in temperate countries. This may be some-where between 0 and 10 °C. Low temperature alone for such breeds, does not pose much problems but wetness and wind are the important factors to be taken care of. Since the climatic conditions prevailing in temperate regions generally favor intensive goat production system, the closed buildings appear necessary for housing the goats. Good insulation may be required particularly in pens of young early weaned kids. In angora goats drastic changes in the chill factor may cause death even at mid summer temperatures, particularly in animals with insufficient hair cover. Young kids have a much narrower zone of thermo neutrality than adult goats. It does not appear to extend below 15 °C during the first two weeks of their life and not below 12 °C until after the fifth week.

The efficiency of ventilation is strongly affected by the direction of the prevailing winds and this should receive adequate consideration when choosing the location of the building. A 15 cm wide continuous slot on the top of both longitudinal walls has given good results. Air outlets are provided by chimneys or by adjustable openings along the ridge. Protected open ridge ventilation with deflectors to eliminate wind striking through the openings constitutes an optimal solution. Walls and roofs are made of diverse materials depending on insulations requirements, availability and price. Straw has very good insulation properties. In a closed house, sensible body heat from the animals is generally sufficient for keeping the environment warm. The cold climate in association of bad indoor conditions, which are not unusual during cold weather environment, may favor the occurrence of diseases of respiratory system.

Hot dry climate

There is great variation in mean maximum temperature in summer and mean minimum temperature in winters in Trans-Gangetic plains. It reaches up to 49°C in summers and falls down up to 2 °C in winters respectively. The upper limit of the zone of thermo neutrality of goats inhabited in temperate climate is reported to be between 25 and 30 °C. Goats like all other domestic animals attempt to maintain a uniform body temperature by continually adjusting their heat loss. As a shade material, hay was found to be about 20% more effective than standard aluminum and 15% more effective than galvanized steel, under typical shade design conditions. Establishment of trees in open yards, in grazing areas and around watering sides to provide shade during the hottest hours of the day, is a simple method, which gave encouraging results. Trees, however, need to be protected from goat damage, particularly at the early stages of their growth.

Warm humid climate

The climate of the coastal regions in India is warm with high humidity for major part of the year. This causes considerable distress and long-term effects on the goats. The humidity of micro-environment within the animal houses is greatly influenced by water evaporated from animal body via respiratory tract, diffusion through the skin, sweat and from urine and faeces. The mean maximum temperature during this period varies from 30 to 35°C and means vapor pressure from 15 to 30 mmHg. The high temperature coupled with high humidity is most stressful to most of the domestic animals in general, and goats in particular. Although the desirability of attempting to maximize the production of this species in the wet tropics remains to be determined; a survey of sheep and goat houses in Indonesia, failed to yield evidence of acute environmental stress for local animals, though relative humidity approached saturation during the night and never fell below 70% during the day.

The most critical factor in rearing kids in hot humid climate is the wet condition of goat house, which may favor the spread of pathogenic microorganisms. Thus besides adequate nutrition the important aspect of kid rearing in hot humid environment seems to be the proper housing. House should be well ventilated and should have projected roof to prevent rains entering into the houses with the primary aim to keep the floor as dry as possible. Dampness in the house has to be avoided as much as possible. Provision of thin bedding may be beneficial in nursery houses for not allowing kids to come into direct contact with the soil. Bedding should be changed frequently to maintain floor dry all the time. The traditional stilted-type goat houses of Malaysia and Indonesia appear to be very well suited to the specific conditions of the humid tropics. Space boarding on the sidewalls and slatted floors raised above the ground provide for good ventilation. In this type of housing, the floor is elevated approximately 1-1.5 meter to facilitate cleaning. A roof overhang of about one meter prevents the entry of driving rain from the sidewalls and a supplementary roof may be constructed to the side of the house.

Variable type of climate

Regions with a semi-arid climate as in western India are known for combination of hot and cold weather. The maximum temperature during summer season reaches beyond 45 °C and the minimum temperature in winter falling to less than 0 °C. The only solution under such climatic conditions seems to be flexible housing to provide protection from rain, strong winds and cold during winter and cutting down the radiant heat load during summer seasons with minimum hindrance to the proper ventilation. A Northeast to Southwest direction of the building to benefit as much as possible from the morning sun is desirable. Relevant experimental data with goats are lacking, but in beef cattle air velocities of 0.5 to 2.0m/s provided by air fan were found to improve daily gain and feed conversion under California conditions. It should be noted, however, that increased velocities of air movement could be detrimental at air temperatures above 40 °C, because the nonevaporative heat transfer would then be reversed. At wintertime, on the other hand, care should be taken to protect young animals from cold, particularly during the early postpartum period. Unless good ventilation has been provided for, bad indoor climates may be the result. Air temperatures reaching 18-20 °C in the afternoon and falling down to 0 °C in the early morning hours of the day, may call for adjustable windows.

Housing requirements for goats and sheep

It is rather not possible to prescribe a small ruminant house, which will be suitable in all types of climates discussed above. Discussion on the basic principles of housing in terms of heat gain and heat loss from animals housed inside and from building structure in different environments to attain desirable microenvironment economically will help in deciding the type of goat house for a particular zone. The optimum environmental conditions for different species of animals have been determined under laboratory conditions. But the effects of interactions of the various parameters are not well known. However the limits of thermoneutrality for goats and sheep may be taken as a climatic environment having an air temperature of 13°C-27°C, relative humidity of 60-70%, a wind velocity of 5-8 km/hr and a medium level of solar radiation.

Orientation of sheds

Orientation of the shade is a paradox. Sheds with long axis running East-West provide a cooler environment underneath than the one with a North-South orientation. The latter, however, keeps the shed dry and promotes sanitation (because of the sun rays falling inside for a longer period) though this orientation may impose a greater stress on animals, if left underneath during the daytime in hot arid climate. A North East to South West orientation of the shed is expected to provide the maximum benefit from the morning sun and the cooler microenvironment within the sheds in the hotarid environment like the latter orientation, East to West and North-East to South-West oriented sheds provide more opportunity for radiation exchange with cooler North sky at night. One slope of the roof is shaded by the roofline of 'A' shaped sheds in such orientations for a greater part of the day, resulting in lower floor temperature. Thus these orientations favour heat loss from animal body to environment both by radiation and conduction. Paddocks on North side of the shed in hot regions and on South side in temperate climates are recommended for better comfort. North to South orientation needs free movement of animals within the shelter and the paddock on all sides around it. Since in general it is difficult to provide paddocks on all sides of the goat house for free movement, the utility of North to South orientation is limited. The structure with long axis north and south will help to dry up the urine and faces and to promote sanitation. Where as a shade with long axis east to west will provide a cooler environment than one with a north-south orientation. Hence, East-west orientation with generous provision for ventilation/air movement to help dry up threshed will be most suitable. Further more the south façade has the advantage of receiving larger solar radiation during winter than during summer. Small over hang (75 cm-1 m) on south facades, can cut off direct solar radiation during summer and allows it during winter. It also gives protection from rains.

Roof and roofing materials

Roof of shade contributes a major part of radiant hat load to an animal. Cooler the material less heat will be radiated to the animals. Generally, in Indian villages thatch roof are common for animal structures and in organized goat and sheep farms, corrugated asbestos cement sheets or galvanized iron sheets are more popular due to their long life. Roofing material in the goat shed is an important factor, which determines the cost of construction and the micro-environment within the shed. A wide range of roofing materials is available in different climates, which differ to a great extent in their thermal characteristics. The worth of over 50 materials was tested for use as roofing materials in California, ranging from hay or straw, galvanized steel and plywood to several types of plastics. In Indian villages, thatch roof are common for animal structures and in organized goat and sheep farms, corrugated asbestos cement sheets or galvanized iron sheets are more popular due to their long life. Nowadays red mud plasters (RMP) sheets which are having good insulation value are also available in the market Thin thatch panels may cover the G.I. sheets to make it more effective. On a summer day, the difference in the radiant heat load, under sheds covered with straw versus galvanized iron or plastics, was of the order of 163 k cal/hr/m^2 of the animal's surface.

In a study at the CIRG, Makhdoom, it has been observed that the improved thatch provided the coolest microenvironment during hot part of the year. Different roofing materials commonly used in India were tested for their efficacy and protection from heating the microenvironment within goat houses and they can be graded as, the most to least effective in that order, improved thatch, thatch, asbestos, light roof with top surface painted white and nonpainted light roof. The life of the improved fireproof thatch is reported to be 8 years as against about 1 to 2 years for ordinary thatch. The process of making improved thatch roof involves four main steps

1. Making of thatch panels
2. Preparation of nonerodable mud plaster
3. Fire retardant treatment
4. Preparation of stabilized cow dung slurry

1. Making of thatch panels

Prepare two identical frames of half spilt bamboos of 5 cm diameter by placing them across each other about 15 to 20 cm apart. These are tied with each other with the help of 20 SWG GI wire or strong rope. Length and breadth of the panels is decided as per the size of the structure. Spread thatching material on one of the frames. The thatching material should be about 10 cm thick. After this the other frame is placed over the thatching material. Both the frames are tied together with the help of 20 SWG GI wire and by putting body weight over joints, applying pressure and jerks. The thickness of the thatch material should become about 5 cm after compression. Then the thatch panel should be fixed properly on the roof structure of the shed.

2. Preparation of nonerodable mud plaster

It consists of the following steps-

(a) Preparation of the mud mortar

Pond based soil containing at least 25% clay and wheat straw (preferably one year old) lopped in 2 cm length are used for preparation of mud mortar. Add straw at the rate of 64 Kg per cubic meter of soil and allow decomposing in presence of water, needing it daily 3-4 times a day for about seven days in summer and fourteen days in winter. Mud mortar should not be allowed to dry during this process or during the construction work.

(b) Preparation of bitumen cut-back

80/100-grade bitumen is mixed with kerosene oil in the ratio of 5:1. Bitumen is heated till melting and then poured into kerosene oil (never pour kerosene into bitumen) keep stirring while pouring bitumen thus mixed with kerosene is called bitumen cut back.

(c) Preparation of nonerodable mud

Pour the bitumen cut back (64 kg of this mixture in one cubic meter of mud mortar) in the earlier prepared mud mortar. Overturn with spade and puddle so that it is thoroughly mixed. It should be kept in mind that no black spots of unmixed cutback are left in the mud.

3. Fire retardant treatment

First of all a layer of mud mortar (without bitumen cut back) is applied on the earlier prepared thatch roof to give the roof an even and smooth finish. Allow the plaster to dry and crack for 1-2 days. Fill the cracks with the same mud mortar. Now this roof is plastered with nonerodable mud mortar (12mm). The roof is left for drying for few days and all the racks are filled with nonerodable mud plaster. Same type of treatment can be given to the ceiling of the structure also.

4. Preparation of stabilized mud-cow dung slurry

Cow dung and soil is mixed thoroughly in equal quantity. Sufficient water is added to form a uniform thin paste. As mentioned earlier prepare and mix bitumen cut back in to the mud-cow dung slurry which is prepared by mixing Soil, Cow dung, Bitumen, Kerosene in the amount of 0.001 M^3 , 0.001 M^3 , 210 g, 46 ml, respectively. Two coats of this slurry are applied on the roof to give a smooth finish. The quantity of materials required for each M^2 of roof area is dry soil-0.014 M^3, wheat straw-900 g, bitumen (80/100 grade) - 750 g and Kerosene-150 ml.

The cost of improved thatch is about 70-80 per cent more than ordinary thatch but its use can overcome the practical difficulties encountered in use of thatch as the former is fire and water retardant and has longer durability. It has been suggested that it would be disadvantageous to use highly reflective materials as roofing because of the reflection of short and long wave radiation back onto housed stock. The dark roof from inside is known to reduce reflection. The low emittance value of the inner surface is also desirable. Roofing materials on outside will absorb less heat if they have a low absorbity for short wave radiation and also a high emissivity. Materials and coating on inside of the shed would reduce the radiation load on the housed goats if they have a high short wave absorbance and a low emissivity. The radiation load on goats in a house may, therefore, be reduced by use of appropriate materials for roofing.

Height and shape of roof

The height at center in 'A' shaped roof is suggested to vary between 3 to 3.5 m. A height of less than 3 m interferes with proper ventilation resulting in reduced convective heat loss from animals. In temperate and hot-humid climate, where more height does not provide any additional benefit, a height of 3 m is expected to suffice. The heat loss through radiation from goats to cool sky is curtailed in low roof sheds. In hot-dry environment, radiant heat load plays a vital role. Within the boundaries of the shed, the radiant load on goats comes from the atmosphere, the roof, the shaded ground and sunny ground. The heat load on goats will be minimum within the shed when the distance from the roof is maximum. A very high shed could also lose its effectiveness by casting its shadow outside the corral for most part of the time. The impedance of the total sun and sky radiation at 3.5 m height is 61% as against 64% at 2.2 m height. A too high shelter without providing any significant additional benefit involves high cost of construction. 'A' shaped roof is indeed better for hot climate regions. In the hot weather one side of 'A' shaped roof saves the other half from direct solar radiation by casting its shadow. This helps in cutting down heat gain from the roof of the shelter. Double roof with both roofs of same or different materials are effective in reducing the heating of shed in hot weather conditions. The additional cost of construction in double roof, however, restricts its use to very high producing animals.

Paint

White washing (with lime and white cement in equal amount) or white painting the roof surface can reduce the temperature by several degrees. But under side of the structure materials should have radiation characteristics of black surface to reduce the reflection of radiation from hot ground and surrounding objects. The wall exteriors should be painted with dull colors. The white painting of sidewalls outside reduces the surface temperature inside the shed by 12-22 °C.

Shelter Surroundings

Surfaces around the shelter are very important in view of the radiation exchange between surrounding surface and the shelter. The temperature of different surfaces varies significantly at the same air temperature. It is well known that the green surface do not heat up as much as other surface like gravel or lose loam. It should be possible to maintain the green vegetation adjacent to the goat shelters except the paddock. It may be possible to increase animal comfort by selection of the proper type of unvegetated ground surface. These vary significantly in view of the difference in reflectivity, thermal conductivity and density etc. Radiation from ground surface and near by buildings add substantially to the animal radiant heat load. There should be grass, hedges, shrubs, shrubs, trees etc. Around the structure to reduce the radiant heat load from ground and near by buildings. The hedges and shrubs planted at a distance of 2 m from the building increase the air movement inside. In case of trees, because of their mass of leaves their shadow is always larger giving a low temperature area. The height of hedges and shrubs should be below the height of opening for ventilation but toward west side height may be kept more to cover the openings so that hot wind coming from west side especially in the after noon of summer may break. There should be greenery all round the shed. Creepers over the roof may also be helpful in providing cool environment. Radiations from ground surface and nearby buildings add substantially to the animal radiant heat load. There should be grass, hedges, shrubs, trees etc. around the structure to reduce the radiant heat load from ground and nearby buildings.

Location

The first step in establishing a goat or sheep farm is the selection of location of the farm. Paying due attention in planning a goat enterprise with respect to the selection of site is of immense importance. The major considerations are:

1. System of farming (intensive, semi-intensive, grazing)
2. Size of the farm
3. Farm should be located on dry, elevated and well drained area.
4. Scope for future expansion
5. The site shall be such that sheds could be oriented towards east to west.
6. Purpose (Breeding farm, Goat production for meat etc.)
7. Availability of grazing land.
8. Easy availability of transport for transporting the input materials and produce.
9. Nearness to the meat-processing unit.
10. Easy availability of feed ingredients.
11. Distance from the habitation.
12. Availability of water, electricity etc.

Facilities should be located on elevated, well-drained sites. When designing a three-sided shelter, the open side should face south away from the prevailing wind. The barn should be easily accessible for deliveries and manure handling. The site should allow for installation of water and electricity.

Lay Out

Planning the layout of a goat farm seldom receives attention it deserves. Many of the farms have been developed in a haphazard way with almost no thought being given to the placement of various units with respect to efficiency of production and management. Office rooms, residential quarters, feed processing and storage unit should have the first approach. Building in which there is maximum labor activities, frequent handling of animals, and need for closer and constant supervision such as isolation ward kidding pens, shelter for kids, milch animal and milking shed, maternity shed etc., should get most central and approachable area. It should be followed by buildings in which there are lesser labor activities, no routine handling of animals and less need for closer supervision such as buck shed, young stock shed and dry animal shed. In the end, ancillary sheds, where no animals are housed but activities relating to feeding and management of stock are performed, such as chaffing shed, silage pits, manure pit etc., should be placed. These should be followed by agricultural farm and/or grazing land. Proper distance (8 m) between two goat houses should be maintained. Surroundings and orientation of the farm should also be taken into account while deciding the layout of the farm. A sufficiently wide and long path containing disinfectant solution should be located at the entrance. Location of establishing renewable source of energy like biogas plant, solar systems, windmills etc. should also be thought off. Provision may be made for segregating new animals for some initial days (about 30 days) before their mixing up with the herd. This quarantine shed should be in the beginning of the farm.

Floor type and space

The surface upon which an animal lies should not be a source of thermal and physical discomfort, injury and infectious diseases. The ideal bed, therefore, needs to be hygienic, dry and reasonably temperature resistant. Deep, lean, dry straw can provide an ideal bed for weaners and growers during the cool period, but a thin layer of straw is likely to be more suitable during warm or hot weather conditions. An inadequate bed of wet filthy straw fails on all accounts. Perforated or slatted floors are mostly drier and more hygienic than solid floors with limited bedding and thus more suitable for humid and high rainfall areas. The type of floor, which provides both comfort and cleanliness with minimal risk of injury, should be given preference.

In a preliminary study at C.I.R.G., five different types of floors viz., slatted wood, slatted plastic, Iron mesh, brick and Kuchcha were tested for their relative acceptability as perceived by goats. On the basis of time spent by the animal in various activities on different types of floors, it was observed that the highest preference was for slatted wooden floor followed by slatted plastic. Wooden floors for less arthritis and mastitis; concrete rocks in yards for better hoof wear have been recommended.

Floors of low thermal resistance are suitable for hot climate to keep the animals cool. For hot-humid climate conditions slatted floors raised above the ground provide good ventilation, easy leaning and collection of faeces and urine. Wet floors encourage skin infection, fungi and pathogens. The use of concrete floors allows easy cleaning but it is hard for standing and sitting. The cases of mastitis are reported to be more frequent in milch goats housed in concrete floors sheds. Deep litre system on floor increases the chances of Para tuberculosis and brucellosis. If the cost of construction is considered, then clay floor in regions with predominant hot-dry climate and slatted floors for hot–humid predominant weather conditions are more suitable. Bedding with straw or grasses during cooler part of the year in variable type of climate and temperate climate reduce the loss of heat through conduction from animal body to floor. Frequent replacement of the bedding is, absolutely essential to maintain hygienic conditions. In a flexible house, hurdles made of wood, iron or iron-framed mesh can be used. Under most system of intensive goat production subdivision into several groups (e.g. does in late pregnancy; does in early lactation, lactating or dry does weaned of their kids; replacement or primiparous goats, etc.) appears essential. Further grouping may be required according to age and dominance status.

The floor space for different age groups should be slightly more in hot weather conditions in comparison to cool weather. This helps in radiant heat losses and convective removal of heat and water from the animal body. In tropical climates, huddling is disadvantageous for health of the animals and their productivity. The knowledge on air space requirement per animal is thought to be important, as the cleanliness of ambient air, with regard to air-borne wastes from animal body, must be directly proportional to the actual volume of air into which those wastes are dispelled. Conversely, concentration of pollutants is directly proportional to stocking density. Systematic studies to delineate the optimum floor space requirements of different goat breeds in different environmental conditions have been carried out at the CIRG. Providing proper covered and open floor space is of utmost importance for proper growth and management of the animals. The suitable floor space for goat of different age groups is mentioned in table 2. Information available in other ruminants and the observations made in goat flocks suggest that pregnant goats are very sensitive to various kinds of stress including excessive animal density in the goat house. To avoid these accidents when pregnant goats are confined in a goat house, it is necessary to maintain comfortable conditions and good air circulation without draughts, high humidity, and high variations of temperature. Providing proper covered and open floor space is of utmost importance for proper growth and management of the animals. The suitable floor space for goat of different age groups is mentioned below

Table 1: Optimum floor space requirements for different categories of goats

Sl. No	Age/Category of goats	Covered area (m^2/goat)	Open paddock (m^2/goat)
1.	0 - 3 months	0.2-0.25	0. 4 - 0.5
2.	3 - 6 months	0.5 - 0.75	1.0 – 1.5
3.	6 - 12 months	0.75 - 1.0	1.5 – 2.0
4.	Yearling goats (above 12 months)	1.00	2.00
5.	Adult goats	1.5	3.0
6.	Pregnant and lactating goats	1.5 - 2.0	3.0 - 4.0
7.	Bucks	1.5 - 2.0	3.0 - 4.0

Poor housing hygiene is associated with reduced space allowance of farmed animals: to improve the advantages of intensification, farmers use very specialized flocks and increase the number of animals. The increase in stocking density influences profoundly the quality of air, in terms of airborne microorganisms, gases and dust, thus affecting the welfare of farmed animals. Intensive production systems brought to a change in the type of occurring diseases, which can be considered a combination of pathogen actions and environmental stress (Hartung, 1994). Poor ambient hygiene in intensively managed flocks condition may contribute to increase predisposition to mastitis development (Mavrogianni et al., 2007). Loynes (1983) recommends a space allowance of 0.8 m^2/animal for ewe of 45–60 kg housed in fully slatted pens, with increases by 30% for ewe housed in straw bedded pens, and by 15% for shorn ewes.

Ventilation space

The importance of ventilation in sustaining the welfare of farmed livestock has been underestimated during the winter season, when inadequate ventilation may determine high concentrations of noxious gases and enhanced moisture content in the air and in the bedding. Ventilation is an important, yet often overlooked aspect of animal housing particularly closed housing.

Poor ventilation can be detrimental to animal health and performance. The purpose of ventilation is to provide the desired amount of fresh air, without drafts, to all parts of the shelter, to maintain temperatures within desired limits, to maintain relative humidity within desired limits and to maintain ammonia levels below specified levels. During the winter season, Sevi et al. (2003) compared the effects of programmed ventilation regime operating at 70% relative humidity with the effects of a low (23 m^3/h per animal) and a moderate (47 m^3/h per animal) ventilation rate on the ewe welfare. Results indicate that stress arising from poor winter ventilation has no effects on both the endocrine responses of animals and their immune reactivity. Barns should not be heated or closed up. Respiratory problems (e.g. pneumonia and bronchitis) often result from poor ventilation. If ammonia can be smelled in the barn, ventilation is probably inadequate. Ventilation can be accomplished by either natural or mechanical means, but usually naturally-ventilated cold housing is satisfactory for sheep. It is better to over-ventilate than underventilate.

The efficiency of ventilation is greatly affected by the summer and winter directions of the prevailing wind at any place. The air in-lets should, therefore, be provided at the height of the goat breeds to prevent the drought. An attempt to cover sheds from all sides to protect the animals from low air temperatures may result in an increase of humidity up to 90% and ammonia concentration to 20 ppm. Good ventilation in the sheds is very important in hot-dry and warm-humid climate to promote the heat loss from animals with increased convection and radiation. In tropics, the two long sides of the goat shed should not be provided with solid wall, above 1 m from the floor. This open part of the shed walls should preferably be kept uncovered when the ambient climatic condition is warm - humid or hot humid and should be partially covered when it is hot dry. Protection from hot-winds in the hot-arid zone needs some cover from western side. During the winter in uncertain climates and for most part of the year in temperate zone, the sides may be closed but cross ventilation space is left at the roof height. Panels of thatch or fire proof thatch made from locally available grasses are very cheap and convenient for adjusting the ventilation at will from the two long sides. Thus the open type shed with adjustment of ventilation should provide the desirable comfort within the shed under variable climatic conditions· Top ventilation in the form of space along the length by providing double 'A' shape roof or chimneys has been, otherwise, found to be efficient outlet in goat sheds.

Air is very much needed for oxygen requirement of the animals and for removal of moisture, humidity, other gasses etc., from the shed. The provision of proper ventilation in the goat sheds is essential to permit continuous movement of fresh air to meet the oxygen requirement of the animals and to remove the moisture and gases generating as a result of respiration, urination, defecation etc. This is possible when 30-50 per cent indoor wind velocity is maintained with the provision of sufficient ventilation. The work carried out on this subject at CIRG, Makhdoom suggested providing 25, 70, 100% ventilation (Per cent of floor area) during comfortable, hot dry and hot humid period of the year, respectively. However during winter either 10% fixed ventilation space should be provided or flexible ventilation should be provided i.e. maximum between 10 am to 4 pm, and closing the ventilation space between 4 pm to 10 am. This will allow maximum air flow through the sheds and availability of sunlight to help in removal of moisture from the sheds at the faster rate. In hot humid climate high rate of air motion is needed. Under ideal conditions the maximum average in door wind velocity does not exceed 40% of the out door velocity. Inlet should be 30 to 50 percent of the total fenestration. For achieving benefit from natural wind, the buildings need not necessarily be oriented perpendicular to the prevailing out door wind. It may be oriented at any convenient angle between 0° to 30°. If the prevailing wind is from east to west, buildings can be oriented at 45° to the incident wind for diminishing the solar heat without affecting the air motion indoor. Measures to protect goats from cold during winter are essential. Use of nearly 10 cm thick thatch panels on the open sides of animal sheds is suggested during night time only.

Hygiene in animal housing involves air, bedding and surface hygiene; poor housing hygiene is strictly connected with intensive systems of husbandry and is exacerbated by poor standard of management (Wathes, 1994). The concentration of airborne particulates in animal houses is inversely related to airspace (Hartung, 1989). In pigs, there is evidence of the association of insufficient air volume per animal with prevalence of lung disease (Christiaens, 1987); minimum air volume indications are given for many farm animals (Hilliger, 1990). In sheep houses, the airspace of 7 m^3 per animal is required to ensure a proper relative humidity and air quality: lower volume per animal determines increased air concentrations of staphylococci and of mesophilic bacteria, resulting in deteriorated air and surface hygiene in sheep houses (Sevi et al., 2001). The worsening of air hygiene with a volume allocation lower than 7 m^3 per animal adversely affects the microbial content, the somatic cell and neutrophilic count of sheep milk, increases the incidence of subclinical mastitis (Sevi et al., 2001) and decreases the quality of milk-products originating from such farms (Albenzio et al., 2006). Results from that work clearly show that an insufficient volume allocation, causing a deterioration of bedding conditions, can be considered a direct source of udder infections in lactating ewes. The smaller the air volume per animal, the higher the need for a proper ventilation system within animal houses (Hartung, 1994).

Solar radiation for kids during winter

Provision should be made to provide direct solar radiation for four hours (10 am to 2 pm) to kids during winter that is quite helpful for proper growth.

Dimensions of shelter

Depending on the number of animals need to be housed total covered and open area is determined (i.e. number of animals x area needed per animal). There is no restriction on the length of a shelter however breadth of the shed should not be more than 12 m. If it exceeds 12 m, the natural air movement inside the shed will be adversely affected. Normally the breadth of the sheds is between 6 m to 8 m. However in big sheds where large number of animals are housed it is increased to 12 m, but in this case it is advisable to have paddocks on both side and to make compartment in the covered space. As the height of the shade is increased, the animal in the shadow becomes exposed to a larger percentage of the cooled sky, which increases the cooling effect. But a balance has to be maintained between the increased cost of construction due to increased height and the benefit occurring from it. Generally the wall height at eaves is kept at 2.7 m and roof height in the centre around 3.5 m.

Bedding

Bedding provides warmth, insulation, and comfort to housed animals. Various materials can be used for bedding for sheep, depending upon their cost and availability: straw, hay, dried corn stalks, corn cobs, peanut hulls, cottonseed hulls, oat hulls, sawdust, wood shavings, wood chips, pine shavings, sand, paper products, peat, hemp, and leaves. Each type of bedding has advantages and disadvantages. Straw is the traditional bedding for livestock. It comes from the stems of small grains: oats, wheat, rye or barley. Since straw has many uses other than livestock bedding some times it costs more than alfalfa hay. As a result, hay is often a cheaper alternative than straw. Sawdust is not good bedding for wooled sheep because it gets in their fleeces, but works fine for hair sheep. Wood chips or peanut shells are less absorbent than other materials, but can be used as bedding. Bedding material is usually provided to keep the goats clean and healthy. Available bedding materials vary in their capacity to absorb urine. Spaced wood boards (as described above) make excellent bedding. Sawdust or shavings, bagasse, paddy husk, groundnut hulls, wheat straw, crushed maize cobs, and dry grass are all good, cheap, and available in many tropical countries. If nothing else is available, coarse sand can be used. To increase the effectiveness of the litter rake the droppings into it. The depth of the litter will partially depend on the price and availability of suitable materials. If they are cheap and available, use 7 to 10 cm. If less than 2.5 cm is used it will not absorb all the urine and the floor may become wet Used bedding can be spread in fields and vegetable gardens to increase plant growth. The choice of bedding materials to be used depends upon the absorption factor of the material, which varies from 0.3 (sand) to 10.0 (peat moss). Bedding of soft dry grasses or similar material should be used in the pens of kids and lactating does in order to prevent them from direct exposure to cold surface (Singh et al., 1989).

Housing management for optimum productivity

For goats and sheep, housing needs also vary by climate, lambing and kidding season. If lambing will occur during periods of inclement weather, more elaborate housing is generally required. If lambing will occur on pasture during periods of mild weather, simple shelters may be all that is needed. Lambing percentages are higher when shed lambing is practiced. Housed sheep and goats have lower nutritional requirements. According to the climate and availability of the raw material there are different types of housing that can be used for sheep and goats. Disease remains a major profit limiting factor in animal production in many tropical countries. Sanitary control measures should be incorporated in any building design, so that a good hygienic standard can be easily maintained. Animals, which are well fed and watered in good condition, will have a high resistance to disease. Good housing and management can do much to remove or reduce the effects of adverse environmental factors such as climatic stress, which otherwise would weaken the body's natural defense mechanism.

Environmental modifications (micro climate of animal housing) include provision of shades, enhancement of evaporative cooling and increase air movement in the shed etc are helpful in mitigating the stress to the animals. However to alleviate heat/cold stress in small ruminants, not much studies have been done. Apart from providing optimum floor area and ventilation space, proper cleaning of animals sheds is necessary to maintain hygienic conditions at the livestock farm and it should be done daily. After removing the refusal from the feeders, floor of the shed should be swept preferably at the time when goats and sheep are out for grazing or in resting/exercising paddocks and the cleaned waste materials should be disposed off far away from animal's sheds. Sick animals shed should be cleaned lastly after all sheds are cleaned and disinfected with lime. Except high rainfall areas and research organizations, the animal sheds practiced for goats/sheep generally have soil/

kutcha floor. The maintenance of such floors in comfortable condition is very important. Due to excessive moisture in the soil and continuous use of shed for a longer duration there is a possibility of formation of cake (hard surface) on the upper surface of the floor. It will prevent absorption of urine resulting into occurrence of dampness in the animal sheds whereas goats feel comfortable on dry surface. Excessive moisture conditions will suit to the growth of many pathogenic organisms. Overturning of floor surface at required interval followed by use of lime at the rate of 10 kg /100 m^2 of floor area is very much helpful in removal of excessive moisture and maintaining the floors in soft and dry condition. Replacement of old soil once in every year during the month of March-April is also suggested. The new soil should be dry enough and thoroughly mixed with lime at the rate of 10 kg/ m^3 of soil. The concrete cement or brick floor should have proper drainage so as to maintain desired cleanliness in the animal sheds.

Use of approximately 10 cm thick thatch panels on the open sides of the sheds along with use of tarpaulin or gunny/jute bags during winter in night hours are needed to protect the goats and sheep from excessive flow of strong wind and cold. The type of shade influences the microclimate created under the shadow cast. Agricultural engineers and foresters have evaluated the design characteristics of various shaded environments. For example, the amount of radiation emitted from shade structures made of aluminium siding can be manipulated with paint colour (Bond et al., 1954). Natural shade, such as trees and hedges, vary in their ability to reduce solar radiation, wind speed and temperature depending on the height, spacing and density of various species (Hawke and Wedderburn, 1994). Shades are among the most widely used devices for protecting small ruminants in hot environments. Radiant heat measurements have shown that solar heat load can be reduced 30 to 50 percent in hot dry climates by intercepting the sun. (Kumar et al., 1990). An animal under a shade also receives radiation from shade material (21%) sky (28%) sunny ground (18%) and shaded ground (33%). During summer, sheep exposed to solar radiation display enhanced respiration rate and increased rectal temperature compared with shaded animals. In addition, sheep exposed to direct solar radiation exhibit an increase of inactive behaviours to reduce heat production and show high nonesterified fatty acids plasma concentrations due to enhanced mobilization of body reserves (Sevi et al., 2001). Grazing increases heat production and contribute to the heat load of the animal. Therefore grazing of sheep and goat may be restricted during the daily peak hour of heat stress. Animal should be provided *ad lib* and preferably cooled drinking water as water intake increases in sheep and goat during heat stress (Joshi et al., 1977; Gupta and Acharya, 1987).

Conclusion

Generally for goats, loose housing system is practiced with the long axis of the sheds in east - west orientation. In rural areas, improved thatch roof (Singh et al.,1989) are to be provided for animal houses and in organized farms, corrugated asbestos sheets are more popular (due to their long life). But in summer, white painting of roof surface (outer side) and black in the inner side should be done in time. Rooftop should be covered with materials that curtail radiation. The surroundings of the shed should be covered with grasses, shrubs, trees etc. to reduce the reflected radiant heat load from the ground. The provision of optimum floor area and ventilation space is expected to provide comfortable microenvironment within the animal sheds. The ventilation requirement goes on changing during different seasons and as per agro climatic conditions of the region. Flexible/ interconvertible houses should be encouraged make required changes in them during different seasons of the year. Although small ruminants are resistant to high environmental temperature, but they do suffer from heat stress when exposed to upper critical temperature. Although several methods are followed to alleviate heat stress in cattle, buffalo and pig, but little such measures have been studied in small ruminants. However selection of breed of heat resistant, provision of shelters, nutritional manipulation and modification of management may greatly reduced the heat stress of small ruminants. The thermal environment in animal houses has a direct effect on the efficiency of animal production and on the health and welfare of animals housed therein; poor building designs and inappropriate microclimates can result in thermal stress and risks to welfare. Goats/ sheep houses should provide protection from solar radiation as a strategy to maintain productivity and welfare of animals, in particular during stressful period of the year.

References

Abdel, Samee, Am., Diel, J.R, Abdel-Samee-Am., Marai-IF.M., Metwally, M.G. 1998. First International Conference Animal Production and Health in Semi Arid Tropic, Egypt, 251-259.

Albenzio, M., Caroprese, R., Marino, A., Muscio, A., Santillo and Sevi, A. 2006. Characteristics of Garganica goat milk and Cacioricotta cheese. Small Ruminant Research 64: 35–44.

Bhattacharya, A.N. 1980. Research on goat nutrition and management in Mediterranean, Middle East and adjacent Arab countries. Journal of Dairy Science 63: 1681.

Bond, T.E., Kelly, C.F., Ittner, N.R. 1954. Radiation studies of painted shade materials. Agriculture Engineering 36:389–392.

Borut, A., Dmiel, R. and Shkolnik, A. 1979. Heat balance of resting and walking goats: comparison of climatic chamber and exposure in the desert. Physiological Zool. 52: 105.

Brosh A., Aharoni Y., Degen A.A., Wright A. and Young B.A. 1998. Effects of solar radiation, dietary energy and time of feeding on thermoregulatory responses and energy balance in cattle in a hot environment. Journal of Animal Science 76: 2671–2677.

Casamassima D., Sevi A., Palazzo M., Ramacciato R., Colella G.E. and Bellitti, A. 2001. Effects of two different housing systems on behaviour, physiology and milk yield of Comisana ewes. Small Ruminant Research 41: 151–161.

Christiaens, J.P.A. 1987. Gas concentrations and thermal features of the animal environment with respect to respiratory diseases in pig and poultry. In: J.M. Bruce, M. Sommer (Eds.), Environmental Aspects of Respiratory Disease in Intensive Pig and Poultry Houses, Including the Implications for Human Health. Commission of the European Communities, Publication EUR 10820 EN, Brussels, pp. 29–43.

Clark J.A. and McArthur A.J. 1994. Thermal exchanges. In: C.M. Wathes and D.R. Charles, Editors, Livestock Housing, CAB International, Wallingford, pp. 97–122.

Davis, M.P., Rajion, M.A., Yasin, H.M., Hamzah, R, Djajanegara, a. and Sukmawati, A. 1994. Proc. 7th AAAP Animal Science., Cong., Bali, Indonesia, v (2); 547-548.

Hartung, J. 1989. Practical aspects of aerosol sampling in animal houses. In: M. Whates and R.M. Randall, Editors, Aerosol Sampling in Animal Houses, European Community Commission Publications, Luxembourg, pp. 14–23.

Hartung, J. 1994. Environment and animal health. In: C.M. Wathes and D.R. Charles, Editors, Livestock Housing, CAB International, Wallingford, pp. 25–48.

Hawke, M.F.,Wedderburn, M.E., 1994. Microclimate changes under Pinus Radiata agroforestry regimes in New Zealand. Agriculture Meteorology. 71, 133–145.

Hilliger, H.G. 1990. Housing Air and Ventilation, Ferdinand Enke Verlag, Stuttgart.

Hopkin, P.S. and Pratt, M.S. 1978. Proceedings of Australian Society of Animal Production 11: 153-156.

Kumar, P., Khub, S. and Sood, S.B. 1990. Effect of micro-environment within different types of sheds on physiological responses in Jamunapari goats in hot semi arid zone. Indian Journal of Animal Research 24(2): 93-100.

LeRoy Hahn G. 1981. Livestock Housing and Management to Reduce Climatic Impacts on animals. Journal of Animal Science 52:175-186.

Loynes, I.J. 1983. Sheep house design, Housing Sheep, Farm Building Information Centre, Stoneleigh pp. 4–9.

Mavrogianni, V.S., Cripps P.J. and Fthenakis, G.C. 2007. Bacteria flora and risk of infection of the ovine teat duct and mammary gland throughout lactation. Preventive Veterinary Medicine 79: 163–173.

Canas, R., Romero J. J. and Baldwin R. L. 1982. Maintenance energy, requirements during lactation in rats. Journal of Nutrition 112:1876.

Sevi A., Annicchiarico G., Albenzio M., Taibi L., Muscio A. and Dell'Aquila S. 2001. Effects of solar radiation and feeding time on behavior, immune response and production of lactating ewes under high ambient temperature. Journal of Dairy Science 84: 629–640.

Sevi, M., Albenzio, A., Muscio, D., Casamassima and Centoducati, P. 2003. Effects of litter management on airborne particulates in sheep houses and on the yield and quality of ewe milk. Livestock Production Science 81: 1–9.

Singh, K., Puneet, K., Saini, A.L. and bhattacharyya, N.K. 1989. Influence of commonly used roofing materials on microclimate in animal housing in hot semiarid zone. Indian Journal of Dairy Science 42(3): 505-510.

Stephenson, RG.A., Edwards, J.C. and Pratt, M.S. 1980. Queenceland Agriculture Jounrnal 106(5): 411-418.

Wathes, C.M., 1994. Air and surface hygiene. In: C.M. Wathes and D.R. Charles, Editors, Livestock Housing, CAB International, Wallingford, pp. 123–148.

Joshi, B.C.; Aravindan, M; Singh, K.S. and Bhattacharyya, N.K. 1977. Indian Journal of Animal Science 47(4):200-203.

□□□

14

Effect of Environment Stress on Animal Productivity and its Amelioration through Shelter Management

A.K.Patel
Division of Animal Sciences and Forage Production
Central Arid Zone Research Institute, Jodhpur-342003

Introduction

Indian arid zone covers 31.8 lakh square km nearly to 10.16% of total geographical area. The hot region of nearly 62% lies in the state of Rajasthan covering 12 districts in western parts. The region suffers from low and erratic annual precipitation (100-420 mm), high evapo-transpiration (1500-2000 mm) and poor physical and fertility condition of soil making crop farming a big gamble. Animal husbandry plays an important role in livelihood security and economic sustenance of people. In India animal husbandry contributes about 32% of total agricultural revenue and 27% of GDP whereas in Rajasthan state it contributes 19% of the GDP. Majority of small ruminants in arid regions maintained in extensive range management system, although the various breeds of small ruminants are well acclimatized in different arid environmental conditions but their production potential is undeniably influenced by the extremes of environmental conditions of the region. The thick coat of hair or wool in sheep and goat acts as an insulator for environmental temperature and as ambient temperature exceeds body temperature the hair or wool protects the skin. However heat or cold stress occurs in these animals when they exposed to ambient temperature above and below critical temperature zone. The fetal growth (Ocfemia et al., 1993) and post weaning growth in kids (Patel et al., 2007) are affected by heat stress particularly at high ambient temperature. Apart from decreased growth rate in young, heat stress lengthens estrus cycle, affects ovulation and decrease conception rate in goats and sheep. Heat stress affects production and reproduction in high yielding dairy cows, the conception rate has been reported to be significantly reduced in summer by 5 to 20% (Flamenbaum, 1998). Extremes in the environmental conditions have enormous effects on the productivity of farm animals (Burke, 1998). Numerous studies indicated that the provision of proper shelter improves livestock performance through moderation of environmental factors (Patel, et. al., 2001, Singh, et. al., 2003 and Patel, et al., 2007). The main aim of the shelter is to provide comfort and a sense of well being to animals so that they can produce to their maximum genetic potential. However, in most part of the Indian arid zone, shelter is not generally provided to the small ruminants whereas, thatched roof is common for large ruminants.

Effect of environment stress on animal physiology and productivity

Animal physiology

A major part of arid region is characterized by harsh environmental conditions due to low and erratic rainfall, poor quality of soil, higher variation in air temperature, high wind velocity, high evopo-transpiration etc. Animals are mostly maintained on extensive grazing on rangelands, where they are not provided any kind of shelter, but in extremes of summer animal take shelter under the tree shade, whereas, during extremely cold conditions at night in winters, the sand dune, dense trees or shrubs protect the animals under natural condition. Extremes in the environmental conditions have enormous effects on physiology and productivity of farm animals (Singh, et al., 2001 and Singh and Upadhyay, 2009). Patel et al. (2009) analyzed the stressful and comfortable period based on weekly Temperature Humidity Index (THI) for Central Farm of CAZRI, Jodhpur, the stressful period for animals starts from May to Ist week of October, where THI ranged from 79 to 83 and the comfortable period start from IInd week of October to March, where the THI equal to or below 74. The animals are exposed to cold stress period from IInd week of December to IIIrd week of February during night and early morning hours, especially during cold waves. The average THI values of morning and evening lies 61.62 and 74.75 for winter; 75.58 and 83.81 for summer dry and 77.59 and 83.70 for wet seasons, respectively. A long period of summer, monsoon and post monsoon are more stressful seasons in arid and semi-arid regions. Animals should be protected from direct solar radiation during the hottest hours of the day to ameliorate the effect of heat stress (Shinde et al., 2002).

Adaptability of small ruminants for water restriction

Water being a most limiting factor for survival in desert, the long term effect of heat and water stress in sheep physiology was studied. These studies observed unusual ability of the desert breed to maintain circulation even when faced with considerable haemo-concentration. When water was reduced to below 75 % of normal daily requirement, there was a steady decline in the body water stores. On an average, there was an 18 % loss in body weight after remaining without water for 3 days during winter and 25 % during summer. Interestingly, the digestibility of crude fibres increased in water restricted sheep while nitrogen balance was not affected due to water stress. The rate of passage of feed is slow in water restricted sheep in comparison to normally hydrated animals.

In one study, goat breeds of Beetal and Black Bengal were divided into 2 groups, in one group water was not withheld, whereas in another group, it was withheld for 36 h before exposure to thermal stress (43.00 ± 0.5°C, RH 55%). Maximum respiration rates were observed when goats attained rectal temperature between 40.3°C and 40.5°C. The rectal temperature level at which maximum respiratory frequency was observed was lower when the animals were under combined stress of thermal exposure and water restriction. Significant differences were observed between breeds and groups in pulse and respiration rates (Kaushish et al., 1987).

Effect of heat and water stress on cortisol level in goat

A study was conducted on 5 to 6 months old male kids (Beetal and Black Bengal), they were exposed to 43.00 ± 0.5°C for 2 h. Cortisol concentration in control with thermal stress and thermal stress coupled with water stress groups were 17.6± 2.68, 54.3±1.71 and 38.5±5.13 ng/ml in Beetal and 48.1±3.60, 43.7±5.32 and 55.5±5.72 ng/ml in Black Bengal goats, respectively, Significant increase in cortisol level was observed in Beetal on exposure to thermal stress, but the increase was non-significant in Black Bengal. It was concluded that Black Bengal were more adapted to hot humid conditions than Beetal goats (Kaushish et al., 1997).

Responses of sheep to solar exposure

Native Nali, Chokla and their crosses with Rambouillet and Soviet Merino hoggets were maintained in shade or sun during summer. After first recording, the animals of sun and shade exposed groups were exchanged and the observations were recorded. The respiration rate, rectal temperature, skin temperature and fleece temperature (1 and 2 cm above the skin) were higher in the solar exposed group as compared to the animals maintained in shed and higher at 16 and 13 h than at 9 h. In general the rectal temperature of the crossbred animals was lower than the native; lower in Merino x Nali and highest in Nali. It is concluded that the animals maintained under hot sun experienced greater stress as compared to the animals under shade. It also appeared that in crossbreds the thermolytic mechanism was activated at a lower ambient temperature resulting in their higher respiration rate and lower rectal temperature (Kaushish et al., 1989). The physiological response viz. respiration rate and heart rate were lower in sheep provided shade and nutritionally restricted or fed *ad lib* in comparison to those exposed in sun (Hooda and Naqvi, 1990).

Physiological responses of sheep and goats put to exercise stress under arid conditions

The water intake was higher in exercise group of sheep and goats during summer and winter season. Both the species lost body weights during summer season. Significant diurnal differences were observed in rectal temperature, pulse rate and respiration rate. The rise in rectal temperature was more in the afternoon in exercise group. The differences in rectal temperature, pulse rate and respiration rate between summer and winter seasons were significant. The rectal temperature was lower in goats than in sheep. Differences in rectal temperature between groups were non-significant. In arid conditions of Rajasthan, Magra sheep and Marwari goats can safely grazed within 8 km from their watering point without any ill effect on their health when the average ambient temperature lies around 44°C (Kaushish and Mittal, 1994).

Milk production performance

The milk yield of all mammalian species undergoes seasonal variation. The optimum environmental temperature for lactation depends on the species, breed and degree of tolerance to heat or cold. The milk yield of Holstein cattle declines at temperature above 21°C, in case of Brown Swiss and Jersey cattle it declines at about 24 to 27°C whereas milk yield of Zebu cattle declines only above 34°C. Observations in India on cross-bred cows have shown that the productivity of cross-bred of exotic breeds with indigenous breeds was not seriously affected by the hot dry climate in north western parts. On the other hand in hot humid coastal and eastern region of the country with heavy rainfall, the productivity was severely affected.

Shinde et al. (1990) observed that milk yield per day decreased with simultaneous increase in ambient temperature and humidity. Dutta et al. (1995) reported that temperature and humidity together caused 62.75% of variation in milk yield, which was higher than those exposed to either temperature or humidity. In a study on thermal stress and milk production in half-bred Holstein crosses (Karan Fries) and zebu cattle Sahiwal, the Karan Fries showed higher sensitivity for temperature rise (Singh and Upadhyay, 2009). When THI crosses the index value of 72 milk production declined, the average milk production of Karan Fries and Sahiwal animals was 13.4 and 6.6 litre / day at around THI of 72. The respective milk production decreased to around 9 and 5 litre / day at 82. The increase in each unit of THI reduced the milk production in the range of 72-82 THI by 0.43 and 0.16 litre/day/ animal, respectively. The lactation yield is influenced by season of calving in Tharparkar cattle, it was higher in winter season calvers (1438.8 litre) than summer season (1274.9 litre) in arid condition (Patel et al., 2000). But the milk fat content of Tharparkar cattle was found to be lowered in both hot dry (4.30%) and hot humid seasons (4.64%) whereas, higher percentage of fat was observed during autumn (5.24%) and winter season (5.25%) (Patel et al. 1994). Though the Marwari goat breeds of Thar Desert are well adapted against desert vagaries, but the productivity of these animals affected adversely due to extremes of climatic conditions. Marwari goats yield lower lactation milk yield during winter when housed in open type house (thatched roof animal shelter) in comparison to closed type pucca animal shelter in arid region. These goats yield 38 litres more milk in a lactation period of 154 days with higher milk fat content of 4.77 % (Patel et al., 2001). In a another study it was found 22% more lactation milk yield in Marwari goats when they were housed in closed type improved animal shelter than open type tradition animal shelter during winter season (Patel et al., 2007). The reason for higher milk yield in Marwari goats under improved animal shelter was due to protection of goats against cold exposure in winter season.

Reproductive performance

Heat stress affects the reproductive physiology in farm animal. In a study on effect of thermal stress on superovulatory response, the occurrence of estrus was late (30.6±1.2 h) with shorter estrus period (31.7±3.6 h) in a group of ewes exposed to thermal stress in comparison to group of ewes maintained under shed (Naqvi et al., 2000). However, the thermal protected ewes exhibited estrus earlier (25.5±1.1 h) and the estrus period was longer (37.7±1.6 h). The reproductive performance of Tharparkar cattle in terms of dry period and calving interval was not significantly influenced by season of calving but the results of the study showed that comparative lower dry period (101.9±23.3

days) and calving interval (414.5±27.9 days) was observed in winter season calvers than summer and rainy season calvers (Patel et al., 2000). On the other hand, Patel and Tripathi (1998) also observed that buffaloes calved in rainy season had higher reproductive efficiency in terms of lower service period (198.4±15.1 days) and calving interval (501.4±15.3 days). The optimum service period was 2 months in Tharparkar cattle and milk production and reproduction efficiency was higher (Patel et al., 2001).

The reproductive performance of Kutchi, Marwari and Beetal breeds of goat was studied. The average age at puberty, first conception and first kidding ranged from 311.2±5.43 to 560.0±6.52, 387.4±3.75 to 605.9±4.59 and 509.4±3.45 to 760.3±4.50 days, respectively. The average values for service period and kidding interval were shortest 157.00±1.30 and 305±4.56 days, respectively in Kutchi. The post-partum intervals were shortest in Kutchi and longest in Beetal. The tupping and conception rate were higher in Kutchi (Kaushish et al., 1994).

Growth performance

The body weight gain in young stock is an important aspect for economic benefit in any animal husbandry. The climatic stress particularly due to heat during growth period of animal reduced the body weight gain. Higher body weight gain was observed in the 6 month old male kids of Marwari breed, when reared under closed type improved animal shelter during summer months. Kids gained 9.52 kg body weight in improved animal's shelter than 7.52 kg in traditional animal shelter during 6 months period of experiment from May to October (Patel et al., 2007). The month of birth of lambs affects the body weights, lambs born in January to February were heaviest at 6 months body weight (30.6+0.93 kg) and decreasing trend in lambs born in subsequent months i.e. March to December time period was recorded (Poonia, 2004). Harsh environment conditions of arid zone coupled with low forage availability in grazing area affect the body weights of different goat breeds of semi-arid region. The lowest body weight of adult goats (22.8 kg) was observed in Parbatsari breed followed by Jhakrana and Jamunapari. However, highest body weight (31.0 kg) was recorded in native adult Marwari goats (Patel et al., 1998). But the supplementation enhanced the higher body weight gain in Jhakrana (54%), followed by Jamunapari (53%), Parbatsari (47%) and lowest in Marwari (16.2%). Rohilla and Khem Chand (2004) also observed a significant growth in Marwari kids when they were supplemented with concentrate feeds daily and on alternate day in arid conditions.

Present status of Shelter management practices in the arid region

A survey on shelter management practices in the arid region revealed that in arid western Rajasthan, only 10% farmer provide thatched house for small ruminants, while rest of the farmers keep their sheep and goat in enclosures without any roof structure. The materials used for making the enclosures are mainly thorny bushes. Though, the facilities of minimum shelter were found in majority of the farmers, but they prefer to tie their animals outside the animal house during comfortable season. However, during extreme environmental conditions e.g. rainy hours, extreme hot hours in mid-day in summer and cool hours in nights during peak winter, animals are housed inside the shelter.

Animal houses are often situated near the human dwellings to carryout the work related to animals easily. Many times, when farmers have limited number of animals for their domestic use, the animal houses are part of dwellings. In a survey study for housing, it was observed that 80% of animal houses were in rectangular shape and 20% in round shape. While the surrounding of open animal shelter was in round shape and mainly made by thorny bushes but some time stone slabs were also used for the purpose. The average dimensions of animal shelter were 12′ x 10′ x 7 ′for rectangular shape and 5-8′ radius for round shape. There is no fix set of rules for orientation of animal house but farmers make a wall in the north of the animal house to prevent the entry of cold air during winter. No pucca floor was observed in any animal shelters, in all the cases, only mud floor was seen. A slope was provided in floor towards the open space in most of the shelters, to avoid dampness. All the animal houses were well ventilated, as the height of walls of the house was much lower than the height of the roof. Observations of the microclimate of the thatched animal houses showed that the ambient temperature of the house was 2-4°C lower than the temperature outside the animal houses.

Local plant materials

Farmers use various types of local materials for the construction of thatch roof, wall and other parts of the houses. Most of these materials consisted of basically branches, twigs of shrubs / trees available in abundance in arid region (Table 1). The frequency of repairing of the thatched roof was once in one or two years, before the onset of winter season (October - November).

Feeding manger

Manger are made in almost all animal houses for large ruminants and iron pans are used for goats, but water troughs are found only in 20% animal houses, since the animals are taken for watering to common tanks or other water bodies of the village. The feed mangers are mostly made by stone slab, whereas, iron pan, wooden boxes and used tyres as feed manger. The average dimensions of the manger is 10′ x 1.5′ x 1′ for L x W x D, respectively.

Table 1. List of local plant materials used for making thatch house for livestock

S.No.	Plant Material	Utility area
1.	Aak (*Calotropis procera*)	Used in making side walls and roof
2.	Bui (*Aerva pseudotomentosa*)	Used in thatch roof manufacturing
3.	Bordi (*Zizyphus nummularia*)	Used for making thatch roof and side walls
4.	Babool twigs (*Prosopis juliflora*)	Used for preparation of thatch roof
5.	Khimp (*Leptadenia pyrotechnica*)	Used for preparation of thatch roof
6.	Shinio (*Crotalaria burhia*)	Used for preparation of thatch roof

Drainage system

The drainage system to dispose the urine and faecal material is not common in animal houses since the pacca floor is not found; only soil floor is common in almost every animal house, since, soil floor directly absorbed the animal waste due to low relative humidity in the arid environment.

Ancillary structure

Feed storage structure is common in the region, which could be due to the higher value of feed and fodder for livestock husbandry. Farmers give due care in storing the feed and fodder for longer time to deal with the lean period within year as well as in drought years which are common feature of the area. About 80% farmers construct pacca and semi pacca type structure for feed storage while 20% farmers store their feed material in kutcha or traditional type of structures.

Systematic housing system is not found for small ruminants, where proper alley or passage is present and no separate house is provided to pregnant, sick animals and breeding male but newborn kids or lambs are provided separate closed type house to protect them from predation and cold climate. In general three types of shelters for livestock are observed in the rural areas of the arid zone, viz; open housing system (enclosure without any roof), Kutcha (thatched roof house) and Pucca housing system (closed type pucca house) (Patel et al., 2005).

Improved animal shelter (IAS) for goats

It was observed from the studies conducted on various type of housing systems that a close type housing system with open space is better for both hot and cold weather conditions of the arid zone in comparison to traditional animal housing system i.e. thatched roof semi-open type animal shelter. An improved animal shelter was designed and developed considering orientation, wind direction, sun movement, air temperature, local materials for construction etc. Improved animal shelter consists of angle iron frame, asbestos sheet and stone slabs. Heavy duty angle iron (50x50x6mm) frame was fabricated and fixed on the ground by grouting. Seven heavy duty trusses were also fabricated and fixed at ten feet interval for proper distribution of asbestos roof load (Mishra et al., 2006)

The orientation of the shelter was kept east-west direction; the long axis of shelter is 60 ft, which was open from south direction and north direction. Hence, this orientation with generous provision for ventilation / air movement help to dry up threshold was found most suitable. Furthermore, the south facing shelter has advantage of receiving larger solar radiation during winters than during summer. Small over hang on south faced can cut off direct solar radiation during summer but allow during winter. It also gives protection from rains. The open space of north axis was covered by plastic curtain to minimize the entry of cold winds inside the shelter during winter.

The double slope roof of the shelter was made by corrugated asbestos cement sheets (1x3mtrs.) on angle iron frame. The roof height was 10 feet from centre and 7 feet from sides. Four inch thick thatch panels were fixed just below the asbestos sheets to provide insulation. The sidewalls were erected using stone slabs with 4ft height in north faced and 3ft in south faced. The floor was elevated 1ft from the ground and filled with calcified soil to give compactness, which can absorb the urine and faecal material.

The feeding manger of 50 ft length was constructed along with the wall of north side of shelter using stone slabs of side. The height of manger was kept 1ft 9 inch from the ground level with 9 inch depth and 12 inch width for holding ample quantity of feed material. The manger was also facilitated with slanting slope from outer to inner side, which helps in sliding of feeding materials while feeding to the goats. A ladder type structure of 1" diameter G.I. Pipe has also been fixed on outside wall of the manger to prevent entry of the goats inside of the manger to avoid the wastage of feed materials. In the same direction a 10ft. long water trough with similar dimensions was also constructed in the corner of the shelter.

Microclimate of improved animal shelter

Minimum-maximum temperature and related humidity inside the Improved Animal Shelter (IAS) was recorded. The *'Improved Animal Shelter'* provides more comfortable environment to the goats than the *'Traditional Animal Shelter'* (TAS) as the maximum average temperature in IAS was found lower (35.7°C, range 31-40.3°C) during summer months (March to September) in comparison to TAS (37.2°C, range 32.7-42.4°C). However during winter from October to March the higher values of minimum temperature (14.7°C, range 12.7-18.1°C) was recorded in IAS than TAS (13.1°C, range 11.1-16.4°C). The maximum average temperature in IAS was also found slightly higher (30.8°C) compared to 29.8°C in TAS.

In IAS, the higher value of minimum temperature was mainly due to the absence of direct entry of air temperature inside close type animal house, secondly the minimum temperature was attained usually in absence of thermal radiation during the time beyond midnight, remained higher in closed type animal shelter, because of inadequacies in loss of absorbed heat and low ventilation also add to this effect. The lower values of maximum temperature in IAS during summer months could be due to the failure of direct sunlight to reach inside closed type animal shelter and thatched roof insulation, which prevent the rise of ambient temperature beyond that in open, whereas the refection radiation in addition to direct radiation caused higher maximum temperature in TAS. The higher level of relative humidity in IAS has been observed, which could be due to low ventilation means and less airflow inside shelter.

Production performance of goats under improved animal shelter

Milk production performance

The study showed that despite of better adaptability of Marwari breed to harsh climate of region, goats of traditional animal shelter (TAS) produced lower milk yield (129.3 lit.) during lactation than the goats of IAS group, which produced 157.6 lit of milk. The peak yield of the group was 1.46 lit as compared to 1.38 lit in Group-I (Table-2). The reason for higher milk production performance in IAS was probably due to complete protection of goats from cold exposure during winter season. Whereas, the goats housed in traditional shelter were exposed due to open type shelter with only simple thatched roof at 10′ height. During night in winter, the effective temperature of the outs side was much lower than the absolute air temperature because of increased radiant losses to the sky. This result in increase in the rate of loss of body heat and therefore, the feed energy is utilized for maintaining the optimum body temperature rather than for the production of milk. On the other hand, the provision of proper shelter i.e. closed type with open space reduces the animal requirement for energy. Thus, the energy available with the animal is utilized for production purpose in proper shelter conditions.

Table 2 Lactation performance of Marwari goats under different housing systems

Parameters	Traditional Animal Shelter	Improved Animal Shelter
90 days lactation yield (lit)	64.0±6.2	69.3±5.0
Total lactation yield (lit)	129.3±10.1	157.6±20.8
Lactation length (days)	180.5±17.5	193.0±18.8
Peak yield (lit)	1.38±0.14	1.46±0.16
Fat (%)	3.42±0.13	3.60±0.10
SNF (%)	8.18±0.10	8.29±0.07
Total solid (%)	11.69±0.19	11.89±0.18

The kidding in goats takes place during the period from mid September to December months in arid region. The first two winter months October and November are comfortable for the goats. However in later two to three months i.e. from December to February, animals experience cold stress especially during night hours due to lower ambient temperature and blowing chilled air (Fig.1). As per the lactation curve, peak lactation in goats is achieved during these months. The peak lactation of the goats during winter can be achieved in Improved Animal shelter. Keeping this finding, therefore housing practice should be adopted for achieving optimum milk yield in goats.

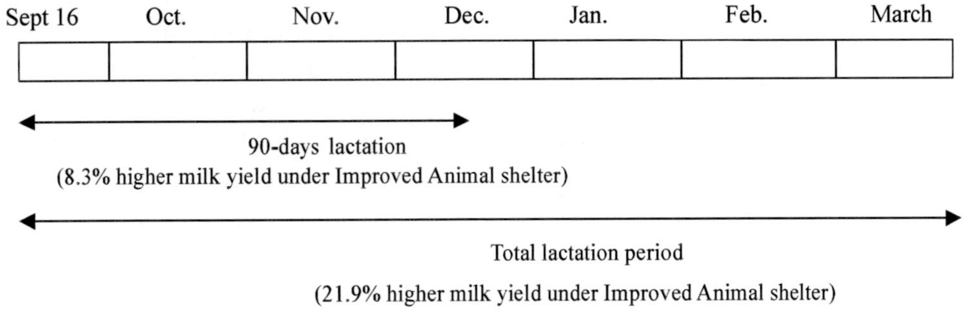

Fig. 1 Lactation period of Marwari goats in a calendar year

Growth performance

Six month old Marwari and Parbatsari kids were maintained under Traditional Animal Shelter (TAS), whereas, kids of another group were kept under Improved Animal Shelter (IAS). The lower minimum temperature was observed in TAS, whereas, the lower maximum temperature was observed in

IAS during the summer period from May to October months. The micro-climate of TAS was close to macro-environment because it was open from all sides and only roof is covered by thatch for providing shade to the animals.

The kids were kept for six months period from May to October, which was hot dry and hot-wet weather. Both the groups were stall fed with 400 g/day of lentil dry fodder and 200 g pellet concentrate feed (CP 18%) up to end of June, after that the quantity of fodder was increased to @ 600 g/day. Kids were also let out for grazing in closed fenced area of the farm from July onwards. The animals of Group-I were let out after 10 AM for three hours and Group-II was let out in early morning from 7 AM to 10 AM. Water was supplied *ad labium* to the animals.

Table 3 Water intake (lit) of male kids in two different housing systems during hot months

Months	Improved Animal Shelter	Traditional Animal Shelter	Difference	Percent Difference
May	1.76	2.18	0.42	23.9
June	1.80	2.45	0.65	36.1
July	1.32	1.60	0.28	21.2
August	1.37	1.41	0.04	2.92
Average	1.56	1.91	0.35	21.03

Higher water intake was observed in kids of Group-I (1.91 lit./day/kid) than the Group-II (1.56 lit/day/kid).The difference between water intake in two groups was more visible during hot dry months in comparison to hot humid months (Table 3). Higher body weight gain was achieved in kids of Group II. The average body weight gain was 10.2 kg in kids kept under Improved Animal Shelter, whereas it was 7.8 kg in kids of Group I (Traditional Animal Shelter).

When these breeds were compared, higher body weight gain was found in Parbatsari than Marwari kids, but the difference in between two breeds was more visible in IAS group (Fig. 4). Parbatsari kids gained 10.85 kg body weight and Marwari gained 9.52 kg in Group II, whereas, body weight gain was more or less similar in both breeds in Group I, which was 7.52 and 8.00 kg for Marwari and Parbatsari kids, respectively (Table 4).

Body weight trend in lactating goats

The study showed that the body weights of Marwari goats were not influenced by type of shelters (Patel et al., 2007). Month wise body weight of adult Marwari goats from January to December are presented in the Table 5. The body weight of the goats were observed to be constant from January to June, but in the first months of monsoon i.e. in July, animals lost their body weights may be due to change in availability of feed and fodder. The animals are totally dependent on available green grasses in pasture, which contained more water during early monsoon. Later on, the body weight of adult goats increased continuously from August onwards till October, due to advancing pregnancy. The body weight again decreased slightly in November month due to kidding of the goats (Fig. 3).

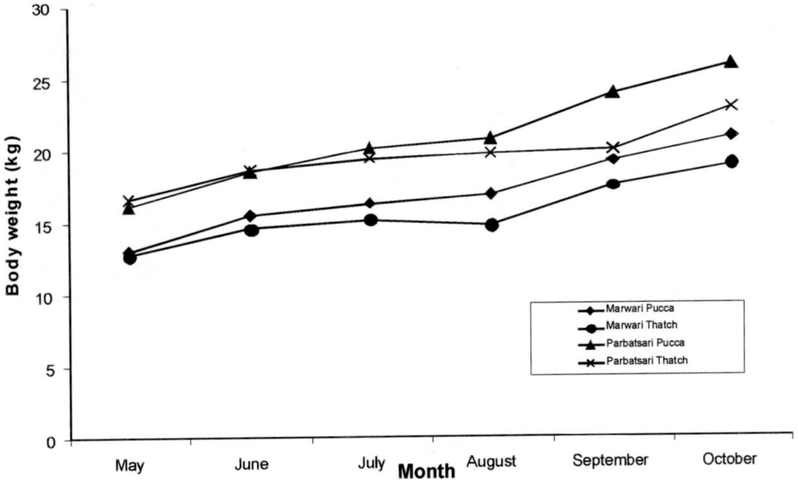

Fig. 2 Body weight gain of male kid under different housing system

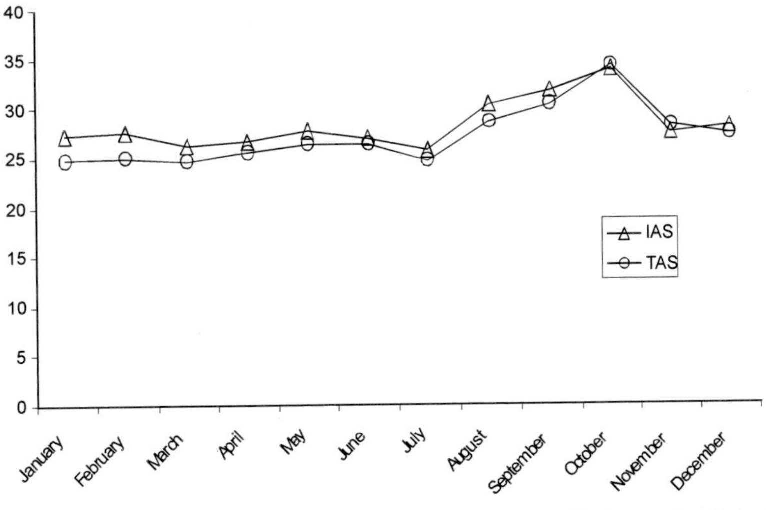

Fig. 3. Monthly body weight of adult Marwari goats in two different animal shelters

Table 4 Body weight of male kids under different housing systems during hot season

Type of shelter/age	Traditional Animal Shelter		Pucca Animal Shelter	
	Marwari	Parbatsari	Marwari	Parbatsari
6 months	12.24±1.84	16.60±1.87	12.52±2.06	15.60±2.21
9 months	14.16±2.14	19.30±1.21	16.24±2.37	20.10±2.18
12 months	19.76±2.00	24.60±2.46	22.04±2.64	26.45±2.34
Body weight gain	7.52±0.60	8.00±0.68	9.52±0.70	10.85±0.43

Table 5. Body weight (kg) of adult Marwari goats in two systems of housing

Months	Traditional Animal Shelter	Improved Animal Shelter
January	24.80±2.33	27.35±2.51
February	24.95±2.01	27.58±2.09
March	24.70±1.68	26.15±1.59
April	25.65±1.63	26.66±1.59
May	26.37±1.74	27.70±1.57
June	26.33±1.41	27.03±1.40
July	24.66±1.18	25.82±1.25
August	28.47±1.05	30.38±1.53
September	30.40±0.89	31.69±1.98
October	34.13±1.29	33.80±1.51
November	28.23±2.49	27.45±1.32
December	27.25±1.80	28.11±1.49

Behavioural changes

The behavioural changes in goats due to climatic variations under different housing system were also studied. During early morning hours of cold days, when minimum temperature was 8 degree °C with cold waves from north direction, goats in open housing system showed shelter-seeking behaviour. Animals tried to conserve body heat by reducing the body surface area with erected coat hair and huddling. While, the goats of pacca housing system (closed type) remained inside the closed area of the shelter. The low atmospheric temperature together with chilled winds affects the productivity to a greater extent because wind increases the loss of body heat from the surface of an animal.

Conclusions

Although, the livestock breeds of arid region are resistant to high and low environmental temperature, but they do suffer from extremes of hot and cold seasons, when exposed to upper and below critical temperature. Tree shed is common available shelter for the livestock. Closed type shelter with open space for free movement for livestock, is found to be most suitable animal shelter in arid zone.

References

Burke, S. 1998. Wind breaks. Butterworth-Heinemann, Woburn, Massachusetts, USA.

Dutta, T., Taneja, V.K. and Singh, A. 1995. Effect of climatic variables on average daily milk production in crossbred cattle. Indian Journal of Animal Sciences, 65(a): 1004-1007.

Flamenbaum, I. 1998. Management of dairy cows in hot climatic conditions. Pashudhan 13(6):1

Hooda, O.K. and Naqvi, S.M.K. 1990. Effect of thermal load and feed restriction on the relative adaptability of Malpura and Avikalin sheep in semi-arid region. Indian Journal of Animal Sciences, 60:608-611.

Kaushish, S.K and Mittal, J. P. 1994. Physiological responses of sheep and goats to exercise stress under arid conditions. Indian Journal of Animal Sciences 64:423-424.

Kaushish, S. K., Singh Dharam and Paul Satya. 1994. Productive and reproductive performance of different breeds of goats under semi-arid conditions. Indian Veterinary Journal 71: 565-568.

Kaushish, S. K., Georgia, G. C. and Sengupta, B. P. 1987. Effect of heat and water restriction on physiological response of Beetal and Black Bengal goats. Indian Veterinary Journal 66:852-856.

Kaushish, S. K., Karim, S. A. and Rawat , P.S. 1989. Response of native and cross bred sheep to solar exposure during summer in semi-arid region. Indian Veterinary Journal 66: 852-856.

Kaushish, S. K., Sengupta, B. P. and Georgie, G. C. 1997. Effect of thermal stress and water restriction on cortisol level of Beetal and Black Bengal goats. Indian Journal of Animal Sciences 63:1277-1279.

Mishra, Dinesh, Patel, A.K. and Singh, Harpal 2006. Development of improved animal shelter for arid region. National Symposium on Livelihood Security and Diversified Farming Systems in Arid Region, January 14-16, CAZRI, Jodhpur. pp59-60

Naqvi, S.M.K., Maurya, V.P., Gulyani, R., Joshi, A. and J. P. Mittal 2000. The effect of thermal stress on supervolatory response and embryo production in Bharat Merino ewes. Small Ruminant Research 55:57-63.

Ocfenia, G.O., Sharma, A., Miller, H.M. and Holmes, J.H.G. 1993. Reduced foetal growth and lactation by does heat-stressed from mid-pregnancy. Small Ruminant Research 11: 33-43.

Patel, A. K., Rohilla, P.P. and Mathur, A. C. 2007. Performance of Marwari kids and goats under improved and traditional animal shelter. Indian Veterinary Journal 84:1069-1071.

Patel, A.K. and Tripathi, V.N. 1998. Effect of non genetic factors on economic traits of Surti buffalo. Indian Journal of Animal Sciences 68: 566-569.

Patel, A.K., Bohra, H.C. and. Kaushish, S.K. 1998. Effect of supplementation on comparative weight gain of certain goat breeds in arid zone. Indian Journal of Small Ruminants 4 :91-93.

Patel, A.K., Mathur, A.C. and Mishra D. 2005. Traditional shelter management practices for livestock in arid region. In: Proceedings of the National Conference on Bridging Gap between Ancient Technologies to Increase Agricultural productivity. December 16-18, CAZRI, Jodhpur pp53-54

Patel, A.K., Mathur, B.K., Mathur, A.C., Mittal, J.P. and Kaushish, S.K. 2000. Productive and reproductive performance of Tharparkar cattle in hot arid region. Indian Journal Animal Sciences 70 : 530-532.

Patel, A.K., Mathur, A.C. and Mittal, J.P. 1994. Factors affecting composition of milk in Tharparkar cows maintained under arid conditions. Indian Journal Animal Production and Management 10: 102-105.

Patel, A.K., Patil, N.V., Mathur, A. C. and Rao, A. S. 2009. Environmental stress and milk production of Tharparkar cattle in arid zone. International Conference on Nurturing Arid Zones For People and the Environment: Issues and Agenda for the 21st Century CAZRI, Jodhpur November 24-28, pp 248.

Patel, A.K., Paharia, S. and Nagpaul, P.K. 2001. Productive performance of Marwari goats under different shelters in arid region. Indian Journal Animal Production and Management 17: 76-78.

Patel, A.K., Mathur, A. C., Mathur, B. K. and Kaushish, S. K. 2001. Optimum service period of Tharparkar cattle under arid conditions. XVII Annual Convention and National Seminar on Fertility Management of Farm Animals under Adverse Agro-climate Conditions. Jodhpur, October 6-8, pp 108.

Poonia, J.S. 2004. Growth performance of Munjal lambs. Indian Journal of Small Ruminants 10 :137-139.

Rohilla, P.P. and Chand, K. 2004. Effect of supplemental feeding on growth of kids and milk yield of Marwari goats. Indian Journal of Small Ruminants 10 (2):143-146.

Shinde, A. K., Bhatta, Raghavendra., Sankhyan, S. K. and Verma, D.L. 2002. Effect of season on thermoregulatory responses and energy expenditure of goats on semi-arid range in India. Journal of Agricultural Science (Cambridge) 139:1:87-93.

Shinde, S., Taneja, V.K. and Singh. M.K. 1990. Association of climatic variables and production and reproductive trait in crossbred. Indian Journal of Animal Sciences, 60 :81-85.

Singh, M., Tyagi, A. K., Mehla, R. K. and Singh, C. 2003. Milk production performance of cows under two different sets of management during summer. Indian Journal of Animal Sciences 73: 692-694.

Singh, P., Dixit, V. P., Singh, B. and Georgie, G.C. 2001. Plasma aldosterone and major circulatory and urinary electrolytes in buffalo calves as affected by peak summer and winter stress. International Journal of Animal Science 16 :161-166.

Singh, S. V. and Upadhyay, R. C. 2009. Thermal stress on physiological functions, thermal balance and milk production in Karan Fries and Sahiwal cows. Indian Veterinary Journal 86:141-144.

❑❑❑

15

Adaptation of Sheep and Goats to Cold Arid Climates

M.A. Kirmani, N.A. Ganai, and K.A. Shah
Faculty of Veterinary Sciences and Animal Husbandry, Sher-e-Kashmir University of Agricultural Sciences and Technology of Kashmir, Shuhama -190006 Srinagar

Introduction

Despite extreme environmental conditions and persistent hypoxia and limited grazing resources, a great variety of livestock species and wealth of animal life are available in Ladakh. Livestock production is the major land-use in Ladakh region of the Indian Trans-Himalaya, and is a crucial sector that drives the region's economy. Under cold arid desert conditions, where feed resources are restricted in quantity and limited in quality, differences among ruminants in energy requirements and digestive efficiency form a very important criterion for the selection of the most appropriate type to be bred in particular circumstances (Devendra, 1990). The animal genetic resources of the Cold arid desert of Ladakh have evolved to adapt and perform under very adverse climatic conditions. Among the livestock species, sheep and goat contribute the major share towards the livelihood security of the people in the region. These species have evolved special adaptability features. The Changthung goat also known as Pashmina or Cashmere produces a dual cover of the fibre: an outer cover of rough guard fibers and an undercoat of the very fine pashmina of 11-15 micron diameter. The undercoat protects the goat from the very cold temperatures (upto – 40°C) during winter. The small ruminants of the arid desert are also reported to reduce their energy requirements by as much as 65% in response to reduction in feed availability. They are also the most efficient utilizers of high-fiber, low-quality fodder, among ruminants. Animal products like meat and milk provide protein to the diet of people, while products like wool and *pashmina* (soft fibre of goats) find their way to the international market. Livestock in Ladakh are also essential for ploughing the fields and for transportation. Livestock Husbandry is therefore an important part of economy of the district.

Animal production problems associated with weather and climate require a knowledge of how potential environmental stressors (ambient temperature, humidity, thermal radiation, air speed) can directly and adversely affect animal performance such as survival, growth, reproduction, milk, and wool when coping capabilities of the animals are exceeded The indirect consequences of weather episodes, such as feed quality and availability, must also be recognized, to evolve the best possible strategies to make these animals perform better to augment the nutritional and livelihood security of the people in the region.

Ladakh topography and climatic conditions

The typical geographic location of J & K state coupled with varied physiography divides it into three main climatic zones: sub-tropical Jammu region, temperate Kashmir region and cold –arid Ladakh region. The cold arid region of western Himalayas mainly comprise of Ladakh area of J & K and some parts of the Lahul-Spiti and Kinnaur districts of Himachal Pradesh. The Ladakh region covers an area of 96701 km^2 accounting to 43% of the geographic area of J & K. The terrain is mostly mountainous and denuded with exception of some parts of Kargil district. Geographically Ladakh has several natural divisions, separated from each other by many passes and mountain ranges. The region has highest average elevations ranging from 12000 to 18000 ft above mean sea level. The temperature in Leh shows wide seasonal variations and diurnal fluctuations. The latter are due to very clear skies and quick loss of heat from bare soils during night rains are scanty, snowfall is little, dry and powdry. Ladakh is aptly classified as an arctic desert for its aridity and coldness. The monsoon clouds hardly penetrate Ladakh, as it is situated in the rain-shadow of the Greater Himalaya. Thus the magnitude of precipitation is low and erratic. The mean annual precipitation hardly crosses 93 mm. The precipitation is mostly in the form of snow in winter, which is associated with the extra-tropical disturbances of mid-latitudes known as "Western Disturbances". Howling winds, cold night temperatures and frigid winters with temperatures dropping to -40°C in peak winter (Dec-Jan) to ±35°C in summer. Table 1 gives an insight of the extreme weather conditions in comparison to the other agro-climatic zones of the country.

Table 1 Metrological data in 4 different climatic zones in the Country

Month	Temperature (°C) Min.	Max.	Mean Total Rainfall (mm)	Mean No. of Rainy Days	Mean Number of days with Hail	Thunder	Fog	Squall
Hot-Arid	7	45	673.9	36.8	0.4	46.0	1.7	4.4
Hot-Humid	15	38	1542.2	73.0	0.5	77.5	11.3	3.7
Cold-Arid	**- 25**	**35**	**< 100**	**< 15**				
Temperate	- 3	30	674.9	55.1	0.8	6.3	4.7	0.0

Vegetation in ladakh

The Trans-Himalayan cold desert is included in the Oriental zoo-geographic realm, though biologically it confirms largely to the Palaearctic, the landscape is characterized by a distinct lack of natural forests, the vegetation being primarily sparse characterized by dry alpine steppe, showing a high degree of endemism (Rawat and Adhikari, 2002). There are no trees in the area except in glens and oases. The major trees along the river banks and valleys are poplar *Populus* spp. and willow *Salix* spp. The most common vegetation includes *Caragana* spp., *Artemisia* spp. and *Eurotia* sp., which are found almost everywhere in the area. *Aconogonum* sp. The major graminoid species are *Stipa* spp., *Poa* spp., *Elymus* spp., *Festuca* sp., *Carex* spp. and *Kobresia* sp., the latter two mostly occurring along streambeds *Thermospsis* sp. occurs on sandy slopes where the sheep prefer to rest. Some other common forbs in the area include *Potentilla* spp., *Oxytropis* spp., *Astragalus* spp., *Dracocephalum* sp. etc.

Animal biodiversity in ladakh

Despite extreme environmental conditions and persistent hypoxia and limited grazing resources, a great variety of livestock species and wealth of animal life are available in Ladakh. Livestock production is the major land-use in Ladakh region of the Indian Trans-Himalaya, and is a crucial sector that drives the region's economy. Animal products like meat and milk provide protein to the diet of people, while products like wool and *pashmina* (soft fibre of goats) find their way to the international market. Livestock in Ladakh are also essential for ploughing the fields and for transportation. Animal Husbandry is and will continue to be an important part of economy of the district. Livestock rearing is an important occupation of the village folk. Such high utility of livestock and their support to the livelihood have resulted in the increase in the in livestock population (Rawat and Adhikari, 2002). Table 2 and 3 gives the type and numbers of the livestock species and the status pashmina production in the region.

Adaptability features of goat and sheep

Goats and sheep generally perform better than other ruminants in terms of survival, reproduction and expression of their genetic potential for growth, fibre, and milk yield under adverse climatic conditions.

Pashmina- the under-coat in goats to counter cold stress

As a natural adaptation to the freezing temperatures of the cold arid desert conditions of Ladakh region, the fleece of Changthangi goats is made up of two distinct fibers: the coarse outer hair and the ultra-fine pashmina (cashmere) undercoat. The coarse outer hair is called guard hair. The fine undercoat (under 15 microns) is the source of Cashmere fiber for clothing. Pashmina popularly known as Cashmere is a unique textile fiber well known for its fineness, softness, warmth and having desirable handle and aesthetic value. The high cost and the rare availability are the notable features of the cashmere. The overall pashmina production by Changthangi pashmina goats is 248 ± 4.2 g (Ganai et al., 2004).

Table 2 Livestock biodiversity in Ladakh region

<table>
<tr><th rowspan="2">Category of Animals</th><th colspan="4">Number of Heads</th></tr>
<tr><th>1987</th><th>1992</th><th>1997</th><th>2002</th></tr>
<tr><td>Cattle</td><td>23907</td><td>24836</td><td>34813</td><td>37,829</td></tr>
<tr><td>DZo-Dzomes</td><td>11756</td><td>11855</td><td>18525</td><td>10,627</td></tr>
<tr><td>Sheep</td><td>56879</td><td>79579</td><td>94788</td><td>1,56,581</td></tr>
<tr><td>Goat
Pashmina Goat</td><td>108944</td><td>110930</td><td>1,50,000</td><td>2,53,493</td></tr>
<tr><td>Yak</td><td rowspan="2">18454</td><td rowspan="2">19916</td><td>9256</td><td>13276</td></tr>
<tr><td>Others</td><td>16106</td><td>12355</td></tr>
<tr><td>Camel (doule humped)</td><td></td><td></td><td></td><td>150</td></tr>
<tr><td>Total</td><td>219820</td><td>247116</td><td>333759</td><td>47,3111</td></tr>
<tr><td>Poultry</td><td>8659</td><td>8858</td><td>10972</td><td>20,494</td></tr>
</table>

Table 3 Sheep and Goat Production in Leh (Wani et al., 2007)

Year	Pashmina Production	Pashmina Goat Population	Non-Pashmina Goat population	Total Goat Population	Sheep
1995-96	32000	146216	70604	364685	147865
1996-97	32400	147812	77385	373961	148764
1997-98	31900	145980	84784	383905	153141
1998-99	32500	146890	93389	396160	155881
1999-00	32656	133288	105891	397813	158634
2000-01	34532	157663	97957	421188	165568
2001-02	34200	156493	80048	399024	162483
2002-03	41900	209821	84042	471161	177298
2003-04	42000	229656	70227	482627	182744
2004-05	48000	227416	67534	479388	184438
2005-06	40000	196383	62339	396475	137753
CGR (%)	3.70	4.94	-2.02		

Energy requirements

Low body weight (BW) and low metabolic rates help desert goats to maintain a frugal energy and water economy. *Some of* the desert breeds of goat are reported to reduce their energy requirements by as much as 65% in response to reduction in feed availability. The digestibility of dry matter and structural carbohydrates found in some breeds of desert goats fed on highly-lignified diets exceeds considerably than other domesticated ruminants. The capacity of goats to consume high-tannin browse and to detoxify the tannin is higher than that found in sheep and cattle under comparable conditions. These advantages are probably related to the ability of goats to control effectively their rumen environment. Maintaining a spacious rumen allows a longer retention time of feed particles without negatively affecting feed intake. In addition, maintaining a steady pH in the rumen, and efficient recycling of key nutrients such as nitrogen and sulfur, enable goats to maintain a maximal. ruminal fermentation rate at given conditions.

Table 4 Body Weights (kg) of Changthangi goats at different ages (Ganai et al., 2004)

Age	Sex	N	Mean with SE
Birth	Male	341	1.47 ± 0.08
	Female	346	1.54 ± 0.07
	Overall	687	1.51 ± 0.05
3 months	Male	325	7.89 ± 0.28
	Female	316	7.45 ± 0.18
	Overall	641	7.68 ± 0.07
6 months	Male	340	14.45 ± 0.38
	Female	333	14.45 ± 0.37
	Overall	673	14.30 ± 0.27
9 months	Male	352	15.94 ± 0.20
	Female	356	13.40 ± 0.17
	Overall	608	15.51 ± 0.14
18 months	Male	385	16.67 ± 0.17
	Female	372	16.12 ± 0.17
	Overall	757	16.71 ± 0.12
24 months	Male	398	23.22 ± 0.29
	Female	398	23.42 ± 0.8
	Overall	796	23.32 ± 0.20

Small body size in goats in adverse environments

Bergmann's rule (1847) is probably the best known rule in zoogeography. It states that in warm-blooded animals, races from warm regions are smaller than races from cold regions. It is a purely empirical generalization, describing a correlation between morphological variation and ambient temperature

(Mayr, 1970). Other scientists suggested that body size is better correlated with primary plant productivity (Rozenzweig, 1968), desiccation (James, 1970), and type and quality of food (Nab, 1971; Calder, 1984), than with temperature. However, body size may be determined by a combination of all these factors which in desert areas are highly interrelated. Therefore under harsh conditions, goats are of small size. Three factors seem to account for this (Epstein, 1971): natural selection, artificial selection, and inbreeding. Natural selection is most likely the most important single factor: under unfavourable conditions, dwarfed individuals are better adapted than the bulk of the ordinary stock. The pressure of selection brought a gradual alteration in the size of the stock through the slightly higher survival and reproduction rates of small animals.

Low metabolic requirements

The classical concept of Kleiber (1961) that the energy requirements of a mammal is a simple function of 'body mass' imply that the energy requirement per kg weight of body tissue in small mammals is relatively greater than that in large mammals. The enhanced metabolic requirements of a small ruminant cannot be met by diets rich in cellulosic matter, because anaerobic fermentation is a relatively slow process and is bioenergetically less efficient than other forms of digestion (Van Soest, 1982). However, small desert breeds of goat have been found to be the most efficient utilizers of high-fiber, low-quality food, among ruminants (Silanikove, 1986a,b). In general, it appears that there is a contradiction between Bergmann's rule and the mass-metabolic requirement concept, because body size does not explain morpho-physiological feeding type in ruminants (Hofmann, 1989).

Digestive efficiency in relation to feeding strategies

With high-fiber, low-quality forages, goats have better digestive efficiency than other ruminants, one of the main reason for this being their longer mean retention time of digesta in the rumen (Devendra, 1990; Tisserand et al., 1991). Numerous experimental results strongly suggest that in most grazing areas in which goats are raised, the forage available to them is highly fibrous, with a relatively high lignin content, and a moderate to low protein content (Ramirez, 1996). In addition, the forage available to goats frequently contains secondary metabolites, such as tannins, which further constrain food utilization (Lu, 1988; Kababya, 1994). This situation is in accordance with the finding that in most cases, breeds of goats which are indigenous to semi-arid and arid areas are able to utilize high-fibre low-quality, food more efficiently than other types of indigenous ruminants, or exotic breeds of goats (Tisserand et al., 1991). The most remarkable feature of the intermediate selector ruminants is their short-term or seasonal anatomical adaptations to changes in forage quality

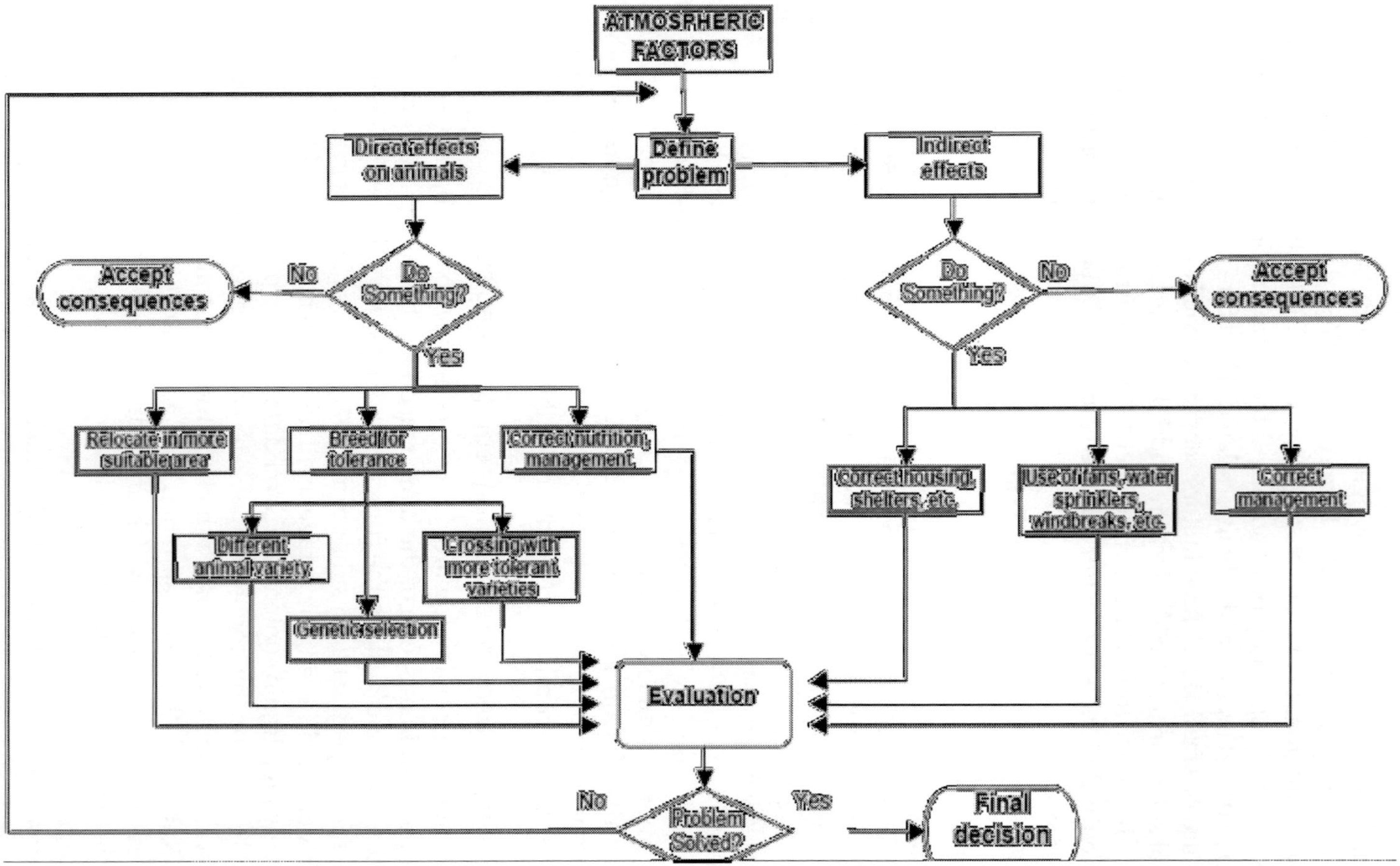

Fig. 1. Decision diagram for managers, considering livestock environment modification

(Hofmann, 1989). The corresponding morphophysiological adaptations are: (i) larger salivary glands, which ensure a higher capacity to secrete serosal buffered parotid saliva than that of grass and roughage eaters and (ii) a higher surface area of absorptive mucosa than is found in grass and roughage eaters.

Conclusion

Animal production problems associated with weather and climate require a knowledge of how potential environmental stressors (ambient temperature, humidity, thermal radiation, air speed) can directly and adversely affect animal performance such as survival, growth, reproduction, milk, and wool when coping capabilities of the animals are exceeded (Figure 1). The indirect consequences of weather episodes, such as feed quality and availability, must also be recognized.

Weather and climate influence both farm animal production and agronomic production. However, there are many differences, some obvious and some subtle, in the way animals and plants respond directly and indirectly to given environments. Management intervention is needed not only to improve the genetic potential of the animals but to ameliorate the constraints on production set by the climate, the physical environment and the health hazards in a region. On-farm decisions usually involve selection, design and management of production facilities, while the collective impacts may guide regional or national policy, determine responses to potential large-scale changes, or influence other decisions. The case for understanding the implications of regional and local climates affecting those decisions is self-evident, as is the need for timely forecasts to trigger management anticipation and response to adverse conditions.

References

Bergmann, C. (1847). Uber die verhaltnisse der warmekonomie der thiere zu Ihrer grosse. Gottinger Studien, 1 : 595-708.

Calder, W.A. (1984). Size, Function and Life History. Harvard University Press, Cambridge.

Devendra, C. (1990). Comparative aspects of digestive physiology and nutrition in goats and sheep. In: Ruminant Nutritiona and Physiology in Asia, Devendra, C. and Imazumi, E. (Eds). pp. 45-60.

Epstein, H. (1971). The Origin of the Domestic Animals of Africa. Vol. II. Edition Leipzig, Germany.

Ganai, T. A. S., Tundup, T., Kirmani, M. A. and Ganai, N. A. (2004). Pashmina growth in Changthangi goats beyond period of longest and shortest day. Paper presented in National Symposium on Conservation and propagation of Livestock and Poultry.

Feb. 26-28, 2004. GB Pant University of Agricultural Sciences and Technology, Pantnagar, Uttaranchal.

Hofmann, R.R. (1989). Evolutionary steps of ecophysiological adaptation and diversification of ruminants: A comparative view of their digestive system. Oecologia, 78: 443-457.

James, F.C. (1970). Geographic size relation in birds and its relationship with climate. Ecology, 70: 1526-1 539.

Kababya, D. (1994). Grazing behaviour and nutrition of goats in Mediterranean woodland. Master Thesis, The Hebrew University of Jerusalem.

Kleiber, M. (1961). The Fire of Life: An Introduction to Animal Energetics, Willey, New York.

Lu, C.D. (1988). Grazing behaviour and diet selection of goats. Small Ruminant Research, 1: 205-216.

Mayr, E. (1970). Population, Species and Evolution. Harvard University Press, Cambridge.

Nab, B.K. (1971). On the ecological significance of Bergmann's rule,. Ecology, 52: 845-854.

Mill, E. (1990). Investigation into the grazing of the Mediterranean shrub vegetation of northeast Tunisia by goats, particularly in relation to stocking density. Animal Research Development, 32: 7-39. CIHEAM - Options Mediterraneennes ires

Ramirez, R.G. (1996). Feed value of browse. In: International Conference on Goats, International Academic Publishers, Beijing, China, Vol. 2, pp. 510-527.

Rawat, G. S. and Adhikari, B. S. 2002. Vegetation characteristics and patterns of livestock grazing in Changthang plateau, eastern Ladakh. Report submitted to ICIMOD, Nepal and WII, Dehra Dun. 32p.

Rosenzweig, M.L. (1968). The strategy of body size in mammalian carnivores. American Midland Naturalist, 80: 299-315.

Silanikove, N. (1986a). Interrelationships between feed quality, digestibility, feed consumption, and energy requirements in desert (Bedouin) and non-desert (Saanen) goats. Journal of Dairy Science, 69: 2157-2612 .

Silanikove, N. (1986b). Feed utilization, energy and nitrogen balance in desert black Bedouin goats. World Review of Animal Production, 2 : 93-96.

Tisserand, J. L., Hadjipanayiotou, M. and Gihad, E.A. (1991). Digestion in Goats. Chapter 5. In: Goat Nutrition, Morand-Fehr, P. (ed.).

van Soest, P.J. (1 982). Nutritional Ecology of Ruminant. Corvallis, Or, O. and B. Books Inc.

Wani S. A. and Wani M. H. (2007). Economics of Pashmina production under pastoralist Nomadic System of Management in Cold arid region of Jammu and Kashmir. World Journal of Agricultural sciences 3(6):788-795.

❑❑❑

16

Physiological Adaption of Sheep to Hot Environmental Conditions with Special Reference to Climate Change

S.M.K. Naqvi* and V. Sejian
Division of Physiology & Biochemistry
Central Sheep & Wool Research Institute, Avikanagar, District Tonk, Rajasthan-304501

Introduction

A major proportion of sheep population (>70%) thrives well in arid and semi-arid areas of western region and southern plateau (southern peninsular region). As per the livestock census (2003), only five states of the country i.e. Andhra Pradesh, Rajasthan, Karnataka, Tamil Nadu and Jammu and Kashmir cover about 60 % of the sheep population. It is clearly indicated that sheep is densely populated in hot-arid and semi-arid regions. The productive potential of sheep in these areas is influenced by the exposure to harsh climatic factors namely, high ambient temperature, solar radiation and wind velocity; and long distance walking in search of feed resources. Sheep production in the changing scenario of environment, shrinking of grazing land / rangeland and diminished feed resources, is likely to be influenced to a greater extent in future. Drivers of changing climates may force to shift from existing extensive system of sheep management to intensive or semi-intensive management.

Heat stress seems to be one of the several intriguing factors making animal production of many world areas difficult. In fact the animals can adapt to the hot climates, nevertheless the response mechanisms are helpful for survival but are detrimental to performance. In farm animals exposure to different environmental stressors elicit various physiological changes. Some of these changes are under emergency involving activation of adrenomedullary system that results in the release of catecholamines. The other change is the general adaptation response, which involves activation of pituitary–adrenal axis resulting in release of corticosteroids that controls the metabolic activity. Among the glucocorticoids, cortisol is the major stress relieving hormones in ruminant species, which plays a major role in adapting to the extreme environments. Well adapted animals are characterized by minimum production loss (McManus et al., 2009). Environmental factors and thermoregulatory mechanisms have a significant impact on the energy exchange between the animal and the environment (Srikandakumar et al., 2003).

Heat stress is considered a major limiting factor for sheep production under hot semi-arid environment (Naqvi and Hooda, 1991; Maurya et al., 2004). Thermal environment is a major factor that can negatively affect sheep performance (Al-Haidary, 2004). The changes in the biological functions of sheep due to exposure to heat stress include the depression in feed intake and utilization, disturbances in the metabolism of water, protein, energy, enzymatic reactions, hormonal secretions and blood metabolites (Habeeb et al., 1992; Marai et al., 2004; Marai et al., 2007). Sheep grazing under hot semi-arid environment face extreme fluctuations in the quantity and quality of feed on offer throughout the year (Martin et al., 2004). High ambient temperature augments the effort by sheep to dissipate body heat. As a result the rate of respiration, body temperature, heart beat, and water consumption are increased (Hooda and Naqvi, 1990). Increase in body temperature is associated with marked reduction in feed intake, redistribution in blood flow and changes in endocrine functions that negatively affect the productive and reproductive performance of sheep (Naqvi et al., 2004). Exposure to more heat suppresses the production of hormone releasing factors from the hypothalamic centre, causing a decrease in pituitary hormone secretion (Habeeb, 1987). Such variations in hormone concentration, in fact allow the animals to adapt their metabolic balance to different environmental conditions, variation in nutrient requirement and availability, and to homoerotic changes during different physiological stages (Todini, 2007).

Measurement of severity of heat stress in sheep

The severity of heat stress on livestock production can be measured using certain weather parameters, which measure the intensity of heat stress. The most noteworthy weather parameters included in such heat stress severity measurements were the ambient temperature (including dry and wet bulb temperature) and relative humidity. Few formulas developed by various researchers for measuring intensity of heat stress during summer season have been successfully used under hot semi-arid condition of Rajasthan (Naqvi and Hooda, 1990). Certain mathematical formulas have been designed by various researchers and research institutes for measuring the severity of heat stress (Table 1). All these formulae calculate the heat stress severity in terms of score on a 100 scale and finally these scores are compared on a standard 'Temperature Humidity Index' (THI) chart to asses the stress imposed by the impending climatic condition on livestock over a period of time. The THI is used as a guide to measure heat stress and it combines the effects of temperature and humidity into one value. There are three stress categories (temperatures given in Fahrenheit): Livestock alert is 75-78 degrees, Livestock danger is 79-83 degrees, and Livestock emergency is 84+ degrees. The higher the humidity the lower is the temperature for the Livestock alerts; for danger and emergency levels to occur. Generally for sheep two THI indexes were used to evaluate heat stress severity under tropical countries - one index was designed by LPHSI (1990): $THI = db°F - \{(0.55 - 0.55RH)(db°F - 58)\}$ and the other by Marai et al. (2001): $THI = db°C - \{(0.31 - 0.31RH)(db°C - 14.4)\}$. Among these two indices the one index which was designed by Marai et al. (2001) has been used widely under hot semi-arid environments to establish heat stress effects in sheep.

One of the major limitations of THI is that it does not account for wind velocity and solar radiation. Devising a single index encompassing all the components of environment and use of such index in predicting the climatic stress would be desirable. Several attempts have been made over the past to develop a satisfactory and practical index to describe the climatic stress but most have fallen short of expectations. The simple reason for this drawback is the difficulty to measure the combined influence of temperature, humidity, radiation, wind velocity and their diurnal variation on various species of livestock because of experimental complexity.

Table 1. Commonly used indices for evaluating heat stress effect on domestic animals

S.N.	THI indices	References
1	tdb+0.36tdp+41.5	Thom, 1958
2	(0.8xAmb tem)+{[(RH/100)x (Amb tem - 14.4)} +46.4	Thom, 1959
3	[0.4x(Tdb+Twb)]x 1.8+32+15	Thom, 1959
4	(0.15xTdb+0.85xTwb)x1.8+32	Bianca, 1962
5	(0.35xTdb+0.65xTwb)x1.8+3.2	Bianca, 1962
8	0.55DB + 0.2DP+17.5	Johnson,1965
9	(Tdb+Twb) x 0.72+40.6	National Research Council, 1971
10	(0.55xTdb+0.2xTdp) x 1.8 + 32 + 17.5	National Research Council, 1971
11	0.72 (Td + Tdp) + 40.6	McDowell, 1972
13	Tdb + (0.36xTdp) + 41.2	Yousef, 1985
14	0.72 (Td+Tw) + 40.6	World Mateorological Organization, 1989
15	db°F - {(0.55- 0.55RH) (db°F - 58)}	LPHSI, 1990
16	(9/5 Temp °C + 32) - (11/2 - 11/2x Humidity) x (9/5 Temp °C - 26)	Ravagnolo and Misztal, 2000
17	db°C - {(0.31 - 0.31RH) (db°C - 14.4)}	Marai et al., 2001
18	t - {(0.31 - 0.31RH) (t - 14.4)}	Marai et al., 2002
19	(0.85 x DBT + 0.15 x WBT) x $V^{-0.058}$	Tao & Xin, 2003
20	t air - [0.55 - (0.55xRH/100)] x (t air - 58.8)	Oklahoma State University, 2003
21	Temp - (0.55 - (0.55x(RH/100) x (Temp - 58)	Amundson et al., 2005
22	BGHI=tbg + 0.36 tdp + 41.5	Buffington et al., 1981
23	THVI= (0.85 x DBT + 0.15 x WBT) x $V^{-0.058}$	Tao & Xin, 2003
24	WBGTI= (0.7Twb) + (0.2Tbg) + (0.1Tdb)	Al-Tamimi, 2005
25	$HLI_{BG>25}$=8.62 + (0.38xRH) + (1.55xBG temp) - (0.5xwind speed) + ($e^{2.4\text{- wind speed}}$)	Gaughan et al., 2008
26	$HLI_{BG<25}$= 10.66 + (0.28xRH) + (1.3xBG) - wind speed	Gaughan et al., 2008

Abbreviations: THI = Temperature Humidity Index; tdp = Dry bulb temperature; twb = Wet bulb temperature; tbg = Black globe temperature; Tdp = Dew point temperature; Tw = wet bulb temperature; Td = Dry bulb temperature; RH = Relative Humidity; T air = Air temperature; HLI = Heat Load Index; BG temp = Black Globe temperature; WBGTI = Wind Black Globe Temperature Index; THVI = Temperature Humidity and Velocity Index; DBT = Dry Bulb Temperature; WBT = Wet Bulb Temperature; BGHI = Black Globe Humidity Index

Genetic variation in heat stress adaptation

Keeping in view the global distribution of the sheep, as determined by temperature and rainfall, many distinct groups of sheep were recognized. In India about 51 breeds of sheep parameters and different types of sheep were determined but the important thing to note is that there are many distinct types of sheep available. The research findings from one type of sheep may not be necessarily applicable to the other kind of sheep. Other limitation is that most of studies were for short-term and conducted in laboratories located in the temperate zone on British/Merino breeds. Physiological responses in homeotherms are important indicators for reflection of homeostasis. In normal course, there are fluctuations in physiological responses and sweating rates, which give a normal range. These ranges vary with the changes in season in an effort to maintain normal body temperature irrespective of fluctuation in environmental temperature. Hence these are considered as important indices for comparative adaptability of different genotypes (Gupta and Acharya, 1987). Genotype differences were observed in physiological response at high temperature (Table 2). Exotic sheep breeds from temperate and sub-temperate countries were reported to be less heat tolerant as compared to indigenous native breeds (Singh et al., 1978; Rai et al., 1979; Singh, 1980). More et al. (1975) assessed exotic fine wool type Rambouillet sheep with indigenous carpert wool type Chokla sheep for their adaptability in hot environment. They indicated that Rambouillet sheep was less adapted as compared to Chokla breed to hot environment. Diwivedi (1976) also established that exotic animals showed highest respiration rate, pulse rate and rectal temperature. Native breeds showed superior adaptive capability than exotic breeds with respect to physiological responses. Mittal and Ghosh (1979) also reported similar finding in Marwai and Magra sheep for their adaptability in arid zone of Rajasthan during hot months. Indian sheep in arid and semi-arid areas under thermal stress utilizes cutaneous evaporative cooling mechanisms for dissipation of body heat more than respiratory evaporative cooling. Further Rai et al. (1983) and Singh et al. (1983) showed that exotic breeds of sheep experienced more stress than native breeds at 40°C. Karim et al. (1985) reported significant difference in stress responses between native and crossbred sheep watered on alternate days during summer. Dang et al. (1998) had reported significant difference in physiological responses between native and crossbred sheep under hot semi-arid environment. They suggested that native breeds were able to better adapt to heat stress in terms of physiological adaptability. Crossbreds produced with Rambouillet or Merino germplasm (Avikalin, Avivastra and Bharat Merino) are better adapted to hot environment than pure temperate breeds of sheep but less adapted than their native counterpart (Malpura, Chokla, Sonadi and others).

Table 2. Physical Responses of different breeds of sheep during hot summer months under semi-arid region

S.N.	Breed	Morning (07:00)			Afternoon (14:30)		
		RR (Breaths/ min)	PR (Beats/ min)	RT (°C)	RR (Breaths/ min)	PR (Beats/ min)	RT (°C)
1	Garole	20.0	70.3	38.2	60	74.0	38.6
2	Malpura	29.6	69.0	38.3	58.0	74.0	38.7
3	Merino	94.4	78.8	39.1	120.2	85.9	39.6
4	Chokla	24.0	54.7	39.5	61.0	68.3	40.6
5	Nali	26.4	54.0	39.5	68.7	67.5	40.6
6	Avikalin	28.0	53.0	39.7	58.8	67.5	40.7
7	Rambouillet	24.0	53.5	39.6	114.0	68.1	40.8

(Sources: Kaushish and Sahni, 1975; Rai et al., 1979; Gupta and Acharya, 1987 and Maurya et al., 2009)

Effect of heat stress on physiological adaptability

To improve production, apart from infusion of high producing genes, the agro-climatic conditions have an important role to play by influencing the physiological mechanism(s). Physiological responses in homeotherms are important indicators of homeostasis. Normal fluctuations in physiological responses, i.e. respiration rate, pulse rate, rectal temperature and sweating rate vary with the changes in season in an effort to maintain normal body temperature independent of the fluctuation in environmental temperature. Hence these are considered important indices for comparative adaptability of different genotypes. Increased respiration rate is the first reaction when animals are exposed to environmental temperatures above the thermo neutral zone (Kamal, 1975; Maurya et al., 2007). This response ensures direct heat stimulation of the peripheral receptors, which transmit nervous impulses to the heat centre in the hypothalamus. With the increasing environmental temperature, the respiration rate continues to rise linearly until a certain temperature afterwards rate of respiration slows down and depth of breathing increases (Singh et al., 1982; Kaushish et al., 1989). At this level, the respiratory muscle reach a threshold of maximum activity and thus the respiration rate cannot increase further. Respiration rate can be an indicator of heat stress (Habeeb et al., 1992).

Ambient temperature is known to influence the body temperature and cardio respiratory responses of sheep. In a study conducted in our laboratory, higher values of physiological responses (body temperature, pulse and respiration rates) were reported during summer months in Garole and Malpura sheep (Maurya et al., 2008). Other reports on various breeds of sheep viz: Marwari, Soviet Merino, Nali and Chokla also indicated that ambient temperature influences the physiological responses of sheep. Many researchers utilized the physiological responses during stressful period to assess the comparative ability of heat tolerance like Corriedale compared with Bikaneri sheep, Soviet Merino with Marwari and Malpura, Romney March with Bikaneri, Rambouillet with Coimbatore, Corriedale with Marwari and Magra, Rambouillet with Malpura and Corriedale with Nali. Heat tolerance of non-pregnant adult ewes of Chokla, Nali and their crosses with Merino and Rambouillet were studied under solar exposure during summer. Native had lower rectal temperature and pulse than exotic breeds, while crossbred had intermediate values. The magnitude of physiological responses evoked by thermal stress and time required for their subsequent return to normalcy after removing the stress were considered useful indices for assessing the thermal ability of animals. Rai et al. (1983) showed that Rambouillet x Chokla experienced more stress at 40°C than Chokla when exposed for short duration (2 h) and both breed attained normalcy within 2h after removing from the hot chamber and exposure to 20°C.

The physiological response under hot semi-arid environment varied enormously during forenoon and afternoon. This is because the animals maintained under semi-arid condition are usually exposed to high ambient temperatures during hot summer months (Naqvi, 1987). The increase in ambient temperature through the morning and towards the afternoon may explain the reason for rise in the physiological responses in the afternoon when compared to morning values (Maurya et al., 2004). The type of nutrition consumed and body condition scoring (BCS) also seem to affect the respiration rate under heat stress conditions (Sejian et al., 2008b). Among the physiological response, respiration rate showed significant changes with respect to the different BCS than the pulse rate and rectal temperature. The reason for this could be that the homoeothermic animals initially react to stress by enhancing the thermoregulation mechanism, such as respiration rate, to avoid an increase in rectal temperature. These findings are in agreement to the previous study conducted in our laboratory by Maurya et al. (2003).

Effect of high ambient temperature on sweating in sheep

Sweating in sheep is considered to be important in heat dissipation than respiratory evaporative cooling. The native animals were found to utilize cutaneous evaporative cooling relatively more than exotic animals during thermal stress at high ambient temperature (Singh and Acharya, 1977 and

Ghosal et al., 1981). A series of experiments were conducted at CSWRI Avikanagar on sweating rate (Rai et al., 1979), sweat composition (Rai et al., 1982) and sweating from different region of body (Rai et al., 1979). Rai et al. (1979) observed no breed difference among Rambouillet, Chokla, Malpura and their half-breed in response of increase in sweating rate from 20°C to 35°C, but at 42°C Chokla showed a considerable rise. It might reflect that stimulation for increasing the sweating activity is dependent on the temperature. Rai et al. (1979) also found a linear increase in the sweating from birth to adult age and ram had high sweating rate than ewes at high temperature (41-43°C). Significant differences were observed between sweating rate at different regions of body of sheep at high ambient temperature (43-44.5°C). The sweat samples collected from Malpura, Chokla, Rambouillet and their crosses at 38-40°C did not show difference in sodium, potassium and protein contents, but chloride content was higher in Rambouillet samples (Rai et al., 1982). At high ambient temperature (41°C) sodium and potassium increased in Rambouillet and decreased or remain unchanged in Malpura and Chokla. The sweating rate of nutritionally depleted sheep under natural summer condition and under hot chamber maintained at 40°C/6h/d was reduced similarly (Naqvi and Rai., 1987). The environmental variables viz; ambient temperature relative humidity and wind velocity have been found to influence sweat gland structural dimensions and coat characteristics in cattle and sheep.

Importance of nutrition to heat tolerance

Thermal stress and feed scarcity are the major predisposing factors for the low productivity of ewes under hot semi-arid environment (Naqvi and Hooda, 1991; Maurya et al., 2004). Sheep grazing under hot semi-arid environment face extreme fluctuations in the quantity and quality of feed on offer throughout the year (Martin et al., 2004). Beside thermal stress, sheep under hot semi-arid environment are also exposed to the nutritional stress. Heat tolerance of sheep under the conditions of restricted feed and water availability are of applied significance. In a series of experiments conducted at CSWRI, Avikanagar to adjudge the heat tolerance of various breeds under different watering and feeding regimens it was found that the thermal stress was accentuated by scanty availability of water and feed resources. Singh et al. (1982) compared the relative adaptability of Chokla and Rambouillet x Chokla half-bred under thermal stress accentuated with water restriction or 1, 2, and 3 days. The native and crossbreed tolerated summer heat when watered everyday. Heat stress was accentuated during water restriction and resulted in decrease in feed intake and body weight. Karim et al. (1985) exposed Chokla and their half-breds with Rambouillet to simulating semi arid field condition and watering on alternate days. Physiological responses indicated better tolerance of heat in Chokla as compared to crossbreds. Naqvi and Rai, (1987) exposed the native Chokla and crossbred (Avivastra) to natural summer condition with different feeding regimens. The percent disturbance in responses indicated lowered heat tolerance of nutritionally depleted sheep.

Restricted feeding to the tune of 30% of *ad libitum* feeding was able to induce nutritional stress in sheep (Naqvi and Hooda, 1991; Maurya et al., 2004). When nutrition is not a limiting factor native sheep in hot semi-arid condition can tolerate thermal stress in field or in controlled condition in chamber (Naqvi and Hooda, 1991; Karim and Patnayak, 1998) without influencing much on productive and reproductive efficiency of sheep. However, the precise nature of these interactions is very complex and often unclear and the exact mechanisms underlying these interactions are yet to be elucidated in farm animals. Maurya et al. (2004) also showed that restricted feeding during hot summer months significantly reduced the body weight of ewes. This shows that proper nutrition during thermal stress is more important to maintain body weight without much variation. Karim and Patnayak, (1998) were also of same opinion that when sheep under thermal stress were fed adequately they could maintain normal body weight. Hooda and Naqvi (1990) also indicated that heat tolerance of sheep was influenced by level of feed and walking stress. Further in a recently conducted experiment in our laboratory we have observed that *ad libitum* feeding during summer months significantly reduced the negative effects of hot environment over the performance in Malpura breed of sheep (Sejian et al., 2008b). It is well documented that under nutrition affects reproductive function in ruminants at different levels of the hypothalamus-pituitary-gonadal axis (Boland et al., 2001; Chadio et al., 2007). The manipulation of reproduction using nutrition is an inexpensive management tool to control ovulation rate and litter size particularly in low cost, extensive production systems in marginal environment such as the semi-arid regions of the world (Scaramuzzi et al., 2006). These findings establish the importance of proper nutrient regimen to be followed during thermal stress. It is also evident from these studies that when nutrition is not a limiting factor then ewes were able to better cope up with thermal stress. Further studies are required to have a clear understanding of these associations at a mechanistic level if we have to fully exploit the potential of nutritionally manipulated reproduction in ewes under hot semi-arid environment. It is presumed that this approach will be valuable in gaining a thorough understanding of adjusting the nutrient requirement to deal with existing environments and will therefore aid in developing rational managerial decision taking tools to optimize productivity in sheep.

Effect of heat stress on blood biochemical parameters

Mechanism of homeostasis in an animal body exposed to heat will involve metabolic reactions which in part will reflect in changes in blood constituents as well as in body fluid compartments. Environmental temperature influences the body fluid space in sheep (More and Sahni, 1975; Sodhi, 1983). More et al. (1980b) found no breed differences among exotic (Rambouillet), native (Chokla and Malpura) and halfbreds (Rambouillet x Malpura and Rambouillet x Chokla) for extra cellular fluid volume, plasma volume, red cell volume and water intake on exposure to 40°C /6h/d for consecutive 6 days, period. An increase in haemotocrit values was noted in Rambouillet. Seasonal variations in the hemoglobin concentration and PCV in blood of corriedale rams were reported by Chahal and Rattan (1981). The plasma and blood volume of Chokla and Malpura in terms of percent body weight was found to be significantly higher than that of Rambouillet during summer. Balanced studies conducted on Rambouillet (R), Malpura (M), Chokla (C), R x C and R x M in climatic chamber (40°C/6h/d) or during summer did not show breed differences in excretory pattern of water, potassium or sodium (More and Rawat, 1984). The blood biochemical concentration of plasma sodium, serum inorganic phosphorus and erythrocyte, reduced, glutathione increased and blood urea and phospholipids and phosphorus also did not reflect any changes in above breeds when exposed to 40°C/6h/d (More and Rawat, 1986). During thermal stress there is a decrease in the hemoglobin concentration (More and Sahni, 1979; Yousef, 1985; Maurya et al., 2007), which could be attributed to hemodilution and increase in the blood volume of these animals. The packed cell volume (hematocrit percentage) also decreases in heat stressed animals either due to red cell destruction or hemodilution (Marai et al., 1991). Srikandakumar et al., (2003) reported that there was no effect of heat stress on haemoglobin in Omani sheep but was decreased in Merino.

Blood glucose concentration was found to decrease during short-term exposure of sheep to 35°C ambient temperature for 24 h and as well as during 5 days. However, when exposed to 40°C there was either small (in native Nali sheep) or no decline (in half breds Soviet Merino x Nali sheep) at all. Several researchers have studied the effect of thermal stress on the blood glucose concentrations but the results reported by them were conflicting. The decrease in glucose level during heat exposure relates to decrease in concentration of insulin and thyroxin, which are closely associated to energy metabolism during heat exposure. Decrease in plasma glucose could also be due to the marked dilution of blood (and body fluid as a whole or increase in the plasma glucose utilization to produce more energy for greater muscular expenditure required for high muscular activity (More et al., 1980a; Habeeb,

1987; Naqvi and Hooda, 1991). Other study showed that glucose concentration is increased during thermal exposure of animals because there was decrease in the glucose utilization, depression of the catabolic and anabolic enzyme secretions leading to subsequent reduction of metabolic rate, and also due to breakdown to glycogen into free glucose. Serum proteins, particularly albumin concentration, usually decrease in heat exposed cattle (Habeeb, 1987). A negative correlation between plasma protein and elevated environmental temperature has also been reported in some studies. The decrease in the plasma protein may be due to dilution of plasma proteins and decrease in protein synthesis as a result of depression of anabolic hormone secretion. In addition to this, there is also increase in glucocorticoids concentration. The reduced feed intake in heat stressed animals also leads to decrease in nitrogen concentration in the body, which leads to low protein level. The serum total lipid concentration was also decreased in the animals exposed to prolonged thermal stress, which might be due to increase in utilization of fatty acids for energy production as a consequence of decrease in glucose concentration (Daader et al., 1989; Kamal et al., 1989). Plasma free fatty acids, total lipids and cholesterol concentration were decreased during prolonged exposure of hot environment. Lower levels of ruminal ammonia and blood urea nitrogen were also reported in Merino sheep maintained at high temperature (35°C) than those of same animals when kept at low temperature (15°C).

Heat stress causes an increase in the activities of serum glutamic oxaloacetic transaminase (SGOT) and serum glutamic pyruvic transaminase (SGPT) due to increased stimulation of gluconeogenesis by corticoids (Kamal et al., 1989; Hooda and Naqvi., 1990). However, More and Sahni, (1980) observed no change in serum SGOT and alkaline phosphatase activities in Chokla sheep and Sirohi goat exposed to high ambient temperature (42.5°C). But Singh et al. (1983) reported increased alkaline phosphatase activity in Nali and Nali x Soviet Merino sheep exposed to heat stress. However, Rai et al. (1983) and (El-Masry, 1987) reported significant reduction in alkaline phosphatase by heat stress which was attributed to the reduction in thyroid hormone that occurred under heat stress. However, acid phosphatase generally is not affected more in heat stressed animals. Lactic acid and serum protein concentrations were increased at 35°C and 40°C exposure. Blood plasma vitamin A level was decreased as the ambient temperature increased while atmospheric pressure was decreased in rams but in ewes it did not show specific trend. Further the activity of plasma acid phosphates and LDH were comparatively higher during summer than spring season while GOT, GPT and alkaline phosphates did not change much in ewes. Higher levels of blood glucose and cholesterol, and lower levels of total plasma proteins and blood lactate were observed during summer as compared to spring in Corriedale rams.

In a study conducted on Iranian fat tailed sheep, reduced serum concentrations of total protein, glucose, cholesterol, total lipid, calcium, inorganic phosphorus, magnesium, creatine kinase, lactate dehydrogenase, triiodothyronine and thyroxine were reported after thermal exposure (Nazifi et al., 2003). They also reported increased levels of serum aspartate aminotransferase and alanine aminotransferase in heat stressed animals. Packed cell volume, total plasma proteins RBC and haemoglobin concentration had high positive correlation between each other indicating the significance of these parameters for heat tolerance in Brazilian sheep (Mc Manus et al., 2009). Al-Haidary. (2004) reported significant increase in PCV while there was no effect on haemoglobin concentration after exposed to heat stress in Naimey sheep. Srikandakumar et al. (2003) conducted an experiment on Omani and Merino sheep and observed varying degrees of changes in blood chemistry. They established significant reduction in plasma calcium, creatinine phosphokinase and aspartate aminotransferase after imposing both the breeds to heat stress. Heat stress also increased BUN in Omani while it was decreased in Merino sheep. Likewise, heat stress increased the plasma glucose in Merino while it was decreased in Omani breed. These results indicated that Omani sheep was more heat tolerant than Merino sheep.

Effect of heat stress on endocrine response

Hormones play a critical and important role in the thermoregulation of animal's body. On prolonged heat exposure, hypothalamic releasing hormones is suppressed which in turn drastically affects the release of pituitary hormones (Magiakou et al., 1997). During stress, various endocrine responses are involved to improve the fitness of the individual animals. Endocrine responses to stress in general work towards suppressing productive functions such as growth and reproduction, in favour of maintenance and survival. The front-line hormones overcoming stressful situations are the glucocorticoids and catecholamines. The secretion of glucocorticoids is a classic endocrine response to stress (Kannan et al., 2000). The association between thermal stress and increased secretion of cortisol, the principal glucocorticoid hormone in small ruminants, is well documented (Ali and Hayder, 2008; Sejian et al., 2008a). Currently it appears that glucocorticoids provide an initial integrating signal, which in conjunction with other hormones and paracrine secretions may determine specific behavioural and physiological responses to adapt to different environmental conditions (Wingfield and Kitaysky, 2002). Heat stress is associated with significant depression in thyroid gland activity resulting in lowering of thyroid hormones level (Ross et al., 1985; Nazifi et al., 2003). However, other investigators did not detect any significant changes in thyroid hormones (Al-Haidary, 2004). In a study conducted in our laboratory on Malpura rams, it has been established that BCS of sheep under hot semi-arid environment had significant influence on plasma cortisol, T_3, T_4 and testosterone concentrations. Recent reports suggest the involvement of melatonin to counteract heat stress in farm animals (Collier et al., 2008; Sejian et al., 2008a). Further there is evidence for the role of melatonin and prolactin to up regulate heat shock protein (HSP) 70 gene expression during heat stress (Collier et al., 2008).

Effect of heat stress on sheep reproduction

It is an established fact that reproduction processes are influenced during thermal exposure (Naqvi et al., 2004; Kornmatitsuk et al., 2008). From these studies it is pertinent to conclude that glucocorticoids are paramount in mediating the inhibitory effects of stress on reproduction. In support of this notion, various studies have shown that administration of natural or synthetic glucocorticoids can inhibit the secretion of the gonadotrophins in sheep (Juniewicz et al., 1987; Tilbrook et al., 2000). Further glucocorticoids are capable of enhancing the negative feedback effects of estradiol and reducing the stimulation of GnRH receptor expression by estrogen (Adams et al., 1999; Daley et al., 1999). Glucocorticoids may also exert direct inhibitory effects on gonadal steroid secretion and sensitivity of target tissues to sex steroids (Magiakou et al., 1997).

In a study conducted on Malpura ewes, Maurya et al., (2005) reported significant influence of heat stress on their sexual behavior. Thermal stress influence on estrous incidences is a well established fact (Das et al., 2001; Naqvi et al., 2004; Tabbaa et al., 2008). Further in another study Naqvi et al. (1999) concluded that estrous synchronization success percentage was more in winter than in summer season in Kheri sheep. This could be related to high plasma progesterone concentration in thermal stressed ewes. Presumably, therefore, the longer estrous cycles were due to a slower rate of follicular maturation after CL regression. Naqvi et al. (2004) demonstrated that thermal stress significantly altered the superovulatory response and embryo production in Bharat Merino ewes. Further it has been established that sheep embryo is most susceptible to maternal heat stress (Thwaites, 1971). In addition Lawson and Cahill (1983) postulated that variations in the physiological range of peripheral progesterone concentration due to management factors such as nutrition may induce asynchrony between the embryo and uterus resulting in failure of establishing pregnancy. The birth weight of lambs of heat stressed ewes was generally lower, which could be attributed to the fact that heat stress may cause a temporal impairment of placental size and function resulting in a transient reduction in foetal growth rate (Ali and Hayder, 2008).

In a study conducted in our laboratory on Malpura rams, it has been established that BCS had significant influence on sexual behavior, scrotal and testicular measurements and various semen attributes. The rams of 3.0-3.5 BCS had performed better in terms of reproductive efficiency than lower and higher BCS rams. This indicates that maintaining rams under optimum nutrient regimen is very important under hot semi-arid environment. Heat stress affects the spermatogenesis and fertility in rams. Testicular and scrotal measurements and sexual behavior of rams was also found to be affected by heat stress (Naqvi et al., 2009).

Measurement of thermal adaptability

The evaluation of the level of adaptation to heat stress, based on the lowest rectal temperature, respiratory frequency and physiological variables as the main parameters under high temperatures, was found to be insufficient. The average relative deviations (ARD) from normal (regardless either positive or negative), due to exposure to hot climates, in thermal, water and/or nitrogen balances of the animals (or in all traits measured), could be used in the estimation of parameters for detection of adaptability to a hot climate (Habeeb et al., 1997; Marai and Habeeb, 1998) as follows:

$$\text{Adaptability } (\%) = [100 - \text{ARD}] \times 100$$

In males, El-Darawany (1999) and Marai et al. (2006) used tunica dartos indices (TDI) to measure the ability of the male to tolerate increased ambient temperatures. The scrotum actively controls its own temperature through the function of the tunica dartos muscle which is interpreted as the distance between the testes and the abdominal wall. This muscle thus defines the magnitude of vascular heat exchange and is performed by the contraction of the tunica dartos muscle of the scrotum pulling the testes toward the body to increase its warmth, when the environmental temperature is low. During high ambient temperatures, the reverse process occurs in dissipating of the excess heat as much as possible from the testes (Taylor and Bogart, 1988). The TDI can be used as an index to measure the ability of male to tolerate increased ambient temperatures, as it reflects the magnitude of vascular heat exchange.

Climate change and sheep production

Sheep production system in India is changing rapidly due to change in climate conditions, feed scarcity, urbanization and change in transhumance/

migration of sheep rearing. Impact of climate change in a region needs to be assessed by ambient temperature, RH, difference in maximum and minimum temperature in 24 h, rainfall, wind velocity, solar radiation, IR radiation, evaporation rate and atmospheric CO_2 (Folk, 1974; Hulme, 2005). Heat stress and feed scarcity are the two most important determinants that are likely to alter the sheep production in arid / semi-arid tropical regions.

The impact of climate change on animal production has been categorized by Rotter and Van de Geijn (1999) on (a) availability of feed grain, (b) pasture and forage crop production and quality, (c) health growth and reproduction and (d) disease and their spread. The climate change may result in decrease or increase in population of a livestock species in a region. Animals which are more hardy and adapted to reference climate condition may thrive well while others may either shift to more suitable region or suffer stressful environment. Sheep adapted to hot environment will be preferred in hot semi-arid /arid region of the country over high producing and less thermal tolerant sheep. Thermal stress is known to influence more severely to non-adapted and high producing sheep. The production performance and survivability of Bharat Merino sheep was unsatisfactory at Avikanagar (semi-arid tropical area) but their transportation to Mannavanur (sub-temperate location) resulted in marked increase in production and health performance (growth, reproduction and survivability). Mitigation of climatic stresses becomes necessary if a high producing and less tolerant sheep are to be reared in harsh environmental conditions. More than 70% of total sheep in India thrive in arid and semi arid regions of the country. There has been frequent drought and decrease in annual rainfall over last few decades. The pasture quality is deteriorating and total availability of feed and fodder resources are constantly diminishing. In some areas C_3 grasses are being replaced by lower quality C_4 tropical grasses (Barbehenn et al., 2004).

Size and colour of sheep changing due to climate change

A novel study by a team of scientists in Britain reported that average body size of a wild Soay sheep of Hirta (Scottish island) in the St Kilda archipelago has decreased by approximately 5% over the last 24 years. This is in contradiction to evolutionary theory which suggests that average size of wild sheep increases during process of evolution in colder environment and tend to be more likely to survive and reproduce than smaller ones. The reason for bringing down the size of Soay sheep was attributed to shorter and milder winters caused by global climate change. In the changing climate conditions, the weight gain by the lambs during early months of life was diminished as compared to few decades back when winters were colder. The lambs had to put more weight to survive under extreme cold for survival.

The advantage of dark coloured coat of animals over lighter counterparts in colder environment is linked to conservation of solar energy and saving food energy for maintenance of homeothermy. The change in climate (warmer cold season) has been associated with the change in the proportion of light colored Soay sheep in total population. A study has revealed that dark colored Soay sheep have decreased over the past 20 years as the ambient temperature was increased.

Conclusions

The mechanisms underlying the adaptive capability of sheep to heat stress are complex in nature. Several systems of the body respond in different manner in combating thermal stress in sheep. There are genetic variations and breed differences in determining the adaptive capability of an individual. The immediate response by which the sheep counteract heat stress is the physiological response while endocrine response is the one which plays a major role in combating thermal stress. It is also evident from the various study conducted that when nutrition is not a limiting factor then ewes were able to better cope up with thermal stress. Further studies are required to have a clear understanding of these associations at a mechanistic level to fully exploit the potential of nutritionally manipulated reproduction in ewes under hot semi-arid environment. Sheep kept under the conditions of a hot, semi-arid environment should be maintained at moderate (3.0–3.5) BCS during breeding stage to ensure maximum reproductive efficiency from these animals. This will in turn ensure economically viable return in sheep farms. Research efforts are going on in our laboratory on multiple stress factors influencing sheep production under hot semi-arid environment (involving thermal, nutritional, walking and radiation stresses) for understanding the physiological mechanisms and nutrient requirements of sheep to deal with impending climate change and also develop rational managerial decision making tools to optimize productivity in sheep.

References

Adams, T.E., Sakurai, H. and Adams, B.M. 1999. Effect of stress like concentrations of cortisol on estradiol dependent expression of gonadotrophin-releasing hormone receptor in orchidectomized sheep. Biology of Reproduction 60: 164-168.

Al-Haidary, A.A. 2004. Physiological responses of Naimey Sheep to heat stress challenge under semi-arid environments. International Journal of Agriculture and Biology 2: 307-309.

Ali, A. and Hayder, M. 2008. Seasonal variation of reproductive performance, Foetal development and progesterone concentrations of sheep in the subtropics. Reproduction in Domestic Animal Doi: 10.1111/j.1439-0531.2007.00980.x

Al-Tamimi, H.J. 2005. Effect of solar radiation on thermophysiological and growth parameters of indigenous black bedwin goat kids in Southern Jordan. Journal of Biological Sciences 5(6): 724-728 .

Amundson, J., rasby, R.J., Mader, T.L. and Hu, Q.T. 2005. The effects of temperature and temperature-humidity index on pregnancy rate in beef cows. Nebrasca Beef Cattle Reports 10-12.

Barbehenn,R.V., Chen, Z., Karowe, D.N. and Spickard, A. 2004. C3 grasses have a higher nutritional quality than C4 grasses under ambient and elevated atmospheric CO_2. Global Change in Biolology 10: 1565-1575.

Bianca, W. 1962. Relative importance of dry and wet bulb temperatures in causing heat stress in cattle. Nature 195: 251-252.

Boland, M. P., Lonergan, P. and O'Callaghan, D. 2001. Effect of nutrition on endocrine parameters, ovarian physiology, and oocyte and embryo development. Theriogenology 55: 1323-1340.

Buffington, D.E., Colazon-Arocho, A., Canton, G.H. and Pitt, D. 1981. Black globe humidity index (BGHI) as comfort equation for dairy cows. Trans American Society for Agriculture and Engineering 24: 711-714.

Chadio, S.E., Kotsampasi, B., Papadomichelakis, G., Deligeorgis, S., Kalogiannis, D., Menegatos, D. and Zerwas, G. 2007. Impact of maternal under nutrition on the hypothalamic - pituitary-adrenal axis responsiveness in the sheep at different ages postnatal. Journal of Endocrinology 192: 495-503.

Chahal, A.S. and Rattan, P.J.S. 1981. Seasonal variation in the contents of hemoglobin and the packed cell volume in the blood of Corriedale rams. Journal of Research (PAU, Ludhiana, India) 18:341-344.

Collier, R.J., Collier, J.L., Rhoads, R.P. and Baumgard, L. H. 2008. Invited Review: Genes Involved in the Bovine Heat Stress Response. Journal of Dairy Science 91:445–454.

Daader, A.H., Marai, I.F.M., Habeeb, A.A. and Yousef, H.M. 1989. Improvement of growth performance of Friesian calves under Egyptian sub-tropical conditions. 1. Internal cooling technique using diuretics and drinking cool water. In: Proceedings of the 3rd Egyptian British Conference on Animal, Fish and Poultry Production, Vol. 2, Alexandria, Egypt, pp. 595–605.

Daley, C.D., Sakurai, H., Adams, B.M. and Adams, T.E. 1999. Effect of stress like concentrations of cortisol on gonadotroph function in orchidectomized sheep. Biology of Reproduction 60: 158-163.

Dang, A.K., Naqvi, S.M.K., and Mittal, J.P. 1998. Comparative physiological response of native and crossbred lambs under semi-arid conditions. Indian Veterinary Journal 75:546-547.

Das, G.K., Naqvi, S.M.K., Gulyani, R., Pareek, S.R. and Mittal, J.P. 2001. Estrus response and fertility in post-partum ewes using progesterone and PMSG in tropical environment. Indian Journal of Animal Sciences 71: 1124-1126.

Diwivedi, I.S.D. 1976. Studies on the adaptability of exotic breeds of sheep and their crosses with indigenous breeds I. Fluctuation in body temperature, pulse rate and respiration. Indian Veterinary Journal 53:938-942.

El-Darawany, A.A. 1999. Tunica dartos thermoregulatory index in bull and ram in Egypt. Indian Journal of Animal Sciences 69: 560-563.

El-Masry, K.A. 1987. The role of thyroxine in improving productivity of heat-stressed animals with different techniques. Ph.D. Thesis, Faculty of Agriculture, Zagazig University, Zagazig, Egypt.

Folk, G.E. 1974. Textboo of environmental physiology. Lea & Fabiger, Philadelphia.

Gaughan, J.B., Holt, S.M., Mader, T.L. and Lisle, A. 2008. Journal of Animal Sciences 86: 226-234.

Ghosal, A.K., Purohit, S.K., Goswami, A.K., Singh, L.B. and Jatkar, P.R. 1981. Rate on physiological responses and coat characteristics of Nali and Corriedale sheep during canary season in India. Indian Journal of Animal Sciences 51: 243-245.

Gupta, U.D. and Acharya, R.M. 1987. Heat tolerance in different genetic groups of sheep in Semi-arid conditions. Indian Journal of Animal Sciences 57: 1314-1318.

Habeeb, A.A. 1987. The role of insulin in improving productivity of heat-stressed farm animals with different techniques. Ph.D. thesis. Faculty of Agriculture, Zagazig University, Zagazig, Egypt.

Habeeb, A.A., Marai, I.F.M. and Kamal, T.H. 1992. Heat stress. In: Philips, C., Piggens, D. (Eds.), Farm Animals and the Environment. CAB International, pp. 27–47.

Habeeb, A.A., Marai, I.F.M., Kamal, T.H. and Owen, J.B. 1997. Genetic improvement of livestock for heat adaptation in hot climates. In: Proceedings of the International Conference on Animal, Poultry and Rabbit production and Health, Dokki, Cairo, Egypt, pp. 11-16.

Hooda, O.K. and Naqvi, S.M.K. 1990. Physiological responses of Malpura and Avikalin sheep during thermal, nutritional and walking stress. Indian Journal of Animal Sciences 60: 958-961.

Hulme, P.H. 2005. Adapting to climate change: is there scope for ecological management in the face of a global threat. Journal of Applied Ecology 42:784-794.

Johnson, H.D. 1965. Response of animals to heat. Agricultural Meteorology 28: 109-114.

Juniewicz, P.E., Johnson, B.H. and Bolt, D.J. 1987. Effect of adrenal steroids on testosterone and luteinizing hormone secretion in the ram. Journal of Andrology 81: 90-196.

Kamal, T.H. 1975. Heat stress concept and new tracer methods for heat tolerance in domestic animals. Proceedings of 1st Scientific Conference in Peaceful Uses of Atomic Energy for Scientific and Economic Development. Atomic Energy Commission, Baghdad, Iraq.

Kamal, T.H., Habeeb, A.A., Abdel-Samee, A.M. and Abdel-Razik, M.A. 1989. Supplementation of heat-stressed Friesian cows with urea and mineral mixture and its effect on milk production, in subtropics. Proceedings of the International Symposium on the Constraints and Possibilities of Ruminant Production in the Dry Subtropics. Cairo, Egypt. pp 183-185.

Kannan, G., Terrill, T. H., Kouakou, B., Gazal, O. S., Gelaye, S., A.Amoah E. and Samake, S. 2000. Transportation of goats: Effects on physiological stress responses and live weight loss. Journal of Animal Science 78:1450–1457.

Karim, S.A. and Patnayak, B.C. 1998. Relationship of dietary energy and heat tolerance in sheep. Indian Journal of Animal Science 68: 1193-1197.

Karim, S.A., Rai, A.K., More, T. and Singh, M. 1985. Responses of native and half-breed sheep watered on alternate day during summer in semi-arid region. Indian Journal of Animal Health 24:109-111.

Kaushish, S.K. and Sahni, K.L. 1975. Seasonal variation in rectal temperature, pulse and respiration rates of Russisn Merino sheep in semi arid climate. Indian Journal of Animal Sciences 45:860-63.

Kaushish, S.K.; Karim , S.A. and Rawat, P.S. 1989. Responses of native and crossbred sheep to solar exposure during summer in semi-arid region. Indian Veterinary Journal 66:852-856.

Kornmatitsuk, B., Chantaraprateep, P., Kornmatitsuk, S. and Kindahl, H. 2008. Different types of postpartum luteal activity affected by the exposure of heat stress and subsequent reproductive performance in Holstein lactating cows. Reproduction in Domestic Animal 43 (5): 515-519.

Lawson, R.A.S. and Cahill, L.P.1983. Modification of the embryo-maternal relationship in ewes by progesterone treatment early in the estrous cycle. Journal of Reproduction and Fertility 67: 473-475.

LPHSI, 1990. Livestock and poultry indices, Agriculture engineering guide, Clemenson university, Clemenson SC., 29634, USA.

Magiakou, M.A., Mastorakos, G., Webster, E. and Chrousos, G.P. 1997. The hypothalamic-pituitary-adrenal axis and the female reproductive system. Annals of the New York Academy of Sciences 816: 42-56.

Marai, I.F.M. and Habeeb, A.A. 1998. Adaptation of *Bos Taurus* cattle under hot climate conditions. Annals of Arid zone 37: 253-281.

Marai, I.F.M., Abdel-Samee, A.M. and El-Gafaary, M.N. 1991. Criteria of response and adaptation to high temperature for reproductive and growth traits in rabbits. Options Mediterraneennes Series A 17:127-134.

Marai, I.F.M., Ayyat, M.S. and Abd El-Monum, U.M. 2001. Growth performance and reproductive traits at first parity of New Zealand white female rabbits as affected by heat stress and its alleviation under Egyptian condition. Tropical Animal Health and Production 33: 457-462.

Marai, I.F.M., Ei-Darawani, A.A., Abou-Fandoud, E.I. and Abdel-Hafez, M.A.M. 2004. Reproductive traits and the physiological background of the seasonal variations in Egyptian Suffolk ewes under the condition of Egypt. Annals Arid Zone (India) 42 (2): 1-9.

Marai, I.F.M., Ei-Darawani, A.A., Abou-Fandoud, E.I. and Abdel-Hafez, M.A.M. 2006. Tunica dortos index as a parameter of adaptability of rams in sub-tropical conditions of Egypt. Animal Science (Japan) 77: 487-494.

Marai, I.F.M., El-Darawany, A.A., Fadiel, A. and Abdel-Hafez, M.A.M. 2007. Physiological traits as affected by heat stress in sheep – a review. Small Ruminant Research 71: 1-12.

Marai, I.F.M., Habeeb, A.A.M. and Gad, A.E. 2002. Rabbits productive, reproductive and physiological performance traits as affected by heat stress: A review. Livestock Production Science 78: 71-90.

Martin, G.B., Rogar, J. and Blache, D. 2004. Nutritional and environmental effects on reproduction in small ruminants. Reproduction, Fertility and Development 16: 491-501.

Maurya V.P., Naqvi S.M.K., Gulyani, R., Joshi, A. and Mittal J.P. 2005. Effect of thermal stress on sexual behaviour of super ovulated Bharat Merino. Asian-Australasian Journal of Animal Sciences 18: 1402-1405.

Maurya V.P., Naqvi, S.M.K., Joshi, A. and Mittal, J.P. 2007. Effect of high temperature stress on physiological responses of Malpura sheep. Indian Journal of Animal Sciences 77: 1244-1247.

Maurya, V.P., Naqvi, S.M.K. and Mittal, J.P. 2003. Physiological responses and growth of native (Malpura) and crossbred (Bharat Merino) female lambs born in autumn season under semi-arid ecology of India. Indian Journal of Animal Sciences 73: 916-919.

Maurya, V.P., Naqvi, S.M.K. and Mittal, J.P. 2004. Effect of dietary energy level on physiological responses and reproductive performance in Malpura sheep in hot semi-arid region of India. Small Ruminant Research 55:117-122.

Maurya, V.P., Naqvi, S.M.K., Sejian, V., Kumar, D. and Joshi, A. 2008. Effect of thermal stress on physiological response and blood profile of Garole and Malpura ewes. Indian Veterinary Journal (*In press*).

Maurya, V.P., Naqvi, S.M.K., Sejian, V., Kumar, D. And Joshi, A. 2009. Effect of thermal stress on physiological response and blood profile of Garole and Malpura ewes. Indian Veterinary Journal (*In press*).

Mc Manus, C., Paludo. G.R., Louvandini. H, Gugel. R., Sasaki. L.C.B. and Paiva. S.R. 2009. Heat tolerance in Brazilian sheep: physiological and blood parameters. Tropical Animal Health and Production 41: 95-101.

McDowell, R.E. 1972. Improvement of livestock production in warm climates. W.H. Freeman and Co., San Francisco, CA.

Mittal, J.P. and Ghosh, P.K. 1979. Effect of shearing on certain physiological responses of Corriedale rams under arid conditions during summer. Indian Journal of Animal Sciences 49:152-154.

More, T. and Rawat, J.S. 1984. Plasma electrolytes of H. K. and L.K. Sheep given long term intermittent watering under semi-arid conditions. Indian Veterinary Journal 61:837-841.

More, T. and Rawat, P.S. 1986. Effect of long term intermittent watering on certain blood metabolites of HK and LK sheep under semi-arid condition. Indian Journal of Animal Sciences 56:262-269.

More, T. and Sahni, K.L. 1975. The blood potassium level, certain haematological and wool characteristics of Rambouillet sheep under semi-arid conditions. Indian Veterinary Journal 52:181-185.

More, T. and Sahni, K.L. 1979. Some haematological changes during three months after birth of Chokla lambs under semi-arid conditions. Indian Veterinary Journal 56:646-649.

More, T. and Sahni, K.L. 1980. Certain biochemical responses of sheep and goat exposed to thermal stress. Indian Journal of Animal Sciences 50:1012-1014.

More, T., Rai, A.K. and Singh, M. 1980. Effect of thermal exposure on body fluid composition of different breeds and breed crosses of sheep. Indian Journal of Animal Sciences 50: 207-209.

More, T., Singh, M. and Rai, A.K. 1980. Observations on excretory patterns of sodium, potassium and water in different genetic groups of sheep under high ambient temperature. Indian Journal of Animal Sciences 50:182-186.

Naqvi, S.M.K. 1987. Physiological adaptation of sheep during energy crisis and thermal stress. Ph.D. thesis submitted to Kurukshetra University, Kurukshetra, India.

Naqvi, S.M.K. and Hooda, O.K. 1990. Animal Environment and its measurement to assess the environment stress. Livestock Advisor 15(12):20-24.

Naqvi, S.M.K. and Hooda, O.K. 1991. Influence of thermal, nutritional and exercise stress on some blood parameters of native and crossbred sheep. Indian Journal of Animal Sciences 61:660-662.

Naqvi, S.M.K. and Rai A.K. 1987. Heat tolerance of nutritionally depleted Avivastra and Chokla sheep. Abstracts, National Seminar on small ruminant Production Jan. 5-7, CSWRI, Avikanagar (Rajasthan).

Naqvi, S.M.K. and Rai, A.K. 1991. Influence of dietary energy level on sheep for mutton during winter: Effect on cardio respiratory responses, rectal temperature, some blood metabolites, enzymes and thyroidal hormones. Indian Journal of Animal Sciences 61:1126-1131.

Naqvi, S.M.K., Kumar, D. and Pareek, S.R. 2009. Testicular development of Malpura ram lambs under extensive and intensive feeding regimen. Indian Journal of Small Ruminants (*In press*).

Naqvi, S.M.K., Maurya, V.P., Gulyani, R., Joshi, A. and Mittal, J.P. 2004. Effect of thermal stress on superovulatory response and embryo production in Bharat Merino ewes. Small Ruminant Research 55: 57-63.

Naqvi, S.M.K.Gulyani, R., Das,G.K., Pareek ,S.R. and Mittal, J.P. 1999. Effect of season on estrus synchronization in Kheri sheep. Indian Journal of Small Ruminants 5(2): 85-86.

National Research Council. 1971. A guide to environmental research on animals. National Academy of Science Washington, DC.

Nazifi, S., Saeb, M., Rowghani, E. and Kaveh, K. 2003. The influence of thermal stress on serum biochemical parameters of Iranian fat-tailed sheep and their correlation with triiodothyronine (T_3), thyroxine (T_4) and cortisol concentrations. Comparative Clinical Pathology 12: 135-139.

Oklahoma State University. 2003. Livestock : Managing heat stress returns dividends. Extension Service-West Virginia University 1-3.

Rai , A.K., Mehta, B.S. and Singh, M. 1979. Thermal sweating in different body regions of sheep. Journal of Agricultural Sciences (Cambridge) 92:511-512.

Rai, A.K., More, T. and Singh Manohar. 1982. Composition of sweat in sheep exposed to high ambient temperatures. Indian Journal of Animal Sciences 52:1056-1059.

Rai, A.K., More, T. and Singh, M. 1983. Certain blood attributes in different genetic groups of sheep on feed lot ration. Indian Veterinary Journal 60:839-841.

Ravagnolo, O. and Misztal, I. 2000. Genetic component of heat stress in dairy cattle, parameter estimation. Journal of Dairy Science 83: 2126-2130.

Ross, T.T., Goode, L. and Linnerud, A.C. 1985. Effects of high ambient temperature on respiration rate, rectal temperature, fetal development and thyroid gland activity in tropical and temperature breedsof sheep. Theriogenology 24:259-269.

Rotter, R. and Van De Geijn, S.C. 1999. Climate change effects on plant growth, crop yield and livestock. Climate Change 43: 651-681.

Scaramuzzi, R.J., Cambel, B.K., Downing, J.A, Kendall, N.R., Khalid, M., Gutierrez, M. and Somchit, A. 2006. A review of the effect of supplementary nutrition in the ewe on the concentration of reproductive and metabolic hormones and the mechanism that regulate folliculogenesis and ovulation rate. Reproduction, Nutrition and Development 46:339-354.

Sejian, V., Srivastava, R.S. and Varshney, V.P. 2008a. Pineal-adrenal relationship: Modulating effects of glucocorticoids on pineal function to ameliorate thermal-stress in Goats. Asian-Australasian Journal of Animal Sciences 21: 988-994.

Sejian, V., Maurya, V.P., Naqvi, S.M.K., Kumar, D. and Joshi, A. 2008b. Effect of induced body condition score differences on physiological response, productive and reproductive performances of Malpura ewes kept in a hot, semi-arid environment. Journal of Animal Physiology and Animal Nutrition (*In press*).

Singh, L.B., Singh, M., Amrit, L. and Dwarakanath, P.K. 1978. Effect of some biochemical characters on production traits in sheep. I. Some body traits. Indian Journal of Animal Health XVII: 69-74.

Singh, M. 1980. Problems of adaptation by sheep to hot arid conditions. Annals of arid zone 19:301-306.

Singh, M. and Acharya, R.M. 1977. A note on the mode of heat dissipating in different types of sheep. Indian Journal of Animal Science 47(6):367-368.

Singh, M., More T., Rai, A.K. and Karim, S.A. 1982. A note on the adaptability of native and crossbred sheep to hot summer conditions of semi arid and arid areas. Journal of Agricultural Science (Cambridge) 99:525-528.

Singh, M., Rai, A.K. and Karim, S.A. 1983. Relative heat tolerance of Indian Nali and Soviet Merino x Nali halfbred sheep to continuous 35 C and 40 C temperature conditions. Journal of Animal Physiology and Animal Nutrition 49:18-23.

Singh, Manohar., More, T., Rai, A.K. and Karim, S.A. 1982. A note on the adaptability of native and crossbred sheep to hot summer conditions of semi-arid and arid areas. Journal of Agricultural Sciences (Cambridge) 99(3):525-528.

Sodhi, S.P.S. 1983. Effect of seasonal variation in blood volume in rams. Indian Journal of Animal Sciences 53:342-343.

Srikandakumar, A., Johnson, E.H. and Mahgoub, O. 2003. Effect of heat stress on respiratory rate, rectal temperature and blood chemistry in Omani and Australian Merino Sheep. Small Ruminant Research 49: 193-198.

Tabbaa, M.J., Alnimer, M.A., Shboul, M. and Titi, H.H. 2008. Reproductive characteristics of Awassi rams. Animal Reproduction 5: 23-29.

Tao, X. and Xin, H.2003. temperature-humidity-velocity Index for market size broilers. ProPAPER N. 034037. Nevada-USA.

Taylor, R.E. and Bogart, R. 1988. Scientific farm animal production. Macmillan Publishing Company, New York, USA.

Thom, E.C. 1958. Cooling Degree days. Air conditioning, heating and ventilating 55: 65-69.

Thom, E.C. 1959. The discomfort index. Weather wise 12: 57-59.

Thwaites, C.J. 1971. Short term heat stress and embryo mortality in sheep. Australian Journal of Experimental Agriculture and Animal Husbandry 11(50): 265-267.

Tilbrook, A.J., Turner, A.I. and Clark, I.J. 2000. Effect of stress on reproduction in non rodent mammals: the role of glucocorticoids and sex differences. Reviews in Reproduction 5: 105-113.

Todini, I. 2007. Thyroid hormones in small ruminants: effects of endogenous, environmental and nutritional factors. Animal 1: 997-1008.

Wingfield, A.S. and Kitaysky, J.C. 2002. Endocrine responses to unpredictable environmental events: stress or anti-stress hormone, Integrative and Comparative Biology 42: 600-609.

World Meteorological organization (WMO). 1989. Animal Health and Production in Extreme environments. WMO Technical Note. No. 119. pp 181.

Yousef, H.M. 1985. Studies on some environmental factors affecting production and reproduction in some farm animals. M.Sc. thesis. Faculty of Agriculture, Zagazig University, Zagazig, Egypt.

Yousef, M.K. 1985. Stress physiology in livestock. CRC Press, Boca Raton, FL.

□□□

17

Effect of Climatic, Thermal and Nutritional Stresses on Reproduction of Goats

A. K. Goel* and N. Ramachandran
Physiology, Reproduction and Shelter Management Division, Central Institute for Research on Goats, Makhdoom, Farah , Mathura- 281 122, Uttar Pradesh

Introduction

The goats have occupied a unique place in their long association with human civilization, being the one of the earliest domesticated animals and probably next oldest to the dog. During the course of domestication, the goat has undergone intense natural selection pressure for various phenotypes. India is rich in goat genetic resources by having 20 well established and recognized goat breeds and many more are in the process of evaluation and characterization. Goats play a vital role in the livelihood security, poverty alleviation and employment generation to millions of marginal and small farmers and landless rural population. Goats in India contribute around 3.90 and 8.64% of milk and meat (chevon) production, respectively. The total annual contribution of this species is around 14335 crores of rupees through meat (6773 crores INR), milk (4583 crores INR) and skin (648 crores INR), which accounts for around 8 % of GDP from livestock sector. Since the domestication of the goats, the different breeds have developed in a wide range of environments and have consequently evolved a variety of reproductive strategies to adapt these environments. Small ruminants (Goat and Sheep) are mostly reared under extensive system of range management, hence directly affected by the influence of climate change in terms of biomass availability and changes in rearing environment. Increasing animal production and productivity in the face of diminishing feed and land resources has been a major challenge and in the wake of climate change scenario, task has become more and more challenging to all of us. Under these circumstances, it is imperative to reorient our research priorities to face these challenges. To mitigate deleterious effects of elevated environmental temperature more emphasis is needed for mineral and vitamin supplementation, embryo transfer to bypass heat stress, hormonal therapy and alternate breeding practices. This paper focuses on the role of climatic, thermal and nutritional stressors affecting reproduction and probable nutritional manipulation and mitigation strategies related to climatic variables in the successful management of goats for increased production.

Stress (climatic, thermal, nutritional) and reproduction process

Different livestock species contribute significantly in the rural economy of the country. The effects of climatic changes that are likely to affect reproduction of Indian livestock is relatively neglected area of research. The factors responsible for the initiation of stress pathways are known as *'stressors'*. The term *'Stress'* is defined as a constellation of events including a stimulus (stressor), a reaction at the level of nervous system due to the stimulus (stress perception) and a physiological activation of the 'fight or flight' system (Mc Ewen, 2002). A stressor is not always harmful. It can be considered harmful only by assessing the way in which the animal is able to cope with it and to regain the previous homeostasis (Von Borrell, 2001). Thus, the stress does not always have unfavorable consequences and often its positive effects in terms of adaptation and health are neglected. According to Mc Ewen (2002) stress can be harmful when it is long lasting and the animal is unable to successfully cope with it. Thus, the stress can be classified on the basis of its duration. Acute or short stress lasts minutes, hours or a few days while chronic stress persists for months or years.

The climatic changes in the present scenario have enhanced the environmental temperature and given rise to the concept of thermal stress. This acts as a potential stressor at the level of hypothalamus to initiate the stress pathways and this pathway is termed as Hypothalamic-Hypophyseal-Adrenal Axis. Activation of this system affects most of the visceral physiological functions leading to the imbalanced internal homoeostasis in animals. Increased temperature and humidity result in decreased expression of oestrus and reduction in feed intake. Heat stress at ovarian level reduces the degree of dominance of the recruited ovarian follicles and this can be seen as reduced steroidogenic capacity of its theca and granulosa cells and a fall in blood oestradiol levels. Plasma progesterone levels can be increased or decreased depending on whether the heat stress is acute or chronic. These endocrine changes reduce follicular activity and alter the ovulatory mechanism, leading to a decrease in oocyte and embryo quantity and quality. The uterine environment is also modified, reducing the chances of embryo implantation. Appetite and dry matter intake both are reduced by heat stress thus prolonging the post partum period of negative energy balance and thus increasing the inter kidding interval. The formation of gametes is thermal sensitive. Normal spermatogenesis requires a temperature that is below the normal body temperature and recent evidences suggest that the development of oocytes is also temperature sensitive. The effect of heat stress on fertility might then be the result of a direct effect of high ovarian temperature on oocyte quality. Heat stress induces oxidative stress, as a result of imbalance between the antioxidant defense mechanism and the formation of reactive oxygen radicals, may damage life important membrane lipids, proteins, DNA and carbohydrates. Heat stress is associated with reduced total antioxidant activity in blood plasma and there is some evidence that elevated temperatures involves increased free radical production in the body.

Underlying mechanism of stress on reproduction processes

Reproduction is one of the most complex functions of the animal body. Reproductive functions are not only regulated by the gonads but also hypothalamic-hypophyseal system. Stress affects the central hypothalamic axis leading to alteration of the process of reproduction both in male and female. This altered axis eventually impairs animal production. Stress also leads to a depression in immunological system of the body. The adrenal- cortical system and the immuno competent cells mediate this system. In this way, stress lead to impaired reproduction, which is reflected in the form of increased age at puberty, aberrations in oestrous cycles (short and long oestrus cycles, short and prolonged oestrous periods) decreased growth, size and recruitment of ovarian follicles, abnormal shedding of ova, decreased fertilization rate, repeat breeding, embryonic/fetal mortality, stress induced abortions in late pregnancy, still births, premature births, longer post partum oestrus interval leading to anoestrus and increased incidence of reproductive diseases in females; abnormal spermatogenesis and sperm abnormalities and decreased conception rate etc. in males. Studies have also shown that under stress increased numbers of free radicals (reactive oxygen species) are generated in steriodiogenic cells and mononuclear phagocytes in the corpus luteum and influence progesterone synthesis. Under stress body cells fail to by pass from reactive oxygen species through enzymes or antioxidants.

Thermo regulatory mechanisms in goats

Goats like for other homeotherms, regulate internal body temperature by balancing the amount of heat produced through metabolism with the heat flow from the animal to the surrounding environment to avoid hyperthermia or hypothermia. Heat flow occurs through processes dependent on surrounding temperature (sensible heat loss; i.e. conduction, convection, radiation) and humidity (latent heat loss; evaporation through sweating and panting). The magnitude of sensible heat loss via conduction and convection is dependent on the surface area per unit body weight, the magnitude of the temperature gradient between the animal and the air, and the conductance of heat from the body core to the skin and from the skin to the surrounding air. Heat exchange by radiation depends upon surface area as well as the reflective properties of the hair coat. Light-colored hair coats and hair coats that are sleek and shiny reflect a greater proportion of incident solar radiation than hair coats that are dark in color or more dense and wooly (Stewart, 1953; Hutchinson and Brown, 1969; Finch, 1986; Hansen, 1990). The thick coat of hair or wool in goat acts as an insulator for environmental temperature and as ambient temperature exceeds body temperature the hair or wool protects the skin and cutaneous blood flow from warming effects of solar radiation and thus help to prevent excessive increase in core body temperature even in places where temperature shoots very high.

Goats are also thought to be less susceptible to environmental stress because of its unique water conservation capacity, higher sweating rate, lower basal heat metabolism, higher respiration rate, higher skin temperature and constant cardiac output and water output (Lu, 1989). However, heat stress does occur in these animals when they are exposed to ambient temperature above critical temperature zone with in certain limit. Heat stress is caused primarily due to high air temperature but can be intensified by high humidity, thermal radiation, low air movement and physiological status of the animals. Like other animals, small ruminants undergo several physiological and behavioral adjustments to cope with the heat stress. Increased physiological reactions, decreased voluntary feed intake, feed digestibility, thyroid function, blood insulin and increased in cortisol etc. have been observed during heat stress in small ruminants (Bhattacharyya and Hussein, 1974; Joshi et al., 1977). Heat stress during summers disrupts the homeostasis of animals by evoking thermoregulatory reactions, which try to maintain the heat tolerance. Since the animals are dumb, the magnitude of the environmental stress can only be measured indirectly through the behavioral response of the animal (Fraser and Broom, 1997). Dairy farmers can utilize knowledge of animal behavior to improve the production performance of livestock (Shabi et al., 2005). The consequences of these changes are the decreased production and reproductive functions of animals under stress. However, the effect of heat stress on reproduction of goats is not studied in detail barring meager studies around the world.

Climatic/thermal stress and male reproduction

In goats and sheep, heat load and photoperiod are two of the most important environmental factors influencing the reproduction as in case of other livestock species like pigs, cattle and equines. Chemineau (1993) reported that seasonal variations in sexual activity among small ruminants depend on latitude and day length. Melatonin secreted during the night by the pineal gland enables the animals to determine the length of day. This hormone can be used to advance the mating season of sheep and goats and increase their fecundity. The use of artificial photoperiodic variations and/or melatonin eliminates or alters the seasonality of semen production. Numerous research reports concerning the influence of thermal stress on male reproductive efficiency revealed that high temperature was found to cause a significant decline in libido and semen production like lower sperm concentration, lower motility, increasing percentage of morphologically abnormal sperms and lower fertilizing ability in goats, the greatest effect being on the first stage of spermatogenesis with resultant delayed effects on fertility in male sheep and goats of tropical as well as Mediterranean regions (Casu et al.,1991). Al-Sheikh (2000) studied the effect of increasing ambient temperature on spermatogenesis and semen quality of 1-2 year old Aardi bucks of Saudi Arabia by maintaining them in thermo regulated room at 21°C for 5 weeks followed by 45°C for 9 weeks and reported that heat stress impaired spermatogenesis and decreased semen volume significantly from 1.51 to 0.68 ml. Santos et al. (1998) demonstrated the effect of heat stress on the characteristics of the scrotum and ejaculate before and after insulation of the scrotum in a double-walled plastic bag in 6 crossbred Moxoto-Brown Alpine bucks. Decrease in scrotal volume and degeneration of testicular consistency and sperm quality was observed in all animals. Morphological abnormalities began to appear in spermatozoa seven days after the initiation of heat stress. Sperm motility reached its lowest value three weeks after initiation of insulation and returned to normal at 8-9 weeks. Seminal degeneration was observed in all animals at week 4, comprising a reduction in sperm concentration, increase in morphological abnormalities and reduction in cellular vigor, culminating in akinesia and necrospermia. Ten weeks after the start of the experiment all animals regained normal scrotal circumference, testicular consistency and spermatozoa profile. Kang and Chung (1976) found significant effect of season on semen volume in Korean native goats, whereas Jankiraman et al. (1990) found volume to be maximum in summer. Mittal (1982) reported significant effect of season on per cent live sperms. Sinha et al. (1981), however, observed seasonal variation in semen volume and of sperms. The individual sperm motility was also found to be affected by season (Kang and Chung, 1976; Chaudhary and Mehmood, 1984; Jankiraman and Mehta, 1990).

As early as 1955 Casady and Co workers reported that the critical temperature for inhibition of spermatogenesis in dairy bull was estimated to be 29°C. However, critical temperature for inhibition of spermatogenesis in goats is yet to be explored except the studies on effect of seasons on semen quality traits in bucks. Even though indigenous and crossbreed bucks in tropical zone maintains fertility throughout the year (Cupps, 1991; Jainudeen and Hafez, 1993), seasonal variation in semen quality is reported in many studies and various environmental variables are attributed to this variation (Elwishy et al, 1971; Kang and Chung, 1976; Mittal 1982,1986, 1987; Chaudhary and Mehemood,1984). Shukla and Bhattacharyya (1952) carried out studies on seminal characteristics of goats in India. Semen volume was highest in summer and least in winter. Sharma et al. (1957) observed higher semen volume in summer than in winter, and highest sperm concentration in winter and least in spring. Sperm motility was more during autumn than winter. Sinha et al. (1981) in Jamunapari bucks reported a higher sperm concentration, motility and percentage of live sperms during spring than during winter. A number of researchers (Shukla and Bhattacharyya, 1952; Sharma et al., 1957; Mishra and Sengupta, 1966; Tiwari, 1967) revealed seasonal variation in seminal attributes in indigenous buck semen. Semen of poor quality was observed due to high humidity, summer and winter seasons. Extensive studies carried out at the Veterinary College, Mathura by Sahni (1967) on semen quality, cryopreservation and artificial insemination (AI) in goats revealed that semen of consistently good quality suitable for artificial insemination could be obtained in any season of the year from Barbari, Jamunapari, Saanen and crossbred bucks. Photoperiodicity and environment had practically no effect in hot arid areas of tropics as compared to temperate area located at greater distance from equator.

Semen evaluation studies carried out on different breeds of goats by various workers in different regions of India revealed that although there was significant fluctuation in seminal attributes between seasons and breeds, the semen of optimum quality fit for artificial insemination could be obtained throughout the year from native bucks. In one of the studies on Black Bengal goats in Northern plains of India (Raza Nasir et al., 1978) high ambient temperature accompanied by high humidity during hot humid period had a significant deleterious effect on the motility of spermatozoa and sperm concentration significantly lowered during this period in comparison to other periods. The average pH higher during hot humid period and the initial fructose was significantly higher in both hot humid as well as hot dry periods than other periods including cool period. Although the semen volume was higher during hot dry period than cool period, the differences were not significant. The hotter part of the year in tropical countries seems to be more conducive for sexual activity and semen quality as compared to the cooler part of the year. The reaction time during cool dry period (December, January and February) was significantly higher than hot-dry (April, May and June), hot humid (July, August and September) and moderate dry (October and November) periods (Raza Nazir et al., 1978).

Climatic/ thermal/transport stress and female reproduction

The well-known high reproductive efficiency of goats is evident in the dry tropics and sub-tropics also, where climate is predominantly hot, both in indigenous and European breeds and their crosses breeds (Mukundan and Rajgopalan, 1971; Mukundan, 1976, Singh et al, 1978; Devendra and Burns, 1983; CIRG, Makhdoom 1985; Khan et al, 1986, 1987; Goel, 1998; Goel and Agrawal, 2000). Inadequacies of favorable environmental conditions, however, restrict the harvesting of optimum fertility and prolificacy due to higher kid mortality, poor nutrition and longer inter kidding intervals.

In India, dairy and other animals in oestrus are often transported to distinct places for breeding (Natural/Artificial Insemination). A great proportion of these animals transported around the onset of Luteinizing Hormone (LH) surge are expected to release sub normal LH and thus suffer anovulatory oestrus resulting in infertility. Avoiding stress to such animals will resulting optimizing fertility in dairy animals. (Nanda, 1995).

Effect on Sexual Rhythm

The average duration of oestrous cycle in goat is 20 to 21 days but occurrence of short oestrous cycles seems to be more frequent in hot climate conditions (Sahni and Roy, 1967; Prasad and Bhattacharyya, 1979). The short cycles are likely to be infertile cycles and apparently are a symptom of hormonal imbalance. The rate of conception in Malabari goats and their crosses with Saanen and Alpine in hot humid climate of southern India was reduced by 33% due to short and long cycles (Mukundan, 1976).

The goats in temperate climate are seasonal breeders and this seasonality governed by photoperiodicity. The hot climate countries being near to equator do not experience changes in daily duration of sunlight to that extent and thus goats should breed round the year without exhibiting the seasonality in sexual activity. In most of the studies in various countries, having predominantly hot climate, goats have shown distinctly reduced activity during some months of the year. These months, however, are not similar and differ from region to region (Roy et al., 1966; Rajkonwar and Borgohain, 1978; Agrawal et al., 1986; Aboul - Naga, 1987; Amoah and Gelaye, 1990; Jankiraman and Mehta, 1990; Srivastava et al., 1991). Agrawal et al. (1986) in one of the studies in hot semiarid climate of India observed highest incidence of estrus from May to July and September to October in Jamunapari and Barbari goats, the incidence is almost nil in Jamunapari from December to April and poor in Barbari goats. Misra and Biswas (1966) observed highest number of oestrus in October and then in June and lowest in March. Studies on month-wise occurrence of oestrous cycle in hot-arid zone of India in Surti and Marwari breeds (Jankiraman and Mehta, 1990) revealed that although the oestrous cycles are exhibited in both the breeds, the frequency of occurrence was not uniform. There were distinct periods of higher activity in both the breeds. Singh and Sengar (1979) reported two distinct seasons May to June and September to November. The Assam goats, however, exhibit greater incidence of oestrus between July and October (Rajkonwar and Borgohain, 1978). It is evident from all these studies that this type of restricted seasonality in reproductive activity in goats of tropics is an adaptive effort by different breeds in relation to changes in ambient temperature, onset of rain and availability of herbage.

A common observation in the tropics is that oestrus in goats occurs shortly after the onset of rainy season or even after sporadic rains during dry season. Oestrus behavior in tropical breeds of goats (Barbari, Jakhrana and Jamunapari) has been studied elaborately by Goel and Agrawal (1994, 2004) and Goel and co workers (2003). Monthly variation in oestrus occurrence was observed in different months of the year in Jamunapari goats. Goats started cycling from May (90.00%) and oestrous activity reached to maximum (100%) in September through December.Oestrous activity started declining from January with complete cessation in March -April. Nearly 70.00% goats expressed oestrus during morning and 30% in evening hours. Duration of oestrus averaged 39.75±1.30 hours. In majority (80%) oestrus duration ranged 24 - 48 hours. Nearly 86% (91/106) oestrous cycles were of normal length average: 21.14±0.15 days, range: 18 -24 days). Incidence of short (average: 8.40 ± 1.69 days, range: 5 -13 days) and long cycles (average: 37.40 ±2.11 days, range: 28 - 47 days) was of lower magnitude (5% and 9%, respectively). Study revealed Jamunapari to be a non seasonal breeder having peak oestrous activity in certain period of the year. The nomadic nature of particular breed seems to continue to play an important role in restricted seasonality in reproductive activity. The other possibility appears to be that some environmental stimuli affect the neuro-endocrine mechanism to cause this phenomenon particularly when viewed closely that one or more pre monsoon showers during summer causes a sudden outburst in estrus exhibition. The restricted seasonality in oestrous cycle expression is more marked in European breeds in the tropics or even in their crossbreeds with local breeds. The increase in Angora inheritance leads to seasonality in breeding in crosses with local goats in hot semi arid zone of India (Srivastava et al., 1991). Hakusugawara and coworkers (1989) reported that in Saanen goats 'prolactin' concentration increased according to prolonging day of the light and season. Circulating levels of prolactin in goats are higher during summer than during in monsoon and winter. High level of prolactin suppresses the gonadal activities by making the refractory to gonadotrophins (Jankiraman 1977; Singh and Madan, 1989).

As early as 1979, Agrawal and Bhattacharyya compared the effect of comfortable environment in psychrometric chamber (average ambient temperature and absolute humidity was 20.59°C, 11.98 mm Hg) with natural summer shed environment (32.90°C, 26.17 mm Hg) on the favorable tubo-uterine condition of nannies of Barbari goats 10 -15 hours after onset of oestrus and reported that histologically, the epithelial cells in the reproductive tract appeared to be more well developed and secretary in nature in the comfortable environment. The endometrium was thicker and the myometrium and serosa were thinner with a reduced number of cells per unit volume, indicating hypertrophy of the muscle cells. The lamina propria of the vagina was edematous with fewer cells per unit volume. Histochemically, the intensity of PAS reaction in the fallopian tube and uterus was similar in the two groups, but in the cervix was more intense in the comfortable environment. The compactness and regression of tissue in the tropical summer environment may indicate lowered oestrogen and raised progesterone blood levels, possibly resulting from reduction in LH levels through environmental heat stress.

Casu et al. (1991) studied the effect of heat stress in small ruminant females and reported that in the ewe, high temperature reduces the length of the oestrous cycle or suppresses oestrus, depending on the time at which heat stress occurs, where as in the doe, heat stress lengthens the oestrous cycle. Heat stress has adverse effects on ovulation in both species, the greatest effect in the ewe being observed in the first 3 days after ovulation. In the ewe, exposure to heat in the 2nd half of pregnancy results in damage to the fetus, and decreased birth weight and viability. These effects, which are observed in the tropical regions, occur also in the Mediterranean area. Chemineau

(1993) reported that heat stress reduced the oestrous period and level of fecundity and increased early embryonic mortality. The hyperthermia resulting from heat stress can also compromise cellular function and result in physiological changes inimical to animal production. This physiological adjustment is particularly true for reproduction. Culture of oocytes and embryos get impeded at temperatures characteristic of those experienced by heat-stressed animals influenced subsequent embryonic development (Rivera and Hansen, 2001; Krininger et al., 2003; Roth and Hansen, 2004).

Effect on recruitment of ovarian follicles

Ozawa et al. (2005) investigated the changes in follicular dynamics and steroidogenic activity during heat stress in goats by exposing adult female goats to heat stress at 36°C and 70% relative humidity for 48 h and then injected with PGF2µ (the time of PGF2 µ injection was designated as 0 h). In control (non-heat-stressed) goats, ovulatory follicles were mainly recruited from -24 h to 0 h, whereas no follicles recruited during that period were ovulated in the heat-stressed goats. The timing of the recruitment of ovulatory follicles was delayed by heat stress by approximately 24 h. The plasma concentration of oestradiol in the heat-stressed goats was significantly lower from 36 to 54 h compared with the controls, although the concentrations of FSH and progesterone did not differ between the treatments. In addition, the concentration of oestradiol, the aromatase activity, and the LH receptor level in the follicles from heat-stressed goats were significantly lower compared with the controls. These results indicated that heat stress during follicular recruitment suppresses subsequent growth to ovulation, accompanied by decreased LH receptor level and oestradiol synthesis activity in the follicles. A number of hormones (Thyroid, Growth and Insulin) synergistically act on the granulosa cells of the follicles in the presence of transforming growth factor- B and helps granulosa cell division that enhances the granulosa cells population (Hafez and Hafez, 1993) which further helps in increasing oestradiol 17b production of follicles. Timely surge of oestradiol 17b helps in the release of LH from the pituitary and brings ovulation and finally formation of functional corpus luteum to release progesterone in circulation (Abilay et al., 1975).

Effect on Pregnancy and Conceptus Development

It is well established that fertility (Hall et al., 1959; Gwazdauskas et al., 1975; Badinga et al., 1985) and other production and reproduction traits (Collier et al., 1982; Moore et al., 1992) are reduced in response to elevated ambient temperatures and humidity. Lu (1989) suggested that heat stress (HS) in goats can be defined as the disruption of homeostasis by ambient temperatures which are greater than an animal's upper critical temperature, resulting in heat production primarily due to a rise in body temperature. Two external measurements, rectal temperatures and respiration rates, were elevated in heat stress goats. Continuous application of this temperature regime resulted in an increase in respiration rates during the experiment period in HS goats. Such an increase may reflect an inability to totally dissipate heat gained from the previous day(s) and likely contributed to the higher rectal temperatures in heat stress goats. Small increments (<1°C) in rectal temperatures have been associated with adverse affects on fertility (Ulberg and Burfening, 1967;Gwazdauskas et al.,1973; Wolfensen et al.1988) reduced conceptus and corpus luteum weights (Biggers et al.,1987), and early luteal regression (Wolfensen et al., 1988) in livestock. Goats exposed to HS from Day 8 to Day 17 of pregnancy had increased plasma levels of primary circulating metabolite of PGF2µ, 13, 14 - dihydro - 15 - keto - prostaglandin F2µ (PGFM) on Day 17 of pregnancy. An increase in circulating concentrations of prostaglandins appears to be a common response to heat stress in a number of other species. In vivo heat stress resulted in increased circulating concentrations of PGFM and reduced luteal function in gilts (Hoagland and Wetteman, 1984) and post partum cattle (Lewis et al.,1984). Increase in plasma PGFM concentrations in response to HS may reflect uterine PGF2µ secretion (Guilbault et al.,1984). Heat stress alters plasma membrane lipid composition (Anderson and Parker,1982) and affects phospholipase activity and phosphoinositide turnover (Calderwood et al.,1987).Therefore, the increased concentrations of PGFM in heat stressed goats may be the result of increased availability of substrates and/or activity of the enzymes involved in uterine prostaglandin synthesis (Flint et al., 1986). Alternatively, the increased levels of PGFM in plasma of heat stressed goats may have originated from extra uterine sources. Prostaglandins of the E series are thought to act on the central nervous system as final mediators of the febrile response (Milton and Wendandt, 1970; Stitt, 1973; Bernheim et al., 1980). Prostaglandin levels are elevated in the systemic circulation during fever (Skarnes et al., 1981; Rotondo et al., 1988) and may act peripherally to increase heat loss through vaso dilatation (Shimada at al., 1990; Long et al., 1991). Concentrations of Progesterone hormone have been reported to decrease (Folman et al.1983), increase (Abilay et al., 1975; Vaught et al., 1977; Thatcher and Ponce-Roman, 1980), or remain unchanged (Hoagland and Wetteman, 1984; Biggers et al.,1987) in response to elevated ambient temperatures. Although at 24 hours mean progesterone levels were unaffected by heat stress. Pregnant goats had elevated plasma concentrations of Progesterone in the afternoon, concomitant with the observed afternoon increase in body temperature and respiration rates. The biological significance of this phenomenon is not known but may be due to an increase in secretion or a reduced metabolism of Progesterone (Collier et al., 1982). Heat stress from day 8 to day 17 of pregnancy did not alter uterine responsiveness to oxytocin although plasma levels of PGFM were increased by oxytocin in two of four breeds/non pregnant goats. The critical period for maternal recognition of pregnancy in goats occurs between day 15 and day 17 of pregnancy (Gnatek et al., 1989). The presence of a viable conceptus suppresses uterine release of PGF2μ in response to oxytocin in goats. In contrast, endometrium from Day 17 pregnant cattle, when perfused at thermo neutral (TN) temperatures, does not respond to oxytocin with an increase in PGF2μ secretion. However, endometrium perfused at elevated temperatures (42°C) responds to oxytocin with a rapid increase in PGF2μ secretion, as does endometrium from cyclic cows regardless of perfusion temperature (Putney et al., 1988a). Similar increases in PGF2μ secretion were observed *in vitro* when endometrium from pregnant gilts was heat stressed and challenged with oxytocin (Gross et al., 1989). Similarly, Wolfensen et al. (1993) were unable to demonstrate a significant effect of short - term heat stress on oxytocin- induced secretion of PGF2μ in pregnant or cyclic heifers, but greater variation was associated with the PGFM response to oxytocin in heat stressed heifers, probably suggesting that the conceptus may not be fully capable of inhibiting PGF2μ secretion by pregnant endometrium during heat stress conditions (Wolfensen et al., 1993). Such a mechanism could have contributed to the increase in plasma concentrations of PGFM in heat stressed goats. In summary, goats that received heat stress from Day 8 to Day 17 of pregnancy had elevated respiration rates and rectal temperatures. Endocrine responses to heat stress included increased circulation concentrations of Progesterone and PGFM but uterine sensitivity to exogenous oxytocin was unaffected in pregnant goats.

Fertility is lower during periods of heat stress. Reduced conception rates (Alliston et al., 1961) and early embryonic losses have been reported in sheep (Dutt, 1963), cattle (Gwazdauskas et al., 1973; Thatcher, 1974), and swine (Wetteman and Bazer, 1985) exposed to elevated temperatures and humidity. This may be partially due to direct effects on the early embryo because dairy cattle exposed to elevated ambient temperatures from Day 1 to Day 7 of pregnancy have a greater incidence of abnormal or retarded embryos (Putney et al., 1988b). However, maternal heat stress during the critical period of maternal recognition of pregnancy may also reduce reproductive efficiency in livestock. Heat stress applied solely during the period of conceptus elongation (approximately at Day 10 - 20) reduced productivity in ewes and gilts (Dutt and Jabara,1976; Omtveld et al.,1971), modified protein secretion by endometrial and conceptus tissues (Malayer and Hansen,1989) and resulted in lower conceptus and corpora lutea weights (Biggers et al.,1987). Cows exposed to heat stress on Day 17 post insemination have higher circulating levels of PGFM than non-stressed cows (Putney et al., 1989a). Finally, cyclic cows exposed to heat stress undergo luteal regression earlier than cows exposed to thermo neutral (TN) temperatures (Wolfensen et al., 1988); it is not known to what extent heat stress during early pregnancy effects early regression of the corpus luteum (CL). *In vitro,* heat stress reduces conceptus secretion of the anti luteolysin bovine interferon'tau' (previously called type 1 trophoblast interferon and bovine trophoblast protein-l) by 72% (Putney et al.,1988a). Furthermore, the response of endometrium, obtained from cattle on Day 17 of pregnancy, to oxytocin was restored during *in vitro* heat stress (Putney et al., 1988b). These data indicated that heat stress influenced conceptus development and might have altered alter endometrial responsiveness to oxytocin during early pregnancy. Enhanced uterine sensitivity to oxytocin during early pregnancy could result in premature regression of the corpus luteum (CL) and contribute to non geno toxic embryonic loss. Luteolysis in goats is achieved through mechanisms similar to those reported for cattle and sheep. Inter oestrus interval in goats is prolonged after immunization against oxytocin (Cooke and Homeida, 1985). Oestrous cycle length is shortened from 21 to 7 days after oxytocin administration (Cooke and Knifton, 1981; Cooke and Homeida, 1982). Oxytocin-induced pulsatile release of prostaglandin F2μ (PGF2μ), the uterine luteolysin in goats was attenuated during early pregnancy suggested that the anti luteolytic effects of the goat conceptus were similar to those for other ruminants (Bazer, 1992). But studies documenting ovarian and uterine responses to heat stress during early pregnancy in goats are lacking. Therefore, researchers tested the hypothesis that heat stress applied during the period of conceptus elongation (Days 8-17), would influence basal and/or oxytocin-stimulated plasma concentrations of PGFM, and/or plasma concentrations of progesterone.

Emesih et al. (1995) studied the effects of heat stress (HS; 37°C 12 h per day, 30°C 12 h per day) on plasma concentrations of progesterone (P) and PGFM in pregnant goats (biphasic temperature pattern delivered to heat stress goats was provided to simulate normal daily temperature variations characteristic of the summer months in Texas). Goats experienced constant relative humidity (35%) with either heat stress (n=16) or thermo neutral (TN; 21°C; n =20) temperatures from Day 8 to Day 17 of pregnancy and reported that Plasma levels of PGPM tended to be higher (P=< 0.08) in pregnant goats exposed to heat stress compared to those maintained at TN temperatures (458.1 & 37.4 and 360.45 37.0 pg per ml, respectively). Pregnant goats exposed to heat stress (HS) had elevated plasma concentrations of P in the afternoon (HS, 8.33 k 0.36 ng per ml; TN, 6.38 + 0.42 ng per ml) but not in the morning (HS, 6.84 ± 0.42; TN, 6.58 ± 0.42 ng per ml; temperature X time, $P<0.05$). Therefore, elevated ambient temperatures during Days 8 - 17 of pregnancy increased plasma concentrations of progesterone and PGFM in pregnant goats and concluded that a rise in uterine prostaglandin secretion may influence corpus luteum function during early pregnancy and affect conceptus growth and development.

Thermal/climatic stress and embryo transfer technology

Of late Embryo Transfer Technology has been recognized as one of the most suitable technology for proliferation of superior female gene pool after artificial insemination in most of the domestic species including cattle, sheep and goat (Armstrong and Evans, 1983). Climatic/ Thermal Stress is one of the important factors deciding the different facets of embryo transfer like super ovulation, embryo recovery and embryo survival after transfer. (Armstrong, 1983a, 1983b). It has been reported that super ovulation and embryo collection at different time/season of the year with the same regimen or protocol elicited variable response in transferable embryo production in goats (Goel and Agrawal,2005) occur in a favorable climatic conditions. Any adverse climate directly affects the energy balance in animals. During stress, animal system promptly cuts down the energy inflow to the reproductive system for maintaining its immediate requirement for survival. Thus the hormone production related to energy metabolism is diverted to other vital organs for the survival of the animals. The gonadotrophins and gonadal hormone synthesis decreases drastically (Badinga et al., 1993). The folliculogenesis, ovulation and the process of implantation are affected due to its imbalance of hormones leading to sub fertility or infertility (Udompraset and Willimson, 1987; Hansen, 1997). External manipulation with the hormone fails to augment the proper reproduction to the animals under the above circumstances (Thatcher et al., 2001; Putney et al., 1989).

Induction of super ovulation with exogenous hormones increases endogenous hormone milieu leading to changes in normal homeostasis of animal and thus fails to produce proper folliculogenesis, ovulation and embryo development (Wolfenson et al., 1995; Wilson et al., 1998). High humid climate has been shown to cause much more adverse effect than of cold climate (West et al., 1991). It may be due to the fact that to lower heat load, animal decreasing the energy production by decreasing feed intake, digestion and assimilation in one hand, decreasing the hormone production on other hand. However during cold stress, the energy utilization is more which causes stress to the hormones related to energy metabolism and for survivability, the energy is curtailed from the proper level needed for reproduction, ultimately these events leads to reduced reproduction.

Nutritional stress and reproduction

The nutritional environment and physiological stage of animals varies widely under prevailing production systems. To meet fluctuating nutritional demand and cope up with stress, the animals have developed physiological strategies to make efficient use of the available nutrients. During period when nutrient availability is surplus to the physiological need, it is stored in depot fat and in insufficiency and/or stress conditions the reserve is mobilized to supplement the body requirement. Generations of goat breeders have understood that the nutritional status of their animals is central to reproductive performance with sub-optimal nutrition associated with following reproduction related events:

- Delayed onset of puberty/sexual maturity.
- Reduced expression of reproductive behaviors (oestrus expression, sexual vigor and Mounting behavior).
- Aberrations in oestrous cycle.
- Reduced reproduction rates.
- Poor kid growth.
- Prolonged post- partum anoestrus.
- Increased reproductive ailments.

Seasonal variation in feed availability is the major deriving force behind the evolution of seasonal breeding at least in photo responsive temperate breeds (Bronson, 1989) but the nutrition is also important as a direct or proximate regulator of reproduction. At one extreme, reproductive behavior and ultimately gamete production is inhibited as nutrition becomes progressively more limiting and at the other, optimum levels of nutrition are required if animals are to express their full genetic potential for reproduction. Nutritional manipulation in both the male and female remains a useful tool in the successful management of goats for increased production.

Underlying mechanism of nutrition in fertility regulation

Recent studies have improved the understanding of the metabolic mechanism that mediate nutritional effects on puberty, post- partum anoestrus and ovulation rate with leptin emerging as a potentially important candidate. Metabolic hormones such as insulin and IGFs and their binding proteins appear to synchronize with gonadotrophins at the level of gonads. Nutrition is known to affect at the level of both the ovaries and the reproductive tract. It is understood that some of the nutrient mediated effects act directly on the gonads and other reproductive organs, while other produce similar effects indirectly via hypophyseal -pituitary-gonadal axis (Smith and Akinbamijo, 2000).

Nutritional regulation of reproduction in male

i) Attainment of puberty

Puberty as defined by complete separation of the prepuce and the penis. Ejaculation of motile spermatozoa is attained at the age of 5 -14 months of age in most of the tropical breeds of goat, although full reproductive potential may take further few months. In most ungulates, attainment of puberty is dependent on achieving satisfactory body weight usually between 40-70% of adult weight and goats appear to be no exception. Studies to examine the relationship between reproduction and nutrition in goat kids revealed that in case food security, supplementation of energy and phosphorus hastened the puberty, growth and reproduction (Hernandez and Peraza, 1982).

ii) Sperm production

Effective male reproduction requires both production of adequate viable spermatozoa and libido to ensure deposition of the sperms in the female genital tract. The endocrine regulation of these two functions differs and there is increasing evidence that they may also differ in their responses to altered nutrition. Scrotal measurements are excellent predictors of testicular size, which in turn an excellent indicator of sperm production. Thus testicular size has been commonly used as an indicator measure of spermatogenic function in goats. Goats are responsive to change in nutrition so that under nutrition reduces and improved nutrition increases both testicular size and sperm production. Poor nutritional regimen that resulted in weight loss can also cause reduction in semen volume; sperm count per ejaculate, percent live sperms, sperm motility and an increase in sperm abnormalities. Vitamin A is considered vital for spermatogenesis. During the lean period when the availability of green fodder is scarce, supplementation of vitamin A / carotene significantly improved sperm quality in terms of total sperm abnormalities and tail abnormalities (Deshmukh and Honmode, 1982).

Nutritional regulation of reproduction in female

In females the complete process of reproduction involves pregnancy, lactation and potential capacity to reproduce in the following year. From energy point of view, the mechanism of regulating reproduction should include both the present nutritional status and the level of body reserves, as security for the whole reproductive process. Much of the research on nutrition and fertility has concentrated on energy requirements since this is probably the major factor limiting reproductive performance. This is partly because the animals in their early lactation has a higher energy requirement than can be supported by feed intake, and is therefore usually in a state of negative energy balance. In case of dairy goat it is probable that the large negative energy balance that occurs during early lactation will further delay the resumption of sexual activity as has been observed in dairy cattle (Canfield and Butler, 1991). Research in USA has shown that high levels of dietary protein are associated with low pregnancy rates in large ruminants, which appears to be due to rumen-degradable protein. Recently, there has been great interest in understanding the role of Leptin in the relationship between nutrition and reproduction in livestock. Leptin is an adipocyte-derived hormone, which reflects the state of nutrition and energy reserves in many species including ruminants (Chilliard et al., 1998). Studies have shown that leptin might act as a chronic metabolic signal for the reproductive system by indicating the level of fat reserves available to meet the caloric demands of reproduction.

i) Nutrition and attainment of puberty and oestrus behavior

Expression of first oestrus is usually taken to represent the onset of puberty in doe and several episodes of silent oestrus precede the first behavioral oestrus (ovulatory oestrus). It is well known that inadequate nutrition during the growing period retards growth and delays puberty in young doe. It is generally considered that does should be mated when they reached 50-60% of their adult body weight. Pubertal body weight can be attained at varying ages according to availability of dietary intake. The condition of goats, whether directly or due to poor nutrition or indirectly through parasitic infestations (external and/or internal) or some debilitating disease like Johne's disease, may influence the occurrence of oestrous cycles, which may be weak or entirely missing. Vitamin A, B_{12} and D, manganese, cobalt, zinc, selenium and phosphorus deficiencies /imbalances have all been implicated in infertility. Vitamin A deficiency causes changes in the uterine lining, which make conception and implantation difficult thus leading to embryonic mortality. Vitamin A deficiency has also been associated with decreased ova production from ovary.

ii) Nutrition and post-partum ovarian cyclicity

A number of factors influence the post-partum ovarian activity in goats. It has been documented that negative energy balance caused by low dry matter intake during early lactation period suppresses LH pulse frequency and maturation of dominant follicles. LH frequency starts to increase after the nadir of energy balance. Post - partum anoestrus in rigidly photoperiodic breeds of small ruminants depends on photoperiod, with no cyclicity observed under long photoperiods. In suckling does, for a given level of feed there is a strong positive relationship between the duration of nursing and duration of post -partum anoestrus, which is reinforced the natural effect of season (Delgadillio et al., 1999). Resumption of both oestrus and ovulation is not related to the body weight of the dam at kidding but to body weight changes (i.e., energy balance). In the tropics or with non- photo responsive breeds, there is better evidence that nutrition is a primary regulator of reproduction. Time of the year is the major factor affecting litter size, which is lowering during the dry season. Alpine dairy goats also exhibit year round variation in reproductive performance, which is related to rainfall and ambient temperature changes.

iii) Effect of flushing on ovulation

It is the process of increasing the nutritional status of animals just prior to and during breeding season to increase ovulation and conception rates. Goats like sheep, are capable of responding to increased level of nutrition. (Henniawati and Fletcher, (1986). Flushing raises the level of ovarian function. Nevertheless this practice does not end with constant response. Detailed studies, in this area however, have not been documented for adult goats.

iv) Nutrition and embryo transfer

The nutritional status of donor and recipient affects the success of an embryo transfer programme. The first biological system to fail due to imbalanced/sub optimal nutrition is the reproductive system. Animal's body systems are designed with a level of priorities. Maintenance of own body itself has utmost priority. Under adequate nutritional conditions, entire energy source is directed towards the life sustaining systems i.e. respiration, digestion and circulation. The reproductive system requires a large amount of energy to carry, maintain and deliver a live fetus. Under poor body conditions, the animal shut down the reproductive system resulting in cessation of oestrus expression. Embryo transfer programme requires that the donor should be normally cycling in order for optimum collection of embryos. Thus the maintenance of donor on acceptable level of nutrition is foremost in reproductive management. It has been demonstrated that embryo survival is independent of the nutritional status of donor. Carryover effect of donor's nutrition is visible on fetal growth. Similarly the embryo survival rate has been reported to be related to level of feeding of recipient doe, as over feeding reduces the peripheral progesterone level leading to embryonic loss. In ewes it has been reported that increase in the ovulation rate can be brought about by feeding lupin seed or soyabean meal.

v) Nutrition and reproduction rate

The low reproduction rate of the Angora breed of goat is uniquely a typical of the goat population as a whole. Abortion is a major problem in this breed and as much as a portion of population is 'habitual aborters' and abort following some stress situation. Wentzel et al. (1974) reported that a high incidence of abortion accompanied sub maintenance energy nutrition during the last third of pregnancy. This was likely a result of a drop in blood glucose concentration triggering endocrinological activity, a rise in plasma oestrogen and expulsion of fetus (Wentzel et al., 1976). Abortions were controlled by feeding 300 g per day of high energy concentrate.

Points to remember to get optimum reproductive performance of animals

- Reproduction can be affected by both excess as well as nutritional deficiencies.
- Balanced feeding is necessary throughout different physiological stages (lactation, gestation and dry period) of animals.
- Interactions exist between the factors affecting fertility so that the combined effects are additive.

References

Abilay, T.A., Johnson, H.D.and Madan, M.1975. Influence of environmental heat on peripheral plasma progesterone and cortisol during the bovine estrous cycle. Journal of Dairy Science 58:1836 -1840.

Aboul - Naga, A. M.1987. Extensive flock management of goats in arid rangeland. Case Study of South Western Coast of Egypt. In: Proceedings of the 4th International Conference on Goats, Brazil, Volume II. pp. 853 -865.

Agrawal, K, P. and Bhattacharyya, N. K. 1979.Histological and certain histochemical evidences of favorable tubo uterine condition at comfortable temperature in Barbari nannies (goat). Indian Journal of Animal Sciences 49(2): 127 - 135.

Agrawal, K. P., Goel, A. K. and Bhattacharyya, N. K. 1986. Annual Scientific Report. CIRG Makhdoom, Farah Mathura, U. P. India. pp. 35 - 45.

Alliston C. W. and Ulberg L. C.1961. Early Pregnancy Loss in Sheep at Ambient Temperatures of 70° and 90 ° F as Determined by Embryo Transfer. Journal of Animal Science 20: 608 - 613.

Al-Shaikh, M. A. 2000. Effect of elevating ambient temperature on reproduction performance of Aardi goats. Vertebrate Anatomy and Embryology 33 (B): 1- 7.

Amoah, E. A. and Gelaye, S. 1990. Reproductive performance of female goats in South Pacific countries. Small Ruminant Research 3:257 - 267.

Anderson, R.L. and Parker, R. 1982. Analysis of membrane lipid composition of mammalian cells during the development of thermo tolerance. International Journal of Radiation Research 42: 57 - 69.

Armstrong D T, Pfitzner A P, Warnes G M, Ralph M M and Seamark R M. 1983a. Endocrine responses of goats after induction of super ovulation with PMSG and FSH. Journal of Reproduction and Fertility 67:395 - 401.

Armstrong D T, Pfitzner A P, Warnes G M, Ralph M M and Seamark R M. 1983b. Super ovulation treatments and embryo transfer in Angora goats. Journal of Reproduction and Fertility 67:403 - 410.

Armstrong, D.T. and Evans, G. 1983. Factors influencing success of embryo transfer in sheep and goats. Theriogenology 19: 31 - 42.

Badinga L, Thatcher WW, Diaz T, Drost M, Wolfenson D. 1993 Effect of environmental heat stress on follicular development and steroidogenesis in lactating Holstein cows. Theriogenology 39:797- 810.

Badinga, L., Collier, R.J., Thatcher, W.W. and Wilcox, C.J. 1985. Effects of climate and management factors on conception rate of dairy cattle in a sub tropical environment. Journal of Dairy Science 68:78 - 85.

Bazer, F.W. 1992. Mediators of maternal recognition of pregnancy in mammals. In: Proceedings of the Society for Experimental Biology and Medicine 199: 373 - 384.

Bernheim, H.A., Gilbert, T.M. and Stitt, J.T. 1980. Prostaglandin E levels in the third ventricular cerebrospinal fluid of rabbits during fever and change in body temperature. Journal of Physiology 301: 69 -78.

Bhattacharyya, A.N. and Hussein, F.1974. Intake and utilization of nutrients in sheep fed different levels of roughage under heat stress. Journal of Animal Science 38: 877-886.

Biggers, B.G., Geisert, R.G., Wetteman, R.P. and Buchanan, D.S. 1987. Effect of heat stress on early embryonic development in the beef cow. Journal of Animal Science 64:1512 -1518.

Bronson F H.1989. Mammalian Reproductive Biology. University of Chicago Press, Chicago, USA.

Calderwood, S.K., Stevenson, M.A. and Hahn, G.M. 1987. Heat stress stimulates inositol triphosphate release and phosphorylation of phosphoinositides in CHO and Balb C 3T3 cells. Journal of Cell Physiology 130: 369 - 376.

Canfield R W, and Butler W R.1991. Energy balance, first ovulation, and the effect of naloxone on LH secretion in early post partum dairy cows. Journal of Animal Science 69: 740 -746.

Casady, R. B., Myers, R. M. and Legates. J. E. 1953. The effect of exposure to high ambient temperature on spermatogenesis in the dairy bull. Journal of Dairy Science. 36:14.

Casu, S., Cappai, P. and Naitana, S. 1991. Effects of high temperatures on reproduction in small ruminants. In: Animal Husbandry in Warm Climates 103 -111.

Chaudhary, S.A. and Mehmood, Ul.H. 1984. Some observations on semen collection technique and morphological abnormalities of buck spermatozoa. Pakistan Veterinary Journal 4: 227-228.

Chemineau, P.1993.Environment and animal reproduction. World Animal Review.77: 2-14.

CIRG.1985. Annual Scientific Report. CIRG, Makhdoom. Farah, Mathura, U.P. pp.85 - 88.

Collier, R.J., Doelger, S.G., Head, H.H., Thatcher, W.W. and Wilcox, C.J. 1982. Effects of heat stress during pregnancy on maternal hormone concentrations, calf birth weight and postpartum milk yield of Holstein cows. Journal of Animal Science 54: 309 - 319.

Cooke, R.G. and Homeida, A.M. 1982. Plasma concentrations of 13, 14 - dihydro-15-ketoprostaglandin F2 µ and progesterone during oxytocin-induced estrous in the goat. Theriogenology 18: 453 - 460.

Cooke, R.G. and Homeida, A.M. 1985. Suppression of prostaglandin F2 µ release and delay of luteolysis after active immunization against oxytocin in the goat. Journal of Reproduction and Fertility 75: 63 - 68.

Cooke, R.G. and Knifton, A. 1981. Oxytocin-induced estrous in the goat. Theriogenology 16: 95 - 97.

Cupps, P.T. 1991. Reproduction in Domestic Animals. Harcourt Brace Jovanovich Publishers. 4th Edition. pp. 506 - 510.

Delgadillio JA, Canedo GA, Chemineau P, Guillaume DF, Malpaux B.1999. Evidence for an annual reproductive rhythm independent of food availability in male creole goats in subtropical northern Mexico. Theriogenology 52: 727-737.

Deshmukh GB and Honomode J.1982. Effect of Vitamin and Carotene on reproductive efficiency of Bucks. In: Proceedings of the 3rd International Congress on Goat Production and Diseases, Tucson, Arizona (USA). January 10 -15, p.369.

Devendra, C. and Burns, M. 1983. Goat Production in the Tropics. CAB International U. K. p.184.

Dutt, R.H. 1963. Critical period for early embryo mortality in ewes exposed to high ambient temperature. Journal of Animal Science 22: 713 - 1218.

Dutt, R.H. and Jabara, C.K.1976. Gestation stages and embryo loss in ewes heat stressed during the placentogenesis. Journal of Animal Science 43: 282.

Elwishy, A.B. Elsawat, S.A. Elmikkawi, F. and Omar, A.A. 1971. Monthly and seasonal variations in sexual activity of male Damascus goats. Indian Journal of Animal Sciences 41(7):562 - 569.

Emesih, G C. Newton, G R. and Weise, D.W. 1995. Effects of heat stress and oxytocin on plasma concentrations of progesterone and 13, 14 - dihydro - 15 keto prostaglandin F2µ in goats. Small Ruminant Research 16:133 -139.

Finch, V.A., 1986. Body temperature in beef cattle: its control and relevance to production in the tropics. Journal of Animal Science 62:531 - 542.

Flint, A.P.F., Lest, W.M.F., Sheldrick, E.L. and Stewart, H.J.1986. Stimulation of phosphoinositide hydrolysis by oxytocin and the mechanism by which oxytocin controls prostaglandin synthesis in the ovine endometrium. Biochemical Journal 237: 797- 805.

Folman, Y., Rosenberg, M., Ascarelli, I., Kaim, M. and Herz, Z. 1983. The effect of dietary and climatic factors on fertility, and on plasma progesterone and estradiol -17â levels in dairy cows. Journal of Steroid Biochemistry 19: 863 - 868.

Fraser AF and Broom DM. 1997. Farm Animal Behavior and Welfare. 3rd Edition, CAB International U.K. pp.79 - 98.

Gnatek, G.G., Smith, L.D., Duby, R.T. and Godkin, J.D.1989. Maternal recognition of pregnancy in the goat: effects of conceptus removal on inter estrus interval and characterization of conceptus protein production during early pregnancy. Biology of Reproduction 41: 655 - 663.

Goel A K. 1998. Augmentation of Reproductive Efficiency in Jakhrana Goats. Ph. D. Thesis, Dr. B. R. Ambedkar University, Agra (Formerly Agra University) U. P. India.

Goel, A K and Agrawal, K P. 1994. Breeding behavior of indigenous goats in semi arid zone. Indian Journal of Animal Reproduction 15: 32 - 35.

Goel A K and Agrawal K P.2000. Distribution pattern of oestrus in Jakhrana goats. Indian Journal of Animal Sciences 70:589 - 590.

Goel, A K and Agrawal, K P. 2004. Onset of puberty and oestrus behavior in Jakhrana goats. Indian Journal of Animal Sciences 74(11): 1130 - 1131.

Goel A K and Agrawal K P.2005. Ovulatory response and embryo yield in Jakhrana goats following treatments with PMSG and FSH. Tropical Animal Health and Production (U K) 37: 549 - 558.

Goel A K, Kharche S D, Jindal S K. and Sinha N K. 2003. Oestrus behaviour of Jamunapari goats under tropical environment. In : Abstract and Souvenir, 14th Annual Convention and National Symposium on "Current Reproductive Technologies for Improvement of Livestock Production in India". Salt Lake City, Kolkata (West Bengal) August, 22 –24, Abstract No. BPL-1, pp. 86.

Gross, T.S., Putney, D.J. and Thatcher, W.W. 1989. Effect of *in vitro* heat stress on prostaglandin and protein secretion by endometrium from pregnant and cyclic gilts at day 14 after oestrus. Journal of Reproduction and Fertility 85: 541- 550.

Guilbault, L.A., Thatcher, W.W., Foster, D.B. and Caton, D.1984. Relationship between15-keto-13,14-dihydro-prostaglandinF2µ concentrations in peripheral plasma with local uterine production of F series prostaglandins and changes in uterine blood flow during the early post partum period of cattle. Biology of Reproduction 31: 879 - 889.

Gwazdauskas, F.C., Thatcher, W.W. and Wilcox, C.J. 1973. Physical, environmental and hormonal factors at insemination which may affect conception. Journal of Dairy Science 56: 873 - 877.

Gwazdauskas, F.C., Wilcox, C.J. and Thatcher, W.W. 1975. Environmental and managemental factors affecting conception rate in a subtropical environment. Journal of Dairy Science 58:88 -92.

Hafez E S E and Hafez B. 1993. Folliculogenesis, Egg Maturation and Ovulation. In: Reproduction in Farm Animals (B, Hafez; Hafez, E S E, Eds.) Lippin Cott Williams and Wilkins, Philadelphia, pp.68 - 81.

Hakusugawara, Masakazu katayana and Tackokimura. 1989. Effect of prolonged lightening on the plasma concentration of prolactin and electro encephalogram in goats. Japanese Journal of Zootech. Science 16: 567-77.

Hall, J.G., Branton, C. and Stone, E.J. 1959. Estrus, estrous cycles, ovulation time, time of service and fertility of dairy cattle in Louisiana. Journal of Dairy Science 42: 1086 - 1094.

Hansen PJ. 1997 Effects of environment of bovine reproduction. In: Current Therapy in Large Animal Theriogenology(Youngquist RS, Editor) Philadelphia: WB Saunders;.pp.403 - 415.

Hansen,P.J.1990. Effects of coat color on physiological and milk production responses to solar radiation in Holsteins. The Veterinary Record 127: 333 - 334.

Hennaiawati and Fletcher J C.1986. Reproduction in Indonesian sheep and goats at low levels of nutrition. Animal Reproduction Science 12:77- 84.

Hernandez P and Peraza Carlos. 1982. Some aspects of the reproduction of goat kids. In: Proceedings of the 3rd International Congress on Goat Production and Diseases, Tucson, Arizona(USA). January 10-15, p.366.

Hoagland, T.A. and Wetteman, R.P. 1984. Influence of elevated ambient temperatures after breeding on plasma corticoids, estradiol and progesterone in gilts. Theriogenology 22:15-24.

Hutchinson, J.C.D., Brown, G.D.1969. Penetrance of cattle coats by radiation. Journal of Applied Physiology 26 454 - 464.

Jainudeen, M.R. and Hafez, E.S.E.1993.Gestation, Prenatal Physiology, and Parturition. In: Reproduction in Farm Animals (B, Hafez; Hafez, E S E, Eds.) Lippin Cott Williams and Wilkins, Philadelphia, pp.140 -155.

Jankiraman, K. 1977. Aspects of endocrinological imbalance interfering with reproductive efficiency in buffalo. Joint Indo-Soviet Symposium on Buffalo Breeding. No.16 -18. National Dairy Development Board, Anand, India.

Jankiraman, K. and Mehta, V. M. 1990. Final Technical Report of PL- 480 Goat Project. Gujarat Agricultural University, Anand, India.

Joshi, B.C.; Aravindan, M; Singh, K.S. and Bhattacharyya, N.K. 1977. Effect of high environmental stress in the physiological responses of bucks. Indian Journal of Animal Sciences 47(4):200 -203.

Kang, S. W. and Chung, K. S. 1976. Studies on the semen characteristics of Korean native goats. Korean Journal of Animal Science 18: 117-124.

Khan, B. U., Roy, R., Prakash, B. and Singh, S. K. 1987. Annual Scientific Report. CIRG, Makhdoom. Farah Mathura, U. P. India. pp. 15 -32.

Khan, B. U., Roy, R., Prakash, B., Singh, L. B. and Singh, S. K. 1986. Annual Scientific Report. CIRG, Makhdoom. Farah Mathura, U. P. India. pp. 3 -22.

Krininger III, C.E., Block, J., Al-Katanani, Y.M., Rivera, R.M., Chase Jr., C.C. and Hansen, P.J. 2003. Differences between Brahman and Holstein cows in response to estrous synchronization, superovulation and resistance of embryos to heat shock changes in inhibitory effects of arsenic and heat shock on growth of pre implantation bovine embryos. Molecular Reproduction and Development 63: 335 -340.

Lewis, G.S., Thatcher, W.W., Bliss, E.L., Drost, M. and Collier, R.J. 1984. Effects of heat stress during pregnancy on postpartum reproductive changes in Holstein cows. Journal of Animal Science 58: 174 -186.

Long, N.. Morimoto, A., Nakamori, T., Yamashiro, O. and Murakami, N.1991. Intra peritoneal injections of prostaglandin E2 attenuate hyperthermia induced by restraint or interleukin-1 in rats. Journal of Physiology 444: 363 - 373.

Lu,C.D.1989.Effects of heat stress on goat production.Small Ruminant Research2:151 - 162.

Malayer, J.R. and Hansen, P.J. 1989. Differences between Brahman and Holstein cows in heat-shock induced alterations of protein synthesis and secretion by oviducts and uterine endometrium. Journal of Animal Science 68: 266 -280.

Mc Ewen, B., 2002. The end of stress as we know it. Joseph Henry Press / Dana Press, Washington, DC, USA.

Milton, A.S. and Wendandt, S. 1970. A possible role for prostaglandin E1 as a modulator for temperature regulation in the central nervous system of the cat. Journal of Physiology 207:76 -77.

Mishra , M. S. and Sengupta, B. P. 1966. Semen quality of rams and goat in autumn. Indian Veterinary Journal. 42: 742 -745

Misra, H. R. and Biswas, S. C. 1966. A study on distribution of estrus in desi goats. Indian Journal of Dairy Science 19: 132 -134.

Mittal, J. P. 1987. Male reproductive characteristics of indigenous and crossbred goats under Indian arid zone. Indian Journal of Animal Sciences 57:158 -161.

Mittal, J.P. 1986. Reproduction characteristics of indigenous and crossbred bucks maintained under desert condition. Indian Journal of Animal Sciences 56 (6): 688 - 692.

Mittal, J.P.1982. Seasonal variation in semen quality of Barbari bucks. Indian Veterinary Journal 59: 957-959.

Moore, R.B., Fuquay, J.W. and Drapala, W.J. 1992. Effects of late gestation heat stress on postpartum milk production and reproduction in dairy cattle. Journal of Dairy Science 75: 1877 -1882.

Mukundan, G. and Rajgopalan, T. G.1971. An evaluation of influence of age of the dam on the frequency of multiple births in Malabari goats. Kerala Journal of Veterinary Science 2: 95 -98.

Mukundan,G.1976. In: Proceedings of the 2nd Workshop of All India Coordinated Research Projects (AICRP)on Goat Breeding, National Dairy Research Institute, Karnal, India.

Nanda A S. 1995. Stress as a cause of abnormal LH surge and ovulatory disturbances. In: Recent Advances in Animal Reproduction and Gynecology (Ed. A S Nanda). USG Publishers and Distributors, Ludhiana (India) pp.69 - 74.

Omtvedt, IT., Nelson, R.E., Edwards, R.L., Stephens, D.F. and Thurman, E.J. 1971. Influence of heat stress during early, mid and late pregnancy in gilts. Journal of Animal Science 32:312 - 317.

Ozawa, M., Tabayashi, D., Latief, T. A., Shimizu, T., Oshima, I. and Kanai, Y. 2005. Alterations in follicular dynamics and steroidogenic abilities induced by heat stress during follicular recruitment in goats. Reproduction Cambridge. 129(5): 621 - 630.

Prasad, S. P. and Bhattacharyya, N. K. 1979. A note on the characteristics of pubertal estrus and oestrous cycle in Barbari nannies. Indian Journal of Animal Sciences 49 : 969 - 970.

Putney, D.J., Gross, T.S. and Thatcher, W.W. 1988a. Prostaglandin secretion by endometrium of pregnant and cyclic cattle at Day 17 after oestrus in response to *in-vitro* heat stress. Journal of Reproduction and Fertility 84: 475-483.

Putney, D.J., Drost, M. and Thatcher, W.W. 1988b. Embryonic development in superovulated dairy cattle exposed to elevated ambient temperatures between day 1 to 7 post insemination. Theriogenology 30: 195 -209.

Putney, D.J., Torres, C.A.A., Thatcher, W.W., Plante, C. and Drost, M. 1989a. Modulation of uterine prostaglandin biosynthesis by pregnant and non pregnant cows at day 17 post estrus in response to *in vivo* and *in vitro* heat stress. Animal Reproduction Science20:31 - 47.

Putney D J, Mullins S, Thatcher W W, Drost M. and Gross. T. S. 1989b. Embryonic development in superovulated dairy cattle exposed to elevated ambient temperatures between the onset of estrus and insemination. Animal Reproduction Science.19:37 - 51.

Rajkonwar, C. K. and Borgohain, B. N. 1978. A note on the incidence and signs of estrous in local does (*Capra hircus*) of Assam. Indian Journal of Animal Sciences 48 :546 - 548.

Raza Nazir, M. M., Agrawal, K. P. and Singh Khub and Bhattacharyya, N. K. 1978. Physico chemical studies on the semen of Black Bengal bucks. Annual Scientific Report, Division of Physiology and Climatology, IVRI, Izatnagar U P India. pp. 29 -31.

Rivera, R.M. and Hansen, P.J. 2001.Development of cultured bovine embryos after exposure to increased temperatures in the physiological range. Reproduction 121:107-115.

Roth, Z. and Hansen, P.J. 2004. Sphingosine-1-phosphate protects cultured bovine oocytes from physiologically relevant thermal stress. Reproduction, Fertility and Development 6:282.

Rotondo, D., Abul, H.T., Milton, AS. and Davidson, J.1988. Pyrogenic immunomodulators increase the levels of prostaglandin E2 in the blood simultaneously with the onset of fever. European Journal of Pharmacology 154:145 -152.

Roy, A., Dutta, I. C., Sahni, K. L., Singh, B. and Sengupta, B. P. 1966. Studies on certain aspects of sheep and goat husbandry, artificial breeding, telescoping and breeding season and certain reproductive phenomena in sheep and goats. Indian Journal of Veterinary Science and Animal Husbandry 32. 269 -275.

Sahni, K. L. 1967. Studies on quality, preservation and fertility of semen of sheep and goats. Ph. D. Thesis. Agra University, Agra, Uttar Pradesh, India.

Sahni, K. L. and Roy, A. 1967. A study on the sexual activity of the Barbari goat and conception rate through AI. Indian Journal of Veterinary Science and Animal Husbandry 37. 269 -276.

Santos, D. O., Simplicio, A. A. and Machado, R. 1998. Characteristics of the scrotum, testes and ejaculate in crossbred male goats subjected to scrotal insulation. Arquivo Brasileiro de Medicina Veterinaria-e-Zootecnia. 50(3): 287- 291.

Shabi S, Murphy M R and Moallem U. 2005. Within day feeding behavior of lactating dairy cows measured using a real time control system. Journal of Dairy Science 88:1848 -1854.

Sharma, G.P. Suri, K. and Vall, K.N. 1957. A study on reaction time and some of semen characteristics of Beetal breed of goat. Research Bulletin, Punjab University No.101:217-227.

Shimada, S.G., Stitt, J.T. and Angelogianni, P.1990. Effects of cold and capsaicin desensitization of prostaglandin E hypothermia in rats. Journal of Applied Physiology 68: 2618 -2622.

Shukla, D.D. and Bhattacharyya, P. 1952. Seasonal variation in reaction time and semen quality in goat. Indian Journal of Veterinary Science 22. 179 -190.

Singh, C. S. P., Shrivastava, S. N. and Singh, S. K.1978. A note on the incidence of estrus in goats. Indian Journal of Animal Sciences 48 : 67-70.

Singh J. and Madan M L. 1989. Hyperprlactinaemia. A possible cause of summer anoestrus in buffaloes. In: Proceedings, National Symposium on applied Reproduction in Farm Animals, College of Veterinary Science, Anand (Gujarat) India.

Singh, S. N. and Sengar, O. P. S. 1979. Technical Report, PL-480 Research Project, RBS College, Bichpuri (Agra), Uttar Pradesh, India.

Sinha, N. K., Wani, G. M. and Sahni, K. L 1981. Effect of seasons and age on seminal attributes of Jamunapari bucks. Indian Veterinary Journal 58: 963-965.

Skarnes, R.C., Brown, S.K., Hull, S.S. and McCraken, J.A. 1981. Role of prostaglandin E in the biphasic fever response to endotoxin. Journal of Experimental Medicine 154: 1212 -1224.

Smith O B and Akinbamijo O O. 2000. Micronutrients and reproduction in farm animals. Animal Reproduction Science 60 - 61:549.

Srivastava, A. K., Kortkar, D. P., Narawada, Bansod, R.S. and Jagtap, D. Z.1991. Studies on oestrous behavior in Angora local and crossbred goats. Indian Veterinary Journal 68 (7): 648 - 651.

Stewart, R.E.. 1953. Absorption of solar radiation by the hair of cattle. Agricultural Engineering 34:235-238.

Stitt, J.T. 1973. ProstaglandinE1 induced fever in rabbits. Journal of Physiology 232:163 - 179.

Thatcher W W, Moreira F, Santos J E, Mattos R C, Lopes F L, Pancarci S M, Risco C A. 2001. Effects of hormonal treatments on reproductive performance and embryo production. Theriogenology 55(1):75 - 89.

Thatcher, W.W. 1974. Effects of season, climate and temperature on reproduction and lactation. Journal of Dairy Science 57: 360 - 368.

Thatcher, W.W. and Ponce-Roman, H. 1980. Effects of climate on bovine reproduction. In: D. Morrow (Editor), Current Therapy in Theriogenology. W.B. Saunders, Philadelphia, pp. 441- 448.

Tiwari, S. B. 1967. Studies on certain aspects of semen production and artificial insemination in goats. M. V. Sc. Thesis, Agra University, Uttar Pradesh, India.

Udompraset P, Williamson NB. 1987. Seasonal influences on conception efficiency in Minnesota dairy herds. Theriogenology 28:323 -336.

Ulberg, L.C. and Burfening, P.J. 1967. Embryo death resulting from adverse environment on spermatozoa or ova. Journal of Animal Science 26:571 - 577.

Vaught, L.W., Monty, Jr., D.E. and Foote, W.C.1977. Effect of summer heat stress on serum luteinizing hormone and progesterone values in Holstein Friesian cows in Arizona. American Journal of Veterinary Research 38: 1027-1030.

Von Borrell, E.H. 2001. The biology of stress and its application to livestock housing and transportation assessment. Journal of Animal Science 79 (Supplement E):260 - 267.

Wentzel D, Le Roux, Marita M and Botha J. J. 1976. Effect of the level of nutrition on blood glucose concentration and reproductive performance of pregnant Angora goats. Agroanimalia 8: 59 -62.

Wentzel D, Morgenthal JC, Van Niekerk CH and Roclofse C S. 1974. The habitually aborting Angora doe. II. The effect of an energy deficiency on the incidence of abortion. Agroanimalia 6: 129 -132.

West J W, Mullinix B G and Sandifer TG. 1991 Effects of bovine somatotropin on physiologic responses of lactating Holstein and Jersey cows during hot humid weather. Journal of Dairy Science 74(3): 840 - 851.

Wetteman, R.P. and Bazer, F.W. 1985. Influence of environmental temperature on prolificacy of pigs. Journal of Reproduction and Fertility (Supplement) 33:199 -208.

Wilson SJ, Marion RS, Spain JN, Spiers DE, Keisler DH, Lucy MC.1998. Effect of controlled heat stress on ovarian function in dairy cattle: I. Lactating cows. Journal of Dairy Science 81:2124 - 2231.

Wolfensen, D., Bartol, F.F., Badinga, L., Barros, C.M., Marple, D.N., Cummins, K., Wolfe, D., Lucy, M.C., Spencer, T.E., and Thatcher, W.W. 1993. Secretion of PGF2 μ and oxytocin during hyperthermia in cyclic and pregnant heifers. Theriogenology 39: 1129 -1141.

Wolfensen. D., Flamenbaum, I. and Berman, A.1988. Hyperthermia and body energy store effects on estrous behavior, conception rate, and corpus luteum function in dairy cows. Journal of Dairy Science 71: 3497 - 3504.

Wolfenson D, Thatcher WW, Badinga L, Savio J D, Meidan R, Lew BJ. 1995. The effect of heat stress on follicular development during the estrous cycle dairy cattle. Biology of Reproduction 52:1106 –1113.

□□□

18

Physiological Adaptation of Goats to Climate Change

Puneet Kumar
Physiology, Reproduction and Shelter Management Division, Central Institute for Research on Goats, Makhdoom, P.O. Farah, Mathura -281 122, Uttar Pradesh

Introduction

World's climate may be generally considered as being tropical, semi-tropical, temperate and arctic. Each of these climatic zones represents a complex of the physical or meteorological and biological factors, which constitutes the natural environment. Each climate complex encompasses a multitude of plant and animal species that have evolved successfully by adaptive processes resulting from interactions with the meteorological environment. An environmental profile includes such factors as daily, seasonal, maximal and minimal temperatures, humidity, wind, radiation, length of season and a biological assessment such as quality and quantity of protein and energy available. The physiological profile is an assessment of selected physiological processes such as thermoregulation, hormonal balance, water balance and energy balance. The fitting of the physiological or production profile to the environmental profile would be the basis for a bioclimatic index. An animal with a good bioclimatic index would be an individual that has a high physiological predictability for ability to produce milk, grow, and reproduce in the environment. The application of meteorological and physiological principles to animal selection and management practices will increase the availability of animal protein, especially in climatic-limiting zones of the world.

The goat is an important source of milk, meat and fibre for the people throughout the world. Goats are found in many climatic regions of the world ranging from the arctic cold, temperate, deserts and mountains to subtropical and tropical dry and humid zones. They are recognized as one of the most successful domestic ruminants of the tropics and subtropics, which involve the arid, semi-arid, sub-humid, humid and the super humid climates. In these regions, climatic stressors, limitations of food, water quality and quantity add challenges to the adaptability of goats in addition to presence of internal and external parasites. For the goat to be successful survival and reproduce in all of these environments it must be highly adaptable.

Global climate change

Global climate change is an integrated system of several atmospheric phenomena and their products. At the surface, concentrations of greenhouse or radiative gases such as carbon dioxide, chlorofluorocarbons, methane and nitrous oxide have clearly increased since the onset of the industrial revolution. These trace gases, in addition to warming the surface air temperature by trapping some of the energy from the outgoing radiation, when transported into the stratosphere (10-15 km above the surface), destroy the beneficial ozone layer naturally present at that height. Such a loss in the thickness or thinning of the ozone layer will permit the increased penetration to the surface of deleterious wavelengths of solar radiation (Ultraviolet or UV [B- band], 280-315 nanometers, 1 nanometer = one billionth of meter). Average global air temperature has increased by about 0.8 C above pre-industrial levels and a report by the Intergovernmental Panel on Climate Change projected a rise from 1.4 to 5.8 °C by the year 2100. Local climate in different geographic areas may very well become warmer and drier, cooler and wetter or remain unchanged. Any change in the climate is expected to manifest itself as increases in the frequency of extreme events such as hurricanes, blizzards, heat waves and the number of days without precipitation during the plant-growing season (drought). Increases in air temperature (in winters in India) can accelerate crop growth and consequently shorten the growth period. In cereal crops (wheat) for example, such changes can lead to poor vernalization (e.g., hastened flowering) and reduced yield. Equally importantly agricultural emissions of greenhouse gases are governed by the use of nitrogen fertilizers (increased nitrous oxide emissions from the soil as a greenhouse gas) and animal husbandry (increased ammonia emissions from manure leading to atmospheric nitrogen fertilization by deposition, for example, in precipitation).

India and China are ranked among the top countries in net human consumption of primary food production. India also ranks at the top in the withdrawal of more than 40% of its total available fresh water supply, in comparison to China (20-40%) and the USA (10- 20%). By the year 2050, a majority of the global population is projected to be at a high risk of suffering from water stress. Currently Asia supports more than one half of the global population, with a projected increase of 29% by the year 2030. In comparison, population is expected to increase in Africa by 65%, North America by 26%, and South America by 31% and in contrast, a decrease by 6% is predicted for Europe. It is very educative to examine the status of the present and projected global agricultural production within these overall scenarios. Currently the ratio of rural to total populations is for: the world - 52%, China - 65%, India - 71% and the USA- 20%. Similarly the ratio of agricultural to rural populations is for: the world - 80%, China - 94%, India - 73% and the USA - 10%.

Climate change implications

Rise in global temperature

Observations show that global temperatures have risen by about 0.8 °C over the 20th century. There is strong evidence now that most of the observed warming over the last 50 years is caused by human activities. Climate models predict that the global temperature will rise by about 6°C by the year 2100.

Rise in sea level

In general, the faster the climate changes, the greater will be the risk of damage. The mean sea level is expected to rise 9 - 88 cm by the year 2100, causing flooding of low lying areas and other damages.

Food shortages and hunger

Water resources will be affected as precipitation and evaporation patterns change around the world. This will affect agricultural output. Food security is likely to be threatened and some regions are likely to experience food shortages and hunger.

India could be more at risks than many other countries. Models predict an average increase in temperature in India of 2.3 to 4.8°C for the benchmark doubling of Carbon-dioxide scenario. Temperature is expected to rise more in Northern India than in Southern India. It is estimated that 7 million people would be displaced, 5700 km^2 of land and 4200 km of road would be lost, and wheat yields could decrease significantly. Climate change will cause draughts at some places, floods at others, rise in sea level, non-availability of fresh water for drinking, low water table and increased salinity in water, heat stress due to high intensity of solar radiation, non-availability of green fodder to the animals due to land degradation. Camels and goats seem to be better adapted under such harsh changed climatic conditions.

All domestic animals are homeotherms. When an animal is exposed to environment outside the optimum range of temperature, food, water and oxygen supply, it acclimatizes. If acclimatization fails, there is disease and death. The responses for acclimatization include metabolic, circulatory, endocrine, and behavioral readjustments. The ability to acclimatize by making strain adjustments is, of course, genetic in origin. Each breed of goat has its genetic range of potential for the acclimatization. The concept of animal adaptation refers to the genetic and physiological changes taking place in an animal in response to internal and external stimuli. Genetic adaptation concerns selection by nature and man, whereas; physiological adaptation concerns changes occurring within an individual, over shorter or longer periods. The concept of physiological adaptation may imply the capacity and process of adjustment of the animal to itself, to other living material, and to its external physical environment. The greater the extent of adaptation, the more the animal will tend to survive or to reproduce itself so that its biological characteristics may persist. The maintenance of high level of production in hot regions is made difficult by the large amount of simultaneously produced excess heat, which has to be dissipated in addition to the heat imposed by the environment besides other factors. Biological productivity depends not only on the flow of energy, food and water within the system, but also on the adaptability of organisms to the environment and on their interactions.

Adaptive physiological differences involve three concepts - *alarm* which may last minutes or hours; the *resistance* stage that may last hours and days, and the third stage *adaptation* which may exist for days, months or years. In the adapted stage the responses are stabilized. Initial reactions to stressor i.e. the alarm stage, involves the surges of many hormones regarded as stress hormones (epinephrine, norepinephrine, cortisol) and others which usually decline as the acclimatization to the environment proceeds. This decline of the alarm stage responses is of advantage to the animal's body to avoid tissue degeneration and immuno suppression from prolonged elevated plasma and tissue levels of alarm stage hormonal factors. If the animals do not stabilize or adapt, pathological problems develop which may result in mal-adaptation and possibly death. These stages of adaptation vary with the intensity and duration of the heat, cold or other environmental stressors and with the genetic resistance of the individual, breed, or species of animals to the stressor(s). The physiological adaptation of goats under changing climatic scenario may be discussed as below.

Water Turnover Rate

The water turnover rate is important channel for the protection of homeotherms against overheating.

(i) Water intake

The main factors affecting water metabolism and free water intake of goats are related to: (a) dry matter intake, (b) composition of feeds and especially their water, salt and mineral contents and taste factors, (c) live weight, (d) level of milk production, (e) physiological status (maintenance for a dry and non-pregnant goat, pregnancy and lactation) and (f) environmental factors

Animals derive their water from three sources: (a) water consumed by drinking, (b) water that is present in or on food and (c) water formed during metabolism of food and body tissue, known as metabolic water. Different amounts of metabolic water are formed for each food type metabolized: for protein 0.396g/g food; for fat 1.071 g/g; and for starch 0.556 g/g (Schmidt-Nielsen, 1964). As a consequence of drought, animals produce metabolic water during periods of body weight loss. A goat losing 1 kg of body weight per week, a common live weight loss during seasonal summer droughts on annual pastures in southern Australia (McGregor, 1998), will generate about 130 g of metabolic water per day. In tropical arid and semi-arid environments, the water requirements of animal rises during summer season due to loss of water via skin and lungs however; availability of free water during this season is scarce and they have to go without water for a longer or shorter period. Under such conditions the ruminants often imbibe huge volume of water into the rumen during one short drinking bout. In winter, when evaporative cooling is not necessary; goat, sheep and camels obtain sufficient water from the feed to remain in water balance.

Kumar (1998) reported that total water intake in goats was significantly higher in hot environment than that in cool and moderate environments. Exposure to solar radiation during hot period resulted in significantly higher total water intake in Barbari breed than that in Marwari, Sirohi and Jamunapari breeds. Normally water intake in cool, moderate and hot-dry environment was 4.97, 7.48 and 13.88 l/100 kg body weight, respectively. Sirohi bucks drank significantly less amount of water than those of Marwari, Jamunapari and Barbari bucks, when maintained within the shed. Water ingestion in the morning was almost negligible in cool period. But in hot period bucks ingested almost equal amount of water in the morning as well as in the afternoon in hot radiation environment. This indicated that the bucks in hot radiation environment stored sufficiently higher amount of water in the rumen, which can be considered as "water reservoir" in the goat. This water is then utilized for thermoregulatory purposes throughout the day.

The ratio of water intake to dry matter intake showed a positive trend with the increase in air temperature. Kumar (1998) reported water intake (l) per kg of dry matter intake in Marwari, Sirohi, Jamunapari and Barbari breeds was 2.00, 1.85, 2.12 and 1.60, respectively in cool environment; 2.61, 2.06, 2.33 and 2.20, respectively in moderate environment and 4.72, 4.62, 5.17 and 4.33, respectively in hot environment. This ratio was increased as the bucks were exposed to solar radiation in the hot environment. It was 5.82, 6.44, 5.82 and 5.42 in the four breeds, respectively. In Anglo-Nubian goats it was observed that the water consumption, drinking frequency and time spent in drinking increased from 20°C (2.3 to 4.0 l/day/goat) except for a pronounced decrease at 40 °C (Appleman and Delouche, 1958).

When the heat load causes the animal to initiate steps to increase rate of evaporation from the body, the water initially comes from the blood. This must be replenished by water mobilized from a number of sources. They are stomach, intestine, interstitial fluid, faeces and oxidation of some stored carbohydrates, fat or protein. As the water is drawn from these sources, some action through the blood or more likely through nerve impulses act on the *'thirst centre'* in the brain for creating a desire for restoration of the body water to normal levels. The regulation of the water intake is controlled within narrow limits by sodium-osmosensitive cells in the hypothalamus (Mckinley et al., 1980). Food deprivation had caused lower Na concentration (Olsson et al., 1995) but this did not prevent the goats from drinking in excess. Many factors influence blood osmolarity and volume viz., food intake and loss of water and electrolytes during heat stress. Water intake or renal-reabsorption of water has to be increased in order to maintain water balance during the periods of thermo-regulatory sweating or panting. An interaction between cerebral thermal sensors and sensors regulating thirst and release of vasopressin has, therefore, been suggested (Taylor, 1970; Fitzsimons, 1979; Baker and Dawson 1985).

(ii) Water output

In all ruminants so far studied, evaporative water loss exceeds faecal and urinary water losses combined. Evaporative water loss provides a cooling mechanism for goats in hot dry conditions. Environmental factors affect the evaporative (insensible) water loss by goats. Water output through urine and faeces exhibits a declining trend with the increase in environmental temperature, as water is diverted towards the evaporatory heat loss mechanisms.

Through Urine

Kumar (1998) reported urine excretion 60.74% of the total water intake in cool environment. In moderate environment, it was 42.46% and in hot environment it was drastically reduced to 18.45% under shade and to 13.43% in solar radiation. Barbari bucks drank significantly higher water, but the urine excretion was significantly lower indicating higher water economizing capacity of this breed. In Jamunapari bucks, the ratio of urine excretion to water intake was almost of the same magnitude in hot environment under shade (18.01%) and in solar radiation (19.68%) indicating lower effect of radiant heat load in this breed, may be due to its white colour. In Marwari bucks, the ratio of urine excretion to water intake was reduced to almost half in solar radiation (12.58%) than that in shade (24.21%) during hot period. Urine excretion was significantly lower in Sirohi bucks than that in Marwari, Jamunapari and Barbari bucks.

Through Faeces

In the hot environment, the animal's ability to desiccate its faces helps in economizing water use for thermo-regulatory purposes. Kumar (1998) reported that the daily faeces output in hot environment were significantly lower than that in cool and moderate periods. Reduction in faeces output in hot environment from that of moderate environment was 30.28%. The amount of water loss through faeces when examined as percentage of total ingested water was 15.98, 20.75, 18.44 and 15.53 percent in Marwari, Sirohi, Jamunapari and Barbari breeds respectively. In hot environment it was 8.34, 4.41, 5.86 and 4.81 percent in four breeds in shade and 3.83, 3.25, 4.23 and 2.15 percent in solar radiation. The ratio of total water excreted through urine and faeces to that of total water ingested, accounted 52 to 69 percent in different breeds of goats (Kumar, 1998).

Through evaporation

Kumar (1998) reported that water diverted towards evaporative cooling accounted (percent of total drinking water) to 76.05, 67.45, 76.13 and 87.23 percent of total water drank by Marwari, Sirohi, Jamunapari and Barbari breeds, respectively. The evaporative water loss for many goats and sheep breeds of temperate climate is 60% breathing (respiration) and 40% sweating (cutaneous) under hot dry conditions (Wilson 1989). In desert adapted Bedouin goats the relative evaporative water loss is 33% respiration: 67% cutaneous. When environmental temperatures increase from 20°C to above 40°C, respiration rates in East African goats increased from about 20 to over 250 breaths/minute (Maloiy and Taylor, 1971).

Goats and sheep are regarded as having a more efficient renal system (kidney function) which reduces water loss compared with temperate and Zebu cattle (Wilson, 1989). In the Rajasthan desert during summer, the adapted goats were considered to be more efficient at economizing on water use than sheep from the same region (Khan and Ghosh, 1982). Many authors have concluded that goats that have had access to shade were better adapted to more arid conditions than sheep. However, the arid environments to which goats are *"so well adapted"* are characterized by low rocky ridges and scrubland plant communities. These environments allow goats to use shade during the hottest part of the day (McGregor, 1986; Burke, 1990). On dry annual pasture in southern Australia, particularly during drought, the moisture content of pasture is very low and much pasture and crop-lands have been cleared leaving little shade. Thus goats are more exposed to direct sunlight and must control their body temperature by panting and sweating, particularly on hot days with strong winds (McGregor, 1986).

Drought, scarcity of drinking water and dehydration stress

One of the major adaptations of goats to arid environment relates to their ability to withstand long periods of water deprivation and therefore search for food in an area far away from water resources, thus utilization of the range forage resources avoiding overuse of area close to water resources. Ruminants exposed to dehydration conserve body water excretion through various excretory routes. Yet these animals continue to lose their body weight partly due to lower intake of feed, loss of body fluids and catabolism of various metabolites or body components. Intensity of these changes proceeds with the advancement of dehydration.

A progressive loss in body weight was observed with the increase in water deprivation period in Marwari, Sirohi, Jamunapari and Barbari bucks. During hot period, the loss in body weight after 3 days of water deprivation was 27.73, 14.57, 24.46 and 22.39 percent in the four breeds respectively (Kumar, 1998). Sirohi bucks tolerated the water deprivation more efficiently as the loss in body weight was minimal. Giger-Reverdin and Gihad (1991) reported 25-30 % decrease in live weight of Bedouin goats after 4 days of water deprivation in addition to a decrease in milk production and growth of kids. Dm'iel (1986) reported loss of 19.5 % in body mass of black Bedouin goats exposed to summer conditions in the desert after 72 h of water deprivation.

Shkolnik et al. (1972) reported that after 2 weeks of water deprivation on a dry diet at 30 °C and 30% RH, black Bedouin goats lost about 2 % of their body weight daily. Barmer goats lost about 1.5 % of body weight per day when deprived of water absolutely for 4 days at a maximum temperature of 35-37 °C and minimum temperature of 16-20 °C (Khan et al., 1978). The desert goats when maintained under intermittent or partial watering schedule, usually gained in body weight. The goats, which were provided with only 1/4th of normal daily water intake, did not show any loss in body weight (Khan et al., 1979).

Body mass loss in the Sinai goats was largely due to reduction in total body water volume of the body water, plasma volume loss was 49.2% for Sinai goats (Shkolnik et al., 1972). A greater loss in the proportion of plasma volume can put a strain on the circulatory system and cannot be sustained for an extended period (Degen and Kam, 1992). Some of the desert animals like camels (Schmidt - Nielsen et al., 1956; Macfarlane et al., 1962), Burros (Yousef et al., 1970) and Kangaroos (Denny and Dawson, 1975) resist large losses in plasma volume even during rapid dehydration. In Marwari breed of goats, 4 days of water deprivation during summer brought down plasma volume by about 13 % of normal (Khan et al., 1979) in contrast to 43 % reported in Marwari sheep (Purohit et al., 1972).

The scarcity of water combined with heat load of a hot desert environment requires some specific physiological adaptations. They can be identified as follows.

(i) Ability to desiccate the faeces

When an animal is deprived of water, one of its physiological adaptations would be to reduce water loss through faeces by desiccating it (Maloiy and Taylor, 1971). Reduction in loss of water through faeces after 3 days of water deprivation in hot period was 87.80, 84.64, 92.94 and 76.67 percent in Marwari, Sirohi, Jamunapari and Barbari breeds, respectively.

(ii) Ability to reduce urine excretion

Decrease in feed intake in water deprived goats reduces the quantity of waste material to be excreted in urine and hence the amount of water needed to accompany these materials in the urine is less. Kumar (1998) reported 65.55 %, 77.76 %, 67.40 % and 50.66 % reduction in urine volume in Marwari, Sirohi, Jamunapari and Barbari bucks, respectively after 3 days of water deprivation in hot period. Urine volume was reported to decline by about 50 % in dehydrated animals (Maloiy and Taylor, 1971; Maloiy, 1974). Normally the concentration of urine does not exceed 1200 mOsm / kg if water is available. Schmidt-Nielsen (1964) reported a rise in urine osmalarity up to 2800 - 3000 mOsm / kg H_2O giving a urine plasma ratio of 10, a level comparable to many desert ungulates. Kumar (1998) observed dark brown colour of urine of water deprived bucks.

The desert animals possess long loops of Henle than non-desert animals. Longer the loop of Henle in the kidney medulla, the higher is the possible urine concentration. The ratio of the thickness of medulla to cortex is a good index of the potential water re-absorption capacity. The conservation of water is regulated by the hypothalamo-neurohypophysical system through the mediation of antidiuretic hormone (ADH). ADH release occurs with increase in plasma osmolarity, for example, during water deprivation which stimulates osmoreceptors that are located in the hypothalamus and possibly in other areas of the central nervous system (CNS). Neural pathways carry the impulses from osmoreceptors through the median eminance and into the neurohypophysis.

(iii) Ability to reduce evaporative water loss

Ability to reduce evaporative water loss is an important physiological adaptation which an animal requires during the scarcity of water combined with the heat load (Maloiy and Taylor, 1971; Shkolnik et al., 1972). Reduction in sweating rate on the first day of water deprivation during hot period was 27.36, 30.10, 30.14 and 32.56 percent in Marwari, Sirohi, Jamunapari and Barbari breeds, respectively. On second day of water deprivation reduction in sweating rate was 39.22, 40.85, 39.17 and 41.74 percent in the four breeds, respectively. On third day of water deprivation, sweating rate in bucks of all the four breeds was decreased to almost 50 % (Kumar, 1998). In black Bedouin goats (Choshniak, 1978), the reduction in evaporation was achieved by suppression of sweating up to 75 % after 4 days of water deprivation in hot environment.

Under normal conditions when water is available *ad-lib,* a rise in body temperature will be accompanied with increase in respiratory rate. In water deprived bucks, respiratory rate may decline, particularly in hot environment, as to reduce the water loss through respiratory evaporation. Respiratory rate of Marwari, Sirohi, Jamunapari and Barbari bucks decreased due to water deprivation (Kumar, 1998). Hassan (1989) observed significantly decreased respiratory rate after 3 days of water deprivation in summer in Egyptian Baladi, Anglo-Nubian and their crossbred. Baker (1989) reported similar respiratory frequency and respiratory evaporation in dehydrated and hydrated goats. Robertshaw and Dm'iel (1983) reported that dehydrated Israeli black Bedouin goats deprived of water for four days increased respiratory rate and respiratory evaporation above hydrated levels when they were exposed to high ambient temperatures.

Although there is a reduction in evaporation and therefore less cooling, the phenomenon of heat storage was not observed in goats (Maloiy and Taylor, 1971) as it is in some wild desert ungulates (Taylor, 1970). However, the black Bedouin goat maintained a slightly higher but significant temperature when dehydrated (Robertshaw and Dm'iel, 1983). Rectal temperature of Marwari, Sirohi, Jamunapari and Barbari bucks increased due to water deprivation, however; the magnitude of increase was higher in hot environment than cool and moderate environment (Kumar, 1998). A higher rectal temperature in dehydrated than hydrated Alpine X Toggenberg and Nubian goats was observed (Baker, 1989).

Two consequences of dehydration are: (a) an elevation in the concentration in solutes in body fluids and (b) a reduction in the blood volume, influence thermo-regulatory water loss (Trulejska and Baker, 1986). Evidence that elevated body fluid solute concentration is an important stimuli for the thermo-regulatory adjustments occurring in dehydration comes from the studies of Nielsen (1974), Baker and Doris (1982), in which hypertonic solutions were infused into hydrated animals. When body fluid osmolarity was elevated by intragastric or intravenous administration of hypertonic solution in heat stressed mammals, thermo-regulatory evaporation was reduced and body temperature rose. A number of observations support the possibility that intracranial osmoreceptors play a role in this reduction of evaporative heat loss. Thus, thermal panting in hydrated dogs and rabbits (Baker and Dawson, 1985; Trulejska and Baker, 1986) and sweating in monkey (Owen et al., 1987) are inhibited by intracarotid or intracerebroventricular infusion of hypertonic solution. It is expected that water deprivation will reduce metabolic heat production, since feed intake is reduced. Heart rate, under such circumstances should show a declining trend, but an increase in the heart rate due to water deprivation was observed in Marwari, Sirohi, Jamunapari and Barbari bucks (Kumar, 1998).

(iv) Utilization of the rumen as a water reservoir

During the hot period the bucks of Marwari, Sirohi, Jamunapari and Barbari breeds drank 36.92±3.29, 22.18±1.24, 24.93±1.06 and 32.32±4.59 litres of water per 100 kg body weight on rehydration after 3 days of water deprivation (Fig. 1). These values were 165.94, 83.29, 71.93 and 99.37 % more than the water intake during pre-water deprivation period in the four breeds, respectively. The water intake before water deprivation in hot environment was 13.88±1.21, 12.10±0.77, 14.50±0.96 and 16.21±0.72 litre/ 100 Kg body weigh/ day in the four breeds respectively (Kumar, 1998). This voluminous amount of water on rehydration was ingested within 2-3 minutes. This would have raised the problem of intravascular haemolysis because of sudden sharp reduction in plasma osmolarity but it did not happen.

Choshniak and Shkolnik (1977) reported the way Bedouin goats manage to circumvent the hazards likely to follow its voluminous drinking. They found that the osmotic concentration of the goat's blood is maintained at a fairly constant level in the face of these great and sometimes very rapid changes in the total body water content. The rumen of Bedouin goat played a major role in maintaining the osmotic homeostasis of the body fluid (Choshniak and Shkolnik, 1978). By employing (^{51}Cr) EDTA as non-absorbable marker it was demonstrated that even 5 hours after the voluminous drinking, over 80% of the volume consumed was retained in the reticulo-rumen complex. During this 5 hours time the osmotic concentration of the rumen fluid, which dropped to 90 mOsm/ kg immediately following drinking, increased in the fasting animals to 131 mOsm / kg. In the animals having free access to food, osmolality achieved a concentration iso-osmotic to the blood during this period. The rate of flow through the reticulo- omasal orifice, which is the passage of fluid from the rumen to the more permeable parts of the gastro-intestinal tract, was assessed by calculating the rate of disappearance of the (^{51}Cr) EDTA. From the values of 73 ml/ hr during the first hour following rehydration the outflow from the rumen in the fasting goat increased continuously to a rate of 250 ml/ hr during the fifth hour. When dehydrated goats consumed saline instead to tap water, the flow during the first hour amounted to 600 ml/ hr. The rate at which the plasma volume increased following the drinking of saline considerably exceeds the rate recorded in animals that had drunk tap water. Changes in blood plasma osmolality in both cases were minor. Presumably, factors related to the osmotic difference between the ruminal and body fluids controls the out flow from the rumen and adjust its rate to avoid osmotic shock likely to occur following rapid rehydration. It was suggested that the '*rumen water reservoir*' provides the essential mechanism for water balance, enabling the desert goats to circumvent hazards likely to follow rapid rehydration.

In a pastoral system, however, the rates at which that ruminant can be stocked in the system are also of great significance to the breeder. In the arid rangelands the great distance between watering sites often interferes with the animal's capacity to evenly exploit the area's meager pasture, and as a result hampers its stocking rates. Under such conditions, the ability of a ruminant to withstand prolonged periods of water deprivation becomes a major factor in determining its stocking rates fig. 1.

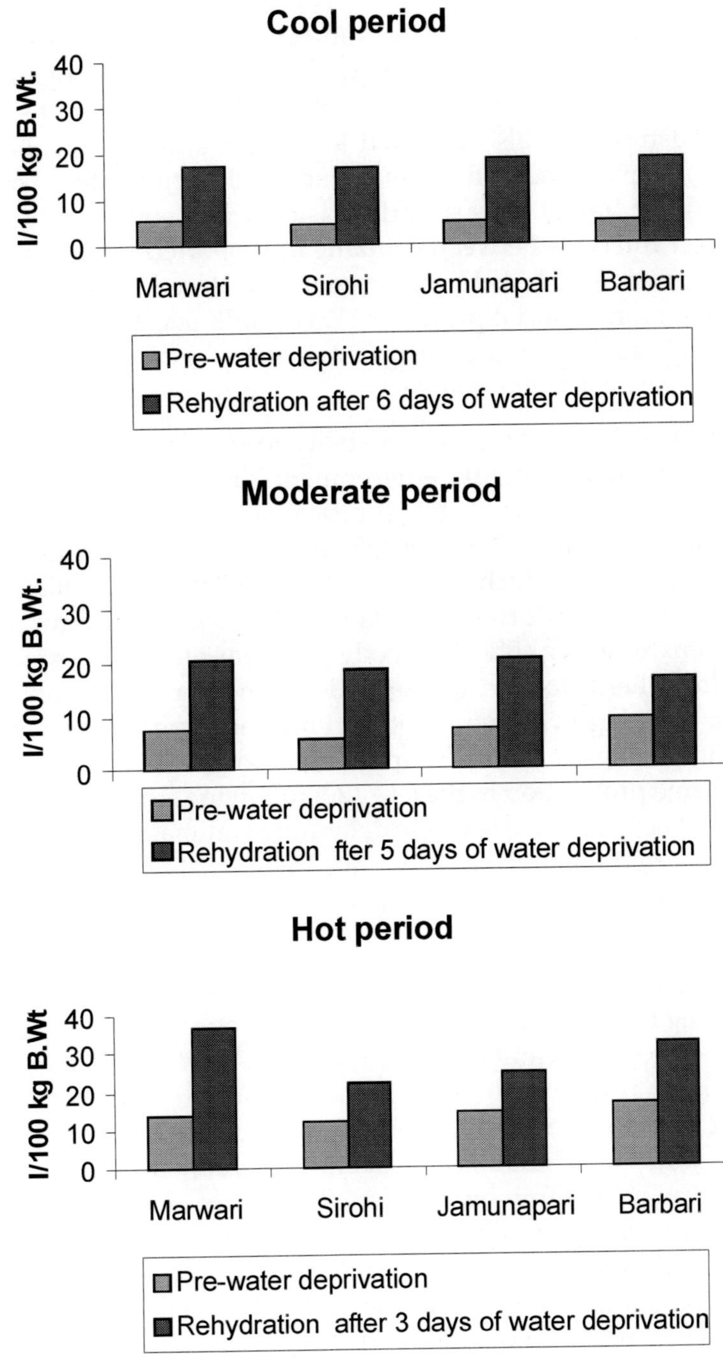

Fig 1. Volume of water intake on rehydration on three environmental periods in bucks of four breeds

Herbivores, indigenous to the sub-tropical aid areas of the world, are famous for their capacity to graze far away from the sparsely available watering sites, and while doing so withstand prolonged periods of water deprivation. Sheep in Australia are also reported to possess similar capacities. Drinking regimens of goats in the arid zones are not well documented. Local breeds in the hot dry Rift Valley of East Africa visit a water source only once every 2 days. Longer intervals between drinking are reported for Indian breeds. The East Mediterranean black Mumber goat is watered only once daily, even during mid-summer and it produces 1½ l of milk per day. The black Bedouin goat, throughout its sun-scorched distribution, is often seen to walk for 2 days for the nearest water source.

Complementary to an animal's ability to regularly withstand periods of water deprivation in a hot, dry environment is a capacity to rapidly replenish considerable water losses. The significance of such a capacity was first described and discussed in the camel. Following its demonstration in the camel, voluminous drinking which accounted to 20 to 30% of the animal body mass was also observed in other herbivores of the xeric environment. Water consumption exceeding 40% of the body mass was measured in many members of the Bedouin herds following four mid-summer days of continuous grazing. Even with these high volumes of body fluids, no increase in urine output was observed following the animal's rapid rehydration. As if to conserve the water imbibed, urine production in the 6 to 12 h following drinking was even below the volume recorded in the severely dehydrated animals. A similar observation has been reported for sheep in Australia. In the goats, however, it was shown that a reduced renal blood flow underlies this ability to help retain the high volume of body fluids.

Apparently the excess serves as a *'reservoir'* to meet the animals demands while grazing far away from water. Indeed, throughout 4 days of continuous grazing the goats continued their foraging activities and maintained their *'dry body mass'* at its initial value. The water and animals consumed during their short visits to the water hole was always sufficient to replenish the entire amount of water which had been lost and restore their body water *'reservoir'*. In no case was the voluminous drinking by the goat followed by any ill effect such as hemolysis. The red blood cells of the goat, however, when tested in a hypotonic salt solution, were found to be highly fragile. The osmotic concentration of the goat's blood is maintained at a fairly constant level in the face of these great and sometimes very rapid, changes in the total body water content. The osmotic stability of the red blood cells of the goat is never challenged *in vivo*; consequently, the osmotic stability of the goat's erythrocytes is irrelevant to the animal's capacity to rapidly rehydrate. Even following drinking that resulted in the expansion of the H_2O space of the goat by over 50% of its value before rehydration; the drop in the plasma osmolality never exceeded to 30- 40 mOsm/kg.

The rumen plays in maintaining the osmotic homeostasis of the body fluids. It was demonstrated that even 5 h after the voluminous drinking over 80% of the volume consumed was still retained in the reticulo-rumen complex. During this period of time the osmotic concentration of the rumen fluid, which dropped to 90 mOsm/kg immediately following drinking, increased in the fasting animal to 131 mOsm/kg. In the animal having free access to food, osmolarity achieved a concentration isoosmotic to the blood during this period. From a value of 73 m /h during the first hour following rehydration, the outflow from the rumen in the fasting goat increased continuously to a rate of 250 m /hr during fifth hour. When dehydrated goats consumed saline instead of tap water, the flow during the first hour amounted to 600 ml/h presumably; a factor related to the osmotic difference between the ruminal and body fluids, controls the outflow from the rumen and adjusts its rate to avoid osmotic shocks likely to occur following rapid rehydration. It is suggested, therefore, that the rumen, commonly regarded as a specialized compartment of the goat related to cellulose digestion, also plays a major role in the water economy of goats herded in hot and dry environments. This 'rumen water reservoir' provides the essential mechanism for water balance, enabling the desert goat to circumvent hazards likely to follow rapid rehydration. Goats appear to have a large rumen compared to other ruminants. Bhattacharya (1980) reported a rumen volume exceeding 45% of the animal's body mass for the kill-goat of East Antatolia and the Syrian xeric areas. Similar values were also found in the black Bedouin goat. Goat breeds, in more mesic environments, may have smaller rumens than those indigenous to xeric conditions. It means that breeds of goats adapted to the xeric conditions have larger rumens capable of serving as water stores.

Swedish goats (*Capra hircus*) were dehydrated for 24 h. Blood pressure did not change when the goats saw water but was increased when they drank. Seeing water caused arousal in the goats, resulting in an accelerated heart rate. The additional rise in blood pressure during the act of drinking appeared to be a combination of excitement and sensory inputs from the pharyngeal region, causing a temporary activation of the sympathetic nervous system (Olsson and Carlsson, 2004). Wilson (1989) observed that when water stress was imposed and animals become dehydrated and the food intake was reduced whatever the temperature was. Under conditions of heat stress and limited water there are further depressive effects on food intake; the reductions being particularly marked in the domestic species of goats, sheep and cattle. There is some evidence that East African goats may be able to maintain appetite under heat stress. Under drought conditions, when animals are being fed to maintain body weight or to slowly lose body weight, the most important factors contributing to water turnover are the requirements for evaporative cooling (sweating, breathing) and to ensure an adequate intake of food. Goats are able to consume a significant amount of water at a single drinking session (Wilson, 1989). In Black Bedouin goats, a species adapted to the arid deserts of the Sinai region, water intake can reach as high as 45% of body weight without haemolysis of the red blood cells. This response is related to the rumen acting as a water storage preventing water passing directly into the blood stream by reducing water flow into the lower gut thus allowing water to be absorbed over an extended period of time. This response also prevents unnecessary water and salt loss via urine. When saline water is consumed by goats, the outflow from the rumen was much greater than when fresh water was consumed.

Choshniak et al. (1987) concluded that absorption of saline fluid from the rumen into the blood is responsible for an expansion of blood plasma volume. This process enables a rapid return of water to the body. In addition, there was no chance of haemolysis of blood cells after drinking saline water as there was following the drinking of fresh water. The water used by animals is related to the live weight of animals to the power 0.82, not the normally used exponent 0.75 as water is used not only for intermediary metabolism but also for evaporative cooling (Wilson, 1989). Generally there is a log-linear relationship between body water turnover and body weight. Water consumption of adult Angora goats and adult Merino sheep has been measured when grazing dry un-shaded summer pastures in southern Australia (McGregor, 1986). The findings were:

- For both goats and sheep, water intakes on the hottest days (> 33°C) were double the average (when the mean temperature averaged 25°C).
- Water intake of the Angora goats was 36% greater than intake of adult Merino sheep. The intake of the goats was 1.9 compared with the intake for sheep 1.4 litres/day.
- When allowing for the differences in live weight and removing fleece weight, water intake was 50% higher in the goats, Angora goats: 55.6 ml/kg/day; Merino sheep: 36.8 ml/kg/day or Angora goats: 104 ± 4 ml/kg0.82/day; Merino sheep: 70 ± 3 ml/kg0.82/day.

In east Africa a similar finding was reported when shade provision was low (King 1983). King found that the daily water intake of East African goats, weighing 37 kg, averaged 2.2 l/day (equivalent to 114 ml/kg0.82/day) was higher than heavier Dorper type sheep. Boer goats have also been recorded as having a lower water turnover rate than Merino and other southern African sheep breeds. Erasmus (1967) tested these animals at 21°C and 37°C but details of 9 feed, housing and shade provision were not reported. In this study the Boer goats drank 40% less tepid water per kg0.82 than sheep when under heat stress. Goat faeces were also drier, the urinary volume declined at higher temperatures and was lower than that of the sheep. Ferreira et al. (2002) measured the water intake of castrated Boer goat kids (26 kg) and castrated Mutton Merino lambs (32 kg) receiving either a low (8.9 MJ ME/kg DM) or high (10.9 MJ ME/kg DM) energy diet when fed indoors on slatted floors. Both diets contained 12.8% crude protein. On both the high and low energy diets the Boer goats had a lower water intake per kg of feed intake and per kg of live weight gain than the sheep. Both species had a lower water intake on the high energy ration compared with that on the low energy diet. In these shaded conditions the Boer goats had a daily water intake of 129 ml/kg0.82 compared to the 237 ml/kg0.82 of the Mutton Merino. The authors conducted the study during the spring and early summer but did not report environmental temperature. It is unclear how much water intake of goats was reduced by the grazing and browsing of Australian scrub. Goats grazing the greener material will ingest water but may have to excrete more water if the ash content of the material is high (SCA, 1990). The provision of shade in such a situation may provide more benefit in reducing water intake than the actual intake of water from the drought affected plants. The impact of direct sunlight on the water intake of the Boer goats is not reported. It is likely that there may be differences in water consumption between Australian breeds of goat as breed differences are reported for goats in the Middle East.

(v) Behavioural responses

Macfarlane (1982) concluded that dominant goats expend more energy maintaining their dominant position than lower rank goats and in return they obtain better shade and more access to water and food supplies. Henzell (1997) reported upon the dependence of feral goats to drinking water leading them to gather at water points, where they can be trapped, a practice used for many years to capture feral goats. For many years Australian feral goats have been known to be highly dependent on drinking water (Harrington, 1982; Parkes et al., 1996). During hot dry periods more than 80% of feral goats drink water daily. Similar observations have not been recorded on domestic goats. Feral goats have been recorded as dying at dry water holes when water was available within 1.5 km (Harrington, 1982). This suggests that when water sources dry out or are changed during a drought, the manager must be vigilant in ensuring that goats are led to new sources of water.

Water supply and its quality during drought

A good reliable water supply is extremely important in drought. In drought, goats are fed diets very low in water content and therefore, must be supplied with water at all times. Evidence suggests that goats have similar or slightly greater tolerances to salt in water compared with sheep. Providing saline water with up to 10,000 mg/l total dissolved solids (TDS) did not affect food intake or growth of goats. When the TDS was increased to 17,000 mg/l, the food intake of goats fell but not to the extent of the decline observed in sheep. It is possible for goats to tolerate higher TDS than these levels but the goats need to be adapted to this saline water over a long period. During drought the salt content of river and dam water can increase to high levels and TDS should be monitored to ensure salinity remains at safe levels. Failure to monitor TDS can lead to death due to salt poisoning and this has occurred with goats in Australia in recent droughts. Algal blooms can occur where water has high levels of nitrogen, phosphorus and temperature. Algal blooms can be toxic. High water magnesium levels can also be toxic.

Intake of saline and seawater

According to Goatcher and Church (1970), laboratory tests showed that the intake of water by goats and sheep fell rapidly above sodium chloride concentrations of 0.6%. This does not accord well with observations made of feral goats surviving on arid islands (Dunson, 1974; Parkes et al., 1996) or with studies on Egyptian goats (Abou Hussien et al., 1994). In 1905, scientists in the Galapagos Islands observed feral goats apparently drinking from seawater (Dunson, 1974). Observations have been made of goats on beaches apparently drinking seawater in Western Australia (Parkes et al., 1996), Queensland (Dunson, 1974). Drinking seawater by goats may be associated with: (a) drinking fresh ground water or diluted seawater that has followed the water table to the tide mark, (b) sodium deficient animals drinking some seawater for the salt content, (c) eating seaweed as a source of food (Dunson, 1974), (d) drinking large volumes of seawater to obtain free water after salt excretion, and/ or (e) consuming small amounts of seawater to offset insufficient amounts of plant moisture.

Dunson (1974) cites Castro who reported that feral goats on Espanola Island in the Galapagos drank seawater for 10 months when fresh water was not available even though they often exhibited diarrhea. Dunson (1974) observed goats drinking from a seawater seep on Espanola Island and measured the sodium concentration at 470 mM (27,500 mg/l). Burke (1990) investigated the seawater consumption of feral goats on Aldabra Atoll in the Seychelles. During the dry season, goats were seen drinking from tidal pools and the lagoon. These goats appeared to produce very dry faeces, drier than those reported for Bedouin goats. Burke calculated that these goats could produce urine more than twice the osmolarity of seawater, probably enough to allow them to realize a net gain of free water from drinking seawater. It is possible that by drinking seawater it allowed the goats to increase urine volume to enable them to excrete larger amounts of other solutes such as urea. These goats had access to a good supply of browse vegetation with a water content of 17 to 48%. The goats drank from temporary rainwater puddles when available. The goats remained relatively inactive during the day and fed primarily at dusk and dawn. Macfarlane (1982) concluded that since most Merino sheep become partly intoxicated by salt at 1.3% (220 m mol/l) in water (Peirce, 1968) and Turkana goats tolerate 1.5% (257 m mol/l) of salt in drinking water that these goats must be more adapted to higher salt loads by having slightly better sodium pumps than sheep. Macfarlane (1982) noted that within 4 days of being exposed to saline water there is an induction of enzymes in the ilium, liver and kidney. The main enzyme is NaK ATPase that increases the pumping of sodium out of cells and potassium return to the intracellular space. The induction of this enzyme is a powerful adaptive mechanism.

Abou Hussien et al. (1994) examined the response of Egyptian Zaraibi bucks (38 kg body weight), Rahmany rams (55 kg) and camels to three levels of drinking water salinity. Using dried sea salt, the TDS of tap water (260 mg/l) was increased to 9,500 or 17,000 mg/l. The animals were fed good quality hay ad libitum indoors. Increasing water salinity to 17,000 mg/l increased total water intake of goats by 59% to 376 ml/kg0.82 and that of sheep by 99% to 500 ml/kg0.82. The increase in water intake was associated with greater urinary water loss and little change in faecal and insensible water loss (sweating, breathing). Parkes et al., (1996) observed that in Western Australia, feral goats that had drunk seawater would die when chased or stressed.

It is likely that in grazing situations the water consumption of goats will increase as the salinity of the water increases. SCA (1990) reports that for each 1,000 mg TDS/l in excess of 2,000 mg/l water, allowances for sheep increase by 3%. For the last two months of pregnancy and during lactation the SCA (1990) suggest that water allowances increase by 30% and that a further 1 litre be provided for each 1 kg of milk produced. Water consumption will also increase if the feed has been treated with caustic soda or slaked lime. The SCA (1990) recommends that in this circumstance an additional 2 litres per kg of treated feed (sheep) be provided. A similar allowance is suggested for goats. Young sheep have difficulty thriving on water supplies with higher than 5,000 mg/l salt while adult stock can handle up to 10,000 mg/l, especially once they are adapted to the water. Levels above 10,000 mg/l salt need to be treated with caution (Court, 2002). There are differences between the salinity limits advised for sheep (Court, 2002) and those provided by Scarlett (2002) for goats.

It would seem clear that there are differences between breeds of goats in their ability to resist dehydration based on genetics and environmental history. Greenwald (1964) found that desert Hottentot goats from South Africa were more resistant to dehydration with lower water consumption, evaporative and urinary losses compared with Swiss-type milk goats. The capacity of the kidney to concentrate urine and its ability to reduce urinary water loss during dehydration is directly related with the relative kidney medullary thickness (RMT). The greater the RMT, the longer would be the loop of Henle relative to the size of the kidney, so the greater would be the ability of the kidney to reabsorb water. In Australia, Dunson (1974) found that the RMT of feral goats from Queenslands Esk Island was greater than the RMT of domestic Australian goats that in turn had a greater RMT than domestic lambs. Similar findings have been reported by Greenwald (1964) where desert adapted African goats had a greater RMT than Swiss-type dairy goats. Burke (1990) found no unusual morphological effects on the goats' kidneys resulting from drinking seawater. These goats had RMT less than those measured by Dunson but greater than Greenwald's Swiss dairy goats. East African goats and Turkana goats from Kenya (Maloiy and Taylor 1971) both reduced evaporative water losses and increased urine concentration with reduced urinary volume when faced with restricted water supply. With housed domestic goats, Dunson (1974) reported that one of the main mechanisms for reduction of water loss during dehydration appeared to be a decrease in evaporative loss. When he fed seawater to domestic North American goats, all the goats drank seawater but consumption was low and variable. With Australian domestic goats, voluntary consumption of seawater of 3.6% of body weight per day for 24 days occurred with 15 to 20% weight loss but consumption by one goat of 9.1% of body weight was associated with a 30% weight loss over 16 days. Dunson (1974) concluded that seawater consumption can slow the rate of dehydration in goats provided consumption was less than 4% body weight per day, maintenance of food consumption and sources of water loss, particularly evaporative water loss, were reduced.

It is also clear that to minimize dehydration of goats, behavioral avoidance of environmental heat load would be critical as would be a reduction in activity. In the study of Abou Hussien et al. (1994) described earlier, intake of water with 9,500 mg/l TDS reduced the dietary intake of sheep but not of goats.

Increasing the salt content from 9,500 to 17,000 mg/l TDS reduced the dietary intake of both sheep and goats. The increase in urinary output of sodium and chloride and the decrease in urinary potassium associated with drinking water of 17,000 mg/l were evident with sheep and goats. The urea clearance rate of goats was higher than that of sheep. Drinking saline water had no effect on the urea concentration of urine of goats but decreased it in sheep and camels. Abou Hussien et al. (1994) concluded that the mechanism by which sheep and goats control salt load by drinking saline water was different to that of camels. Sheep and goats excreted more urine and increased the filtration rate to reduce the high salt load resulting from their high consumption of saline water. Camels consumed relatively less saline water to reduce salt stress. El-Gawad (1997) studied the responses of 21 to 46 kg doe's fed tap water (total soluble salts, TSS 1,050 mg/l) or saline well water (8,250 mg/l) for 6 weeks. Goats were individually housed in semi open pens and fed on hay and a concentrate mixture. Body weight was not significantly affected, while feed and water intake increased in the group offered saline water. Respiration rate was increased in goats drinking saline water, while rectal temperature and pulse rate were only slightly affected. The effect on health and production of goats, occurring by changing the drinking water from surface run off water (TSS 200 to 500 mg/l) to saline bore water (TSS 5000 to 10000 mg/l) as goats are grazed in different paddocks, have not been documented. The SCA (1990) summarized some data for Merino sheep kept in semi-arid regions of Australia. In Western Victoria, Walkerden et al. (1976) found that there was no effect on the growth of weaned Merino lambs fed typical pasture hay (15% crude protein, 8.8 MJ ME/kg DM) when saline bore water of 3,720 mg/l TSS; 330 mg/l Mg was used instead of freshwater (120 mg/l 12 TSS). Bore water should also be tested for other toxic minerals. Saul and Flinn (1985) reported that 370 to 500 mg/l magnesium had no harmful effect on young sheep.

Effect of intermittent watering in goats

Water is scarce in the semi-arid regions and therefore goats are watered intermittently. This can result in dehydration and decreased animal performance. Nevertheless, more than three days interval between watering during the hot dry season is not recommended since it may jeopardize animal performance and welfare.

Responses to Hot Environment

In arid and semi-arid zones of India, air temperature prevails above 40°C in summer. Sometimes it reaches up to 50°C. The effect of high air temperature is furthermore intensified by solar radiation. During strong sunshine in hot arid areas, the intercepted solar radiation flux can be several times of the rate of metabolic heat production. Evaporation, whether cutaneous or respiratory, is the principal mechanism for dissipating excess heat in mammals, which will increase the water demands. Heat stress, therefore, influences simultaneously both energy and water metabolism. The difference in responses to heat stress among ruminants may relate to diversity in insulation properties and body size. The heat load imposed by solar radiation depends on coat type and colour. Depending on the coat characteristics, part of this is re-radiated to the environment. Therefore, type of the coat would be an important consideration in the thermal balance of animals that live in semi-arid and desert areas. The humid tropical areas provide adequate shade and coat colour would be of less importance from thermoregulatory point of view. It might be predicted that white and light colour would be the predominant colour of animals subjected to high solar radiation. But in the sub-tropical desert areas the goats are either predominantly or entirely black or dark coloured.

Radiation may be divided into infrared or heat radiation (long wavelengths); visible light (medium waves) and ultraviolet radiation (short waves). The proportion of long and medium waves in the total radiation will increase as one move from the poles towards the equator. The proportion of short waves present in the radiation will increase as one move from sea level to high altitudes. It follows that the greatest radiation intensity is encountered by farm animals kept at a high altitude on the thermal equator. The fur or fleece of animals provides a barrier between the skin and the sun and it is the nature of this barrier which is important. The penetration of fur by the solar beam is a function not only of colour but also structure of coat. A few studies (Goyal, 1983) have revealed that free ranging black coloured goats have shown better thermo stability than white coloured goats, whereas; other studies (Acharya et al., 1995) indicated that dark coloured goats were under more heat stress than light coloured goats. It is conveniently believed that a white coat colour should be helpful in maintaining body temperature in a tropical or sub-tropical region, whereas; a black or dark coat colour would be beneficial in a temperate environment. The thinking behind these popular beliefs has been primarily based on the difference in the reflectivity of surfaces of different colours. However, a multitude of factors other than reflectivity alone may be determining the degree of penetration radiant heat load into the body. For example, it has been argued that a white coat, while reflecting back a good deal of the incident radiations, also allows relatively more of the harmful ultraviolet radiation to enter into the body. On the other hand, a black coat absorbs more heat but forms a barrier against harmful radiation. The goats in the Indian desert are mostly of black or dark colour and considered hardy animals. The climatic elements acting on homeotherms evoke physiological responses as they attempt to maintain energy and fluid balance. The magnitude of the responses depends on the thermal state of the environment. While these environmental variables act in different combinations and ways, but are integrated by an animal. Obviously, the thermoregulatory effort by an animal will be governed by its own thermal status. All the productive processes are associated with a high metabolic rate, hence a high rate of heat production making hot environment more stressful. The maintenance of an almost constant core temperature, characteristic of homeotherms, depends on a dynamic equilibrium between heat production and heat loss.

(i) Heat loss mechanisms

As the air temperature exceeds body temperature, evaporative heat loss from upper respiratory tract and skin surface are the only effective mechanisms to get rid off extra heat load from animal body. The goats increase their respiratory rate in the heat. Near the top of the nasal cavity, the capillary mesh of the carotid artery is cooled during panting, so that blood to the brain stem and hypothalamus is cooled more specifically than that to the body at large (Baker and Doris, 1982) This evaporative heat loss increases with the increase in respiratory frequency and minute volume and also depends on the temperature and humidity of the inspired air. The ventilation rate is a function of the respiratory rate of the system. Increase in the deep body temperature is generally considered as a manifestation of break down of homeothermy when thermoregulatory mechanisms get exhausted (Schmidt-Nielsen, 1977). Slight rise in deep body temperature in some of the desert animals like camel is considered as a defense mechanism to reduce the gradient between body and ambient temperature to reduce the rate of heat gain from environment (Schmid, 1976). Heat stress significantly increased the rectal temperature, respiratory rate and minute volume in Jamunapari bucks (Joshi et al., 1977). Tidal volume declined with increase in respiratory frequency. Under field conditions morning, afternoon and mean respiratory frequency in Jamunapari female yearlings was significantly higher during hot-humid period (Kumar et al., 1990). The effect of hot micro-environment was found to be more pronounced on Barbari than Jamunapari goats (Kumar et al., 1988).

Kumar (1998) found that bucks of Marwari, Sirohi, Jamunapari and Barbari breeds were able to maintain their deep body temperature within normal range, when maintained within the shed and protected from solar radiation in hot dry period and from cold during winters, despite large variation in environmental temperature during cool, moderate and hot periods of the year. Sirohi bucks exhibited consistently significant lower mean rectal temperature as compared to other three breeds. The mechanism used by different breeds to get rid of the excess heat load during hot periods varied. Sirohi and Jamunapari bucks loosed excess heat through more efficient mechanism of higher sweating rate. Marwari bucks used respiratory evaporative heat loss to a greater extent than other breeds mainly because long shaggy hair coat interfered in cutaneous evaporative heat loss. Barbari bucks utilized both efficient sweating mechanism as well as higher respiratory evaporative heat loss. Exposure to direct solar radiation during hot-dry period clearly depicted that the rectal temperature rose above normal levels in all the four breeds of goats. Obviously, the extra heat gained through incident solar radiation impinging on body could not be lost even with increase in respiratory as well as surface evaporative loss in all the four breeds. The magnitude of increase in rectal temperature from morning to afternoon on exposure to direct sun was almost similar in Marwari (1.37°C) and in Jamunapari (1.35°C). Marwari bucks being black colour should have absorbed more solar radiation in hot environment than the white coloured Jamunapari bucks. But there was no significant difference in afternoon rectal temperature in hot radiation environment in both the breeds. The long shaggy hair coat of Marwari bucks might have provided a barrier between the skin and the solar radiation. The penetration of fur by the solar beam has been investigated by Hutchinson and Brown (1969) and is a function not only of colour but also structure of the coat. Thus heat absorbed at the surface of black hair or plumage may be dissipated by convection, above 3 ms^{-1} which is a usual phenomenon in the arid and semi-arid areas during summer (Walsberg et al., 1978), whereas a white fur may reflect the incident beam inwards to the level of the skin (Hutchinson and Brown, 1969). Finch et al. (1980) showed that black goat absorbed between 50 to 100% more heat from the sun due to their colour than did a white goat or light brown goat. The extra heat absorbed was not stored but dissipated by evaporation. Kumar (1998) reported the maximum effect of heat stress in Barbari bucks. In this breed, the respiratory rate even in the morning hours was significantly higher (77.27±2.10 no/ min) as compared to Marwari (47.72±2.92 no./min), Jamunapari (37.17±1.08 no./min.) and Sirohi (35.72±1.80 no./min.) bucks. He reported significantly high rate of sweating in Barbari bucks (166±8.67 $g/m^2/h$) accompanied by significantly high intake of water.

Johnson (1976) calculated that at an air temperature of 38 °C, approximately 75% of the total evaporation is from the respiratory tract. Hales (1974) computed it as low as 60%. Borut et al., (1979) reported that black Bedouin goats of mid-eastern desert have to dissipate a greater heat load when exposed to solar radiation by the more efficient sweating as an evaporative heat loss mechanism supplementary to that of panting so that sweating becomes 69% of the total evaporative heat loss. A high rate of cutaneous evaporative heat loss is more efficient mechanism than increasing respiratory evaporative heat loss (Cena and Monteith, 1975). The glands of goats are morphologically similar to those of cattle. Most goat breeds have a lower sweat gland density (100-300 glands/cm^2) than cattle to 1000 glands / cm^2) but the output of sweat per gland is comparable (Dmi'el et al., 1979). However, certain tropical goat breeds, such as the Black Bedoin, have a much greater output of sweat which can be as high as 138 g/m^2/h, which is about four times as great as *Bos Indicus* cattle (Table 1).

Table 1. Sweating rate in two breeds of goats compared to cattle

Animal	Sweat rate (g/m^2/h)	Sweat gland (glands/cm^2)	Sweat rate/ gland (ml/h)	References
Cattle	160	1000	16	Jenkinson and Robertshaw (1972)
Goats (Saanen)	23	170	14	Dmi'el et al., (1979)
Goats (Black Bedouin)	138	215	64	Dmi'el et al., (1979)

In British Saanen goats, the phenomenon of *'muscle fatigue'* was observed as sweating rate was not consistent throughout the exposure of high temperature but Kumar and Singh (1994) observed consistency in sweating high sweating rate in some of the goats breeds of semi-arid region on prolonged exposure to high ambient temperature (Table 2).

Table 2. Pattern of sweating rate (g/m^2/h) in Jamunapari and Barbari adult bucks exposed to direct sun

Time	Ambient temperature and vapour pressure	Jamunapari	Barbari
09 00 hr	39.5 °C, 13 mm Hg	239.96±25.89	274.74±20.45
13 00 hr	44.0 °C, 12 mm Hg	288.09±24.42	320.84±25.59
14 00 hr	46.0 °C, 12 mm Hg	300.22±23.73	349.54±31.76
15 00 hr	46.5 °C, 13 mm Hg	289.93±25.27	286.24±27.79
16 00 hr	46.0 °C, 12 mmHg	172.07±20.47	199.45±15.64
17 00 hr	44.5 °C, 12 mm Hg	197.18±16.24	256.55±24.42

Borut et al. (1979) reported that in a heated environmental room, either while resting or walking, respiratory evaporation in the Bedouin goat considerably exceeded cutaneous water loss. However, when tested the Bedouin goat under desert outdoor conditions, surprisingly they found cutaneous evaporation to be twice as high as respiratory evaporation. Evaporative cooling accounted for 75 to 83% of the total water turnover rate of the Bedouin goats in the field. When the black and white Bedouin goats were exposed to solar radiation in summer season, the black goats were found to absorb more heat. However, because of the high volumes of the body water the Bedouin goats store and the secretary capacity of their sweat glands, black goats obviously could cope with the extra heat they apparently absorbed because of their dark colouration (Finch et al., 1980). Kumar and Singh (1994) reported significantly lower rectal temperature of hairy bucks of Kutchi and Marwari breeds that those of shorn bucks, indicating that the long hairy goats tolerate radiant heat better than short hairy goats. Acharya et al. (1995) reported that short haired Sirohi goats had higher respiratory and pulse rate than long haired Sirohi goats. Another aspect of heat loss in goats, which has been examined by Taylor (1966), is the blood supply to the base of the horns in goats. Since there are arteries and capillary meshes in this area, some degree of cooling (about 3%) by this means would be possible. Reciprocally however, unless there is good vasoconstriction, heat could be lost in a cold climate.

(ii) Metabolic heat production

Ruminants are slow to reach the post-absorptive phase of metabolism often referred to in measurement of basal metabolism in animals with simple digestive tract. Therefore, the resting metabolic rate of ruminants in a thermo neutral environment is in excess of basal metabolism and rather signifies the total energy costs of maintenance and synthetic processes. Heat is produced in animals by the oxidation of absorbed nutrients in the cells. The simplest and under normal conditions, the most accurate method for measuring energy metabolism is, by the rate of oxygen consumption (plate 1) and combating the heat production by the calorific value of oxygen e.g. 4.825 Cal/ lit., corresponding to an R.Q. of 0.82 (Brody, 1945).

Kumar (1998) reported lower metabolic rate in Marwari, Sirohi, Jamunapari and Barbari bucks in hot period than that in moderate or in cool period. Resting heat production was significantly higher in Barbari breed than that in Jamunapari, Marwari and Sirohi breeds. The overall metabolic rate of Marwari and Sirohi bucks were comparatively lower than that of Jamunapari bucks and significantly lower than that of Barbari bucks. A lower metabolic rate is advantageous to life in arid region where water and food are at a premium, since this would reduce water loss and food requirement (Yousef, 1985). No further reduction in the resting heat production as a result of exposure to solar radiation in hot period was observed in the bucks. The highest rate of heat production in Barbari bucks render these animals more prone to heat load in comparison with other breeds. It was apparent that the changes in metabolic rate in relation to environmental temperature were used by the bucks to maintain a relatively constant body core temperature, and it can be used as a reliable yardstick to express thermosensitivity and thermo adaptability.

Pulse rate responds to heat exposure either by a rise or a fall depending on the nature of heat exposure. Exposure to severe heat for a short period increased heart rate (Bianca and Findlay, 1962). Relatively long periods of exposure to heat decreased heart rate (Worstell and Brody, 1953). This decline was associated with decrease in feed consumption and in the production of metabolic heat. McDowell and Woodward (1982) reported increase in pulse rate of goat and sheep and decline in cattle under hot conditions. The values reported for pulse/min in goat, sheep and cattle at thermo neutral zone (13-18°C) were 94.5, 73.0 and 64.1, respectively. Under hot conditions (above 40°C) the pulse rate was increased to 108.2 and 97 pulse/min in case of goat and sheep, respectively but was reduced to 57.8 pulse/min in cattle.

Kumar (1998) reported significant decline in heart rate in hot environment from that in moderate environment, when the bucks were housed in the shed and protected from the solar radiations. Marwari and Sirohi breeds had lower heart rate than that of Jamunapari and Barbari breeds. Heart rate increased on exposure to solar radiation in hot environment. In hot radiation environment, increased heat dissipation is possibly aided by greater circulation through arteriovenous anastomoses in the skin (Goodall, 1955). Experiments have shown that at 40°C dry bulb temperature (DBT)/20° C wet bulbs temperature (WBT), there was an increase in cardiac output and central blood volume, while the total peripheral resistance and blood pressure fell. These are expected as the peripheral vasodialation occurs in heat stress along with increased heart rate (Whittow, 1968). Vasodialation all over the body helps in the heat dissipation through cutaneous evaporation (Garg and Nangia, 1987). An increase of 14.5% in heart rate of goats from thermoneutral zone (13-18°C) to hot conditions (40°C) has been reported by McDowell and Woodward (1982). Mittal et al. (1992) reported that the pulse rate of Marwari bucks was not affected by the season of the year under the arid conditions of Rajasthan.

(iii) Endocrine strain to heat

Most of the goats live in areas where summer heat is considerable. In adaptation to heat, hormones show complex patterns of strain. Cortisol rises in the blood (Alvarez and Johnson, 1973) when non acclimatized animals are exposed to high levels of heat stress (in the sun at 40°C more) and the level of catecholamines also rise in plasma. In most desert and tropical conditions, plasma concentration and turnover of cortisol is lower than in temperate zone animals. Catecholamines remain at twice normal concentration in cattle even after 24 days at 35°C (Alvarez and Johnson, 1973). In hot environments, there is reduction also in the amount of gonadotrophin, particularly luteinising hormone (Madan and Johnson, 1973) secreted by pituitary gonadotrophs, and less mobilization of fat and sugar by adrenalin and noradrenalin. Since metabolic rates are lower in the heat, this would be a useful adaptation to reduce energy turnover. The water and salt turnovers, of course, increase in the heat because of evaporative cooling, and vasopressin with aldosterone rise in most animals to protect the extracellular volume. With lowered gonadotrophin output there is usually reduced fecundity and poorly adapted ruminants living in hot environments commonly have few offspring, poor growth rate and poor milk output. Evolutionary adaptation and acclimatization has, on the other hand, produced good fecundity, in the desert.

Responses to cold environment

Animals at low ambient temperature are expected to conserve or generate sufficient amount of heat to maintain their body temperature. Heat conservation is done by vasoconstriction/ reduction in respiratory rate. Tidal air volume increases to allow an increase in pulmonary ventilation to burn more food. But in the sub-tropical desert areas, the growth of vegetation is hampered due to very low temperature in winters. The sparse vegetation becomes scarce in these areas and the energy requirements for thermo-regulatory and productive purposes are substantially increased. Under such circumstances any saving of their energy expenditure may indeed be crucial for their survival. Thus, the critical season of the year for the desert goats seems to be the winters.

(i) Fur colour and heat balance: utilization of solar radiant energy

In the sub-tropical desert areas the goats are predominantly or entirely black. Most of the black goat breeds of subtropical desert areas (Mehsana, Zalawadi, Marwari, Kutchi, Jakhrana, Beetal, Black Bedouin) have long rough hairy coat when compared to their contemporaries of white or light colour (Surti, Sirohi, Jamunapari, Barbari) having short and smooth coat. Maximum absorption of solar energy by black coloured goats in cool environment seems to be an important adaptive phenomenon in arid conditions. The extra heat which an animal gets during summer is not required and dissipated (Finch et al., 1980) whereas, the extra heat absorbed during the winter becomes the major benefit to the animals. Under such conditions, the animal need not to generate extra heat within the body system to maintain the body temperature and maximum amount of feed energy is expected to be diverted for productive purposes by reducing temperature gradient between the animal and the environment (Dmi'el et al., 1980).

Maximum increase in rectal temperature from morning to afternoon on 6-8 h exposure to solar radiation in cool environment in Marwari bucks (2.15^{0}C) than in Jamunapari bucks (1.80^{0}C) indicated that Marwari bucks due to their black coat colour absorbed more solar radiation than white coat of Jamunapari bucks. The magnitude of this much deviation in rectal temperature was not observed when the bucks were not exposed to solar radiation in cool environment. The deviation in rectal temperature in unexposed bucks was lesser in Marwari bucks (0.99^{0}C) than in Jamunapari bucks (1.19^{0}C). The resting metabolic rate of Marwari bucks (94.59±11.86 Kcal/ Kg $W^{0.75}$/24 h) and of Jamunapari bucks(97.64±8.54 Kcal /Kg $W^{0.75}$/24h) in winters, when not exposed to solar radiation, was almost of similar magnitude but on exposure to solar radiation in winters, the resting heat production of Marwari bucks was 28.05 % lower than that of Jamunapari bucks. The heart rate of the bucks was correlated with the metabolic heat production of the bucks in cool radiation environment. Maximum reduction in the heart rate of Marwari bucks was observed on exposure to solar radiation in cool environment than when not exposed to solar radiation in cool environment. The change in mean daily heart rate on exposure to solar radiation in cool environment than in unexposed bucks was -12.09% in Marwari and +1.55% in Jamunapari bucks. Dry matter intake was lower in Marwari bucks and not in Jamunapari bucks on exposure to solar radiation in cool environment than in bucks not exposed to solar radiation in cool environment.

The use of the radiant energy in reducing energy expenditure for thermo-regulatory needs during cool period was studied in weaned kids of black, dark tan and white coat colours (Singh et al., 1996). The average daily gain in live weight was higher in weaned kids receiving 8 h daily exposure to solar radiation than their contemporaries kept inside the shed. The difference in daily live weight gain between the kids of two groups was more in black and dark tan colour kids than those of white colour kids. Overall daily live weight gain was higher (53.78 g/d in the experiment 1 and 52.5 g/d in the experiment 2) for kids exposed to solar radiation in comparison to kids of Group II (32.7 g/d in the experiment 1 and 28.4 g/d in the experiment 2), kept inside the shed. Breed-wise examination of data in the experiment 1 revealed that the kids of Marwari breed having black coat exhibited the maximum difference in daily live weight gain and those of Jamunapari breed having the white coat the minimum difference between two groups. The kids having dark coat colour would have absorbed relatively more solar radiation when exposed to direct sun than kids with white coats. During the period of exposure to solar radiation, metabolic rate in kids of exposed group was lower than that in unexposed group. The magnitude of decrease in metabolic rate was more in kids of black coat in comparison to kids of white coat (Kumar et al., 1999). The kids in Group 1 in both the experiments had lower thermo-regulatory needs and thus used more of their feed energy for growth. This contention is fully supported by better feed conversion efficiency in kids of group I getting exposure to Sun than group II kept inside the shed. Differences between the breeds revealed that the ability to absorb solar radiation has a direct effect on energy use for growth. Dmi'el et al. (1980) also reported decrease in metabolic rate of black as well as white goats on exposure to sun in cool environment. They also concluded that the greater decrease in metabolic rate in black goat was due to a greater increase in their surface temperature, resulting from a higher absorption of solar radiation. The black Bedouin goats dominate the herds of the Bedouins in Eastern Sinai and the Southern parts of the Negev desert of Israel. White specimens are only occasionally found in the Bedouin herds. Bedouin goats thrive in herds of varying size over a wide range of desert habitats. Throughout their distribution, these goats encounter severe heat in the summer and bitterly cold temperature in winter (Table 3).

Table 3. Oxygen consumption of Black and White Bedouin goats during a clear winter day in the desert

	Oxygen consumption ml (O_2Ag/hr)		
Breed	**Shade**	**Sun**	**Metabolic reduction (%)**
Black goat	488	351	28.1
White goat	488	436	10.7

Being productive in a hostile environment

Goats in the hot, dry areas of the world are generally tended for their milk production although male kids are used for the meat which is considered a delicacy in many countries. The number of goats in arid and semiarid zones south and east of the Mediterranean basin (North Africa, Arabia, the Levant, Greece, and Cyprus) account for 15% of the total world goat population. Nevertheless, the milk these animals produce accounts for 30% of the total world goat milk production. Some goat breeds indigenous to that area, such as the Damascus goat or the black East Mediterranean Mumber goat, are world famous for their high milk yields.

Animals, which are lactating, require considerably more water and food than they do at their maintenance levels. Therefore, lack of an adequate water supply and a shortage of suitable forage may merely hamper production. In environments where water and food are not consistently available, animals tend to synchronize their productivity with the season of the year characterized by the highest availability of both water and food. In the desert, conditions that favour production prevail for short periods of time. They occur irregularly following sporadic and sometimes torrential rains at the end of the cold winter, during years of drought they may be skipped altogether. Nevertheless, from the middle of the winter to the end of the summer, lactating goats have always been observed in the Bedouin herds. Milk yields in the Bedouin goat were assessed in the laboratory under conditions that favoured maximal production were: Alfalfa hay *ad lib*, water once daily, temperature and relative humidity controlled at 30^0 C and 30%, respectively. The yields measured in these goats matched the yields reported for goat breeds selected during ages of domestication for producing high milk yields (Table 4). Composition of the milk in the Bedouin goat was also similar to that reported for the high yielding breeds. In agreement with such high milk yields, productivity, as measured by the growth rate of kids, is also reported to be very high in the Bedouin goats.

Table 4. Yield and composition of milk in East Mediterranean goat breeds and the Swiss Saanen Goat

Breed	Body mass (kg)	Yield (g/kg/day)	Total solids (%)	Milk fat (%)	Total protein (%)	Lactose (%)
Black Bedouin	23	56	14.5	3.7	2.8	3.7
Black East	50	70	13.2	3.4	3.9	3.3
Mediterranean Swiss Saanen	50	70	12.0	3.0	2.2	3.5

Demands for both water and food are consistently higher in lactating goats compared to those observed in goats just before gestation. Maltz and Shkolnik (1984) recorded water turnover rates 2½ times higher in lactating goats than in non-lactating ones. The daily water consumption of lactating goats was three times the value measured in goats before gestation and their gross energy intake during lactation doubled, as compared to the level recorded in their non-lactating phase.

If the high water requirements of lactating goats rendered these animals dependent on frequent drinking, their grazing area would become limited to vicinity close to watering points at a time when the caloric demands of the animal are greatly increased. Maltz and Shkolnik, 1984) have demonstrated that the Bedouin goat copes with these difficult situations by merely increasing the volume of water it "stores" upon visiting a watering site. The tritiated water space that was measured in a fully hydrated lactating goat often amounted to over 85% of its body mass. During 4 days of water deprivation the "dry weight" in these goats was maintained, but body water that was in excess of the volume measured in non-lactating goats was used up. Even at the end of the 4-day dehydration period, the HTO space in the "water-restricted" lactating goats still amounted to over 70% of their body mass–3 level that enabled these apparently dehydrated goats to forage normally.

Storing extra water for maintaining the goats grazing range in a desert environment implies the expansion of all body fluid compartments. The Evans Blue (EB) dye space that was measured in the fully hydrated lactating goats amounted to twice the volume usually reported for other mammal's blood plasma. Goats, unlike other desert mammals such as camels and gazelles, lack the capacity when dehydrated, to maintain the volume of their blood at the expense of other body fluid compartments. All fluid compartments in the Bedouin goat contribute equally to the loss of body water. Nevertheless, due to its high initial value, plasma volume in the goat is maintained within the limits considered "normal" for mammals in general even with a decrease of 30% in body mass. Because the water loss in the Bedouin goat is evenly distributed throughout the entire body water pool, the osmotic consequences of the loss are minimized. This is in spite of a total loss that exceeds the loss most other animals can tolerate. With such a spacious water "store", deprivation of drinking water for 2 days was not found to affect the high milk yield of the lactating goats. Their yield only began to drop on the third day of the water deprivation period. However, even at the end of the fourth day of that period, the water demands of the goat were met. Furthermore, in the face of continuously repeated periods of water deprivation, the Bedouin goats maintained their capacity to resume their initial yield upon rehydration. Even during peak lactation, dehydrated goats resumed their high yield rates 1 day following drinking. Water, once consumed and "stored" by the desert goat, is economically used for the production of milk. The Bedouin goat requires only 2.5 kg of water for each kilogram of milk produced. Bergman reports a consumption of 3.5 kg water per kilogram milk in dairy goats of the temperate region and a similar value has been recorded in cattle.

In addition to playing a role in the water economy of the lactating goats, the kidney also contributes to the goat's ability to maintain their nitrogen balance while producing high milk yields. As much as 73% of the blood plasma urea that is filtered in the renal glomeruli is reabsorbed in the kidney of the productive goat. In the kidney of the non-lactating goat, only 47% of the urea filtered is reabsorbed. As a result of the kidney's contribution to the retention of the blood urea in the lactating goat, the urine/urea concentration in these animals amounts to only a third of the concentration in non-lactating goats. Moreover, this is the case even though urine osmolarity is higher during lactation. Urea conservation by the kidney helps the lactating Bedouin goat maintain a high urea recycling rate and meet the high demand of protein required by such a highly productive animal (Table 5).

Table 5. Nitrogen kinetics in black Bedouin goats during lactation and before gestation

N Intake (g/day)	N urea body pool (g)	N urea entry rate (g/day)	N urine urea (g/day)	N milk urea (g/day)	N recycled urea (g/day)	N urea recycled (% of entry rate)
			Lactating			
27.1	4.9	28.3	7.3	0.25	20.8	73.5
			Non lactating			
13.6	3.0	17.3	9.6	-	7.7	44.6

The energetic efficiency of milk production in the black Bedouin goat was also demonstrated by Maltz and Shkolnik (1984). They found that the conversion coefficient of digestible energy to energy in milk ranged from 34% during peak lactation to 25% at the end of the lactation period. According to Brody, mammals capable of converting over 25% of their digestible energy intake into energy in milk are considered to possess *'superior dairy merits'*. Only cow breeds selected for high milk production as well as the Alpine goat and the Damascus goat are reported to be included in this category. Bedouin goats, unlike high-yielding milk cows, do not catabolize tissue even during peak lactation though they do maintain their "superior dairy merits" throughout the lactation period. The widely accepted notion that the poor productivity reported for tropical dairy goats is due to poor dairy merit is obviously not valid for the goats of the sub-tropic, xeric environment.

Dry matter digestibility in dry season

While livestock in open range might select for high quality forage to maintain a relatively similar basal diet quality from season to season, the extent to which they can do this and still maximize their intake becomes significantly reduced in extremely dry seasons when forage biomass and its quality are low. This would result in a low quality basal diet, a less dense and less vigorous rumen microflora and hence very low DM digestion. The season (January-March) is the crucial period for high quality forage supplement intervention for all livestock species, and that cattle suffer the most due to their high reliance on grass, the least nutritive of the forage components during the this period. Camels, followed by goats, fare better, in terms of rumen dry matter digestibility (RDMD), than sheep and cattle, and appear to be better adapted in the utilization of available feed resources across seasons (Migongo-Bake and Hansen, 1987).

Silanikove et al. (1980) assessed the gross energy intake in Bedouin and Swiss Saanen goats. When both breeds were fed dry alfalfa hay and watered *ad libitum*, the gross caloric intake of the Bedouin goat, on a metabolic body mass basis, was 30% lower than that recorded in the Swiss breed. However, when wheat straw was fed to the same animals the consumption of the Bedouin goats exceeded that of the Swiss Saanen goats. Wheat straw is considered an inadequate food source for any domesticated animal. The Swiss Saanen goats continuously lost weight when fed this foodstuff. However, when the Bedouin goats were placed on the same diet they maintained their body mass for an extended period of time. Silanikove et al. (1980) also assessed the apparent digestibility in the two breeds. When fed alfalfa hay the apparent digestibility in the Bedouin goat amounted to 72% as compared to 67% in the Swiss goat (55 to 68% being the value usually reported for other ruminants). However, on a diet of wheat straw an apparent digestibility of 53% was recorded in the Bedouin breed while only 39% was found in the Swiss breed. Silanikove demonstrated a slower passage rate in the GI tract of the Bedouin goat than that of the Swiss Saanen breed. They attributed this difference to a longer retention time of the digesta in the rumen of the Bedouin breed. It is well established that a low rate of passage renders digestion more efficient. The spacious rumen which plays a major role in the water economy of the goats in the arid zones additionally provides, the space for retaining the digesta longer, and thus contributes to the economy of the Bedouin goat's energy budget.

Urea Recycling

Wheat straw is high in crude fiber and contains less than 3% crude protein. The ability of the Bedouin goats to sustain their body mass on this poor-quality foodstuff is attributable not only to their efficient digestion but also to their capacity to recycle urea. While being fed wheat straw, 90% of the urea discharged into the bloodstream in the Bedouin goat was transferred into the GI tract (to be used by rumen microorganisms for resynthesis of amino acid, and proteins). Only in camels the higher rate of urea recycling been documented. In the Swiss Saanen goats, the recycled urea amounted to only half the amount recorded in the Bedouin breed; a rate which is similar to values reported for other domesticated ruminant species. The two characteristics demonstrated in the black Bedouin goat, namely the ability to digest poor quality food stuff and to efficiently exploit nitrogenous metabolic waste, seem to be complementary to each other. They enable this breed to meet their caloric demand and also balance nitrogen metabolism under adverse environmental conditions.

Adaptation to high altitude

At the altitudes of about 2000m, low oxygen pressure acts upon plasma proteins to produce the glycoprotein erythropoietin which enters the bone marrow cells and stimulates the synthesis of DNA and RNA, and the formation of more new red blood cells for oxygen transport in the mountains (Fisher, 1971). Goats live up to altitudes of 4000m in the Himalayas and Andes, where their oxygen carrying capacities are greater than those at ground level by over 30%. At see level goat red blood cells are small (19μm^3) and numerous (13-18 million mm^{-3}), but only 10-12 g dl^{-1} of haemoglobin is available (Choshniak and Shkolnik, 1977).

Anatomical considerations

The goats, indigenous to the humid tropics, tend to be smaller than breeds found in the arid-tropical areas. It might be speculated that since high humidity suppresses evaporative heat loss, there would be selection for factors that enhance non-evaporative heat dissipation. Since non-evaporative heat loss is a function of temperature gradient and surface area and since surface area in proportion to size increases as animals get smaller, it could be that the smaller breeds will have a greater non-evaporative heat loss. On the other hand, there are no constraints on evaporation in the low humidity arid areas but the system of management must ensure adequate provision of water. The goats of the arid and semi-arid areas show an interesting adaptation of the scrotum in that it consists of two discrete sacs thereby increasing surface area and enhancing heat loss in an area of the body that requires preferential cooling and which in desert areas is subjected to a high radiative heat load due to reflected solar radiation and long wave radiation from the hot sandy surface. With a more *'open hair coat'*, thinner skin and low fat covering, the goat will get heat and feel cool more rapidly while low hair density could also cause susceptibility to chilling in goats.

References

Abou Hussien, E.R.M., Gihad, E.A., El-Dedawy, T.M. and Abdel Gawad, M.H. 1994. Response of camels, sheep and goat on saline water. 2. Water and mineral metabolism. Egyptian Journal of Animal Production 31(November): 387-401.

Acharya, R. M., Gupta, U. D., Sehghal. J. P. and Singh, M. 1995. Coat characteristics of goats in relation to heat tolerance in the hot tropics. Small Ruminant Research 18: 245-248.

Alvarez, M. B. and Johnson, H. D. 1973. Environmental heat exposure on cattle plasma catecholamine and glucocorticoids. Journal of Dairy Science 51: 74-77.

Appleman, R. D. and Delouche, J. C. 1958. Behavioral, physiological and biochemical responses of goats to temperature 0-40 °C. Journal of Animal Sciences 17: 326-335.

Baker, M. A. and Dawson, D. D. 1985. Inhibition of thermal panting by intracarotid infusion of hypertonic saline in dogs. American Journal of Physiology 249: R787-791.

Baker, M. A. 1989. Effects of dehydration and rehydration on thermoregulatory sweating in goats. Journal of Physiology 417: 421-435.

Baker, M. A. and Doris, P. A. 1982. Control of evaporative heat loss during changes in plasma osmolality in the cat. Journal of Physiology 328: 535-545.

Bhattacharya, A. N. 1980. Research on goat nutrition and management in Mediterranean, Middle East and adjacent Arab countries. Journal of Dairy Science 63: 16-18.

Bianca, W. and Findlay, J. D. 1962. The effect of thermally induced hyperpnea on the acid - base status of the blood of calves. Research in Veterinary Sciences 3: 38-49.

Borut, A., Dmi'el, R. and Shkolnik, A. 1979. Heat balance of resting and walking goats: Comparison of climatic chamber and exposure in the desert. Physiological Zoology 52: 105-112.

Brody, S. 1945. Bioenergetics and growth. Reinhold, New York, pp. 313-319.

Burke, M.G. 1990. Seawater consumption and water economy of tropical feral goats. Biotropica 22: 416-419.

Cena, K. and Monteith, J. L. 1975. Transfer processes in animal coats. III. Water vapour diffusion. Proceedings of the Royal Society (London) 188: 413-423.

Choshniak, I. 1978. Homeostasis of body fluids in the desert: The Black Bedouin Goat (in Hebrew), Ph.D. thesis, University of Tel Aviv, Israel.

Choshniak, I. and Shkolnik, A. 1978. The rumen as a protective osmotic mechanism during rapid rehydration in the black Bedouin goats. In: Osmotic and Volume Regulation. Alfred Benson Symposium XI, Munksgaard pp. 344-359.

Choshniak, I. and Shkolnik, A. 1977. Rapid rehydration in the black Bedouin goats: Red blood cells fragility and role of the rumen. Comparative Biochemistry and Physiology 56 A: 581-589.

Choshniak, I., Wittenberg, C. and Saham, D. 1987. Rehydrating Bedouin goats with saline: rumen and kidney functions. Physiological Zoology 60: 373-378.

Court, J. 2002. Drought feeding and management of sheep. Department of Natural Resources and Environment, Melbourne, Australia.

Degen, A. A. and Kam, M. 1992. Body mass loss and body fluid shifts during dehydration in Dorper sheep. Journal of Agricultural Sciences (Cambridge) 119: 419-422.

Denny, M. J. S. and Dawson, T. J. 1975. Effects of dehydration on body water distribution in desert Kangaroos. American Journal of Physiology 229: 251-254.

Dmi'el, R. 1986. Selective sweat secretion and panting modulation in dehydrated goats. Journal of Thermal Biology 11(3): 157-159.

Dmi'el, R., Prevolotzky, A. and Shkolnik, A. 1980. Is a black coat in the desert a means to save metabolic energy? Nature (London) 283: 761-769.

Dmi'el, R., Robertshaw, D. and Choshniak, J. 1979. Sweat gland secretion in the Black Bedouin goat. Physiological Zoology 52: 558-564.

Dunson, W.A. 1974. Some aspects of salt and water balance of feral goats from arid islands. American Journal of Physiology 226:662-669.

El-Gawad, E.I.A. 1997. Physiological responses of Barki and Damascus goats and their crossbred to drinking to drinking saline water. Alexandria Journal of Agricultural Research 42: 23-36.

Erasmus, T., 1967. Water metabolism studies with ruminants. DSc (Agric) thesis, University of Pretoria, Experimental Agriculture 26: 639-642.

Ferreira, A.V., Hoffman, L.C., Schoeman, S.J. and Sheridan, R. 2002. Water intake of Boer goats and Mutton merinos receiving either a low or high energy feedlot diet. Small Ruminant Research 43: 245-248.

Finch, V. A., Dm'iel, R., Boxman, R., Shkolnik, A. and Taylor, C. R. 1980. Why black goats in hot desert? Effect of coat colour on heat exchange of wild and domestic goats. Physiological Zoology 53:19-25.

Fisher, J. W. 1971. Kidney hormones. Academic Press, London.

Fitzsimons, J. T. 1979. The physiology of thirst and sodium appetite. Cambridge University Press, New York.

Garg, S. K. and Nangia, O. P. 1987. Effects of climatological variation on the cardiac output and related heart functions in buffalo calves. Indian Journal of Animal Sciences 57(2): 101-105.

Giger-Reverdin, S. and Gihad, A. 1991. Water metabolism and intake in goats. Goat Nutrition, Morand-Fehr, P (ed). p. 37 - 45 Pudoc, Wageningen, Netherland.

Goatcher, W.D. and Church, D.C. 1970. Taste responses in ruminants. IV. Reactions of pygmy goats, normal goats, sheep and cattle to acetic acid and quinine hydrochloride. Journal of Animal Sciences 31: 373-382.

Goodall, A. M. 1955. Arterio-venous anastomoses in the skin of the head and ears of the calf. Journal of Anatomy (London) 89: 100-106.

Goyal, S. P. 1983. Coat colour and body temperature regulation in Indian desert goats. Annals of Arid Zone 22: 59-63.

Greenwald, L., 1964. Water economy of the desert dwelling springbok (*Antidorcas marsupialis*). M.Sc. Thesis, Zoology. Syracuse University; New York.

Hales, J. R. S. 1974. Physiological responses to heat. In: MPT International Review of Science, Environmental Physiology, D. Robertshaw (ed), Butterworths, London.

Harrington, G.N. 1982. The feral goat. Chapter 1 in "Goats for Meat and Fibre in Australia". SCA Technical Report Series No. 11. (CSIRO: Melbourne).

Hassan, G. E. A. 1989. Physiological responses of Anglo-Nubian and Baladi goats and their crossbreds to water deprivation under sub-tropical conditions. Livestock Production Science 22: 295-304.

Henzell, R. 1997. The ecology and pest potential of feral goats. Bulletin 1997-08, Primary Industries South Australia: Port Augusta.

Hutchinson, J. C. D. and Brown G. B. 1969. Penetrance of cattle coats by radiation. Applied Physiology 26: 454-464.

Johnson, K. G. 1976. Evaporative temperature regulation in sheep. In: Progress in biometeorology, H.D. Johnson (ed.). Swetz and Zeitlingen, Amsterdam.

Joshi, B. C., Arvindan, M., Singh, K. and Bhattacharyya, N. K. 1977. Effect of high environmental temperature stress on physiological responses of bucks. Indian Journal of Animal Sciences 47: 200-204.

Khan, M. S., Ghosh, P. K. and Sasidharan, T. O. 1978. Effect of acute water restriction on plasma proteins and on blood and urinary electrolyte in Barmer goats of the Rajasthan Desert. Journal of Agricultural Sciences (Cambridge) 91: 395-398.

Khan, M. S., Sasidharan, T. U. and Ghosh, P. K. 1979. Water regulation in Barmer goat of the Rajasthan desert. Experientia 35: 1185-1189.

Khan, M.S. and Ghosh, P.K. 1982. Comparative physiology of water economy in desert sheep and goats. Proceedings of the 3rd International Conference on Goat Production and Disease: 337. Dairy Goat Publishing Co., Scottsdale, USA.

King J. 1983. Livestock water needs in pastoral Africa in relation to climate and forage. ILCA Research Report 7, Addis Ababa.

Kumar Puneet and Singh, K. 1994. Effect of shearing on thermoadaptability in goats of arid and semi-arid zone of India. Indian Journal of Animal Sciences 64: 290-294.

Kumar Puneet, Saini, A.L. and Singh, K. 1988. Effect of microenvironment on sweating rate in Jamunapari and Barbari bucks maintained in convertible shed module. In: Proceedings of the IV Annual Conference of the Society Animal Physiologists of India, Central Institute for Research on Goats, Makhdoom, pp.5-6.

Kumar Puneet, Singh, K. and Sood, S. B. 1990. Effect of microenvironment within different types of sheds on physiological responses in Jamunapari goats in hot semi-arid zone. Indian Journal of Animal Research 24: 93-110.

Kumar Puneet 1998. Thermoregulatory characteristics in some breeds of goats of hot arid and semi-arid zone. Ph.D. thesis, Dr. B.R. Ambedkar university (formerly Agra University), Agra.

Kumar Puneet, Singh, K., Singh, D. and Misra, R. P. 1999. Resting heat production and cardinal physiological responses of kids exposed to different duration of solar radiation in cool period. In; Proceedings of the 86th Indian Science Congress, Chennai, January 3-7.

Macfarlane, W. V., Morris, R. J. H. and Howard, B. 1962. Water metabolism of Merino sheep and Camels. Australian Journal of Animal Sciences 25: 112-116.

Macfarlane, W.V., 1982. Concepts in animal adaptation. In: Proceedings of the 3rd International Conference on Goat Production and Disease: 375-385. Dairy Goat Publishing Co., Scotttsdale, USA.

Madan, M. L. and Johnson, H. D. 1973. Environmental heat effects on bovine luteinizing hormone. Journal of Dairy Science 56: 1420-1423.

Maloiy, G. M. O. 1974. Digestion and renal function in East African goats and haired sheep. East African Journal of Agricultural Forestry 40: 177-188.

Maloiy, G. M. O. and Taylor, C. R. 1971. Water requirements of African goats and haired sheep. Journal of Agricultural Sciences (Cambridge) 77: 203-288.

McDowell, R. E. and Woodward, A. 1982. Concepts in animal adaptation - comparative suitability of goats, sheep and cattle to tropical environments. Proceedings of 3rd International Conference on Goat Production and Disease, Tucson, Arizona, pp.387-390.

Maltz, E. and Shkolnik, A. 1984. Milk composition and yield of the black Bedouin goat during dehydration and rehydration, Journal of Dairy Research 51: 23–27.

McGregor, B.A. 1986. Water intake of grazing Angora wether goats and Merino wethers. Australian Journal of Agricultural Science (Cambridge) 77: 203-208.

McGregor, B.A. 1998. Nutrition, management and other environmental influences on the quality and production of mohair and cashmere with particular reference to mediterranean and annual temperate climatic zones: A review. Small Ruminant Research 28: 199 - 215.

Mckinley, M. J. Denton, D. A., Leksell, L., Tarjan, E. and Weisinger, R. S. 1980. Evidence for cerebral sodium sensors involved in water drinking in sheep. Physiological Behaviour 25: 501-504.

Migongo-Bake, W. and Hansen, R. M. 1987. Seasonal diets of camels, cattle, sheep and goats in a common range in eastern Africa. Journal of Range Management 40:76-79.

Mittal, J. P., Singh, M. and Khan, M. S. 1992. Adaptive responses in goat under heat and dehydration stress. In: Research in Goats, Indian Experience. R.R. Lokeshawar, N.K. Bhattacharyya and K. Singh (Eds), Central Institute for Research on Goats, Makhdoom pp. 135-146.

Nielsen, B. 1974. Effects of changes in plasma volume and osmolarity on thermoregulation during exercise. Acta Physiologica Scandiva 90: 725-730.

Olsson, K., Josater-Hermelin, M., Hossaini-Hilali, J., Hydbring, E. and Dahlborn, K. 1995. Heat stress causes excessive drinking in fed and food deprived pregnant goats. Comparative Biochemisry and Physiology 110:309-317.

Olsson, K. and Carlsson, E. 2004. Cardiovascular changes associated with dehydration and drinking in saline water. Alexandria Journal of Agricultural Research 42: 23-36.

Owen, M. D., Matthes, R. D. and Gisolfi, C. V. 1987. Increase in CSF osmolarity reduces sweat rate in the heat-stressed Patas monkey. Federation Proceedings 46: 323-327.

Parkes, J., Henzell, R., and Pickles, G. 1996. Managing Vertebrate Pests: Feral Goats. Australian Government Publishing Service: Canberra, 129 pp.

Peirce, A.W. 1968. Studies on salt tolerance of sheep. VIII The tolerance of grazing ewes and their lambs for Proceedings of the 3rd International Conference on Goat Production and Disease: 337. Dairy Goat Publishing Co., Scottsdale, USA.

Purohit, G. R., Ghosh, P. K. and Taneja, G. C. 1972. Water metabolism in desert sheep. Australian Journal of Agricultural Research 23: 605-610.

Robertshaw, D. and Dmi'el, R. 1983. The effect of dehydration on the control of panting and sweating in the black Bedouin goat. Physiological Zoology 56: 412-418.

Saul, G.R. and Flinn, P.C. 1985. Effects of saline drinking water on growth and water and feed intake of weaner heifers. Australian Journal of Experimental Agriculture 25: 734-738.

SCA, 1990. Feeding Standards for Australian Livestock: Ruminants. Standing Committee on Agriculture (CSIRO: East Melbourne) pp. 266.

Scarlett, T. 2002. Drought feeding of goats. New South Wales Agricultrue: Sydney. http//www.agric.nsw.gov.au/reader/5337 22/11/02.

Schmid, W. D. 1976. Temperature gradients in the nasal passage of some small mammals. Comparative Biochemistry and Physiology 54A: 305-308.

Schmidt-Nielsen, B., Schmidt-Nielsen, K., Houpt, T. R. and Jarnum, S. A. 1956. Water balance of the camel. American Journal of Physiology 185: 185-194.

Schmidt-Nielsen, K. 1977. Problems of scaling : locomotion and physiological correlates. In:Scale Effects in Animal Locomotion, T.J.Pedley (ed), pp.1-21. Academic Press, New York and London.

Schmidt-Nielsen, K. 1964. Desert Animals-Physiological problems of heat and water. Clarendon Press, Oxford.

Shkolnik, A., Borut, A. and Choshniak, J. 1972. Comparative Physiology of Desert Animals. Maloiy, G.M.O. (ed.), Academic Press, London, pp. 229-242.

Silanikove N., Tagari H. and Shkolnik A. (1980). Gross energy digestion and urea recycling in the desert black Bedouin goat. Compedium of Biochemistry and physiology. 67A: 215-218.

Singh, K., Singh, D. and Kumar Puneet 1996. Use of radiant energy to promote growth rate in kids in cool season. In: Proceedings of the VI International Conference on Goats. Vol I, 6-11 May, 1996, Beijing, China. International Academic Publishers, pp. 471-472.

Taylor, C. R. 1970. Dehydration and heat. Effects on temperature regulation of East African ungulates. American Journal of Physiology 29: 1136-1139.

Taylor, C. R. 1966. The vascularity and possible thermoregulation function of the horns of goats. Physiological Zoology 39: 127-139.

Trulejska, E. and Baker, N. A. 1986. Elevated CSF osmolality inhibits thermoregulatory heat loss response. American Journal of Physiology 251: R749-R754.

Walsberg, G. E., Campbell, G. S. and King, J. R. 1978. Animal coat colour and radiative heat gain; a re-evaluation. Journal of Comparative Physiology 126: 211-222.

Whittow, G. C. 1968. Cardiovascular response to localized heating of the anterior hypothelamus. Journal of Physiology 198: 541-548.

Wilson, R.T. 1989. Ecophsiology of the Camelidae and desert ruminants. Springer-Verlag, Berlin.

Worstell, D. M. and Brody, S. 1953. Environmental physiology and shelter engineering with special reference to domestic animals. XX Comparative Physiological Reactions of European and Indian cattle to Changing Temperature. Missouri Agricultural Experiment Station Research Bulletin No. 515.

Yousef, M. K. 1985. Stress Physiology in Livestock. Vol.II, Ungulates. C.R.C. Press, Inc. Boca Raton, Florida, pp. 261.

Yousef, M. K., Dill, D. B. and Mayes, M. G. 1970. Shifts in body fluids during dehydration in the burro, *Equus asinus*. Journal of Applied Physiology 29: 345-349.

□□□

19

Stress Factors Influencing Preservation of Ram Semen: Approaches for Ameliorating Their Adverse Consequences

Anil Joshi*, Davendra Kumar and S.M.K. Naqvi
Division of Animal Physiology and Biochemistry, Central Sheep and Wool Research Institute
Avikanagar, via Jaipur- 304501, Rajasthan

Introduction

Sheep are among the first domesticated animals and have continued to be a major livestock animal used for food and fibre. The availability of optimized methods for ram sperm preservation would have a significant impact on improving the efficiency of sheep production systems worldwide by preserving valuable genetic stock for genetic variability and protecting genetic diversity (Hollinshead et al., 2004; Ehling et al., 2006; Nel-Themaat et al., 2006). The life span of spermatozoa is prolonged by preservation of semen either through reduction (*'short-term preservation'*) or arrest (*'long-term preservation'*) of their metabolic activity. The principal advantage of using liquid semen is that fertility is possible with low numbers of spermatozoa and the storage is also economical. However, during short-term preservation of ram semen there is decline in fertility beyond 24 h of storage (Maxwell and Salamon, 1993). Frozen storage has the advantage to preserve important genes for future use, provide insurance against loss of a particular sire, permit transport of semen over long distances and allow large numbers of females to be inseminated at different season or location.

Landmark breakthroughs in semen preservation first came into prominence with the discoveries of the protective agents in egg yolk for cooling (Phillips, 1939) and glycerol for freezing (Polge et al., 1949). The consequences of multiple stresses imposed on ram spermatozoa during cryopreservation leads to impaired transport and poor survival of frozen-thawed in the female reproductive tract. Concerted research efforts are going on worldwide to improve the methods of freezing and insemination for obtaining good post-thaw recovery and fertility with frozen ram spermatozoa. The progress made on various aspects of ram semen freezing and artificial insemination (AI) such as diluent composition, processing, freezing and thawing methods, cryoinjury to sperm plasma membrane and fertility has been extensively reviewed by researchers from time to time (Sadler, 1966; Visser, 1974; Graham et al., 1978; Watson, 1979; Maxwell, 1984; Evans, 1988; Salamon and Maxwell 1995 a, b; Watson, 1995; Maxwell and Watson, 1996; Bailey et al., 2000; Curry 2000; Watson, 2000; Salamon and Maxwell, 2000; Naqvi et al., 2001; Evans et al., 2004; Gillan et al., 2004; Anel et al., 2006; Barbas & Mascarenhas, 2009).

Unfortunately, the success achieved with the cryosurvival of bull sperm has not been translated into most commonly raised farm animal species including the ram (Salamon and Maxwell, 2000). Advances in cryopreservation of ram spermatozoa have not kept pace with the developments that have occurred in some other ovine reproductive technologies. Only minimal changes in protocols for processing and freezing ram semen have been implemented in the past two decades. This limited rate of progress is due to a lack of complete understanding of the factors and interactions that alter spermatozoal viability during processing, freezing and thawing. If the spermatozoal membrane is damaged during the freeze-thaw process; intracellular components may be damaged or destroyed, thereby rendering the spermatozoon useless for AI (Salamon and Maxwell, 2000; Anel et al., 2006). Thus, current fertility rates with cryopreserved ram spermatozoa do not satisfy the demand of the sheep industry (Gillan et al., 1999).

It has been well known that sperm undergoes considerable cellular, biochemical and osmotic changes during epididymal maturation and after the addition of seminal fluids for normal fertilization (Yeung et al., 2006). Several studies have been conducted regarding osmotic tolerance, cold-shock sensitivity and hydraulic conductivity to understand some of the cryobiological properties of ejaculated ram sperm, but these properties have not been fully investigated for epididymal ram sperm (Curry and Watson, 1994; Duncan and Watson, 1992). Appropriate retrieval and optimal cryopreservation of epididymal spermatozoa following accidental deaths would also greatly help in preserving biodiversity (Hishinuma et al., 2003; Fernandez-Santos et al., 2006).

Understanding the effects of low temperature, osmotic stress and cryoprotective agents (CPAs) on cellular systems during cryopreservation procedures and utilizing this knowledge in developing improved cryopreservation protocols are the principle aims of fundamental cryobiology. Cryopreservation is a multi-step procedure in which sperm have to withstand serious deleterious conditions created by imposition of low-temperature stress during freezing followed by reverse high-temperature stress during thawing. Thus, it is essential to systematically study the fundamental ramifications of ram sperm that are undergoing several stresses during: (i) semen collection and dilution (ii) cooling spermatozoa below physiological temperatures in the presence of permeating (e.g. glycerol) or non-permeating (e.g. sucrose) CPAs for suspended quiescence (iii) thawing from -196°C to physiological or slightly elevated temperature for their resuscitation and (iv) sperm sorting and preserved of sorted spermatozoa.

Stress imposed during semen collection

The use of an effective method of semen collection ensures maximum survival to spermatozoa. Semen can be collected from live animals by using artificial vagina or electroejaculation. Semen collection with the aid of an artificial vagina resembles natural service, but usually requires a preliminary training period (Wulster_Radcliffe et al., 2001). However, for obtaining semen from a large number of rams unresponsive to training, electroejaculation could be a useful procedure but has attracted adverse comments on welfare grounds (Foote, 2002). However, in some cases where semen donor rams may be stressed by handling; electroejaculation under general anaesthesia is the only real option for obtaining ejaculated semen. Epididymal sperm have been successfully recovered and frozen, either from animals under anaesthetic or post-mortem conditions. Flaws in electroejaculation methodology have been observed as it could affect the ejaculation reflex or provide insufficient stimulation in rectal mucose. Extreme resilience of epididymal ram sperm to various stress factors during cryopreservation provides a fundamental cryobiological explanation for their high post-thaw survival. The information gained about electroejaculated and epididymal ram sperm motility and acrosomal integrity responses to various cryobiological relevant stressors will be useful to predict better the potential damage caused to spermatozoa during cryopreservation (Varisli et al., 2009).

The effects of semen collection methods on fresh and frozen–thawed spermatozoa have also been evaluated in order to develop a feasible methodology for the creation of the cryopreserved sperm bank. The main findings from the study were that: (i) electroejaculation resulted in lower recovery efficiency (80% of the cases) as a consequence of contamination with urine or lack of response to the electrical stimulation, (ii) fresh seminal quality was not significantly different between collection methods, except for the concentration of spermatozoa, but the total number of spermatozoa and the consequent number of possible seminal doses for artificial insemination were similar, and (iii) higher functional frozen–thawed spermatozoa were obtained by electroejaculation compared to artificial vagina (Marco-Jimenez et al., 2005). In order to explain how the collection method affects the frozen–thawed sperm function, one hypothesis could be the differences in seminal plasma composition secreted from sex glands. The addition and removal of a variety of proteins during epididymal maturation and at ejaculation play an important role(s) in the capacitation of sperm and fertilization of the egg (Yanagimachi, 1994). Barrios et al. (2000) suggested that the acquisition of seminal plasma proteins by adsorption to the sperm cell surface modifies the functional characteristics of damaged spermatozoa. Assuming the advantages and limitations of both treatments; quick application of electroejaculation methodology (without the need for a training period) can be useful for *ex situ* conservation of sheep breeds in the form of spermatozoa (Marco-Jimenez et al., 2005).

Stress imposed during sperm storage at ambient and refrigeration temperature

Storage of sperm at ambient temperature can provide a simplified alternative to the established cryopreservation method. Handling and logistics would become much simpler if it becomes feasible to preserve sperm in liquid extender for longer duration. This would have potential benefits to the sheep farmers in the organized and unorganized sectors where for AI semen needs to be transported to different places (Holt, 1997; Foote, 2002). The unpredictability in motility changes resulting from ambient temperature fluctuations is an important factor that needs to be taken into consideration. The strategy for liquid storage of ram spermatozoa should therefore, involve: (i) identification and minimization of the major stress factors contributing to cellular degradation and (ii) study of temperature dependence to predict motility damage as a function of storage temperature.

The major factor contributing to the disruption of cellular function in sperm during storage at near ambient conditions is the formation of reactive oxygen species (ROS). ROS are mainly composed of peroxides (H_2O_2), superoxide anions (O_2 E-) and hydroxyl free radicals (OH E) ions (Vishwanath and Shannon, 1997; Benaroudj et al., 2001). Recent study has shown that the reactions producing these free radicals are more active at higher storage temperatures than in the cryopreserved state (Sitaula et al., 2009). ROS molecules combine with cellular components and transform them into oxygen-based damage products. Sperm plasma membranes are highly sensitive to peroxidation caused by free radicals because of high content of unsaturated fatty acids in their membranes. Lipid peroxidation causes the membrane to be leaky and leads to complete loss of motility and membrane integrity. Since sperm do not possess any internal repair mechanism against cellular damage (Vishwanath and Shannon, 1997), an environment where damage is minimized is essential to protect it from ROS-induced damage. For similar reasons, a reduced oxidative stress environment is equally desirable in cryopreservation or storage of cells at near ambient temperature in the partially desiccated state (Kanias and Ackar, 2006).

Superoxide anions have a short half-life (1ms) and they are broken down into peroxides spontaneously or enzymatically. H_2O_2 is relatively more stable compared to the super oxide anions or the hydroxyl radical. It has a long half-life and accumulates in the media after being generated. On the other hand, hydroxyl radical can be formed by reaction between superoxide anion and hydrogen peroxide or by the reduction of peroxide by ferrous ion. The deleterious effect of hydroxyl radical lies in its extremely high reactivity, a very short half-life (of the order of 1ns) and hence it cannot be eliminated by enzymatic actions (de Lamirande et al., 1997). Reducing the oxidative stresses through the use of antioxidant(s) and chelating agents can target the increase in the short-term storage ability of ram sperm in liquid suspension. The hypothesis is that the addition of an optimal amount of antioxidant or chelating agents can reduce the oxidative stresses, thus minimizing motility loss and membrane and/or mitochondrial damage. Antioxidants counteract the formation of superoxide anions and peroxides while chelators sequester the free metal ions, thereby minimizing the production of hydroxyl radical by the transition metal (Sitaula et al., 2009).

Stress imposed during sperm storage at ultra-low temperature and thawing

The combinations of storage temperature, chemical composition of extender and the hygienic control are the key factors that affect the life span of spermatozoa (Yoshida, 2000). Unlike some mammalian species, ram spermatozoa are susceptible to various stresses during freezing and thawing. Cryopreservation of ram semen also depends upon several interrelated factors

(Fiser and Fairfull, 1986, 1989; Schmehl et al., 1986; Pontbriand et al., 1989; Joshi and Mathur, 1994; Joshi et al., 1998a, 1998b, 2000, 2001, 2005, 2006, 2008; Bag et al., 1998, 1999, 2002a, 2002b, 2004; Kumar et al., in press a) but their adverse effects are manifested on thawing (Holt et al. 1992; Holt and North, 1994). The problem, still, is that even with the best preservation a technique to date post-thaw survival is restricted to about 50 % of sperm population (Watson, 1995). The complex anatomy of ewe cervix (Halbert et al., 1990) is also a major factor affecting the fertility with frozen-thawed semen (Eppleston and Maxwell, 1993, Naqvi et al., 1998, 2001). Despite thorough research, progress in the preservation of ram semen has reached a plateau. As evidence of this, Salamon et al. (2004) reported that ram semen cryopreserved 35 years ago yielded fertility results after laparoscope-aided intrauterine AI that were within the current acceptable standards. Nevertheless, over the past 30 years there has been much knowledge gained on the functional behaviour of the spermatozoa after preservation.

Although ram semen has also been frozen in ampoules but the most common packages for its storage are pellets and polyvinyl chloride (PVC) straws. Ram semen can be successfully stored in pellets (Salamon et al., 1996) and straws (Salamon and Maxwell, 2000) for prolonged period of time with no detrimental effect on the subsequent survival of spermatozoa after thawing. Noteworthy results on cryopreservation of ram semen have obtained by workers from different countries (Fiser and Fairfull, 1989; Abdelhakeam et al., 1991; Mathur et al., 1991; Sanchez-Partida et al., 1992; Payne et al., 1994; Gonzalez et al., 1996; Valcarel et al., 1996; Soderquist et al., 1997; Joshi et al., 1998a; Aisen et al., 2000; Gil et al., 2000; Joshi et al., 2001; Paulenz et al., 2004). The mean percent post-thaw motility achieved among them ranged from 41 to 70%. The Australian in pellet freezing (Sanchez-Partida et al., 1992) while Argentinean (Aisen et al., 2000), Swedish (Gil et al., 2000) and our group in straw freezing have reported more than 70% post-thaw motility of ram spermatozoa. The wide variation in this may be contributed by the adoption of different freezing protocol by each laboratory. Pellet freezing is advantageous because of easy handling and simple equipment required for it. However, there is no control on freezing rate and variability exists even between pellets of the same sample. Moreover, there is also a difficulty in maintaining identity of stored pellets, as they cannot be coded distinctly like straws. Programmable cell freezers have been designed for the controlled cooling and subsequent warming of biological specimens specially sperms and embryos. They provide variable cooling and heating rates within the temperature range of + 30 to –180 °C. The operation of the freezer relies upon the controlled influx of atomised liquid nitrogen into the work chamber by a microprocessor-based programmer with an associated temperature controller allowing pre- set linear cooling rates to be obtained. A resistance temperature probe situated within the work chamber detects temperature and the signal is fed to the controller and also to a digital display. A second temperature probe, also within the chamber, provides signal to the chart recorder for maintaining permanent record of the freezing cycle.

In order to overcome the disadvantage of proper identification of stored pellets and lack of repetition in freezing conditions, further studies were done in our laboratory by freezing ram semen in French plastic mini and medium straws. The protocol for cryopreservation of ram semen in straws is based on programmable freezing and computer-assisted sperm analysis (CASA) techniques (Joshi and Mathur, 1996; Mathur and Joshi, 1996; Joshi et al., 1998a; Bag et al., 1999; Joshi et al., 2001; Bag et al., 2002a, 2002b, 2004; Joshi et al., 2005). The main advantage of using this protocol is complete automation of the freezing and evaluation processes. The results were consistent and reproducible giving an average post-thaw recovery of 70% motile spermatozoa using rams of exotic (Joshi *et al.*, 1998b), crossbred (Bag et al., 1998; Joshi et al., 1998a; Bag et al., 2002a; 2004) or native breeds (Mathur and Joshi, 1996; Bag et al., 1999; Joshi et al., 2001; Bag et al., 2002a, 2004; Joshi et al., 2005). The high post-thaw recovery may be attributed to the criteria of processing only those ejaculates for cryopreservation which have thick consistency, rapid wave motion, 90% initial motility and >3000 x 10^6 spermatozoa per ml.

Recent studies have revealed that preservation techniques do not merely suspend spermatozoa in time, but induce sub-lethal damages that affect their functional capacity and making them behave very differently to fresh spermatozoa Many studies aimed to improve the fertility of preserved spermatozoa have addressed the issue by increasing the number of motile spermatozoa for insemination (Gillian et al., 2004). Frozen-thawed ram spermatozoa are immediately capable of penetrating oocytes whereas fresh spermatozoa require pre-incubation (Garde et al., 1993). This led Watson (1995) to suggest that the spermatozoa emerge from frozen storage in a state resembling that of capacitation having by-passed some of the normal development process. The observations of Gillan et al. (1997) that a high proportion of ram spermatozoa were capacitated after freezing and thawing compared to fresh spermatozoa confirmed the assumptions of Watson (1995). The premature capacitation as a consequence of freezing and thawing curtails the life span of frozen-thawed spermatozoa and they have a short time to achieve fertilization compared to fresh spermatozoa. There is also increased embryonic loss after insemination with preserved semen, which decreases the fertility. Furthermore, the advanced stage of development of embryos fertilized by spermatozoa that have bypassed normal capacitation process may result in abnormal embryo development (Gillan et al., 1997). An attempt to alter the membrane state was made by Maxwell et al. (1999) by post-thawing addition of seminal plasma to ram spermatozoa that resulted in less capacitation.

Moses et al. (1995) by computer-aided semen analysis (CASA) observed that sperm kinematics parameters were changed significantly after freezing and thawing of ram spermatozoa. Our studies on CASA have confirmed those observations (Joshi et al., 1998 a,b; Bag et al., 2002 a,b; 2004; Joshi et al. 2005, 2008; Kumar et al., in press b). It has been reported that there is a disruption to the axonemal elements of the tail (Watson, 1995) and this may not only reduce the number of motile spermatozoa but also affect the type of motility. The architecture of the mitochondria in the midpiece is altered during freezing and thawing resulting in a loss of structure and this damage has been shown to decrease the respiratory rate of spermatozoa (Windsor and White, 1995; Windsor, 1997). Using the fluorochrome rhodamine 123 (R123), which accumulates in the mitochondria of actively respiring spermatozoa, Gillan and Maxwell (1999) reported that the mitochondrial respiration of frozen-thawed spermatozoa decreases more rapidly than that of fresh spermatozoa when subject to thermal resistance test at 37°C. Also using R123, Windsor (1997) observed the effect of cryoinjury on mitochondrial respiration and demonstrated that mitochondrial respiration is important for ram spermatozoa to be able to successfully penetrate the cervix. Although at present it is not known how damage to mitochondria can be prevented, but it would be expected that methods that can avoid direct damage to spermatozoa or minimize the sub-lethal effects due to cryoinjury might be beneficial. There are reports that the proportion of double-stranded decreases after freezing and thawing (Gillian and Maxwell, 1999) and the surface area of the sperm head also decreases significantly possibly owing to the over condensation of the chromatin in the nucleus (Gravance et al., 1998). Freezing and thawing disrupts the stability of ram sperm chromatin, suggesting that the reduced fertilizing efficiency of cryopreserved semen *in vivo* might partly be due to abnormal DNA structure (Peris et al., 2004). Variation between individual animals in their ability to withstand the preservation process may be owing to the susceptibility of their DNA to the freeze-thawing induced damage to spermatozoa. This can be used to visualize differences in DNA sequences between individual rams classified as having poor, average and good post-thaw recovery of motile spermatozoa as assessed by CASA, plasma membrane integrity and acrosome integrity (Gillan et al., 2004).

There is a lack of information regarding lipid peroxidation and antioxidant capacity in cryopreserved ram semen. Cryopreservation is associated with the production of ROS which lead to lipid peroxidation of sperm membranes; resulting in a loss of motility, viability and fertility of sperm. It has been reported that addition of antioxidants generally could not maintain the level of antioxidant(s) following thawing of semen. The question regarding inexistence of consistency among antioxidative capacities following the thawing of ram semen still unanswered. Related to spermatozoal concentration, it may be possible that some antioxidant systems are destroyed during the freezing-thawing process. Changes in preservation protocols, extender formulations, antioxidant concentration and animal species may explain different behaviours of antioxidant capacities. Further studies are required to obtain more results on the determination of lipid peroxidation and antioxidant capacities in cryopreserved ram semen (Bucak et al., 2007).

New concepts of research to minimize stress during freezing

In a recent study it has been shown that ram sperm can be held at 5 degrees Celsius for up to 48 hours prior to freezing with no injurious effects on motility, membrane integrity, or fertilizing potential (Purdy, 2007). The purpose of this study was to determine the fertilizing capacity of ram semen collected at distant locations while being shipped to semen laboratory for cryopreservation. In our laboratory we have started programmable freezing from the ambient temperature itself at a slow rate simulating the slow cooling upto 5°C in a cold handling cabinet prior to the use of cell freezer. This step will allow the elimination of cold handling cabinet and large number of semen doses can be preserved under controlled rate cooling and freezing using a large capacity cell freezer. Moreover, the complete run of the freezing protocol in the cell freezer can make this reproducible at any time of the year and any research laboratory. For this step we have added an additional step in the existing protocol that allows the controlled rate of cooling up to 5°C.

Ram spermatozoa can tolerate a wide range of freezing rates (Watson and Martin, 1974; Fiser and Fairfull, 1986; 1989; Pontbriand et al., 1989; Kumar et al., 2003). In our study the overall cooling rate of straws achieved under uncontrolled conditions was approximately at the rate of 0.15°C per min from 25 to 5°C, which was close to the approximate cooling rate of 0.14°C per min reported by Morrier et al. (2002) on cooling straws from 30 to 5°C in the cold chamber. However, under uncontrolled conditions, cooling over the period of 135 min was not at a linear rate, commencing at the rate of 0.4°C per min from 25°C for 15 min, and continuing at the rate of 0.2°C per min for 15 min, 0.13°C per min for 60 min and thereafter progressed at the rate of

0.06°C per min for 45 min up to 5°C. Kumar et al. (2003) observed optimal cryosurvival of ram spermatozoa when cooled at the rate of 0.2°C per min from 22 to 5°C over a period of 90 min followed by freezing at the rate of 30°C per min from 5 to –50°C and concluded that careful control of the cooling and freezing rates are essential for maximal recovery of viable and functional cells. In our earlier studies we have observed higher post-thaw survival of sperm frozen at –125°C, compared to -25 or –75°C (Bag et al., 2002a; b). Similarly, the higher survival of post-thaw incubated sperm under controlled rate of cooling achieved might be attributed to lesser structural damage to frozen-thawed spermatozoa due to uniform cooling at the rate of 0.15°C from 25 to 5°C followed by freezing at the linear rate of 25°C per min from 5 to –125°C. The results indicated that controlled-rate (linear) cooling has a significant effect on post-thaw motility and acrosomal integrity of frozen-thawed ram spermatozoa, compared to uncontrolled-rate (non-linear) cooling prior to programmable freezing (Joshi et al., 2008; Kumar et al., in press).

In Israel a novel freezing technology based on "multi- thermal gradient (MTG) directional solidification for freezing bulk quantity of semen has been developed and patented (Arav, 1999). The semen in the test tube is moved in a constant velocity through a linear temperature gradient so that the cooling rate and ice front propagation are precisely monitored. The MTG apparatus is designed to control ice crystal propagation by changing the thermal gradient or the liquid- ice interface velocity and so it can optimise the ice- crystal morphology during freezing of semen (Arav et al., 2002a,b; Gacitua and Arav, 2005). Although acceptable post-thaw motility of ram spermatozoa has been reported with MTG protocol but it will be most applicable in future for banking frozen semen in large volumes. The use of large volume has advantages over that in small volumes in straws because it reduces wastage of semen during packaging and also allows insemination of large group of animals. However, freezing or thawing large volumes had problems associated with heat transfer that tend to cause varied cooling rates during cooling and recrystallization during warming. To overcome the problem of recrystallization during warming, the Israeli workers have also developed a new container (Hollow-Tube ™, IMT, Israel) that works by causing high temperature water to flow inside the tube causing uniform warming inspite of large volume (Gacitua and Arav, 2005).

Seminal plasma proteins: functions and interaction with protective agents during semen preservation for ameliorating stress

Seminal plasma is a complex mixture of secretions from the testes, epididymides and accessory sex glands (seminal vesicles, ampulla, prostate, bulbourethral glands). Despite its physiological significance as the carrier of spermatozoa to the female reproductive tract, the biochemical characteristics and physiological roles of the various seminal plasma proteins are poorly understood. While some seminal plasma proteins appear to be beneficial to sperm functions such as motility, capacitation, acrosome reaction, viability and/or sperm-egg interaction; others seem to be detrimental, particularly to sperm preservation (Manjunath and Therien, 2002; Bergeron and Manjunath, 2006).

In bovine, the major protein fraction of seminal plasma (30-50 mg/ml) constitutes a family of closely related proteins named BSP proteins (Manjunath, 1984; Manjunath and Sairam, 1987). Homologues of BSP proteins have been isolated and characterised in ram seminal plasma named as RSP (Bergeron et al., 2005; Jobim et al., 2005). These RSP proteins were designated RSP-15 kDa, RSP-16 kDa, RSP-22 kDa, and RSP-24 kDa. The BSP proteins and their homologs are a family of structurally related proteins characterized by the presence of tandem fibronectin type II domain (Manjunath et al., 2009). They bind to sperm membrane choline phospholipids at ejaculation. They also bind to capacitation factors, namely, high-density lipoproteins and glycosaminoglycans and promote sperm capacitation induced by these molecules, indicating their beneficial role in sperm function and fertility. In contrast to their beneficial role in sperm function, BSP proteins may be detrimental to sperm in the context of sperm storage. This is because BSP proteins stimulate cholesterol and phospholipids efflux from the sperm membrane in a time and concentration dependent manner (Therien et al., 1998, 1999). Therefore, continuous exposure of sperm to seminal plasma (as in the case of semen collected for *in vitro* storage) that contains BSP proteins, causes continuous cholesterol and phospholipid removal from the sperm membrane, which can render sperm very sensitive to storage in the liquid or the frozen states (Bergeron and Manjunath, 2006; Manjunath et al., 2007). Thus, BSP proteins are beneficial or detrimental to sperm depending on the concentration and duration of exposure. Interestingly, BSP proteins specifically bind low-density lipoproteins present in egg yolk, a compound commonly used in semen extenders. This interaction minimizes lipid removal from the sperm membrane, which positively influences sperm storage in liquid or frozen states (Bergeron et al., 2004). Therefore, BSP proteins in seminal plasma act like a double-edged sword, being both beneficial and detrimental to sperm (Manjunath et al., 2007).

Upon ejaculation, BSP proteins secreted by the seminal vesicles are added to sperm (Manjunath et al., 1994). BSP proteins then bind to the sperm membrane (Desnoyers and Manjunath, 1992; Manjunath et al., 1994) and induce cholesterol and phospholipid efflux (Therien et al., 1998, 1999). If semen is not diluted, sperm are continuously exposed to a high concentration of BSP proteins and the lipid removal continues, resulting in decreased sperm resistance to cold shock and freezing. Since ejaculates are diluted with egg yolk extenders within minutes after collection, low-density lipoproteins (LDL) sequestrate most of the BSP proteins present in semen. This could result in minimal modification of the sperm plasma membrane and allow better sperm storage. Thus, LDL may offer protection to sperm by reducing the deleterious effect of BSP proteins on the sperm membrane. A 50-80% less BSP proteins associate with sperm and concomitantly, lipid (cholesterol and phospholipid) efflux from the sperm membrane is prevented during storage when semen is diluted with egg yolk- or LDL-containing extenders (Bergeron et al., 2004). Consequently, sperm functions such as motility, acrosomal integrity and viability are protected. Since BSP proteins are involved in sperm capacitation and sperm binding to oviductal cells (Manjunath and Therien, 2002; Gwathmey et al., 2003, 2006), the decrease in sperm-bound BSP proteins in the presence of egg yolk extender may be one of the reasons why cryopreserved sperm have impaired fertility compared to fresh semen.

The addition of seminal plasma proteins to frozen–thawed ram spermatozoa improved sperm quality parameters (Ollero et al., 1997a; Maxwell et al., 2007; Rebolledo et al., 2007), reverted the cryodamage on the ram sperm membrane (Rebolledo et al., 2007) and prevented cold-shock membrane damage to ram spermatozoa (Perez-Pe et al., 2001; Colas et al., 2009), which was also reflected in increased fertility of spermatozoa (Rebolledo et al., 2007). Both protective and repairing effects are highly specific because neither BSP nor BSA has the ability to restore ram sperm membrane integrity (Garcý´a-Lo´ pez et al., 1996; Colas et al., 2009) and might be due to the antioxidant enzyme activity (Marti et al., 2007, 2008). Moreover, thermal denaturation of seminal plasma proteins removes these effects (Garcý´a-Lo´ pez et al., 1996), confirming that the active constituent(s) are proteinaceous. Seminal plasma lipoproteins are not involved in the recovering effect, because the addition of lipoproteins isolated from ram seminal plasma was unable to reverse the cold-shock-induced damage (Barrios et al., 2000). However, the fractionation of ram seminal plasma proteins by exclusion chromatography provided three fractions that are able to repair the damage (Barrios et al., 2000). Differences in composition between the separated fractions, characterized by polyacrylamide gel electrophoresis (SDS-PAGE), mainly resulted from two major bands of approximately 14 (P14) and 20 (P20) kDa, which must be responsible for the beneficial effects (Barrios et al., 2005). The protein profile in the same molecular weight range has been identified by several authors in ram seminal plasma of different breeds (Bergeron et al. 2005; Jobim et al., 2005; Maxwell et al., 2007). The major proteins in ram seminal plasma, which are able to protect and repair the cold-shock damage to sperm, contain fibronectin-II domain (Bergeron et al., 2005; Muino-Blanco et al., 2008).

Recently the presence of melatonin in ram seminal plasma and differences in its concentration in this fluid has been demonstrated between the breeding and non-breeding season. These results prove that melatonin has a direct effect on ram spermatozoa in the non-productive season. This can be explained, at least in part, by the melatonin capacity as a reactive oxygen species scavenger and antioxidant. These findings might help to select the optimal experimental conditions for IVF and to improve sperm preservation protocols (Casao et al., 2009). Melatonin treatment in rams during non-breeding season increases sperm progressive motility and number of spermatozoa bound to zona pellucida of immature oocytes, and also modifies other kinematic motility parameters. However, only the increase on progressive motility rate seemed to be related with a slight improvement of *in vivo* fertility rate. Further studies are required to determine if these results are the consequence of either a direct or indirect action of the pineal hormones on the spermatozoa (Casao et al., 2008a, b).

Advances in evaluation of ram semen subjected to stress during preservation

Sperm motility is one of the most important characteristics for evaluating the fertilizing potential of ejaculated and frozen-thawed spermatozoa. Although traditional semen quality evaluation procedures based on visual assessment are simple but the subjective nature of the method leads to variability of results between observers. Sperm motility assessed microscopically is not well correlated with either *in vivo* or *in vitro* fertilization due to human and technical limitations of the method for assessing detailed sperm movement characteristics. The objective methods of evaluating sperm motility based on CASA technique give better prediction of fertility (Saacke, 1982) and the results are ideal for comparison within and between research laboratories (Dunphy et al., 1989).

The three main factors those can provide erroneous CASA results are settings of the semen analyzer on the basis of sperm dimensions, sperm concentration and image digitization. CASA technique is accurate for objective measurements of sperm kinematics, if care is taken when preparing the semen samples and proper setting of the instrument. The results of CASA are inaccurate if the sperm count for analysis is below 20×10^6 sperm/ml or above 50 X 10^6 sperm/ml. Hence, it is necessary that all the samples should be diluted to approximately to the recommended range and the digitization rate along with the settings of the instrument are kept constant prior to CASA analysis for all the observations so as to ensure reliability and repeatability of the results. It is very important to identify the dilution medium that should not have any adverse effect on the sperm motion characteristics. Therefore, before interpretation of any CASA results it must be ensured that dilution medium does not influence any sperm motion attributes. Moreover, the time lapse between semen dilution and the CASA analysis should be short thereby enabling the spermatozoa to survive until completion of analysis. Apart from these three there are several other factors, which can also decide on the accuracy of the CASA results. The role of all these factors is very important for meeting the operational standards and comparability of automated semen analyzers (Davis and Katz, 1992, 1993).

Validated CASA procedures are now being applied in most laboratories during freezing of ram spermatozoa. Apart from identifying motile and static spermatozoa CASA can also categorize spermatozoa on the basis of velocity of each motile sperm. It also measures the mean sperm velocity and related sperm track dimensions (Edward et al., 1995; Holt and Palomo, 1996; Joshi et al., 2003; Kumar et al., 2007, Kumar et al., 2009; a, b *in press*). Moses et al. (1995) by CASA determined that sperm kinematics parameters changed significantly after freezing and thawing of ram spermatozoa. Our studies based on CASA observations have confirmed these observations. It has been observed that prior to freezing the sperm motility is high and almost all spermatozoa are rapidly motile. After thawing even if the motility may be $\geq$ 70 % and majority of the frozen-thawed sperms are rapidly motile but there are significant numbers of medium and slow moving sperms. CASA can also provide valuable information of the effect of post- thaw incubation on sperm kinematics of ram spermatozoa (Bag et al., 2002a, b; Bag et al., 2004; Joshi et al., 2005). Computer automated sperm- head morphology (ASMA) can also be performed with the analyzer that is equipped with additional morphometry software. The morphology option provides morphometry measurements for total, normal and abnormal sperms, number and percent of total, normal, bent and coiled tail sperms and number and percent of total, distal and proximal cytoplasmic droplets (Gravance et al., 1997; Rijsselaere et al., 2004).

Stress imposed during separation and preservation of sorted sperm

The development of sperm sexing technique has added new dimensions on semen processing for the associated uses of the semen (Evans et al., 2004). It is well documented that the only marker in sperm that can be effectively used for the separation of X and Y- bearing chromosome is DNA and the method used worldwide is a patented technique known as the 'Beltsville Sperm Sexing Technology'. The technique involves staining of DNA in the sperm nucleus with a DNA- permeant fluorescent dye bizbenzimide (Hoechst 33342) followed by excitation by a UV laser. The sperms are passed under pressure through an orienting nozzle in single file and the degree of fluorescence is measured optically as the sperms are sorted in which X chromosome bearing sperm fluoresce more brightly than Y chromosome bearing sperms (Johnson et al., 1989; Johnson et al., 1999). The complete sperm sorting process is not only time consuming but also factors like dilution, high pressure and mechanical stresses alter the functional integrity of sperms, while staining and UV exposure affect the integrity of sperm DNA (Garner, 2001; Evans et al., 2004). The sorting technique requires two stages of extensive semen dilution depending on the species. The first involves a 20- 1000 fold extension of the neat semen for staining and the second involves further final dilution of 200-30000 folds after passage through the flow cytometer, when the sorted spermatozoa combine with the sheath fluid in the collection tube. The overall influence of these factors can have an adverse effect on the viability and function of sorted sperms (Siedel and Garner, 2002; Hollinshead et al., 2003).

Freezing of sorted sperms require an additional step of reconcentration by centrifugation to enable packaging thereby imposing additional stress to the sperm. Inspite of these steps samples of sexed sperm with high proportion of motile and acrosome intact sperm can be obtained from frozen ram sperm (O'Brien et al., 2003). Standard freezing protocols have been modified for post-sorting cryopreservation of sperm (Evans et al., 2004). For sorted ram sperm no difference was observed in post-thaw motility or pregnancy rate of inseminated ewes after freezing sorted sperm in either Zwitterion or Test-yolk-buffered freezing media (Hollinshead et al., 2002). The ability of these samples to bring about conception *in vivo* has not been reported but lambs have been born after frozen semen has been thawed, sorted, refrozen, thawed and used following *in vitro* fertilization and transfer of resultant embryos to surrogate dams (Hollinshead et al., 2002; Hollinshead et al., 2004b). The high cost of the sperm flow cytometry sorter and skilled personnel presently restrict the widespread use of this technology in small ruminants. The central location of any such facility will require transport of semen in special media for which short-term liquid storage of semen before and after sorting holds promise. The future use of this technology lies in conjunction with MOET, AI and associated reproductive technologies those are expected to provide a large scope for more efficient use of sexed sperm for specialized research program (Maxwell et al., 2004). High-purity sorting of frozen-thawed spermatozoa for immediate use or re-cryopreservation for later use would enhance the commercial and conservation applications of sperm sexing technology.

Summary

Ram spermatozoa undergo several stresses during semen preservation. It is essential to systematically study the basic ramifications of ram sperm that are undergoing several stresses during semen collection and dilution, cooling below physiological temperatures in the presence of cryoprotective agents; and thawing from -196°C to physiological or slightly elevated temperature. Semen can be collected from donor rams by using artificial vagina or electroejaculation. Electroejaculation could be a useful procedure but has attracted adverse comments on welfare grounds. The major factor contributing to the disruption of cellular function in sperm during storage at near ambient conditions is the formation of reactive oxygen species (ROS). ROS on one hand are required for maturation, capacitation and acrosome reaction but on the other hand they combine with several peroxidable cellular components and transform them into oxygen-based deleterious products. The maintenance of a suitable ROS level is, therefore, essential for adequate sperm functionality. Since sperm do not possess any internal repair mechanism against cellular damage, an environment where damage can be minimized is essential to protect it from ROS-induced damage. Reducing the oxidative stresses through the use of antioxidant and chelating agents can increase the short-term storage ability of ram sperm in liquid suspension. Unlike some mammalian species, ram spermatozoa are susceptible to various stresses during freezing and thawing. Premature capacitation as a consequence of freezing and thawing curtails the life span of frozen-thawed spermatozoa. Addition of antioxidants generally does not maintain the level of antioxidant(s) following thawing of semen. The seminal plasma (BSP) proteins bind to capacitation factors, namely, high-density lipoproteins and glycosaminoglycans and promote sperm capacitation, indicating their beneficial role in sperm function and fertility. In contrast to their beneficial role in sperm function, BSP proteins may be detrimental to sperm in the context of sperm storage as they also stimulate cholesterol and phospholipids efflux from the sperm membrane in a time and concentration dependent manner. Continuous exposure of sperm to seminal plasma that contains BSP proteins can render sperm very sensitive to storage in the liquid or the frozen states. Recently the presence of melatonin in ram seminal plasma and differences in its concentration in this fluid has been demonstrated between the breeding and non-breeding season. Melatonin has a capacity to act as a ROS scavenger and antioxidant. Further studies are still required to determine if there is either a direct or indirect action of the pineal hormones on the spermatozoa. The development of sperm sexing technique has added new dimensions on semen processing for the associated uses of the semen. The sperm sorting process is not only time consuming but also factors namely; dilution rate, high pressure and mechanical stresses alter the functional integrity of sperms; while staining and UV exposure affect the integrity of sperm DNA. Freezing of sorted sperms require an additional step of reconcentration by centrifugation to enable packaging thereby imposing additional stress to the sperm. Inspite of these steps samples of sexed sperm with high proportion of motile and acrosome intact sperm can be obtained from frozen ram sperm. The ability of these samples to bring about conception *in vivo* has not been reported but lambs have been born after frozen semen has been thawed, sorted, refrozen, thawed and used following *in vitro* fertilization and transfer of resultant embryos to surrogate dams.

References

Abdelhakeam, A. A., Graham, E. F., Vazquez, I. A. and Chaloner, K. M. 1991. Studies on the absence of glycerol in unfrozen and frozen ram semen. Cryobiology 28, 43-49.

Aisen, E. G., Alvarez, H. L., Venturino, A. and Garde, J. J. 2000. Effect of trehalose and EDTA on cryoprotective action of ram semen diluents. Theriogenology 53, 1053-1061.

Anel, L., Alvarez, M., Martinez-Pastor, F., Garcia-Macias, V., Anel, E. and de Paz, P. 2006. Improvement Strategies in Ovine Artificial Insemination. Reproduction in Domestic Animals 41 (Suppl. 2): 30-42.

Arav, A. 1999. Device and methods for multigradient directional cooling and warming of biological samples. US Patent 5 873 254.

Arav, A., Yavin, S., Zeron, Y., Natan, D., Dekel, I and Gacitua, H. 2002 a. New trends in gametes cryopreservation. Molecular and Cellular Endocrinology 187, 77- 81.

Arav, A., Zeron, Y., Shturman, H., Zeron, Y. and Gacitua, H. 2002 b. Successful pregnancies in cows following double freezing on large volume of semen. Reproduction Nutrition Development 42, 1- 4.

Bag, S., Joshi, A., Mathur, A. K. and Mittal, J. P. 1998. Controlled freezing and automated evaluation of frozen-thawed ram spermatozoa packaged in 0.5 ml straws. Indian Journal of Animal Reproduction 19, 136-139.

Bag, S., Joshi, A., Mathur, A. K., Rawat, P. S. and Mittal, J.P. 1999. Effect of thawing temperature on motion characteristics of frozen-thawed ram spermatozoa. Indian Journal of Animal Science 69, 16-18.

Bag, S., Joshi, A., Naqvi, S.M.K and Mittal, J.P. 2004. Effect of post-thawing incubation on sperm kinematics and acrosomal integrity of ram spermatozoa cryopreserved in medium-sized French straws. Theriogenology 62: 415-424.

Bag, S., Joshi, A., Naqvi, S.M.K., Rawat, P.S. and Mittal, J.P. 2002b. Effect of freezing temperature at which straws were plunged in to liquid nitrogen, on post thaw motility and acrosomal status of ram spermatozoa. Animal Reproduction Science 72: 175-183.

Bag, S., Joshi, A., Rawat, P.S. and Mittal, J.P. 2002a. Effect of initial freezing temperature on the semen characteristics of frozen-thawed ram spermatozoa. Small Ruminant Research 43: 23-29.

Bailey, J.L., Bilodeau, J.F. and Cormier, N. 2000. Semen cryopreservation in domestic animals: A damaging and capacitating phenomenon. Journal of Andrology 21: 1-7.

Barbas, J.P. and Mascarenhas, R.D. 2009. Cryopreservation of domestic animal sperm cells. Cell Tissue Bank 10: 49–62.

Barrios, B., Fernandez-Juan, M., Muino-Blanco, T. and Cebrian-Perez, J. 2005: Immunocytochemical localization and biochemical characterization of two seminal plasma proteins that protect ram spermatozoa against cold shock. Journal of Andrology 26: 539–549.

Barrios, B., Perez-Pe, R., Gallego, M., Tato, A., Osada, J., Muino- Blanco, T. and Cebrian-Perez, J.A. 2000. Seminal plasma proteins revert the cold-shock damage on ram sperm membrane. Biology of Reproduction 63: 1531–1537.

Benaroudj, N., Lee, D.H. and Goldberg, A.L. 2001. Trehalose accumulation during cellular stress protects cells and cellular proteins from damage by oxygen radicals. Journal of Biological Chemistry 276: 24261–24267.

Bergeron, A. and Manjunath, P. 2006. New insights towards understanding the mechanism of sperm protection by egg yolk and milk. Molecular Reproduction and Development 73: 1338-1344.

Bergeron, A., Crete, M.H., Brindle, Y. and Manjunath, P. 2004. Low-density lipoprotein fraction from hen's egg yolk decreases the binding of the major proteins of bovine seminal plasma to sperm and prevents lipid efflux from the sperm membrane. Biology of Reproduction 70: 708-717.

Bergeron, A., Villemure, M., Lazure, C. and Manjunath, P. 2005. Isolation and characterization of the major proteins of ram seminal plasma. Molecular Reproduction and Development 71: 461-470.

Bucak, M.N., Atessahin, A., Varish, O., Yuce, A., Tekin, N. and Akcay, A. 2007. The influence of trehalose, taurine, cysteamine and hyaluronan on ram semen, Microscopic and oxidative stress parameters after freeze-thawing process. Theriogenology 67: 1060-1067.

Casao, A., Mendoza, N., Perez-Pe, R., Grasa, P., Abecia, J.A., Foreada, F., Cebrian-Perez, J.A., and Muino-Blanco, T. 2008a. Melatonin prevents capacitaion and apoptotic-like changes of ram spermatozoa and increases fertility rate. Journal of Pineal Research doi: 10.1111/j.1600-079x.2009.00722.x

Casao, A., Vega, S., Palacin, I., Perez-Pe, R., Lavina, A., Quintin, F.J., Sevilla, E., Abecia, J.A., Cebrian-Perez, J.A., Foreada, F. and Muino-Blanco, T. 2008b. Effects of melatonin implants during non-breeding season on sperm motility and reproductive parameters in Rasa Aragonesa rams. Reproduction in Domestic Animals doi: 10.1111/j.1439-0531.2008.01215.x

Colas, C., Junquera, C., Perez-Pe, R., Cebrian-Perez, J.A. and Muino-Blanco, T. 2009. Ultrastructural study of the ability of seminal plasma proteins to protect ram spermatozoa against cold-shock. Microscopy Research and technique 72: 566-572.

Curry, M.R. and Watson, P.F. 1994. Osmotic effects on ram and human sperm membranes in relation to thawing injury. Cryobiology 31: 39–46.

Curry, M.R. 2000. Cryopreservation of semen from domestic livestock. Review of Reproduction 5: 46-52.

Davis, R. O and Katz, D. F., 1992. Standardization and comparability of CASA instruments. Journal of Andrology 13, 81- 85.

Davis, R. O and Katz, D. F., 1993. Operational standards for CASA instruments. Journal of Andrology 14, 385- 394.

de Lamirande, E., Jiang, H., Zini, A., Kodama, H. and Gagnon, C. 1997. Reactive oxygen species and sperm physiology. Review of Reproduction 2: 48–54.

Desnoyers, L. and Manjunath, P. 1992. Major proteins of bovine seminal plasma exhibit novel interactions with phospholipid. Journal of Biological Chemistry 267: 10149-10155.

Duncan, A.E. and Watson, P.F. 1992. Predictive water loss curves for ram spermatozoa during cryopreservation: comparison with experimental observations. Cryobiology 29: 95–105.

Dunphy, B.C., Kay, R., Barratt, C.L.R and Cooke, I.D. 1989. Quality control during the conventional analysis of semen, an essential exercise. Journal of Andrology 10, 378- 385.

Edward, A. Y., Windsor, D. P., Purvis, I. W., Sanchez-Partida, L. G. and Maxwell, W. M. C. 1995. Distribution of variance associated with measurement of post- thaw function in ram sperm. Reproduction Fertility and Development 7,129- 134.

Ehling, C., Rath, D., Struckmann, C., Frenzel, A., Schindler, L. and Niemann, H. 2006. Utilization of frozen–thawed epididymal ram semen to preserve genetic diversity in Scrapie susceptible sheep breeds. Theriogenology 66: 2160–2164.

Eppleston, J. and Maxwell, W. M. C.1993. Recent attempts to improve the fertility of frozen ram semen inseminated into the cervix. Wool Technology and Sheep Breeding 41, 291-302.

Evans, G. 1988. Current topics in artificial insemination of sheep. Australian Journal of Biological Sciences 41: 103-116.

Evans, G., Hollinshead, F.K. and Maxwell, W.M.C. 2004. Preservation and artificial insemination of sexed semen in sheep. Reproduction Fertility and Development 16: 455-464.

Fernandez-Santos, M.R., Esteso, M.C., Montoro, V., Soler, A.J. and Garde, J.J. 2006. Cryopreservation of Iberian red deer (*Cervus elaphus hispanicus*) epididymal spermatozoa: effects of egg yolk, glycerol and cooling rate. Theriogenology 66: 1931–1942.

Fiser, P. S. and Fairfull, R. W. 1986. Combined effects of glycerol concentration, cooling velocity and osmolality of skim milk diluents on cryopreservation of ram spermatozoa. Theriogenology 25: 473-484.

Fiser, P. S. and Fairfull, R. W. 1989. The effect of glycerol-related osmotic changes on post-thaw motility and acrosomal integrity of ram spermatozoa. Cryobiology 26: 64-69.

Foote, R.H. 2002. The history of artificial insemination: selected notes and notables. Journal of Animal Science 80 (electronic suppl 2).

Gacitua, H. and Arav, A. 2005. Successful pregnancies with directional freezing of large volume buck semen. Theriogenology 63, 931- 938.

Garcýa-Lopez, N., Ollero, M., Cebrian-Perez, J.A. and Muino-Blanco, T. 1996. Reversion of thermic-shock effect on ram spermatozoa by adsorption of seminal plasma proteins revealed by partition in aqueous two-phase systems. Journal of Chromatography B 680: 137–143.

Garde, J., Gutierrez, A., Artiga, C. G. and Vazquez, I. 1993. Influence of freezing process on in vitro capacitation of ram semen. Theriogenology 39, 225.

Garner, D. L. 2001. Sex-sorting mammalian sperm: concept to application in animals. Journal of Andrology 22, 519- 526.

Gil, J., Soderquist, L and Rodriguez-Martinez. 2000. Influence of centrifugation and different extenders on post-thaw sperm quality of ram semen. Theriogenology 54, 93-108.

Gillan, L. and Maxwell, W.M.C. 1999. The functional integrity and fate of cryopreserved semen in the female tract. Journal of Reproduction and Fertility (Suppl) 54: 271-283.

Gillan, L., Evans, G. and Maxwell, W. M. C. 1997. Capacitation status and fertility of fresh and frozen-thawed ram spermatozoa. Reproduction Fertility and Development 9, 481-487.

Gillan, L., Maxwell, W.M.C. and Evans, G. 2004. Preservation and evaluation of semen for artificial insemination. Reproduction Fertility Development 16: 447-454.

Gonzalez, C. I. M., Oba, E., Bicudo, S. D. and Souza, M. I. L. 1996. Cryopreservation of semen of ideal rams with egg yolk-milk extender. 13th International Congress on Animal Reproduction, Sydney, Vol 3, p 2-9.

Graham, E. F., Crabo, B. G. and Pace, M. M. 1978. Current status of semen preservation in the ram, boar and stallion. Journal of Animal Sciences 47 (Suppl): 8-103.

Gravance, C. G., Vishwanath, R., Pitt, C., Garner, D. L and Casey, P. J. 1998. Effects of cryopreservation on bull sperm head morphometry. Journal of Andrology 19, 704-709.

Gravance, C. G., White, C., Robertson, K. R., Champion, Z. J and Casey, P. J. 1997. The effects of cryopreservation on the morphometric dimensions of caprine sperm heads. Animal Reproduction Science 49, 37- 43.

Gwathmey, T.M., Ignotz, G.G. and Suarez, S.S. 2003. PDC-109 (BSP-A1/A2) promotes bull sperm binding to oviductal epithelium in vitro and may be involved in forming the oviductal sperm reservoir. Biology of Reproduction 69: 809-815.

Gwathmey, T.M., Ignotz, G.G., Mueller, J.L., Manjunath, P. and Suarez, S.S. 2006. Bovine seminal plasma proteins PDC-109, BSP-A3, and BSP-30- kDa share functional roles in storing sperm in the oviduct. Biology of Reproduction 75: 501-507.

Halbert, G.W., Dobson, H., Walton, J.S. and Buckrell, B.C. 1990. The structure of the cervical canal of ewe. Theriogenology 33: 977-992.

Hammerstedt, R. and Parks, J. 1987. Changes in sperm surfaces associated with epididymal transit. Journal of Reproduction and Fertility (Suppl) 34: 133–149.

Hishinuma, M., Suzuki, K. and Sekine, J. 2003. Recovery and cryopreservation of sika deer (Cervus nippon) spermatozoa from epididymides stored at 4 degrees C. Theriogenology 59: 813–820.

Hollinshead, F. K., Evans, G., Evans, K. M., Catt, S. L., Maxwell, W. M. C. and O'Brien, J. K. 2004 a. Birth of lambs of a pre-determined sex after in vitro production of embryos using frozen-thawed sex-sorted and re-frozen-thawed ram spermatozoa. Reproduction 127, 557- 568.

Hollinshead, F. K., Gillan, L., O'Brien, J. K., Evans, G. and Maxwell, W. M. C. 2003. In vitro and in vivo assessment of the functional capacity of flow cytometrically sorted ram spermatozoa after freezing and thawing. Reproduction Fertility and Development 15, 351- 359.

Hollinshead, F. K., O'Brien, J. K., Gillan, L., Meyers, M., Maxwell, W. M. C and Evans, G. 2004 b. Liquid storage of flow cytometrically sorted ram spermatozoa, Theriogenology 62, 587- 605.

Hollinshead, F. K., O'Brien, J. K., Maxwell, W. M. C and Evans, G. 2002. Production of lambs of pre-determined sex after the insemination of ewes with low numbers of X- or Y-chromosome bearing spermatozoa. Reproduction Fertility and Development 14, 503- 508.

Holt, W.V. 1997. Alternative strategies for the long-term preservation of spermatozoa. Reproduction Fertility and Development 9: 309–319.

Holt, W.V and North, R.D. 1994. Effects of temperature and restoration of osmotic equilibrium during thawing on the induction of plasma membrane damage in cryopreserved ram spermatozoa. Biology of Reproduction 51: 414-424.

Holt, W. V and Palomo, M. J. 1996. Optimization of a continuous real- time computerized semen analysis system for ram sperm motility assessment and evaluation of four methods of semen preparation. Reproduction Fertility and Development 8, 219-230.

Holt, W.V, Head, M.F. and North, R.D. 1992. Freeze-induced membrane damage in ram spermatozoa is manifested after thawing: Observation with experimental cryomicroscopy. Biology of Reproduction 46: 1086-1094.

Jobim, M.I., Oberst, E.R., Salbego, C.G., Wald, V.B., Horn, A.P. and Mattos, R.C. 2005. BSP A1 / A2-like proteins in ram seminal plasma. Theriogenology 63: 2053–2062.

Johnson, L. A., Flook, J. P. and Hawk, H. W. 1989. Sex preselection in rabbits: live births from X and Y sperm separated by DNA and cell sorting. Biology of Reproduction 41, 199- 203.

Johnson, L. A., Welch, G. R. and Wim, R. 1999. The Beltsville sperm sexing technology: High- speed sperm sorting gives improved sperm output for in vitro fertilization and AI. Journal of Animal Science 82, 213- 220.

Joshi, A. and Mathur, A. K. 1994. Influence of freezing rate on post-thaw motility and velocity of ram spermatozoa. In: Proceedings of the 7th International Symposium on Spermatology, Cairns, Australia, pp 9.3-9.4.

Joshi, A. and Mathur, A. K. 1996. Assessment of sperm kinematics of frozen-thawed ram spermatozoa. Indian Journal of Animal Reproduction 17, 42-44.

Joshi, A. Mathur, A.K., Naqvi, S.M.K. and Mittal, J.P. 2006. Influence of osmolality of complete semen extender on motion characteristics of frozen-thawed ram spermatozoa. Asian-Australasian Journal of Animal Sciences 19: 1716-1721.

Joshi, A., Bag, S. and Mittal, J. P. 1998 a. Freezability of ram spermatozoa packaged in mini and medium size straws. In: Proceedings of 8th World Conference of Animal Production Seoul, Korea, OR 1-13, pp 258-259.

Joshi, A., Bag, S., Mathur, A. K., Rawat, P. S. and Mittal, J. P. 2000. Effect of osmolality of Test-yolk-glycerol extender on motion characteristics of frozen-thawed ram spermatozoa. In: Proceedings of the 14th International Congress of Animal Reproduction, Stockholm, Sweden, 2, 132.

Joshi, A., Bag, S., Naqvi, S.M.K., Sharma, R.C. and Mittal, J.P. 2005. Effect of post-thawing incubation on sperm motility and acrosomal integrity of cryopreserved Garole ram semen. Small Ruminant Research 56: 231-238.

Joshi, A., Bag, S., Naqvi, S.M.K., Sharma, R.C., Rawat, P.S. and Mittal, J.P. 2001. Effect of short-term and long-term preservation on motion characteristics of Garole ram spermatozoa: A prolific microsheep breed of India. Asian-Australasian Journal of Animal Sciences 14: 1527-1533.

Joshi, A., Bag, S., Rawat, P. S. and Mittal, J. P. 1998 b. Influence of storage period on motion characteristics of frozen-thawed Awassi ram spermatozoa. Indian Journal of Animal Science 68, 1032-1033.

Joshi, A., Kumar, D., Naqvi, S.M.K. and Maurya, V.P. 2008. Effect of controlled and uncontrolled rate of cooling, prior to controlled rate of freezing, on motion characteristics and acrosomal integrity of cryopreserved ram spermatozoa. Cell Preservation Technology 6: 277-284.

Joshi, A., Naqvi, S.M.K., Bag, S., Dang, A.K., Sharma, R.C., Rawat, P.S. and Mittal, J.P. 2003. Sperm motion characteristics of Garole rams raised for a prolonged period in a semi-arid tropical environment. Tropical Animal Health and Production 35: 249-257.

Kanias, T. and Acker, J.P. 2006. Mammalian cell desiccation: facing the challenges. Cell Preservation Technology 4: 253–277.

Kumar D., Joshi A. and Naqvi S.M.K. 2009. Sperm motion characteristics of Malpura ram lambs reared under semi-arid tropical environment. Tropical Animal Health and Production DOI: 10.1007/s11250-009-9472-y

Kumar D., Joshi A. and Naqvi S.M.K. a. Effect of post-thaw incubation on motion characteristics and acrosomal integrity of ram spermatozoa, cryopreserved in straws under controlled and uncontrolled rate of cooling, prior to controlled rate of freezing. Animal Reproduction (In press)

Kumar, D., Joshi, A. and Naqvi, S.M.K. b. Comparative Semen Evaluation of Malpura and Bharat Merino Rams by Computer-aided Sperm Analysis Technique under Semi-Arid Tropical Environment. International Journal of Animal and Veterinary Advances (In press).

Kumar, D., Joshi, A., Naqvi, S.M.K., Kumar, S., Mishra, A.K., Maurya, V.P., Arora, A.L., Mittal, J.P. and Singh, V.K. 2007. Sperm motion characteristics of Garole X Malpura sheep evolved in a semi arid tropical environment through introgression of FecB gene. Animal Reproduction Science 100: 51-60.

Kumar, S., Millar, J.D. and Watson, P.F. 2003. The effect of cooling rate on the survival of cryopreserved bull, ram and boar spermatozoa: a comparison of two controlled-rate cooling machines. Cryobiology 46: 246-253.

Manjunath, P. 1984. Gonadotropin release stimulatory and inhibitory proteins in bull seminal plasma. In: Gonadal Proteins and Peptides and their Biological Significance, Edited by Sairam, M.R. and Atkinson, L.E., World Science Publishing, Singapore, pp. 49-61.

Manjunath, P. and Sairam, M.R. 1987. Purification and biochemical characterization of three major acidic proteins (BSP-A1, BSP-A2 and BSP-A3) from bovine seminal plasma. Biochemical Journal 241: 685-692.

Manjunath, P. and Therien, I. 2002. Role of seminal plasma phospholipid-binding proteins in sperm membrane lipid modification that occurs during capacitation. Journal of Reproductive Immunology 53: 109-119.

Manjunath, P., Bergeron, A., Lefebvre, J. and Fan, J. 2007. Seminal plasma proteins: functions and interaction with protective agents during semen preservation. In: Spermatology, Edited by Roldan, E.R.S. and Gomendio, M., Nottingham, pp. 217-228.

Manjunath, P., Chandonnet, L., Leblond, E. and Desnoyers, L. 1994. Major proteins of bovine seminal vesicles bind to spermatozoa. Biology of Reproduction 50: 27-37.

Manjunath, P., Lefebvre, J., Jois, P.S., Fan, J. and Wright, M.W. 2009. New Nomenclature for Mammalian BSP Genes1. Biology of Reproduction 80: 394–397.

Marco-Jimenez, F., Puchades, S., Gadea, J., Vicente, J.S. and Viudes-de-Castro, M.P. 2005. Effect of semen collection method on pre- and post-thaw Guirra ram spermatozoa. Theriogenology 64: 1756–1765.

Marti, E., Mara, L., Marti, J.I., Munio-Blanco, T. and Cebrian-Perez, J.A. 2007. Seasonal variations in antioxidant enzyme activity in ram seminal plasma. Theriogenology 67: 1446-1454.

Marti, E., Marti, J.I., Munio-Blanco, T. and Cebrian-Perez, J.A. 2008. Effect of cryopreservation process on the activity and immunolocalization of antioxidant enzymes in ram spermatozoa. Journal of Andrology 29: 459-467.

Mathur, A. K. and Joshi, A. 1996. Freezability of ram spermatozoa in organic amine-based semen diluents. In: Proceedings of13th International Congress of Animal Reproduction, Sydney, Australia, June 30th to July 4th, P 2-10.

Mathur, A. K., Srivastava, R. S., Joshi, A. and Kalra, D. B. 1991. Cryopreservation of ram semen in Egg yolk lactose raffinose citrate glycerol extender. International Journal of Animal Science 6, 79-81.

Maxwell, W.M.C. 1984. Current problems and future potential of artificial insemination programmes. In: Reproduction in Sheep. (Eds Lindsay D R and Pearce D T), Cambridge Press, Cambridge, pp. 291-298.

Maxwell, W.M.C. and Salamon, S. 1993. Liquid storage of ram semen: A review. Reproduction Fertility and Devlopment 5: 613-638.

Maxwell, W.M.C. and Watson, P.F. 1996. Recent progress in the preservation of ram semen. Animal Reproduction Science 42: 55-65.

Maxwell, W. M. C., Evans, G., Hollinshead, F. K., Bathgate, R., De Graaf, S. P., Eriksson, B. M., Gillan, L., Morton, K. M. and O,Brien, J. K. 2004. Integration of sperm sexing technology in to the ART toolbox. Animal Reproduction Science 82-83, 79- 95.

Maxwell, W. M. C., Evans., Mortimer, S. T., Gillan, L., Gellatly, E. S. and McPhie, C. A. 1999. Normal fertility in ewes after cervical insemination with frozen-thawed spermatozoa supplemented with seminal plasma. Reproduction Fertility and Development 11, 123-126.

Maxwell, W.M.C., de Graaf, S.P., Ghaoui, R.E.H. and Evans, G. 2007. Seminal plasma effects on sperm handling and female fertility. Society of Reproduction and Fertility Supplement 64: 13–38.

Moses, D. F., de las Heras, M. A., Valcarel, A., Perez, L and Baldassarre, H. 1995. Use of computerized motility analyser for the evaluation of frozen-thawed ram spermatozoa. Andrologia 27, 25-29.

Muino-Blanco, T., Perez-Pe, R. and Cebrian-Perez, J.A. 2008. Seminal Plasma Proteins and Sperm Resistance to Stress. Reproduction in Domestic Animals 43: 18–31.

Naqvi, S. M. K., Joshi, A., Bag, S., Pareek, S. R. and Mittal, J. P. 1998. Cervical penetration and transcervical AI of tropical sheep (Malpura) at natural estrus using frozen-thawed semen. Technical Note. Small Ruminant Research 29, 329-333.

Naqvi, S.M.K., Joshi, A., Das, G.K. and Mittal, J.P. 2001. Development and application of ovine reproductive technologies: an Indian experience. Small Ruminant Research 39: 199-208.

Nel-Themaat, L., Harding, G.D., Chandler, J.E., Chenevert, J.F., Damiani, P., Fernandez, J.M., Humes, P.E., Pope, C.E. and Godke, R.A. 2006. Quality and freezing qualities of first and second ejaculates collected from endangered Gulf Coast Native rams. Animal Reproduction Science 95: 251–261.

O'Brien, J. K., Hollinshead, F. K., Evans, K. M., Evans, G. and Maxwell, W. M. C. 2003. Flow cytometric sorting of frozen- thawed spermatozoa in sheep and non-human primates. Reproduction Fertility and Development 15, 367- 375.

Ollero, M., Cebrian-Perez, J.A., Muino-Blanco, T. 1997. Improvement of cryopreserved ram sperm heterogeneity and viability by addition of seminal plasma. Journal of Andrology 18: 732–739.

Paulenz, H., Soderquist, L., Adnoy, T., Nordstoga. A., Gulbrandsen, B and Berg, K. A. 2004. Fertility results after different thawing procedures for ram semen frozen in minitubes and mini straws. Theriogenology 61,1719-1727.

Payne, S. R., Oliver, J. E. and Upreti, G. C. 1994. Effect of antifreeze proteins on the motility of ram spermatozoa. Cryobiology 31,180-184.

Perez-Pe, R., Cebrian-Perez, J.A. and Muino-Blanco, T. 2001. Seminal plasma proteins prevent cold-shock membrane damage to ram spermatozoa. Theriogenology 56: 425-434.

Peris, S.I., Morrier, A., Dufour, M. and Bailey, J.L. 2004. Cryopreservation of ram semen facilitates sperm DNA damage: Relationship between sperm andrological parameters and the sperm chromatin structure assay. Journal of Andology 25: 224-233.

Phillips, P. H. 1939. Preservation of bull semen. Journal of Biological Chemistry 130: 415.

Polge, C., Smith, A. U. and Parkes, A. S. 1949. Revival of spermatozoa after vitrification and dehydration at low temperatures. Nature 164: 666.

Pontbriand, D., Howard, J.G., Schiewe, M.C., Stuart, L.D. and Wildt, D.E. 1989. Effect of cryoprotective diluent and method of freeze-thawing on survival and acrosomal integrity of ram spermatozoa. Cryobiology 26: 341-354.

Purdy, P. H. 2007. Preserving ram semen: New science shows it can be stored for up to two days before freezing. Sheep Magazine March 1, pp.40-41.

Rebolledo, A.D., Sierra, L.N., Tamayo, A.C., Loria, A.A., Denis, S.E., Oses, R.B., Parra, E.G., Monsreal, L.P., Ugalde, J.R. 2007. Fertility in hair sheep inseminated with freeze spermatozoa rediluted with seminal plasma. Rev Cient Fac Cienc Veter 17: 73–76.

Rijsselaere, T., Soom, A. V., Hoflack, G., Maes, D and de Kruif, A. 2004. Automated sperm morphometry and morphology analysis of canine semen by the Hamilton-Thorne analyser. Theriogenology 62, 1292- 1306.

Saacke, R. G. 1982. Components of semen quality. Journal of Animal Science 55 (Suppl 2), 1- 13.

Sadler, R.M.F.S. 1966. The preservation of mammalian spermatozoa by freezing. Laboratory Practicals 15: 413.

Salamon S, Gillan L, Evans G and Maxwell W M C. 1996. Fertility of ram semen after long-term frozen storage. Proceeding of the 13th International Congress on Animal Reproduction, Sydney, Australia, Vol 3 , P 24-25

Salamon S, Gillan L, Evans G and Maxwell W M C. 2004. Fertility of ram semen after 35 years of frozen storage. In:Proceedings of the 15th International Congress on Animal Reproduction, Porto Segura, Brazil.

Salamon, S. and Maxwell, W.M.C. 1995 a. Frozen storage of ram semen. I. Processing, freezing, thawing and fertility after cervical insemination. Animal Reproduction Science 37: 185-249.

Salamon, S. and Maxwell, W.M.C. 1995 b. Frozen storage of ram semen. II. Causes of low fertility after cervical insemination and methods of improvement. Animal Reproduction Science 38: 1-36.

Salamon, S. and Maxwell, W.M.C. 2000. Storage of ram semen. Animal Reproduction Science 62: 77-111.

Sanchez-Partida, L. G., Maxwell, W. M. C. and Palez, L. G. 1992. Proline and glycine betaine in cryoprotective diluents for ram spermatozoa. Reproduction Fertility and Development 4, 113-118.

Schmehl, M.K., Anderson, S.P., Vazques, I.A. and Graham, E.F. 1986. The effect of dialysis of extended ram semen prior to freezing on post-thaw survival and fertility. Cryobiology 23: 406-414.

Seidel, G. E. Jr and Garner, D. L. 2002. Current status of sexing mammalian spermatozoa. Reproduction and Fertility 124, 733- 743.

Sitaula, R., Guo, M. and Bhowmick, S. 2009. Developing Predictive Tool for ROS Damage During Bovine Sperm Storage at Ambient Temperature. Biopreservation and Biobanking doi: 10.1089/bio.2009.0004

Soderquist, L., Madrid-Bury, N. and Rodriguez-Martinez. 1997. Assessment of ram sperm membrane integrity following different thawing procedures. Theriogenology 48,1115-1125.

Therien, I., Moreau, R. and Manjunath, P. 1998. Major proteins of bovine seminal plasma and high-density lipoprotein induce cholesterol efflux from epididymal sperm. Biology of Reproduction 59: 768-776.

Therien, I., Moreau, R. and Manjunath, P. 1999. Bovine seminal plasma phospholipid-binding proteins stimulate phospholipid efflux from epididymal sperm. Biology of Reproduction 61: 590-598.

Valcarel, A., de las Heras, M. A., Moses, D. F., Perez, L. J. and Baldassarre, H. 1996. Comparison between Sephadex G-10 and percoll for preparation of normospermic, asthenospermic and frozen/thawed ram semen. Animal Reproduction Science 41, 215-224.

Varisli, O., Uguzb, C., Agcac, C. and Agcac, Y. 2009. Motility and acrosomal integrity comparisons between electro-ejaculated and epididymal ram sperm after exposure to a range of anisosmotic solutions, cryoprotective agents and low temperatures. Animal Reproduction Science 110: 256–268.

Vishwanath, R. and Shannon, P. 1997. Do sperm cells age? A review of the physiological changes in sperm during storage at ambient temperature. Reproduction Fertility Development 9: 321–331.

Visser, D. 1974. Recent advances in the deep-freeze preservation of ram semen. South African Journal of Animal Sciences 4: 275-288.

Watson, P.F. 1979. The preservation of semen in mammals. In: Oxford Reviews of Reproductive Biology (Ed Finn C A) Clarendon Press, Oxford, London, U.K., Vol I, and pp. 283-350.

Watson, P.F. 2000. The causes of reduced fertility with cryopreserved semen. Animal Reproduction Science 60-61: 481-492.

Watson, P.F. 1995. Recent developments and concepts in the cryopreservation of spermatozoa and the assessment of their post-thawing function. Reproduction Fertility Development 7: 871-891.

Watson, P.F. and Martin, I.C.A. 1974. Regions of the freezing curve causing changes in structure and viability of ram sperm. Nature 251: 315-316.

Windsor, D. P and White, I. G. 1995. Mitochondrial injury to ram sperm during procedures associated with artificial insemination or frozen storage. Animal Reproduction Science 40, 43-58.

Windsor, D. P. 1997. Mitochondrial function and ram sperm fertility. Reproduction Fertility and Development 9, 279-284.

Wulster-Radcliffe, M.C., Williams, M.A., Stellflug, J.N. and Lewis, G.S. 2001. Technical note: artificial vagina vs. a vaginal collection vial for collecting semen from rams. Journal of Animal Sciences 79: 2964–7.

Yanagimachi, R. 1994: Fertility of mammalian spermatozoa: its development and relativity. Zygote 3: 371–372.

Yeung, C.H., Barfield, J.P. and Cooper, T.G., 2006. Physiological volume regulation by spermatozoa. Molecular Cellular Endocrinology 250: 98–105.

Yoshida, M. 2000. Conservation of sperms: current status and new trends. Animal Reproduction Science 60-61: 349-355.

❐❐❐

20

Impact of Body Condition Score on Productive and Reproductive Capability of Sheep

V.P.Maurya*, V.Sejian and S.M.K. Naqvi
Adaptation Physiology Laboratory, Division of Physiology and Biochemistry
Central Sheep and Wool Research Institute, Avikanagar, via Jaipur-304 501, Rajasthan

Introduction

In the arid and semi-arid region; scarcity of feed, water and adverse climatic conditions lead to lower body condition score (BCS) of ewes, which is the main hindering factor in sheep production system. Every year sheep die during scarcity of feed and harsh climatic condition because they do not have sufficient body reserves to sustain them against the demand of the inclement weather. Reproduction is a major and important component of the productive efficiency for a ewe-lamb system. Ewes must have adequate amount of body fat as an indicator of energy store to maintain their health, reproductive function and productive capacity (Atti et al., 2001). Body scoring is based on a subjective assessment of the fat level and muscle thickness on the backbone behind the last rib, according to a five-point scale described by Russel et al. (1969). A sheep flock consists of ewes of different sizes, body conditions and different levels of production and therefore they have varying nutritional needs. Although it is impossible to treat each ewes needs separately, many a times it is beneficial to divide the flock into groups of ewes having similar needs. To improve body condition score of ewes by one score requires good grazing for 6 to 10 weeks. Over-conditioned ewes can have reduced reproductive performance and therefore over-fat ewes should be separated off and grazed optimally before the breeding season. Body condition scoring in sheep can be useful means for assessing the flocks at mating time (Gordon, 1997). The ewes with low body fat reserves have fewer large ovarian follicles due to which less number of follicles reach to the final stage of development and ovulate with greater possibility of reproductive failure and reduction in the production level (Michels et al., 2000). The ewes with appropriate body condition score (BCS) throughout gestation and after lambing, have higher productivity than ewes of poor BCS (Russel et al., 1969). To optimize the productivity of sheep, it is therefore, essential to have a simple and reliable indicator to assess nutrition level of ewes and decide when and how to supplement the flock (Maurya et al., 2009). The BCS method is a simple, noninvasive, time saving and effective technique to rank ewes according to their body reserve by sight and touch. Though a large body of literature on effect of BCS on reproductive and productive efficiency of exotic sheep is available but meager information is available in Indian context. This paper presents the impact of BCS on productive and reproductive capabilities of sheep in semi-arid region of India.

How to condition score?

Accurate condition scoring depends on handling the animal in the areas outlined. Visual scoring is not recommended unless the operator has considerable previous experience at condition scoring by touch. Condition score is independent of body size. Condition score measures the amount of soft tissue (meat and fat) over the bones of the animal and not the size of the animal. The smallest breed Garole and medium sized breed Malpura sheep can have the same body condition score. Generally there are three types of BCS system followed worldwide. In the United States and Ireland a 5-point system is used, whereas Australia and New Zealand use 8-point and 10-point scale respectively (Roche et al., 2004). In India the 5-point system followed in United States is more suitable. BCS is measured in our institute subjectively in 5-point scale as per method described by Russel et al. (1969) and Maurya et al. (2008a) and is briefly described in Table 1.

Point-wise description of methodology

i. The animal should be standing in a relaxed position.

ii. It should not be tense, crushed by other animals or held in a crush. If the animal is tense it is not possible to feel the short ribs and get an accurate condition score.

iii. Locate the last rib (the 13th). Using the balls of the fingers and thumb, try to feel the backbone with the thumb and the end of the short ribs with the finger tips immediately behind the last rib.

iv. Feel the muscle and fat cover around the ends of the short ribs and over the backbone.

v. Feel the fullness of the loin muscle.

vi. The degree of roundness of the ends of the bones, the amount of tissue between the bones and the fullness of the lattissimus muscle determines the condition or finish of the animal.

Table 1. General description of 5-point scale scoring system

Score	Assessment	Description
1	Emaciated	Ewes in this body condition have no fatty tissue detectable between skin and bone. These ewes appear weak and unthrifty.
2	Thin	Ewes in this body condition have only a slight amount of fatty tissue detectable between skin and bone. Spinous processes are relatively prominent. These ewes appear thrifty but have only minimal fat reserves.
3	Average	Ewes in this body condition have average flesh but do not have excess fat reserves. This condition score includes ewes in average body condition.
4	Fat	This condition score includes ewes that are moderately fat. Moderate fat deposits give sheep a smooth external appearance
5	Obese	Includes ewes that are extremely fat. Excess fat deposits can easily be seen in the brisket, flank and tail-head regions. These ewes have excess fat reserves to the point that productivity may be impaired.

Body condition score and ewe reproduction

Ewes with low BCS have been associated with higher prenatal and neonatal mortality (Nordby et al., 1986) and lower lamb survival (Khan, 1994). Undernutrition of donor ewes reduces the body weight (BW) and BCS with a negative effect on oocyte quality which inturn results in lower rates of cleavage. BCS also affect the numerous reproductive functions including hormone production, fertilization and early embryonic development (Boland and Lonergan, 2005). In ewes, undernutrition during late pregnancy or in early postnatal life can permanently and irreversibly reduce the lambing rates of ewes throughout adult life (Gunn et al., 1995). Nutritional status has also been correlated with embryo survival in ewe and marked as key factor influencing efficiency in animal reproduction technology (Webb et al., 2004).

Nutrition has an important impact on the reproductive performance in sheep, but the magnitude of nutritional effect on reproduction can vary with season (Cumming, 1977; White et al., 1983). Such conditions are more difficult for the sheep, which enjoy a lower priority, compared to cattle production in India and are often subjected to starvation/semi-starvation condition. This leads to heavy losses in sheep body weight and a decline in reproductive function. The depleted body condition of sheep during a period of energy deficiency also reduces heat tolerance (Sleiman and Abi Saab, 1995; Naqvi, 1987), which in turn affects the reproductive potential of sheep. Rhind and Mc Neilly (1986) showed that ewes with low body fat reserves had fewer large ovarian follicles and therefore fewer follicles capable of undergoing the final stage of development and ovulation.

The lower energy level significantly decreases PCV, blood hemoglobin, glucose and albumin concentration (Maurya et al., 2004). The biochemical parameters indicate the need for animal metabolic profile monitoring with the aim of determining the nutritive and environmental status of animals (Maurya et al., 1998). In addition to this restricted dietary energy level decreases the total protein of the body. The transportation of ewes adversely affects the physiological responses and blood metabolites (Parrott et al., 1998). Sheep can resist well even after drinking saline water during draught conditions (Assad and Elsherif, 2002). It's indeed a moot point that how animals are accommodating themselves with existing nutritional and thermal stress for a period of 3 to 4 months during summer in semi-arid region and they are unable to produce their full potential even after getting access to feed 7 to 8 month in a year.

The body condition of ewes drastically affects the manifestation of sexual behaviour. The behavioral manifestation of estrus (circling, tail fanning, head turning, standing and approaching to ram) ranges from a phase of low intensity to a phase of high intensity occurring 8 to 12 hour after commencement and ends with another phase of low intensity with gradual disappearance as ewes enter in the diestrus stage (Maurya et al., 1998). The ewes with less than 2.5 BCS have less intensity of sexual behaviors as compared to the ewes having good body condition scoring i.e. a score of 3 to 3.5. The incidence of estrus and receptivity of ewes are important factors, which can affect overall embryo production (Tompkins and Bryant, 1974). The ewes of lower body condition have less duration of estrus and more estrus interval as compared to ewes having more body condition scoring (Sejian, et al., 2008).The proper assessment of sexual behaviour and receptivity before breeding of ewes treated for superovulation may increase the possibility of fertile mating and the overall success rate of embryo transfer performance. Various studies have been conducted in our laboratory to observe the effect of simulated body condition score on productive and reproductive parameters of different breeds of ewes from the laboratory (Table 2).

Table 2: Effect of simulated body condition score on productive and reproductive parameters of different breeds of ewes

Breeds	Parameter	Body Condition Score			
		2..5	3.0	3.5	4.0
Malpura	Gestation Length(Days)	149.9±0.69	150.3±0.29	151.1±0.35	151.0±0.39
	Lambing (%)	75	84.8	86.1	70
	Birth weight(kg)	2.80±0.17	3.2±0.07	3.5±0.07	3.9±0.23
Avikalin	Gestation Length(Days)	151.5±0.45	150.7±0.17	150.3±0.34	150.2±0.97
	Lambing (%)	80	93.8	92.1	71.4
	Birth weight(kg)	2.75±0.10	3.15±0.04	3.27±0.08	3.72±0.12
Bharat Merino	Gestation Length(Days)	156.0 ± 0.83	150.9±0.36	149.5 ± 0.37	151.0 ± .29
	Lambing (%)	22.2	64.5	71.4	55.5
	Birth weight(kg)	3.1 ± 0.12	3.2 ± 0.11	3.6 ± 0.21	3.8 ± 0.08
Garole	Gestation Length(Days)	150.4±0.72	149.6±0.42	149.4±0.61	-
	Lambing (%)	83.8%	91.4	80	-
	Birth weight(kg)	2.94 ±0.17	2.81 ±0.09	3.1 ±0.15	-

Source: Maurya et al., 2008a; Maurya et al., 2008c; Sejian et al., 2008

Body conditioning at different stages of pregnancy

Condition score cannot be altered rapidly. It generally takes around eight weeks to modify condition by one score. Clearly the best time to attempt to modify the condition score is at weaning or, at the very latest, eight weeks before tupping. It is unacceptable to neglect or ignore thin and weak ewes in a flock. It is the responsibility of all shepherds and flock owners to take all possible practical measures to ensure that the body condition of every sheep in the flock is maintained. Rhind et al. (1998) reported that the birth weight of lambs born to ewes restricted in adulthood ($P<0.01$) were lower than those of lambs born to unrestricted ewes.

Feed flushing usually begins about 2 weeks prior to joining with rams and continues for about 2 to 3 weeks into the breeding season, for a total flushing period of 4 to 6 weeks. In early pregnancy the nutrient requirements of embryos are extremely small. However, nutrition can affect embryo survival indirectly by affecting the hormonal status of the ewe. Inadequate nutrition or body condition has been associated with delayed onset of the breeding season, decreased pregnancy rate, low birth weight of lambs (Maurya et al., 2004).

Excessive weight gain in mature ewes can be detrimental to placental development and thus reduce fetal growth. In contrast to mature ewes, ewe lambs and hogget's cannot compensate for under-nutrition in mid-pregnancy and should continue on a high plane of nutrition to ensure they reach 75 and 95% of their mature weight pre-lambing respectively. Late pregnancy is the period when nutrition has the greatest effect on total potential lamb production. Sheep lambing in moderate to good condition (2.5-3.0) will have a significantly shorter interval to first estrus, compared to those lambing in poor condition (< 2). Body condition affects the economics of wintering, fertility, lambing difficulties, and milk yield (West et al., 1991)

Ewes with a lambing rate of 2.5 and a body condition score four weeks prior to lambing of 3.5, produced heavier lambs and more total lamb weight than ewes that had a body condition score of 2.5 (Maurya et al., 2008b). The relationship between birth weight and survivability is high (Michels et al., 2000). Therefore, farmers must feed so that ewes entering the last 4 to 6 weeks of gestation will be provided with optimum nutrition to ensure normal fetal growth and development. Ewes should be condition scored prior to flushing. It is important that ewes be kept at 3.5 for at least 30 days following breeding (Maurya et al., 2008c). Failure to keep a ewe in good condition after breeding could result in the loss of eggs. Based on the experimental findings, the optimum BCS recommended for each stage of production cycle under hot semi-arid environment have been depicted in Table 3.

Table 3: Some recommended (optimal) condition score values for the various stages of the production cycle of sheep under semi-arid condition

Production stages of sheep condition score	Optimum
Breeding	3.0
Mating	3.0-3.5
Early-Mid Gestation	3.0
Late gestation	3.5
Lambing	3.5
Twining	3.5-4.0
Lactation	3.0
Rams at mating	3.5
Weaners	2.5 or more

BCS and ram reproductive efficiency

In rams, reproductive activity is affected by a range of external factors, including socio-sexual cues, temperature, photoperiod and nutrition. Among these factors, nutrition is arguably the most powerful. The responses of ram to nutritional manipulations can be divided into short-term effects that act mainly on the neuroendocrine system controlling testicular activity (Blache et al., 2000) and long-term effects that act on testicular growth and sperm production (Oldham et al., 1978). Under extensive management system, level of nutrition may have a greater influence on reproductive activity of rams than photoperiod (Perez et al., 1997). Reproduction is a physiologically costly process that consumes significant amounts of energy, and the mechanisms controlling energy balance are therefore closely linked to fertility. The Energy balance, appetite and reproductive function are closely associated and influence the hypothalamo-hypophyseal-gonadal axis which inturn influences gonadal functions. Regulation of normal reproductive development is a complex process involving the coordinated interaction of neurotransmitter systems, hypothalamic releasing factors, pituitary hormones, gonadal sex steroid hormones and various growth factors. It is well known that rams exhibit seasonal fluctuation in sexual behavior, hormonal activity, gametogenesis and also in testicular weight and volume (Tajangookeh, et al., 2007). Sperm production and testicular size in rams has been found to be influenced by the plan of nutrition (Murray et al., 1990). Testicular size is significantly correlated with reproductive activity. Positive correlations between testis size, reproductive hormone concentration, semen volume, sperm output and mating frequency were reported in rams (Yarney and Sanford, 1985).

Nutritional effects on sexual behavior have generally not been well characterized (Wierzbowski, 1978). The reduced sexual behavior in the lower BCS rams could be attributed to the reduced scrotal and testicular morphological characteristics and further due to reduced plasma testosterone concentration as a result of low energy feeding in these rams. Scrotal circumference and testicular weight have been widely used in predicting the reproductive capacity of male domestic animals (Sarder, 2005). Scrotal circumference, a high heritable trait, is considered as an excellent index of sperm production in the ram (Kafi et al., 2004). Level of nutrition and daily body growth has been shown to influence on scrotal circumference (Cameron et al., 1988). There are reports which suggest nutritional management does have an influence on scrotal circumference, scrotal fat, scrotal weight, testicular weight and testicular volume of young rams (Naqvi et al., 2009). The decrease in scrotal circumference of lower BCS rams is due to high sensitivity of testicular tissue to nutritional fluctuations. The response in losing or gaining weight of testes is more quickly than the rest of the body (Masters and Fels, 1984).

The positive relationship between ram live weight and testicular size was reported (Murray et al., 1991). Adult and heavier rams generally having bigger testes. Changes in testicular size can be caused by nutrition, and are accompanied by changes in sperm production per testis and per gram of testicular parenchyma (Oldham et al., 1978). It has been shown that scrotal circumference along with testicular diameter are excellent indicators of spermatogenic function (Elmaz et al., 2008). Further a significant relationship was found between testosterone levels, scrotal circumference, body weight, the prepubertal morphological and physiological characteristics, and the postpubertal reproductive performance in rams (Bielli et al., 1997).

The level of feeding has been shown to influence sperm production of rams (Braden et al., 1974). Spermatogenic activity, sperm content of the epididymis, and other variables were also lower in underfed than in *ad libitum* fed rams (Hotzel et al., 1992). Supplying low-quality feeds to rams decreases the proportion of morphologically normal spermatozoa and increases the proportion of immature spermatozoa (Dana et al., 2000). It has also been reported that undernutrition reduces serum luteinizing hormone and follicle stimulating hormone secretion, impairing testicular growth in ram lambs which ultimately led to low sperm concentration (Martin and White, 1992).Improvement of testicular efficiency by feeding was also reported by Oldham et al. (1978) who showed that rams maintained on a high plane of nutrition produced more sperm than those raised under deficient nutrition. According to Walkden-Brown (1994) overfeeding of sires (boars, bulls and rams) can have detrimental effects on their reproductive capacity. He further emphasized that increasing the energy intake of the ram had a greater effect on the daily sperm production, compared to increasing the protein intake. These results indicate that diet has a marked effect on the rate of sperm production in rams. Furthermore, it was suggested that energy intake probably has no direct effect on spermatogenesis or on testosterone production, but may influence these parameters indirectly via an effect on gonadotrophin secretion (Fourie et al., 2004). Coulter et al. (1997) found a detrimental effect of high energy diets on fertility of young bulls. Both semen quantity and quality were significantly and negatively affected by the high energy content of the diet. The results in terms of sperm concentration and motility in the present study was similar to those recorded by Fourie et al. (2004), who reported a high energy diet to have a detrimental effect on sperm concentration and motility in Dorper rams. These differences can mainly be attributed to greater amounts of subcutaneous fat in the scrotal skin. This scrotal fat may interfere with the thermoregulatory mechanisms of the testis and vital for spermatogenesis (Labuschagne et al., 2002). The nutrient deficiency along with high ambient temperature might have caused a severe impact on the semen attributes in the lower BCS group in the present study.

The rams having a moderate BCS between 3.0 and 3.5 performed better than lower and higher BCS rams for most reproductive parameters studied. This study indicates the importance of maintaining optimum body condition for rams to ensure best reproductive performance under hot semi-arid environment. The additional energy supplied to higher BCS (BCS 4.0) rams did not reflected in substantial increase in reproductive performance. Further the optimum BCS rams (BCS 3.0-3.5) performed better in terms of reproductive efficiency in comparison to higher BCS (BCS 4.0) rams. The results indicates that the rams kept under the conditions of a hot, semi-arid environment should be maintained at moderate (3.0–3.5) BCS during breeding stage to ensure maximum reproductive efficiency from these rams. This will in turn ensure economically viable return in sheep farms.

Impact of BCS on carcass quality of sheep

Body condition affects both sheep and lamb performance. Poor body condition is associated with reduced income per sheep, increased post-partum interval, weak lambs at birth, and lower weaning weights (Rossi and Wilson, 2006). Increasing post-partum interval will result in a younger, smaller lamb at weaning and will result in lower incomes if sold at weaning. Weak lambs at birth may not get adequate colostrum and are more susceptible to disease, reduced weaning weights, reduced feedlot performance and less desirable carcass traits. This supports the conclusion that BCS is one of the most important factors in determining the desirable carcass traits (Apple, 1999). Condition scoring sheep at slaughter has shown that, among animals of the same age and sex, live weights, carcass weights, and edible tissue yield are highly correlated with condition score. Thus those involved in marketing of live sheep would find condition scoring useful in estimating expected saleable sheep meat (Hassen et al., 1999).There is an association between live weight and body condition scores in beef cows (Apple, 1999). As the animals increase in live weight, their body condition scores tend to increase and as sheep lose live weight their body condition scores tend to decrease (Hassen et al., 1999).

Relationship between BCS & carcass characteristics

Generally the carcass weight and live weight increased as the BCS increased (Gregory et al., 1998). However, carcass length did not showed this trend, suggesting that the increase in weight occurred in the soft tissues rather than in skeletal size. Animals having low condition score had limited body fat reserves. The fatness in carcass increased as condition score increased. The interactions among the individual factors affecting dressing percentage are great, making it rather difficult to accurately predict carcass yield or quality by visual examination of the live animals. However the single factor which affect maximum the carcass characteristics is the body condition (Shelton et al., 1984). In a experiment conducted on Malpura ewes, a strong correlation had been achieved between BCS and carcass characteristics (Maurya et al., 2008a). The ewes belonging to the BCS between 3.0-3.5 possessed the supreme carcass characteristics as compared to lower and higher BCS ewes (Table 4).

Table 4: Effect of BCS on carcass characteristics of Malpura ewes

Trait	2.5BCS	3.0BCS	3.5BCS	4.0BCS
Pre slaughter weight (kg)	28.3±1.12	34.55±1.16	35.05±1.37	45.00±1.80
Hot carcass weight (kg)	10.38±1.13	15.05±0.69	16.02±1.32	20.86±1.12
Dressing (%)	40.31±2.19	46.23±1.47	48.16±1.49	50.31±1.31
Fat content (kg)	3.13±0.020	5.42±0.06	7.35±0.11	10.18±0.14
Lean content (kg)	5.44±0.14	7.40±0.19	7.83±0.18	9.37±0.23
Bone content (kg)	1.65±0.02	1.75±0.03	1.79±0.03	1.84±0.03

Source: Maurya et al., 2008a

Absolute gross and net values of sheep carcass were affected by the different BCS. Within the grade of Cutter, carcasses from BCS-1 sheep had the lowest and carcasses from BCS-4 sheep had the highest gross and net values. Among utility carcasses, the gross and net values of BCS-5cows were greater than the gross values of BCS-1, 2, 3, and 4; however, the live value of cows producing utility carcasses was unaffected by BCS (Apple et al., 1999). Across both quality grades the gross and net value increased linearly as BCS increased from 1 to 4. Sheep designated with a BCS of 4 and 5 had greater gross and net values than Sheep assigned a BCS of 3 or lower. Moreover, BCS-3 sheep had higher gross and net values than BCS-1, and 2 sheep; BCS-1 sheep had the lowest gross and net values.

Conclusion

Condition scoring is a system of describing or classifying breeding animals by differences in relative body fatness. It is a subjective scoring system but provides a fairly reliable assessment of body composition. BCS is a simple but useful procedure, which can help producers in making management decisions regarding the quality and quantity of feed required to optimize performance. Under Indian farming condition, 5-point body condition scoring system, similar to the one followed in United States is preferable. BCS provides a reasonable indicator of status of ewes at different production phases, which allow to assess ewe's nutrition level and to decide when, and how to supplement the flocks. It is desirable to have ewes in 3 or 3.5 BCS at the time of mating to get higher lambing rate and as well as more birth weight of lambs per lambing. Further the mutton industry could optimize returns to producers and processors by marketing sheep with a BCS of 3.0-3.5. Carcasses from BCS-3.0-3.5 sheep are the most valuable from economic point of view, and its live value is similar to BCS-4 sheep. It is therefore, essential to have a simple and reliable indicator like BCS at hand, which will allow to assess nutrition level of ewes particularly in production systems where the availability of feed is not constant and to decide when and how to supplement the flock for getting maximum productivity from the flock.

References

Apple, J.K. 1999 Infuence of Body Condition Score on live and carcass value of cull beef cows. Journal of Animal Science 77: 2610-2620.

Apple, J.K., Davis, J.C. and Stephenson, J. 1999. Influence of Body Condition Score on by-product yield and value from cull beef cows. Journal of Animal Science 77: 2670-2679.

Assad, F. and Elsherif, M.M.A. 2002. Effect of drinking saline water and feed shortage on adaptive responses of sheep and camel. Small Ruminant Research 45: 279-290.

Atti, N., Theriz, M. and Abdennebi, L. 2001. Relationship between body condition at mating and reproductive performance in the fat tailed Barbarine breed. Animal Research 50: 135-140.

Bielli, A., Gastel, T., Perez, R., lopez,A., Castrillejo, A., Regueiro, M., Forsberg, M., Lundeheim, N. and Rodriguez-Martinez, H. 1997. Influence of nutrition on seasonal variations in testicular morphology and function in Corriedale rams. Journal of Reproduction and Development 43(2): 171-180.

Blache, D., Chagas, L.M. Blackberry, M.A., Vercoe P.E. and Martin, G.B. 2000: Metabolic factors affecting the reproductive axis in male sheep. Journal of Reproduction and Fertility 120: 1–11.

Boland, M. P. and Lonergan, P. 2005: Effects of nutrition on fertility in dairy cows. Advances in Dairy Technology 15: 19-33.

Braden, A.W.H., Turnbull, K.E., Mattner, P.E. and Moule, G.R. 1974. Effect of protein and energy content of diet on the rate of sperm production in rams. Australian Journal of Biological Sciences 27: 67-73.

Cameron, A.W.N., Murphy, P.M. and Oldham, C.M. 1988. Nutrition of rams and output of spermatozoa. Proceedings of Australian Society for Animal Production 17: 162–165.

Coulter, G.H., Cook, R.B. and Kastelic, J.P. 1997: Effects of dietary energy on scrotal surface temperature, seminal quality and sperm production in young beef bulls. Journal of Animal Science 75: 1048-1052.

Cumming, I.A. 1977. Relationships in the sheep of ovulation rate with liveweight, breed season and plane of nutrition. Australian Journal of Experimental Agriculture and Animal Husbandry 17:234-241.

Dana, N., Tegegne, A. and Shenkoru, T. 2000. Feed intake, sperm output and seminal characteristics of Ethiopian highland sheep supplemented with different levels of leucaena (Leucaena leucocephala) leaf hay. Animal Feed Science and Technology 86: 239-249.

Elmaz, O., Dikmen, S., Cirit, U., Demir, H. 2008. Prediction of Postpubertal Reproductive Potential According to Prepubertal Body Weight, Testicular Size, and Testosterone Concentration Using Multiple Regression Analysis in Kývýrcýk Ram Lambs. Turkish Journal of Veterinary and Animal Sciences 32: 335-343.

Fourie, P.J., Schwalbach, L.M.J., Neser, F.W.C. and Van der Westhuizen, C. 2004. Scrotal, testicular and semen characteristics of young Dorper rams managed under intensive and extensive conditions. Small Ruminant Research 54(1-2): 53-59.

Gordon, I.1997. Controlled reproduction in sheep and goats. Ist edn. CAB International Wallingford, Oxon Ox 10 8 DE U.K.

Gregory, N.B., Robins, J.K., Thomas, D.G. and Purchas, R.W. 1998. Relationship between body condition score and body composition in dairy cows. New Zealand Journal of Agricultural research 41:527-532.

Gunn, R.G., Sim, D.A. and Hunter, E.A. 1995. Effects of nutrition in utero and in early-life on the subsequent lifetime reproductive-performance of Scottish Blackface ewes in two management-systems. Journal of Animal Science 60: 223-230.

Hassen, A., Wilson, D.E. and Rouse, G.H. 1999. Evaluation of carcass, live, and real-time ultrasound measures in feedlot cattle: I. Assessment of sex and breed effects. Journal of Animal Science 77: 273-282.

Hotzel, M.J., Martin, G.B.and Caraty, A. 1992. Effect of nutrition on testicular growth in rams immunized against GnRH. In: Proceedings of the Endocrine Society of Australia, 35: 87-93.

Kafi, M., Safdarian, M. and Hashemi, M. 2004. Seasonal variation in semen characteristics, scrotal circumference and libido of Persian Karakul rams. Small Ruminant Research 53: 133–139.

Khan, K. 1994. Effects of body condition and pre-lambing supplementation on ewe productivity. Masters Thesis. Oregon State University, Corvallis.

Labuschagne, H.S., Schwalbach, L.M.J., Taylor, G.J. and Webb, E.C. 2002. The effect of age on reproductive and productive characteristics of young Bonsmara Bulls fed a high-energy diet. In: Proceedings of the 39th National Congress of the South African Society of Animal Science, Christiana May 13–16, p. 154.

Martin, G.B. and White, C.L. 1992. Effect of dietary zinc deficiency on gonadotrophin secretion and testicular growth in young male sheep. Journal of Reproduction and Fertility 96: 497-507.

Masters, D. G. and Fels, H. E. 1984. Seasonal changes in the testicular size of grazing rams. Proceedings of the Australian Society of Animal Production 15: 444-7.

Maurya, V.P., Naqvi, S.M.K. and Mittal, J.P. 2004. Effect of dietary energy level on physiological responses and reproductive performance in Malpura sheep in hot semi-arid region of India. Small Ruminant Research 55:117-122.

Maurya, V.P., Naqvi, S.M.K. and Mittal, J.P. 1998. Reproductive behaviour of Malpura and Bharat Merino ewe lambs under semi-arid condition. Indian Journal of Animal Sciences 68: 533-535.

Maurya, V.P., Sejian V., Kumar, D., Joshi, A., Naqvi, S.M.K. and Karim, S.A. 2008a. Body condition scoring system: A simple tool for optimizing productivity in sheep farms. Published by CSWRI, Avikanagar. pp-1-35.

Maurya, V.P., Kumar, S., Kumar, D., Gulyani, R ., Joshi, A., Naqvi, S.M.K., Arora, A.L. and Singh, V.K 2008b Effect of Body Condition Score on Reproductive Performance of Chokla Ewes. Indian Journal of Animal Sciences (*In press*).

Maurya, V.P., Prince, L.L.L., Naqvi, S.M.K., Sejian, V., Kumar, D. and Joshi, A. 2008c. Effect of body condition score on productive and reproductive performance of Avikalin ewes. Indian Veterinary Journal (*In press*).

Maurya, V.P., Sejian, V., and Naqvi, S.M.K. 2009. Body condition scoring system – a strategic tool for optimizing productivity in sheep farms. Indian Farming, March 2009, PP 28-33.

Michels, H., Decuypere, E. and Onagbesan, O. 2000. litter size, ovulation rate and prenatal survival in relation to ewes body weight: genetic review. Small Ruminant Research. 38: 199-209.

Murray, P.J., Rowe, J.B. and Pethick, D.W. 1991. Effect of season and nutrition on scrotal circumference of Merino rams. Australian Journal of Experimental Agriculture 31: 753-756.

Murray, P.J., Rowe, J.B., Pethick, D.W. and Adams, N.R. 1990. The Effect of Nutrition on Testicular Growth in the Merino Ram. Australian Journal of Agricultural Research 41: 185-195.

Naqvi, S.M.K. 1987. Physiological adaptation of sheep during energy crisis and thermal stress. Ph.D. thesis submitted to Kurukshetra University, Kurukshetra, India.

Naqvi, S.M.K., Kumar, D. and Pareek, S.R. 2009. Testicular development of Malpura ram lambs under extensive and intensive feeding regimen. Indian Journal of Small Ruminants (*In press*).

Nordby, D. J., Field, R. A., Riley, M. L., Johnson, C. L. and Kercher, C. J. 1986. Effects of maternal undernutrition during early pregnancy on postnatal growth in lambs. Proceedings of Western Section of American Society for Animal Science 37: 92-97.

Oldham, C.M., Adams, N.R., Gherardi, P.B., Lindsay, D.R. and Mackintosh, J.B. 1978. The Influence of Level of Feed Intake on Sperm-producing Capacity of Testicular Tissue in the Ram. Australian Journal of Agricultural Research 29: 173-179.

Parrot, R.F., Hall, S.J.G., Lloyd, D.M., Goode, J.A. and Broom, D.M. 1998. Effect of a maximum permissible journey time (31h) on physiological response of fleeced and shorn sheep to transport, with observations on behaviour during a short (1h) rest-stop. Animal Science 66: 197-207.

Perez, C.R., Lopez, A., Castrillejo, A., Bielli, A., Laborde, D., Gastel, T., Tagle, R., Queirolo, D., Franco, J., Forsberg, M. and Rodriguez-Martinez, H. 1997. Reproductive seasonality of corriedale rams under extensive rearing conditions. Acta Veterinaria. Scandiva 38: 109-117.

Rhind, S.M., Elston, D.A., Jones, J.R., Rees, M.E., Mc Millen, S.R. and Gunn, R.G. 1998. Effect of restriction on growth and development of Brecon Cheviot ewe lambs on subsequent lifetime reproduction performance. Small Ruminant Research 30: 121-126.

Rhind, S.M. and Mc Neilly, A.S. 1986. Follicle populations, ovulation rates and plasma profiles of LH, FSH and prolactin in Scottish Blackface ewes in high and low levels of body condition. Animal Reproduction Science 10: 105-115.

Roche, J. R., Dillon, P. G., Stockdale, C. R., Baumgard, L. H. and VanBaale, M. J. 2004. Relationships Among International Body Condition Scoring Systems. Journal of Dairy Science 87: 3076-3079.

Rossi, J. and Wilson, T.W. 2006. Body condition scoring beef cows. In the bulletin published by university of Goergia.

Russel, A. J. F., Doney, J. M. and Gunn, R. G. 1969. Subjective assessment of body fat in live sheep. Journal of Agricultural Science (Cambridge) 72: 451–454.

Sarder, M.J.U. 2005. Scrotyal circumference variation on semen characteristics of artificial insemination (AI) bulls. Journal of Animal and Veterinary advances 4(3): 335-340.

Sejian, V., Maurya, V.P., Naqvi, S.M.K., Kumar, D. and Joshi, A. 2008. Effect of induced body condition score differences on physiological response, productive and reproductive performance of Malpura ewes kept in a hot, semi-arid environment. J. Anim. Phys. Anim. Nutr. DOI: 10.1111/j.1439-0396.2008.00896.x.

Shelton, M., Smolder, G. and Figueiredo, E.A.P. 1984. Meat Production and Carcass Characteristics of the Goat. USAID Title XII. Small Ruminant Collaborative Research Support Program, Texas A & M University, San Angelo.

Sleiman, F.T. and Abi Saab, S. 1995. Influence of environment on respiration rate, heart rate and body temperature on filial crosses compared to local Awassi sheep. Small Ruminant Research 16: 49-53.

Tajangookeh, H.D., Shahneh, A.Z., Shahrebabak, M.M. and Shakeri, M. 2007. Monthly variation of plasma concentration of testosterone and thyroid hormones and reproductive characteristics in three breeds of Iranian fat-tailed rams throughout one year. Pakistan Journal of Biological Sciences 10(19): 3420-3424.

Thompkins, T. and Brayant, M.J. 1974. Oestrus behaviour of ewes and the influence of treatment with progesterone. Journal of Reproduction and Fertility 41: 121-132.

Walkden-Brown, S.W., Restall, B.J. and Taylor, W.A. 1994. Testicular and epididymal sperm content in grazing Cashmere bucks: seasonal variation and prediction from measurements in vivo. Reproduction Fertility Development 6: 727-736.

Webb, R., Garnsworthy, P.C., Gong, J.G. and Armstrong, D.G. 2004. Control of follicular growth: local interactions and nutritional influences. Journal of Animal Science 82: E63-E74.

West, K.S., Meyer, H.H. and Nawaz, M. 1991. Effect of differential ewe condition at mating and early post mating nutrition on embryo survival. Journal of Animal Science 69: 3931-3938.

White, D.H., Bowman, P.J., Morley, F.H.W., Mc Manus, W.R. and Filan, S.J. 1983. A simulating model of the breeding ewe flock. Agricultural Systems 10: 149–189.

Wierzbowski, S. 1978. The sexual behaviour of experimentally underfed bulls. Applied Animal Ethology 4: 55-60.

Yarney, T.A. and Sanford, L.M. 1985. Relationship between prepubertal reproductive-endocrine parameters and postpubertal testicular size and function of rams. In: Proceedings of the10th International Congress of Animal Reproduction and Artificial Insemination, Vol. 2. Urbana-Champaign, IL, p. 178.

❑❑❑

21

Development and Dissemination of the NARI Suwarna Strain of Deccani Sheep: Genetic Improvement of Production Performance while Maintaining Adaptability

C. Nimbkar*, P.M. Ghalsasi and B.V. Nimbkar
Animal Husbandry Division, Nimbkar Agricultural Research Institute
P.O. Box 23, Phaltan- 415 523, Maharashtra

Introduction

Deccani sheep are reared by smallholders on the Deccan plateau having a dry, monsoonal climate. They are reared in Maharashtra, Karnataka and Andhra Pradesh States of India. The Deccani sheep population in the three States is estimated to be 3.4 million, 7.2 million and 8.5 million respectively, thus making a total of 19.1 million (Anthra, 2007). They are traditionally reared by communities such as the Dhangar in Maharashtra, Kuruba in Karnataka and Kuruma in Andhra Pradesh. The traditional system of rearing is still followed although there is some use of vaccination and modern veterinary medicines. Sheep are usually reared in flocks of 25 to 200 breeding ewes and one to four breeding rams. Rams are always with the flock and lambs are not artificially weaned by separating them from their mothers. Eighty per cent of the flocks migrate for about eight months of the year- from November to June- to areas of higher rainfall or irrigated areas, over distances of 100 to 500 km.

More than 90% of the income from rearing Deccani sheep is earned from the sale of 3-4 months old, unweaned lambs weighing about 15 kg. Lambs are sold young because there is market demand for them and sheep owners consider it beneficial to have the dams return to oestrus and conceive again once the lamb is sold. Sheep are herded for grazing by flock owners (referred to as 'smallholders' in this paper) all day. They are grazed mainly on public, often degraded grazing lands including hilly areas, road and canal sides and farm bunds. They also graze on crop residues of grain sorghum, sunflower, groundnut, pearl millet, maize, chickpea, cotton, okra, vegetables and other crops. Sheep are penned at night either on a field for manuring or near the owner's house. Sale of manure collected from the pen and manuring of fields are sources of cash income. Deccani ewes usually have only a single lamb (Acharya, 1982). The average litter size of Deccani sheep is 1.02 and the average lambing interval is 10 months (Nimbkar et al., 2002; Waghmode, 2007). Lambs are reared with careful personal attention. Lambs that do not get sufficient milk from their mothers are cross-fostered to ewes that have surplus milk. Usually there are a few goats in the flock and lambs may also be cross-fostered to goat does. If there are no surplus lambs in the flock for cross-fostering to ewes whose lambs die, orphan lambs are purchased and suckled to such ewes. Lambs are given a small amount of supplement such as ground nut cake and wheat flour dough. Given the system of management and the high and increasing demand and market price of lambs, a moderate increase in the litter size of Deccani ewes would lead to an increase in the number of saleable lambs and in the incomes of shepherds. An increase in sheep productivity and meat production also conforms to Indian national agricultural priorities and would help to tackle the serious problem of protein malnutrition especially among women and children. It would therefore be profitable to improve the reproductive performance of Deccani sheep by genetic means.

A breeding program was initiated in 1998 at the Nimbkar Agricultural Research Institute (NARI), Phaltan in Maharashtra State of India to introduce prolificacy in the Deccani breed from the prolific Garole breed of Sundarban in West Bengal State (Nimbkar et al., 2002). Garole ewes are small weighing only 15 kg compared with the 28 kg adult weight of a Deccani ewe. They are also prolific with an average litter size of 1.74 in the management system at NARI (Nimbkar et al., 1998). Garole sheep are likely to be the 'diminutive' Bengal sheep which were taken to Australia from Calcutta, India in 1792-93 and were postulated as the source of the *FecB* gene discovered in a highly prolific strain of Merino sheep in the 1980s (Turner, 1982; Ghalsasi & Nimbkar, 1993). It was confirmed later that the Garole indeed possessed the same *FecB* mutation as the highly prolific Booroola Merino (Davis et al., 2002). *FecB* (*Fec* for fecundity and *B* for Booroola) is an autosomal dominant gene having a large effect on ovulation rate in sheep. $FecB^B$ is the allele promoting higher fecundity at this locus while $FecB^+$ is the wild type allele (COGNOSAG *ad hoc* committee, 1995). The genotype carrying two $FecB^B$ alleles is called the genotype homozygous for $FecB^B$ or BB, the heterozygous B+ and the non-carrier ++.

The *FecB* mutation was introduced into the Lonand strain, which is one of four strains within the Deccani breed based on geographic separation: Lonand, Sangamneri, Sangola and Kolhapuri (Gokhale, 2003). The *FecB* carrier Deccani strain has been named 'NARI Suwarna'. This paper describes the development of the NARI Suwarna, its benefits and how it has been disseminated.

Introgression of the *FecB* gene into Deccani sheep

The beginning

The Garole is the only reported prolific sheep breed in India (Fahmy and Mason, 1996). A Garole flock in Phaltan (18^0 N 74^0 E) in Maharashtra State was established by importing two rams and two ewes in April 1993 and 10 rams and 30 ewes in May 1994 from Sundarban, West Bengal State (21^0N 88^0E) over a distance of about 1500 km (Nimbkar et al., 1998). The Bannur is a non-prolific meat sheep breed from Karnataka State adjacent to Maharashtra and is known for its blocky conformation and superior meat quality. Lamb production and gastrointestinal parasite resistance of the three breeds- the Deccani, Garole and Bannur- were evaluated at NARI from 1996 to 1999 with the aim of developing recommendations for the appropriate breed combination for a likely composite (Nimbkar et al., 2003). It was only speculation at that time that the prolificacy of the Garole was due to the *FecB* gene. An 'incomplete diallel' mating design was used in which both ewes and rams of Deccani and Bannur breeds were used with only rams of the Garole breed included. Over four years, 290 Deccani ewes and 265 Bannur ewes were inseminated with the semen of 8 Deccani, 9 Bannur and 15 Garole rams and the resulted progeny were evaluated. Artificial insemination was used because the small size of Garole rams precluded natural mating. It was found that crossing the Deccani and Bannur with Garole reduced live weight at birth, three and six months and thus lamb growth rates significantly compared with Deccani. However, lambs sired by Garole rams (i.e. carrying 50% Garole genes) were more resistant to naturally acquired gastro-intestinal nematode infections and to artificial challenge with *Haemonchus contortus* than those sired by Deccani or Bannur rams (i.e. not carrying any Garole genes). Despite the enhanced resistance to *H. contortus,* lambs sired by Garole rams had reduced rates of survival (Nimbkar et al., 2003).

Early investigation of the genetic basis of Garole prolificacy

Matings were also carried out to demonstrate segregation of a postulated single major gene for prolificacy in the Garole breed (Nimbkar et al., 2002). B+ F1 Garole cross rams were mated to Deccani ewes and the ovulation rate of the resulting ¼ Garole ewes was measured. If the Garole prolificacy was due to a single gene, half the ewes would be expected to inherit one prolificacy allele of the gene from the sire and the other half would be expected to inherit the wild type allele. After the first lambing, about half of the daughters of each F1 sire had a mean ovulation rate of one while the other half had a mean ovulation rate of two, indicating single gene inheritance of prolificacy in the Garole. After the confirmation of the existence of the *FecB* mutation in the Garole, the PCR-RFLP DNA test to identify the mutation (Wilson et al., 2001) was established in 2002 at the National Chemical Laboratory (NCL) in Pune, India. All crossbred progeny produced in the breeding program thereafter were genotyped for the *FecB* locus using this test. Deccani and Bannur animals and their crosses were not routinely genotyped for *FecB* because they are not prolific and are unlikely to carry the *FecB* mutation. This was confirmed by genotyping a number of sheep of these two breeds (Pardeshi et al., 2005).

Development of the breed improvement program using the *FecB* gene

In 2000, 86 F1 ewes generated from the diallel breeding program were added to the main breeding ewe flock of Deccani and Bannur ewes. Inseminations with Deccani, Bannur, Garole and Garole X Deccani ram semen were carried out to compare the maternal performance of the crosses with that of pure Deccani and Bannur ewes and to produce further crosses for determination of appropriate contributions of each breed to a possible composite. It was also planned that no lamb should have more than 25% Garole genes, the remaining being made up by Deccani and Bannur breeds. A reduction in Garole proportion was deemed necessary because of their small size, poor lamb-rearing ability, poor milk production, existence of horns in males, wide foreheads and other features of appearance of Garole crosses considered undesirable by local shepherds. The benefit from the better worm resistance of the Garole therefore had to be sidelined. The Improved Awassi Dairy Sheep strain from Israel, which was available at NARI (Nimbkar and Ghalsasi, 1992), was used for crossbreeding from 2001 to improve milk yield, lamb weight and growth rate. Awassi rams and crossbred rams with >50% Awassi genes were used for breeding. In each year, Deccani X Deccani and Bannur X Bannur matings were also carried out to produce contemporary animals for comparison with crosses. In 2002, four 25% Garole, 75% Deccani rams genotyped to be B+ were used widely to cross with Deccani and Bannur ewes. Additionally, Awassi-Garole B+ crossbred rams were mated to Deccani-Bannur crossbred ewes.

The NARI Suwarna at NARI and in smallholder flocks

From 2003 onwards, the focus was on developing two prolific strains, the fecund Deccani (later named the NARI Suwarna) and the fecund Composite (later named the NARI Composite) with the attributes of high fertility and prolificacy, good lamb rearing ability and fast growth. The NARI Suwarna was to have up to 25% Garole proportion with the remaining proportion being Deccani. The NARI Composite was to have up to 25% Awassi and/or Bannur genes, <25% Garole genes and the remaining Deccani. The objective was to generate BB, B+ and ++ ewes of both the NARI Suwarna and Composite breeds for testing in shepherds' flocks. The mate selection approach (Kinghorn et al., 2002) was used for allotting rams to ewes using the Total Genetic Resource Management Program (TGRM™) (X'Prime Pty Ltd., 2005). An index of Estimated Breeding Values (EBV) for reproductive and weight traits was used. The ratio of index weights on the different traits was 1:4:12 for fertility, 3 months weight and live litter size at birth respectively. This was based on economic values for a breeding objective calculated by Nimbkar (2006) for the animals in this introgression program. There was a trade-off between increasing the frequency of the *FecB*^{B} allele and controlling inbreeding because of the relationships among *FecB* carrier sires and between *FecB* carrier sires and dams. There was also a trade-off between increasing frequency of the *FecB*^{B} allele and increasing the progeny EBV for 3 month weight (Nimbkar. 2006). An attempt was therefore made to maximize genetic merit, increase frequency of the *FecB*^{B} allele up to a target of 0.5 to 0.6 and control inbreeding by keeping the predicted progeny mean inbreeding coefficient around 0.02 and the mean coancestry of selected parents around 0.02.

Forty eight B+ NARI Suwarna (fecund Deccani) ewes, 40 ++ ewes having Deccani and Garole genes, 12 B+ NARI Composite ewes and 20 ++ Composite ewes were introduced into 14 smallholder flocks in 2003 and 2004. Two of these flocks were seasonally migratory. In addition, B+ and BB rams were introduced into 25 smallholder flocks every year from 2003 to 2007. Rams were kept in smallholder flocks for 35 to 90 days and then brought back to NARI as the same rams were used for breeding in NARI's flock. There are now 20 BB ewes and more than 300 B+ ewes in these smallholder flocks which were born there. Flock owners manage twin lambs just like their single-born lambs. In some cases, they provide extra care and attention to twin lambs such as cross-fostering them to ewes other than their dams if the dams do not have enough milk. Sometimes they also provide nutritious fodder such as Lucerne and grain such as wheat or maize to lambs. Recently, 96 early pregnant heterozygous and 24 non-carrier lambed ewes and their lambs were sold to 12 smallholder shepherds belonging to Birdev Farmer Shepherds' Club in Bhadali village near Phaltan who got loans from the State Bank of India to purchase sheep.

Open nucleus flock

This open nucleus flock at NARI, continued since 2000, now has 521 ewes: 113 homozygous BB, 267 B+ and 141 non-carrier ++ ewes. This flock strength is after the recent sale of 120 ewes to local smallholder shepherds. Phenotypically superior Lonand Deccani rams from shepherds' flocks are brought regularly to the NARI flock for breeding to improve the appearance of NARI's animals, increase genetic diversity in the NARI flock and control inbreeding. Non-carrier ewes are maintained with a view to generate heterozygous rams and ewes for dissemination. All matings are done by cervical artificial insemination (AI) with fresh, diluted semen. Ewes are inseminated on natural oestrus detected by vasectomized rams. Insemination programs are carried out three times a year, for 32-34 days or over the length of two oestrus cycles. Oestrus is detected early in the morning and in the evening. Ewes found to be on oestrus in the morning are inseminated at about 2 p.m. in the afternoon while ewes exhibiting oestrus in the evening are inseminated at 10 a.m. the next morning. Ewes that don't conceive after the first insemination within the 32-day period are inseminated again. Detailed records are kept. In the AI program carried out from 25 June to 25 July 2009, 243 ewes conceived out of 274 ewes inseminated, yielding a conception rate of 88.7% to first AI.

Nucleus flock ewes are maintained on NARI's Lundy farm at Rajale village, 15 km east of Phaltan. The farm is 19 ha. and there is canal irrigation facility available only for 8 months in the year. The farm has pastures of *Stylosanthes hamata*, *Stylosanthes seabrana*, *Cenchrus setigerus*, *Desmanthus variegatus* and Mulato (a *Brachiaria* hybrid). Additionally, silage of sorghum fodder is prepared for summer feeding and loppings of *Leucaena leucocephala* (Subabhul) are given to lambed ewes and young lambs. As NARI's own pastures are not adequate to graze all nucleus flock sheep year round, sheep are grazed on road and canal sides, on common grazing lands and on other farmers' lands in return for manure. A sustainable symbiotic relationship has been established with farmers from Rajale village such that they invite NARI's sheep for grazing on their crop residues, fallow plots, weeds on plots that are going to be ploughed and in orchards. In return, NARI provides them the agreed quantity of sheep manure at times convenient to them. This arrangement has allowed NARI to maintain the nucleus flock for the last ten years and because of the similarity of management, NARI's animals adapt easily when they are introduced into local smallholder flocks. Since NARI's sheep often share grazing grounds with other sheep from the village, no anthelmintic resistance has developed yet in NARI's flock to any class of anthelmintics, probably because of their exposure to refugia larval populations from non-drenched sheep.

Sheep are grazed in two flocks of about equal size. They are given a concentrate supplement of 100-200 g per day for one month during breeding and from one month before to three months after lambing. Lambs are grazed separately on NARI's pastures after the age of one month. Lambs are given supplementary feed up to the age of six months which consists of maize grain at 1% of their body weight and cotton seed cake at 0.5% of body weight.

PCR-RFLP DNA Test for *FecB* mutation detection established at NARI

Under a new project funded by the Department of Biotechnology, "Increasing profitability of sheep production by genetic improvement using the *FecB* (Booroola) mutation and improved management", a molecular biology laboratory has been established at NARI and the PCR-RFLP DNA test for the detection of the *FecB* mutation in DNA isolated from blood samples on FTA paper has been standardized successfully in our laboratory. About 700 Garole and crossbred sheep have been genotyped at the *FecB* locus in this laboratory so far. The DNA test is necessary for this breeding program because:

- The phenotype of *FecB* carriers (increased number of ovulations and lambs) cannot be measured in males and before the age of puberty in females and
- The phenotype is not completely associated with genotype in females (a female with two lambs is more likely to carry the *FecB* mutation but often will not be a carrier and carrier ewes do not have twins at every lambing).

Benefits of *FecB* introgression

One copy of *FecB*^{B} led to an increase in ovulation rate from 1.0 to 2.0 eggs and an increase in live litter size at birth from 1.0 to 1.6 in the NARI flock and from 1.0 to 1.4 in smallholder flocks (Nimbkar et al., 2009). Litter size of homozygous ewes was similar. Thus only about 40% of the *FecB* carrier ewes in smallholder flocks had twins and less than 5% of the litters of carrier ewes were triplets. The increased litter size was found to be moderate and manageable under the existing production system of smallholders. The small changes in management with increased twinning in smallholder flocks were keeping young lambs behind in the pens when ewes went grazing and providing lambs with a small amount of supplementary feed. Compared to 0.9 lambs of three months age weaned by non-carrier ewes, B+ ewes weaned 1.3 and 1.2 lambs in NARI and smallholder flocks respectively. This was a 33% increase in productivity and income for a negligible amount of extra expenditure on feed and some extra care. A higher gain in productivity and income is expected from progeny of the more recent batches of *FecB* carrier rams sent to smallholder flocks as they are the products of more generations of backcrossing, leading to a smaller Garole proportion, larger size and more of the phenotypic features desired by smallholders. Smallholders were given free veterinary care and sheep insurance for the first four years. Training in ewe and lamb management and health care is, however, an integral part of the project since the beginning.

Conclusions

Introgression of the *FecB* mutation was the starting point of the breeding program at the Nimbkar Agricultural Research Institute to develop the more productive NARI Suwarna strain of Deccani sheep, having the ability to produce twin lambs. This strain has the potential to be biologically and economically more efficient than single-bearing Deccanis. It would thus help to make the sheep production system more sustainable in the changing demographic, economic, and agricultural milieu.

References

Acharya, R.M. 1982. Sheep and goat breeds of India. FAO Animal Production and Health Paper 30, FAO, Rome.

Anthra. 2007. Summary of the seminar. In: Proceedings of the National Seminar on Sustainable Use and Conservation of the Deccani Sheep, Hyderabad, pp.3.

COGNOSAG *ad hoc* committee 1995. Revised guidelines for gene nomenclature in ruminants 1993. Genetics Selection Evolution. 27: 89-93.

Davis, G.H., Galloway S.M., Ross I.K., Gregan S., Ward J., Nimbkar B.V., Ghalsasi P.M., Nimbkar C., Gray G.D., Subandriyo, Inounu I., Tiesnamurti B., Martyniuk E., Eythorsdottir E., Mulsant P., Lecerf F., Hanrahan J.P., Bradford G.E. and Wilson T. 2002. DNA tests in prolific sheep from eight countries provide new evidence on origin of the Booroola (*FecB*) mutation. Biology of Reproduction. 66:1869-1874.

Fahmy, M. H. and Mason, I. L. 1996. Less known and rare breeds. In: Prolific sheep. M. H. Fahmy (Ed). CAB International, Wallingford, U.K. pp. 178-186.

Ghalsasi, P.M. and Nimbkar B. V. 1993. The "Garole" - microsheep of Bengal, India. Animal Genetic Resources Information, FAO, 12:73–79.

Gokhale, S.B. (Ed.) 2003. Survey, evaluation and characterization of Deccani sheep breed. Final Report under the Network Project on Animal Genetic Resources. BAIF Development Research Foundation, Pune pp.119 .

Kinghorn, B. P., Meszaros S. A. and Vagg R. D. 2002. Dynamic tactical decision systems for animal breeding. In: Proceedings of the 7th World Congress on Genetics Applied to Livestock Production. Montpellier, France, CD Rom Communication No. 23-07.

Nimbkar, C. and Ghalsasi P.M. 1992. Observations on the performance of the first flock of improved Awassi sheep in India. In: 'Recent Advances in Animal Production'. In: Proceedings of the 6th AAAP Animal Science Congress, Bangkok, Thailand. III, pp. 250.

Nimbkar, C., Ghalsasi P. M., Ghatge R. R. and Gray G. D. 1998. Establishment of prolific Garole sheep from West Bengal in the semi-arid Deccan Plateau of Maharashtra. In: Proceedings of the 6th World Congress on Genetics Applied to the Livestock Production, Armidale, pp. 257- 260.

Nimbkar, C., Ghalsasi, P.M., Walkden-Brown, S.W. and Kahn, L.P. 2002. Breeding program for the genetic improvement of Deccani sheep of Maharashtra, India. In: Proceedings of the 7th World Congress on Genetics Applied to Livestock Production, Montpellier, France, CD-ROM Communication No. 25-11.

Nimbkar, C., Ghalsasi P. M., Swan A. A., Walkden-Brown S. W. and Kahn, L. P. 2003. Evaluation of growth rates and resistance to nematodes of Deccani and Bannur lambs and their crosses with Garole. Animal Science 76:503-515.

Nimbkar, C. 2006. Genetic improvement of lamb production efficiency in Indian Deccani sheep. Ph.D. Thesis. University of New England: Armidale, NSW, Australia.

Nimbkar, C., Ghalsasi, P.M., Nimbkar, B.V., Ghalsasi, P.P., Gupta, V.S., Pardeshi, V.C., Maddox, J.F., van der Werf, J.H.J., Gray, G.D. and Walkden-Brown, S.W. 2009. Biological and economic consequences of introgression of the *FecB* (Booroola) gene into Deccani sheep. 2009. In: Use of the *FecB* (Booroola) gene in sheep-breeding programs. Proceedings of the Helen Newton Turner Memorial International Workshop held in Pune, Maharashtra, India, 10–12 November 2008. S.W. Walkden-Brown, J.H.J. van der Werf, C. Nimbkar and V.S. Gupta (eds). ACIAR Proceedings No. 133. Australian Centre for International Agricultural Research. pp. 90-99.

Pardeshi, V.C., Sainani M. N., Maddox J. F., Ghalsasi P. M., Nimbkar C. and Gupta V. S. 2005. Assessing the role of FecB mutation in productivity of Indian sheep. Current Science 89:887-890.

Turner, H.N. 1982. Origins of the CSIRO Booroola. In: 'The Booroola Merino'. L.R. Piper, B.M. Bindon and R.D. Nethery (eds). Proceedings of the Workshop held at Armidale, NSW, Australia. CSIRO Division of Animal Production. pp. 1-7.

Waghmode, 2007. Sustainable use and conservation of the Deccani sheep for meat and wool. In: Proceedings of the National Seminar on Sustainable Use and Conservation of the Deccani Sheep, Hyderabad, pp. 39-53.

Wilson, T., Wu X., Juengel J., Ross I., Lumsden J., Lord E., Dodds K., Walling G., McEwan J., O'Connell A., McNatty K. and Montgomery G. 2001. Highly prolific Booroola sheep have a mutation in the intracellular kinase domain of bone morphogenetic protein IB receptor (ALK-6) that is expressed in both oocytes and granulosa cells. Biology of Reproduction 64:1225-1235.

X'Prime Pty Ltd 2005, Total Genetic Resource Management™. http://www.xprime.com.au/ products/ tgrm/.

❑❑❑

22

Genetics of Stress Resistance and its Application in Sheep Breeding

A.L. Arora*, Ved Prakash and L. L. L. Prince
Division of Animal Genetics and Breeding, Central Sheep and Wool Research Institute, Avikanagar, via Jaipur-304 501, Rajasthan

Introduction

Stress adversely influence cellular mechanisms, individual physiology and genetic variations at the population level and process of natural selection. There is a growing awareness that environmental stress plays a significant role in the evolution of biological systems, from the level of the gene to ecosystem. The change in a biological system caused by stress is potentially injurious (Hoffmann and Parsons, 1991) with adverse consequences on health (Bijlsma and Loeschcke, 1997). Genetic stress arises from inbreeding or a disturbance of co-adapted gene complexes by hybridization and is similar to environmental stress as both lead to an up regulation of molecular chaperones (Kristensen et al., 2002).

In the last century, environmental stress has adversely influenced the biosphere primarily due to increasing human population and the growing demand for more space and resources. This has caused major environmental changes, such as climatic shifts, habitat destruction, reduced livestock population sizes and increased rates of inbreeding. Habitat destruction and fragmentation has accelerated the rate of species extinction while global warming has exerted thermal and desiccation stress on the animals. Understanding the nature and consequences of environmental stress at a global level from ecological and evolutionary perspectives and their potential synergistic interactions with genetic stress is of paramount importance for the development and evaluation of mitigation measures. Therefore, in depth investigations are essential to understand the mechanism(s) that allow organisms to cope with environmental and genetic stresses

Breed performance under stress and breeding strategy

The tropical and sub-tropical breeds are low producing but well adapted to harsh conditions. It is essential to match the adaptation of animal to existing environment and management system to improve production efficiency of tropical animals. High production from temperate animals may not be possible due to their susceptibility to heat, diseases, parasites and poorer nutrition especially in tropics. Hence a compromise must be sought and breeding goal may be carefully designed. In tropical and sub-tropical areas, expression of productive traits such as growth and fertility is restricted by the effects of environmental stresses such as ecto- and endo- parasites, endemic diseases, heat TstressT resulting from high temperatures, humidity, seasonality and nutrition. The knowledge of variances and co-variances between all these traits is therefore, required for designing effective breeding programmmes for sheep in the tropics and sub-tropics. Further advances in molecular genetics and protein and gene polymorphism identification will make it possible to identify markers for stress resistance and incorporate them in the sheep breeding and selection programmes.

Selection for adaptation

Survival of animals in the situation of multiple stresses (heat, parasites and disease and poor nutrition) is one of the most important traits (Upton, 1985; S¨olkner et al., 1998). Therefore, adaptability traits such as survival rates and reproductive performances may be considered (Ponzoni, 1992). There are two options to improve the adaptation of animals. One option is to concentrate on selection for production traits and allow natural selection. This option has several drawbacks. Such selection will be useful only if the environment in which the population is selected is same. It may not be possible to duplicate the environment of smallholding on large stations. Finally the indirect response in adaptation through selection may be a function of level of adaptation and an initially un-adapted population may be of very little genetic variability (low frequency of resistance genes) or a small contribution of adaptation to economic value. The other alternative is to develop some strategies for adaptation and attempt to select the individually directly. It involves developing care of animals capable of economic production in tropical region by direct selection for adaptation and production. For example we can select for animal's ability to vary its metabolic rate as well as its production according to level of available feed or increase adaptation to ambient temperature, which an animal can tolerate without adversely effecting reproduction and production. For implementing such a complex selection strategy, it is necessary to give suitable weightage for each trait. Simple economic weights may not be appropriate as initial impact on production from selection for adaptation may be very small. We must somehow design our programmes on future economic gains rather than current values.

Selection goals

Traits, which can be readily identified for adaptation to tropics, are: resistance to local disease and parasites, mechanism for thermoregulation, low metabolic rate, low appetite and light coat colour. Besides this, there are many other traits associated with particular environment such as ability to digest low quality feed, wool and hair cover, distribution of body fat and lipids or walking efficiency for longer distances and surfaces. It is also possible that late sexual maturity and long lambing interval are adaptations to humid tropics or to particular management.

Negative genetic correlations between production and fitness traits

Intensive selection aims for higher production yields is negatively correlated to fitness traits (e.g. reproduction and stress susceptibility) in several domestic species. Increasing stress susceptibility reduces longevity and lifetime production of high-yielding breeding animals and reduces economic returns. Selection for fitness traits or functional traits is inefficient, mainly because of low heritabilities. According to Vollema (1998), heritability estimates for functional herd life of dairy cows ranged from 0.02 to 0.10 and for stayability from 0.01 to 0.06. Thus, accurate breeding values for fitness traits require daughter groups as high as 100 to 150. In addition, selection on fitness traits increases generation intervals and consequently reduces selection responses of production traits. Therefore, breeding programmes, aimed at genetic improvement of fitness traits in high yielding populations, are rare and the results are not very encouraging. So far, the only successful breeding strategy for improving stress resistance has been systematic crossbreeding, which exploits additive and non-additive genetic effects.

Crucial areas for reducing stress and development of future breeding programmes

Selection for heat tolerant breed

To avoid the effect of high environmental stress, heat tolerant breeds of sheep should be selected for tropical environment. Small ruminants of tropical origin are more tolerant than breeds of temperate origin (Singh et al., 1982, Gupta and Acharya, 1987). Sheep breeds like Chokla, Malpura and Nali are more tolerant than purebred Merino or Rambouillet (Gupta and Acharya, 1987). Crossbred is fairly comparable to native or in between native and exotic sheep in their heat tolerance.

The relationship between metabolic rate, adaptation and production

Basic physiological conflict between adaptation and high production is well known. If we select for high production, heat load will increase and therefore need to select animal for higher heat dissipation efficiency, beyond the range normally found in tropical well-adapted breeds.

The effect of increased body temperature on fertility and production

Now it is well known that elevated body temperature is the major cause of infertility in animals of tropics. Higher negative genetic and phenotypic correlations between rectal temperature and fertility and negative relationship between rectal temperature and growth have been reported. Selection of animals, which can withstand higher ambient temperature, is desirable.

Heat balance in tropics and mechanism of cooling

It is now possible to measure total radiant and metabolic heat gain and heat loss through sweating and respiration routes. Respiration accounts for an insignificant proportion of total evaporative heat loss. It is desirable to select animals with light colour coat cover and has able to increase sweating rates in response to increase in rectal temperature.

Inheritance of parasite and disease resistance

Ecto and endo parasites like gastro intestinal helminthes and protozoan parasites, tick and flies, bacterial and viral disease are the major factors for limiting animal production in tropics. Drugs, dips and drenches can control disease and parasitic problems. But these add to the cost of production and there may be problem of drug resistance in parasites. Increasing awareness of undesirable levels of insecticide and drug residue in meat and milk reinforces the need for genetic solutions. Genetic variability in animals exists for resistance to many diseases and selection for resistance or tolerance may be followed as a major part of selection programme. Breed differences in resistance to nematode infections have been well documented, particularly *H. contortus* (Bishop and Morris, 2007). Many studies have quantified within-breed heritabilities, using faecal egg count (FEC) as the indicator of relative nematode resistance. In almost all studies (Woolaston and Windon, 2001; Morris et al., 2000; Bishop et al., 2004; Gruner et al., 2004; Swarnkar et al., 2009; Prince et al., 2009). FEC, once appropriately transformed, is a moderately heritable trait in lambs and responds to selection. Vagenas et al. (2002) showed that responses to selection for decreased FEC could be achieved over a short time period. In the peri-parturient ewe, FEC is moderately heritable trait as well as genetically correlated with resistance in the lamb (Morris et al., 1998). At CSWRI, Avikanagar resistant and susceptible lines to *H. Contortus* (Malpura and Avikalin breeds of sheep) are developed by divergent selection based on sire group FEC. The trends in intensity of infection from R line revealed reduced FEC and increased ability of sheep to withstand infection and maintain productivity without drenching (Singh et al., 2009).

Tolerance to food shortages

Webster (1993) suggests that selection should include traits, which increase tolerance to long-term consequences of prolonged food shortage, not just shortage of energy, but also of nitrogen, phosphorus, copper and selenium. Woolliams et al. (1986) showed that lambs from two genetic lines selected for low or high copper status differed substantially in mortality and resistance to infection. Differences in grazing behaviour between and within breeds indicate that breeds or individuals within breeds are better adapted to extensive conditions. The differences between sheep breeds exist for grazing time. For example, out of six breeds studied by Dudzinski and Arnold (1979) Suffolks had the longest grazing times, followed by Border Leicester, Dorset Horn and Romney sheep, whilst Cheviot and Southdown sheep had the shortest grazing times.

It is reported that breeds that remain close together are not suited to areas where favoured herbage patches are distance apart such as in extensive grazing systems (Hunter, 1960). Sheep are selective in their diet (Fraser and Broom, 1990). Sheep may select between different plant species, individual plants, and parts of the plants available (Lynch et al., 1992). However, there is considerable variation between individuals of the same breed (Arnold, 1981; Lynch et al., 1992). Arnold (1981) showed that sheep from the Australian rangelands preferred different pasture plants to sheep kept on sown pastures, and differences are strongly influenced by the previous nutritional history of the animal. In future, more emphasis on research on within breed genetic variation in grazing behaviour, and associations with production and animal welfare may be given.

Genotype –Environment interaction

The domestication of farm animals starting with sheep (about 12000 years ago) was accompanied and followed by a modification of their genome in several respects, particularly in relation to docility and several major production traits. A major problem of the present animal husbandry system is the increasing ease with which animal genotypes can be transported from their region of origin. This means that present day animal genotype have to contend with range of environments, not only in terms of location but also in terms of disease challenge and nutrition. The genotypes developed in high input husbandry systems in temperate areas are being exposed to tropical and sub-tropical conditions and high disease challenge systems, and are often compounded with seasonal nutritional constraints. With the variation in the environment, genotype-environment interaction is expected whereby genotypes show different expression of traits in different environments. Comstock and Moll (1963) suggested that the benefit from genotype and environment should be based on the increase in additive genetic variance resulting from a positive correlation between genotype and genotype × environment interaction.

Cold stress

Newborn lambs of different breeds reared in same cold weather, differed significantly in mortality and resistance to hypothermia (Table 1). Slee (1986) showed significant genetic variation for cold resistance in shorn adult sheep. Experiments at Animal Breeding Research Organization (ABRO) U.K involving genetic selection for cold resistance in newborn Scottish Blakface lambs showed response to selection for cold resistance (Slee and Stott, 1986).

Heat stress

In sheep, genotype x environment (GE) interaction is a well-known phenomenon because of wide range of environments in which sheep are kept. Information on such interaction comes from comparison of native and exotic genotype under stressful environments. Olsson and Beyne (1990) compared the Arsi sheep native to Ethiopia with crossbred sheep sired by introduced rams of the Belu de Maine, Hampshire and Corriedale breeds (Table 2). Many sheep breeds evolved in the sub-tropical semi-arid areas of the world have a fat tail, which have a significance analogus to the hump of the camel. It is also a means of energy storage without impending heat loss capacity. However, observations on animals where the tail has been docked do not support this hypothesis (Marai et al., 1987).

Table 1. Viability and cold resistance in newborn lambs of eight breeds

Type of breeds	Field observations			Laboratory measurements		
	Mortality within 24hrs		Hypothermic lambs	Cold resistance time (min) to reduce body temp		
	No of lambs	%	No of lambs	%	No of lambs	Time
Hill breeds						
Welsh Mountain	181	3.3	47	8.5	21	89
Scottish Blackface	307	4.2	64	1.6	33	87
South country Cheviot	105	9.5	22	9.1	35	98
Small low land breeds						
Merino	104	9.6	16	68.8	21	45
Finnish Landrace	165	10.9	13	64.6	23	38
Southdown	68	13.2	17	47.1	26	51
Large low land breeds						
Oxford	50	2	12	0	21	79
Broder Leicester	77	9	17	36.4	23	80

Source: Marai and Owen, 1987

Table 2. Influence of genotype x environment interaction on breed characteritics

Genotype	Barreness %	Total weaning weight/ewe joined (kg)
Group 1 (1974-79)		
Arsi	9.6±4.8	13.7
25% Exotic	8.9±5.7	16.2
58% exotic	15.5±5.5	17.5
Group 2 (1978-1987)		
Arsi	3.8±2.6	14.3
50% Exotic	8.8±2.4	17.5
75% Exotic	18.9±2.5	15.5
87.5% Exotic	36.4±3.7	12.6

Photoperiod

The influence of season on ewe productivity is well documented. Glimp (1971) reported that the interval to first estrus and conception was longest during August breeding, while prolificacy was maximal during October breeding. Fogarty et al. (1984) reported that fertility and prolificacy under an accelerated lambing program increased in May (71% and 1.8, respectively) and January (57% and 1.9, respectively) compared to September lambing (17% and 1.5, respectively). It was observed that ewes exposed for breeding in August after having lambed in May had a period of postpartum and post-lactational recovery under conditions of hot, stressful summer. In contrast, ewes lambed in January and exposed for breeding in April avoided any heat stress that impaired recovery. Lower fertility and litter size during early season and gradually increasing from January to February–April followed by declining in May lambing has been reported (Glimp, 1971).T T There is a possibility that influence of season on the various genetic parameters due to average differences in the reproduction and growth traits may exist.

The annual pattern of fibre growth in sheep and fibre producing goats is photo dependent and regulated by hormone action. In sheep and Angora goats, fibre growth rate is higher in summer than winter with the amplitude varying between breeds. Cashmere-producing goats grow fibre between the longest and shortest day after which it is shed. The variation in day length between seasons affect the growth of wool (Nagorcka, 1979), mohair (Stapleton, 1978), and cashmere (Mc-Donald et al., 1987) with fibre growth being lowest in mid-winter and highest in mid-summer. The finding of Hulet et al. (1974) on ewes demonstrated the need for assessing the performance of sheep during breeding season before introducing new genotypes in different locations particularly where latitude differences are involved. Aboul Ela and Aboul Naga (1987) analyzed the reproduction of sub-tropical fat tailed sheep and showed that although seasonality is much reduced at low latitudes, the small photoperiod changes the oestrous activity of sub-tropical sheep. It can be concluded that search for adaptable sheep for frequent breeding system may be concentrated on local sheep breeds or sheep breed from other subtropical areas rather than sheep from northern latitudes to avoid complication of GE interaction.

Feed choice and feeding system

The feeding behaviour of modern farm animals is dominated by their wild progenitor's genome with some modification since domestication. There is little documented evidence to assess to what extents animals bred for generations under confinement, have lost the ranging behaviour of their wild pastoral relatives. With regard to feed choice, there is evidence that animal subjected to new choices show a differential development of innate wisdom associated with their wild environment. Pregnant ewes given free choice to feed materials had variable success and many chose very badly (Gordon and Tribe, 1951). Wiggans and VanVleck (1978) not detected GE interactions between high forage and grain feeding systems. It is well known that the digestibility of the diet increases early in the grazing season in many parts of the world suggesting the presence of a genotype x environment interaction in animal performance.

Disease challenge

The existence of genetic resistance (or tolerance of) to disease challenge implies a GE interaction since resistant genotype could be expected to perform relatively better in a high challenge than in low challenge environment. Diseases covered include gastrointestinal nematode infections, diseases due to mycotoxins, bacterial diseases including foot rot and mastitis, ectoparasites such as flies and lice and scrapie. In all cases there is well-documented evidence for between-animal genetic variation in resistance to the disease and, in some of the infectious diseases, resistance to infection. These heritable differences between animals lead to opportunities to breed animals for enhanced resistance to the disease. For some diseases, including nematode parasite infections, resistance to various forms of mycotoxin poisoning and fly-strike, the feasibility of breeding for resistance has been demonstrated in experimental flocks. Importantly, in other cases, including nematode parasite infections and some forms of mycotoxin poisoning, but also mastitis, foot rot and scrapie, now there are breeding programmes are continuing where animals are selected for enhanced resistance. In almost all cases, the evidence for genetic variation and the documented success of breeding for resistance in sheep rather than goats has been observed (Table 3). Breed differences in resistance to nematode infections have been well documented, particularly for *H. contortus* challenge in tropical and sub-tropical sheep. (Bishop and Morris, 2007).

Table 3. Genetic parameters estimates

Trait	hP2P	Reference
Worm resistance	0.27±0.07	Bisset et al. (1992)
Worm resistance	0.21±0.06	Woolstan and Windon (2001)
Fleece root (incidence)	0.17±0.02	Li et al. (1999)
DOMI / LW (9month)	0.08±0.05	Lee et al. (2002)
Digestibility 9 month	0.17±0.00	Lee et al. (2002)
(IgG) specific to *T.colubriformis*	0.18	Douch et al. (1995)
Antibodies specific to *T. circumcincta*	0.31	Douch et al. (1995)
Liability to foot rot	0.34	Baker et al. (1986)
Liability to severe foot rot.	0.03	Baker et al. (1986)
Prevalence of fly strike	0.53	Raadsma (1991)
Cold resistance	0.70	Slee el al. (1991)

Biochemical and molecular variation

The study of Rutherford and Lindquist (1998) showed that genetic variation in stress resistance or stress susceptibility (buffering capacity) may be due to polymorphisms at loci responsible for the regulation of stress response (e.g. heat shock) genes. The polymorphic loci developed produced many biochemical and molecular variation in genes and proteins required during stress responses. At the phosphoglucose isomerase (PGI), locus, the more anodal allozyme/isozyme is favoured under stressful conditions including high temperature, high salinity, anoxia and desiccation in wide range of animal and plant taxa. This suggests at least one locus in natural populations of major importance in determining resistance to stress (Riddoch, 1993). This particular situation is not surprising, since *in vitro* biochemical studies of PGI allozymes suggest that this enzyme, which catalyzes a metabolic reaction and regulates flux through glycolysis, is a direct target of selection of such stresses (Watt, 1985).

The distribution of whole blood potassium concentration in sheep shows marked bimodality varying about two modes one with higher concentration of potassium and other with lower concentration. These are designated as high (HK) and low potassium types (LK). Genetically two types are controlled by a pair of genes (HK is recessive and LK dominant). Taneja (1967) have shown higher proportion of HK animals in Rajasthan deserts which may give them advantage in adaptation as HK animals have higher haemoglobin, WBC count and maintain lower body temperature than LK (Table 4). This also indicates a relatively inefficient thermal regulation of LK in tropical conditions of India.

Table 4. Mean and variances for potassium concentration in LK and HK sheep

Breed	Number	Means	Variances
Polwarth	25	8.74	1.60
Rambouillet	9	7.61	1.35
Polwarth x Rambouillet	19	8.41	1.08
Malpura	74	33.81	21.65
Marwari	106	24.38	12.44
Nali	42	27.38	15.10
Pugal	19	29.91	8.96
Magra	75	27.53	4.82
Chokla	168	26.78	4.11
Jaisalmeri	18	23.68	7.76

(Source: Taneja, 1972)

Ipate et al. (2009) found different genotype based on mutation in certain region gene coding for prion proteins. The coding for alanine (A) by codon 136 confers resistance to the prion protein undergoing the structural change associated with scrapie. The coding for valine (V) by codon 136 can produce susceptibility to structural change associated with scrapie. V at site136 is linked with Q at site 171, such that R cannot be found at site 171 in combination with V at site 136 (Table 5).

Table 5. Genotype based mutation producing structural change associated with scrapie

Susceptibility to Scrapie	Genotype (136, 171)
Negligible	AR/AR
Very low	VQ/AR
Intermediate	VQ/AQ
High	VV/QQ, AQ/AR, AQ/AQ

Gene regulation during stress

Preliminary results of Loeschcke et al. (2004) showed a drastic change in gene regulation in response to a short-term hardening treatment, and a different time resolution of different genes. Up regulated genes include the well-known heat shock genes, and also many other genes involved in cellular defence, immune response and metabolism are being up regulated (Leemans et al., 2000; Kayo et al., 2001; Lee et al., 2001; Pletcher et al., 2002; Seroude et al., 2002). Genes involved in housekeeping functions are up regulated with inbreeding (Kristensen et al., 2002). Also, other genes of importance for the stress response and metabolism are affected by inbreeding. The results of Loeschcke et al. (2004) from array analyses on inbred lines in drosophila also revealed that the up or down regulation of genes involved in stress resistance were more pronounced with fast compared to slow inbreeding (inbred to the same inbreeding level at different rates). This finding was in support of the hypothesis that slow inbreeding reduces the inbreeding depression as deleterious alleles have been purged. Slow inbred lines therefore, have a lower *'need'* for gene products related to stress resistance.

Candidate-gene approach for fitness traits

The first successful example for the application of the candidate-gene approach for fitness traits was the porcine stress syndrome (CRC-locus). The study of Rutherford and Lindquist (1998) showed that genetic variation in stress resistance or stress susceptibility (buffering capacity) might be due to polymorphisms at loci responsible for the regulation of stress response (e.g. heat shock) genes. Destabilising selection observed by Belyaev (1979) in silver foxes and by Yang and Siegel (1998) in chicken, might be due to similar molecular mechanisms. Thus, the candidate-gene approach could help to map the relevant loci and to isolate genetic variants, which are responsible for additive and non-additive genetic effects on fitness traits in high-yielding livestock populations.

References

Aboul Ela, M.B. and Aboul Naga, A. M. 1987. Improving fecundity in subtropical fat tailed sheep: In: New Techniques in Sheep Production (Ed: Marai I.F.M and Owen, J.B.), Butterworths London.

Arnold, G.W. 1981. Grazing behaviour. (Ed. F.H.W. Morley), World Animal Science, Bl,

Baker, R.L., Clark, J.N., Harvey, T.G., Meyer, H.H. 1986. Inheritance of foot and jaw abnormalities in sheep. Proceedings of the New Zealand Society of Animal Production 46: 93-100

Belyaev, D. K. 1979. Destabilizing selection as a factor in domestication. Journal of Hereditary 70: 301–308.

Bijlsma, R. and Loeschcke, V.1997. Environmental Stress, Adaptation and Evolution Published by Birkhäuser Verlag, Switzerland.

Bishop, S. C. and Morris, C. A. 2007. Genetics of disease resistance in sheep and goats. TSmall Ruminant ResearchT 70: 48-59.

Bishop, S. C., Jackson, F., Coop, R.L., Stear, M. J., 2004. Genetic parameters for resistance to nematode infections in Texel lambs. Animal Science. 78:185–194.

Bisset, S. A., Vlassof, A., Morris, C. A., Southey, B. R., Baker, R. L., Parker, A.G. H. 1992. Heritability and genetic correlations among faecal egg counts and productivity traits in Romney sheep. New Zealand Journal of Agricultural Research 35: 51-58

Douch, P. G. C., Green, R. S., Morris, C. A., Bisset, S. A., Vlassof, A., Baker, R. L., Watson, T. G., Hurford, A. P., Wheeler, M. 1995. Genetic and phenotypic relationships among anti-*Trichostrongylus* traits in grazing Romney sheep. Livestock Production Science 41: 121–132.

Dudzinski, M. L. and Arnold, G. W. 1979. Factors influencing the grazing behaviour of sheep in a Mediterranean climate. Applied Animal Ethology 5: 125-144.

Fogarty, N. M., Dickerson, G. E. and Young, L.D. 1984. Lamb production and its components in pure breeds and composite lines. I. Seasonal and other environmental effects. Journal of Animal Science T58: T285–300.

Fraser, A. F. and Broom, D. M. 1990. Farm Animal Behaviour and Welfare. Balliere Tindall, London

Glimp,1971. H. A. Glimp, Effect of breed and mating season on reproductive performance of sheep. Journal of Animal Science T32T:1176–1182.

Gordon, J. G and Tribe D. E. 1951. The self selection of diet by pregnant ewes. Journal of Agricultural Sciences 41:187-190.

Gruner, L., Bouix, J., Brunel, J. C. 2004. High genetic correlation between resistance to *Haemonchus contortus* and *Trichostrongylus colubriformis* in INRA 401 sheep. Veterinary Parasitology 119: 51–58.

Gupta, U. D. and Acharya, R. M. 1987. Heat tolerance in different genetic groups of sheep in semi arid conditions . Indian Journal of Animal Sciences. 57:1314-1318.

Hoffmann, A. A. and Parsons, P. A. 1991. Evolutionary genetics and environmental stress New York: Oxford University Press

Hulet, C.V., Shelton, M., Gallaghar, J. R. and Price, D. A. 1974. Effects of origin and environment on reproductive phenomena in Rambouillet ewes.1 breeding season and ovulation. Journal of Animal Sciences 38: 1210-1217.

Hunter, R. F. 1960. Aims and methods in grazing behaviour studies on hill pastures. Proceedings of the 8th International Grassland Congress, pp 454-458.

Ipate, I. G., Brembogda, A. T., Monika, Gutscher, Seregi, I., Toba, G. F., Sivana, L. Zoldag, A. Maroti-Agots, M. Parvu, N. Popescu. 2009. Genes assisted selection as instrument of the biodiversity and pooling the genetic diseases Lucrãri °tiinþifice Zootehnie °i Biotehnologii, 42 (1): 568-574

Kayo, T., Allison, D. B., Weindruch, R. and Prolla, T. A. 2001. Influences of aging and caloric restriction on the transcriptional profile of skeletal muscle from rhesus monkeys. Proceeding of the National. Academic Science. USA 98 5093–5098.

Kristensen, T. N., Dahlgaard, J. and Loeschcke, V. 2002. Inbreeding affects Hsp70 expression in two species of *Drosophila* even at benign temperatures. Evolution Ecology Research 4: 1209–1216.

Lee, J. 1986. The genetics of adaptation to cold climates with particular reference to sheep. Proceedings of the Third World Congress of Genetics Applied to Livestock Production 11: 462-473.

Lee, J. H., Cho, K. S., Lee, J., Yoo, J. and Chung, J. K. 2001. Diptericinlike protein: an immune response gene regulated by the antibacterial gene induction pathway in *Drosophila*. Gene 271: 233–238.

Lee,?S.H.,?Engle,?T.E.,?Hossner,?K.L. 2002. Effects of dietary copper on the expression of lipogenic genes and metabolic hormones in steers. Journal of Animal Science 80: 1999–2005.

Leemans, R., Egger, B., Loop, T., Kammermeier, L., Haiqiong, H., Hartmann, B., Certa, U., Hirth, F. and Reichert, H. 2000. Quantitative transcript imaging in normal and heat-shocked *Drosophila* embryos by using high-density oligonucleotide arrays; Proceedings of the National Academic Science USA 97:12138–12143.

Li, Y., Swan, A. and Purvis I. 1999 Genetic variation in resistance to fleece rot in CSIRO's fine wool flock. Proceedings of the Association for the Advancement of Animal Breeding and Genetics 13: 524–527.

Loeschckel, V., Sørensen, J. G. and Kristensen, T.N. 2004. Ecologically relevant stress resistance: from micro arrays and quantitative trait loci to candidate genes – a research plan and preliminary results using *drosophila* as a model organism and climatic and genetic stress as model stresses Journal of Bioscience. 29: 503-511.

Lynch, J. J., Hinch, G. N., Adams, D. B. 1992. The Behaviour of Sheep. Biological Principles and Mediterranean climate. Applied Animal Ethology 5: 125-144.

Marai, I.F.M., Nowar, M.S., Bahagat, L.B. and Owen, J.B. 1987 Effects of docking and shearing on growth and caracass traits of fat tailed Ossimi sheep. Journal of Agricultural Sciences 109: 513-518.

Marai, M. and Owen, J.B. 1987. New techniques in sheep production Butterworths, London, Boston

McDonald, B. J. and Hoey, W. A. 1987. Effect of photo-translocation on fleece growth in cashmere goats. Australian Journal of Agricultural Research 38:765–773.

Morris, C. A. 1998. Responses to selection for disease resistance in sheep and cattle in New Zealand and Australia. In: Proceedings of the 6PthP World Congress of Genetics of Applied Livestock Production 27: 295–302.

Morris, C. A., Bisset, S. A., Vlassoff, A., West, C. J., Wheeler, M. 1998. Faecal nematode egg counts in lactating ewes from Romney flocks selectively bred for divergence in lamb faecal egg count. Animal Science 67: 283–288.

Morris, C. A., Vlassoff, A., Bisset, S. A., Baker, R. L., Watson, T. G., West, C. J., Wheeler, M. 2000. Continued selection of Romneysheep for resistance or susceptibility to nematode infection: estimates of direct and correlated responses. Animal Science 70: 17–27.

Nagorcka, B. N. 1979. The effect of photoperiod on wool growth. In: Physiological and Environmental Limitations to Wool Growth (Eds Black, J.L. and Reis, P.J.), University of New England Publishing, Armadale, New South Wales, pp.127–137.

Olsson, A. and Beyne, T. 1990. Performance of indigenous and crossbred sheep in the highlands of Ethiopia. In: Proceedings of the Fourth World Congress Genetics and Applied Livestock Production vol. 15. pp. 406–409

Pletcher, S. D., Macdonald, S. J., Marguerie, R., Certa, U., Stearns, S. C., Goldstein, D. B. and Partridge, L. 2002. Genome-wide transcript profiles in aging and calorically restricted *Drosophila melanogaster*; Current Biology 12 712–723.

Ponzoni, R. W. 1992. Genetic improvement of hair sheep in the tropics. FAO Animal Production and Health paper, 101, Rome, Italy, pp.168.

Prince, L. L. L., Gowane, G. R., Swarnkar, C.P., Singh, D. and Arora, A.L. 2009. Estimates of genetic parameters for faecal egg count of *Haemonchus contortus* infection and relationship with growth traits Avikalin sheep. Tropical Animal Health Production DOI 1.1007/s11250-009-9487-4.

Raadsma, H. W. 1991. Fleece rot and body strike in Merino sheep. V. Heritability of liability to body strike in weaner sheep under fly wave conditions. Australian Journal of Agricultural Research 42: 279- 293.

Riddoch, B.J. 1993. The adaptive significance of electrophoretic mobility in phosphoglucose isomerase (PGI). Biological Journal of the Linnean Society, 50: 1- 1 7.

Rutherford, S. L., Lindquist, S. 1998: Hsp 90 as a capacitor for morphological evolution. Nature 396: 336–342.

Seroude, L., Brummel, T., Kapahi, P. and Benzer, S. 2002. Spatiotemporal analysis of gene expression during aging in *Drosophila melanogaster*; Aging Cell 1 47–56.

Singh, D., Swarnkar, C.P., Kumar, Sushil., Prince, L.L.L. and Arora, A.L. 2009. Performance of Avikalin sheep selected for resistance to *Haemonchus contortus*. Journal of Veterinary Parasitology 23: 23-27.

Singh, M., More, T. T., Rai, A. K. and Karim, S. A. 1982. A note on the adaptability of native and crossbred sheep to hot summer conditions of semi arid and arid areas. Journal of Agricultural Sciences 99:525-528.

Slee, J. and Stott, A.W. 1986. Genetic selection for cold resistance in Scottish black face lambs. Animal Production 43: 397-404.

Slee, J., Alexander, G., Bradley, L. R., Jackson, N., Stevens, D. 1991. Genetic aspects of cold resistance and related characters in newborn Merino lambs. Australian Journal of Experimental Agriculture 31:175–182.

Stapleton, D. L. 1978. Mohair production and seasonal variability in the fleece of the Australian Angora goat. Ph. D. Thesis, University of New England, Armadale, New South Wales.

Swarnkar, C.P., Singh, D., Kumar, Sushil., Mishra, A. K. and Arora, A.L. 2009. Study on Malpura sheep selected for resistance to *Haemonchus contortus*. Indian Journal of Animal Sciences 79: 577 – 581.

Taneja, G. C. 1967. Water intake in relation to blood potassium types in desert sheep Experientia 23:645-646.

Taneja, G. C. 1972. Genetic control and adaptive significance of blood potassium types in some indigenous and exotic breeds of sheep in India. Journal of Genetics 61: 64-77.

Upton, M. 1985. Returns from small ruminant production in southwest Nigeria. Agricultural System. 17:65–83.

Vagenas, D., Jackson, F., Russel, A. J. F., Merchant, M., Wright, I. A., Bishop, S. C. 2002. Genetic control of resistance to gastrointestinal parasites in crossbred cashmere producing goats: responses to selection, genetic parameters and relationships with production traits. Animal Science 74:199–208.

Vollema, A., 1998. Selection for longevity in dairy cattle. Doctoral thesis, Animal Breeding and Genetics group. Wageningen, Agricultural University, the Netherlands.

Watt, W. B. 1985. Bioenergetics and evolutionary genetics: opportunities for new synthesis. Amnican Naturalkt 125 118-143.

Webster, A. J. F. 1993. Environment: heat and cold tolerance. Proceedings of the Sheep Veterinary Society 17: 123- 128.

Wiggans, G. R. and VanVleck, L. D. 1978. Evaluation of sires in herds feeding differing proportions of concentrates and roughages. Journal of Dairy Science 61 246-249.

Woolaston, R. R., and Windon, R. G. 2001. Selection of sheep for response to *Trichostrongylus colubriformis* larvae: genetic parameters. Animal Science 73: 41–48.

Woolliams, C., Suttle, N. F., Woolhams, J. A., Jones, D. G., Wiener, G. 1986. Studies on lambs from lines genetically selected for high and low copper status. 1. Differences in mortality. Animal Production 43: 293-302.

Yang, A. and Siegel, P. B. 1998. Asymmetries and heterosis of bilateral traits in parental lines of chickens and their F1 crosses. Journal of Animal Breeding and Genetics 115:105–111.

❑❑❑

23

Breeding Strategies for Sustainable Livelihood, Conservation and Improvement of Small Ruminants *vis-à-vis* Global Plan of Action for Animal Genetic Resources

S.K. Singh
Central Institute for Research on Goats, Makhdoom, Farah
Mathura- 281 122, Uttar Pradesh

Introduction

Most of the genetic diversity in small ruminants of the world exists in developing and underdeveloped countries. The *'Ranchi Declaration (2009) on Conservation and Management of Farm Animal Genetic Resources'* confirms availability of 34 goat and 62 sheep breeds in India. These figures are higher than that discussed by Acharya (1982) and reported by NBAGR, Karnal. A few breeds may be added or deleted from the list, if proper genetic evaluation studies are undertaken in time framed manner at the national level. The vast area within the country i.e. Madhya Pradesh, Andhra Pradesh, Chhattisgarh and Karnataka do not possess any classified breed of goat while the goat population in these states is very high. Similar is the condition in sheep also. On other hand some states i.e. Rajasthan and Gujarat possess high number of goat breeds. This suggests necessity of conducting a country level survey for the existence of exact number of breeds that are available and constitution of a national authority entrusted with powers under land of law for accreditation of the breeds based on scientific lines. The improvement programmes for classified breeds of small ruminants are either absent or undertaken on small scale by various agencies on experimental basis. Significant number of programmes have been discontinued (i.e. Indo Swiss Goat Project on Sirohi goats and many breed centres of AICRP/Network projects on sheep and goat) due to one or other reasons. This is indicator of lack of will power to undertake the genetic improvement programmes at appropriate stages. In principle, breed improvement programmes tend to be a long-term activity covering a sizable population of a breed, but in practice, reality is far from the principles and theories involved and being evolved. Responsibilities are not appropriately marked and shared because of presence of many stakeholders i.e state government and its agencies, agricultural and veterinary universities, ICAR Institutions, Central Government and associated organizations and various non- government organizations (NGO's). The present paper envisage to evaluate the present status of improvement programmes on small ruminants genetic resources conservation and improvement programmes vis-à-vis declarations made in by *'Global Plan of Action for Animal Genetic Resources'* and in Ranchi declaration.

Components of breeding programme

Before discussing the breeding programmes and review the research programmes meant for small ruminants, it will be appropriate to design the modern breeding programmes being adopted by countries following modern breeding practices and technologies. The fundamental requirement of a breeding programme is characterization and inventory of small ruminant genetic resources. While different organizations depict variable figures not only for number of breeds available in sheep and goat but also the breed characteristics at phenotypic and genetic levels are loosely defined. The first major effort in this respect was made by Acharya (1982) and recently in Ranchi declaration. However, a national authority is required to approve and accept a breed and its characteristics. The much needed inventory of breeds will depend on these characteristics. In such situations, it is really difficult to report the exact number of breeds and their habitat of the country.

Monitoring of breed base, trends and risk status

Since, breed-wise survey has been recently included under livestock census being carried out periodically by the Government of India; it is difficult to predict the changes in population of breeds' overtime. However, lack of breed descriptors in appropriate format makes it even more difficult for surveyors of livestock census to count the animals breed-wise. In some states, the surveyors do not posses requisite qualification in animal husbandry and therefore, some times doubts are raised on animal counts reported for a particular breed. Since population dynamics breed-wise for livestock species in general and for small ruminant in particular are not available; it is difficult to monitor production trends and therefore, profits and loss in terms of biological consequences and also with respect to risk status. Such situations create hindrance in strategic planning and implementation of breeding programmes in the country specially when crucial information required for formulation of breed are not available.

Sustainable use and development

A viable breeding programme has to be sustainable in existing environment and prevailing social systems. Since breeding programmes are long-term activity and very costly; therefore results are mostly evolutionary in nature. The design of breeding programme has to be done in a manner that it has little effect on climate change, farming systems, inputs and stability of the breed. The social system do affect the longevity of breed i.e. sale and purchase of few breeds of goat viz. Jakharana, Jamunapari, Surti has been at very high rate threatening the existence of these breeds. Jamunapari because of its popularity, size, look and milk production has been in high demand world over. As such it has been regularly taken out of its home tract due to which the population of this breed has gone down below ten thousand. Similarly, the goats of Jakhrana from the its home tract in Alwar district because of its proximity to New Delhi and Surti to Mumbai have been over sold for meat purposes at premium higher prices. The Beetal is other goat breed which has gone up to level of extinction because of high intensity of crop production in its home tracts. As such the very existence of these breeds is threatened. Further, the drop in wool prices has made sheep breeds known for wool production as uneconomic proposition *vis-a-vis* crop and other livestock species.

Conservation

Recent classification standards for breeds being adapted by FAO are welcome from the perspective planning point of view. The livestock genetic resources of India as per these guidelines have been classified in Ranchi declaration. Very few breeds of goat i.e. Bengal, Gaddi and Tibetan have been categorized as *'Regional Transboundary'* and Barbari, Beetal and

Jamunapari as *'International Transboundary'* breeds. Similarly Hissardale, Madras Red, Poonchi and Tibetan breeds of sheep have been categorized as *'Regional Transboundary'* category. As majority of breeds of small ruminants are classified in 'local category'; funding, genetic improvement and conservation programmes have to be local in nature. The donors for breed improvement programmes with respect to sheep and goats are few while very large breed-based breeding programmes require heavy investment for their operation. The conservation and improvement of Animal Genetic Resources as a subject is dealt by State Governments which are not properly equipped to run such programmes on long-term basis without financial support. Further, the major thrust of State Animal Husbandry Departments and Associated Organization has been in disease monitoring. Many programmes, policies and infrastructure development are dedicated to large ruminant species. As the flock size varies according to the breed, location, farmer's capacity, landscape and vegetation available; it will be of great help if breeding programmes are formulated area-wise. Further, loss of threatened breeds will not only have negative impact on social and cultural systems but also on climate change, biodiversity of the locality and biological behavior of associated organisms. Loss in one species/breed disturbs biological chain and livelihood system also. Therefore, effective *in situ* and *ex situ* programmes are required for all threatened small ruminant breeds.

Programmes, policies and infrastructure development

Few National programmes are in operation and that too they are in large ruminants. The *'National Cattle and Buffalo Breeding Project'* run by Department of Animal Husbandry and Fisheries and implemented by State Agencies has to show its impact on conservation and improvement of cattle and buffalo. However, such programmes on small ruminants are lacking. The network projects on *'Sheep Improvement'* and *'AICRP on Goat Improvement'* projects being run by research institutions have had their own limitations, problems in implementations and are run on small populations. As such the impact of these programmes on conservation and genetic improvement of farmer's flock cannot be properly assessed. Therefore, conservation and improvement of small ruminant genetic resources of the country has been a barren field. Such conditions may not lost long as rapidly changing global environment, markets and social systems may have devastating effect on existence of an number of breeds of Indian origin. Small ruminants husbandry has being practiced by relatively weaker section of the society. Therefore, they have been unable to make a lobby so as to impress upon the government system to support small ruminant husbandry in same enthusiasm and zeal as they do for large ruminants and other industrial sectors.

Creation of statuary authorities for conservation and genetic improvement

Developed world has created various societies, organizations, constitutional bodies and legal system to promote conservation and implement genetic improvement programmes. The equitable participation of stakeholders is mandatory in improvement programmes in developing countries. This has made programmes become sustainable while in developing countries such system is lacking. Therefore, the breeding has been indiscriminate, unplanned and basically unorganized. On one hand such breeding practices produced many known genotypes as well as non-descript animals. The productivity of future generations where parents are from non-descript origin can not be predicted. The existence of approximately 85% of goat population of the country under the non-descript category is a strong indicator of unplanned and indiscriminate breeding practices being adopted by farming community and also lack of institutional set-up at country level for planning and implementation of breeding programmes. It is therefore, essential to create breeding societies with respect to each breed in a manner that they are sustainable on long term basis. The role of government departments and non government organization are crucial in this respect.

Infrastructure development and capacity building

The basic and fundamental infrastructure requirement of the breeding programme must be created in order to run such programme on long term basis. This requires policy and plans for animal identification, performance recording, movement monitoring and sharing of profits arising out of small ruminant husbandry among stakeholders. The required infrastructure at each level is lacking therefore, making it really difficult to implement the programme on sizable population over widely distributed area of the home tract. Further more ignorance among the farmers regarding benefits of planed breeding and lack of incentives to workers under rural farming system has rendered many breeding programme ineffective as they met with little success. The Indo-Swiss goat project implemented at Ramsar and Network/ AICRP projects have faced such problems in implementation of breeding programme. Further more, lack of adequate knowledge on small ruminant husbandry practices and technologies among development workers further complicates implementation of programmes.

Genetic evaluation center

The immediate requirement is to create a body for development of National and Regional animal evaluation centres on the line of INTERBULL and recording as suggested by *'International Committee for Animal Recording'*. The body should be given adequate powers and technical hands so as to develop protocols for performance recording, animal identification devices, electronic data ware houses and software etc as applicable in Indian conditions. The statistical software i.e. ASREML, WOMBAT, PEST, VCE, MTREML etc. should be available for BLUP and BLUE estimations to predict genetic merit of animals. The BLUP's are used for ranking of animals to facilitate selection. Presently the genetic and phenotypic variance estimation on production traits in livestock of India is extremely difficult because of very small populations under performance recording, the controlled environment they are maintained in, changing animal husbandry practices and policies. As genetic and phenotypic variances are the foundations of any selection criterion, unreliable estimates on small population reduce the selection accuracy and thereby selection response. This might be the main reason for variation in means of population being selected over generations. The response to genetic selection has been either negative or non significant in most selection experiments being carried out on livestock species. Therefore, intense review of selection experiments are required to reformulate the breeding policy and programmes and change the organizational set up of livestock improvement in the country.

Review of organizational structure of livestock improvement

At present many organizations are responsible for livestock improvement in the country. That makes implementation of breeding programmes even more difficult. The major government departments involved in animal husbandry are Department of Animal Husbandry, Dairying and Fisheries, Government of India, ICAR, New Delhi, state animal husbandry departments and associated bodies and state agricultural universities. In spite of so many actors, the ground level breeding programme involving farmers and stakeholders are lacking. Therefore, their is need to develop synergy among government actors for greater cooperation in, policy development, execution of programmes benefit and responsibility, impact evaluation and sharing of benefit equitable and proper sharing of benefits arising out of small ruminants husbandry.

Recommendations

In order to implement Global Plan of Action on Animal Genetic Resources (GPA) and Ranchi Declaration (RD) following recommendations are made for immediate action:

1. Creation of Breed societies/authorities for most breeds. These societies must be made responsible for implementation of breeding programmes and GPA and RD. Therefore adequate administrative authority must be ensured to these authorities.

2. Identification of farmers (covering at least 10% breed population for normal and all animals for threatened breeds). These farmers will make the core group in breed improvement programmes.
3. Animal identification for all animals of threatened breeds and at least 10 percent of other breeds.
4. Development of infrastructure for performance and pedigree recording.
5. Molecular Genotyping of most animals under performance recording for SNP's. The help of research institutions and NBAGR, Karnal may be sought.
6. Development of National Animal Evaluation Authority for technical guidance, genetic parameters and BLUP and BLUE Estimations.
7. Selection of animals on the basis of BLUP value and in situ conservation of threatened breeds.
8. Exploring local, regional and international markets for commercial gains.
9. Storage of appropriate biological samples and material for ex-situ conservation.

References

Acharya, R. M. 1982. Sheep and goat breeds of India. FAO Animal Production and Health Paper, Rome.

FAO, Commission on Genetic Resources for Feed and Agriculture 2007. Global Plan of Action for Animal Genetic Resources and the Interlaken Declaration, 37 p.

Ranchi Declaration on Conservation and Management of Farm Animal Genetic Resources. 2009 Trust for Advancement of Agriculture Sciences. Avenue II IARI, New Delhi.

□□□

24

Iranian Sheep and Goat Industry at a Glance

Reza Valizadeh
Ferdowsi University of Mashhad, P.O. Box: 91775-1163, Mashhad, Iran

Introduction

Iran as the seventeenth largest country in the world (1,648 million km^2) is located at the heart of Middle-East and bridges the Caspian Sea to Persian Gulf and East of Asia to the West of Asia. The total population of the country is 70.5 million with urban and rural population of 68.4 and 31.6%, respectively with the average population growth rate of 1.6%. The mean annual rainfall of the country is 250 mm or one third of the world (National Cartographic Centre, 1999). Iran has various agro-ecological zones from arid to semi-arid, humid to temperate and highland cold types, but most of the country is under the arid and semi-arid environment. There is about 14.2 million-hectare forestland in the whole country. Although, this country has 86 million hectare pastoral land in form of natural pastures (rangeland) and mostly are of low and medium in quality (more than 91%). Agricultural land area is about 17.7 million hectare with various types, quality and water availability (Statistical and Technology Office, 2007).

Agricultural sector accounts for about 1/3 of the national GDP and 1/4 of the country work force. More than 90% of the Iranian food requirements are produced in the country and its export ranking is third after oil and industrial goods (National Cartographic Centre, 1999). There are 128.7 million animal units (one mature sheep) in Iran. The number of sheep and goats are 52.2 and 25.9 million heads, respectively. The per capita consumption of red meat, meat, milk and eggs are 12.7, 28.4, 115 and 9.8 kg/ person/ year, respectively (Ministry of Agricultural Jahad, 2001). The domesticated sheep and goat breeds are probably originated from the wild sheep and goat species, which are still found in many parts of Iran. Two main stocks of wild sheep, Asian mouflons (*Ovis orientalis*) and the smaller type Asiatic Urial (*Ovis vignei*), as well as the main wild progenitor of domesticated goat (*Capra hircus*) by name of Bezoar goat (*Capra aegagrus*) are easily found in the protected natural areas and national parks in Iran (Coop, 1982; Ensminger et al., 1986).

Major characteristics of Iranian sheep and goat industry

Sheep and goats form the most important group of ruminants in Iran mainly in rural areas. More than 57% of the available animal units in the country are sheep and goats (Ministry of Agricultural Jahad 2001). Most of the sheep and goat keepers, mainly small farmers keep this enterprise as a complementary enterprise to plants culture or horticulture. On average every sheep or goat keeper has 38 and 25 heads of animals, respectively.

The main characteristics Iranian sheep and goat industry reported by Satari (1975) and Saadat-Noori and Siah-Mansoor (1987) are as follows:

i. Owned by small farmers

ii. Based on extensive grazing

iii. Highly influenced by the environmental variables (rain fall, weather, feed supply, drought etc) (Rancourt et al., 2006; Ministry of Agricultural Jahad, 2001)

iv. Economic variability due to uncertainty in feed availability, weather, rainfall, market, export and import animal products mainly food materials.

v. Its number or increment rate is declining in comparison with the past decades (because of urbanizations industrialization, low income, etc).

vi. Genetic structure and physiological characters of the most Iranian sheep and goats are not clear.

vii. No comprehensive standard investigation had been carried out on distinguishing different breeds of these animals. What is known as breed of sheep or goat is based on the apparent physical conformation.

viii. All of the Iranian sheep breeds, except one (Zel breed) are fat-tail types.

ix. Although Iranian sheep and goats are grouped according to their main product, but generally they are kept for providing different products or sources of income including meat, milk, fiber and hide.

x. These small ruminants are resistant to high level of inorganic minerals in feed and forages.

xi. Iranian sheep and goat live and produce over a remarkable wide range of environments from the desert type dry and warm climate to the mountainous cold zones.

xii. Iranian sheep and goats appear in different color from white to the completely black and many classes in between.

xiii. Iranian sheep produce mainly coarse fibre, which is suitable for Iranian carpet industry.

xiv. Most of Iranian breeds are high–set animals, which is a suitable character for grazing over the rocky and mountainous areas.

The main obstacles of Iranian agriculture, which affects its animal agriculture as well as other agricultural disciplines, are outlined as follows:

- Desertification
- Deforestation
- Water shortage
- Erosion
- Low efficiency and out-put
- Mostly illiterate small farmers

In this paper some elements and fluctuation of the Iranian sheep and goat husbandry under the present conditions are briefly reviewed.

Breeds of sheep in Iran

It has been noted that there are more than 28 distinctive breeds of sheep in Iran, which appear in a variety of size, shapes, types and color. Broadly speaking, there are 4 main types of sheep as follows (Saadat-Noori and Siah-Mansoor, 1987; Satari, 1975; Shoridea, 2001; Tavakolian, 2000).

(i) Meat type

a. Moghani (Shahsavan)
b. Loribakhtiyari
c. Zel
d. Afshari
e. Shal or Chal Ghazvin
f. Sangsari

(ii) Dual purpose (wool and meat) type

a. Baluchi
b. Yazdi
c. Kermani
d. Sanjabi
e. Makoei
f. Mehraban Hamadah
g. Kalkuei
h. Naeni
i. Farahani

(iii) Fur type

a. Karakul Siyah Sarakhs
b. Kabode Shiraz (Khakestari Shiraz)
c. Zandi Ghom

(iv) Milk type

a. Ghezel
b. Kordi

The following is the brief description of the 3 typical breeds of sheep in Iran.

Baluchi

This is undoubtedly, the most important breed of sheep in Iran and probably in western part of Pakistan. This fat-tail medium size sheep is well adapted to the harsh marginal arid sub-tropical areas around the two big deserts Kavir Lot and Dashte Kavir in central and eastern part of Iran. It is easily recognized by its white coat and black spots in head and legs (Shoridea, 2001; Yazdi, 1997). Baluchi breed accounts to over 29% of the Iranian sheep population. Body size varies between 40-60 kg with 1.5-2 kg of medium-quality wool. This breed provides the best fiber for making famous Persian carpets. The milk yield of lactating ewes over a period of 125 days is around 50 kg. Some Baluchi ecotypes produce a wool fiber as fine as Merino. Although, this breed of sheep has been grouped as a dual-purpose breed but currently it is kept mainly for meat production, which is popular among urban consumers in the area. Wool price is quite low and has no determinable economical impact on the farmers' budget. Unfortunately unlike other agricultural sectors sheep and goat industry receive no subsidizes from the government.

Karakul

Karakul sheep known as Karakul Siah (Black) and Sarakhs (a city in North–East of Iran).The lambs of this breed are well-adapted for fur production, but the adult animals have very low–quality coarse wool which is not comparable the attractive fur of lambs. Karakul sheep are also distributed in Turkmenistan, Uzbekistan Kazakhstan, and Afghanistan (Ensminger and Parker, 1986; Mason, 1967). It is believed that this sheep is originated from Bokhara area in Uzbekistan. However, mature Karakul sheep are gray in color, fat–tail in conformation and an average body weight of 60-70 for ewes and 80-90 for rams. In the past Karakul sheep were bred primarily for the suitability of lamb pelts for fur production. Persian lamb is famous for fur production and they are slaughtered in age of 3-10 days. The fiber over skin of these lambs is undeveloped, grows in different directions, and reflects light and giving the pelt unique attractive appearance. However, nowadays these sheep are kept for producing meat as the first sealable product, but in a special desert type climate known as Gharagham. The population of Karakul sheep in Iran is less than 6% of the total sheep population.

Zel

Zel is the only breed of sheep, which has tail instead fat-tail. This small sheep has an average body weight of 40-45 kg. The coat of Zel sheep appeared in different colors from white to black or brown. The sheep is resistant to the humid and wet environment and parasites. The home and production area of this breed is around Caspian Sea with high rainfall and mostly covered by forests. It is believed this breed is the ancestor of Merino sheep.

Breeds of goats in Iran

Unlike sheep, Iranian goats are not grouped well according to the importance of their products, color or conformation. Although, more than 20 breed of goats have been recognized in Iran but the typical breed are as follows (Tavakolian, 2000):

i. Tali or Saheli
ii. Adani
iii. Marghoz
iv. Najdei
v. Raeni
vi. Baluchi
vii. Mamasani
viii. Yazdi (Nadoshan)

Similar to sheep, goats are kept for producing different products including, meat, milk, fiber, hide, etc (Cannas and Pulina, 2008; Coop, 1982; Ensminger and Parker, 1986). The two main breeds are known for their Mohair and Kashmir production:

Marghoz

This small breed of goat is distributed over the western and North-West of Iran near to the Turkey and Iraqi borders. They produce quite fine Mohair with different colors e.g. white, golden, brown, gray and even black. The average mohair production is about 0.6 kg per year. This fiber is expensive and mainly exported. Marghaz goats are fertile animals with twin kidding over 30%. It is believed the Angora goats are originated from this breed of goat. Angora goats appear in one color, which is white to silver, but Marghoz goats produce Mohair in different natural colors which are a unique character of these goat breed.

Raeni

This type of goat is famous for producing a fine Kashmir fiber with a mean diameter around 18-20 microns. Mean raw Kashmir production by the adult Raeni goats is around 1kg per year which remarkably high. The average body weight of this type of goat is between 30-35 kg. Raeni goats are also important for their ability to survive in the arid sub-tropical environmental areas in Central dry provinces such as Kerman and Yazd.

Transition in Iranian sheep and goat population

Small ruminant systems in Iran are changing rapidly in response to variety of drivers. In 1967 the census figures clearly indicated that there were 30,467,000 head sheep and 13,329,000 head goats in the country (Table 1). Sheep and goat numbers reached 52,117,000 and 25,757,000 head in 1997 respectively. The population of these animals was 52,271,000 head sheep and 25,833,000 head goats in 2007.

Table 1. Number of sheep and goats (×1000 head) in Iran during different periods

Class of animal	Animal unit factor	Periods		
		1967	1997	2007
Sheep	1.00	30467	52117	52271
Goat	0.75	13329	25757	25833
Cattle (Large breeds)	8.00	-	1855	4619

The annual increment rate for sheep during the 30 years period (from 1967 to 1997) was 721,667 head sheep per year. The increment rate of sheep population for the last decade (1997 – 2007) was only 15,400 head sheep per year. These figures clearly show the reduction rate for sheep population during the noted decade was 46.9 times in comparison with previous period (30 years). This trend was even worse for Iranian goat population. The average increasing rate for Iranian goats was 414267 head goats per year during 30 years Period from 1967 – 1997. This figure was only 7600 head goats per year for the last decade (1997-2007). These values show a reduction rate equal to 54.5 times for the Iranian goat numbers during recent years.

In comparison with the small ruminant population trend the number of cattle (large breeds) has been increased 2.5 times during the decade from 1997 to 2007. Several factors have contributed to the declining trend in sheep and goat numbers rates, including; (a) low rainfall and climatic changes, (b) rangeland deterioration and rapid increasing the cost of animal feeds, (c) lower returns and higher risks from small ruminants than for pure–bred and cross–bred cattle, (d) rapid urbanization, (e) increasing the cost of production mainly feed resources and wages and (f) uncertainties in the public markets and governmental policies for import and export of animal products. Similar situation is also going on in many nearby countries (Thornton et al., 2009).

Carcass weight and slaughtering conditions

The average carcass weight of Iranian sheep and goats are summarized in Table 2. In general the carcass weight of both sheep and goats increased with advancing the seasons, probably due to their growth pattern and maturity. In other words in spring and summer lambs grow faster but their body weight is lighter. In autumn and winter they grow slower but have heavier body weight. Although, large variation in carcass weight and characteristics exists between and within the Iranian sheep and goat breeds as other breeds of these animals throughout the world, but generally the carcass weight of fattening small ruminants in Iran is over 55% of their live weight. Fat content of Iranian sheep carcasses is lower than 20%. Typically Iranian sheep carcasses have significant lower amount of fat within the muscles in form of marbling, probably because of their fat-tail, which is a pure fat reservoir.

Table 2. Mean carcass weights (kg) of Iranian sheep and goats during different seasons

Class of animal	Spring	Summer	Autumn	Winter	Average
Sheep	17.5	18.1	19.5	19.9	18.8 ± 1.1
Goat	13.0	13.1	13.5	13.6	13.3 ± 0.3

A summary of the results on sheep and goat slaughtering in industrial and semi-industrial slaughterhouses is presented in table 3. The table revealed that about 52.3% of sheep and goats are slaughtered under the legal controlled healthy conditions. Although no formal figure was found on this subject but it was suggested from the hide (skin) production in the country, which is formally published every year. Hide or skin marketing mainly of small ruminants is an open and real ongoing market throughout the year in all Iranian cities. Nearly all of the produced skins are exported. Therefore, the published data in skin production are correct. According to these data the real percentage of slaughtered sheep and goats in slaughterhouses is 28.3% in 1997 and 28.2% in 2007.

Table 3. Number of live and slaughtered sheep and goats in industrial and semi-industrial slaughterhouses and skin (hide) production on Iranian sheep and goat industry during two different periods

Item	Periods	
	1997	2007
Live sheep and goats	77874000	78104000
Slaughtered sheep and goats	11215024	11837000
Skin (hide) number	22077278	22023513

The recorded data in table 3 indicate that around 48% of Iranian sheep and goats are slaughtered out of the slaughterhouses in spite of its danger to the public health. It must be noted that different bodies in the government and non-governmental organizations encourage the farmers or butchers to slaughter the animals in the healthy condition provided free of charge in slaughterhouses but this behavior is changing quite slow and needs some kind of restricted roles with considerable penalties.

Reproductive performance

The average frequencies of reproductive traits are given in Table 4. These data show the overall reproduction performances of Iranian sheep and goats are lower than the exotic pure breeds. Some of the noted negative transition of small ruminants in Iran could be due to these lower performances. A higher reproductive performance have been reported by applying the advanced techniques in intensive sheep and goat farming, but their applications in large scales or in the extensive systems is under the critical question.

Table 4. Reproductive performances (%) of Iranian sheep and goats

Trait	Sheep	Goat
Fertility	93 ± 4	95 ± 6
Prolificacy	99 ± 5	110 ± 3
Survival (Birth to weaning)	96 ± 6	103 ± 5
Twins	9 ± 5	18 ± 4
Triplets	2 ± 0.4	9 ± 1

The main obstacle in applying these new techniques is lower income of small farmers. Unfortunately, the poor farmers receive no help or subsidy from the government. About 70% of Iranian ewes show estrus cycles in late summer. The other 30% come into heat at the end of winter or early spring. Although two lambings have been observed in some sheep herds under the controlled condition but it is hard to apply in the extensive system in rural areas or nomadic systems.

Conclusion

The different aspects of sheep and goat husbandry, interactions between industrialization, urbanization and the trends of small ruminant production in Iran are still not well understood. This fact is well-known that Iranian sheep and goat population will be decreased and changed dramatically with respect to their systems, locations and flock sizes in the future but at the same time the price of their products mainly meat will be increased. It seems the variability in environmental patterns such as low rainfall and feed shortage, uncertainty in farmers' income and market conditions will be the most important factors in pushing the inevitable transition in the Iranian sheep and goat industry. This transition may have critical effects on the animal based food security mainly red meat from small ruminants, which is popular for Iranian consumers. Therefore, more systematic approach is required by the government and non-governmental organizations for handling this trend in the right direction.

References

Cannas, A. and G. Pulina. 2008. Dairy goats feeding and Nutrition. CAB International, USA. pp. 293.

Coop. I. E. 1982. World Animal Science Production-System Approach. No 1 Sheep and Goat Production. Elsevier Science. Publication Co. pp. 492.

Ensminger, M. E. and R. O. Parker. 1986. Sheep and goat Science (Animal Agriculture Series). The Interstate Printers and Publication Inc., Danville, Illinois, USA. pp. 643.

Mason, I. L. 1967. Sheep Breeds of the Mediterranean. FAO, Rome, Italy, pp. 215.

Ministry of Agricultural Jahad. 2001. Jahad of Agriculture in the Mirror of Statistics. Ministry of Agricultural Jahad press, Tehran Iran. (www. maj.ir)

National Cartographic Centre. 1999. National Atlas of Iran Animal Husbandry. Islamic Republic of Iran, Plan and Budget Organization, Tehran. Iran, pp. 52.

Rancourt, M. de., N. Fois, M. P. Lavin, E. Tchakerian and F. Vallerand. 2006. Mediterranean sheep and goat production: An uncertain future. Small Ruminant Research. 62:167-179.

Saadat-Noori, M., and S. Siah-Mansoor. 1987. Sheep husbandry and management. Asharfi Pub. Co. Tehran, Iran. pp 494.

Satari, M. 1975. Sheep husbandry in Iran, breeds, feeding and production. Tehran University press, No 1276, Second edition, pp. 328.

Shoridea, A. R. 2001. Winter nutrition of breeding ewes with bagasse pith. MS Thesis, Ferdowsi University of Mashhad, Mashhad, Iran, pp. 103.

Statistical and Technology Office. 2007. Agricultural Statistics. Ministry of Agricultural Jahad, Tehran, Iran.

Tavakolian, J. 2000. An introduction to genetic resources of native farm animals in Iran. Department of Education and Research, Animal Science Research Institute. Karaj, Iran, pp. 451.

Thornton P. K., J. van de Steeg, A. Notenbaert, and M. Herrero. 2009. The impact of climate change on livestock and livestock systems in developing countries: A review of what we know and what we need to know. Agricultural system. 101:113-127.

Yazdi, M. H. 1997. Genetic studies in Baluchi sheep, biometric analyses of body development, wool production and reproductive performance. Ph.D. Thesis, Swedish University of Agricultural Sciences, Uppsala, Sweden.

❑❑❑

25

Exploration of Genetic to Diseases for Improving Small Ruminant Production

D. Singh* and C.P. Swarnkar
Division of Animal Health, Central Sheep and Wool Research Institute
Avikanagar – 304501 (Rajasthan)

Introduction

Securing and building the assets of the poor is a cornerstone of poverty alleviation. Animal health and well-being have become increasingly important issues for animal producers and consumers. Diseases causing morbidity and mortality significantly decreases profitability of animal production and have direct impact on livelihood and nutritional security of farmers and human health. Livestock diseases like anthrax, ectoparasites, gastrointestinal helminths heart water, fascioliasis, pneumonia, PPR and Pox in the tropical developing world have been ranked for their impact on poverty in terms of their direct effect on production and their indirect effects on international trade and marketing (Perry et al., 2002). The cost of existing endemic diseases is estimated to be 17% of the turnover of livestock industries in the developed world and 35% to 50% in the developing world (Bishop et al., 2002). Disease control strategies focus on either the pathogen or the host. Traditionally, control of animal disease has involved the destruction of the pathogen or the vector carrying the pathogen, e.g. through vaccination, treatment with antibiotics and other drugs and spraying pesticides. Disease can also be controlled through culling. This latter approach requires defined animal populations for the replacement in flock (eg. scrapie and JD) and substantial political support to cover the huge financial burden involved (eg. brucellosis, slaughter campaign to eradicate FMD virus from the UK). Current fear of a worldwide human influenza pandemic caused by transmission of avian influenza and swine flu viruses to humans has increased public awareness of a need to control animal diseases (Wong and Yuen, 2006). Despite the success of these traditional strategies in combating specific diseases, it was found that current systems of disease control are vulnerable (Bishop et al., 2002) and losses imposed by diseases continue to impede the growth of livestock industries and have also become the major hindrance in the up-liftment of society.

Emerging and re-emerging diseases related to climatic changes, more intensive production, and transmission of diseases from wildlife to livestock and vice versa (Daszak et al., 2000), increasing restriction on the use of antibiotics in livestock, sizeable costs and long lag phase associated with new drug development are making it more difficult to manage animal health. Additionally, consumer concern for improved food-safety, animal well-being and the implications for human health to the emergence of drug resistant organisms (BOA, 1999; Singh et al., 2002), demands alternative approaches to disease prevention which do not rely on the extensive use of chemotherapeutics (Singh and Swarnkar, 2007). Thus, the goal must be to implement non-traditional prophylactic approaches to improve disease resistance of livestock, particularly during periods of production stress such as pregnancy, parturition, weaning, shipping and handling.

Genetic resistance to disease is a widespread phenomenon and has been area of research for a long time in order to explore its utility as an alternate means of disease control (Axford et al., 2000). It has been well established that rarely will all the animals in a population when exposed to an infectious disease exhibit clinical symptoms. However, it is difficult to determine why some animals become sick while others remain healthy. Animal health is influenced by many factors including genetics, nutrition, age, stress, management system, season, pathogen dosage, immunological background, epidemiology, animal biological status and many other variables. These factors interact, thus confounding our ability to understand the mechanisms of disease resistance. This may best be accomplished through improved understanding of the phenotypes and genotypes that control host defence and regulate disease resistance or susceptibility. Livestock genetic resources have evolved in diverse environments and carry unique genes that define productive and adaptive capabilities. Within the boundaries of the Tropics of Cancer and Capricorn like the tropical and subtropical zones, where human, their crops and livestock usually suffer much greater ravages from a plethora of different diseases and pests than in the more temperate climate. Although, possibly lacking the productivity and performance potential of their counterparts in the temperate regions, one great advantage of a number of indigenous tropical breeds of livestock is their genetic ability to tolerate or resist diseases. The unimproved breeds have evolved disease resistance trait through a process of natural selection over several centuries, whereby only the fittest have survived in the face of severe challenge of environmental stress, malnutrition and massive challenge by pathogens with very little use of chemotherapeutics (Sanyal, 2002). There is phenotypic variation in the expression of resistance in a population and studies on nature of variation exhibited that some of the observed variation is genetic or heritable. This suggests that it is possible to increase the average level of resistance by conventional selection programme. Improved disease control strategies through use of disease resistant livestock and improved diagnostics and vaccines will help secure livestock assets and increase productivity, while also reducing chemical and drug usage hence improving environmental health.

Issues in disease management

Presently the disease control is accomplished by vaccination, medication, isolation, improved sanitation and better management system. However, in developing countries, it is not even possible for poor farmers to provide minimum veterinary services to keep the stock healthy. The major issues before us in disease management are:

- Availability and approach to health care delivery system
- Feasibility in implementation
- Emergence of drug resistant strains of organisms
- Cost effectiveness
- Availability of infrastructural facilities
- Remoteness of localities
- Consumer's preference and drug residue in animals based products.

Immune system

Knowledge of the mode of disease infection and host response is essential to comprehend the complexity of selecting for disease resistance. First, the pathogen must be present in the host's environment. The pathogen must penetrate the host cell barriers in sufficient numbers, attack target cells and replicate. Sub-clinical or clinical expression of the disease is dependent on the pathogen's virulence and the interaction between pathogen and host characteristics. Thus, in terms of infectious organisms, the response of the host largely reflects the relationship or adaptation between the host and agent. This response is influenced through genotype by environment interactions both at the individual and population level. It may be that disease is largely the product of incompatible gene by environmental interaction. It is therefore, particularly relevant to understand host-pathogen relationships and adaptations under various stress and management conditions. Improved understanding of the biology and genetic relationships between the host and pathogen, particularly those that affect the immune system during periods of production stress should facilitate implementation of non-traditional approaches to improve the health of intensively reared livestock. To maintain health, following three immune defences against infection must be present and functioning:

(i) Natural immunity

This is the first barrier and is comprised of skin, hair, mucous membranes, secretions (tears, urine, stomach, saliva, mucous, skin secretions, etc.), grooming behaviour (licking, dust rolling, tail swishing, etc.) and favourable microorganisms that compete directly or indirectly against pathogens. There are also nutritional components to natural immunity. Dehydration and malnutrition can decrease natural secretions making some tissue more susceptible to infection. Vitamin and mineral deficiencies result in suppressed immune systems.

(ii) Innate immunity

This refers to the immune system one is born with and is the initial response by the body to eliminate microbes and prevent infection. It involves white blood cells (natural killer cells, neutrophils, eosinophils, monocytes, and macrophages), complement proteins (C1 - C4) that adhere to pathogens and cytokines (interferons and chemokines) that attract immune cells to the site of infection. The innate immune system constantly searches for antigens (bacteria, fungi, and viruses). The innate system is not specific to any one type of pathogen and has no memory of previous exposure to a pathogen or antigen. Breed differences in the innate immune system have been reported. A higher haemolytic complement activity in *Bos indicus* breeds was associated with their higher resistance to tick infestation and subsequent tick borne diseases when compared to *Bos taurus* breeds (Wambura et al., 1998).

(iii) Acquired immunity

This is developed from previous exposure to pathogens or vaccines and is antigen specific. The acquired immune system is comprised of T and B cells, which are specialized white blood cells. The T cells destroy pathogen-infected cells (cell mediated immunity). The B cells develop into specific antibody producing cells (humoral immunity). Acquired immunity occurs in active or passive form. Passive or maternal immunity is passed from the dam to the offspring via colostrum and is temporary. Disease resistance of very young lambs / kids is highly dependent on passive immunity. This type of protection is short lived because soon after birth, the lambs's intestinal tract has a significant reduction in its ability to absorb immunoglobulins and the ewes's production of colostrum decreases as lactation progresses. Half of the colostrum antibodies absorbed by the lamb will be excreted, broken down or absorbed at 8 to 16 days postpartum and most will be gone by 30 to 60 days postpartum (Besser et al., 1988). Recently DNA markers associated with failure of passive immunity have been reported in cattle (Clawson et al., 2004). Therefore, it is important that the lambs's own immune system (active immune system) develops at an early age to produce cell mediated immunity and antibodies in response to antigens and vaccines to take over when passive or maternal immunity diminishes.

Disease Resistance

In population, lowered incidences of disease may be reached in several ways including, management and rearing measures, vaccination programmes and preventive medications as well as breeding for improved disease resistance (Magnusson, 2001). The justification for including disease resistance in breeding programs can be challenging to establish. Most importantly, the economical cost of the disease must be sufficiently high to rationalize selecting for resistance. Certainly, if consumers shun a product because of its potential health threat from antibiotic residue or non-treatable communicable diseases (i.e., BSE, Avian Influenza) then selection may be a favourable alternative. If antibiotics and other drugs have become inefficient because of microbial resistance, selection for disease resistance may be logical. Genetic selection for disease resistance may be useful against diseases for which neither vaccines nor therapeutics have been found. Organic meat production systems that cannot use vaccines or therapeutics may also find it economically important to select for disease resistance.

Approaches in breeding for disease resistance

There are four approaches that can be used for breeding livestock for disease resistance.

(i) Breeding directly for resistance to infectious diseases

The most obvious is to record disease incidence in the progeny and select those parents that produce the progeny with the lowest incidence of disease. Indeed, the heritability has been shown to be high enough for some diseases to permit such a direct selection (Lundeheim, 1988) eg., inclusion of the predisposition to mastitis in the cattle breeding programmes in Sweden. The heritability for clinical and subclinical mastitis in Swedish dairy cattle was reported as 0.02 and 0.15, respectively (Mark et al., 2000). Possibly one such disease complex is intestinal helminths in sheep and indeed a heritability of 0.2 to 0.4 of worm egg counts in faeces in different sheep-lines has been demonstrated suggesting a genetic control of resistance to helminths in sheep (Windon, 1996).

(ii) Using breeding stock possessing certain major histocompatibility complex (MHC) antigens

Another approach is to use a breeding stock possessing certain major MHC antigens, which are involved in the regulation of the immune response eg., chickens possessing the B2 haplotype are resistant to Marek's disease (Hepkema et al., 1993).

(iii) Including immune function traits with high heritability in breeding programmes

A third approach is to analyse the heritability for a set of immune functions or related traits crucial for resistance to infections. Traits important for resistance to infections with high heritability may then be included as selection criteria in breeding programmes. An example of this is the discovery of a very high heritability for the number of circulating neutrophils in the pig (Edfors-Lilja et al., 1994).

(iv) Genetic selection for animals with a high combined immune response

Finally, one may genetically select animals for high immune response using an index that combines estimated breeding values for several immunological traits, e.g., in a pig herd such low and high responder lines (LIR and HIR, respectively) have been maintained for several generations. In a challenge experiment with *Mycoplasma hyopneumonie* the HIR pigs had a better protection against polyserositis but suffered more from arthritis (Magnusson et al., 1998). Moreover, the HIR pigs responded better to vaccination against *Actinobacillus pleuropneumonie,* i.e., an indirect way to improved resistance (Magnusson et al., 1997). This approach needs an establishment of certain breeding lines.

Genetic selection for disease resistance : Genetic regulation of immune response and selection for disease resistance in livestock is well documented and should be considered as an economical and prophylactic approach to improve animal health. Livestock selection from population for the purpose of disease resistance can be either by direct or indirect process (see box)

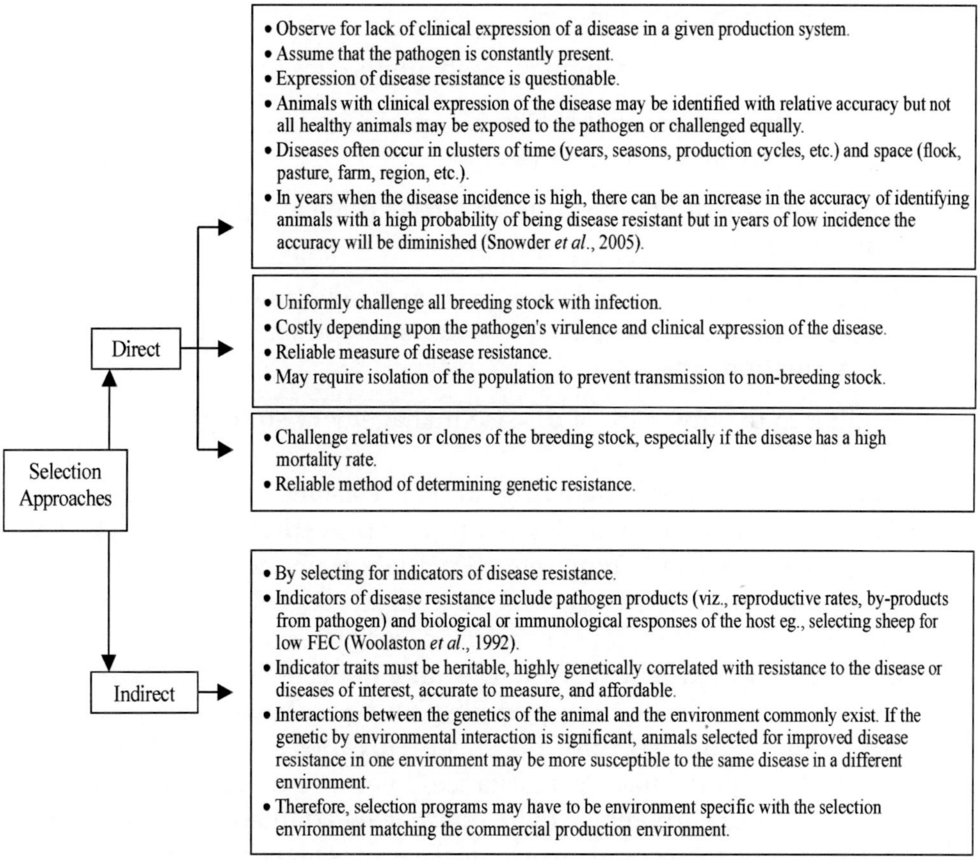

In most species, heritability estimates for humoral and cell-mediated immune responses are stable and moderate to high indicating that genetic selection is feasible. For many livestock diseases, evidence has been found for genetic variation to the extent in which host animals are susceptible. In developing breeding programmes, it is very important to distinguish between the following two terms: ***resistance*** and ***tolerance.*** Resistance refers to the ability of a host to resist infection, while tolerance signifies a condition in which the host is infected by the pathogen but displays very limited adverse effects. If the goal is to stop the spread of infection to another population, as with zoonoses, then resistance to a disease is far more advantageous than tolerance. Managing genetic resources in order to enhance the resistance or tolerance found in livestock populations offers an additional tool for disease control. A number of advantages of incorporating genetic elements in disease management strategies have been recognized (FAO, 1999) including:

- The permanence of genetic change once it is established,
- The consistency of the effect,
- The absence of the need for purchased inputs once the effect is established,
- The effectiveness of other methods is prolonged as there is less pressure for the emergence of resistance,
- The possibility of broad spectrum effects (increasing resistance to more than one disease),
- The possibility of having less impact on the evolution of macroparasites such as helminths, compared to other strategies such as chemotherapy or vaccination, and
- Adding to the diversity of disease management strategies.

Genetic investigations involving animal resistance to infections caused by pathogens of varying etiologies can be determined at three genetic levels namely; species, breed and unique genetic variation among individual animals. The impact of genetic resistance towards a' causative agent of disease is greatest in cases where all levels of genetic resistance act synergistically. For example, studies of differences in genetic resistance among species to the infective agents that cause footrot, indicate that goats display a greater resistance/tolerance to these causative agents than do sheep (Jovanovic et al., 2009). When considering the significance of resistance/tolerance at the breed level, the intrinsic evolutionary advantage of breeds that are adapted to an environment should be taken into account. In tropical regions, where extreme endemic diseases are widespread, due to their evolutionary roots, locally adapted autonomous breeds display a far greater level of genetic resistance and adaptation, as compared to imported breeds (Saviæ et al., 1995).

Based on data from FAO (2007), genetic resistance/tolerance to a variety of diseases has been reported in 59 breeds of cattle, 33 breeds of sheep, 5 breeds of horses and three breeds of pigs, all of which confirms that certain breeds express greater resistance to a larger number of pathogens than others. An overview of documented evidence for genetic resistance / tolerance to individual diseases in sheep and goats is presented in Table 1.

Table 1. Examples of diseases documented for genetic resistance or tolerance in sheep and goats

Species Infectious agent	Disease	Comment
Prion	Scrapie	Variation in resistance dominated by a known gene
Bacteria	Footrot	Variation in resistance and vaccine response
	Mastitis	Genetic effects subtle but well established
	Paratuberculosis	Anecdotal evidence of within breed variation
	Dermatophilosis	Selection of resistance successful in Merinos
	Salmonellosis	Heritable within-breed resistance
	Cowdriosis	Breed tolerance
Protozoa	Trypanosomosis	Tolerant breeds exist
Nematodes	Helminthosis	Combination of resistance and tolerance
Plathyhelminths	Liver fluke	Combination of resistance and tolerance
Flies	Cutaneous myiasis	Selection for resistance successful in Merinos

Research investigations have identified genetic resistance in sheep to parasites, such as *H. contortus, T. columbriformis and O. circumcinta*; which has further confirmed a significant correlation between the occurrence of certain parasitic diseases and particular loci on the OLA complex (chromosome 20). Footrot in goats provides a classic example of how environmental control strategy can be used in disease prevention. Studies have revealed an extremely complex immunological response, which involves approximately 26 alleles at two gene loci of the OLA complex. Since it appears that a potentially large number of genes are responsible for resistance to footrot, genetic markers that have been thus far identified, represent merely the first step towards the eradication of genetically vulnerable individuals from a population. The emergence of prion disease, along with the identification of responsible genes, represents the newest challenge in the study of inherited predispositions to disease in sheep. Several tests have been developed which identify those mutations (at codons 171, 136, 141 and154) that appear in individuals susceptible to scrapie.

Breed/genetic variation for disease resistance

A number of studies carried out in different production systems clearly demonstrated breed difference in resistance or tolerance to viral, bacterial and parasitic diseases. Genetic resistance may be found with discrete or continuous phenotypic variation and inherited by simple mendelian mechanism or polygenic inheritance. Selective breeding to take advantage of within-breed variation in disease resistance is an important strategy in the control of a number of diseases. For endemic diseases, which are continuously present in the relevant production systems (e.g. mastitis, helminthosis) selection based on phenotypic response to disease challenge is possible. In the case of mastitis, somatic cell count in milk (an indicator of bacterial infection) or clinical cases of the disease can be used as phenotypic indicators of susceptibility (Rupp and Boichard, 2003). The information on the extent of genetic variation to a disease is an essential prerequisite for inclusion of disease resistance in breeding programme. The first indication of genetic variation for disease resistance often comes from the observation that some breeds have ability to tolerate endemic diseases compared to other breeds (Table 2). In India, sound reports of breed variation in susceptibility from experimental flocks have been reported. However, most of the studies are not aimed to assess genetic variation in breeds. Comparative disease susceptibility to sheep pox, blue tongue, ovine adenovirus, FMD and haemonchosis has been reported (Sharma et al., 1986; Dubey et al., 1988; Yadav et al., 1993).

Viral diseases

It has been long recognized that certain breeds within an animal species are more resistant to acute viral infection than others eg. capripox is endemic in Africa, India and Middle East and virulent strain of the virus from these regions of the world have been shown to cause severe generalized lesions and death of British breeds contrary to a severe but local reactions in indigenous animals (Kitching et al., 1987). Since last 3 decades the growth of molecular biology have provided new insights in to host defence mechanism against viral infections and the possibility of side stepping traditional breeding methods to generate resistant animals using genetic engineering techniques. A lot of information is available on individual virus genes and the function of the proteins they specify (structure-function relationship). These functions include (i) ability of structural proteins to aggregate spontaneously to form virus particles of specific dimension, (ii) capacity of proteins on the surface of virus particles to adsorb to particular receptor proteins on the plasma membrane of cells and (iii) ability of viral coded enzymes to replicate virus genetic material inside the infected cells. Murty and Singh (1971) reported that though morbidity rate of sheep pox in Mandya (28%) and Bikaneri (24%) sheep were almost similar in an outbreak but case fatality was higher (76%) in Mandya compared to Bikaneri (51%) sheep. Mahajan (1979) observed greater susceptibility for sheep pox in mutton breeds of sheep compared to the fine wool breeds. Among mutton type sheep, Sonadi breed was found more susceptible than the Malpura breed and among fine wool breeds, Nali breed was more susceptible than Chokla breed (Sharma et al., 1986). Relatively lack of antibody response in native sheep (Malpura, Marwari, Nali and Sonadi) compared to 33-34% seroprevalence of BTD in exotic sheep (Rambouillet and Merino) was attributed to the resistance of the native sheep to blue tongue (Dubey et al., 1988). Like-wise Rambouillet sheep were found to have higher susceptibility to BTD than native Nali and Sonadi sheep (Mahajan *et al.*, 1991). No antibodies against ovine adenovirus were detected in native sheep (Malpura, Chokla, Nali and Sonadi) compared to 33-50% positivity in exotic and their crosses at CSWRI, Avikanagar (Dubey et al., 1988). In goat flock at Avikanagar, Nagpal et al., (1990) observed low, medium and high susceptibility to goat pox in Sirohi, Kutchi and Marwari goats, respectively. In another report it was observed that the mortality due to got pox was negligible (0.6%) in Sirohi goat compared to 10-fold higher mortality in crosses of Sirohi with Alpine and Toggenberg (ISGP, 1998). Against FMD, Barbari goats were found to possess low susceptibility compared to Jamunapari and Jhakrana (Shankar et al., 1992).

Bacterial diseases

Bacterial diseases that spread rapidly and do not induce natural acquired immunity tend to have a higher economic impact while diseases that occur sporadically, had low prevalence and induce natural acquired immunity tend to have a lower economic impact (Table 3). In contrast to viral diseases, well defined clinical manifestation and diagnostic techniques have been established for most bacterial diseases so that animals can be classified as resistant or susceptible after a disease outbreak. Resistance to bacterial diseases in manifested by (a) failure to develop disease after challenge (innate resistance), (b) failure to develop disease after repeat challenge /vaccination (acquired resistance), (c) expression of less severe signs and/or resilience after challenge and (d) measurement of protective immunological responses after vaccination.

(i) Johne's Disease

It is caused by *Mycobacterium Paratuberculosis* and characterized by chronic enteritis and wasting. Although culling of clinically affected animals is recommended, eradication is considered almost impossible because of the high number of healthy carriers and no clear diagnostic tests, a long incubation period in host and long survival times of the organism in the environment. Difference in climate, management and nutritional conditions prevent conclusive evidence on breed differences in susceptibility. Singh et al. (1990) reported breed differences (Barberi goats were highly susceptibility compared to Jamunapari goats) and small sire effects ($h^2 = 0.01 - 0.15$) in the prevalence of JD in goats in India. Difficulties with diagnosis and epidemiological features of the disease will be a challenge for genetic studies aimed at evaluating the scope for genetic improvement.

Table 2. Selected studies indicating breed difference in resistance / tolerance to diseases

Disease/ Infectious agent	Breed(s) showing greater resistance	Compared to which breed(s)	Experimental conditions	Results	Reference
Pox	North Yamen Black goat	British goat	Challenge infection	Higher susceptibility of British goat	Kitching et al. (1987)
BTD	Soya sheep	Dorset Horn Merino sheep	Natural infection	Severe clinical signs before death in Dorset Horn and Merino sheep	Jeggo et al. (1986)
Trypanosoma congolense	Djallonke sheep	Djallonke × Sahelian cross-breeds	Artificial Infection	Lower parasitaemia level, a longer prepatent period and a higher antibody response than crossbreeds	Goosens et al. (1999)
Ticks	N'Dama cattle	N'Dama × Zebu, Zebu	Field conditions	Fewer ticks	Claxton and Leperre (1991) Mattioli et al. (1993)
Theileria annulata	Sahiwal cattle	Holstein-Friesian	Artificial infection	Less severe clinical symptoms	Glass et al. (2005)
Anaplasma marginale	N'Dama cattle	Gobra Zebu	Field conditions	Lower serological prevalence, fewer ticks	Mattioli et al. (1995)
Haemonchus contortus	N'Dama cattle	Zebu	Village herds in the Gambia	Fewer abomasal worms, lower FEC	Claxton and Leperre (1991)
	Red Masaai sheep Small East African goats	Dorper lambs Galla	field flocks in subhumid coastal Kenya	Lower FEC, higher PCV, lower mortality then Dorper lambs	Baker (1998)
	Santa Ines sheep	Ile de France, Suffolk	on pastures in Brazil	Lower FEC, higher PCV, lower worm counts	Amarante et al. (2004)
Fasciola gigantica	Indonesian Thin Tailed sheep	Merino	Artificial Infection	Lower number of flukes in liver, differences in immune response	Hansen et al. (1999)
	Indonesian Thin Tailed sheep	St Croix			Roberts et al. (1997)
Footrot	East Friesian × Awassi cross-bred sheep	Pure-bred Awassi	Natural outbreak in Israel	Lower prevalence	Shimshony (1989)
	Romney Marsh, Dorset Horn, Border Leicester sheep	Peppin Merino, Saxon Merino	On irrigated pasture in Australia	Less serious lesions, faster recovery	Emery et al. (1984)

Table 3. Major bacterial diseases of small ruminants and their importance (Raadsma, 1995)

Disease	Importance (Prevalence/Economic)		Management	Vaccine efficacy	Zoonotic nature	Contagiousness
	Sheep	Goat				
Actinobacillosis	+	+	Antibiotics	No	No	Yes
Anthrax	++	+	Antibiotics, hygiene	Yes (***)	Yes	Yes
Brucellosis	++	++	Antibiotics, hygiene	Yes (**)	No	Yes
Caseous lymphadinitis	++	++	Antibiotics, hygiene	Yes (**)	No	
Bacillary haemoglobinuria	-	NR		No	No	-
Black disease	++	+	Hygiene, vaccine	Yes (***)	No	-
Blackleg	+	-	Vaccine	Yes (***)	No	-
Botulism	+	+	Hygiene, vaccine	Yes (*)	No	-
Enterotoxaemia	+++	+++	Vaccine	Yes (**)	No	-
Malignant oedema	+	-	Hygiene, vaccine	Yes (***)	No	-
Tetanus	+++	+++	Hygiene, vaccine	Yes (***)	Yes	-
Colibacillosis	-	-	Antibiotics	No	Yes	Yes
Vibriosis	-	-	Antibiotics, hygiene	Yes ?	No	-
Salmonellosis	++	++	Antibiotics, hygiene	No	Yes	Yes
Yersiniosis	-	-	Antibiotics, hygiene	No	Yes	Yes ?
Footrot	+++	++	Antibiotics, vaccine, hygiene	Yes (**)	No	Yes
Listeriosis	+	++	Antibiotics ?	Yes ?	Yes	-
Mastitis	-	+	Antibiotics ?	No	No	-
JD	+	+	Slaughter	Yes (*)	No	Yes
Mycoplasmosis	-	++	Antibiotics	No	No	Yes
Ovine enzootic abortion	+	-	Antibiotics	Yes (*)	Yes	-
Pasterellosis	++	++	Antibiotics	Yes (*)	No	Yes

(Importance: - = Unimportant, +++ =Very important, NR = Not relevant
Vaccine efficacy: * = partial protection, short term immunity, *** = Highly protective, long term immunity)

(ii) Salmonellosis

In small ruminants it takes the form of acute enteritis with severe diarrhoea or dysentery. Usually the disease precipitates under stresses like transport, nutritional deprivation, cold exposure, weaning, lambing / kidding, concurrent infections and over-crowding. No reports are available on genetic differences between breeds of sheep and goats, however, identification of specific loci (*Ity* and *Lps*) associated with innate resistance to *S. typhimurium* infection in mice, provides a powerful option to screen for similar genetic variants in other species (Lantier et al., 1990).

(iii) Enterotoxaemia

The disease is peracute and death takes place within hours. Normally disease progress is so rapid that no treatment is possible. Vaccination is recommended as a highly successful control strategy. No genetic variation in susceptibility to this disease has been documented.

(iv) Caseous lymphadenitis

It is caused by *Corynebacterium pseudotuberculosis* and animals with lesions are a major reason for carcass condemnation on slaughter. Differences between breeds in susceptibility to experimental infection have been reported (Pepin et al., 1988). A possible association has been reported between involvement of Class I gene from the ovine MHC and onset of abscess formation (Millot, 1989).

(v) *Pasteurellosis*

There is no evidence for genetic variation between or within breeds of the sheep in susceptibility to the infection. Further sporadic nature and relatively low prevalence will make genetic comparisons difficult.

(vi) *Mycoplasmosis*

No examples of genetic difference in susceptibility of the host have been documented.

(vii) *Mastitis*

It is considered as a complex of infections, with predisposing factors as important as opportunistic bacterial agents. A wide range of pathogens have been implicated in mastitis, the most common being *Staphylococcus aureus, Streptococcus* spp, *Pseudomonas aeruginosa, Corynebacterium pyogenes, Escherichia coli, Mycoplasma* spp and *Pasteurella haemolytica*. Breed differences in prevalence of udder infection in small ruminants has been reported by Watson et al. (1990) and Jones (1991). Larsgard and Vaabenone (1993) reported possibility of genetic variation within sheep flocks (h2 = 0.13±0.16) against mastitis. Though, the complex nature of mastitis may prevent carefully controlled genetic studies and environmental factors may prevent the expression of genetic variation as shown in cattle (Eriksson, 1991), there is need to generate information on between breed and within-breed genetic differences in mastitis.

(viii) Collibacillosis

Barberi goats were observed highly susceptible for collibacillosis compared to Jamunapari breed (Vihan and Singh, 1988; Singh et al., 1992).

(ix) Footrot

It is caused by the highly contagious bacterium *Dichelobacter nodosus*. Virulent infection causes severe lameness in sheep and goats with under-running of the hoof and inflammation. The occurrence of footrot in a flock is extremely disheartening and stressful for the farmer as it resulted in 20% drop in lambing rate, 40% reduction in wool yield and increase in death rate from 5 to 10%. The expression of footrot in a flock is governed by three factors namely; (a) virulence of organism, (b) the suitability of environment and (c) inherent susceptibility of host (Egerton, 1989). Sources of genetic variation in resistance to footrot have been reviewed by Egerton and Raadsma (1991). Skermam and Moorhouse (1987) developed blood lines in Romney Marsh and Corriedale breeds with increased resistance to footrot and reported differences between sires for resistance within a range of breed. In New Zealand, a moderate (0.28 – 0.55) heritability was derived from the prevalence of affected and non-affected sheep (Baker et al., 1986). The heritability of footrot based on a single observation was 0.14±0.04 for natural exposure and 0.15±0.05 for experimental footrot. The genetic marker (MHC genes) for natural resistance in sheep to footrot was discovered during 1997-1999 that indicates whether a sheep has high, medium or low natural resistance to footrot.

(x) Fleece rot and Dermatophilosis

Fleece rot is a mild superficial dermatitis induced by moisture and bacterial proliferation at skin level. A range of pseudomonads are the major causative agents. Dermatophilosis is caused by chronic infection with *Dermatophilus congolensis* coupled with extensive wetting of the skin. These entities are intricately linked to body strike (Raadsma et al., 1988, 1989). There is no conclusive evidence for differences between breeds in their susceptibility to fleece rot. However, considerable evidences are available that reflect significant variation in the susceptibility to fleece rot between flocks of Merino sheep. Increased resistance from strong-wool to medium-wool to the fine-wool strains is now well documented (Raadsma et al., 1989). The heritability of liability to fleece rot is 0.3 to 0.4 (McGuirk and Atkins, 1984) indicating that disease susceptibility is partly under genetic control and there is potential scope for within-flock genetic improvement. Similarly for resistance to experimental dermatophilosis the h^2 ranged from 0.14±0.05 to 0.42±0.18 (Raadsma et al., 1992).

(xi) Anthrax

It is endemic in many tropical and subtropical countries in usually well defined endemic areas. No documented evidences of differences in susceptibility of sheep to anthrax have been reported. However, in mice Shibaya et al. (1991) demonstrated variation between inbred strains in resistance to *Bacillus anthracis,* with the possibility of a gene with large effect.

(xii) Listeriosis

At the Arid Region Campus of the CSWRI, at Bikaner (Rajasthan), Bohra (1988) observed incidence of listeriosis only in native Marwari sheep but failed to get incidence in exotic Karakul sheep on the same premise.

Parasitic diseases

Grazing animals are continuously exposed to infestation with larvae of gastrointestinal nematodes (GIN). The control of GIN is solely dependent on use of anthelmintics, however this tactics resulted in widespread emergence of anthelmintic resistance in parasites (Singh et al., 2002; Singh and Swarnkar, 2008; Swarnkar et al., 2008) in addition to having chances of residues in livestock products. In worm management the alternative approaches includes grazing management, nutritional management, biological control, genetic control and vaccination (Swarnkar and Singh, 2005). Among these strategies, exploitation of host genetic resistance seems to be an attractive sustainable solution for control of GIN infections (Baker, 1998). A relatively simple and cheap method of reducing the effects of nematode infestation would be selection and breeding of genetically nematode-resistant animals and there are many reports on variation among breeds of sheep in resistance to common internal parasites, such as *H. contortus, Trichostrongylus* spp., *Ostertagia* spp. (Gasbarre and Millar, 2000). Worm resistant animals can be found in any flock, whether they are in a wormy, high rainfall environment or a dry area as demonstrated in sheep breeds like East Africa Masai, Florida Native,

Barbados Blackbelly, St. Croix and others (Baker, 1996). Selecting for worm resistant sheep is a gradual but permanent approach to the sustainable control of internal parasites. Modelling predictions indicate that it would take 10-12 years selection with a high emphasis on breeding for worm resistance to be able to eliminate one drench from the annual program. These predictions are supported by results from a CSIRO experimental flock that has been selected for worm resistance for about 20 years.

Genetic variation in host resistance to GIN

Resistance to internal parasites varies considerably between animals and 20-30% of this variation is due to genetic differences between animals (Swarnkar et al., 2000; Nimbkar et al., 2003; Yadav et al., 2006; Mandal and Sharma, 2008). Presently the largest source of genetic variation in resistance is between sheep within a flock, rather than between different flocks (Kumar et al., 2006). Resistance to internal parasites is under genetic control and subject is vividly reviewed by (Stear et al., 1990; Stear and Wakelin, 1998). It has been recognized for decades that breeds of sheep differ in their resistance to nematode infection (Table 4). In France, Romanov ewes were found more susceptible than Lacaune ewes (Gruner et al., 1986) and more susceptible than Merinos and crossbreds (Gruners et al., 1992). In India Nimbkar et al. (2003) indicated that lambs sired by Garole rams had significantly lower FEC than lambs sired by Deccani rams while lambs sired by Bannur rams were intermediate between the two. Further Nimbkar (2005) confirmed the relatively high worm resistance of the Garole breed, followed by the Bannure, compared to the Deccani and Awassi breeds. Yadav et al. (1997) reported no significant differences in parasitological, pathophysiological and immunological parameters in native Nali and Merino crosses experimentally infected with *H. contortus.* Hooda et al. (1999) observed higher haematological values, fewer pathological lesions and significantly lower worm burden in responders of Sonadi x Corriedale lambs. It was observed in the flocks of CSWRI that native Malpura breed was more tolerant to heavy worm burden (Pachalag et al., 1972) and out of 13 Malpura sires tested, rogenies of 8 sires had low mean FEC (Swarnkar et al., 1997a). Chauhan et al. (2003 a, b) observed that in semi-arid region of India, Jamunapari lactating goats had significantly higher FEC than that of dry and pregnant does but there was no peri-parturient rise in FEC in resistant Barberi goats. Variations among breeds were not consistent in response to primary infection and suggest that observed breed differences may be due to differences in acquired immunity. Singh et al. (2006) observed that in Malpura and Avikalin lambs there was no difference in intensity of infection between resistant and susceptible line at naïve stage however, among exposed animals due to expression of variability in resistance to infection, the mean FEC remained significantly higher in susceptible line. At CSWRI, Avikanagar, study on effect of *FecB* gene inheritance on faecal egg count exhibited that on majority of occasions mean FECs for strongyle worm remained lower in *FecB* carrier sheep (Garole followed by its crosses with Malpura) compared to *Fec B* non carrier Malpura sheep (Singh et al., 2009b).

In Australia and New Zealand, the genetic variation in host response to GIN has been exploited to develop sheep resistant to *H. contortus*. Romney and Merino sheep were successfully selected for high and low immune response to *H. contortus* and *T. columbriformis* (Bisset et al., 1991; Woolaston and Piper, 1996). The heritability of resistance to GIN infection in sheep, as measured by faecal egg count (FEC) varied from 0.01 to 0.50 (Table 5). Baker et al. (1998) reviewed that average h^2 to the tune of 0.32 for a single FEC measurement while a weighted mean of 0.27 of several literature h^2 estimates of FEC in sheep was reported by Safari et al. (2005). The disparity in h^2 estimates of FEC indicates that some of the important genes for resistance had been fixed in certain breeds eg. Red Maasai after many centuries of natural selection under endoparasitic challenge resulting in low estimate in resistant breeds. Until recently, little was known of the extent of variation in resistance between flocks. Studies of 57 bloodlines across six research stations in various parts of Australia found that between-flock variation in resistance was quite small compared with within-flock genetic variation. Of the total genetic variation in FEC, typically only 4% was accounted for by between-strain differences, 9% by bloodlines within strains and 85% by within-flock genetic differences (Woolaston and Eady, 1995).

Using FEC as phenotypic marker for within breed selection of resistant and/or susceptible animals at CSWRI, Avikanagar it was observed that this trait is low to moderately heritable. Creation of divergent lines either resistant (R-line) or susceptible (S-line) could be possible through regular screening for FEC at naïve and exposed stage of infection and selection of progenies. In this attempt study undergoing at CSWRI, Avikanagar revealed that animals of R-line had lower FEC over the years compared to their counterparts in S-line. The animals of S-line required strategic as well as tactical anthelmintic intervention while animals of R-line were maintained without any anthelmintic intervention (Swarnkar et al. 2008) Selection of resistant individual or breed is feasible using phenotypic markers such as FEC, packed cell volume, peripheral eosinophil counts etc. However, one of the major difficulties inherent in using phenotypic markers in naturally infected animals is the need for same uniformity of challenge. Since artificial challenge of large number of animals in different environment also possess problems, researchers are seeking to identify appropriate genetic markers. Though, candidate genes and alleles associated with resistance are known however, to date not a single common gene could be identified.

Genes controlling resistance to GIN

The genetic markers allow detection of specific region of DNA which is associated with worm resistance. The usefulness of these depends initially on the genetic control of the resistance trait and on the proximity of the markers on the chromosome to the gene of interest. If the trait is due to the combined action of several genes of small effect (polygenic) it is unlikely that genetic markers will be useful in identifying animals of superior resistance status. However, if the resistance is due to the effect of a single gene, or the action of one or a few genes of moderate or large effect (i.e. Quantitative Trait Loci, QTL) the probability of identifying useful markers is much greater. The inclusion of resistance to GIN in sheep breeding programme might be facilitated by the identification of QTL or closely linked markers. However, the investigation of QTL for resistance to GIN in sheep is a difficult area of research, mainly due to a large number of problems associated with phenotypic and analytical complexity of this trait. A number of studies have investigated QTL for resistance in sheep with a diverse range of approach and have identified regions of interest on different chromosomes (viz., 1, 3, 6 and 20). A QTL conferring resistance to *H. contortus* and accounting for about $1/3^{rd}$ of the total genetic variation in FEC was detected in the "Golden Ram" Merino flock in Australia. Similarly evidence has been found for a putative QTL in mean FEC on primary challenge with *H. contortus* in Indonesian Thin Tailed sheep.

The preliminary results with established experimental lines in New Zealand indicate that there may be several genes that have substantial effect on host resistance. Further, the use of Marker Assisted Selection (MAS) techniques are considered as the most effective tools for future to identify sheep that are both resistant and resilient to worm infection. The advantages of MAS techniques include:

- No need to subject animals to prolonged worm challenge, so production cost associated with the test procedure as well as costly and messy sampling procedures will be avoided.
- Higher possibility to determine an animal's genetic status at an early age.
- Overcome the problem associated with recessive or over-dominant genes under traditional selection pressure.
- Valuable in overcoming the antagonistic association between low FEC and some production traits.

Table 4. Resistance to parasites in different sheep breeds

Breed	Compared with	Type of infection	Results	Reference
Navajo	Suffolk, Targhee, Rambouillet, Corriedale	Natural	Reduced number of worms	Knight et al. (1973)
Barbados black belly	Dorset and its crosses	Artificial/natural	Decreased FEC, worm count	Yazwinski et al. (1981)
Florida Native	Rambouillet, Hampshire	Artificial/natural	Decreased FEC, Hb, worm count	Loggins et al. (1965)
Florida Native, St. Croix, Barbados	Rambouillet, Finn Dorset X Rambouillet	Artificial/natural	Reduced or no PPR	Courtney et al. (1984)
Florida Native, St. Croix	Finn Dorset X Rambouillet, Barbados blackbelly	Artificial/natural	Decreased FEC, No difference in worm count	Courtney et al. (1985a, b)
Florida Native	Dorset X Rambouillet	Artificial/natural	Decreased FEC, worm count	Zajac et al. (1988)
St. Croix	Dorset	Artificial/natural	Decreased FEC, worm count, globular leucocytes	Gamble and Zajac (1992)
Targhee x Barbados	Targhee	Artificial	No difference in FEC, worm count, PCV and weight gain	Todd et al. (1978)
Florida Native	Rambouillet	Artificial	Low FEC, worm count, PCV, abomasal eosinophils, pepsinogen	Bradley et al. (1973) Radhakrishnan et al. (1972)
Florida Native, St. Croix	Dorset X Rambouillet	Artificial	Low FEC, PCV, Total protein	Zajac et al. (1990)
Malpura	Sonadi	Natural	Low susceptibility	Pachlag and Kumar (1974)
Coimbatore	Merino, Rambouillet		Lower FEC, mortality, morbidity	Sanyal (1988)
Munjal (Nali X Lohi)	Hisardale (Nali X Corriedale)		Low susceptibility	Yadav et al. (1993)

Table 5. Heritability of FEC following natural / artificial infection of GIN in sheep and goats

Breed	Age	Infection type	h^2	Reference
Merino	Weaners	Artificial *T. colubriformis* after vaccination with irradiated *T. colubriformis*	0.41 ±0.04 0.41 ±0.09	Windon and Dineen (1984)
Romney and crosses	Weaners	Natural *T. columbriformis, O. circumcincta*	0.34 ±0.19	Watson *et al.* (1986)
Merino	Weaners	Artificial *H. contortus*	0.34 ±0.10	Albers *et al.* (1987)
Merino	18 months	Artificial *H. contortus*	0.23 ±0.13	Piper (1987)
Merino	Weaners	Natural *H. contortus*	0.42 ±0.14	Cummins *et al.* (1991)
Romney	Weaners	Natural *H. contortus*	0.34 ±0.09	Baker *et al.* (1991)
Merino	Sheep	Artificial *H. contortus*	0.30 – 0.50	Woolaston *et al.* (1991)
Romney	Weaners	Natural *H. contortus*	0.13 ±0.07	Mc Ewan *et al.* (1992)
	Sheep		0.28	Nowosad *et al.* (1992)
Romanov	Sheep	Artificial mixed GIN infection	0.55	Gruner and Lantier (1995)
Polish long wool	Sheep	Artificial mixed GIN infection	0.28	Gruner and Lantier (1995)
B. Merino	Hogget	Natural *H. contortus*	0.42 ±0.27	Swarnkar *et al.* (1997b)
Red Maasai	Lambs		0.06	Baker *et al.* (1998)
Polish long wool	Lambs	Natural *H. contortus* and *O. circumcincta*	0.22 to 0.33	Bouix *et al.* (1998)
	Ewes	Natural *H. contortus* and *O. circumcincta*	0.18 to 0.25	
Avikalin	Hogget	Natural *H. contortus*	0.35 ±0.18	Singh *et al.* (1999)
	Sheep		0.20 – 0.42	Morris *et al.* (2002)
Garole crosses	Sheep	Natural *H. contortus*	0.09 – 0.12	Nimbkar (2005)
Dorper	Lambs		0.35	Wolf *et al.* (2008)
Barbari	Goat	Natural *H. contortus*	0.05 – 0.13	Mandal and Sharma (2008)
Malpura	Hogget	Natural *H. contortus*	0.010 – 0.246	Swarnkar *et al.* (2009)
Avikalin	Hogget	Natural *H. contortus*	0.114 – 0.223	Singh *et al.* (2009a)

For genetic analysis of the DNA polymorphism more than 200 microsatellite markers were tested spaced at regular intervals (about 20 cM) across the entire genome. Preliminary results of QTL analysis show that an expected heterozygosity index was 50%, and 45% for polymorphism information content (PIC). These data suggest that parasite-resistance is related to acquired immunity, associated with the IFNG gene. The gene was also found as QTL for resistance to gastrointestinal nematodes in sheep. The relevant investigation to identify QTLs for resistance to GIN was arranged in 1979 in New Zealand (Diez-Tascon et al., 2002). Divergent sheep selection lines resistant and/or susceptible to nematode parasites were used to find the respective QTLs. The QTL for resistance was localized in chromosome 3 and mapped to about a 5 cM region. The gene located to this region codes for the interferon gamma (IFNG) and is considered a putative candidate gene for resistance to nematode parasites. In Australia the study to identify QTL for resistance to *T. colubriformis* in Merino sheep revealed the respective QTL on chromosome 6 (Beh et al., 2002). Recently, a genome scan performed by Crawford et al. (2006) using divergent lines and naturally infected animals detected a significant QTL on chromosome 8. Studies with Soya sheep exhibited that three loci appear to be associated with parasite resistance: INFG on chromosome 3 (Coltman et al., 2001), MHC on chromosome 20 (Paterson et al., 1998) and the adenosine deaminase gene (ADA) on chromosome 13 (Gulland et al., 1993). In Germany the study on QTL for resistance to parasites in Rhönschaf sheep showed significant association between parameters of resistance (faecal egg count) and the markers *OarCp73*, *DYMS1* and *BM1815*. The *DYA* gene (belonging to the class IIb subregion of the MHC) closely linked to the microsatellite *DYMS1*, is a possible candidate gene for resistance to *H. contortus* in sheep (Janssen et al., 2002). In Scotland an ovine MHC class II antigen was identified being associated with 98% lower FEC in Scottish Blackface sheep naturally infected with *Ostertagia circumcincta* (Schwaiger et al., 1995), a subsequent study showed that DRB1 class II antigen was associated with 10-fold reduction in FEC. Thus number of studies (Outteridge et al., 1996; Paterson et al., 1998; Schwaiger et al., 1995; Van Haeringen et al., 1999) provided evidences that were significantly associated with ruminant resistance to intestinal nematodes is MHC.

Special attention is paid to the MHC class II molecules that induce the immune response in case of extracellular infection. The widest polymorphism among the MHC genes is found in *locus DRB*. This gene encodes the beta chain of the DR molecule, protein found in high concentrations on the surface of antigen-presenting cells. The most frequently investigated fragment of the *DRB* gene covers exon 2, which codes the binding site for a foreign protein.

Primitive Heatherheaded sheep showed a significant association between microsatellite polymorphism in *DRB1* gene and FEC (Charon et al., 2002). The investigated gene fragment was found highly polymorphic and a total of 23 alleles were identified. Alleles 482 bp and 530 bp showed significant association with resistance to GIN, while the 568 bp allele was found related to susceptibility to parasites (Charon, 2004).

At CSWRI investigations research efforts were carried out to observe the polymorphism of MHC Ovar-DRB1 in R and S lines developed against *H. contortus* and to measure the association of RE patterns with R and S lines in both Malpura and Avikalin breeds. The Ovar-DRB1 of 296bp was amplified through nested PCR using primers ERB1, HL031 and XRB1. In Malpura, SacI RE produced three genotypes viz; AA, AB and BB in R and S-line with frequencies of 0.36, 0.54,01 and 0.60, 0.30, 0.1 respectively. The frequency of allele 'A' (0.75) was significantly higher in S-line as compared to R-line (0.64) and the frequency of allele 'B' (0.36) was significantly higher in R-line as compared to S-line (0.25). These two alleles 'A' and 'B' may be associated with resistance/susceptibility in Malpura sheep. There was no significance difference of frequency of RE pattern produced by NcI and Hin1I in both the lines. In Avikalin, there was no significant difference in the genotype produced by NciI, SacI, SacII and Ecor1 enzymes between the R and S lines. The frequency of AB (0.59) and AA (0.46) produced by Nci1 were more in resistant and susceptible line, respectively. The allele frequency of 'A' was 0.69 and 0.67 in R and S-line respectively. The frequencies of three genotypes produced by SacI enzyme in R and S-lines were AA (0.49) AB (0.49) BB (0.02) and AA (0.60) AB (0.38) BB (0.22), respectively. Over all in both the lines the allele frequency of 'A' (0.76) was observed to be more than that of 'B' (0.24). It was observed that the genotype frequency of BB produced by SacII enzyme was nil. The genotype frequency of AA was highest in R (0.79) as well as in S (0.85) lines. The allele frequency of 'A' and 'B' in R lines were 0.89 and 0.11, respectively and in S line was 0.92 and 0.08.

Challenges of selecting for disease resistance

Selection for disease resistance is much more complicated than selecting for production traits which can be measured directly or indirectly on each animal. The success of selection for disease resistance is dependent on correctly identifying the phenotype for disease resistance. Identifying the phenotype for disease resistance is difficult. It is a false assumption that in a population of sick and healthy animals all healthy animals are disease resistant. Some susceptible animals may not have been sufficiently exposed to the disease organism to get sick. Animals that appear healthy may have sub-clinical infections and represent pathogen reservoirs. Often the clinical expression of a disease can be confounded with a similar disease, for example pneumonia can be confused with bronchitis, emphysema, pleuritis, pulmonary adenomatosis, upper respiratory infection and pleural fibrosis. Selection for disease resistance may be unfavourable for animal production. If the genetic factors that improve disease resistance reduce production traits such as growth or feed efficiency then selection for disease resistance will decrease production. There is sufficient evidence that such negative genetic correlations do exist. If these genetic correlations are unfavourable, then a selection index for total merit may be feasible to maintain production levels while selecting for disease resistance. Perhaps, the biggest challenge of selecting for disease resistance is to accurately identify the phenotype for disease resistance and/or to have reliable genetic markers with high predictive values for a disease phenotype. For some diseases, disease resistance may include sub clinical and clinical infection while for other diseases only the clinical expression may be considered. The difficulties associated with breeding for improved responsiveness are as follows:

- Immune response is complex in nature and a good response to one antigen does not necessarily mean a superior reaction to another antigen. It means, breeding for enhanced immune responsiveness as a consequence of the presence of a particular haplotype, reduces the MHC polymorphism and increases the risk of susceptibility as a result of immunological unresponsiveness.
- Complex nature of genotype - environment interaction influences the immune response and disease resistance.
- Breeding for improved immune response and disease resistance may have a negative effect on desirable production traits.

The Near Future

We do not know at this time to predict whether or not selection for disease resistance can be effective in livestock. Basic research into the complexities underlying diseases will likely reveal effective approaches for many disease problems. It may be difficult to select for animals resistant to a wide range of diseases, it may be possible to breed or identify animals that are genetically more responsive to anti-viral vaccines or other therapies. Certainly, genetic selection will not solve all of our livestock disease problems. Therefore, management, nutrition, vaccination, culling, therapeutic treatment, stress reduction practices and other measures must accompany genetic approaches to reduce the impact of livestock disease on profitability and animal well being.

(i) Polygenic Effects

The complexity of the immune system clearly infers that many genes are involved in disease resistance. It is highly doubtful that many single genes will be discovered and associated with major diseases. Chromosome mapping may lead to quantitative trait loci or regions related to disease resistance. As the human and mice genomes are further investigated for disease related genes, it is highly plausible that quantitative trait loci (QTL) associated with disease resistant in livestock may also be identified in the near future. New and novel gene mapping approaches are being developed specifically for detection of complex disease loci (Pareek et al., 2002). Micro array technology is advancing rapidly to enable association of livestock DNA with human (Chitko-McKown et al., 2004) and mice DNA. Comparative genomics may make the identification of disease loci easier and more affordable. It may be possible to identify similar genes associated with disease susceptibility/ resistance among human, mice, and livestock.

(ii) Gene Mapping

Sequencing of the mice and human genomes and construction of similar maps in livestock have led to discovery of several genetic markers and even genes related to the immune system. Most genes related to disease resistance have been discovered using inbred strains of mice. Only a few genes have been linked to disease resistance in cattle. The Nramp1 gene (natural resistance-associated macrophage protein) is associated with the innate immune system. Nramp1 has been linked with resistance to brucellosis (Harmon et al., 1989), tuberculosis and salmonellosis (Qureshi et al., 1996). Homologues for Nramp1 have been identified, sequenced and/or mapped in chickens, swine, and sheep (Adams and Templeton, 1998). The major histocompatibility complex (MHC) genes are linked to specific immunological responses. MHC genes were some of the first mapped and sequenced genes related to disease resistance. The MHC have a high degree of polymorphism, more than one variant (allele) for a gene exists in a population. Over 50 MHC alleles have been identified (Adams and Templeton, 1998). The high degree of polymorphisms for MHC genes which is unique for each individual (over 100 million combinations possible) partially explains how the host immune system can attack such a great number of antigens which requires the ability to distinguish self from foreign. In dairy cattle, the bovine MHC complex has been linked to disease resistance of economically important traits (Batra et al., 1989). In chickens, MHC has been linked to resistance to Marek's disease and fowl cholera (Lamont, 1989). Other examples of recently discovered single genes influencing disease resistance in livestock include the fimbriae F4 (K88) gene in swine for reducing *E. coli* intestinal infection (Moon et al., 1999), the prion protein (PrP) gene related to scrapie susceptibility in sheep and the TNC gene related to salmonellosis in chickens (Hu et al., 1997).

(iii) Nuclear Techniques

Conventional approaches of disease diagnosis involving isolation and direct detection of microorganism by microscopy and immunoassay usually take long time while nucleic acid hybridization techniques are very promising in terms of time and sensitivity. Remarkable improvements in livestock productivity in the developed countries have achieved through research into how animals grow and how yields can be influenced and protected, followed by the widespread uptake of new techniques and materials. Biological processes responsible for disease resistance in different farm animals are manipulated for greater productivity through the use of radioisotopes (Dargie, 1990; FAO/IAEA, 2008). Nuclear techniques have played the vital role in the field of animal health. Ionizing irradiation from 60Co or X-ray sources have been used to eliminate the virulence of some parasites to produce safer and cost effective vaccines.

(iv) Disease resistant genetically modified animals

The combination of new methodology that enables the efficient production of genetically-modified (GM) animals with exciting new tools to alter gene activity makes the applications of transgenic animals for the benefit of animal (and human health) increasingly likely. This technology is likely to have specific application where genetic variation does not exist in a given population or species and where novel genetic improvements can be engineered. With either approach, the intention would be to enhance the ability of the animals to mount an appropriate immune response against the pathogen or to generate an effective system that would directly block pathogen entry or directly destroy the pathogen (Whitelaw and Sang, 2005). The *Mx* genes of vertebrates were first discovered in mice because of the ability of functional alleles to induce a potent antiviral state in response to infection by specific groups of viruses, including influenza. Chickens also have an *Mx* gene, but the allele present in most commercial lines is apparently not functional due to a single amino acid substitution (Ko et al., 2002). Following are the possible strategies:

- *Dominant-negative proteins*: The introduction of mutant versions of key factors in pathogen infection, such as cell surface receptors, can block disease progression (Ono et al., 2004).
- *Ribonucleic acid interference* (RNAi): It relies on the ability of specific short RNA sequences to anneal with the RNA of the pathogen, causing

destruction of the foreign RNA. RNAi requires access to the target RNA, which may limit this approach to viruses (Clark and Whitelaw, 2003; Mello and Conte, 2004).

- *Ribonucleic acid decoys*: expression of RNA sequences that mimic specific sequences within a pathogen can disrupt the activity of the pathogen's replication machinery (Luo et al., 1997). Again, this approach is probably restricted to specific viruses, with influenza being a good candidate
- *Antibodies*: the transgenic production of antibodies in the host animal may act in an analogous manner to vaccination (Kolb et al., 2001; Marasco, 2001).

Genetically modified animals resistant to disease could be used by our society in two ways. First, these engineered animals would provide valuable models with which to investigate disease progression and evaluate this approach to controlling the disease. Alternatively, the GM disease-resistant animal could be introduced into the breeding stock.

Conclusions

Disease control programme of selective breeding for resistance should first be justified economically and second by the lack of alternate control methods. A primary requirement for inclusion of diseases resistance in breeding programme is knowledge of the extent of genetic variation. The genetic variation among indigenous sheep and goat breeds in the tropics is likely to be larger than that found among breeds in temperate region. Genetic manipulation of the host offers an alternate long-term solution and we must utilize this effectively to improve the performance of our stock and to reduce morbidity and mortality losses. The inclusion of host genetic resistance to diseases as an alternate tool in integrated disease control strategies will generally be more sustainable, cost effective, enhance consumer acceptance, increase international trade, decrease spreading of disease and will take care of animal welfare. There is a need to evaluate our genetic resources for genetically based resistance in different agroclimatic and production systems as well as to investigate genetic correlation between resistance to the disease of interest and all major production traits including resistance to other production diseases. The genetic differences within the flock are most likely under polygenic control and thus reliable heritability estimates are a basic requirement for designed breeding programmes.

References

Adams, L.G. and Templeton, J.W. 1998. Genetic resistance to bacterial diseases of animals. Review of Scientific and Technical OIE 17: 200-219.

Albers, G.A.A., Gray, G.D., Piper, L.R., Baker, J.S.F., Le Jambe, L.F. and Barger, I.A. 1987. The genetics of resistance and resilience to *Haemonchus contortus* in young Merino sheep. International Journal for Parasitology 17: 1335-1363.

Amarante, A.F.T., Bricarello, P.A., Rocha, R.A. and Gennari, S.M. 2004. Resistance of Santa Ines, Suffolk and Ile de France sheep to naturally acquired gastrointestinal nematode infections. Veterinary Parasitology 120: 91–106.

Axford, R.F.E., Bishop, S.C., Nicholas, F.W. and Owen, J.B. 2000. Breeding for Disease resistance in Farm Animals. 2nd ed. CAB International, Wallingford, UK.

Baker, R.L. 1996. Characterization and utilization of sheep and goat breeds that are resistant to helminths. In: L.F. Le Jambre and M.R. Knox (Eds) Sustainable Parasite Control in Ruminants, ACIAR Proceeding No. 74: 172-177.

Baker, R.L. 1998. Genetic resistance to endoparasites in sheep and goats. A review of genetic resistance to gastrointestinal nematode parasites in sheep and goats in the tropics and evidence for resistance in some sheep and goat breeds in sub-humid coastal Kenya. Animal Genetic Resources Information 24: 13–30.

Baker, R.L., Clark, J.N., Harvey, T.G. and Meyer, H.M. 1986. Inheritance of foot and jaw abnormalities in sheep. Proc. The New Zealand Society of Animal Production 46: 93-100.

Baker, R.L,, Watson, T.G., Bisset, S.A., Vlassoff, A. and Douch, P.G.C. 1991. Breeding sheep in New Zealand for resistance to internal parasites. In: Grey, G.D. and Woolaston, R.R. (Eds) Breeding for Disease Resistance in Sheep, Australian Wool Corporation, Melbourne pp. 19-32.

Baker, R.L., Rege, J.E.O., Tembely, S., Mukasa-Mugerwa, E. Anindo, D., Mwamachi, D.M., Thorpe, W. and Lahlou-Kassi, A. 1998. Genetic resistance to gastrointestinal nematode parasites in some indigenous breeds of sheep and goats in East Africa. In: Proceedings of the 6th World Congress on Genetics Applied to livestock Production, Armidale, Australia 25: 269-272.

Batra, T.R., Lee, A.J., Gavora, J.S. and Stear, M.J. 1989. Class I alleles of the bovine major histocompatibility system and their association with economic traits. Journal of Dairy Science 72: 2115-2124.

Beh, K.J., Hulme, D.J., Callaghan, M.J., Leish, Z., Lenane, I., Windon, R.G. and Maddox, J.F. 2002. A genome scan for quantitative trait loci affecting resistance to *Trichostrongylus colubriformis* in sheep. Animal Genetics 33:97-106.

Besser, T.E., McGuire, T.C., Gay, C.C. and Pritchett, L.C. 1988. Transfer of functional immunoglobulin G (IgG) antibody into the gastrointestinal tract accounts for IgG clearance in calves. Journal of Virology 62:2234-2237.

Bishop, S.C., De Jong, M. and Gray, D. 2002. Opportunities for incorporating genetic elements into the management of farm animal diseases: policy issues. Commission on Genetic Resources for Food and Agriculture, FAO, Rome, pp. 36.

Bisset, S.A., Vlassoff, A. and Pulford, H. 1991. Rotational grazing/grazing interchange systems. In: Proc. Sheep and Beef Cattle Society of the New Zealand Veterinary Association 21: 47-54.

BOA. 1999. The use of drugs in food animals: benefits and risks. Washington DC. Board on Agriculture, National Academies Press.

Bohra, S.D.J. 1988. Genetic resistance to diseases and parasites in sheep. In: Proceedings of the 2nd National Seminar on Sheep and Goat Diseases, CSWRI, Avikanagar, 16-22.

Bouix, J., Krupinski, J., Rzepecki, R., Nowosad, B., Skrzyzala, I., Robarzynski, M., Fuldalewicz-Niemczyk, W., Shalzka, M., Malezewski, A. and Gruner, L. 1998. Genetic resistance to gastrointestinal nematode parasites in Polish long-wool sheep. International Journal for Parasitology 28: 1797–1804.

Bradley, R.E., Radhakrishnan, C.V., Patil-Kulkarni, V.G. and Loggins, P.E. 1973. Responses in Florida Native and Rambouillet lambs exposed to one and two doses of *Haemonchus contortus*. American Journal of Veterinary Research 34: 729-735.

Charon, K.M. 2004. Genes controlling resistance to gastrointestinal nematodes in ruminants. Animal Science Papers and Reports 22: 135-139.

Charon, K.M., Moskwa, B., Rutkowski, R., Gruszczynska, J. and Œwiderek, W. 2002. Microsatellite polymorphism in DRB1 gene (MHC class II) and its relation to nematode faecal egg count in Polish Heath Sheep. Journal of Animal and Feed Sciences 11:47-58.

Chauhan, K.K., Rout, P.K., Singh, P.K., Mandal, A., Singh, S.K. and Roy, R. 2003a. Genetic resistance of Barbari and Jamunapari kids to natural infection with gastrointestinal nematodes. Tropical Animal Health and Production 35: 397-408.

Chauhan, K.K., Rout, P.K., Singh, P.K., Mandal, A., Roy, R. and Singh, S.K. 2003b. Susceptibility to natural gastrointestinal nematode infection in different physiological stages in Jamunapari and Barbari goats in the semi-arid tropics. Small Ruminant Research 50: 219-223.

Chitko-McKown, C.G., Fox, J.M., Miller, L.C., Heaton, M.P., Bono, J.L., Grosse, W.M. and Laegreid, W.W. 2004. Gene expression profiling of bovine macrophages in response to Escherichia coli 0157:H7 lipopolysaccharide. Development in Comparative Immunology 28: 636-645.

Clark, J. and Whitelaw, B. 2003. A future for transgenic livestock. National Review of Genetics 4: 825-833.

Clawson, M.L., Heaton, M.P., Chitko-McKown, C.G., Fox, J.M., Smith, T.P.L., Snelling, W.M., Keele, J.W. and Laegreid, W.W. 2004. Beta-2-microglobulin haplotypes in the U.S. beef cattle and association with failure of passive transfer in newborn calves. Mammalian Genetics 15:227-236.

Claxton, J. and Leperre, P. 1991. Parasite burdens and host susceptibility of Zebu and N'Dama cattle in village herds in the Gambia. Veterinary Parasitology 40: 293–304.

Coltman, D.W., Wilson, K., Pilkington, J.G., Stear, M.J. and Pemberton, J.M. 2001. A microsatellite polymorphism in the gamma interferon gene is associated with resistance to gastrointestinal nematodes in a naturally parasitized population of Soay sheep. Parasitology 122: 571-582.

Courtney, C.H., Parker, C.F., Maclure, K.E. and Herd, R.P. 1984. A comparison of the peri-parturient rise in faecal egg counts of exotic and domestic ewes. International Journal for Parasitology 14: 377–381.

Courtney, C.H., Parker, C.F., Maclure, K.E. and Herd, R.P. 1985a. Resistance of exotic and domestic lambs to experimental infection with *Haemonchus contortus*. International Journal for Parasitology 15: 101–109.

Courtney, C.H., Parker, C.F., Maclure, K.E. and Herd, R.P. 1985b. Resistance of non lambing exotic and domestic ewes to naturally acquired gastrointestinal nematodes. International Journal for Parasitology 15: 239–243.

Crawford, A.M., Paterson, K.A., Dodds, K.G., Diez-Tascon, C., Williamson, P.A., Thomsom, M.R., Bisset, S.A., Beattie, A.E., Greer, G.J., Green, R.S., Wheeler, R., Shaw, R.J., Knowler, K. and McEwan, J. C. 2006. Discovery of quantitative trait loci for resistance to parasitic nematode infection in sheep: I. Analysis of outcross pedigrees. BMC Genomics, 7.

Cummins, L.J., Thompson, R.L., Yong, W.K., Riffin, G.G., Goddard, M.E., Calinen, A.P.L. and Sounder, M.J. 1991. Genetics of *Ostertagia* selection lines. In: Grey, G.D. and Woolaston, R.R. (Eds) Breeding for Disease Resistance in Sheep, Australian Wool Corporation, Melbourne pp. 11-18.

Dargie, J.D. 1990. Helping small farmers to improve their livestock. International Atomic Energy Agency, Vienna.

Daszak, P.A., Cunningham, A. and Hyatt, A.D. 2000. Emerging infectious diseases of wildlife – threats to biodiversity and human health. Science 287:443-449.

Diez-tascon, C., Macdonald, P.A., Dodds, K.G., Mcewan, J.C. and Crawford, A.M. 2002. A screen of chromosome 1 for QTL affecting nematode resistance in ovine outcross population. Proceedings of the 7th World Congress on Genetics Applied to Livestock Production, Montpellier, France, pp. 13-37.

Dubey, S. C., Rao, T.R.M., Srivastava, C.P., Lonkar, P.S. and Maru, A. 1988. Seroprevalence of blue tongue disease in Rajasthan. Indian Journal of Animal Sciences 58: 68-70.

Edfors-Lilja, I., Wattrang, E., Magnusson, U. and Fossum, C. 1994. Genetic variation in parameters reflecting immune competence of swine. Veterinary Immunology and Immunopathology 40: 1-16

Egerton, J.R. 1989. Footrot of cattle, goats and deer. In: Egerton, J.R., Yong, W.K. and Riffkin, G.G, (Eds) Footrot and Foot Abscess of Ruminants, Boca Raton, Florida, CRC Press, pp 47-56.

Egerton, J.R. and Raadsma, H.W. 1991. Breeding sheep for resistance to foot rot. In: Owen, J.B. and Axford, R.E. (Eds) Breeding for disease resistance in farm animals, CAB international, Wallingford, UK, pp 347-370.

Emery, D.L., Stewart, D.J. and Clark, B.L. 1984. The susceptibility of five breeds of sheep to foot rot. Australian Veterinary Journal 61: 85–88.

Eriksson, J.A. 1991. Mastitis in cattle. In: Owen, J.B. and Axford, R.E. (Eds) Breeding for disease resistance in farm animals, CAB International, Wallingford, UK, pp 394-411.

FAO. 1999. Opportunities for incorporating genetic elements into the management of farm animal diseases: policy issues. In: S. Bishop, M. de Jong and D. Gray (eds) Background Study Paper Number 18. Commission on Genetic Resources for Food and Agriculture. Rome.

FAO. 2007. The state of Agricultural biodiversity in the livestock sector: Animal genetic resources and resistance to disease, Section E, 101-111.

FAO/IAEA. 2008. Nuclear technology serving agriculture. The Joint FAO/IAEA Programme of Nuclear Techniques in Food and Agriculture in *http://www-naweb.iaea.org/nafa/index.html.*

Gamble, H.R. and Zajac, A.M. 1992. Resistance to St, Croix lambs to *Haemonchus contortus* in experimentally and naturally acquired infections. Veterinary Parasitology 41: 211-225.

Gasbarre, L.C. and Miller, J.E. 2000. Genetics of helminth resistance. In: Breeding for Disease Resistance in Farm Animals. 2nd ed. Axford, R.E.F., Bishop, S.C., Nicholas, F.W. and Owen J.B. (editors), CAB International, 129-152.

Glass, E.J., Preston, P.M., Springbett, A., Craigmile, S., Kirvar, E., Wilkie, G. and Brown, C.G.D. 2005. *Bos taurus* and *Bos indicus* (Sahiwal) calves respond differently to infection with *Theileria annulata* and produce markedly different levels of acute phase proteins. International Journal for Parasitology 35: 337–347.

Goosens, B., Osaer, S., Ndao, M., Van Winghem, J. and Geerts, S. 1999. The susceptibility of Djallonké and Djallonké-Sahelian crossbred sheep to *Trypanosoma congolense* and helminth infection under different diet levels. Veterinary Parasitolog, 85: 25–41.

Gruner, L. and Lantier, F. 1995. Breeding for resistance to infectious diseases of small ruminants in Europe. In: Grey, G.D., Woolaston, R.R. and Eaton, B.T. (eds) Breeding for Resistance to Infectious Diseases in Small Ruminants, ACIRA, Canberra, Australia pp. 99-117.

Gruner, L., Cabaret, J., Sauve, C. and pailhories, R. 1986. Comparative susceptibility of Romanov and Lucaune sheep to GI nematode and small lungworms. Veterinary Parasitology 19: 85-93.

Gruners, L., Bouix, J., Cabaret, J., Boulard, C., Cortet, J., Sauve, C., Molenat, G. and Calamel, M. 1992. Effect of genetic type, lactation and management on helminths infection of ewes in an intensive grazing system on irrigated pasture. International Journal for Parasitology 22: 919-925.

Gulland, F.M., Albon, S.D., Pemberton, J.M., Moorcroft, P.R. and Clutton-Brock, T.H. 1993. Parasite-associated polymorphism in a cyclic ungulate population. In: Proc. Royal Society of London B Biological Sciences 254: 7-13.

Hansen, D.S., Clery, D.G., Estuningsih, S.E., Widjajanti, S., Partoutomo, S. and Spithill, T.W. 1999. Immune responses in Indonesian thin tailed sheep during primary infection with *Fasciola gigantica*: lack of a species IgG2 antibody response is associated with increased resistance to infection in Indonesian sheep. International Journal for Parasitology 29: 1027–1035.

Harmon, B.G., Adams, L.G., Templeton, J.W. and Smith, R. 1989. Macrophage function in mammary glands of *Brucella abortus*-infected cows and cows that resisted infection after inoculation of *Brucella abortus*. American Journal of Veterinary Research 50:459-465.

Hepkema, B.G., Blankert, J.J., Albers, G.A., Tilanus, M.G., Egberts, E., Zijpp, A.J. van der Hensen, E.J. 1993. Mapping of susceptibility to Marek's disease within the major histocompatibility (B) complex by refined typing of White Leghorn chickens. Animal Genetics. 24: 283-287.

Hooda, V., Yadav, C.L., Chaudhri, S.S. and Rajpurohit, B.S. 1999. Variation in resistance to haemonchosis: selection of female sheep resistant to *Haemonchus contortus*. Journal of Helminthology 73:137-142.

Hu, J., Bumstead, N., Burrow, P., Sebastiani, G., Olien, L., Morgan, K. and Malo, D. 1997. Rsistance to almonellosis in the chicken is linked to NRAMP1 and TNC. Genome Research 7: 693-704.

ISGP. 1998. Indo-Swiss Goat Development and Fodder Production Project, Biennial Report (1986-88), Department of Animal Husbandry, Rajasthan.

Janssen, M., weimann, C., Gauly, M. and Erhardt, G. 2002. Association between infections with *Haemonchus contortus* and genetic markers. In: Proceedings of the 7th World Congress on Genetics applied to Livestock Production, Montpeller, France, pp. 13-11.

Jeggo. M.J., Corteyn, A.H., Taylor, W.P., Davidson, W.L. and Gormam, B.M. 1986. Virulence of bluetongue virus for British sheep. Research in Veterinary Science 42: 24-28.

Jones, J.E.T. 1991. Mastitis in sheep. In: Owen, J.B. and Axford, R.E. (Eds) Breeding for disease resistance in farm animals, CAB International, Wallingford, UK, pp 412-423.

Jovanoviæ, S., Saviæ, M. and Živkoviæ, D. 2009. Genetic variation in disease resistance among farm animals. Biotechnology in Animal Husbandry 25: 339-347.

Kitching, R.P., Hammond, J.M. and Taylor, W.P. 1987. A single vaccine for the control of capripox in sheep and goats. Research in Veterinary Science 42: 53-60.

Knight, R.A., Vegors, H.H. and Glimp, H.A. 1973. Effect of breed and date of birth of lambs on gastrointestinal nematode infections. American Journal of Veterinary Research 34: 323 - 327.

Ko, J.H., Jin, H.K., Asano, A., Takada, A., Ninomiya, A., Kida, H., Hokiyama, H., Ohara, M., Tsuzuki, M., Nishibori, M., Mizutani, M. and Watanabe, T. 2002. Polymorphisms and the differential antiviral activity of the chicken *Mx* gene. Genome Research 12: 595-601.

Kolb, A.F., Pewe, L., Webster, J., Perlman, S., Whitelaw, C.B.A. and Siddell, S.G. 2001. Virus-neutralizing monoclonal antibody expressed in milk of transgenic mice provides full protection against virus-induced encephalitis. Journal of Virology 75: 2803-2809.

Kumar, S., Swarnkar, C.P., Singh, D., Kolte, A.P. and Singh, V.K. 2006. Genetic resistance to parasitic nematodes - a review. Indian Journal of Small Ruminants 12: 131-145.

Lamont, S. J. 1989. The chicken major histocompatibility complex in disease resistance and poultry breeding. Journal of Dairy Science 72:1328-1333.

Lantier, F., Tien, J.V., Oswald, I.P., Bioux, J., Guerrin, G., Nguyen, T.C., Gros, P., Shurr, E., Skamene, E., Boivin, R., Pepin, M. and Pardon, P. 1990. Resistance to abortusovis infection: is there an equivalent to the Ity gene in sheep?. Annals de Researches Veterinaires 21: 305-306.

Larsgard, A.G. and Vaabenone, A. 1993. Genetic and environmental causes of variation in mastitis in sheep. Small Ruminant Research 12: 339-347.

Loggins, P.E., Swanson, L.E. and Kager, M. 1965. Parasite levels in sheep as affected by heredity. Journal of Animal Science 24: 286 – 287.

Lundeheim, N. 1988. Health disorders and growth performance at a Swedish pig progeny testing station. Acta Agric. Scandinavica 38: 77-88.

Luo, G., Danetz, S. and Krystal, M. 1997. Inhibition of influenza viral polymerases by minimal viral RNA decoys. Journal of General Virology 78: 2329-2333.

Magnusson, U. 2001. Breeding for improved disease resistance in organic farming - possibilities and constraints. Acta Veterinaria Scandinavica Suppl. 95: 59-61.

Magnusson, U., Mallard, B.A., Bosse, J.T., Kennedy, B.W. and Wilkie, B.N. 1997. Antibody response to *Actinobacillus pleuropneumoniae* antigens after vaccination of pigs bred for high and low immune response. Vaccine 15: 997-1000.

Magnusson, U., Wilkie, B.N., Mallard, B.A., Rosendal, S. and Kennedy, B.W. 1998. Mycoplasma hyorhinis infection of pigs selectively bred for high and low immune response. Veterinary Immunoogy and Immunopathology 61:83-95.

Mahajan, J.M. 1979. Studies on factors affecting preweaning survivability in lambs. Ph.D. Thesis, Kurukshetra University, Haryana.

Mahajan, N.K., Prasad, G., Jain, N., Dhanda, J.S. and Gupta, Y. 1991. Epizootiological studies on blue tongue at an organised sheep breeding farm near Hissar, Haryana. Indian Journal of Animal Sciences 61: 1-5.

Mandal, A. and Sharma, D.K. 2008, Inheritance of faecal egg count in Barbari goats following natural *Haemonchus contortus* infection. Veterinary Parasitology 155: 89-94.

Marasco, W.A. 2001. Intrabodies as antiviral agents. Current Topics in Microbiology and Immunology 260: 247-270.

Mark, T., Fikse, W.F., Sigurdsson, A. and Philipsson J. 2000. Feasibility of international genetic evaluations of dairy sires for somatic cell count and clinical mastitis. Interbull Bulletin 25: 154-162.

Mattioli, R.C., Bah, M., Faye, J., Kora, S. and Cassama, M. 1993. A comparison of field tick infestation on N'Dama, Zebu and N'Dama × Zebu crossbred cattle. Veterinary Parasitology 47: 139–148.

Mattioli, R.C., Bah, M., Kora, S., Cassama, M. and Clifford, D.J. 1995. Susceptibility to different tick genera in Gambian N'Dama and Gobra zebu cattle exposed to naturally occurring tick infection. Tropical Animal Health and Production 27: 995–1005.

McEwan, J.C., Mason, P., Baker, R.L., Clarke, J.N., Hickey, S.M. and Turner, K. 1992. Effect of selection for productive traits on internal parasite resistance in sheep. Proceedings of New Zealand Society for Animal Production 52: 53-56.

McGuirk, B.J. and Atkins, K.D. 1984. Fleece rot in Merino sheep. I. The heritability of fleece rot in unselected flocks of medium-wool Peppin Merinos. Australian Journal of Agricultural Research 35: 424-434.

Mello, C.C. and Conte, D. 2004. Revealing the world of RNA interference. Nature 431:338-342.

Millot, P. 1989. Sheep major histocompatibility complex (OLA): Apparent involvement in a flock endemic infection by *Corynebacterium pseudotuberculosis*. Experimental and Clinical Immunogenetics 6: 225-235.

Moon, H.W., Hoffmann, L.J., Cornick, N.A., Boother, S.L. and Bosworth, B.T. 1999. Prevalences of some virulence genes among *Escherichia coli* isolates from swine presented to a diagnostic laboratory in Iowa. J. Vet. Diagn. Invest. 11: 557-560.

Morris, C.A., Cullen, N.G., Green, R.S. and Hickey, S.M. 2002. Sire effects on antibodies to nematode parasites in grazing dairy cows. New Zealand Journal of Agricultural Research 45: 179-185.

Murty, D.K. and Singh, P.P. 1971. Epidemiological studies on an outbreak of sheep pox in a mixed flock in Uttar Pradesh. Indian Journal of Animal Sciences 41:1072-1079.

Nagpal, A.K., Vihan, V.S., Singh, D., Singh, S.V. and Singh, N. 1990. Epidemiological study of an outbreak of goat pox and its effect on the performance of kids. Indian Journal of Animal Sciences 60: 544-546.

Nimbkar, C. 2005. Importance of genetic resistance to gastrointestinal nematodes in sheep in developing countries with special reference to the Garole breed. In: Proceedings of the FAO Symposium on "Integrated Animal Parasite Management: From Academic Interest to Reality" pp. 34 – 40.

Nimbkar, C., Ghalasasi, P.M., Swan, A.A. Walkden-Brown, S.W. and Kahn, L.P. 2003. Evaluation of growth rates and resistance to nematodes of Deccani and Bannur lambs and their crosses with Garole. Animal Science 76: 503-515.

Nowosad, B., Krupinski, J., Niemczyk, W., Malczewski, A., Gruner, L. and Bouix, J. 1992. Genetic sheep resistance to helminths parasites in Poland: Results of the first year in a Polish long-wool type. VIth EMOP Sep 7-11, The Hague, Netherlands, pp 117.

Ono, E., Amagai, K., Taharaguchi, S., Tomioka, Y., Yoshino, S., Watanabe, Y., Cherel, P., Houdebine, L.M., Adam, M., Eloit, M., Inobe, M. and Uede, T. 2004. Transgenic mice expressing a soluble form of porcine nectin-1/herpesvirus entry mediator C as a model for pseudorabies-resistant livestock. Proceedings of National Academy of Sciiences USA 101:16150-161555.

Outteridge, P.M., Anderson, L., Douch, P.G.C., Green, R.S., Gwakisa, P.S., Hohenhaus, M.A. and Mikko, S. 1996. The PCR typing of MHC-DRB genes in the sheep using primers for an intronic microsatellite: application to nematode parasite resistance. Immunology and Cell Biology 74: 330-336.

Pachlag, S.V. and Kumar, P.N. 1974. Studies on the gastrointestinal helminthiasis in sheep. In : *Annual Report,* CSWRI, Avikanagar.

Pachalag S.V., Chattopadhyay, S.K. and More, T. 1972. A note on the field observations on the susceptibility of sheep to helminths infection. Indian Journal of Animal Sciences 42: 238-239.

Pareek, C.S., Pareek, R.S. and Walawski, K. 2002. Novel linkage mapping approach using DNA pooling in human and animal genetics I. detection of complex disease loci. Journal of Applied Genetics 42:175-192.

Paterson, S., Wilson, K. and Pemberton, J.M. 1998. Major histocompatibility complex variation associted with juvenile survival and parasite resistance in a large ungulate population (*Ovis aries*L.). In: Proceedings of the National Academy of Sciences, USA 95: 3714-3719.

Pepin, M., Lantier, F. and Pardon, P. 1988. Breed susceptibility to experimental *Corynebacterium pseudotuberculosis* infection in lambs. In: Proc. 3rd World Congress on Sheep and Beef Cattle Breeding 19-23 June, INRA, Paris Volume 1 pp 646-648.

Perry, B.D., Randolph, T.F., McDermott, J.J., Sones, K.R. and Thornton, P.K. 2002. Investigating in Animal Health Research to Alleviate Poverty. ILRI, Nairobi, Kenya.

Piper, L.R. 1987. Genetic variation in resistance to internal parasites. In: McGuirk, B.J. (ed) Merino Improvement Programme in Australia, Australian Wool Corporation pp 351-363.

Qureshi, T.J., Templeton, W. and Adams, L.G.. 1996. Intracellular survival of *Brucella abortus, Mycobacterium bovis* (BCG), *Salmonnella dublin* and *Salmonella typhimurium* in macrophages from cattle genetically resistant to *Brucella abortus.* Veterinary Immunology and Immunopathology 50:55-66.

Raadsma, H.W. 1995. Genetic variation in resistance to bacteria. In: Grey, G.D., Woolaston, R.R. and Eaton, B.T. (Eds) Breeding for Resistance to Infectious Disease in Small Ruminants, ACIAR, Canberram Australia pp. 15-42.

Raadsma, H.W., Gilmour, A.R. and Paxton, W.J. 1988. Fleece rot and body strike in Merino sheep. 1. Evaluation of liability to fleece rot and body strike under experimental conditions. Australian Journal of Agricultural Research 39: 917-934.

Raadsma, H.W., Gilmour, A.R. and Paxton, W.J. 1989. Fleece rot and body strike in Merino sheep. 2. Phenotypic and genetic variation in liability to fleece rot following experimental induction. Australian Journal of Agricultural Research 49: 207-220.

Raadsma, H.W., Sandeman, R.M., Sasiak, A.B., Engwerda, C.R. and O'Meara, T.J. 1992. Genetic improvement in resistance to body strike in Merino sheep. Where are we at with indirect selection? In: Proc. Australian Association of Animal Breeding and Genetics 10: 143-146.

Radhakrishnan, C.V., Bradley, R.E. and Loggins, P.E. 1972. Host response of worm-free Florida Native and Rambouillet lambs experimentally infected with *Haemonchus contortus*. American Journal of Veterinary Research 33: 817–823.

Roberts, J.A., Estuningsih, E., Widjayanti, S., Wiedosari, E., Partoutomo, S. and Spithill, T.W. 1997. Resistance of Indonesian thin tail sheep against *Fasciola gigantica* and *Fasciola hepatica*. Veterinary Parasitology 68: 69–78.

Rupp, R. and Boichard, D. 2003. Genetics of resistance to mastitis in dairy cattle. Veterinary Research 34: 671–688.

Safari, A., Fogarty, N.M. and Gilmour, A.R. 2005. A review of genetic parameter estimates for wool, growth, meat and reproduction traits in sheep. Livestock Production Science 92: 271-289.

Sanyal, P.K. 1988. The epizootology and control of gastrointestinal nematodiasis of sheep. Proceedings of 2nd National Seminar on Sheep and Goat Diseases, CSWRI, Avikanagar.

Sanyal, P.K. 2002. Sustainable control of parasitic gastroenteritis in ruminants in India. Journal of Veterinary Parasitology 16: 87-94.

Savic, M., Jovanovic, S. and Trailovic, R. 1995. Some genetic markers in blood of Balkan goat. Acta Veterinaria 45: 5-6.

Schwaiger, F.W., Gostomski, D., Stear, M.J., Duncan, J.L., Mckellar, Q.A., Epplen, J.T. and Buitcamp, J. 1995. An ovine major histocompatibility complex DRB1 allele is associated with low faecal egg counts following natural, predominantly *Ostertagia circumcincta* infection. International Journal for Parasitology 25: 815-822.

Shankar, H. Singh, S.V., Singh, N. and Vihan, V.S. 1992. occurrence of foot and mouth disease in small ruminants. In:Lokeshwar, R.R. (Ed) Pre-conference Proceedings, Abstracts of contributory papers, 5th International Conference on Goats, New Delhi, India Volume I pp 505.

Sharma, M.M., Uppal, P.K., Lonkar, P.S. and Mathur, P.B. 1986. Epidemiology of a sheep pox outbreak in mutton and fine wool type sheep at an organised farm. Indian Journal of Animal Sciences 56: 1183-1186.

Shibaya, M., Kubomichi, M. and Watanabe, T. 1991. The genetic basis of host resistance to *Bacillus anthracic* in inbred mice. Veterinary Microbiology 26: 309-312.

Shimshony, A. 1989. Footrot in Awassis and the crosses with East Friesian sheep. New Zealand Veterinary Journal 37: 44.

Singh, D. and Swarnkar, C.P. 2007. Alternative methods of control of gastrointestinal nematodes in small ruminants. In: Vihan, V.S., Kumar Ashok, Gupta, V.K. and Singh, N.P. (Eds) Small Ruminant Emerging Diseases, Containment under WTO regime, Satish Serial Publishing House, Delhi, pp. 269 – 304.

Singh, D. and Swarnkar, C.P. 2008. Role of refugia in management of anthelmintic resistance in nematodes of small ruminants – a review. Indian Journal of Small Ruminants 14: 141-180.

Singh, D., Swarnkar, C.P., Khan, F.A., Jayasankar, J. and Bhagwan, P.S.K. 1999. Heritability of faecal egg counts in Avikalin sheep. Indian Journal of Animal Sciences 69: 983-985.

Singh, D., Swarnkar, C.P. and Khan, F.A. 2002. Anthelmintic resistance in gastrointestinal nematodes of livestock in India. Journal of Veterinary Parasitology 16: 115-130.

Singh, D., Swarnkar, C.P., Sushil Kumar, Kumar, S. and Arora, A.L. 2006. Variability of sheep resistance to natural gastrointestinal nematode infection. In: Proceedings of the 17th National Congress of Indian Association for the Advancement of Veterinary Parasitology, Rajiv Ghandhi College of Veterinary Sciences, Puducherry, 15 - 17 November.

Singh, D., Swarnkar, C.P., Kumar, Sushil, Prince, L.L.L. and Arora, A.L. 2009a. Performance of Avikalin sheep selected for resistance to *Haemonchus contortus*. Journal of Veterinary Parasitology 23: 23-27.

Singh, D., Swarnkar, C.P., Satish Kumar and Khan, F.A. 2009b. Effect of FECB gene inheritance on faecal egg count in sheep naturally infected with gastrointestinal nematodes in semi-arid Rajasthan. In: Proceedings of the 19th National Congress of Indian Association for the Advancement of Veterinary Parasitology, GADVASU, Ludhiana, Punjab, 3 - 5 February.

Singh, N., Kala, S.N., Vihan, V.S. and Singh, S.V. 1990. Genetic study on the susceptibility to Johne's disease in goats. Indian Journal of Animal Sciences 60: 1163-1165.

Singh, N. Vihan, V.S., Singh, S.V. and Tiwari, H.A. 1992. Prevalence and pathology of *Escherichia coli* infection in neonatal kids. In:Lokeshwar, R.R. (Ed) Pre-conference Proceedings, Abstracts of contributory papers, 5th International Conference on Goats, New Delhi, India Volume I pp 512.

Skermam, T.M. and Moorhouse, S.R. 1987. Broomfield Corriedales, A strain of sheep selectively bred for resistance to footrot. New Zealand Veterinary Journal 35: 101-106.

Snowder G.D., Van Vleck L.D., Cundiff L.V. and Bennett G.L. 2005. Influence of breed, heterozygosity and disease incidence on estimates of variance components of respiratory disease in pre-weaned beef calves. Journal of Animal Sciences 83: 507-518.

Stear, M.J. and Wakelin, D. 1998. Genetic resistance to parasitic infection. Revues Scientifiques at Technicales de I' Office Internationale de Epizooties 17: 143-153.

Stear, M.J., Hetzel, D.J.S., Brown, S.C., Gershwin, L.J., Mackinnon, M.J. and Nicholas, F.W. 1990. The relationships among ecto- and endoparasite levels, class I antigens of bovine major histocompatibility system, immunoglobulin E levels and weight gain. Veterinary Parasitology 34:303-321.

Swarnkar, C.P. and Singh, D. 2005. Nutritional intervention in management of gastrointestinal nematodes in small ruminants. In: Proceedings of FAO Symposium on "Integrated Animal Parasite Management: From Acedemic Interest to Reality" pp. 41 – 54.

Swarnkar, C.P., Khan, F.A., Singh, D., Dixit, S. and Bhagwan, P.S.K. 1997a. Genetic variation in resistance to nematode parasites of sheep. In: Proceedings of the IXth National Congress Veterinary Parasitology, PAU, Ludhiana, 6-8 October.

Swarnkar, C.P., Singh, G., Singh, D. and Khan, F.A. 1997b. A pilot study on genetic variation in resistance to nematode parasites in fine wool sheep. In: Proceedings of the IIIrd National Seminar on Small Ruminant Diseases, CIRG, Makhdoom, 2-3 December.

Swarnkar, C.P., Khan, F.A., Jayasankar, J., Singh, D. and Bhagwan, P.S.K. 2000. Repeatability of faecal egg count and haematological values in sheep experimentally infected with *Haemonchus contortus*. Indian Journal of Animal Sciences 70: 791-796.

Swarnkar, C.P., Singh, D., Lal Krishna and Khan, F.A. 2008. Epidemiology and Management of Gastrointestinal Parasites of Sheep in Rajasthan. CSWRI, Avikanagar pp 1- 145.

Swarnkar, C.P., Singh, D., Kumar, Shushil, Mishra, A.K. and Arora, A.L. 2009. Study on Malpura sheep selected for resistance to *Haemonchus contortus*. Indian Journal of Animal Sciences 79: 577-581.

Todd, K.S., Mansfield, M.E. and Levine, N.D. 1978. *Haemonchus contortus* infection in Targhee and Targhee-Barbados Blackbelly cross lambs. American Journal of Veterinary Research 39: 865–866.

Van Haeringen, W.A., Gwakisa, P.S., Mikko, S., Eythorsdottir, E., Holm, L.E., Olsaker, I., Outteridge, P.M. and Anderson, L. 1999. Heterosigosity excess at the cattle *DRB* locus revealed by large scale genotyping of two closely linked microsatellites. Animal Genetics 30:169-176.

Vihan, V.S. and Singh, N. 1988. Epidemiological and clinicopathological studies on collibacillosis in kids. Indian Journal of Animal Sciences 58: 233-236.

Wambura, P.N., Gwakisa, P.S., Silayo, R.S. and Rugaimukamu, E.A. 1998. Breed associated resistance to tick infestation in *Bos indicus* and their crosses with *Bos taurus*. Veterinary Parasitology 77: 63-70.

Watson, T.G., Baker, R.L. and Harvey, T.G. 1986. Genetic variation in resistance or tolerance to internal nematode parasites in strains of sheep at Rotomahana. Proceedings of New Zealand Society for Animal Proceeding 46: 23-26.

Watson, D.L., Franklin, N.A., Davies, H.I., Kettlewell, P. and Frost, A.J. 1990. Survey of intra-mammary infections in ewes on the New England Tableland of New South Wales. Australian Veterinary Journal 67: 6-8.

Whitelaw, C.B.A. and Sang, H.M. 2005. Disease-resistant genetically modified animals. Review of Scientific and Technical OIE 24: 275-283.

Windon, R.G. 1996. Genetic control of resistance to helminths in sheep. Veterinary Immunology and Immunopatholgy 54: 245-54.

Windon, R.G. and Dineen, J.K. 1984. Parasitological and immunological competence of lambs selected for high and low responsiveness to vaccination with irradiated *Trichostrongylus colubriformis* larvae. In: J.K. Dineen and P.M. Outteridge (eds) Immunogenetic Approaches to the Control of Endoparasites Melbourne, 13–28.

Wolf, B.T., Howells, K., Nakielny, C., Haresign, W., Lewis, R.M., Davies, O. and Davies, M.H. 2008. Genetic parameters of strongyle and Nematodirus faecal egg counts in lambs and their relationship with performance traits. Livestock Science 113: 209-217.

Wong, S.S. and Yuen, K.Y. 2006. Avian influenza virus infections in humans. Chest 129:156-68.

Woolaston, R.R. and Eady, S.J. 1995. Australian research on genetic resistance to nematode parasites. In: Grey, G.D., Woolaston, R.R. and Eaton, B.T. (eds) Breeding for Resistance to Infectious Diseases in Small Ruminants, ACIRA, Canberra, Australia pp. 53-75.

Woolaston, R.R. and Piper, L.R. 1996. Selection of Merino sheep for resistance to *Haemonchus contortus*: Genetic variation. Animal Science 62:451-460

Woolaston, R.R., Windon, R.G. and Gray, G.D. 1991. Genetic resistance in variation to internal parasites in Armidale experimental flocks. In: Grey, G.D. and Woolaston, R.R. (Eds) Breeding for Disease Resistance in Sheep, Australian Wool Corporation, Melbourne pp. 1-9.

Woolaston, R.R., Elwin, R.L. and Barger, I.A. 1992. No adaptation of *Haemonchus contortus* to genetically resistant sheep. International Journal for Parasitology 22: 377-380.

Yadav, C.L., Grewal, H.S. and Banerjee, D.P. 1993. Susceptibility of two cross breeds of sheep to *Haemonchus contortus*. International Journal for Parasitology 23: 819-822.

Yadav, C.L., Singh, Z., Banerjee, D.P. and Chaturvedi, G.C. 1997. Breed difference in acquired resistance of sheep to *Haemonchus contortus*. Indian Journal of Animal Sciences 67: 95-99.

Yadav, N.K. Mandal, A., Sharma, D.K. Rout, P.K. and Roy, R. 2006. Genetic studies on faecal egg counts and packed cell volume following natural *Haemonchus contortus* infection and their relationships with liveweight in Muzaffarnagri sheep. Asian-Australian Journal of Animal Sciences 19: 1524-1528.

Yazwinski, A.A., Goode, L., Moncol, D.J., Morgan, G.W. and Linnerud, A.C. 1981. *Haemonchus contortus* resistance in strightbred and crossbred Blackbelly sheep. Journal of Animal Sciences 51: 279-284.

Zajac, A.M., Herd, R.P. and McClure, K.E. 1988. Trichostrongylid parasite population in pregnant or lactating and unmated Florida Native and Dorset / Rambouillet ewes. International Journal for Parasitology 18: 981–985.

Zajac, A.M., Krakowka, S., Herd, R.P and McClure, K.E. 1990. Experimental *Haemonchus contortus* infection in three breeds of sheep. Veterinary Parasitology 36: 221–235.

□□□

26

Broiler Rabbit Production under Prevailing Climate Change

Rajeev Gulyani
Rabbit Unit, Central Sheep and Wool Research Institute
Avikanagar, via Jaipur, 304 501 Rajasthan

Introduction

Climate change and stress, in all likelihood, are going to impact seriously on animal productivity over the next decade and beyond. Production losses due to impaired physiology are quiet distinct. More serious are the losses due to disease occurrence and the morbidity accompanying such diseases. Heat stress affects animals in several ways (West, 2003): elevated body temperature, increased respiration rates, increased maintenance energy requirements and reduced energy available for productive functions, and decrease in reproductive performance (Jordon, 2003). Lower feed efficiency, higher incidences of disease outbreaks and lower reproductive efficiency are likely to increase the cost of livestock production, which may have far reaching economic implications. Thus there is an urgent need to understand these complex issues so that we can device suitable managemental practices to reduce the adverse effects of climate change. This is of particular significance in rabbits as these animals are generally housed indoors where the micro-climate can be controlled. Day length plays a crucial role in rabbits and is responsible for the seasonality in reproduction observed in rabbits (Sittman et al., 1964). This seasonality in reproduction can be overcome by providing artificial light to breeding does during short day length periods (Bhasin et al., 1990). At the same time, more emphasis can be given on selecting rabbit genotype which is more adapted to high ambient temperature and has better feed efficiency under stress. Also, temperature humidity index (THI) and temperature maximum (T*max*) or temperature minimum (T*min*) need to be analyzed along with production and disease data in different climatic zones and among different breeds of broiler rabbits. Only Rocca et al. (2005) has used the THI modified for rabbits by Marai et al. (2002) and showed that the acute exposure to high THI had immediate negative effects on sperm concentration, total number of spermatozoa per ejaculate, sperm motility, and variables related to viability and sperm normalcy.

Influence of climate change and stress on rabbits

Climate change is not only affecting the normal physiological functions of the animal body but it also induces metabolic disorders, reproductive malfunctions and endocrinological disturbances and genetic alterations (Madan, 2009). The internal milieu of functions in an animal body is regulated by both intrinsic and extrinsic factors. As an extrinsic factor, climate change plays a significant role, which not only affects animal health but also affects animal production. Due to altered endocrine functions, there can be a decrease in the efficiency of nutrient utilization and feed intake depending upon the intensity and duration of heat stress. This often results in feed intake decrease of 10-20 % in hot summer days while the decrease in reproductive performance can be prolonged and impact the animal for months after the heat exposure. High ambient temperatures can cause infertility in breeding rabbits, bucks being more sensitive than does (Lukefahr and Cheeke, 1991; Alvarino, 2000). Therefore, it is always advisable to provide a cooling system in the rabbitry during the hot periods to prevent male rabbits (bucks) from becoming sterile resulting in lower conception rates in females (does). The does also exhibit poor receptivity, lower litter size, early embryonic deaths and decreased fetal growth if exposed to heat stress. The impairment of rabbit doe performance under heat stress conditions is well described both in experiments carried out during summer in Spain and Egypt (Mendez et al., 1986; Marai et al., 2002) or in climatic chambers (Fernandez-Carmona et al., 2003). In these studies it is observed that a hot climate reduced feed and digestible energy intake, milk production, litter size and growth, rabbit doe weight and increased kit mortality. Kits and weaners are particularly sensitive to hot and humid conditions, which causes rapid spread of coccidiosis and thereby heavy mortality due to enteritis. To overcome this problem, prophylaxis is employed against coccidiosis or breeding schedule planned in a manner so as to avoid kindling and weaning during the hot-humid months and instead intensive rabbit breeding and production is practiced during the remaining good part of the year to maintain the overall production. However, if the exposure is over long periods, the rabbits get acclimatized to constant stress situations, also termed as adaptation, to withstand the onslaught of adverse climate. Such adaptive changes are of advantage in terms of disease resistance and ability to withstand climatic stress but disadvantageous in terms of production performance. In general, growth rates of rabbits range from 10-20 g/day in the tropical regions compared to temperate countries where growth performance typically is between 35-40 g/day (Samkol and Lukefahr, 2008).

The universal distribution of rabbits throughout the world, from cold temperate to hot tropical regions, speaks favourably about the adaptability of rabbits to different climatic conditions. The broiler rabbit breeds available in the country were imported from cold temperate former USSR and the UK. These were initially introduced into our country in the Kullu Valley of Himachal Pradesh at NTRS Garsa. Later in 1982, these were introduced in the hot semi-arid region at CSWRI Avikanagar to study their adaptability and performance. The performance over the years at Avikanagar has shown that broiler rabbits can be reared successfully in the hot semi-arid regions of our country (Gulyani et al., 2000) which constitute roughly 65 % of the total geographical area of our country and where temperatures reach 45-47°C during peak summer. Since Broiler rabbits are mostly reared indoors, these become most suitable for livestock production under prevailing and future global warming conditions. With a few modifications in their shelter management, they can tide over the difficult summer phase, which may extend beyond the two to three months period at present, but at an increased cost of production.

The severity of heat stress experienced by rabbit depends on a number of factors. The key ones include the actual temperature and humidity inside the shed, housing type, the length of heat stress period, water availability, the degree of night cooling, ventilation and air flow, the size and age of animal, breed (native, exotic or crossbred) and density of fur and the level of production. According to Siloto et al. (2008), environmental conditions and housing systems should be in accordance with the essential biological characteristics of the species. In tropical areas, environmental temperature along with relative humidity is the environmental factor that has the most profound impact on the efficiency of rabbit production and welfare conditions.

The ranges of temperature and relative humidity recommended for laboratory rabbits (16 to 22°C and 30 to 70%; NRC, 1996) are often exceeded under natural conditions. Housing systems for rabbit should minimize the negative effects of natural environment on the animals.

Rabbits are highly susceptible to heat stress as they have few functional sweat glands and have a difficult heat output situation when the environmental temperature is high (Cheeke et al., 1987; Stephan, 1980). In a study undertaken at Avikanagar on the effect of season and breed on the thermoregulatory responses of broiler rabbits in hot semi-arid environment, Naqvi et al. (1995) observed that winter and spring seasons are relatively comfortable than summer for broiler rabbits on the basis of their respiration rate (RR), which could go up to 450-500 breaths/min. during hot summer temperatures of 35-45°C. Under similar elevated temperature condition (37.8°C), the RR of New Zealand White (Kasa and Thawaites, 1990) and Angora rabbits (Lee, et al., 1941) were 700-800 breaths/min. The comparatively lower rate of RR at Avikanagar could be due to acclimatization of rabbits to hot semi-arid environment as they had been reared for more than seven years by the time of the study (Naqvi et al., 1995). They also observed that Soviet Chinchilla (SC) rabbits could maintain relatively lower rectal temperature as compared to White Giant (WG) during peak of thermal stress by increasing the respiratory evaporative cooling through increase in RR, and that this breed characteristic in SC could be of help to tolerate high environmental temperature, which is manifested in lower mortality (15%) as compared to WG (40%).

Role of rabbits in providing food security and income under changed climate scenario

It is projected that there will be a deficit of ruminant meat production and a deficit of non-ruminant meat production in most countries of Asia (Table-1) and at the same time an increase in per capita demand for livestock products in Asia (Table-2) (Samkol and Lukefahr (2008). This situation is likely to intensify further under changing climate scenario. Since all reasonable options to increase livestock production in our country need to be explored, rabbit can play a major role as an alternative source of meat. According to Lukefahr and Cheeke (1991), a breeding doe could produce 20 marketable offspring from 4 litters/year and ten does could yield 200 fryers annually on forage based diet and using supplement produced from farm. The inclusion of purchased concentrate feed could increase doe production to 6 litters per year.

Table 1. Forecast of ruminant and non-ruminant meat production and demand (kg per capita) in the year 2010 in Asia

Country	Ruminant meat demand	Ruminant meat production	Non-ruminant meat demand	Non-ruminant meat production
Bangladesh	3.0-3.4	1.7	1.0-1.2	0.8
Cambodia	5.2-5.9	3.3	14.2-16.3	9.1
China	5.8-7.4	8.5	54.5-71.3	49.8
India	5.1-6.2	3.8	1.5-1.9	26.2
Indonesia	4.6-6.0	2.5	12.3-16.7	26.2
Laos	4.8-5.4	3.0	12.4-14.2	7.8
Malaysia	6.3-7.9	0.6	73.7-93.9	139.6
Pakistan	16.9-20.3	14.6	19.8-24.5	9.8
Philippines	4.4-4.9	2.7	27.8-31.7	29.8
Sri Lanka	2.7-3.3	1.2	3.4-4.3	3.8
Thailand	10.1-14.8	6.3	35.5-53.5	42.3
Vietnam	10.1-14.8	3.0	21.5-25.2	18.9

Table 2. Projected per capita demand for livestock products in Asia (kg/year)

Livestock product	South Asia			Southeast Asia			East Asia (including Japan)		
	1990	2010	2020	1990	2010	2020	1990	2010	2020
Beef	1.2	1.4	1.5	2.5	4.5	6.0	1.3	2.3	3.1
Pork	0.3	0.4	0.4	5.5	8.6	10.5	18.8	30.6	38.2
Sheep meat	1.0	1.1	1.2	0.3	0.5	0.7	1.0	1.0	1.2
Poultry meat	0.5	0.6	0.7	4.2	6.9	8.5	3.0	5.2	6.5
Eggs	1.3	1.6	1.8	3.3	5.5	7.0	6.8	10.9	13.6
Milk	63.4	84.9	95.3	3.2	3.8	3.5	7.7	9.3	10.2

Rabbits have small body size, short generation interval, high reproductive potential, rapid growth rate, genetic diversity and the ability to utilize forages and by products as major diet components that make this animal appropriate for small livestock keeping in developing countries (Cheeke, 1986; Das and Yadav, 2007). According to Rastogi (2000), the advantages of small scale rabbit production are: small size and quite nature of rabbits make it easy to raise them in cities, suburbs and villages; larger litter size and short generation interval allows for economic returns in short term; rabbits are 2.5 and 4 times more efficient in extracting protein from forages than sheep and beef cattle; rabbits can easily subsist on waste materials from vegetable garden, family kitchen and institutional canteens/cafeterias; low investment is required for establishing a small rabbitry with 3-5 breeding does; meat of rabbits is an excellent, alternative source of healthy food being low in fat, salt and cholesterol.

Livestock play a significant role in improving living conditions of the poor. The purpose of livestock keeping of small farmers is for draught power, food, cash income and organic fertilizer. Poor households rarely keep one species, due to risk of diseases, and so raise several livestock species for sustainability. Rabbit can be added to this list as according to FAO (2001), backyard rabbit keeping provides additional income and supplies additional protein for poor rural and urban households with low investment and labour inputs. It is not only a prolific breeding animal but also adjusts to varied agro-climatic conditions and different feed sources (Bhasin et al., 1990).

Indirect effects on livestock production have been investigated by observations on changes in survival of pathogens, disease vectors and parasites, but livestock production system may also be affected by the impact of climate change on forage production. Under such a scenario, rabbit production assumes importance as rabbits can easily be incorporated into integrated farming systems as they covert a vast variety of plant material, often of low nutritive value, to high quality meat, as well as provides organic manure. According to Lukefahr (1992), one clear advantage of rabbits is their ability to directly consume forage and convert proteins into animal protein. The potential of local feed resources can be successfully exploited for growing rabbits in terms of cost effectiveness and sustainability. Therefore, poor families with limited resources could be sustained and helped through increased income and increased consumption of rabbit meat to meet the families' nutritional needs.

Recent outbreaks of Avian Influenza in poultry have occurred in several countries in the world. Rabbit production, which is a comparatively new development, can play an important role in view of the economic risks by spread of Asian Bird Flu (Otte et al., 2007) and ensure the supply of 'white' meat for health conscious meat eating population as rabbit meat has well known nutritious characteristics like low cholesterol and high protein (Hernandez and Gondert, 2006). It is a lean meat rich in proteins of high biological value and is characterized by high levels of essential amino acids, low content of purines and absence of uric acid (Hernandez, 2008).

Adaptability of broiler rabbits in the hot semi-arid environment

Rabbits are highly susceptible to heat stress as they have few functional sweat glands and have a difficult heat output situation when environmental temperatures are high. In the semi-arid region, the rabbits show lower body weights from April to August and improvement in body weights as environment becomes favourable (Table 3). The rabbits maintain a lower body weight in the semi-arid region as compared to the temperate and sub-temperature regions of the country, indicating that during the course of adaptation to harsh environment there is a reduction in their adult body weights (Gupta, 1987).

Table. 3. Average adult body weight (kg) of broiler rabbits

Breed	Jan	Feb	Mar	Apr	May	June	July	Aug	Sept	Oct	Nov	Dec
WG	3.36	3.33	3.40	3.36	3.19	3.05	3.07	3.21	3.24	3.34	3.34	3.51
GG	3.04	3.05	3.09	3.02	2.90	2.69	2.70	2.74	2.78	2.81	2.98	3.01
SC	3.20	3.25	3.22	3.25	3.07	2.79	2.84	2.80	2.90	3.12	3.17	3.27

Studies on thermoregulatory responses of SC and WG rabbits in the semi-arid environment have demonstrated that the period from October to March is favourable for rabbits while the April to July period is stressful. As compared to WG, SC is more tolerant to hot environmental conditions because of its ability to achieve higher respiration rates i.e., higher evaporative cooling (Naqvi et al., 1995).

Survivability of broiler rabbits in the hot semi-arid environment

The survivability of rabbits varies among different age groups (Table 4). The mortality in kits (0-6 weeks) was highest in all the breeds, particularly in the first week of life as the kits are naked and depend totally on the mothering ability of the doe as well as the climatic conditions prevailing at that time. During winter kits generally die of hypothermia and in summer due to hyperthermia. Similar results were reported by Damodar and Jatkar (1985). The overall survivability was high in GG and SC breeds and low in WG breed.

Table 4. Survivability (%) in rabbits among different age groups and breeds

Age group	WG	NZW	GG	SC
0-6 Weeks	79.82	70.83	78.15	83.17
7-12 weeks	89.32	95.85	92.24	82.89
13-24 Weeks	92.56	95.48	93.70	97.38
Adults	82.44	85.73	88.25	88.13

Growth performance of broiler rabbits in the hot semi-arid environment

Growth is important aspect of broiler rabbit production. The growth performance of different broiler rabbit breeds is presented in Table 5. The average birth weight ranged from 46.08 in BB to 54.57 g in SC while WG and NZW had comparable birth weights. Similar results have been reported by Swai et al. (1985). The body weights at 6 weeks of age ranged from 708.1 g in BB to 764.4 g in WG which compare favourably with those reported by Lahari and Mahajan (1982) for broiler rabbits in the temperate region. The 12-week weight ranged from 1554.60 g to 1580.6 g showing no marked breed difference.

Table 5. Growth performance of broiler rabbits.

Breed	Body Weights in grams			
	At birth	6 weeks	12 weeks	24 weeks
WG	54.05	806.41	1853.00	2645.30
SC	54.57	876.98	1788.46	2502.80
BB	46.08	769.76	1711.11	2448.60

The body weight at 12 weeks is of crucial significance as the broiler rabbit is usually marketed and slaughtered at this age. The growth is fastest during 7-12 weeks period. The higher the body weight at 12 weeks, the more the carcass yield and profitability. Under experimental *ad lib* complete diet feeding system, average weight of 2.0 to 2.3 kg at 12 weeks has been achieved at this Institute (Prasad et al., 1996). However, exposure of the growing rabbit to heat stress during summer adversely affected growth (Marai et al., 2001) Now efforts are being made to achieve 2.0 kg body wt. at 12 weeks by increasing the milk yield of does and improving the feed accessibility to the weaner rabbits under routine management.

Reproductive performance of broiler rabbits in the hot semi-arid environment

Short generation time and high reproductive potential of rabbit makes it the ideal meat producing small livestock for our country. Rabbits are induced ovulators and can be bred within 24 hours of parturition. Thus it is theoretically possible to produce over 11 litters per year under intensive production system. The average number of kindling/doe/year and average number of offspring/doe/year achieved in the semi-intensive production system are 3.5 and 23.9, respectively (Table 6), while under intensive system it was marginally higher at 4.0 litter/doe/year (Singh, 1998). Fertility is adversely affected in the semi-arid region as the semen quality of bucks deteriorates during summer and this condition continues up to the first half of the rainy season (Mathur et al., 1989). However, in the temperate region it was possible to achieve an average of 5.16 litters/doe/year (range 4-9) or 35-40 offspring/doe/year under the intensive production system (Gulyani and Rai, 1987).

Table 6. Kindling performance of broiler rabbit does

Breed	No. of kindling/ doe/ year	No. of kits born	No. weaned
WG	3.3	25.9	17.3
SC	3.7	22.4	16.6
BB	3.3	22.9	15.5
Overall	3.5	23.9	16.7

The reproductive performance of broiler rabbits is presented in Table 7. The litter size at birth (LSB) ranged from 6.46 to 7.26 while the litter size at weaning (LSW) ranged from 4.92 to 6.17 in different breeds. These results are in agreement with those reported by Damodar and Jatkar (1985). High LSB and LSW were recorded in Grey Giant (GG) and White Giant (WG) breeds. Similarly, high litter weights at birth (LWB) and weaning (LWW) were recorded in GG and WG breeds. The average LWB and LWW ranged from 325.34 to 390.82 g and 3023.80 to 3488.22 g, respectively.

Table 7. Reproductive performance of broiler rabbits.

Breed	Litter size (n) at		Litter weight (g) at	
	Birth	Weaning (6 wks)	Birth	Weaning (6Wks)
GG	7.26	6.17	374.19	3488.22
WG	7.23	5.70	390.80	3681.09
NZW	6.46	5.18	345.99	3300.50
SC	6.65	5.26	258.00	3023.80
BB	7.06	4.92	325.34	3304.34

Studies on reproductive efficiency of broiler rabbits by Kumar et al. (1998) revealed that the overall conception rate was 50.25% and number of services/ conception was 1.98. Highest conception rate (53.33%) was recorded in Soviet Chinchilla, followed by White Giant (48.80%) and Black Brown (46.80%).

Milk production of broiler rabbit does in the hot semi-arid environment

The growth of the young during the suckling period, especially during the first three weeks, greatly affects their later performance (Cheeke et al., 1987). Apart from milk yield, the liter size and doe's nursing ability also influence the pre-weaning growth. Milk production by a rabbit doe is thus an important indicator of growth and health of young rabbits in their first month of life and is intimately related to the body weight achieved at the slaughter age of 12 weeks of age. Gulyani et al. (1998) in their earlier study on milk production of broiler rabbit does in the semi-arid region showed that the total milk yield of SC does was higher (3481.6 g) as compared to WG (3278.18 g) and BB (3205.00 g) in a 28 days lactation period. The pre-weaning growth of kits is entirely dependent upon the does milk yield, particularly during the first 21 days of life. The milk yield and nursing ability of doe increases with parity order. A high milk yield of 4370.90 g was achieved in SC does as compared to WG (4326.43 g) and BB (4179 g) in a 35 days lactation period (Table 8). There is, however, a sudden decline in milk production in all the three breeds studied from 31.32 onwards if lactation is continued beyond 28 days. Therefore, in order to take more number of kindlings per doe per year, it is recommended to go for early weaning at 28 days as by this time the young start consuming some solid feed as well as roughage and the role of milk in their diet declines.

Table 8. Milk production in broiler rabbit does

Lactation Period	Milk yield/doe (g) Soviet Chinchilla	White Giant	Black Brown
0-7 days	531.38	561.25	527.14
8-14 days	903.33	797.50	808.57
15-21 days	1055.83	923.75	892.50
22-28 days	941.11	975.45	915.83
28-35 days	700.00	680.00	725.00
0-28 days	3481.66	3278.18	3205.00
0-35 days	4370.90	4326.43	4179.00

Carcass characteristics of broiler rabbits reared in hot semi-arid environment

The first step in slaughtering rabbit is stunning before bleeding. In small scale operations, dislocation of neck is generally the method of choice, while on a commercial scale electrical stunning is mostly used. Feed is withheld at least 12 hours before slaughter to ensure an almost empty gut. After separation of head, the whole body is suspended by inserting the hook in the hock joint of the hind leg and skinning is carried out carefully to avoid any cut on the skin as it reduces the value of the skin, which is an important by-product of rabbit. This is followed by evisceration of all the visceral organs and separation from the carcass. The carcass is then cut into hind quarters, loin and fore quarters. Killing out percentages of 55-60 % saleable meat yields are achievable in rabbit (Table-9).

Table 9. Carcass traits of broiler rabbits

Traits	Soviet Chinchilla	Grey Giant	Pooled
Pre-slaughter weight (g)	2131.90	2206.60	2169.20
Blood weight (g)	80.40	80.60	80.50
Head weight (g)	186.40	191.90	189.20
Skin Weight (g)	224.00	238.40	231.20
Inedible offal weight (g)	477.10	516.20	496.60
Edible offal (g)	81.40	80.10	80.70
Head meat weight (g)	61.70	58.40	60.10
Leg cut weight (g)	423.40	422.50	422.90
Loin cut weight (g)	249.40	237.90	243.60
Rack, neck & BF cut Weight (g)	409.80	433.00	421.40
Total cut weight (g)	1082.60	1099.30	1090.90
Saleable meat yield (g)	1225.70	1237.80	1231.80
% PSW	57.45	55.68	56.57

Some 70% of rabbit carcass is composed of edible meat as compared to 50% in chicken. Rabbit meat is also comparable to chicken in terms of low fat content (3.8 %) and high protein (20.7 %) and these values are favourable than most other meats. Moreover the digestibility of rabbit meat is as high as 98.9 %. Rabbit meat is in fact appreciated for its low content of total fat and cholesterol and high proportion of polyunsaturated fatty acids (PUFA) and phospholipids, which make rabbit meat a healthy meat for humans.

Rabbit diseases and their control

Disease and death are an integral part of any livestock operation. The same is true in rabbit raising. Mortality usually averages between 20-25% of all animals born in most of the rabbitaries. This high rate of mortality in other livestock enterprises would be very discouraging but is tolerable in rabbit raising because of its short generation interval and faster production. Since most diseases occur due to management mistakes, it is possible to keep rabbit diseases at a minimum. Ventilation, sanitation and observation are three of the most important factors involved in disease control. Less respiratory problems are encountered in well-ventilated rabbitaries, as air dilution is a very effective method of reducing the number of certain disease causing organisms. Physical or chemical removal of such organisms, called sanitation, is another effective method of reducing the number of potential disease organisms. Observation means training oneself to look for signs of discomfort in animals. A sick animal is usually off-feed and water, is lethargic and has a dull appearance. If one misses these signs, it is generally too late to do anything. However, in the initial stages, the treatment may be helpful and save the life of the animal.

The two most important specific rabbit diseases are pasteurellosis and enteritis. Pasteurellosis is caused by the organism *pasteurella multocida* and this term covers a multitude of clinical conditions like snuffles, pneumonia, abscesses, weepy eyes, orchitis, metritis and wryneck. The first signs of *P. multocida* infection are snuffles or cold. Strict isolation / culling and treatment with antibiotics will control the problem. Ventilation is very important as both ammonia levels and humidity are involved in the transmission and development of snuffles. Treatment involves draining the pus properly and putting the rabbit on antibiotics. Another major cause of death in weaner/ grower rabbits is the complex of diseases called enteritis. Enteritis complex includes enterotoxaemia, mucoid enteritis, coccidiosis and Tyzzer's disease. The clinical signs of enterotoxaemia are profuse diarrhoea, dehydration and reduced feed intake. It is most commonly seen in weaners and the post-mortem reveals an enlarged and reddish caecum. Enterotoxaemia is more common when diets low in fiber and high in energy are fed to rabbits. Causing agents are generally *Clostridium perfringens* and *E. coli.* Oxytetracycline in water gives some relief but feeding of hay or straw is more helpful in prevention of this disease.

Conclusions

Rabbit production, though of recent origin in India, has a great scope. Due to rapidly increasing human population and climate change, food shortage may become a major problem in future. Since all reasonable options have to be explored, rabbit can play a major role as an alternative source of meat in the changing climate scenario. Studies at the Central Sheep and wool Research Institute has shown that rabbit can be reared successfully in most regions of the country in either a small-scale backyard or as a large-scale commercial enterprise. Rabbit production, therefore, now deserves better attention of our policy makers than what has been given in the last two decades. Development of infrastructure facilities in States where rabbit rearing enjoys popular support, in terms of germplasm, housing, feeding, health care, marketing, training, testing and processing of raw materials, etc., may be a good step forward in the successful implementation of rabbit production programme in our country.

References

Alvarino, J.M.R. 2000. Reproductive performance of male rabbit. In: Proceedings of the 7th World Rabbit Congress, Valencia, Spain, Vol. A. 13-35.

Bhasin,V., Shastry, V.R.B., Singh, D., Gulyani, R., Malhi, R.S., Kishore, K., Singh, R.N., Lahiri, S.S., Rai, R.B. and Das, P.K. 1990. Performance of broiler rabbits in sub-temperate Himalayan region. Journal of Applied Rabbit Research 12: 263-265.

Cheeke, P.R. 1986. Potentials of rabbit production in tropical and sub-tropical agricultural systems. Journal of Animal Science 63: 1581-1586.

Cheeke, P.R., Patton, N.M., Lukefahr, S.D. and McNitt, J.I. 1987. Rabbit Production. Interstate Publishers, Danville III.

Damodar, N. and Jatkar, V.D. 1985. Adaptability of rabbits under sub-tropical climate. Indian Journal of Animal Sciences 55(7): 610-611.

Das, S.K. and Yadav, B.P.S. 2007. Effect of mating system, parity and breed on the reproductive performance of broiler rabbits under the agro-climatic conditions of Meghalaya. Livestock Research for Rural Development 19 (2).

FAO 2001. FAO recognizes the increasingly important role of rabbit breeding: Global rabbit production exceeds 1 million tons. Press Release 01/57, FAO, Rome, Italy.

Fernandez-Carmona, J., Alqedra, I., Cervera, C., Moya, J. and Pascual, J.J. 2003. Effect of Lucerne based diets on performance of reproductive rabbit does at two temperatures. Animal Science 76: 283-295.

Gulyani, R. and Rai, R.B. 1987. Annual Report, CSWRI, Avikanagar.

Gulyani, R., Kumar, S. and Singh, R.N. 1998. Milk production of broiler rabbit does in the semi-arid region. In: Proceedings of the Golden Jubilee seminar on sheep, goat and rabbit production and utilization, 24-26 April, Jaipur, pp 32.

Gulyani, R., Kumar, S. and Singh, R.N. 2000. Status of broiler rabbit rearing technology in the semi-arid region of India. In: Proceedings of the 7th World Rabbit Congress, Valencia, Spain, Section of FAO short papers pp1-6.

Gupta, S.C. 1987. Performance of rabbits in the semi-arid tropics of India. Proceedings of Short Course on Advances in Rabbit Production, 29 June to 5 July, Garsa, Kullu, H.P.

Hernandez, P. 2008. Enhancement of nutritional quality and safety in rabbit meat. Proceedings 9th World Rabbit Congress, June 10-13, Verona, Italy, 1287-1299.

Hernandez, P. and Gondret, F. 2006. Rabbit Meat Quality. In: Maertens, L. and Coudert, P. (Eds). Recent Advances in Rabbit Sciences. ILVO, Merelbeke, Belgium, 269-290.

Jordan, E.R. 2003. Effect of heat stress on reproduction. Journal of Dairy Sciences 86: E104-E114.

Kasa, W. and Thawaites, C.J. 1990. The effect of elevated temperature and humidity on rectal temperature and respiration rate in the New Zealand White rabbit. International Journal of Biometeorology 34: 157-160.

Kumar, S., Gulyani, R., Singh, G. and Singh, R.N. 1998. Reproductive efficiency and reproductive performance of broiler rabbit does in the semi-arid region. In: Proceedings of the Golden Jubilee seminar on sheep, goat and rabbit production and utilization, 24-26 April, Jaipur, pp 33.

Lahiri, S.S., and Mahajan, J.M. 1983. Weaning characteristics of different mating types in rabbits. Indian, Journal of Animal Science 53(12): 1363-1365.

Lee, D.H.K., Robinson, K. and Hines, H.J.G. 1941. Reactions of rabbit to hot atmospheres. Proceedings of Royal Society of Queensland 53: 129-144.

Lukefahr, S.D. 1992. A Trainer's Manual for Meat Rabbit Project Development. The Rabbit Manual: A Heifer Project International Publication, Little Rock, AR, USA, 36-39.

Lukefahr, S.D. and Cheeke, P.R. 1991. Rabbit project development strategies in subsistence farming systems. World Animal Review 6: 60-70.

Madan, M.L. 2009. Climate change affecting animal functions. Compendium of DUVASU National Seminar, September 24-25, Mathura.

Mathur, A.K., Srivastava, R. S., Rawat, P. S. and Kalra, D.B. 1989. Seasonal variation in the semen characteristics of Soviet Angora bucks. Animal Reproduction Science 19:293-298.

Marai, I.F., Ayyat, M.S. and Abd El-Monem, U.M. 2001. Growth performance and reproductive traits at first parity of New Zealand White female rabbits as affected by heat stress and its alleviation under Egyptian conditions. Tropical Animal Health Production 33: 451-462.

Marai, I.F.M., Habeeb, A.A.M. and Gad, A.E. 2002. Rabbits' productive, reproductive and physiological performance traits as affected by heat stress: a review. Livestock Production Science 78: 71-90.

Mendez, J. de Blas, C. and Fraga, M.J. 1986. The effect of diet and remating interval after parturition on the reproductive performance of commercial rabbit doe. Journal of Animal Science 62: 1624-1634.

Naqvi, S.M.K., Gulyani, R. and Singh, Gurmej. 1995. Physiological responses of broiler rabbits in hot semi-arid environment. Indian Journal of Animal Science 65(6): 718-720.

NRC (National Research Council). 1996. Guide for the Care and Use of Laboratory Animals. National Academy Press, Washington, USA.

Otte, J., Pfeiffer, D., Tiensin, T., Price, L. and Silbergeld, E. 2007. HPAI risk, bio-security and small holder adversity. In Proceedings of World Poultry Science Association-

Asian Pacific Working Federation Group on Small Scale Family Poultry Farming Symposium, Bangkok, Thailand, 1-8.

Prasad, R., Singh, G. and Patnayak, B.C. 1996. Growth performance of broiler rabbits maintained on different diets. World Rabbit Science. 4(1):11-14.

Rastogi, R.K. 2000. Periurban small livestock production for food and community development. Department of Food Production, Faculty of Agriculture and Natural Sciences, UWI, St. Augustine, Trinidad.

Rocca, J., Martinez, S., Orengo, J., Vazquez, J.M. and Martinez, E.A. 2005. Influence of constant long days on ejaculate parameters of rabbits reared under natural environment conditions of Mediterranean area. Livestock Production Science 94: 169-177.

Samkol, P. and Lukefahr, S.D. 2008. A challenging role for organic rabbit production towards poverty alleviation in Southeast Asia. Proceedings 9th World Rabbit Congress, June 10-13, Verona, Italy, 1479-1497.

Siloto, E.V., Zeferino, C.P., Moura, A.S.A.M.T., Fernandes, S., Sartori, J.R. and Siqueira, E.R. 2008. Temperature and cage floor enrichment affect the behaviour of growing rabbits. In: Proceedings of the 9th World Rabbit Congress, June 10-13, Verona, Italy, 1245-1249.

Singh, G. 1998. A study on the intensive reproduction of broiler rabbits under hot semi-arid climate. Proceedings of the Golden Jubilee seminar on sheep, goat and rabbit production and utilization, 24-26 April, Jaipur, pp 34.

Sittmann, D.B., Rollins, W.C., Sittmann, K. and Casady, R. 1964. Seasonal variation in reproductive traits of New Zealand White Rabbits. Journal of Reproduction and Fertility 8: 29.

Stephan, K. 1980. The influence of environmental temperature on meat rabbits of different breeds. In: Proceedings of the II World Rabbit Congress, Barcelona, Spain, pp 399.

Swai, G.D., Mtenga, L.A. and Mgheni, M. 1986. Observations on the effect of sex, litter size and age on body weight of rabbits. Animal Breeding Abstracts 54: 2477.

West, J.W. 2003. Effect of heat stress on production in dairy cattle. Journal of Dairy Sciences 86: 2131-2144.

❑❑❑

27

Angora Wool Production in the Country under Changing Climate and Market

S. R. Sharma* and S. A. Karim
North Temperate Regional Station, Central Sheep and Wool Research Institute
Garsa, Kullu - 175 141, Himachal Pradesh

Introduction

Animal products like skin, fur and fibre had always been a preference of mankind to cover and protect its body from external environments, since time immemorial. These products are being used either in raw or processed form and have undergone lot of changes with the passage of time and introduction of new technological innovations. The animal fibre is primarily used throughout the world for making of apparels, knitwear products, woolens and other textile products. With the technological advancements, lot of synthetic fibre or products are available in the world markets that could satiate the human needs and pride, but the fascination of the human being for natural animal fibre, especially finer types, has remained unchanged over the time. There are five major fibres from animal origin, which have significant economic importance in the world and governing the significant GDP of many countries. Wool (fine) from sheep remains the major fibre, whereas the four others are mohair, angora, cashmere and alpaca. These fibres are preferred for their original qualities of fineness, luster, feel and warmth. Hairs or wool obtained from the Angora rabbits are known as angora and often considered as one of the noble fibre. Angora is preferred over cashmere, mohair, wool and alpaca due to its fineness, warmth, fluffiness, odorless, lightness and anti-static property to repel the dirt. Angora being about 8 times warmer than sheep wool is used either in pure or blended form for making the garments throughout the world. It is often blended with animal or plant fibre to make the yarn and other products and hence, is required in a very little quantity while blended.

Historical background

Rabbits have a very recent history of domestication as compared to the other domesticated animals like cattle, sheep, pigs and poultry. This can be traced to the late middle ages and dates back no further than the present millennium. Angora is considered to be one of the oldest domestic rabbits; originating in Ankara, Turkey and spread from there to Europe and other parts of the world. During the sixteenth century, several breeds of rabbits were known and rabbit breeding seems to have spread across France, Italy, Flanders (Belgium) and England. As early as 1606, Olivier de Serres classified three types of rabbits namely, the wild rabbit, the semi-wild rabbit or warren (rabbits raised inside walls or ditches) and the domesticated (hutch-bred) rabbit (Lebas et al., 1997). At the beginning of nineteenth century, rabbit rearing spread all over Western Europe and was introduced to countries like Australia and New Zealand. From this time onwards there is frequent mention of the fur as a by-product and the already long existing Angora mutant was recorded. The Angora rabbit industry came into existence in Europe during 17th and 18th centuries. Angora rabbits have been reported to be introduced to France from England in 1723. The use of angora in garments was recorded in 1870, whereas the modern angora industry was started in 1930s. During the 20th century, hutch rearing combined with selection, protection and multiplication of breeds and mutants un-adapted to the wild led to the rabbit population explosion and founded the basis of contemporary rabbit husbandry. There are about 45 recognized breeds of rabbits in the world with total estimated population of about 709 million rabbits. The scientific interventions have brought an immense change in the rabbit production, as exampled below (Table 1):

Table 1. Production trends in the most productive Rabbitries of France

Criteria	1950	1960	1970	1980	1990
Rabbits produced (sold) per breeding doe	20-25	30	45	60	65
Average interval between litters (days)	90-100	70	54	42	40
Concentrate feed necessary to produce 1 kg live rabbit (kg)	(*)	6	4.5	3.6	3.3
Type of rabbit	Common, no specific breed	Pure breeds	Pure-bred does crossed with improver buck	Specialized hybrid strains	Specialized hybrid strains
Working hours per doe per year (hours)	16	16	10	7.5	6.0
Labour used to produce 1 kg carcass (minutes)	27	22	9.5	6.2	4.3
Number of breeding does in breeding units	80-100	100-150	200-250	350-400 up to 1000	600-4000
Percentage of investment in retail price of rabbit	<3	5-8	12-15	18-20	18-20

*Rabbits were not fed concentrates at this date; (Source: Lebas et al., 1997)

Angora rabbit and angora

Angora rabbits are herbivores, prolific producers and efficient converter of fodder into meat and wool. With shrinking land holdings due to continuous increase in population, reduced grazing areas and changing climatic conditions in the many countries particularly developing one; the traditional livestock rearing has become difficult and uneconomical and there is shifting towards smaller animals like rabbits for steady and sustainable income, and nutritional security against protein hunger. There are many breeds of Angora rabbits and four major breeds recognized by the American Rabbit Breeders Association (ARBA) namely, English (British), French, Giant and Satin. Few other breeds include German, Chinese, Russian, Swiss and Finnish. However, two major commercial angora breeds are French and German (Rochambeau and Thebault, 1990). French angora breed is bristly (bristle contents 0.2 to 1.8%) with a double coat, which is plucked after giving a fodder Lagodendron. This fodder with a depilatory effect makes the lifting easier, faster and respects the well-being of the animal. On the other hand, German Angora developed as a result of intensive selection for wool production, is wooly type and the wool is removed by shearing. China, Central Europe and South American Countries use angora producing rabbits based on crosses containing 70 to 90% German and 5 to 10% French Angora types. The Chinese Angora rabbit, which contributes for 90% of present international angora trade, was developed by crossing the German Angora with French Angora and the New Zealand White (meat rabbit breed) rabbits and weighs about 4.1 to 4.4 kg at 11 months of age (Thebault, 1993).

The parameters which determine the quality of angora are: (a) fibre (Staple) length, (b) mean fibre diameter, (c) the proportions of the different fibres, (d) crimp and (e) the absence of felt (Herrmann et al., 1996). Angora rabbit pelage has three types of hairs *viz.* the bristle or guard hairs (longest, thick and tight hairs with 25 - 100μm diameter); the awn or guard hairs (medium in length having a thick and tight top and a thin curly body with 16-30 μm diameter), and the down (shortest, thin and curly lying under guard hairs with 6-18 μm diameter) (Schlolaut, 1974; Vrillon and Thebault, 1988). The bristle content varies from breed to breed and is desirable within permissible limits; as these prevent felting on the rabbits and provide fluffiness to the yarn or angora products. All hairs have a hollow structure -medulla characterized by tiny air chambers, which makes them lighter (low specific weight) than wool and increase their insulating properties. Clean, pure and soft angora with mean fibre diameter of about 13μm, staple length > 6cm and guard hairs less than 5% is graded as "A or first grade" and preferred by the industry.

The Chinese rabbit fleece contains approximately 15% bristle fibres. The bristle content of the Chinese angora is significantly higher than the 0.2 to 1.8% recorded for the French Angora rabbit, which makes it coarser in nature and undervalued. Angora rabbits mainly German and French were introduced in to China from England, Germany, Japan and Hungary around 1950s (Gu et al., 2008) and multiplied extensively both for wool and meat purpose rather than exclusively for wool unlike India. Though, no official statistics are published in China on the production and consumption of rabbit meat, however, it does appear that rabbits for meat export (mainly to Europe) come from the nearly 20 million Angora rabbits produced, which are usually slaughtered very young, after the second or third clipping at most. Thus, financially, meat appears to be the by-product and angora wool the main product, fetching 55 to 70 % of the return from each animal (Lebas et al., 1997).

Why Angora rabbit farming?

Angora rabbit rearing can be practically done under rural, peri-urban and urban setups due to various inherent assets with this species. Some of the exceptional advantages and economic considerations which tempt for Angora rabbit farming are:

- The value of angora per unit of weight is 40 to 50 times higher to that of greasy wool and 1 kg angora could be produced by 30% less digestible energy as compared to 1 kg sheep wool.
- Angora rabbits do not compete with human for food being herbivore and require less space as compared to other livestock. These animals convert plant proteins of little or no use to people as food into high-value animal protein in the form of meat and wool.
- In a backyard rabbitry, about 50 animals could be reared on kitchen waste and about 100 rabbits can be easily managed by a household with out affecting daily routine. A unit comprising of 100 adults rabbits can generates an additional income of Rs. 2000-3000 per month.
- Angora rabbits with concurrent pregnancy and lactation and short generation interval can multiply very fast. A single female can produce as many as 30-40 young-ones in a year.
- Angora are considered premium product; as these are directly influenced by the fashion industry and are always a temptation among the elite consumers. Moreover, angora can be blended easily with natural and synthetic fibres to produce quality products, which had demand in most of the developed countries.
- Angora has been found to possess medicinal properties and its garments because of electrostatic properties are recommended for arthritis.
- Angora rabbit meat is categorised as white meat, which is rich in poly unsaturated fatty acids and low in cholesterol. Meat is usually advised to persons having cardiac problem and hypertension.
- Rabbit manure is very rich in nitrogen contents and could replace inorganic urea on per unit basis in agricultural and horticultural crops. Rabbit manure can be used for organic farming and indirectly higher returns could be obtained for such agricultural and horticultural crops or products. Further, rabbit faeces can be used for vermi-composting for additional income from sale of compost. Moreover dried rabbit faeces can be added up to 10% in the ration of rabbits without affecting production and thereby, reducing the feed cost.
- Angora rabbit rearing can sustain multifarious activities in the area and can generate employment for youth, woman and skilled artisans, thereby, improving the social status.

International angora production and marketing

Angora is used mainly in textiles and forms a special sector of the international wool trade characterized as other fine animal fiber under trade code 5102.19: Fine or coarse animal hair, not carded or combed: fine animal hair - other (Schlink and Liu, 2003). World angora production is modest and ranked third largest animal fibre industry (Fig. 1) with about 8,500 tons annual production, though no specific records are maintained for international trading. The angora production estimates in different countries of the world has been summarized (Table 2).

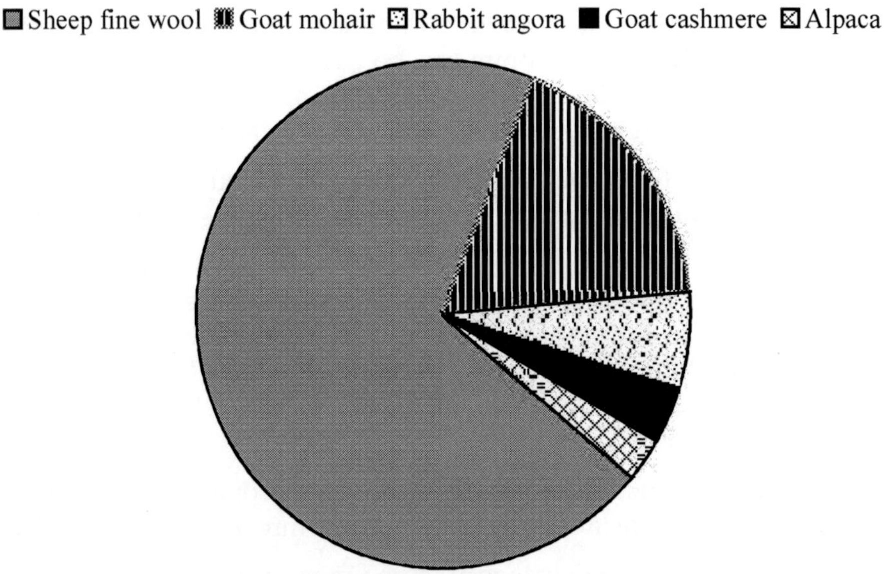

Fig. 1. World production of animal fibres
(Source: Leeder et al., 1998)

Table 2 Country-wise angora wool production

Country	Production per year
Czech Republic and Slovakia	80 to 120 tons
France	100 tons
Hungary	50 to 80 tons
Germany	30 to 40 tons
UK, Spain, Switzerland, Poland & Belgium	Small quantity
China	8000 to 9000 tons
Japan	50 to 60 tons
Argentina, Korea and India	Small quantity

Source: (Lebas et al., 1997)

Europe's share of the ever-growing world output estimated to the tune of 8000 to 10000 tons has reduced to about 250 to 300 tons a year, in recent times, as a result of marketing problems. Currently China is the dominant angora producing country with export of about 3000 tons of angora. China is now effectively dominating the international Angora fibre market both for raw wool and spun yarn and thus sets the world price. With about 50 million Angora rabbits, China produces about 10000 tons rabbit fibre per year and exports about 50% of the fibre into the international market (Tang, 2002). Concurrently, China has also developed angora processing capacity to produce more than 4000 tons of processed products per year according to market requirements and had refined the processing technology to overcome the problems like shrinkage, felting and pilling in the fabrics. In addition, it has developed a capacity to rapidly build numbers should the international prices for Angora fibre increase (Schlink and Liu, 2003).

Comprehensively, the world angora production for last five decades (1950 to 1995) has been analyzed for production patterns and economic returns (Fig. 2). Until 1970 world angora production was stable at around 1,000 tons per year (Ossard et al., 1995). However, from 1976 to 1988 there was a sharp increase in demand, which encouraged Argentina, Chile and Hungary to increase the production significantly. At the same time, looking into the prospects of angora New Zealand and Australia have also made attempts to restart their Angora fibre industries. However, with more and more angora production, the prices have fallen below the traditional levels.

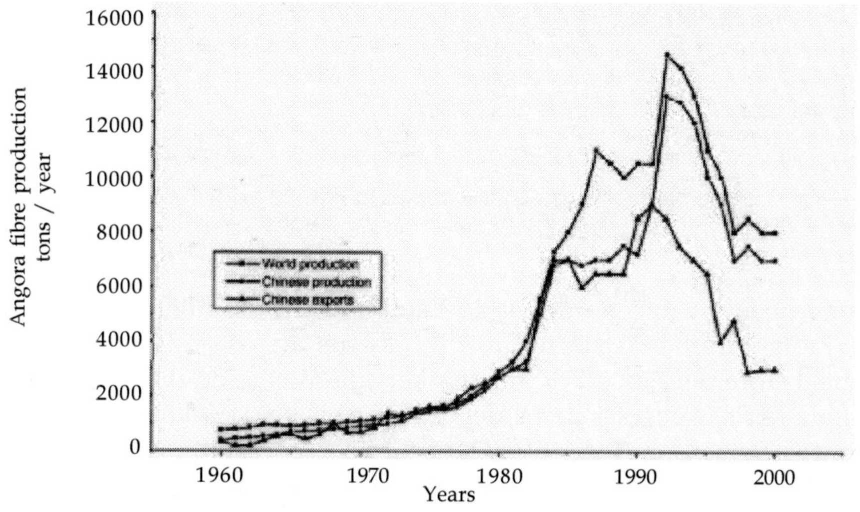

Fig. 2. World Angora fibre production, Angora fibre production in China & amount of Chinese Angora fibre being traded in the international fibre market in tons / year *(Source: Schlink and Liu, 2003)*

In the international trade, angora production is an international industry with separate angora producing, processing and consumer countries, France is not a large consumer angora, but it had been a number one angora producer and exporter till 1965. The main end-user countries of angora are Japan, the United States, Germany and particularly, Italy. The trade is characterized by regular four-year cycles due to fluctuations in demand dictated by fashion and not due to production, which otherwise is regular (Lebas et al., 1997). Since 1985, however, world prices have remained at rock-bottom levels as illustratable from the French angora fibre import prices (Fig. 3).

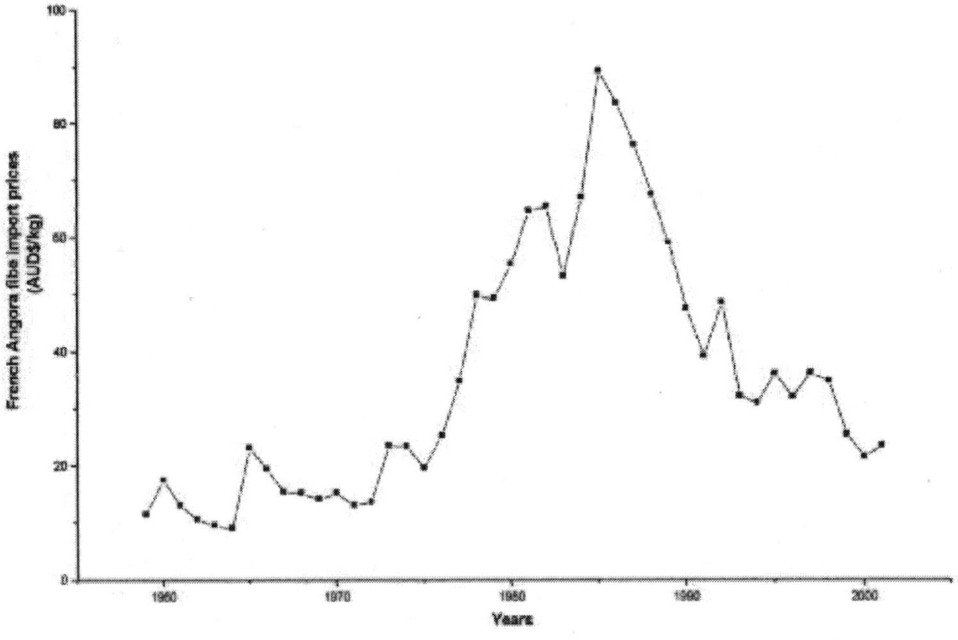

Fig. 3. Price paid for Angora fibre import in France from 1959 to 2001
(Source: Schlink and Liu, 2003)

Consequent to uncertainty and fluctuations in the international angora prices, France itself has started to process the angora into either yarn or garments before releasing in to the market and almost doubling the value of the angora to its farmers. The model of France is being followed by Finland, though it is a small producer of angora. Chile exports angora to Europe and hand spun yarn to United States. India is a significant angora producer but had not entered International angora market so far and processes all angora produced internally for yarn and other products for its own consumption (Gupta et al., 2000).

National angora wool scenario

In India, rabbit rearing of indigenous stock as a pet had been a fancy since ages. The rabbit as a commercial livestock was introduced into the country by private sector long back but was kept in isolation. Around 1940s, the New Zealand White breed of rabbit was introduced by British in the Southern parts of the Country, whereas the Angora (British Angora) rabbit farming was started during 1962 by Mr. Butter Worth at Dharamshala in Himachal Pradesh (the then Punjab). Thereafter, certain individuals and agencies made efforts to spread angora farming in Kullu, Mandi and Kangra districts of Himachal Pradesh and Nilgiri hills of Tamil Nadu. Around 1979, Indian Council of Agricultural Research (ICAR) established a Division of Fur Animal Breeding (DFAB) at Garsa, Kullu (HP) under the Central Sheep and Wool Research Institute (CSWRI) to initiate the scientific work on British angora (BA) and Russian angora (RA) imported from UK and USSR, respectively; under Indian sub-temperate conditions.

The research efforts were initiated to understand and evolve suitable strains adaptable to local conditions and develop packages of practice for small and large scale production. After initial success in its endeavors, the DFAB [presently North Temperate Regional Station (NTRS)] introduced German Angora (GA) during 1986 & 1992 (purchased locally) and 1998 (imported from Germany) into its livestock inventory and is continuously improving the Angora rabbit germplasm by scientific means (Bhasin, 2004). The improvement in GA, BA and RA stocks (Breeding and General Flock) at NTRS Garsa has been consistent and continuous and the improvement for the period from 2001 to 2005 is presented in the Tables 3 and 4. The consistency of the angora characteristic within desired limits over the years (2001 to 2005) has been presented in the Table 5. Moreover, the crossbreds as well as pure bred GA have better adaptability, less reproductive problems; better mothering ability, higher wool yield and wool quality under natural rearing conditions in India. The improvement in BA and RA germplasm maintained at this station has also been consistent as presented in the Tables 6 and 7.

Table 3. Wool yield (g) in German Angora breeding stock at NTRS Garsa

Clip\Year	2001	2002	2003	2004	2005
1st	164.3±4.7(54)	152.8±2.9(97)	170.4±4.3(67)	199.2±3.1(87)	212.4±2.1(99)
2nd	150.7±5.6(49)	157.5±4.6(96)	153.9±4.7(62)	194.8±4.2(84)	189.8±2.1(91)
3rd	147.7±4.2(46)	159.5±4.6(92)	161.4±4.9(59)	169.2±3.9(79)	184.3±3.5(84)
4th	150.9±3.5(47)	165.3±4.0(91)	185.0±5.0(56)	172.3±3.7(73)	184.5±2.4(71)
5th	143.5±5.2(10)	177.9±6.8(31)	205.0±5.2(51)	193.4±4.5(65)	207±1.8(130)
Annual	**757.1 ± 5.3**	**813.0 ± 4.3**	**875.7 ± 7.5**	**928.9 ± 6.2**	**956.7 ± 4.8**

(Source: NTRS Report, 2006)

Table 4. Wool production (g) in general flock of German Angora

Clip\Year	2001	2002	2003	2004	2005
1st	122.9±3.8 (208)	110.5±2.9 (433)	157.7±1.9 (304)	165.3±2.0 (369)	175.5±1.6 (274)
2nd	145.2±2.4 (168)	142.3±3.7 (379)	163.6±2.5 (178)	173.2±2.1 (294)	177.1±1.5 (236)
3rd	163.3±2.4 (160)	157.4±4.8 (274)	152.2±2.5 (140)	153.2±1.9 (229)	169.9±1.6 (219)
4th	139.6±3.1 (153)	138.8±4.5 (261)	151.8±3.1 (120)	153.0±2.2 (167)	155.5±1.6 (197)
5th	133.7±2.6 (125)	146.7±4.4 (216)	178.7±3.6 (96)	172.5±2.6 (136)	164.0±2.0 (104)
Annual	**704.7±5.8**	**695.7±7.8**	**804.0±2.6**	**817.6±4.5**	**842.1±4.1**

(Source: NTRS Report, 2006)

Table 5. Wool Quality in German Angora rabbits

Parameter	2001	2002	2003	2004	2005
Staple Length (cm)	6.1 ± 0.03	6.1 ± 0.03	6.2 ± 0.05	6.1 ± 0.03	6.1 ± 0.03
Fibre Diameter (μ)	12.9 ± 0.3	13.1 ± 0.1	13.3 ± 0.1	13.4 ± 0.0	13.4 ± 0.0
Guard hair (%)	2.5 ± 0.1	3.2 ± 0.1	4.1 ± 0.2	3.7 ± 0.1	3.7 ± 0.1

(Source: NTRS Report, 2006)

Table 6. Wool production (g) in adult BA rabbits

Clip \ Year	2001	2002	2003	2004	2005
1st	92.5±8.1 (16)	107.3±2.4 (40)	135.6±6.7 (31)	155.6±4.7 (39)	144.9±4.4 (28)
2nd	108.3±11.7 (15)	108.3±3.9 (38)	114.7±5.9 (29)	135.0±5.6 (38)	129.4±5.8 (26)
3rd	99.7±11.9 (15)	110.8±4.1 (37)	124.8±4.5 (29)	98.3±4.8 (32)	127.3±6.0 (23)
4th	92.1±5.2 (14)	107.2±3.0 (37)	151.6±4.9 (25)	106.9±6.0 (22)	128.0±5.9 (11)
Annual	**392.6**	**433.6**	**526.7**	**495**	**529.57**

(Source: NTRS Report, 2006)

Table 7. Wool production (g) in RA rabbits

Clip \ Year	2001	2002	2003	2004	2005
1st	112.7 ± 6.2 (36)	99.5 ± 3.7 (29)	116.9 ± 6.1 (23)	137.7 ± 4.5 (32)	147.5 ± 3.9 (23)
2nd	116.9 ± 5.0 (35)	119.3 ± 5.8 (28)	107.6 ± 4.7 (21)	121.4 ± 4.7 (28)	136.1 ± 3.7 (23)
3rd	102.8 ± 4.9 (32)	103.6 ± 5.4 (28)	121.8 ± 4.8 (20)	95.7 ± 4.6 (13)	136.2 ± 5.4 (22)
4th	94.1 ± 3.2 (31)	117.6 ± 5.3 (28)	129.4 ± 5.1 (17)	99.7 ± 9.3 (6)	136.7 ± 2.0 (3)
Annual	**426.5**	**440.0**	**475.7**	**454.5**	**556.39**

(Source: NTRS Report, 2006)

The NTRS Garsa has now been recognized as the National Germplasm Centre for Angora rabbits and making available superior germplasm to farmers, Universities, NGOs, different development agencies and private entrepreneurs in the states of Himachal Pradesh, Jammu & Kashmir, Uttarakhand, Rajasthan, Sikkim, Meghalaya and West Bengal (Darjeeling hills). An appreciable number of rabbitries had been established in Himachal Pradesh and producing the angora to meet the local demand of the handlooms, Khadi institutions, wool cooperatives and textile industries. With the initiatives and support from UNDP through the Central Wool Development Board (CWDB), the Angora rabbit farming, aimed at generating the employment and foreign exchange earning potential, have been extended to the hilly areas of Uttarakhand, Darjeeling and Sikkim. On account of such integrated efforts, Uttarakhand is also making steady progress in Angora farming and local germplasm centers were set up, which are providing rabbit germplasm in the surrounding areas. In addition, the involvement of Defense Agricultural Research Laboratory (DARL) in propagation of Angora rabbits in Pitthoragarh District has been quite successful. An NGO namely Himalayan Institute for Environment, Ecology and Development (HIFEED) at Ranichauri is not only motivating and training the rural youth for Angora rabbit farming; but also concentrating on angora processing and product design development. Similarly, in Jammu & Kashmir as well, the Angora rabbit farming is regaining its position after initial set backs during 1990 due to sharp fall in angora prices and other input constraints. The angora blending with Merino and

Pashmina wool had been beneficial to the most versatile shawl industry of the state.

As per the conservative estimates, the total angora production in India is about 25 to 30 tons per annum. Though, Himachal Pradesh State Animal Husbandry estimated its Angora rabbit population to be around 60,000 with an annual production of 40 tons angora (Bist, 2004). In fact, it is quite difficult to ascertain the exact angora production due to lack of organized market channels, involvement of middlemen and due to barter system of trading with feed and other inputs. Nevertheless, the angora spinning industries established several years back are flourishing and even new industries have been added during recent past. This development certainly indicates that there is big demand, production and fulfillment of angora locally and indirectly a contractual system of rabbit farming possibly exists between growers and industrialists.

In India, the angora prices has fluctuated drastically, consequent to WTO agreement, as coarser angora from china was imported at cheaper rates leading to slump in the domestic market. Over the years, fluctuation of angora market price in India ranged from Rs 300–1200 per kg and never got stabilized. Due to yearly variability in angora prices, the producers are getting discouraged and confused. Since, the cost of all inputs has been increasing steadily, the angora producers at present are hardly meeting out the expenses from the sale of angora. Moreover, there is no relief or intervention from state or central Govt. to angora producers. Because of all these circumstances, angora producers are feeling helpless. As such, already existing farmers are abandoning the Angora rabbit farming and no more new farms are coming up.

Hilly regions of the country (between 4000 and 6000 ft. above mean sea level) with colder climate have been found to be suitable for Angora rabbit production under natural and conventional system of rearing. The Angora rabbit can be reared successfully in areas having temperature range between 5 to 30^{0}C and humidity levels of 60-70% in conventional housing system. Between 15-25^{0}C of ambient temperature the Angora produces more wool (Rochambeau and Thebault, 1990) and feels very comfortable (Chiericato et al., 1992). However, best productive performances have been achieved with a temperature between 15-20^{0}C under controlled conditions (Casamassima et al., 1988). Around 30^{0}C temperature, the feed consumption reduces as much as by 30% (Matheron and Martial, 1981) and the wool yield starts decreasing significantly, which further decreases substantially with every 1^{0}C rise in the temperature (Xu et al., 1992). Further, environmental conditions have been found to influence the fiber quality as well. This implies the importance of environmental temperature and its critical influence on the Angora rabbit farming. Likewise, increase in relative humidity beyond desired levels makes animal uncomfortable and sick as the levels of ammonia inside the rabbitries increases significantly. Higher humidity increases the incidence of conjunctivitis and respiratory diseases, thereby, affecting both production and livability of the animals. With changing climatic conditions, rainfall has become erratic in the hilly areas and summer months are becoming hotter, which are of great concern for Angora rabbit production. Untimely rainfall during summer develops very hot and humid conditions and animals generally die of heat stroke. In addition, with higher humidity, the incidences and outbreaks of enteritis, coccidiosis and aflatoxicosis increases considerably and causes great loss to the farmers due to heavy mortality and reduced production. Unfortunately, these natural climatic changes cannot be avoided and producers or farmers only have to modify the rearing systems and introduce new innovations to mitigate the influence of climate change.

Strategies for mitigating maladies associated with angora wool production

To get the Indian Angora rabbit farming revitalized, make it profitable enterprise and to protect the producer's interests, there is a strong need to redraw the strategies against price fluctuations and climatic changes, which otherwise would be detrimental in the long run. Following steps could be advantageous in mitigating these maladies:

- Develop strong linkages between the angora producer and processor (wool processing industry, handlooms, etc.); so that assured market and remunerative prices for angora exist round the year. Further, such linkage will reduce the exploitation of producers at the hands of middlemen and the profit will directly reach to the producers.
- Intervention by the Government in the form of Fixation of Minimum Support Price (MSP) for domestic angora and regulating the import of angora under OGL system would be a useful. This will stabilize the angora prices and control the fluctuation thereby encouraging the farmers for angora farming.
- Development of organized and strong marketing facilities for angora and its product, regulated by independent agency.
- Contractual system of Angora rabbit farming need to be introduced, which will benefit all concerned with angora.
- Strengthening the concept of Angora based farming (which includes all components from production to utilization) than Angora farming will make angora more demand oriented and profitable.

- Re-look into the concept of Angora rabbit farming. It must be promoted in line with Chinese model and aimed at both meat and fibre rather than exclusively for fibre.
- In National context, we must set our goals for export of angora yarn and its products than fibre for better remuneration like France and Finland.
- Since, angora is a premium produce with huge export potential, private entrepreneur should be encouraged for farming under controlled environment rather than restricting its propagation in the hilly areas only.
- Development of Angora rabbit strains suitable for areas with little warmer climate and conservation of varieties / strains evolved over the years under different climatic conditions irrespective of their genetic inferiority over the purebreds.
- Revisit the packages of practices after through study of climatic changes and their influence on the Angora rabbit farming.

References

Anon. 2006. NTRS Report. Central Sheep and Wool Research Institute, Avikanagar, Rajasthan, India.

Bhasin, V. 2004. An integrated approach for Angora rabbit development. In: Proceedings of the National seminar on Angora Rabbit Wool and Cashmere Production and Utilization, September 25-26, Manali (HP), India. pp: 45- 52.

Bist, B. C. 2004. Status of Angora rabbit and Cashmere fibre production in Himachal Pradesh. In: Proceedings of the National seminar on Angora Rabbit Wool and Cashmere Production and Utilization, September 25-26, Manali (HP), India. pp: 2- 3.

Casamassima, D., Manera, C. and Scarascia, M. G. 1988. Influenza del microclima sulla productivita del coniglio. Rivista di Coniglicoltura 25:28-41.

Chiericato, G. M., Bailoni, L. and Rizzi, C. 1992. The effect of environmental temperature on the performance of growing rabbits. Journal of Applied Rabbit Research 15:723-731.

Gu, Z., Li, S., Chen B., Sun, L., Huang, Y., Liu, Y., Zhao, C. and Guo, W. (2008). Review about rabbit breeding in China. In: Proceedings of the 9th World Rabbit Congress, June 10-13, Verona – Italy, pp:109-113.

Gupta, N. P., Pokharna, A. K., Shakhyawar, D. B. and Singh, R. N. 2000. Status of Angora wool production and utilization in India. World Rabbit Science 8: Suppl 1 Vol B.

Herrmann. S., Wortmann, G. and Wortmann, F. J. 1996. Characteristics of Angora rabbit fibre 1 - The influence of fibre origin on fibre and medulla diameter in Angora wool. World Rabbit Science 4:149-153.

Lebas, F., Coudert, P., de Rochambeau, H. and Thebault, R. G. 1997. The Rabbit - Husbandry, Health and Production. F.A.O. of the United Nations, Via delle Terme di Caracalla, Rome, Italy.

Leeder, J. D., McGregor, B. A. and Steadman, R. G. 1998. Properties and performance of goat fibre-A review and interpretation of existing research results. Rural Industries Research and Development Corporation, Publication No. 98/22, Australia.

Matheron, G. and Martial J. P. 1981. Growth and feed consumption of rabbit does from weaning to 4 months of age in different ambient temperature and humidities. Zootechniques of Physiologiques. ENSA. Rennes.

Ossard, H., Thebault, R. G., Vrillon, J. L., Allain, D. and de Rochambeau, H. 1995. Economic overview of the French and World markets for Angora rabbit wool. European Fine Fabrics Network, Occasional Publication No. 5:35- 46.

de Rochambeau, H. and Thebault, R. G. 1990. Genetics of the rabbit for wool production. Animal Breeding Abstracts 58:1-15.

Schlink, A. C. and Liu, S. M. 2003. Angora Rabbits: A potential new industry for Australia. Rural Industries Research and Development Corporation Publication No. 03/014, Australia.

Schlolaut, W.1974. Stand der Wollproduktion durch Angorakaninchen. Der Tierzuchter 3: 110.

Tang, F. K. 2002. Current production and predicted future of rabbit industries in China. Chinese Journal of Rabbit Farming 1: 3.7

Thebault, R. G. 1993. Rabbit breeding and management. European Fine Fibre Occasional Publication No. 1 Genetic improvement of fine fibre producing animals. Eds. J. P. Laker and S. C. Bishop. Proceedings of the Workshop, November 1993, Macauley Land Use Research Institute, Aberdeen, UK.

Vrillon, J. L. and Thebault, R. G. 1988. Evaluation of Angora wool standardization of testing methods. In: Proceedings of the 4th Congress of World Rabbit Science Association. October 10-14, Toulouse, France.

Xu, L., Chen, C. Z. and Ye, Y. 1992. Studies on the effect of ambient temperature and relative humidity on the feed intake and wool output of angora rabbits. Journal of Applied Rabbit Research 15:1672-1675.

❑❑❑

28

Impact of Climate and Environmental Change on Animal Diseases and Production

S. C. Dubey[1*] and A. K. Shinde[2]
[1]High Security Animal Disease Laboratory, Indian Veterinary Research Institute Anand Nagar, Bhopal-21, Madhya Pradesh [2]Central Sheep and Wool Research Institute Avikanagar, Rajasthan- 304 501

Introduction

According to Dr. Peter Black climate and environmental change is a subset of the larger set of ecosystem changes that promotes the emergence and re-emergence of animal diseases and in turn causes production losses. This is a complex situation that is interconnected to a wide range of factors predisposing the emergence of animal disease. In time to come animal husbandry and veterinary authorities shall have to develop an adaptable, resilient and capable systems and strategies that can deal with the unexpected situations. Millennium Ecosystem Assessment (MEA) reports 918 of 2005 have outlined the key points broadly incriminated for current state of knowledge, ecosystem change, including both climate change and environmental change. According to this report growing demands for food, fresh water, fibre and energy, humans have made unprecedented change to ecosystems in recent decades. No doubt these changes have helped to improve the lives of billions of people, but at the same time they have weakened nature's ability to deliver other key services automatically. The pressure on ecosystems and its impact on every sphere of life is being realized and expressed in guarded and even in exorbitant terms by various experts, but almost all of them have unanimously expressed that gravity of the deteriorating situation will further increase globally in coming decades unless human attitudes and actions change.

Climate change (CC)

A change of climate is attributed directly or indirectly to human activity that alters the composition of the global atmosphere. That is in addition to natural climate variability observed over comparable period. Some aspects of climate variability, including increasing frequency and intensity of extreme weather events such as droughts and floods are attributable to climate change (Dubey et al. 2002).

Environmental change (EC)

A major change in physical and biological systems can be caused either naturally or by human activity. This includes changes in the land use (e.g. deforestation, land clearing, conversion of wet lands, soil degradation), water quality and quantity (e.g. over use and pollution of water supplies), biodiversity (e.g. loss of species), and air quality (e.g. air pollution), but explicitly excludes climate change.

Improvement of animal health, welfare and technical support to control and eradicate animal diseases including diseases transmissible to humans have become the major mandate of international organization for health such as WHO, OIE (the world organization for animal health) and FAO. These organizations also offer expertise to help the member and even the non-member countries to control animal diseases that cause livestock losses and also present a risk to public health. Climate change and environmental change are two different but interrelated factors, hence it may not be explicitly easy to define them separately. OIE experts (Black and Nunn, 2009) have defined both the terms in a very precise and clear wording for better understanding. Through this paper we will try to outline global issues associated with the impact of CC and EC on emerging and re-emerging animal diseases (E & READ) and animal's production.

Causality

A series of factors have been reported about there anticipated direct and indirect effects of global climate change and extreme weather leading to emergence of infectious diseases of humans, animals, and plants. These webs of causation include many factors that are closely interrelated or influenced (either directly or indirectly) by local, regional or global variations in the climate.

A prediction of rise in environmental temperature in Indian subcontinent by 2-3.5^{0}C may lead to increase in sea water level, erratic rains, natural disaster of varied gravity and 9-25% reduction in agricultural and animal husbandry based production.

If it is so the impact of CC and EC on animal diseases and production losses may also emerge with more gravity as an integral consequence of some major climate change. According to Dubey et al. (2006), drought and famine borne excessive migration of animals from sensitive areas may also lead to socio-ecological imbalance in other areas. Similarly erratic rains may also lead to emergence of animal diseases like haemorrhagic septicaemia (HS), skin diseases, pneumonia, parasitic infestation and foot diseases followed by poor production and mortality. Possible animal health consequences of rise in environmental temperature have been summarized in Table 1.

Table 1. Interactive animal health consequences of rise in environmental temperature

Interactive consequences: drought, starvation, low quality water availability, dehydration, poor immunity and diseases		
Nutritional	**Physiological**	**Thermal**
Feed and water scarcity, mineral imbalances, poor intake and exhaustion during grazing and migration and high energy losses lead to LBW, poor immunity, low body depots, starvation, metabolic disturbances- ketosis possibility, secondary complication, still birth, abortion & starvation-exposure syndrome.	Reduced body depots, disturbed production cycle, mis-mothering, low birth weight (LBW), poor survival, stunted growth, debility, still birth, abortion and water toxicity (nitrate, nitrite and fluorine) etc.	Low quality water availability, dehydration, hyperthermia, mineral imbalance, poor immunity, high new-born deaths.

Complexity of the system

Relationship between energy, food and health is very complex raising serious challenges to researchers, policy makers and the executers. Predictions of the behaviour of acute infectious diseases cannot be made simply on the basis of climate projections as their consequential emergence use to be inter-linked in their causation and also depend on public awareness and their response. Therefore, as a matter of public partnership it would be appropriate to handle the consequences of CC and EC as a common issue for lay man and for specific purely technical and scientific outcome at the level of technical experts.

According to King (2004), interrelated factors responsible for diseases emergence and re-emergence converge together and surface in form of a complex system. The major factors include microbial adoption and change, host susceptibility to climate and weather, changing ecosystems, demographics and population, economic development and land use, international trade and travel, technology and industry, reduction in animal and public health services or infrastructure, poverty and social inequality, war and dislocation, lack of political will and the most importantly intent to do harm.

Many researchers working with emerging and re-emerging animal diseases are now appreciating the key importance of considering social and ecological factors together rather than separate factors. To highlight this view, some scientists refer specifically to the complex system as the socio-ecological system or the ecological approach to health. This is adaptive management in which "policies become hypotheses" and management actions use to test the hypotheses and readjust strategy as more information becomes available. Animal husbandry authorities shall have to become more familiar with this approach when dealing with emerging or re-emerging animal diseases.

Role of health professionals in animal husbandry, climate change and human health

In 2004, the WHO and FAO reported that increasing global demand for animal protein in the human diet, associated with the expansion and intensification of animal agriculture, long distance live animal transport and other factors, were partly responsible for the emergence of zoonotic diseases (WHO Report, 2004). Industrial agriculture practices have been blamed for the emergence of bovine spongiform encephalopathy, multi drug resistant, food-borne bacteria and highly pathogenic strains of avian influenza (Gregar, 2007). Historically, chronic diseases, including obesity, have plagued the developed world, whereas developing countries have been more affected by communicable diseases. However, obesity and chronic diseases are increasingly becoming a concern in developing countries also (Popkin and Du, 2003). A global estimate reveals that >1 billion adults are overweight (WHO fact sheet) that increases the risk for diabetes, arthritis, asthma, hypertension and hypercholesterolemia. Worldwide, cardiovascular disease, cancer and diabetes are three of the four main causes of death (Yach et al., 2004).

The worldwide transition from a predominantly plant based diet to a diet high in meat has been identified as a noteworthy contributor to the rise in chronic disease (Popkin and Du, 2003). Health care providers can individually and collectively play a significant role in ensuring healthy and environmentally sustainable policies and practices. Given the animal agriculture sectors considerable role in environmental degradation, zoonotic disease emergence, and chronic disease promotion, reducing livestock production and promoting healthy plant based diet should be global health priority.

Relationship between CC or EC and emerging and re-emerging diseases

Black and Nunn (2009) have proposed a simplified model (Fig. 1) as a basis of discussion on issues pertaining to emerging and re-emerging diseases. According to them, the relative width of the arrows in Fig. 1 reflects the level of influence focused on emerging or re-emerging animal diseases that are likely to exert within overall system. Worldwide response to a questionnaire circulated by OIE to 172 member countries including India revealed that most members identified major relationship at least responsible for one E/READ (Table-2) that was believed to be associated with climate change and environmental changes. The relationship between climate change responses and the increase in incidence of vector-borne diseases in association with climate change are broadly consistent in reports from other workers. Black et al. (2008) conclude that this increase is due to altered vector population size and dynamics, and the increases in pathogen replication rates are influenced directly by ambient temperatures during infection of the poikilothermic arthropod vectored pathogens.

West Nile virus and the climate

West Nile virus is transmitted by urban dwelling mosquitoes to birds and other animals, with occasional spillover to humans. The means by which West Nile virus entered in the Americas in 1999 are still unknown, but climatic conditions like warm winters and spring droughts amplified the disease cycle among urban mosquitoes, birds and humans. This type of information can be useful in generating early warning systems and mobilizing timely and the most environmentally friendly public health interventions. The extreme weather conditions accompanying long term climate change may also be contributing to the global spread of West Nile virus (Epstein, 2001).

Climate change and avian influenza (AI)

Climate change would almost certainly alter bird migration, influence the AI virus transmission cycle and directly affect virus survival outside the host. The joint effects of these changes are rather unpredictable, but it is likely that AI virus circulation in water bird populations will continue with endless adaptation and evolution. In domestic poultry, too little is known about the direct effect of environmental factors on highly pathogenic avian influenza transmission and persistence to allow inference about the possible effect of climate change. Similarly, in the Indian perspective avian influenza emergence and re-emergence is not only the outcome of interplay between wild migratory birds with poultry under commercial or backyard sector, but suitability of local climate to various scavenging birds like crow has got its own direct / indirect impact on disease transmission and control, which may not be truly realized in the temperate countries. The role of these changes will have other flow-on effects within the ecosystem (Nagarajan et al., 2009).

They concluded that the livestock sector was one of the most global (arrow 2 in Fig. 1) entity influenced by CC/EC. Hence livestock production should be the major policy focus when dealing with problems of climate change, land degradation, water shortage, water pollution and loss of biodiversity. The relationship between the change that societies choose to make in their animal production systems in response to the anticipated and observed changes in climate and the environment are equally responsible for E & READ (arrow 3 in fig. 1). There are obviously a very wide range of possible responses that can be implemented at the level of industry, country and region. However, the general trend towards intensification and industrialization is expected to continue as societies seek to improve efficiency and reduce the land area required for livestock production and each of us will experience these trends to some degree, depending on its capacity to adapt to the new challenges likely to surface in future.

Intensification of animal production systems has further implicated the relationship between animal production and E & READs. Animal production systems have been responsible for many E & READs globally for hundreds of years. More recently, many integrated management programs for animal diseases have been developed in response to the changing disease profiles associated with evolving animal production systems. For example, treatment regimes were developed to decrease the incidence of mastitis, which was closely correlated with a range of animal management factors focused on increasing milk production. Similar examples in intensive animal production systems include the prevention and treatment of respiratory disease in feedlots, salmonellae in poultry, PRRS in pigs, internal parasites and emergence of anthelmintic resistance (AR) in semi-intensively and more intensively raised sheep and goat populations, and white spot syndrome in prawns. These were all emerging diseases at one time, but in most cases these diseases are now established within the relevant production systems. In India, the diseases of interest may include bluetongue, tick-borne diseases, AR against gastrointestinal nematodes in small ruminants and avian influenza in poultry.

According to Black and Nunn (2009), generally the intensified production systems will increase the opportunity for E & READs (Nunn and Black, 2006) and management systems need to be developed to minimize their direct and indirect effects on production and profitability. This means that in response to actual or anticipated emerging and re-emerging animal diseases, animal production systems will be adjusted or re-developed (this is the relationship labeled 5 in Fig. 1). The evolution of relationship 4 and 5 is in fact a continuous interplay in which change in one element of the complex system lead to change in other pats of the system.

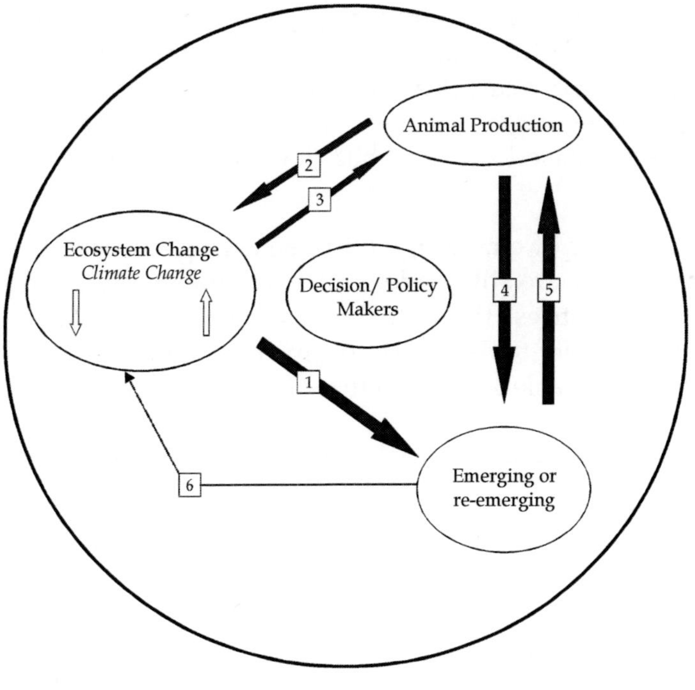

Fig. 1. Schematic representation of environment/climatic factors influencing animal production and disease emergence/re-emergence

Relationships between E & READs and ecosystem change

The policy decision about E & READs that societies implement can indirectly influence ecosystem change. For example, in countries attempting to eradicate a re-emerging disease such as bovine tuberculosis, control strategies could conceivably lead to changes in the density and distribution of other host species such as badgers, possums or buffaloes. This relationship is generally quite diffuse compared to the other relationships described and has therefore been marked as a dotted arrow in fig. 1.

The interactions between the variables shown in Fig. 1 will show their impacts in different ways with scales of time and space as the impacts of climate will not be the same across the world (Stern, 2006). In addition, it will be difficult to forecast accurately the rate, distribution and scale of emergence and re-emergence of many animal diseases except a few diseases for example the emergence of diseases such as arboviral infections can be forecast with some confidence across a range of scale i.e. on country, regional and global basis. On the other hand when and where the diseases like, SARS or Nipah virus will emerge cannot be forecast with any precision. Globally it has been realized by epidemiologists that emergence of new infection is influenced mainly by socio-economic, environmental and ecological factors and in turn zoonotic diseases lead to significant threat to public health worldwide (Jones et al., 2008). In recent years, it has also been realized that more then 70% of zoonotic EIDs have originated from wildlife for which global surveillance resources are not based on risk, but developed countries utilize greater resources.

This is also true of emerging and re-emerging diseases as the necessary surveillance systems are still inadequate for changing animal disease pattern in developing countries. It would be of foremost importance in future to improve our capability to deal with this increasing rate of disease emergence and re-emergence (Table 2) irrespective of their causes.

Table 2 Major relationships responsible for emerging and re-emerging diseases

Diseases mentioned more than twice believed to be associated with	Climate change	Environmental change
Vector-borne		
Bluetongue virus	√	√
Rift Valley fever	√	X
West Nile virus	√	X
African horse sickness	√	X
Lumpy skin disease	√	X
Leishmaniasis	√	√
Epizootic hemorrhagic disease	√	X
Tick-borne disease	√	√
Parasitic diseases (excluding tick-borne)	√	√
Pasteurellosis	√	X
Avian influenza	√	√
Anthrax	√	√
Blackleg	√	X
Rabies	√	√
Tuberculosis	X	√

What needs to be done?

On the basis of responses to OIE questionnaire, Black and Nunn (2009) could conclude that:

- OIE shall have to play a critical role and is also required to do more to assist members to address the issues of the impacts of CC and EC on E and READs,
- Need to design a global strategy to assist members to prevent/ reduce effects of climate and environmental changes on animal disease and production,
- Working with other international organization that are directly involved in climate change and environmental change issues,
- Communicating more frequently with members and
- Monitoring and reviewing the effects of climate change on animal health.

These challenges are global and require global leadership. In addition to this leadership role, OIE has the opportunity to establish regional or sub-regional activities to assist in addressing these impacts of climate change and environmental change on emerging and re-emerging animal diseases. Since impacts are regional, addressing emerging and re-emerging animal diseases at the regional level will result in more targeted and robust strategies.

Being world organization for animal health OIE should continue to collaborate and network with other institutions and agencies that are addressing the broader policy issues linked to climate change, environmental change and animal production. OIE will continue to be the key player supporting the improvement of veterinary services in member countries and territories as a major platform for dealing with E and READs. For evolving *'one world one health'* approach OIE and other international and national institutions shall have to institute a global strategy to reduce the effects of climate and environmental changes on animal disease and production.

References

Black, P. F. and Nunn, M. J. 2009. Impact of climate change and environmental changes on emerging and re-emerging animal disease and animal production. Office International des Épizooties 77th GS/9.

Black, P. F., Murray, J. G. and Nunn, M. J. 2008. Managing animal disease risk in Australia: the impact of climate change. Review on Science and Technology. Office International des Épizooties 27(2): 563-580.

Dubey, S. C., Shinde, A. K. and Singh, B. N. 2006. Applied Animal Husbandry of Cattle, Buffalo, Sheep, Goat, Horse, Swine and Camel (Hindi). International Book Distributing Company Lucknow. pp. 369.

Dubey, S. C., Shinde A. K. and Bhati, Prakash. 2002. Strategies and challenges during drought to prevent animal life and production losses. In: Proceedings of the 5th National Seminar on Strength, Challenges and Opportunities in Small Ruminant Diseases in the New Millennium, Jaipur, December, 30-31. pp 115-127.

Epstein Paul, R. 2001. West Nile virus and the climate. Journal of Urban Health: Bulletin of the New York Academy of Medicine 78: 2.

Gilbert, M., Slingenbergh, J. and Xiao, X. 2009. Climate change and avian influenza. Office International des Épizooties. Author manuscript, available in PMC July 14.

Gregar, M. 2007. The Human / Animal Interface: Emergence and resurgence of zoonotic infectious diseases. CRC Critical Review Microbiology 33:243-99.

Jones, K. E., Patel, N., Levy, M. A., Storeygard, A., Balk, D., Gittleman, J. L. and Daszak, P. 2008. Global trends in human emerging infectious diseases. Nature 451:990-993.

King, L. J. 2004. Emerging and re-emerging zoonotic diseases: Challenges and Opportunities, Compendium of Technical Items Presented to the International Committees or to Regional Commissions of the OIE, pp 21-29.

Mokdad, A.H., Ford E.S. and Bowman B. A. 2003. Prevalence of obesity, diabetes and obesity related health risk factors. Journal of American Medical Association 289: 76-79.

Nagarajan, S., Tosh, C., Murugkar, H. V., Venkatesh, G., Katare, M., Jain, R., Khandia, Tripathi, S, Behera P, Kulkarni, D. D. and Dubey, S. C. 2009. Isolation and molecular characterization of a H5N1 virus isolated from a jungle crow (*Corvus macrohynchos*) in India. (Submitted *to Virus gene*s).

Nunn, M. and Black, P. 2006. Intensive animal production systems. How intensive is intensive enough? 11th Symposium of the International Society for Veterinary Epidemiology and Economics, Cairns, Australia.

Popkin, B.M. and Du, S. 2003. Dynamics of the nutrition transition toward the animal food sector in China and its implications: a worried perspective. Journal of Nutrition 133:3898S-3906S.

Steinfeld, H., Gerber, P., Wassenaar, T., Castel, V., Rosales, M. and de Haan, C. 2006. Livestock long shadow: environmental issues and options. Food and Agriculture Organization of the United Nations, Rome.

Stern, N. 2006. Stern Review: The economics of climate change. http://www.occ.gov.uk/activities/stern.htm (accessed on 11 December 2008). Impact of climate change and environmental change on emerging and re-emerging animal disease and animal production 11.

WHO 2004. Food and Agriculture Organization of the United Nations, World Organization for Animal Health (WHO / FAO / OIE). Report of the WHO / FAO / OIE joint consultation on emerging zoonotic diseases.

WHO fact sheet: obesity and overweight. www.who.int/dietphysicalactivity/publications /facts/ obesity/ en.

Yach, D., Hawkes, C., Gould, C. L. and Hofman, K. J. 2004. The global burden of chronic diseases. Overcoming impediments to preventions and control. Journal of American Medical Association 291:2616-2622.

□□□

29

Newer Approaches of Parasitic Control for Reducing Stresses in Animals and Farmers

P.K. Sanyal
Department of Parasitology, College of Veterinary Science & Animal Husbandry
Indira Gandhi Krishi Viswavidyalaya, Anjora, Durg-491 001, Chhattisgarh

Introduction

Stress is the sum of all physiological responses by which an animal attempts to maintain or reestablish a normal metabolism in the face of a physical and chemical force. The impact of stress upon the dynamics of host and parasite populations is varied. It may be expressed physiologically or behaviorally in either the host or the parasite. At the ecosystem level, stress may be manifested either directly or indirectly on individuals or populations, but the outcome is change in natality or mortality and, hence, in the density of the affected species. The varied response to stressor input at the individual, population and ecosystem levels is dictated by the capacity for adaptability present at each level. The response may be modified by the unique combination of environmental characteristics at the time of stressor input (Esch et al., 1975). Control measures against gastrointestinal parasites of ruminants also induce stress to the animals. Animals do undergo chemical stress induced by the drugs (anthelmintics) at cellular and molecular levels. This stress is always visible in terms of toxic symptoms, sometimes death, following administration of anthelmintics whose safety limits are low. Restraining of animals and forceful drenching resulted in physical stress. Barring aside emergence of anthelmintic treatment, residues in food and environmental degradation; the conventional chemical control also incites physiological responses by which an animal attempts to maintain or reestablish a normal metabolism.

In human beings work-related stress is a pattern of physiological, emotional, cognitive and behavioral reactions to some extremely taxing aspects of work content, work organization and work environment. When people experience work-related stress, they often feel tense and distressed and feel they cannot cope. Small ruminant husbandry system is in the hands of resource poor and self-employed work force belonging to the 'informal sector' of the economy. Thus they are devoid of resources and infrastructure to protect them from work-related stress both in terms of information dissemination and assistance. Work-related psychosocial issues are rarely dealt and are often made worse by a broad spectrum of factors outside the work environment from gender inequalities, poor paths of participation, poor environmental management of industrial pollution to illiteracy, parasitic and infectious diseases, poor hygiene and sanitation, poor nutrition, poor living conditions, inadequate transportation systems and general poverty. The farmers (owner of animals) undergo work-related stress when there is a need for anthelmintic intervention (garnering work force for restraining animals and drench them individually a very taxing procedure) that results in physiological, emotional, cognitive and behavioral reactions. They may also become a victim of intellectual stress by the aggressive campaigning of local chemists and pharmaceutical industries for the use of their drugs. The cost of the drugs itself induce financial stress to the farmers. In the face of experiencing such work-related stress, they often feel tense and distressed.

Researchers are experiencing tremendous intellectual stress the world to come out with parasite control strategies alternative to chemotherapy over at the face of emergence of drug resistance and ever-increasing consumer demand for chemical free food and food products. A closer look on the control strategies alternative to chemotherapy reveals that some of them are in the technology states while others are still under research and development. Biological control by nematophagous fungi, worm vaccine, and exploitation of breed resistance are still undergoing laboratory research, while grazing management and exploitation of nutrition-parasite interaction, self medication and targeted selective treatment can immediately be applied as adjuncts to chemotherapy. The requirement today is a coordinated, continued and committed research, technology transfer and extension education to achieve the goal of sustainable parasite control (Sanyal, 2005).

Self medication

Self medication is a method of delivering anthelmintics in which the animal ingests the anthelmintic on its own without relying on somebody to administer it. It may be of prolonged low level administration in which the animal ingests the drug on a daily basis so that a sustained plasma level is maintained which is independent of the influence of parasite and host related factors or of split dose formulation where the total anthelmintic dose is divided in two split doses. In India, research efforts have been carried out for developing methods for self medication of ruminants (Sanyal, 1997), selection of vehicle for the drug delivery and targeting dose rate so that the animals receive the desired dose of the drug on daily basis. Accordingly, medicated urea molasses blocks and dewormer concentrate feed pellets have been developed, extensively used and widely marketed for worm control using long-term low-level and split dose administration, respectively. The rationale for using the self medication is to prevent the establishment of the parasites during the favourable months of their development and survival. Physical stress of drug administration is zero both for the animals and the farmers.

Targeted selective treatment

For many years it was recommended that all animals in a flock should be treated with an anthelmintic at the same time. However, this strategy has turned out to be unsustainable and parasitologists now favour a selective approach where only those animals in need of treatment actually receive medication. To increase the quantum of refugia (i.e. proportion of susceptible worms in pasture), it is suggested that a portion of flock not be dewormed taking advantage of over-dispersion phenomenon in worm faecal egg counts. The rate at which resistance develops is known to be influenced by the proportion of the population exposed to treatment and can be slowed by maintaining a proportion of the population *in refugia* (unexposed to treatment). Minimising the numbers of treatments (targeting treatments) is one obvious method of maintaining a larger proportion of the total population unexposed to anthelmintic. If this approach can be allied with a 'targeted selective treatment' (TST) strategy (one in which only those animals that will most benefit from treatment are given anthelmintic) then it should, in theory at least, be possible to conserve anthelmintic efficacy whilst maintaining acceptable levels of productivity. Using part flock treatment approach alongside other commonly used whole flock treatment strategies provides an ideal means for optimizing anthelmintic usage. The application of TST approach provided high levels of productivity whilst maintaining efficacy using half the numbers of anthelmintic treatments as compared to the monthly treated group. In the TST group, only 20% of the flock required treatment at any one time and moreover 88% of the animals that were given anthelmintic showed a positive response in performance following the treatment.

The major problem in implementing a selective treatment program for *H. contortus* has been the lack of a simple and reliable field test for anemia. Recently, a clinical on-farm system, called FAMACHA©, was developed in South Africa for categorizing animals based on the level of anemia. The FAMACHA system is aimed at identification of only those animals in a flock that need anthelmintic intervention in *H. contortus* endemic areas (Malan et al., 2001).Because anemia is the primary pathologic effect of *H. contortus* infection, this system can be an effective tool for identifying animals that require treatment (but only for *H. contortus*). To use FAMACHA©, the color of ocular mucous membranes is compared to a laminated card with colored illustrations of the eyes of sheep with different levels of anemia (Vatta et al., 2002). The scale goes from 1 (mucous membranes are red) to 5 (mucous membranes are white). All the animals are examined at regular intervals and only animals scored as being anemic are treated. In evaluation trials in South Africa, the FAMACHA© system reduced the number of anthelmintic treatments given by up to 90 % over previous years. It is successfully used and demonstrated its effectiveness on commercial and small flocks in South Africa and many other countries in the tropics/subtropics. This method also serves as a good tool to identify sheep that repeatedly require anthelmintic intervention so that such animals may be culled from the flock. However, there still a need for a cost-effective and reliable diagnostic technique to identify individual animal needing treatment, where other species like *Trichostrongylus, Oesophagostomum* etc predominates.

Targeted applications of anthelmintics have been conducted with success in horses, based on coproscopical results (Krecek et al., 1994) or in sheep infected with *Haemonchus contortus*, based on clinical signs of anaemia through FAMACHA® system (Van Wyk et al., 1997; Vatta et al., 2001). By restricting anthelmintics to two thirds of the flock, the method reduced substantially the cost of deworming. However, the main advantage of this mode of application of anthelmintics is to delay the onset of resistance by preserving alleles of susceptibility within the trichostrongyle populations (Sangster, 1999; Jackson and Coop, 2000). Coles (2005) stated that it is not known from practical experience that what level of contamination is required on pasture to ensure that resistance only at slow rate and or to decide what proportion of animals in a flock should be left undrenched. Before development of FAMACHA® system for TST it was assumed for sheep that it is a good idea not to drench ewes unless there is necessary on ground of health. *H. contortus* is the only nematode parasite of small ruminants that can be accurately diagnosed without the aid of laboratory testing. Signs of acute anaemia are obvious but past history and discounting other less common conditions causing anaemia will strongly suggest clinical haemonchosis (Krecek and Waller, 2006). The TST approach is highly compatible with host - parasite dynamics. Parasite burdens are highly aggregated in hosts with about 20-30% of animals harbouring about 80% of all the worms. Treating animals with low worm burdens does little to control parasites, but removes an important source of refugia, thereby accelerating the evolution of resistance. In the initial years TST would intend reduce parasite control related stresses to the animals which are left untreated. When the target of realizing a resistant/resilient flock is achieved over the years, the stress to the animals would be drastically reduced even to a negligible level. But this control option needs a specialized way of technology transfer, may be automated technology transfer, and therefore liable to increase intellectual stresses to the farmers.

Control by management

Two related managerial aspects namely; nutrition-parasite interaction and grazing management can form an integral part of integrated management of parasitic gastroenteritis in ruminants.

Nutrition-parasite interaction

Two important nomenclatures, viz., resilience and resistance, are commonly used in describing host-parasite relationship. 'Resilience' is the host's ability to maintain a reasonable level of productivity in the face of a parasitic challenge while 'Resistance' is a measure of the host's ability to limit the establishment, fecundity, growth rate and/or persistence of a parasite population (Coop and Kyriazakis, 1999). The level of nutrition can influence both resilience and resistance of the host to parasitic infection. Improving host resilience and/or resistance to infection through management practices, which involve manipulation of nutrition, can be one component in an integrated approach. These interactions can be considered from two interrelated perspectives. Firstly, the effects of nutrition on the metabolic disturbances and pathophysiology induced by parasitism and secondly, the influence of nutrient availability on the ability of the host to mount an effective response against parasite establishment and/or development and to induce parasite rejection. Gastrointestinal nematodes reduce voluntary feed intake and efficiency of feed utilisation; a key feature being an increased endogenous loss of protein into the gastrointestinal tract (Coop and Holmes, 1996). Overall, there is movement of protein from productive processes into repair of the gastrointestinal tract, synthesis of plasma proteins and production of mucoproteins. Supplementation of the diet with an additional protein does not appear to affect initial establishment of nematode infections but the pathological consequences are generally more severe on lower planes of protein nutrition. The main effects of protein supplementation are to increase the rate of acquisition of immunity and increase resistance to reinfection. This has been associated with an enhanced cellular immune response in the gastrointestinal mucosa. The unresponsiveness of young animals can be improved by dietary protein supplementation (Coop and Holmes, 1996). Trials have shown that growing sheep offered a free choice between a low and a high protein ration are able to modify their diet selection in order to alleviate the increase in protein requirements which result from gastrointestinal nematode infection (Kyriazakis et al., 1994). Studies on the influence of nutrition on the expression of genotype have shown that the benefits of a superior genotype are not lost on a low protein diet, whereas a high protein diet can partially ameliorate the disadvantages of an inferior genotype. In addition to dietary protein, both macro and micro-minerals can influence the host-parasite relationship. Unfortunately the provision of high quality protein is usually not an economic proposition particularly in the developing world. It has been shown in sheep that the provision of non-protein nitrogen supplementation in the form of urea to a low quality roughage diet could reduce the effects of parasitic infection. Urea supplementation could therefore be considered as an integral husbandry practice in order to reduce the debilitating effects of parasitism and minimise the requirement for alternative means of control (Knox and Steel, 1996). Urea molasses block could be a good proposition to deliver urea to the ruminants and can also be used for long-term low-level administration of anthelmintics to cover both the provision of non-protein nitrogen, minerals and anthelmintic drug (Sanyal and Singh, 1993).

Grazing management

It is possible to reduce significantly the number of anthelmintic treatments required by grazing ruminants by employing some relatively simple management procedures based on the knowledge of the epidemiology of the parasites in a particular climatic and production system. Grazing management is one of the ways of reducing frequency of anthelmintic treatment. Grazing management strategies may be of **preventive**, **evasive** and **diluting** (Michel, 1985).

i. *Preventive strategies:* These strategies are those that rely on putting worm free animals on a clean pasture, or by suppressing worm egg output by anthelmintic treatment in the early part of the grazing season until the initial population of infective larvae on pasture has declined to safe levels.

The most common examples are the short, intensive treatment regimes using controlled release devices or conventional deworming regimens at the start of the grazing season (Vercruysse et al., 1995). An extreme form of preventive strategy is the alternation of different host species, usually sheep and cattle over the same pasture. Here the prevention of contamination is achieved by exploiting host specificity of the parasites. Unfortunately, one of the most pathogenic worms, *H. contortus*, widely prevalent in tropical countries, can establish itself both in cattle and sheep (Borgsteede, 1981).

ii. *Evasive strategies:* These strategies do not attempt to restrict contamination of the pasture by worm eggs, but rely on movement of livestock to another pasture just before the larvae resulting from the eggs are likely to appear in significant numbers on the original pasture. A further development was described, which involved frequent rotational grazing system for goats in a wet tropical climate (Barger et al., 1994).

iii. *Diluting strategies:* These strategies exploit the concurrent grazing of susceptible animals with a greater population of non-susceptible animals of the same or different species. Use of anthelmintics in all these strategies is limited specifically to prevent contamination of clean pastures with worm eggs. Because such treatment is characteristically given in conjunction with a move to a clean pasture, reinfection rates are extremely low and the suppressive effect of anthelmintic treatment on egg output is prolonged for several months rather than few weeks seen on contaminated pastures. The basis is if susceptible animals graze with a greater number of non-susceptible animals, then the average rate of contamination of the pasture with worm eggs will be substantially reduced over grazing by susceptible animals alone. Mixed grazing resulted in reduced sheep parasitism and increased productivity of lambs but also in increased cattle parasitism with reduced productivity of the calves (Jordan et al., 1988).

Selection pressure on worms to develop anthelmintic resistance is not simply proportional to the frequency of treatment but depends on how anthelmintics are used in relation to grazing management (Michel, 1985). Selection pressure is measured by the contribution that resistant survivors of anthelmintic treatment make to subsequent generations of worms. This contribution and hence selection pressure, is obviously large when animals are treated frequently and may be equally large in animals treated only once and immediately moved to a clean pasture. Therefore, by adopting one or more of the grazing management practices may result in worm control at a low cost but may not reduce significantly the selection pressure for resistance development (Barger, 1997). A burning example is the apparent failure of worm control programme in the Australian sheep industry (Waller et al., 1995). The important point is not that any specific control method may be non-sustainable when considered in isolation, but that greater the choices, more are they used in combination, hence longer we can synergise the continued effectiveness of all of them.

Reversion of anthelmintic resistance

Another management practice called 'reversion of anthelmintic resistance' is being documented in South Africa either by removing susceptible animals from the pastures infected with the resistant worm strains for at least 12-24 months or attempt to dilute resistant with susceptible worm strains (Van Wyk et al., 1997). The reason behind the practice is the prevalence of rampant anthelmintic resistance in sheep in this region. Total withdrawal of susceptible animals from pasture seemed to be a good option to leave pastures unutilised by susceptible animals until all the free-living larval stages of resistant worms have succumbed. Reversion of a relatively resistant strain of *H. contortus*, paricularly to levamisole resistance, could be achieved by dilution of a resistant worm strain on pasture by intervening in spring (Van Wyk and van Schalkwyk, 1990). While a successful attempt at obtaining reversion was reported (Van Wyk and Van Schalkwyk, 1990), little has been done to overcome practical problems encountered with field application. Pastoral scientists in South Africa have developed a new system of grazing management. They showed that the best method for sustainable improvement in the quality of natural pasture herbage is what they termed the "50/50" system, where all the animals are concentrated on half the available pasture, while the remainder is left ungrazed for at least one full growing season (a full year). This means that practically worm-free pasture is available almost annually. The system appears to offer a solution for application on farms where resistance has become rampant.

Biological control

A number of organisms have been identified that exploit the free living stages of parasites as food source. These include microarthropods, protozoa, predacious nematodes, viruses, bacteria and fungi (Larsen, 1999). Although all are of intrinsic interest, it is from the last group of organisms that breakthroughs in biological control of nematode parasites are likely to emerge. Fungi that exhibit anti-nematode properties have been known for a long time. They consist of a great variety of species which include nematode-trapping fungi, endoparasitic fungi in egg parasitic fungi that invade nematode eggs. The most important group of nematophagous fungi is predacious fungi. These fungi produce specialised hyphal trapping devices, viz., adhesive network, knobs, constricting or non-constricting rings. Within a short period of time following capture of the nematode, the fungus penetrates the worm and destroys it.

Nematode-trapping Fungi

Biological control of animal parasites could become a strong arm for 'Integrated Parasite Control' in the very near future. Though various nematode-destroying fungi received attention, predominantly on academic interest, from 18th Century in Scandanavian countries, work on their application to control animal parasites gathered momentum from 1990s. The philosophy behind biological control is to utilize one or more of the natural enemies of the nematodes, making it possible to reduce the infection on pasture to a level where grazing animals can avoid both clinical and subclinical effects of the parasitic nematodes. The important requirement is the presence of the fungi in the faecal pats where the development of the pre-parasitic larvae takes place. Therefore, to be effective, the fungi should pass through the gastrointestinal tract of the host without loss of viability. The fungus, *Duddingtonia flagrans*, which can be isolated from fresh faeces of ruminants, produces profuse thick walled chlamydospores, the stage responsible for their survival during passage through the gut of ruminants following oral administration. The results had indicated survival of the fungus during gastrointestinal transit in grazing animals and successful reduction of numbers of parasitic nematode larvae on pasture. The dose of fungal spores to be given to an animal and the time of administration for effective parasite control has been standardised. The fungus behaves in density dependent manner and appears to be environment-friendly (Sanyal, 2005). The challenge lies ahead in its field application.

Egg Parasitic Fungi

Wild isolates of egg parasitic fungi, viz., *Paecilomyces lilacinus* and *Verticillium chlamydosporium* were screened out from organic environment of Durg district of Chhattisgarh (Sanyal et al., 2008). Preferred medium of growth for *V. chlamydoaporium* and *P. lilacinus* was Corn Meal Agar followed by Potato Dextrose Agar in the temperature range of 26-40^{0}C with pH range of 4-8 (De et al., 2008). Full grown plates of *P. lilacinus* and *V. chlamydosporium* baited with viable eggs of *Fasciola gigantica* and *Gigantocotyle explanatum* revealed that *V. chlamydosporium* to be more vigorous in its egg parasitic ability compared to *P. lilacinus* (De et al., 2008). Distortion of eggs started on day 2-3 of egg baiting in CMA plates of *V. chlamydosporium* with complete distortion by day 7. *P. lilacinus* and *V. chlamydosporium* revealed no statistically significant differences at 100-1000 mM concentrations of mercuric chloride, sodium arsenate and copper sulphate. Significant inhibition in colony diameters of both the fungi was observed at all concentrations (0.5-4.5 ppm) of carbendazim (benzimidazole fungicide) compared to controls (De et al., *in press*). The polymerase chain reaction (PCR) method to randomly amplify polymorphic DNA (RAPD) was used to differentiate four commonly occurring deuteromycetes viz., *P. lilacinus, V. chlamydosporium, D. flagrans* and *Arthrobotrys oligospora*. The total genomic DNAs from the fungi were amplified using ten arbitrarily selected 10-base primers. A total of 146 scorable amplicons were generated by these fungi. Distinct fingerprints between the fungi were obtained by most of the primers (De, 2007). These egg parasitic fungi had no short-term adverse impact on the environment and could be deployed for use as biological control agents to control long lasting egg stages of trematode and nematode parasites of livestock. Care should be taken while integrating it with anthelmintic control as some benzimidazole anthelmintics possess anti-mycotic property (Singh, 2008).

Control by exploiting breed resistance

Within the boundaries of the Tropics of Cancer and Capricorn lie the tropical and subtropical zones, where man, his crops and his livestock generally suffer much greater ravages from a plethora of different diseases and pests than in the more temperate climate, nematode parasites are no exception (Waller, 1997). Although possibly lacking the productivity and performance capacity of their counterparts in the temperate regions, one great advantage of a number of indigenous tropical breeds of livestock is their genetic ability to tolerate or resist disease. This has been well demonstrated for resistance to nematode parasites in sheep breeds, e.g., East Africa Maasai, Florida Native, Barbados Blackbelly, St. Croix and others (Baker, 1996). These unimproved breeds have evolved this trait through a process of natural selection over several centuries, whereby only the fittest have survived in the face of severe challenge of environmental stress, malnutrition and massive parasitic challenge with very little anthelmintic intervention. Tropics have experienced maximum cross-breeding between native and exotic breeds without much attempt to compare the exotic breeds or their crosses with native breeds. Parsitological advantage of breeding native breeds has been well documented in Maasai breed of sheep in Kenya with a clear economic advantage of farming the more resistant Maasai compared to exotic Dorper breed in Kenya (Baker, 1996). These native breeds should be used in crossbreeding and possibly in breed substitution programme. There are examples where farmers have struggled to keep temperate breeds alive in the humid tropics using suppressive doses of anthelmintics in order to prevent mortalities resulting in development of multiple high level broad spectrum anthelmintic resistance, thus ruling out the benefits of cross-breeding and selection. Planned breed substitution offers a simple, quick and economically viable preventive measure under these circumstances (Waller, 1997).

Resistance to nematode parasites can be improved by selection, but only recently efforts are being made to include the trait in commercial livestock breeding programmes in Australia (Nemesis) and New Zealand (Wormfec). Three approaches have been used; breeding for resistance, resilience, or number of treatments required during parasitism. It is necessary to assess the economic benefits of improving resistance relative to other traits, because their impact varies widely depending on the production environment and on the availability, effectiveness and sustainability of alternative control measures (Woolaston, 1996). It is imperative to say that the level of nutrition can influence both resistance and resilience of the host to parasitic infection.

Mathematical model based decision support

It is now known that the evolution of anthelmintic resistance is determined by the extent to which the survivors of anthelmintic treatment contribute their genes to future parasite generations. The system becomes all the more complex as it is influenced by several important factors such as, drug efficacy, climate, treatment strategy and frequency, rate of ingestion of incoming larvae, fecundity and productive life of adult worm, egg deposition, grazing management etc. Experimenting with or monitoring such a complex system is expensive, time consuming and technically difficult. The only practical way to explore this system is with the aid of a mathematical model. It should however be kept in mind that models will never replace real data from field observations but can play an effective role in worm control programme in view of capital and time intensive process involved in generation of data (Barnes et al., 1995). The minimum requirement of a model is that it should simulate host immunity, parasitic and pre-parasitic populations and genetic selection for anthelmintic resistance. Three such models and their predictions have been developed (Barnes et al., 1995). They can be useful tools for assessing the value of proposed worm control technologies and the best way to use them. Economic traits can be incorporated in the models to compare the cost benefit aspect. Efforts should be initiated in our country on development of mathematical models for prediction of parasitism and impact evaluation studies of alternative control strategies. The User-friendly software named

'FROGIN' (Forecasting of Rajasthan on Ovine Gastrointestinal Nematodosis) developed at CSWRI Avikanagar, is effective for forecasting GIN (particularly *H. contortus*) in sheep as well as on pasture (Singh et al., 2007). The model can help in choosing the number and time of drug treatment to get good worm control and to reduce the use of chemicals. FROGIN gives result as predicted faecal egg counts on the start of month, intensity of faecal egg counts for next 60 days and pasture larval burden for that month (Singh et al., 2007).

Quick technology transfer – Need of the hour

While worm infection has been described as the single most important animal health problem of small ruminants affecting the poor, it is exactly these resource-poor people who at present have little or no access to emerging technologies that could be put to use for improving their situation. Being ubiquitous and omnipresent in small ruminants, management/control of worms presents a particularly difficult challenge following widespread emergence of anthelmintic resistance, further complicated by recent and radical changes in approach to worm management. Various arms of Integrated Worm Management involving TST, grazing management, nutritional management, biological control are now available for widespread adoption. The TST is not only exceptionally affordable in relation to other conventional control programmes but can also help in delaying the selection for anthelmintic resistance. Integration of all these control options as technology arm of sustainable worm control in field needs a specialized way of technology transfer. Lack of dependable infrastructure makes it unlikely that any system of technology transfer dependent on expert extension personnel or on landline infrastructure can offer any solution for parasite management. Groupe Speciale Mobile (GSM wireless- cellphone) technology however, offers a ray of hope for technology transfer. The *per capita* uptake of this technology has apparently been far greater in developing than in developed countries and India is no exception. Can it be practical, for instance, to transmit data on climate, season, dominant worm species and the like to central software via a cellphone, then to be furnished with specific recommendations again via a cellphone to the end users to prevent losses? Challenge lies ahead in its implementation through an integrated and interdisciplinary approach (Sanyal, 2009).

The million dollar question

The question that now comes in mind is: Whether the alternative of parasite control measures would be able to reduce stress in animals and farmers? Reduction in the uses of anthelmintics would definitely minimize physical and chemical stresses to the animals. However, TST would likely to increase physical stresses to animals because frequent individual handling of animals for examination of ocular mucosa in detecting anaemic animals will further cause increase in the physical and chemical stresses to those animals that need anthelmintic intervention. No significant changes were observed in body weight gains and in gross histopathology of vital organs of mice fed on fungal spores for a month but no indicators of biological stresses to the animals were measured. Further, studies are yet been carried out to know the adverse impact, if any, of the fungal spores in target animals like small and large ruminants. However, it is likely that none, in isolation or collectively, will completely replace the need for effective anthelmintics. What is needed is the integration of all methods of parasite control as they come to hand, with the underlying aim of reducing the use and thus preserving the effectiveness of anthelmintics. The cost-effective and simple procedures, based on sound epidemiological principles, can achieve dramatic benefits in worm control but the farmers have poorly adopted them. Tremendous intellectual stresses to the farmers are likely to form the major impediments in adopting the strategies of integrated parasite control management in ruminants.

References

Baker, R.L. 1996. Characterisation and utilisation of sheep and goat breeds that are resistant to helminths. In: Sustainable Parasite Control in Ruminants (L.F. Le Jambre and M.R. Knox eds), ACIAR Proceedings No. 74, pp. 172-177.

Barger, I.A. 1997. Control by management. Veterinary Parasitology 72: 493-506.

Barger, I.A., Siale, K., Banks, D.J.D. and Le Jambre, L.F. 1994. Rotational grazing for control of gastrointestinal nematodes of goats in a wet tropical environment. Veterinary Parasitology 53: 109-116.

Barnes, E.H., Dobson, R.J. and Barger, I.A. 1995. Worm control and anthelmintic resistance: adventures with a model. Parasitology Today 11: 56-63.

Borgsteede, F.H.M. 1981. Experimental cross-infections with gastrointestinal nematodes of sheep and cattle. Zurnal Parasitenkunde 65: 1-10.

Coles, G. C. 2005. Anthelmintic resistance – Looking to the future: A UK perspective. Research in Veterinary Science 78: 99 – 108.

Coop. R.L. and Holmes, P.H. 1996. Nutrition and parasite interaction. International Journal for Parasitology 26: 951-962.

Coop, R.L. and Kyriazakis, I. 1999. Nutrition-parasite interaction. Veterinary Parasitology 84: 187-204.

De, S. 2007. Growth, predatory activity and molecular signature of egg-parasitic fungi *Verticillium chlamydosporium* and *Paecilomyces lilacinus*. MVSc Thesis submitted to Indira Gandhi Krishi Viswavidyalaya, Raipur.

De, S., Sanyal, P.K., Sarkar, A.K., Patel, N.K., Pal S. and Mandal, S.C. 2008. Screening for Indian isolates of egg parasitic fungi for use in biological control of fascioliasis and amphistomiasis in ruminant livestock. Journal of Helminthology 82: 271-277.

De, S., Sanyal, P.K., Sarkar, A.K., Patel, N.K., Pal, S. and Mandal, S.C. 2009. Screening of Chhattisgarh isolates of egg parasitic fungi *Paecilomyces lilacinus* and *Verticillium chlamydosporium* under the influence of heavy metals and a fungicide. In: Proceedings of the National Academy of Sciences, Section-B (in press).

Esch, G.W., Gibbons, J.W. and Bourque, J.E. 1975. An analysis of the relationship between stress and parasitism. American Midland Naturalist 93 (2): 339-353.

Jackson, F. and Coop, R. L. 2000. The development of anthelmintic resistance in sheep nematodes. Parasitology 120: S95-S107.

Jordan, H.E., Phillips, W.A., Morrison, R.D., Doyle, J.J. and McKenzie, K. A 1988. 3-year study of continuous mixed grazing of cattle and sheep: Parasitism of offspring. International Journal for Parasitology 18: 779-784.

Knox, M.R. and Steel, J.W. 1996. Nutritional enhancement of parasite control in small ruminant production systems in developing countries of Southeast Asia and the Pacific. International Journal for Parasitology 26: 963-970.

Krecek, R. C. and Waller, P. J. 2006. Towards the implementation of the 'basket of options' approach to helminth parasite control of livestock : emphasis on the tropics / sub tropics. Veterinary Parasitology 139: 270-282.

Krecek, R. C., Guthrie, A. J., van Nieuwenhuizen, L. C. and Booth, L. M. 1994. A comparison between the effects of conventional and selective antiparasitic treatments on nematode parasites of horses from two management schemes. Journal of South Africa Veterinary Association 65: 97-100.

Kyriazakis, I., Oldham, J.D., Coop, R.L. and Jackson, F. 1994. The effect of subclinical intestinal nematode infection on the diet selection of growing sheep. British Journal of Nutrition 665-677.

Larsen, M. 1999. Biological control of helminths. International Journal for Parasitology 29: 139-146.

Malan, F. S., van Wyk, J. A. and Wessels, C. D. 2001. Clinical evaluation of anaemia in sheep: Early trials. Onderstepoort Journal of Veterinary Research 61: 165-174.

Michel, J.F. 1985. Strategies for the use of anthelmintics in livestock and their implications for the development of drug resistance. Parasitology 90: 621-628.

Willadsen, P., Bird, P., Cobon, G.S. and Hungerford, J. 1995. Commercialisation of a recombinant vaccine against *Boophilus microplus*. Parasitology 110: S43-S50.

Sangster, N. C. 1999. Anthelmintic resistance: past, present and future. International Journal for Parasitology 29: 115-124.

Sanyal, P.K. 1997. Self medicating anthelmintic delivery devices for ruminants. The Blue Cross Book for the Veterinary Profession 8: 12-17.

Sanyal, P.K. 2005. Mycological control of nematode parasites of livestock: From academic interest to reality. In: Proceedings of the National Academy of Sciences, India 75 (B)-Special Issue : 263-271.

Sanyal, P.K. 2009. Automated technology transfer for sustainable control of parasitic gastroenteritis in small ruminants: a review. Indian Journal of Small Ruminants 15: 134-155.

Sanyal, P.K. and Singh, D.K. 1993. Prophylactic and therapeutic efficacy of prolonged low level administration of fenbendazole through urea molasses block against experimental haemonchosis in calves. Journal of Veterinary Parasitology 7: 71-80.

Sanyal, P.K., De, S., Sarkar, A.K., Patel, N.K., S.C. Mandal and S. Pal. 2008. Isolation of egg parasitic fungi from Chhattisgarh. Journal of Veterinary Parasitology 22: 1-3.

Singh, R.K. 2008. Short-term environmental impact of egg parasitic fungi *Verticillium chlamydosporium* and *Paecilomyces lilacinus*. MVSc Thesis submitted to Indira Gandhi Krishi Viswavidyalaya, Raipur.

Singh, D., Swarnkar, C.P. and Khan, F.A. 2007. Performance testing of "FROGIN" a mathematical model for forecasting GIN (particularly *H. contortus*) in sheep of Rajasthan. In: Proceedings of the 5th Annual Scientists' Meet of All India Network Programme on Gastrointestinal Parasitism, pp. 220-223.

Van Wyk, J.A. and Van Schalkwyk, P.C. 1990. A novel approach to the control of anthelmintic resistant *Haemonchus contortus* in sheep. Veterinary Parasitology 35: 61-69.

Van Wyk, J.A., Malan, F.S. and Randles, J.L. 1997. How long before resistance makes it impossible to control some field strains of *Haemonchus contortus* in South Africa with any of the modern anthelmintics? Veterinary Parasitology 70: 111-122.

Vatta, A. F., Letty, B. A., van der Linde, M. J., van Wijk, E. F., Hansen, J. W. and Krecek, R. C. 2001. Testing for clinical anaemia caused by *Haemonchus* spp. In goats farmed under resource-poor conditions in South Africa using an eye colour chart developed for sheep. Veterinary Parasitology 99: 1-14.

Vatta, A. F, Krecek, R. C., van der Linde, M. J., Motswatswe, P. W., Grimbeck, R. J., van Wijk, E. F. and Hansen, J. W. 2002. *Haemonchus* species in sheep farmed under resource - poor conditions in South Africa - effect on haematocrit, conjunctival mucous membrane colour and body conditions. Journal of South Africa Veterinary Association 73: 119–123.

Vercruysse, J., Hilderson, H., Claerebout, E. and Roclants, B. 1995. Control of gastrointestinal nematodes in first-season grazing calves by two strategic treatments with doramectin. Veterinary Parasitology 58: 27-34.

Waller, P.J. 1997. Nematode parasite control of livestock in the tropics/subtropics: The need for novel approaches. International Journal for Parasitology 27: 1193-1201.

Waller, P.J., Dash, K.M., Barger, I.A., Le Jambre, L.F. and Plant, J. 1995. Anthelmintic resistance in nematode parasites of sheep: Learning from the Australian experience. Veterinary Record 136: 411-413.

Woolaston, R.R. 1996. Increasing resistance by selection. In: Sustainable Parasite Control in Ruminants (Eds L.F. Le Jambre and M.R. Knox), ACIAR Proceedings No. 74, pp. 165-171.

❑❑❑

30

Biotic and Abiotic Stresses and Small Ruminant Diseases

V.S. Vihan* , K. Gururaj and Dr Ashok Kumar
Central Institute for Research on Goats, Makhdoom, Mathura, U.P.

Introduction

India ranks first in cattle and buffalo population, second in goat, third in sheep and seventh in poultry. Although the population of livestock during last 10 years has been stable around 485 million, the buffalo population has increased by 8.91 %, while the cattle population has reduced by 6.89%. There has been a significant increase in the population of goats during the last five decades, which is attributed to the decrease in the size of land holdings and persistent drought caused by erratic monsoon, forcing many small farmers to shift from large animals to small ruminants. To meet the rising demand for animal products from indigenous sources, the World Bank estimates that animal production (meat and milk) must increase by 4% per year until 2025 to feed the population, improve nutrition and eliminate imports. Ruminant livestock are primarily raised under traditional systems characterized by low inputs. These systems cannot produce the increased amounts of crop and livestock products for the projected increases in human population. It is estimated that unless steps are taken to address major constraints in production and if current use of inputs remain unchanged, the land area required to support the population by the year 2010 would have to be expanded by more than 100 million ha, or 5% (FAO, 1986).

Major constraints to livestock production include inadequate feed supply, poor animal health, low-yielding animal genotypes and minimal levels of management. Inability to feed animals adequately throughout the year is the most important constraint for most traditional animal farmers. This has made nutrition a major constraint to livestock production. Under nutrition further increases the risk to animals of diseases. Flock productivity may, however, be affected by a wide range of biotic and abiotic stresses particularly caused by various disease problems and reproductive wastage. The impact of disease may be through mortalities and abortions or through morbidity and such sub-clinical effects like weight loss or reduced gains, reduced carcass weight and quality and the cost of time and money involved in controlling or overcoming the effects of disease. Thus, a top priority in operating successful small ruminant enterprises must be given adequate attention to reduce stresses. Losses due to mortality often have severe and easily quantifiable economic impact, but losses in production due to morbidity are commonly underestimated because they are difficult to estimate. Livestock stress and well-being are complex biological phenomena, cutting across both intensively and extensively managed livestock production sector.

Abiotic stresses

Abiotic stress is defined as the negative impact of non-living factors on the living organisms in a specific environment. The non-living variable must influence the environment beyond its normal range of variation to adversely affect the population performance or individual physiology of the organism in a significant way. Abiotic stress factors, or stressors, are naturally occurring, often intangible, factors such as intense sunlight or wind that may cause harm to the plants and animals in the area affected. Abiotic stress is essentially unavoidable. Abiotic stress affects animals, but plants are especially dependent on environmental factors. Research has also shown that abiotic stressors are at their most harmful when they occur together, in combinations of biotic stress factors.

Small ruminant husbandry in relation to productivity has progressed due to intensive and semi-intensive farming by the application of many novel technologies. Over the years, the small ruminants have adapted to minor stresses like changing climatic factors gradually. Off late a drastic climatic change and increasing global temperatures will certainly have a significant effect on these animals. Abiotic stress can have effect on two important parameters, viz. production and reproduction. Most of the times, abiotic stress can cause a direct effect on the animal's homeostasis, but it can also create a conducive atmosphere for biotic stress. For instance, a sudden rise in temperature along with humidity can lead to precipitation of certain bacterial diseases like pneumonia and endoparasites, which are a biotic stress.

Abiotic stress can be of two types viz., natural and induced. Natural abiotic stress can be of many types like change in temperature, humidity, rainfall, wind speed, etc. Climate change affects the small ruminant's adaptability at microlevel. If it is gradual and progressive, the animals acclimatize over the period of its change on the micro and macro-environment. But if it is a dramatic change, it might lead to an increased stress on the animals homeostasis, leading to reduced productivity and affecting its reproduction. On the other hand, abiotic stress can be induced, caused by human intervention. It can be a mechanical stress, which occurs during shearing causing trauma and wound to the small ruminants like sheep. Excess handling can also cause stress on these animals, especially during treatment, dipping and prophylaxis measures. Even a minor change in the feed, dimension of feeding equipment, change of housing, transport of animals, forced breeding and the subsequent production, all of these determinants lead to indefinite stress of the small ruminants. For animals, the most stressful of all the abiotic stressors is heat. This is because many species are unable to regulate their internal body temperature. Even in the species that are able to regulate their own temperature, it is not always a completely accurate system. Temperature determines metabolic rates, heart rates, and other very important factors within the bodies of animals, so an extreme temperature change can easily distress the animal's body.

Abiotic stresses affect animal production in four ways: (a) the impact of changes in livestock feed-grain availability and price; (b) impacts on livestock pastures and forage crop production and quality; (c) changes in the distribution of livestock diseases and pests; and (d) the direct effects of weather and extreme events on animal health, growth and reproduction. Climatic restrictions on vectors, environmental habitats and disease causing agents are important for keeping many animal diseases in check. Alterations of temperature and precipitation regimes may result in a spread of disease and parasites into new regions or produce an increase in the incidence of disease, which, in turn, would reduce animal productivity and possibly increase animal mortality. Direct effects involve heat exchange between the animal and the surrounding environment that are related to radiation, temperature, humidity and wind speed. Under present climate conditions, the lack of ability of animals to dissipate the environmental heat determines that, in many areas in the world, animals suffer heat stress during, at least, part of the year. Heat stress has a variety of detrimental effects on livestock, with significant effects on milk production and reproduction.

Effects of abiotic stress on health and production in ruminants

Indigenous breeds of goats and sheep are fairly well adapted to the tropical environment; and the majority of animals are raised traditionally under extensive free-roaming management systems with no specialized input into housing care, nutrition or disease treatment or prevention. A small percentage of animals are, however, raised intensively, sometimes even under a cut-and-carry system of management. Here, animals are afforded better shelter; nutrition and health care and often achieve higher productivity. The type and impact of diseases on production varies with the level of management. A serious constraint on small ruminant production has been the high prevalence of diseases and parasites, particularly in the more humid areas. This causes high mortality amongst kids and lambs, diminishing the benefits of their high reproductive performance. Pre-weaning mortality up to 40% has been recorded in kids and lambs in India. However, pre-weaning mortality under the extensive system of management may be underestimated. Deaths of the offspring born at the time of grazing usually go unnoticed. In addition, abortions and stillbirths cause further losses.

Climatic conditions affect animal well-being both directly, through the physical effects of climatic extremes, and indirectly, through influences on the levels of pollution in the air, on the agricultural, marine and freshwater systems that provide food and water, and on the vectors and pathogens that cause infectious diseases. Animal health may be affected by both the regional climate and the ambient weather. Climate, or the long-term (decades or longer) average weather conditions in a region, may influence diseases by determining suitable habitats for disease agents.

Temperature related illness and death

Livestock populations have, over time, acclimatized and adapted to local climates and also are able to cope with a range of weather changes. However, within populations, there is a range individual sensitivity to extreme weather events. If heat waves increase in frequency and intensity the risk of death and serious illness would increase. The effects of an increase in heat waves would often be exacerbated by increased humidity and urban air pollution. Although there is considerable higher impact of heat stress related mortalities in developing countries, warmer winters and fewer cold spells will decrease cold-related mortality in many temperate countries. High temperatures cause some well-described clinical syndromes such as heatstroke in tropical countries like India. In some places, the number of deaths of animal due to heat waves is projected to double by 2020.

Extreme weather related health effects

Any increase in frequency of extreme events such as storms, floods, droughts and cyclones would harm ruminant health through a variety of pathways. These natural hazards can cause direct loss of life and injury and affect health indirectly through loss of shelter; population displacement contamination of water supplies; loss of food production (leading to hunger and malnutrition); increased risk of infectious disease epidemics (including diarrhoeal and respiratory diseases); and damage of infrastructure created for health services. Over recent years climate-related disasters have caused hundreds of thousands of deaths of both animals and humans in countries such as Bangladesh, Venezuela and Mozambique. Drought, flood, cyclones and tsunami are disasters due to the global warming in which livestock are affected more because they are more vulnerable. Due to floods, water-born diseases increase as animals rely on the polluted water of flood. Drought leads to the shortage of fodders that cause nutritional stress on animals affecting their optimum productivity.

Impact of rise in sea level

Global warming causes oceans to warm and expand, and therefore rising sea level could submerge the coastal areas. Eventually, the rising waters could take away the land inhabited by people forcing them to move along with their animals. Due to movement, animals particularly ruminants will not adapt to new area and health and production will go down. Salt-water intrusion from rising sea levels will reduce the quality and quantity of freshwater supplies and this in turn will affect the health and production of the animal.

Shortage of feed and fodders

Altered fodder production is due to changes in climate, weather events. There is more demand of fodder in lean season particularly in the urban areas. This will cause increase in the production cost and decrease in the production.

Desertification and land degradation

This is one of the pronounced effects of global warming. Desertification and land degradation primarily causes decrease in the productivity of fodders both in terms of quality and quantity. Nutritional stress thus caused, particularly in the summer season, will drastically reduced productivity.

Direct impact on animals

There is a range of thermal conditions within which animals are able to maintain a relatively stable body temperature by means of behavioral and physiological means. Heat stress results from the animal's inability to dissipate sufficient heat to maintain homeothermy. High ambient temperature, relative humidity and radiant energy compromise the ability of animals to dissipate heat. As a result, there is an increase in body temperature, which in turn initiates compensatory and adaptive mechanisms to reestablish homeothermy and homeostasis. These readjustments, generally referred to as adaptations, may be favorable or unfavorable to economic interests of humans, but are essential for survival of animals. Thus, an increase in air temperature, such as that expected in different scenarios of climate change, would directly affect animal performance by disturbing thermoregulation. Animals higher productivity are more sensitive to heat stress. Heat waves have been found to affect performance of high producing animals in a grazing system. Since climate change could result in an increase of heat stress, all methods to help animals cope with or, at least, alleviate the impacts of heat stress could be useful to mitigate the impacts of global change on animal responses and performance.

A number of changes occur in the animal as a result of heat stress. These include:

1. Elevated body temperature - Body temperatures > 102.5°F (normal is 101.5°F).
2. Increased respiration rates > 70-80/minute.
3. Increased maintenance energy requirement - Animals activate mechanisms in an attempt to dissipate the excess heat and maintain body temperature. The increased respiration rate is one example. The maintenance energy requirement may increase by 20-30% in animals under heat stress. This decreases the intake energy available for productive functions such as milk production. Blood flow to the skin will increase in an attempt to dissipate heat. At the same time, blood flow to the core of the body will decrease.
4. Feed nutrient utilization - An increased loss of sodium and potassium is usually associated with heat stress. This is due to losses associated with the increased respiration rate. This can shift the acid-base balance and results in a metabolic alkalosis. There can also be a decrease in the efficiency of nutrient utilization.
5. Dry matter intake - Dry matter intake decreases in animals subjected to heat stress. This depression in dry matter intake can be either short-term or long-term depending on the length and duration of heat stress.

6. Milk production- there is normally a decrease in milk production (range- 10 to >25%) under heat stress, which can either be transient or for longer period depending on the length and severity of heat stress.
7. Reproduction- Heat stress has also been reported to affect the reproductive performance in following ways.
   - Decreased length and intensity of the oestrus period.
   - Decreased conception (fertility) rate.
   - Decreased growth, size and development of ovarian follicles.
   - Increased risk of early embryonic deaths.
   - Decreased fetal growth and calf size.

Amelioration measures to relieve from abiotic stresses

1. Ration adjustments

a. Select and feed higher quality forages if possible.
b. Lower ration fiber (ADF, NDF-explain) levels slightly.
c. Consider adding some additional fat to the ration.
d. Select feed ingredients that have high digestibility in the animal. This lowers the heat produced by nutrient utilization within the animal.
e. Balance ration protein levels to minimize high levels of soluble and rumen degradable proteins. The animal must spend energy to excrete excess protein from the body.
f. Consider adding buffers (sodium bicarbonate, magnesium oxide, and sodium sesquicarbonate) to help in maintaining a normal rumen environment.
g. Consider increasing ration potassium levels to counteract the higher potassium losses in heat-stressed animals. Magnesium levels in ration may also need to be increased.
h. There may be some benefit to adding yeast or yeast cultures to the ration.

2. Water

a. Do the watering devices contain clean and fresh water?
b. Is there enough water space available?
c. Is fresh water available?
d. Water intake may increase by 20 to > 50% during heat stress conditions. Is an adequate quantity of water available?

3. Housing and facility adjustments

a. Are sheep and goats overcrowded? If so, what can be done to minimize overcrowding?

b. Is shade available? This reduces the effect of radiation.

c. What is the airflow over the housing area? Are there ways to open the facility up to obtain more ventilation? In many cases, the addition of fans will be required to assist in increasing airflow.

Biotic stresses

Stress related important common diseases of small ruminants

1. Diarrhoea (Scours)

Diarrhea is defined as an increased frequency, fluidity, or volume of faecal excretion. There are many causes of diarrhea: bacterial, viral, parasites, and diet. Diarrhoea in lambs and goats is a complex, multi-factorial disease involving the animal, the environment, nutrition, and infectious agents. Diarrhoea should not be considered an illness in or of itself, but rather a symptom of other more serious health problems in sheep and lambs. Diarrhoea is not always the result of an infectious disease. Stress, poor management, and nutrition can induce it. Many of the common causes of diarrhea are self-limiting, and the major goals of treatment are to keep the animal physiologically intact while the diarrhoea runs its course.

Infectious causes of diarrhoea	
Bacterial	*E. coli, Salmonella sp.,Clostridium perfringens*
Viral	Rotavirus, Coronavirus
Protozoa	Cryptosporidia, Coccidia (*Eimera sp.*), *Giardia sp.*
Parasitic	Gastro-intestinal worms (not *Haemonchus*)
Non-infectious causes (or contributing factors)	
Nutritional	Dietary changes, overfeeding, simple indigestion, poor quality milk replacers, inadequate intake of colostrums, poor quality of colostrums, poor quality or stagnant water, lush or wet pasture, inadequate dry matter intake, plant and fungal toxins and allergens
Management (Poor environment)	Overstocking/overcrowding, poor sanitation
Stress	Weaning, handling, weather extremes, shipping/transportation

(A) Diarrhoea in young (neonatal) lambs and kids

Despite improvements in management practices and prevention and treatment strategies, diarrhoea is still the most common and costly disease affecting neonatal small ruminants. A study at the CIRG, Makhdoom showed that diarrhea accounted for 34% of young kid/lamb mortality. The four major causes of diarrhea in lambs and kids during the first month of life are *E. Coli,* rotavirus, *Cryposporidum* sp. and *Salmonella* sp. *E. coli* scours are most common.

E. coli

E. coli scours is an opportunistic disease associated with sloppy environmental conditions and poor sanitation. It is seen in lambs and kids less than 10 days of age, but is most common at 1 to 4 days of age. It usually presents itself as an outbreak in lambs and kids between 12 and 48 hours of age. Fluid therapy is the mainstay of therapy. Antibiotics are used for both treatment and prevention of E. coli scours. Adequate ingestion of colostrum by newborns decreases the incidence of the disease. Treatment of E. coli scours usually involves dehydrating the lamb with oral, subcutaneous or intraperitoneal fluids and treatment with appropriate antibiotics. Prevention of E. coli scours in lambs should really be the key focus for any flock. Lambing barn sanitation and creating a clean, dry environment for newborn lambs are the key factors in preventing outbreaks of E. coli scours.

Rotavirus

Lambs and kids are infected with a group of B rotaviruses, whereas most other animals and humans are infected with group A rotaviruses. Rotavirus generally causes diarrhea in lambs and kids at 2 to 14 days of age. Young animals become very depressed and dehydrated. Rotavirus is treated with supportive care. Vaccinating ewes and does with bovine rotavirus vaccines before parturition will increase passive immunity.

Cryptosporidium

Cryptosporidium parvum is a protozoon that causes diarrhea similar to that of rotavirus infection. Cryptosporidia affect lambs and kids of 5 to 10 days of age. The affected animals are often active, alert, and nursing. The diarrhea is usually very liquid and yellow. No consistently effective treatment for cryptosporidiosis in ruminants has been identified. Decoquinte (Deccox®) and monensin sodium (Bovatec®) may be useful in the control of Cryptosporidiosis. Ammonia and formalin effectively remove *Cryptosporidium* from the environment. The best control of cryptosporidiosis comes from lambs and kids getting adequate immunity through colostrum soon after birth.

Salmonella

Salmonella has thousands of serotypes and all can potentially cause diarrhea in animals including lambs and kids of any age. Animals less than one week of age are more likely to die without clinical signs, whereas animals older than one week are more likely to have diarrhea. *Salmonella* also causes outbreaks of diarrhea in late gestation and is frequently associated with abortion. Bleach is an effective disinfectant to use during an outbreak.

Giardia

Giardia-induced diarrhea is more commonly, but not limited to 2 to 4 week old lambs and kids. The diarrhea is usually transient, but infected animals can continue to shed cysts for many weeks, providing a source of infection for other animals and possibly humans. Infected animals can be treated effectively with fenbendazole.

Nutritional

Infectious agents are not the only cause of diarrhea in neonates. Nutritional problems can result in diarrhea. Nutritional diarrhea is most common in orphaned animals as a result of poor quality milk replacers, mixing errors, and overfeeding. Consumption of lush-green pasture or high-energy diets can also result in diarrhea in young lambs and kids.

(B) Diarrhea in older lambs and kids

The most common causes of diarrhea in older lambs and kids are coccidiosis and gastro-intestinal parasites (worms). Other major causes of diarrhea in older lambs and kids are *Clostridium perfringens*, rumen acidosis, and nutritional.

Coccidiosis

Coccidosis is a protozoan parasitic disease that is a common cause of diarrhea in lambs and kids. It may also cause subclinical production losses. Lambs and kids are most susceptible to the problem at 1 to 4 months of age, although younger animals may be affected. Clinical disease is common after the stress of weaning, feed changes, or shipping. The diarrhea is usually not bloody, but at times it may contain blood or mucous and very watery. Treatment of affected animals includes supportive care and administration of coccidiostats. All animals in a group should be treated during an outbreak. Prevention involves improved sanitation and the use of coccidiostats.

Gastro-intestinal worms

The Barber pole worm (*Haemonchus contortis*) is the major worm species affecting sheep and goats in warm and moist climates that experience summer rainfall. It is not characterized by diarrhea. However, heavy loads of other gastro-intestinal worms can cause diarrhea in sheep and goats: *Ostertagia circumcincta* (medium or brown stomach worm), *Trichostrongylus* (hair worm), *Coopera sp.* (small intestinal worm), and *Nematodirus sp.* (thread-neck worm). Control of gastro-intestinal parasites is best achieved via good pasture, grazing, and animal management, and strategic and/or selective deworming of affected individuals with effective anthelmintics.

Clostridium perfringens

Clostridium perfringens types A, B, C, and D can all cause diarrhea in lambs and kids, though D is the most common type. With type D, the onset of neurologic signs followed by sudden death is more common in sheep, whereas goats are more likely to show signs of diarrhea before death. Treatment is rarely effective but consists of aggressive supportive care and administration of the antitoxin. Clostridium perfringens type C tends to affect very young lambs (<2 weeks of age) and presents itself as bloody diarrhea, hemorrhagic enteritis, and bloody scours.

Rumen acidosis

Acidosis is caused by too much grain or concentrate, which causes a change in rumen acidity and bacteria population. The increase in acid causes inflammation of the rumen wall and a reduction in the bacteria needed to digest fiber. Symptoms may include depression, off feed, bloat, scours, and occasionally death. Treatment includes drenching with mineral oil or antacids. Proper feeding management prevents acidosis. Concentrates (grain) should be introduced in the diet slowly and incrementally to give time for the rumen to adjust.

Nutritional

Nutritional scours can be caused by anything that disrupts normal habits. It can also be the result of low intake of dry matter to fluid ratio. A lamb needs to consume at least 2.5 percent of its body weight in dry matter daily. Young or fast growing lambs turned out to pasture must eat large quantities of grass to satisfy their nutritional needs. Green grass is high in moisture. They may develop diarrhea if they are not getting enough dry matter in their diet.

(C) Diarrhea in adult sheep and goats

Diarrhea in adults is less common than in lambs and kids. Parasitism can cause diarrhea in adult sheep and goats. Coccidiosis can occur in adults under extreme stress or due to lack of immunity. The ingestion of toxins, of which the list is long, can also cause diarrhea. It is not uncommon for sheep or goats to scour when they are grazing lush or wet pasture.

Johne's Disease

Unlike cattle, diarrhea is not a common symptom of sheep and goats affected with Johne's disease. A study at CIRG showed than less than 20 percent of sheep and goats with Johne's show diarrhea. Johne's disease is an incurable, contagious bacterial disease of the intestinal tract. It occurs in a wide variety of animals, but most oftenly in ruminants. Johne's disease is most commonly reported in cattle, but probably underrated as a problem in small ruminants.

2. Abortion

In abortion, pregnancy is terminated and the ewe/doe loses her lambs/ kids or gives birth to weak or deformed lambs that die shortly after birth. There are both infectious and non-infectious causes of abortion. The most common infectious causes of abortion in ewes are *Chlamydia* (Enzootic abortion), *Campylobacter* (Vibrio), and *Toxoplasma.*

Brucellosis

Brucellosis is an infectious disease caused by bacteria of the genus *Brucella.* Various *Brucella* species affect sheep, goats, cattle, pigs, dogs, and other animals. In the infected ruminants, brucellosis commonly induces abortion during the second half of gestation. Ovine brucellosis mainly affects rams, causing lesions in their reproductive organs.

Chlamydial abortion (enzootic abortion, EAE)

Chlamydia psittaci is the most common cause of abortion in ewes. It is transmitted from aborting sheep to other susceptible females. Ewe lambs are usually the most susceptible on farms where organisms are present. *Chylamydia* causes abortion during the last month of pregnancy and may also result in the birth of lambs that die shortly after birth.

Leptospirosis

Sheep are generally more resistant to leptospirosis than cattle, swine, and most other domestic animals. Abortion due to this disease may occur during the last month of pregnancy. A blood test of aborting sheep will confirm diagnosis. The problem can be prevented with annual vaccination with a 5-strain leptospirosis vaccine.

Q fever

Q fever is a disease caused by the rickettsia, *Coxiella burnetti*. The disease is found worldwide except for New Zealand. Sheep, goats, and cattle are most likely to get Q fever. The most common sign of Q fever is abortion during late pregnancy. However, most animals do not show any signs of illness. Animals get Q fever through contact with body fluids or secretions. Q fever is zoonotic.

Salmonella

Salmonella abortion is very common in some countries as a cause of abortion in sheep, but probably occurs more often than recognized. The two major factors determining whether a pregnant ewe will abort from *Salmonella* are stress on the ewe and the number of *Salmonella* a the ewe ingests. Abortions may occur earlier in gestation, but are most common in the last month of gestation. Most of the ewes show diarrhea and some will die from metritis, peritonitis and septicemia. Healthy lambs may also contract the disease and die.

Toxoplasmosis

Toxoplasmosis is common cause of abortion in ewes. It is caused by *Toxoplasma gondii. Toxoplasma* abortion in ewes follows ingestion of feed or water that has been contaminated with oocyte-laden cat faeces. The organism migrates to the placenta and foetuses causing their death and expulsion. Ewes will abort during the last month of pregnancy or give birth to dead or weak lambs that usually die from starvation. Infection in the first two months of gestation results in embryonic death and re-absorption.

Campylobacteriosis (vibriosis)

Campylobacter is the second most common cause of abortion in ewes. Abortion during the last month of pregnancy, stillborn lambs, and the birth of weak lambs are common signs of vibrio abortion. The organisms, which cause vibrio abortion, are *Campylobacter jejuni* or *Campylobacter fetus*. Ewes are infected by oral ingestion. Isolating the aborting ewe, disposal of the fetuses and membranes and disinfecting the affected area can prevent disease spread. Infected ewes usually recover after aborting and are immune to re-infection.

3. Infectious diseases

Changes in temperature, rainfall, humidity and sea level changes can all impact the incidence of infectious diseases. The issue of infectious disease pressure is influenced globally by many factors including migration of people and animals; changes in land use; changes in the public health infrastructure; and the continued increase in drug resistant strains of a number of diseases.

PPR

One of the most serious diseases of small ruminants, *peste des petits ruminants* (PPR), was first recognised as a contagious "rinderpest-like" condition in goats. It was first described in Côte d'Ivoire in 1942 and later in the Benin Republic during 1944. The disease has been difficult to quantify due to the lack of precise statistical records. However, it has been stated that it is the most destructive viral disease among small ruminants. Goats are more susceptible to PPR than sheep and young animals are more susceptible than adult ones. The use of Vero cell culture PPR vaccine is effective in the control of PPR.

Bluetongue

Bluetongue is an insect-transmitted, viral disease of sheep, cattle, goats, and other ruminants, such as white-tailed deer and pronghorn. It is particularly severe in sheep; half the sheep in an infected flock may die. In cattle and goats, however, bluetongue virus causes very mild, self-limiting infections with only minor clinical consequences. The bluetongue virus infection causes inflammation, swelling, and hemorrhage of the mucous membranes of mouth, nose, and tongue. Inflammation and soreness of the feet are also associated with bluetongue. In sheep, the tongue and mucous membranes of the mouth become swollen, hemorrhagic, and may look red or dirty blue in color, thus giving the disease its name. Biting gnats spreads bluetongue viruses from animal to animal.

Foot-and-mouth disease (FMD)

Foot-and-mouth disease is a severe, highly communicable viral disease of cattle and swine. It also affects sheep and goats and other cloven hoofed animals. The disease is characterized by fever and blister-like lesions followed by erosions on the tongue and lips, in the mouth, on the teats, and between the hooves. While many affected animals do recover, the disease results in a weakened state, loss of weight, and reduced production of milk and meat. Foot-and-mouth disease in adult sheep and goats is frequently mild or unapparent, but can cause high mortality in young animals.

Footrot

Footrot is one of the most economically devastating diseases in the sheep industry. It is caused by the interaction between two anaerobic bacteria: *Bacteroides nodosus*, which can only live in the animal's hoof; and *Fusobacterium necrophorum*, which is a normal inhabitant of soil and sheep manure. Lameness in one or more feet is the most common symptom of footrot, though not all lame sheep have footrot. Footrot has a characteristic foul odor. The disease can be controlled and/or eradicated by a combination of hoof trimming, vaccination, foot bathing and soaking and culling. Zinc sulfate is considered to be the most effective foot rot treatment. Footrot is highly contagious.

Pneumonia (respiratory disease complex, pasteurellosis)

Pneumonia is most important disease of the respiratory system. Pneumonia is of multifactorial etiology that includes bacteria, viruses, mycoplasma, fungi and parasites. The most common bacteria isolated from respiratory infections are *Pasteurella haemolytica* or *Pasteurella multocida* or both. Affected animals become depressed and go off feed. They may cough and show some respiratory distress. Temperatures are usually over 104°F. The disease may be acute with sudden deaths or takes a course of several days. Pneumonia is treated with antibiotics.

Caseous lymphadenitis (CLA, boils, abscesses, cheesy gland)

Caseous lymphadenitis is an infectious and contagious disease that involves primarily the lymphatic system, though other organs can be affected. It is caused by the bacteria *Corynebacterium pseudotuberculosis*. Infection results in abscess formation in the lymph nodes which when cut or ruptured discharge pus containing bacteria into the immediate surroundings. When the infection spread internally, affected ewes slowly lose weight and eventually become emaciated. CLA is the third leading cause of carcass condemnation.

Listeriosis (circling disease)

Listeria monocytogenes, the cause of listeriosis, are widely distributed in nature and are found in soil, feedstuffs, and faeces of healthy animals. It is most commonly associated with the feeding of moldy silage or spoiled hay, but because the organism lives naturally in the environment, listeriosis may occur sporadically. Listeriosis usually presents itself as encephalitis, but may also cause abortion in ewes. Sheep with the neurological form of the disease become depressed and disoriented. The affected sheep may walk in circles with the tilted head and facial paralysis. Mortality is high and treatment (high doses of antibiotics) is generally not effective.

Mastitis (hard bag, blue bag)

Mastitis is an inflammation of the mammary gland (udder), which is usually caused by a bacterial infection. The bacteria causing mastitis in ewes are *Staphylococcus aureus* and *Pasteurella haemolytica*. There are two types of mastitis: acute and chronic. The glands of ewes/does with acute mastitis may be discolored and dark, swollen and very warm. The affected ewe may be reluctant to walk, may hold up one rear foot, and may not permit her lambs to nurse. Ewes with chronic mastitis often go undetected. Mastitis is treated with intramammary infusions of antibiotics and systemic antibiotics. There is no vaccine for mastitis. It is best prevented by good management and sanitation.

Soremouth (contagious ecthyma, scabby mouth, pustular dermatitis, orf)

Soremouth is the most common skin disease affecting sheep (and goats). It is a highly contagious viral infection that can also produce painful human infections. The virus causes scab formation on the skin, usually around the mouth, nostrils, eyes, mammary gland and vulva. It first appears as tiny red nodules, usually at the junction of the lips.

Joint ill (navel ill, polyarthritis)

Joint ill occurs in lambs up to one month of age. Affected lambs are often lame in several joints, usually limb joints, including fetlocks, knees, hocks and stifles. Affected joints are hot and painful. The lambs are dull, feverish and clearly unthrifty. Some may have swollen, infected navels, while others may have symptoms of pneumonia or meningitis. The infection is usually caused by strains of *streptococci*, though coliforms and occasionally *Actinomyces pyogenes* may be isolated.

Pink eye (infectious keratoconjunctivitis)

Pinkeye is a highly contagious disease affecting the eyes of sheep. Pinkeye may result from many different infective agents: *Chlamydia*, certain viruses, and mycoplasma. The disease will usually complete its course in three weeks in individual sheep. The use of eye medications containing antibiotics may be helpful in individual cases. There are no effective vaccines available. The agent that causes pinkeye in sheep and goats is different from the one that causes it in cattle.

4. External parasites

Parasitism ranks high among the factors that limit the productivity of small ruminants although its effect is often underestimated. It has been estimated that the losses from parasitic diseases in many countries are higher than those attributable to PPR. External parasites cause extensive losses among small ruminants, especially in humid areas. The two most serious vectors are ticks and mites. The irritation and dermatitis that accompany mange infestation can reduce the value of the skins for sale to the leather industry and the meat for consumption as food. Haemoprotozoans transmitted by ticks are quite common. External parasites affecting sheep include keds, ticks, lice, mites, and nasal bots and mange (sheep scab).

Facial eczema

Facial eczema is a condition of severe dermatitis in cattle, sheep, and goats caused by a toxin in spores of the saprophytic fungus *Pithomyces chartarum,* which lives in dead vegetative material in pastures, especially perennial rye grass. Facial eczema is an example of "secondary photosensitization," in which the skin lesions are really the secondary result of liver damage, rather than the direct result of a plant toxin. The liver damage in facial eczema is caused by the toxin sporidesmin in the fungus spores.

Ringworm

Club lamb fungus is a highly contagious fungal infection of skin of sheep. It is primarily a problem with show lambs that are frequently closed sheared. Club lamb fungus is caused by *Trichophyton*. Infection occurs when the fungus invades the skin and hair (wool) follicles. Fungal spores are transmitted by contaminated clippers, blankets, combs, bedding, bunks, and pens. Lesions can appear anywhere, but most commonly on the head, neck, and back.

4. Metabolic and deficiency Diseases

Cobalt deficiency (vitamin B12 deficiency)

The only known animal requirement for cobalt is as a constituent of Vitamin B12, which has 4% cobalt in its chemical structure. This means that a cobalt deficiency is really a vitamin B12 deficiency. Microorganisms in the rumen are able to synthesize vitamin B12 needs of ruminants if the diet is adequate in cobalt. Ruminants must consume cobalt frequently in the diet for adequate B12 synthesis. Cobalt deficiency causes lack of appetite, lack of thrift, severe emaciation, weakness, anemia, decreased fertility, and decreased milk and wool production. Weeping eyes, leading to a matting of wool on the face, is another common symptom. Cobalt deficiency also impairs the immune function of sheep, which may increase their vulnerability to infection with worms.

Grass tetany

Grass tetany is a complex disease traditionally associated with magnesium deficiency. All ruminants are susceptible. Magnesium deficiency in sheep most commonly occurs in acute form within 4-6 weeks of lambing. Affected ewes exhibit sensitivity to touch and trembling of the facial muscles; some are unable to move, others move stiffly; extreme cases collapse and show repeated tetanic spasms with all four limbs rigidly extended. Low blood magnesium can be caused by low levels of magnesium in lush spring grass or by mineral imbalances such as high potassium and nitrogen or low calcium in the diet. Ewes with grass staggers are often low in calcium as well as magnesium. It is therefore wise to use a combined treatment of calcium borogluconate and magnesium hypophosphite.

Milk fever

Milk fever is a metabolic disease affecting mostly pregnant ewes near term when calcium requirements are highest. It is most commonly caused by an inadequate intake of calcium, but can also be due to ewe's inability to mobilize calcium reserves prior to or after lambing. Milk fever presents similar symptoms as pregnancy toxemia but can be differentiated by the affected ewe's response to calcium therapy. Milk fever can be prevented by providing proper levels of calcium in ewe diets, especially during late gestation.

Pregnancy toxemia

Pregnancy toxemia is a metabolic disease affecting ewes during late gestation. It most commonly afflicts thin ewes, overfat ewes, and/or older ewes carrying multiple fetuses. It is caused by an inadequate intake of energy during late pregnancy, when the majority of fetal growth occurs. Providing adequate energy to ewes during late gestation, usually ½ to 1 lb of grain per head per day more for high producing ewes can prevent pregnancy toxaemia. Adequate feeder space is necessary so that all ewes are able to consume enough feed.

Polioencephalomalacia (cerebrocortical necrosis)

Polioencephalomalacia is a disease of the central nervous system, caused by vitamin B1 (thiamine) deficiency. Since the rumen manufactures B vitamins, polio is not caused by insufficient thiamine, but rather the inability to utilize it. The most common symptom of polio is blindness and stargazing. Polio most commonly occurs in lambs that are consuming high concentrate diets.

Goiter

Goiter is an enlargement or swelling of the thyroid gland. Affected lambs have a swollen throat. They are often born with little or no wool. They are weak and often die of starvation. Goiter in newborn lambs is due to a deficiency of iodine in the pregnant ewe's diet. It can be prevented by providing iodized salt in the diet of gestating ewes. The salt mixture should contain 0.007 per cent of available iodine. The iodine deficiency may also result in reduced yield of wool and reduced conception rate in the flock.

Copper poisoning/toxicity

Sheep are ten times more susceptible to copper toxicity than cattle. When consumed over a long period of time, excess copper is stored in the liver. No damage occurs until a toxic level is reached at which time there is a hemolytic crisis with destruction of red blood cells. Copper is closely related to molybdenum, and copper toxicity occurs when the dietary ratio of copper to molybdenum increases about 6-10:1. Affected animals suddenly go off feed and become weak. Their mucous membranes and white skin will appear yellowish brown color and urine red-brown in color due to hemoglobin in the urine. Treatment of copper poisoning is based on inactivating the copper with molybdate and sulfate.

Effects of disease on inputs

The effects of disease on inputs revolve around the cost of treatment or prophylaxis. This includes drugs, chemicals and vaccines plus the cost of application and/or veterinary care. The cost will accumulate substantially in case treatments are repeated or performed regularly.

Effects of disease on output

1. The effects of disease on output may be direct or indirect. Direct losses include mortality and morbidity. Overall losses due to livestock mortality in sub-Saharan Africa have been estimated at US$ 2 billion. Losses due to morbidity as reflected by reduced growth, lactation, work output and reproduction (judged by lambing interval, lambing percentage, and delayed puberty etc) are probably of the same magnitude. This is best reflected by off take rates for meat, the main purpose for which small ruminants are raised, which remain low. Furthermore, mean carcass weight is only 10-12 kg per head with the result that regional annual mutton/lamb and goat meat production is low.
2. Many a times diseases alter the value of the animal by changing its conformation or rendering the products unfit for human consumption. Furthermore, substantial revenue is lost annually because of the failure of many potential producers to meet the sanitary requirements of lucrative export markets.
3. Among the more indirect effects of disease is the inability of farmers or producers to utilize favorable grazing lands or resources, adopt new

systems of animal management, introduce more productive genotypes or fully utilize specific animal products such as draft power because the presence of disease increases the fear for subsequent morbidity or mortality.

4. Diseases may also indirectly affect production through restrictions imposed on animal products as a result of treatment or vaccination, and the implementation of control regulations following the outbreak of certain diseases. The latter may range from the enforcement of animal movement to the actual slaughter of sick animals or even those in contact.

Combined effects of disease and reproductive wastage on production

The impact of disease and reproductive wastage on small ruminant (sheep and goat) production is best estimated by the annual reproductive rate (RR), which is defined as the number of lambs or kids weaned per ewe (or doe) of reproductive age per year. This estimate is influenced by litter size (S), lamb mortality (M) and lambing interval in years.

Litter size

Litter size in goats ranges from 1.0 to 1.5 indicating that twinning rate in goats ranges from 0 and 50%. But, mean litter size may be less than 1 indicating that the rate of pre- and perinatal losses in the form of stillbirths is greater than the twinning rate in the flock. There are some recognized prolific breeds in India, e.g. the Black Bengal and Garole breeds, which commonly deliver two or more young. Litter size is largely determined by ovulation rate but is also modified by fertilization rate and embryonic and foetal losses.

Young mortality and the role of the dam

Young mortality rates in sheep and goats from birth to weaning range from 5 to more than 50% and represent a serious reduction in biological efficiency. Major causes of mortality include starvation-mismothering-exposure, pneumonia, enteritis, accidents, navel infection and septicaemia . Because starvation and enteritis are two most important causes of neonatal mortality, it is necessary to ascertain if lambs/kids receive adequate colostrum and subsequent nutrition. Maternal behavior is therefore very critical to the newborn with regard to immuniyt and nutritional status. The ability of dams to recognize and bond with their young occurs during the initial sensitive period, a narrow window of time limited to the first few hours. Dam ability to recognize progeny increases with parity and is often impaired by overcrowding. Significance of maternal behavior in young survival varies with management strategy and environmental conditions. But, whatever the subtle signals may be, failure of the maternal-neonatal bond in the first few hours may result in poor maternal behaviour and failure to nurse adequately. Adequate nutrition not only improves conception rates at mating, it increases young birth weight and decreases perinatal mortality. Low nutrition in early pregnancy also results in 90-day foetuses with smaller linear body measurements. Placental size is a reasonably good index of placental function. Decreased placental size limits foetal growth. Placental weights vary widely due to endocrine factors, nutrition, heat stress, and such maternal factors as age and genotype. Although the number of cotyledons is also quite variable, foetal weight is more correlated to the functional cotyledon weight and the chorio-allantoic weight. Finally, newborn rectal temperature is an important factor for survival. Many a times, perinatal death results from the inability to maintain adequate body temperature outside the uterus.

Young adaptation to cold stress

During cold exposure many metabolic hormones like thyroid hormone, growth hormone, insulin, glucagon, gut hormones and adrenal hormones may be involved in altering intermediary metabolism. These may be influenced by somatostatin. In fact, growth potential of young lambs can be maintained during cold stress by active immunization against somatostatin. Somatostatin activity in lambs is suggested to be concentrated in the lower gut where it may be involved in nutrient absorption. These observations have important implications for neonatal mortality rates among sheep raised in the high altitude tropics and may provide useful tools for selecting for perinatal survival.

References

Addo, P.B. 1982. Caseous Iymphadenitis in goats in Nigeria: Prevalence, natural and experimental transmissions. In: Proceedings of the 3rd International Conference on Goat Production and Disease, Tucson, Arizona, USA, 10-15 January 1982. Dairy Goat Journal Publishing Co., Arizona, USA. p. 372 (abstract).

Adeoye, S.A.O. 1985. Disease profiles of sheep and goats in two groups of villages in southwest Nigeria: In: Sheep and Goats in Humid West Africa (J.E. Sumberg and K. Cassady eds), Proceedings of the Workshop on Small Ruminant Production Systems in the Humid Zone of West Africa, held in Ibadan, Nigeria, 23-26 January 1984. ILCA (International Livestock Centre for Africa), Addis Ababa, Ethiopia. pp. 13-16.

Alexander, D. 1984. Constraints to Lamb Survival. In: Reproduction in Sheep (D.R. Lindsay and D.T. Pearce eds), Cambridge University Press, Cambridge, UK. pp. 199-209.

Barlow, R.M., Gardiner, A.C., Angus, K.W., Gilmour, J.S., Mellor, D.J., Cuthbertson, J.C., Newlands, G. and Thompson, R. 1987. Clinical, Biochemical and Pathological Study of Perinatal Lambs in a Commercial Flock. Veterinary Record 120:357-362.

Bell, A.W. 1984. Factors Controlling Placental and Fetal Growth and their Effects on Future Production. In: Lindsay D. R and Pearce D. T. (eds) Reproduction in Sheep (J.E. Sumberg and K. Cassady eds), Cambridge University Press, Cambridge, UK. pp. 144-152.

Chaarani, B., Robinson, R.A. and Johnson, D.W. 1991. Lamb mortality in Meknes Province (Morocco). Preventive Veterinary Medicine 10:283-298.

FAO (Food and Agriculture Organization of the United Nations). 1986. *African Agriculture: The Next 25 Years*. Main Report. FAO, Rome, Italy. p 67.

de Haan, C. and Bekure, S. 1991. Animal Health Services in sub-Saharan Africa: Initial Experiences with Alternative Approaches. World Bank Technical Paper 134. World Bank, Washington, DC, USA. p. 49 .

Hinch, G.N., Kelly, R.W., Davis, G.H., Owens, J.L. and Crosbie, S.F. 1985. Factors affecting lamb birth weight from high fecundity Boroola ewes. Animal Reproduction Science 8:53-60.

Holst, P.J., Killeen, I.D. and Cullis, B.R. 1986. Nutrition of the pregnant ewe and its effect on gestation length, lamb birth weight and lamb survival. Australian Journal of Agricultural Research 37:647-655.

ILCA (International Livestock Centre for Africa). 1987. ILCA's Strategy and Long-term Plan. Addis Ababa, Ethiopia. p. 99 .

Jordan, D.J. and Le Fevre, A.S. 1989. The extent and cause of perinatal lamb mortality in three flocks of Merino sheep. Australian Veterinary Journal 66:198-201.

Krostitz, W. 1991. Medium term outlook for dairying in the developing countries. In: Feeding Dairy Cows in the Tropics (A. Speedy and R. Sansoucy eds), FAO Animal Production and Health Paper 86. FAO (Food and Agriculture Organization of the United Nations), Rome, Italy. pp. 1-8.

Leng, R.A. 1990. Factors affecting the utilization of poor quality forages by ruminants particularly under tropical conditions. Nutrition Research Reviews 3:277-303.

Mukasa E., Said A.N., Lahlou-Kassi A., Sherington J. and Mutiga E.R. 1994. Birth weight as a risk factor for perinatal mortality, and the effects of stage of pregnant ewe supplementation and gestation weight gain in Ethiopian Menz sheep. Preventive Veterinary Medicine 19:45-56.

Ndamukong, K. 1985. Effects of management system on mortality of small ruminants in Bamenda, Cameroon. In: Small Ruminants in African Agriculture (R.T. Wilson and D. Bourzat eds), Proceedings of a Conference held at ILCA, Addis Ababa, Ethiopia, 30 September 4 October 1985. ILCA (International Livestock Centre for Africa), Addis Ababa, Ethiopia. pp. 108-116.

Njau B.C., Kasali O.B., Scholtens R.G. and Mesfin Degefa. 1988. Review of sheep mortality in the Ethiopian highlands, 1982-86. International Livestock Centre for Africa (ILCA) Bulletin (Addis Ababa, Ethiopia) 31:19-22.

Opasina, B.A. 1987. Haemoparasites of village goats in south west Nigeria. Bulletin of Animal Health and Production in Africa 35:130-133.

Parr, R.A., Williams, A.H., Campbell, I.P., Witcombe, G.F. and Roberts, A.M. 1986. Low nutrition of ewes in early pregnancy and the residual effect on the offspring. Journal of Agricultural Science (Cambridge) 106:81-87.

Peeters, R., Buys, N., Kuhn, E.R., Decuypere, E., Siau, O. and van Isterdael, J. 1991. Endocrine changes during the first four hours of extra-uterine life of lambs as related to body weight and rectal temperatures. Small Ruminant Research 5:347-355.

Sadiq, N.A. 1985. Studies on anaplasmosis of small ruminants. In: Small Ruminant Production in Nigeria. Proceedings of the National Conference on Small Ruminant Production, held at NAPRI, Zaria, Nigeria, 6-10 October 1985. National Animal Production Research Institute, Shika-Zaria, Nigeria. p. 271 (abstract).

Smith, O.B. and van Houtert, M.F.J. 1988. Health aspects of intensive management of West African Dwarf goats in the humid forest zone. Bulletin of Animal Health and Production in Africa 36:342-347.

Smith, O.B., Ayeni, A.O., Onawumi, A.O. and Ademosun, A.A. 1986. Helminths and protozoan parasites of dwarf goats in southwestern Nigeria. Bulletin of Animal Health and Production in Africa 34:67-70.

Wilson, R.T., Peacock, C.P. and Sayers, A.R. 1985. Preweaning mortality and productivity indices for goats and sheep on a Masai group ranch in South-Central Kenya. Animal Production 941:201-206

Winrock. 1992. Assessment of Animal Agriculture in sub-Sahahan Africa. Winrock International, Morrilton, Arkansas, USA. p.125.

Yapi, C.V., Boylan, W.J. and Robinson, R.A. 1990. Factors associated with causes of preweaning lamb mortality. Preventive Veterinary Medicine 10: 145-152.

❑❑❑

31

Changing Disease Patterns in Small Ruminants *vis-à-vis* Climate Change

R. K. Singh*, Sanjay Kumar, Sanjay Barua and Rajender Kumar
National Research Centre on Equines, Sirsa Road, Hisar-125 001

Introduction

The World Animal Health Organization (OIE) has reiterated that climate change is widening viral disease among farm animals, expanding the spread of some microbes that are also a known risk to humans. A survey by OIE found 71 per cent of 126 member-states were "extremely concerned" about the expected impact of climate change on animal disease. Among those surveyed, 58 per cent said they had already identified at least one disease that was new to their territory or had returned to their territory, and that they associated with climate change. Bluetongue, which is spread among sheep by biting midges; Rift Valley fever, a livestock disease that can also be picked up by people handling infected meat; and West Nile virus, which is transmitted by mosquito from infected bird to both animals and humans were the three most mentioned diseases. OIE Director General Bernard Vallat said in a statement that more and more countries were indicating that climate change has been responsible for at least one emerging or re-emerging disease occurring on their territory. The statement said "this is a reality we cannot ignore and must help veterinary services throughout the world to equip themselves with systems that comply with international standards of good governance so as to deal with this problem". The Inter-government Panel on Climate Change (IPCC), the UN's Nobel-winning experts, issued a landmark report in 2007 that warned changing weather patterns could widen the habitat of disease-bearing insects. The IPCC said this would have repercussion for human health, in such areas as malaria and dengue fever. The agency is based in Paris and has 174 member countries and territories; it is a clearinghouse of scientific information on livestock and sets down guidelines for sanitary safety and welfare in farm animals.

I. Preamble

Climate encompasses the statistics of temperature, humidity, atmospheric pressure, wind, rainfall, atmospheric particle count and numerous other meteorological elements in a given region over long periods of time. Climate can be contrasted to weather, which is the present condition of these same elements over periods up to two weeks. The climate of a location is affected by its latitude, terrain, altitude, ice or snow cover, as well as nearby water bodies and their currents. Climate change is a change in the statistical distribution of weather over periods of time that range from decades to millions of years. It can be a change in the average weather or a change in the distribution of weather events around an average (for example, greater or fewer extreme weather events). Climate change may be limited to a specific region, or may occur across the whole Earth. **Global warming** is the increase in the average temperature of the Earth's near-surface air and oceans since the mid-20th century and its projected continuation. Global surface temperature increased by 0.74 ± 0.18°C (1.33±0.32°F) between the start and the end of the 20th century.

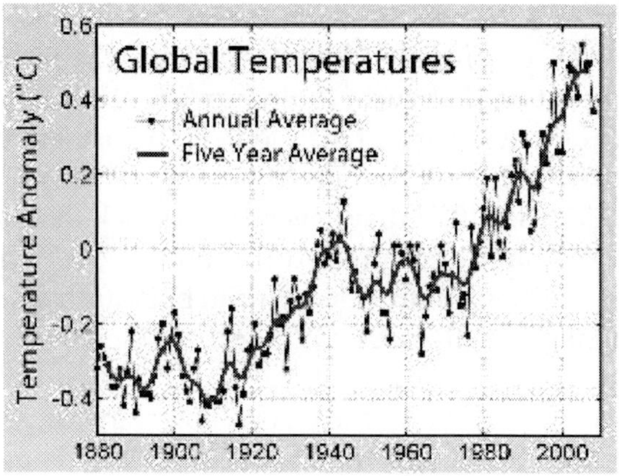

Source: http://en.wikipedia.org/wiki/Global_warming

The most commonly discussed measure of global warming is the trend in globally averaged temperature near the Earth's surface. Expressed as a linear trend, this temperature rose by 0.74°C±0.18°C over the period 1906–2005. The rate of warming over the last half of that period was almost the double that for the period as a whole (0.13°C±0.03°C per decade, versus 0.07°C±0.02°C per decade). The urban heat island effect is estimated to account for about 0.002°C of warming per decade since 1900. Temperatures in the lower troposphere have increased between 0.12 and 0.22 °C (0.22 and 0.4 °F) per decade since 1979, according to satellite temperature measurements. Temperature is believed to have been relatively stable over the one or two thousand years before 1850, with regionally-varying fluctuations such as the Medieval Warm Period or the Little Ice Age.

Human activity since the industrial revolution has increased the amount of greenhouse gases in the atmosphere, leading to increased radiation forcing from CO_2, methane, tropospheric ozone, CFCs and nitrous oxide. The concentrations of CO_2 and methane have increased by 36% and 148%, respectively, since the mid-1700s. These levels are much higher than at any time during the last 650,000 years, the period for which reliable data has been extracted from ice cores. Less direct geological evidence indicates that this high CO_2 values were last seen about 20 million years ago. Fossil fuel burning has produced about three-quarters of the increase in CO_2 from human activity over the past 20 years. Most of the remaining increase is due to land-use change, particularly deforestation. CO_2 concentration continues to rise due to burning of fossil fuels and land-use change. The future rate of rise will depend on uncertain economic, sociological, technological, and natural developments. Accordingly, the IPCC Special Report on Emissions Scenarios gives a wide range of future CO_2 scenarios, ranging from 541 to 970 ppm by the year 2100. Fossil fuel reserves are sufficient to reach these levels and continue emissions past 2100, if these are extensively exploited.

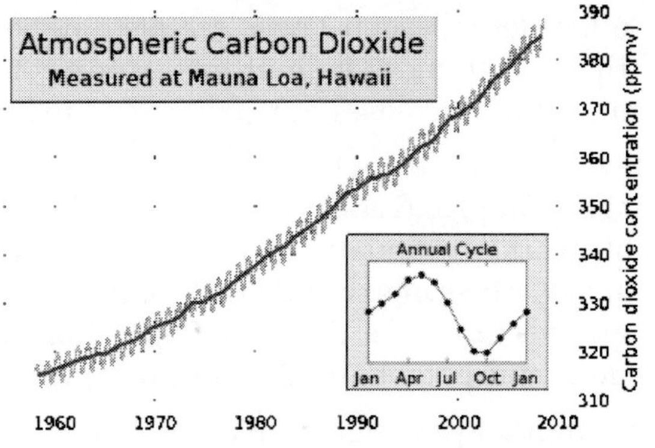

Source: http://en.wikipedia.org/wiki/Global_warming

Ten facts on climate change and human health

Some of the facts established based on the long-term studies about climate change and their effect on human health are described below. As many of the animal diseases are also zoonotic in nature and affect human health, hence the climatic variability is very likely to exert similar effects on these pathogens and, therefore, similar kind of trend in animal diseases as well.

1. Over the last 50 years, human activities - particularly the burning of fossil fuels - have released sufficient quantities of carbon dioxide and other greenhouse gases to affect the global climate. The atmospheric concentration of carbon dioxide has increased by more than 30% since pre-industrial times, trapping more heat in the lower atmosphere. The resulting changes in the global climate bring a range of risks to health, from deaths in extreme high temperatures to changing patterns of infectious diseases.
2. From the tropics to the arctic, climate and weather have powerful direct and indirect impacts on human life. Weather extremes - such as heavy rains, floods, and disasters like hurricane Katrina that devastated New Orleans, USA in August 2005 - endanger health as well as destroy property and livelihoods. Approximately 600,000 deaths occurred worldwide as a result of weather-related natural disasters in the 1990s, and 95% of which took place in the developing countries.
3. Intense short-term fluctuations in temperature can also seriously affect health - causing heat stress (hyperthermia) or extreme cold (hypothermia) - and lead to increased death rates from heart and respiratory diseases. Recent studies suggest that the record high temperatures in Western Europe in the summer of 2003 were associated with a spike of an estimated 70,000 more deaths than the equivalent periods in previous years.
4. Pollen and other aeroallergen levels are also higher in extreme heat. These can trigger asthma, which affects around 300 million people. Ongoing temperature increases are expected to increase this burden.
5. Rising sea levels - another outcome of global warming - increase the risk of coastal flooding, and could cause population displacement. More than half of the world's population now lives within 60 km of shorelines. Floods can directly cause injury and death, and increase risks of infection from water and vector-borne diseases. Population displacement could increase tensions and potentially the risks of conflict.
6. More variable rainfall patterns are likely to compromise the supply of fresh water. Globally, water scarcity already affects four out of every 10

people. A lack of water and poor water quality can compromise hygiene and health. This increases the risk of diarrhoea, which kills approximately 2.2 million people every year, as well as trachoma (an eye infection that can lead to blindness) and other illnesses.

7. Water scarcity encourages people to transport water from long distances and store supplies in their homes. This can increase the risk of household water contamination, causing illnesses.
8. Climatic conditions affect diseases transmitted through water, and via vectors such as mosquitoes. Climate-sensitive diseases are among the largest global killers. Diarrhoea, malaria and protein-energy malnutrition alone caused more than 3 million deaths globally in 2004, with over one third of these deaths occurring in Africa.
9. Malnutrition causes millions of deaths each year, from both a lack of sufficient nutrients to sustain life and a resulting vulnerability to infectious diseases such as malaria, diarrhoea, and respiratory illnesses. Increasing temperatures on the planet and more variable rainfalls are expected to reduce crop yields in many tropical developing regions, where food security is already a problem.
10. Steps to reduce greenhouse gas emissions or lessen the health impacts of climate change could have positive health effects. For example, promoting the safe use of public transportation and active movement - such as biking or walking as alternatives to using private vehicles - could reduce carbon dioxide emissions and improve public health. They cannot only cut traffic injuries, but also air pollution and associated respiratory and cardiovascular diseases. Increased levels of physical activity can lower overall mortality rates.

I. Effect of climate change on infectious disease

Climate change is only one of several 'global change' factors driving the emergence and spread of diseases in livestock and the transfer of pathogens from animals to humans, ecosystem diversity, function and resilience. Other factors include changes in the structure of the livestock industry, in breeding and husbandry practices and in international trade in livestock and animal products. These factors are not independent from each other and climate change interacts with each of them.

Climate change will be especially important to vector-borne diseases and macro-parasites of animals and may also result in new transmission modalities and changes in host species. Changes in species composition and interactions will augment the emergence of unexpected events, including the emergence of new diseases and pests. While most developing countries are already subject to an enormous disease burden, both developing and developed countries will be subject to newly emerging diseases. Bluetongue and Rift Valley fever, as well as tick-borne diseases, will be strongly influenced by climate change. Climate may also have a direct or indirect influence on the onset of complex bacterial syndromes, such as bovine mastitis, which usually require antibiotic treatment leading to residues in foods. Concerns associated with aquaculture in a warming environment include a greater susceptibility to disease, introduction of pathogens and antibiotic-resistant pathogens, heavy use of antibiotics and environmental contamination with pesticides. While much of the discussion on climate change and infectious diseases is applicable to zoonotic disease, the additional impacts of climate, which are specific to zoonotic diseases include (i) increase in the susceptibility of animals to disease, (ii) increase in the range or abundance of vectors/animal reservoirs, and (iii) prolonging the transmission cycles of vectors.

(i) Increase in the susceptibility of animals to disease

Climate may have a direct or indirect influence on the susceptibility of animals to disease. For example, exposure to intense cold, droughts, excessive humidity or heat may predispose cattle to complex bacterial syndromes such as mastitis. Milk from cows with severe clinical mastitis would normally not enter the food chain as the abnormality is easily detected and the milk would be discarded by the producer. But when milk of cows with sub-clinical *mastitis*, *i.e.* with no visible changes, is accidentally mixed into bulk milk, it enters food chain and can be dangerous to humans. Although pasteurization is likely to destroy all human pathogens, there is concern when raw milk is consumed or when pasteurization is incomplete or faulty (Hameed et al., 2006).

(ii) Increase in the range or abundance of vectors/animal reservoirs

Because of the sensitivities of vectors to climatic factors, ecological changes such as variations in rainfall and temperature could significantly alter the range, seasonality and incidence of many zoonotic diseases (CDC, 2008). Examples of sensitivities of vectors to climatic change include:

- Increased night time temperatures will result not only in enhanced vector flight activity (Purse et al., 2005) but also greater competence in supporting replication and transmission of viral pathogens (Baylis and Githeko, 2006).
- Cycles of drought followed by heavy rainfall provide breeding sites for midge and mosquito vectors and are associated with outbreaks of vector-borne livestock diseases (Baylis and Githeko, 2006).

- Changes in precipitation may also affect the range and distribution of arthropod vectors, and there is evidence of ticks expanding their range with decreasing rainfall (Trape et al., 1996). Conversely, increased precipitation increases the abundance of snail hosts for livestock parasites.

Vector-borne pathogens which respond most rapidly to climatic changes are likely to be rapidly evolving promiscuous agents, transmitted by rapidly reproducing, highly mobile and habitat-generalist vectors.

(iii) Prolonged transmission cycles of vectors

Climatic factors can also influence the length of the vector transmission cycle and thus the incidence of human infection. West Nile virus is an example of a vector-borne zoonosis, whose transmission cycle is prolonged by the early onset of spring. Human infections from West Nile virus become more likely as the population of mosquitoes (that bite both birds and humans) increases. In temperate regions, mosquito activity begins in spring and declines in autumn. Thus, an earlier spring would prolong the cycle resulting in an increased incidence of human infection (Greer et al., 2008).

III. Technology use in predicting climate change effects on infectious diseases

(i) Remote sensing: With the help of 14 satellites currently in orbit and the National Aeronautics and Space Administration's (NASA) Applied Sciences Program, scientists have been able to observe the Earth's environment to help predict and prevent infectious disease outbreaks around the world. The use of remote sensing technology aids specialists in predicting the outbreak of some of the most common and deadly infectious diseases today such as Ebola, West Nile virus and Rift Valley fever. The ability of the infectious diseases to thrive depends on changes in the Earth's environment such as the climate, precipitation and vegetation of an area. Through orbiting satellites, data are collected daily to monitor environmental changes. That information is then passed on to agencies such as the Centers for Disease Control and Prevention and the Department of Defense who then apply the data to predict and track disease outbreaks and assist in making public health policy decisions. The use of this technology is essential for the future of curbing the spread of infectious diseases. Further, NASA satellites are also a cost-effective method for operational agencies since they are already in orbit and in use by scientists to collect data about the Earth's atmosphere.

(ii) Predictive models: When available, inferences can be made based on existing data, such as studying disease trends in presence and absence of El

Nino events (Greer et al., 2008). Another approach is the application of mathematical modeling. Finally, molecular-based population genetics studies may provide information on microbial population changes occurring in response to environmental stresses. Some have advocated that the effects of climate variability driven by natural cycles such as the El Nino-southern oscillation (ENSO) can be used to predict, at least in part, the impact of global climate change (Lipp et al., 2002). There is evidence for a correlation between El Nino events and cholera outbreaks, particularly in South America. Climatic changes usually occur on a sub-regional basis rather than continental.

Another emerging field is that of molecular ecology, where scientists use advanced molecular biological methods, specifically nucleic acid sequence comparisons and genomics-based approaches, to characterize complex microbial communities. This field is expanding rapidly and these sorts of studies can provide information about the overall composition of microbial communities; the relationship between pathogens, commensals, and other organisms in the environment; and the effect of environmental changes on these relationships. Furthermore, these methods are applicable to the study of microbial evolution, and virulence factor acquisition and expression as a function of changes in environmental exposures. When combined with geo-informatics (the combination of remote sensing, geographic information systems, and statistical modeling for the characterization of spatial distributions and relationships), it should also be possible to model the distribution and spread of pathogens as a function of climate change.

(iii) Disease surveillance : The need for improved epidemiological surveillance for early identification of emerging infectious diseases is undisputed. Many initiatives have been implemented over the last decade in the developed world. While these have not answered all our questions, they have provided much needed preliminary data about the trends of emerging diseases along with their annual incidence. Ideally, a global approach to epidemiological surveillance should be taken, since the agents (or for that matter, humans) do not respect artificial boundaries. Of particular importance is the rapid investigation of unusual outbreaks, with inclusion of environmental investigation to ascertain if climate change is a factor. In addition, public health systems must be able to mobilize and respond quickly to emerging and re-emerging infectious diseases of infectious origin.

(iv) Pathogen monitoring and surveillance: Ideally, epidemiological surveillance should be supplemented with the direct detection of pathogens in foods and/or the environment. While pathogen detection methods are widely used in the clinical realm, their use in food and environmental applications is complicated. In virtually all instances, pathogen detection

methods involve many steps resulting in a lengthy assay. Most rapid method developments have sought to shorten detection time by introducing methods based on DNA hybridization or enzyme immunoassay. However, since these methods are still relatively insensitive, lengthy cultural enrichment steps remain necessary. Even the highly sensitive and specific polymerase chain reaction (PCR) is hampered by volumetric constraints, matrix-associated inhibition, and the inability to distinguish between viable and non-viable (inactivated) pathogens. There is a clear need to focus research efforts in the development of sensitive and specific methods to detect pathogens in complex sample matrices such as foods. An ideal method would be rapid (results in a few hours), easy, inexpensive, field deployable, and provide enumerative results. We are many years away from this but progress is necessary, particularly for use in the developing world where rapid detection could make a substantial difference in disease containment.

(iv) Good agricultural, animal husbandry, aquaculture and veterinary practices: These practices ensure the safety and quality of agricultural, aquaculture and animal products. They may need to be adapted or revised in light of changing climatic conditions. In relation to good veterinary practices, the appropriate use of veterinary drugs and chemicals in terms of safety, quality, amounts, frequency and timing and withdrawal times, are particularly important in a changing environment. The agriculture and sector offers multiple opportunities for climate change mitigation and environmental protection through the implementation of good animal husbandry and agriculture practices [Green house gases emissions can be reduced through improved diets reducing enteric fermentation, improved manure management and biogas. Water pollution and land degradation can be tackled through better irrigation systems, fertilization schemes, better management of waste, improved animal diets that increase nutrient absorption (LEAD, 2007)].

IV. Infectious diseases of goat and sheep which are likely to be affected by climate change

Sheep and goats are affected by many infectious (bacterial, viral, rickettsial, mycoplasmal) and non-infectious (metabolic) diseases. Many infectious diseases requiring vector for transmission of the pathogen are the diseases which are being affected in their geographic distribution in space and time as well as intensity. Climatic factors are also changing the biodiversity as animal species might shift to new locations in search feed and fodder and, thereby, may be a source of new diseases to other species which have been existing there over a period of time. The section below describes some of the important diseases of small ruminants which are most likely to be affected by climate change.

A. Bacterial and rickettsial diseases affected by climate change

(i) Pasteurellosis

The disease is caused by *Pasteurella haemolytica* or *Pasteurella multocida. P. multocida* causes septicemia in goats and sheep. Disease usually precipitates due to stress (transport - shipping fever, sudden change in climate, overcrowding, feeding stress - feed lot kids, any concurrent chronic infection etc). *Pasteurella hemolytica* is a commensal of nasopharynx and is mainly confined to cattle, sheep and goat. Infection spreads through aerosol route. There is rise in body temperature up to 105-106°F, continuous coughing, sneezing, salivation, lacrymation, nasal discharge, congested mucous membrane, shallow and rapid respiration, localized edema at head, neck and/ or brisket region followed by death.

(ii) Paratuberculosis (Johnes's disease)

The disease is caused by *Mycobacterium avuim* subsp. *paratuberculosis.* It is one of the most important chronic wasting diseases of sheep and goats. Susceptible animals pick up infection through contaminated milk, food and water. Continuous excretions of bacilli in the feces of infected goats contaminate water, feed and fodder, soil, pasture, grazing land and premises. Disease spreads rapidly in farms, where animals are overcrowded and sanitation is poor. The incubation period is variable and may be very prolonged one depending on health status and different factors/stresses (nutritional stress, lactation stress, repeated pregnancies, concurrent parasitic infections, environmental stresses, hygienic conditions and management). Singh and Singh (2000) have reported effect of climate change on Johne's diseases. There are no specific symptoms and affected animals show continuous deterioration in body condition due to fall in body weight even though animals retains normal appetite. Other symptoms include; mild but constant coughing, weakness, hide bound condition, staggering gait, rough coat, intermittent or continuous diarrhea followed by death. The disease is protein loosing entropy and damages the cellular immune system. The affected animals become susceptible to other infections. Disease once enters a herd is difficult to remove and adversely affect the productivity of the animals.

(iii) Listeriosis/circling disease

The disease is caused by *Listeria monocytogenes,* which occurs mainly in temperate climate. Meningeoencephalitis is the most common form in ruminants. Toxaemia leading to meningitis (in young ruminants), abortions and stillbirth, etc. are generally reported. Animals get infection through oral route. The organism causes abortion in pregnant females and encephalitis and toxaemia in general, in all the age group of sheep and goats.

(iv) Spore-forming pathogens (Anthrax & clostridial infections)

The etiological agent of anthrax is *Bacillus anthracis* which is a large gram-positive spore forming bacteria. The spores are highly resistant and often remain viable for longer period in contaminated soil or in animal by-products. The goats are comparatively less susceptible than sheep and cattle. The animals get infection through contaminated feed and water. Like anthrax, clostridial diseases are also due to spore forming bacteria and climatic factors affecting any spore-forming pathogen will also affect clostridial disease epidemiology. Spores are formed when the vegetative bacteria are exposed to atmospheric oxygen, suitable temperature (20-40°C) and relative humidity (> 60 %). Spores may remain viable in the soil or water holes for many years. They may be dispersed by wind, predators, fertilisers or effluent from factories processing contaminated animal products.

Infectious necrotic hepatitis, an acute septicaemic disease of animals especially sheep - is caused by pathogenic strains of *Clostridium norvyi* type B, but the occurrence of a clinical disease is associated with necrosis of the liver tissue which makes the environment favourable for the proliferation of the bacterium and production of a lethal alpha toxin. *Clostridium norvi* 'B' is present in the intestinal tract of normal animals which act as carriers. The occurrence of the disease is related to the distribution of liver flukes (*Fasciola* spp). A seasonal incidence of occurrence of the disease, which is related to the seasonal incidence of *Fasciola* spp and their snail hosts, has been demonstrated. In communal grazing system, overstocking and the congregation of animals in watering points during the dry season can result in outbreaks of fasciolosis and infectious necrotic hepatitis. Irrigation creates favorable habitats for snail hosts of liver flukes and may be associated with high incidences of both fasciolosis and infectious necrotic hepatitis.

(v) Foot abscess and foot-rot

Foot abscess is a disease quite common in Africa, and is usually the result of infection caused by ticks with long mouthparts (especially *Hyalomma* spp. but also *Amblyomma* spp. and *Rhipicephalus glabroscutatum*), but also the sequel of wounds caused by thorns, or the effects of prolonged moisture. As *A. pyogenes* is the most common pathogen, the *A. pyogenes* vaccine is of some value. It is recommended to rather concentrate on tick control, if this is the primary cause (Bath and De Wet, 2000).

Foot-rot in goats and sheep is caused by a large gram-negative rod-shaped bacterium, *Bacteroides nodosus* which is commonly associated with *Treponema penortha. Fusobacterium necrophorum* and other aerobic or anaerobic bacteria may be isolated together with *B. nodosus* from the foot rot lesions. Three serotypes A, B and C of *B. nodosus* exist. Serotypes A and B cross-react while serotype C is antigenically distinct. Wet and warm weather conditions favour the proliferation of the bacteria and soften the animal's skin, thus making it easily breakable and penetrable. Dry and hot conditions are unfavourable for proliferation of *B. nodosus* and transmission of foot-rot and hence, the incidence of foot-rot tend to rise during the rainy season and drop during the dry season. In Tanzania, foot-rot is an important disease in areas of high rainfall and relative humidity and in intensively managed herds. The intermingling and congregation of animals in communal grazing areas, poor floor types and poor disposal of urine and faeces favour the spread of the disease. Carrier animals may harbour the organism for 2-3 years.

(vi) Heartwater

Cowdriosis or heartwater - caused by the rickettsia *Ehrlichia ruminantium* - is a tick-borne disease of sheep, goats, cattle and some wild ruminants. Three-host ticks from the *Amblyomma* genus (bont ticks) act as vectors that can acquire the infection from any of the hosts infected with *E. ruminantium* and probably retain their infectivity for life (Neitz, 1968; Ilemobade, 1976). These ticks occur in frost-free, relatively dry bushed, that is particularly suited to goats, and heartwater may be a major factor affecting profitable goat farming. Sheep and goats are more susceptible to heartwater than cattle and there is a considerable variation between breeds (Uilenberg, 1983; Donkin et al., 1992). Angora goats are highly susceptible to heartwater and their immunity is of short duration (Du Plessis et al., 1983). Genetic resistance, which is due to a recessive sex-linked gene, has been demonstrated in Creole goats in Guadeloupe (Matheron et al., 1987). Wild ruminants, guinea fowl, tortoises and scrub hares are reservoirs of *E. ruminantium* and hence of epidemiological importance where stringent tick control in domestic animals is practised (Oberem and Bezuidenhout, 1987). Factors which are important in the epidemiology of heartwater include immunological strain differences of *E. ruminantium* with variable cross-protection between them (Jongejan et al., 1988; Du Plessis et al., 1989), the presence of wild reservoir hosts and vectors, infection rates in ticks, age and genetic resistance of domestic ruminant populations, seasonal fluctuations in tick abundance and activity, and the intensity of tick control (Uilenberg, 1983). Other factors, especially species, breed, age, degree of natural resistance and immune status play a role in determining whether an animal will develop heartwater or not (Bath et al., 2005). Climate variability will have definite impact on tick vector population.

B. Viral diseases affected by climate change

(i) Bluetongue

In 1943, bluetongue disease was reported in Cyprus, and outbreaks were subsequently reported in Israel, the USA, Portugal, Spain, Pakistan and India. Over the past 30 years evidence of regular virus activity, but not necessarily the disease, has been found in most countries in the tropics and subtropics with substantial populations of ruminants. The virus may be found in a geographic band between latitudes 40°N and 35°S. The presence of bluetongue virus within this band, whether year round or seasonal, depends on the climatic zone type. Genetic studies indicate that the virus exists in discrete, stable ecosystems, probably the result of co-evolution of different strains of the virus and vectors. Numerous countries in the tropics and subtropics have bluetongue virus unknowingly circulating subclinically in cattle and other ruminants. A properly designed serological survey would reveal the presence of the virus. The virus is endemic in areas of some countries, being more or less continuously active. Depending on climatic factors affecting the vector, in most years the virus will seasonally extend to adjacent areas. In exceptionally favourable years, the virus will spread even further, such as to Portugal and Spain in 1956, to British Columbia in 1988, to Bulgaria, continental Greece and Tunisia in 1999 and to Algeria, Sardinia, Corsica, Majorca, Minorca, Sicily and continental Italy in 2000.

Bluetongue virus is an arbovirus that has evolved a life cycle, where alternate cycles of virus replication in vertebrate and invertebrate hosts are essential for virus persistence. Bluetongue is a common, generally subclinical infection of ruminants throughout the tropics and subtropics, within a number of separate ecosystems. Seasonal incursions of the virus into more temperate latitudes, sometimes accompanied by disease, may occur under favorable climatic conditions at certain key locations. There is evidence that infected midges are carried on the wind for long distances. It has been postulated that the major epidemics of bluetongue, in regions where disease occurs only sporadically, can often be traced to wind-borne carriage of infected *Culicoides* from distant areas.

Critical in the understanding of the epidemiology of bluetongue is knowledge of the virus competence of the *Culicoides* species in different ecosystems. Not only may different populations of a species of midge have varying susceptibilities to a strain of virus, but a single strain of the vector may have differing susceptibility to different virus serotypes. Competent midges may be infected when biting viraemic vertebrates. The chance of infection depends in part on the genotype of the midge, the strain of virus, the level of viraemia, and environmental factors. The extrinsic incubation period (the period between feeding on infected blood and the appearance of virus in the saliva of the midge) is 1-2 weeks. Five serotypes of BTV have been isolated in the United States. However, only BTV serotypes 10, 11, 13, and 17 are currently active. The host range of BTV is very broad and includes all ruminant species tested to date. However, the expression of clinical disease varies in different species. Sheep are fully susceptible to BTV. The geographic distribution of the orbiviruses is extensive, but current knowledge is still incomplete. Virus distribution is based on the presence of certain *Culicoides* species, including *C. variipennis, C. imicola, C. brevitaris,* and others. Areas with year-round vector activity could easily maintain the virus by a continuous vector-host cycle. Virus persistence in areas with severe winters is not understood. Re-introduction of virus into the area in the warm months by transportation of infected animals or infected *Culicoides* being carried on the wind is probably common. Some research reports suggest that over-wintering of the virus in these areas occurs by mechanisms such as (1) prolonged viremia (up to 3 months) in certain animals, (2) transplacental transmission of BTV in the late fall and early winter to the late-term developing fetus with subsequent birth of a viremic calf, and (3) over-wintering of the virus in *Culicoides* that may survive through the winter at very low population densities.

Recent spread of bluetongue: In August 2006, Dutch authorities reported the first ever case of bluetongue in Northern Europe. From work performed at the Institute for Animal Health, Pirbright, by the Arbovirus Research Group and the Community Reference Laboratory for bluetongue virus (BTV), the outbreak virus was rapidly identified as serotype 8. It subsequently spread to over 2,000 herds, mostly in the Netherlands, Belgium and Germany with a handful of cases in France and Luxembourg before transmission ceased in the winter. The route by which the virus was introduced into northern Europe remains unknown. On the 13th of June, a sentinel animal on a holding in North Rhein-Westphalia was announced to have displayed evidence of infection with bluetongue virus (BTV) serotype 8 during April. This was the first indication that the virus strain responsible for the outbreak in northern Europe last year had successfully over-wintered in the region. The virus subsequently resurfaced in all countries affected in 2006, with new cases occurring for the first time in Denmark and Switzerland, and the Czech Republic (first case 26th November 2007), as well as the UK.

Arrival of bluetongue in 2007-2008 in the UK: On 21st September 2007, a veterinarian spotted suspicious clinical signs in a cow on a holding near Iipswich. Samples taken from the animal were tested at IAH within 24 hours and were found to be positive for BTV-8. Testing of other animals on the site began immediately, and on 24th September, a second cow at the same holding was found to be positive, as reported by DEFRA. DEFRA announced on the 28th September 2007 of that it believed BTV to be circulating locally within East Anglia. On 22 January, post-import testing indicated that a number of dairy cattle imported from the Netherlands into Northern Ireland had become PCR-positive since importation. Although these events, in brief, suggest that the strain of BTV-8 currently active in northern Europe may be able to cross the placenta and infect the foetus (as well as the possibility of oral infection). This may help to explain its ability to survive the relatively cold winters in northern Europe. This year, BTV-8 has re-emerged across much of its previous range, and has continued to spread rapidly in some areas – particularly France, which had over 15,000 new cases by 1st October. Belgium, France, Germany, Luxembourg, the Netherlands and Switzerland have declared to OIE that they now consider BTV-8 to be endemic within their countries. The presence of BTV-8 has also been confirmed for the first time in Sweden (in September; 2007) Hungary (in September 2007), and Italy (2008).

Climate change and emergence of bluetongue

- 1998, Greek islands close to Turkey.
- 1998 and 2005 -1.5 million sheep deaths in Europe
- Novel vectors- *Culicoides obsoletus* group/ *Culicoides pulicaris* group

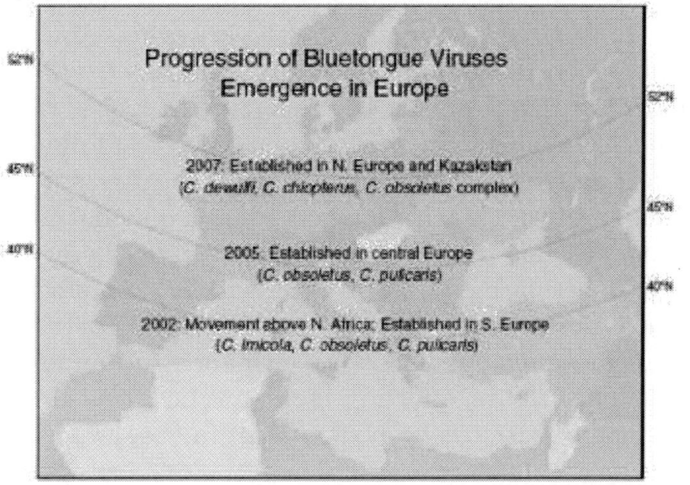

- Vector spread to warmer areas- Turkey, Greece, Bulgaria, several Balkan countries, mainland Italy, Sicily and Sardinia.
- Not spread to cooled areas-north-eastern Spain, Iberia southern continental France and northern Italy.
- Temperature is important determinant of distribution.

(ii) Rift Valley fever (RVF)

This virus has been isolated from many potential vector species inhabiting a range of habitat types. Epidemics in south and east Africa follow periods of high rainfall that create breeding sites for flood-water vectors (*Aedes* mosquitoes), whereas those in north and west Africa, have followed construction work that created breeding sites for large river and dam breeding vectors. In 2000, strains of RVF virus (that probably originated in east Africa) escaped from Africa for the first time and infected the Arabian Peninsula, an area well connected to Europe by a 'ruminant street'. The timing and mode of pathogen responses will obviously depend on the species-specific climatic drivers (Purse et al., 2005).

Rift Valley fever is a mosquito-borne animal and human viral disease in which the vectors are influenced by climate. Rift Valley fever virus (RVFV), is highly promiscuous between vertebrate hosts, ranging from rodents to hippopotamuses, but causes clinical signs only in ruminants and humans. The disease was first described in 1930 in the Rift Valley of Kenya. One of the plagues of Egypt reported in the Bible suggested that it might have been due to RVF. The first outbreak was identified in sheep. The disease was shown to be transmitted by mosquitoes. The losses ceased within a few days, when the sheep were moved to a higher altitude above the Rift Valley. It was recognized in South Africa in 1950-51. Sheep, goats, cattle, camels and man have been affected in epizootics, which have occurred throughout the Ethiopian region. Most cases arise from mosquito bites. The disease follows the rainy seasons in most countries in Africa, where it has a bimodal character. In West Africa for example, this results in RVF virus activity being detected from August to December. In Egypt, most virus activity occurs between the months of May and October, when the onset of frost results in a fall in the vector populations. Peak mosquito population is seen in June, July and August. RVF is an emerging zoonotic disease, affecting the domestic livestock population in Africa. The human disease has been significant in East and West African epizootics.

Important outbreaks of Rift Valley Fever

- 1987: Senegal, Africa, differed from other outbreaks, not associated with rainfall
- 1997-98: Kenya, Africa, largest outbreak reported, 89,000 humans cases - 478 deaths,
- 2000-01: Saudi Arabia and Yemen - first outbreak outside of Africa
- 2003: Egypt, 45 cases; 17 deaths;

- 2006-07: began in Kenya, spread to U.R. Tanzania and Somalia. By May 2007 -over 1000 cases observed with 300 deaths and 23-45%case-fatality.

Evidence from field studies

Virus persistence was studied in artificial flooding in epizootic areas of Kenya. Millions of larvae hatched and were entirely of *Aedes mcintoshi* (previously *Aedes linneatopennis*). RVF virus was isolated from adult *Aedes mcintoshi* mosquitoes (including males), which developed from larvae collected from the field. Trans-ovarian transmission of the virus provides an explanation for the persistence of the virus through the IEP and for its emergence throughout epizootic areas, which experience similar climatic conditions. RVF has been isolated from *Culicoides*, which do not replicate RVF virus but can transmit the virus mechanically. Other biting flies have also been shown to be capable of transmitting RVF mechanically. The epizootics appear to be triggered by periodic cycles of prolonged rainfall. The capacity to predict the risk of RVF epizootic activity exists by Remote Sensing Satellite Imagery (RSSD) data.

(iii) Contagious echthyma

Contagious ecthyma is a viral disease of sheep and goats, which is highly contagious and zoonotic in nature. It is characterized by pustular, scabby and proliferative lesions on the muzzle, lips face, ears, teats or vulva. Contagious ecthyma is caused by an epitheliotropic *Parapox* virus that enters the animals through skin abrasions. The distribution of the disease is world-wide. The virus replicates in proliferating keratinocytes in the damaged epidermis. Scabs that fall to the ground during resolution of lesions have been incriminated as possible agents of transmission to other animals. Carrier sheep and goats may also be an important source of infection to their young ones.

The disease appears in the form of papules which progress rapidly to vesicles, pustules and scabs. Crusty proliferative lesions typically form on the lips but can also affect the face, ears, coronary band, scrotum, teats or vulva. Large masses of granulation tissue develop under the scabs. Bronchopneumonia and gastroenteritis have been observed in goat kids. In malignant form lesions are generalized in nature. Morbidity rate is very high (50-60%), but mortality rate may be 5% in goat kids and lambs. Recently severe ecthymic lesions extending in and aroud buckle cavity and vulvar region have been reported in the flocks concurrently infected or having under current infection with PPR virus. In the absence of prophylactic measures (treatment and vaccine), the disease is frequently reported from sheep and goat farms in young animals immediately after kidding/lambing in new-born and adult animals all over the country. Extreme climatic conditions (summer and winter) also help in the precipitation of the disease. In order to check the spread of infection, infected goats should be isolated and the infected area should be disinfected. The lesions should be treated with mild antiseptic drugs. In generalized or systemic infection, antibiotic should be given to prevent secondary bacterial complication. Very young kids and lambs die due to their inability to suckle. Therefore, the affected animals should be properly supplemented with bottle feeding and succulent fodder.

C. Parasitic Infestations

Alimentary tract harbours a variety of helminthes and protozoan parasites, which in nature, mostly occur as mixed infections and are responsible for parasitic gastroenteritis. Important nematode, fluke, tapeworm and protozoan infections of sheep and goats are given below:

(i) Fluke infections

The prevalence of liver flukes may increase because of warmer, wetter conditions favouring the mud snail vector, and changes in the mixing of cattle and sheep through changes in land use and farming practice, or response to flooding. However, extensive droughts could decrease snail populations. Parasitic pneumonia and gut worm scours increased in cattle in the south-west of GB in 2007 due to the very wet summer.

(ii) Arthropods and arthropod-borne diseases

Ectoparasite infections - e.g. ticks/mites in livestock may enhance prevalence of infections with secondary pathogens such as endemic bacterial pathogens.

Arthropod vector-borne diseases

- In UK: Bluetongue and AHS - both transmitted by *Culicoides* midges
- Worldwide: Tick-borne livestock diseases such as babesiosis, theileriosis, cowdriosis (*Ehrlichia ruminantium*), louping ill, Crimean-Congo haemorrhagic fever & African swine fever; and mosquito-borne diseases viz. VEE, RVF, & West Nile fever

Climate change has capacity to influence animal health both directly and indirectly via altered parasite biology of the parasites and vectors responsible for spreading many vector-borne diseases. Climate variability can alter the relationship of an animal with the parasites and vectors. These climate variability affect the niche where parasites and vectors thrive, altering some geographical regions to be more suitable to the parasites or the vectors while some other ones less amenable in comparison to past years or decades. Climate change can have decisive influence on (i) the time and duration of likely threats from parasites and vectors to agricultural animals, (ii) distribution, transmission, and evolution of the pathogen(s), the drivers of disease emergence and response of animals to emerging disease threats. Recent decades have witnessed significant changes in environmental parameters and effect of these environmental changes has increasingly been reported on livestock husbandry.

D. Metabolic disorders

In small ruminants, most of these production related disorders are mainly caused by dietary irregularities, viz. inadequate feed, irregular feeding, sudden change in feed, spoiled food, change in rumen microbial population, indigestible substances and inadequate nutrients, etc. Because of the difference in the soil type, climate condition, livestock husbandry practices and difference in the feed and fodder among counties, the incidence and gravity of disease is also likely to vary from country to country. Specific problems of sheep and goat industry in India, like hot climate, course roughages, irregular availability of fodder, and imbalance of nutrients causing sub-clinical starvation lead to metabolic diseases, particularly in pregnant and lactating animals. Hence, in most cases, the disease picture is so complicated that the diagnosis becomes difficult.

Characteristics of soils are largely influenced by climate change and they are also very relevant for fungal infestation. The topic is not well investigated but it deserves more focus. Climate change can potentially alter the transfer and the bioavailability of trace elements from the soil to the plant. Deficiency of nutrients or excess of toxic elements may results in lower resistance to insect, pests and plant diseases including the attack of toxigenic fungi and the consequent biosynthesis of mycotoxins. Fertilizer regimes may affect fungal incidence and severity of colonization either by altering the rate of residue decomposition, by creating a physiological stress on the host plant or by altering the crop structure. For *Fusarium* colonization, higher N inputs extend the stages during which wheat is susceptible to infection and a longer flowering period and later ripening was reported. The risk of nitrate leaching in crop fertilized with mineral or organic N is weather and soil dependent. There is a need to better understand this issue. Deficiency of minerals and vitamins like copper, cobalt, iron, sulphur, iodine, sodium, potassium, chlorine, magnesium, zinc, selenium, fluorine, molybdenum, calcium, phosphorus, manganese, and vitamin A, B, D and E deficiencies might be observed due to loss of these minerals and trace elements from the soils because of flooding and leaching and thereby, affecting the content in grains and feed and fodder which ultimately will affect the health of goats and sheep like other livestock.

Phyto-chemicals/chemicals

a) *HCN poisoning*: Hydrocyanic poisoning is also observed in sheep and goats after consuming cyanogenetic plants. In cyanogenetic plants, HCN content generally increased in drought condition and animals are forced to eat such plants. In our country, goats suffer from poisoning on consumption of Remza or raunza (*Acacia leocophea*).

b) *Nitrate and nitrite poisoning*: Over feeding of green oat, maize and other green immature fodder also lead to nitrate and nitrite poisoning in goats which need to be avoided.

Conclusion and futurology

Climate change alters the boundaries between different species and between natural and managed lands. Break down in these boundaries makes it possible for pathogens to switch between hosts including the hosts wherein disease had not been reported earlier. As changing climates widen the range of vector-borne diseases, human and animal health workers need to start talking to each other. The large-scale climate change and global warming have generated intense speculation about the possible adverse effects on animal husbandry. The variations in weather patterns may cause shifts in distribution, frequency, and magnitude of diseases such as arboviruses, Rift Valley fever virus, etc. The potential impacts of climate change on animal health are not yet fully explored but it is indicative that animal health could adversely be affected by rising ambient and ocean temperatures. Climate change may result in changes in the incidence of food-borne zoonoses and animal pests and possibly an increased use of veterinary drugs (FAO, 2008). Consequently, there may be higher and even unacceptable levels of veterinary drugs in foods from animal origin (FAO, 2008). These issues are of concern for environmental contaminants of chemical residues in the food chain. Regular surveillance will provide up-to-date information about changes in pathogen populations. Laboratory and field research will help illuminate how climate changes influence pathogen characteristics, and models will help researchers and producers predict and plan for pathogen threats. With a nationwide network of research facilities and a history of groundbreaking pathogen research, demand Cross-Field Partnerships internationally and nationally.

References

Bath, G.F. and De Wet, J.A.2000. Sheep and Goat Diseases. Tafelberg, Cape Town, South Africa (cited by Bath et al., 2005).

Bath, G.F., van Wyk, J.A. and Pettey, K.P. 2005. Control measures for some important and unusual goat diseases in southern Africa. Small Ruminant Research 60(1-2): 127-140.

Baylis, N., Githeko, A.K. 2006. The effects of climate change on infectious diseases of animals. T7.3. Foresight. Infectious Diseases: preparing for the future. Office and Science and Innovation (www.foresight.gov.uk).

CDC. 2008. Congressional Testimony. Select Committee on Energy Independence and Global Warming United States House of Representatives Climate Change and Public Health. Statement of Howard Frumkin, MD, Dr PH Charron DF, Thomas MK, Waltner-Toews d, Aramini JJ, Edge T, Kent RA, Maarouf AR, Wilson J (2004) Vulnerability of waterborne diseases to climate change in Canada: a review. Journal of Toxocology, Environment & Health 67:1667-1677.

Donkin, E. F., Stewart, C. G., MacGregor, R. G., Els, H.C. and Boyazoglu, P.A. 1992. Resistance of Indigenous and crossbreed goats in heartwater *Cowdria ruminantium*. In: Recent Advances in Goat Production, Proceeding of the Fifth International Conference on Goats, New Delhi, India (1992), pp. 1716–1719 (cited by Bath et al., 2005).

Du Plessis, J. L., Jansen, B. C. and Prozesky, L. 1983. Heartwater in Angora goats. I. Immunity subsequent to artificial infection and treatment. Onderstepoort Journal of Veterinary Research 50**:** 137–143.

Du Plessis, J.L., Van Gas, L., Olivier, J.A. and Bezuidenhout, J.D. 1989. The heterogenicity of *Cowdria ruminantium* stocks: cross-immunity and serology in sheep and pathogenicity to mice, Onderstepoort Journal of Veterinary Research 56: 195–201.

FAO. 2008. Expert Meeting on Climate-Related Transboundary Pests and Diseases Including Relevant Aquatic Species, Food and Agriculture Organization of the United Nations, 25-27 February 2008.

Greer, A., Ng, V. and Fisman, D. 2008. Climate change and infectious diseases in North America: the road ahead. Canadian Medical Association Journal 178**:** 6.

Hameed, K.G.A., Sender, G. and Korwin-Kossakowska, A. 2006. Public health hazard due to mastitis in dairy cows. Animal Science Papers and Reports 25 (2): 73-85.

Ilemobade, A.A. 1976. Study on heartwater and the causative agent *Cowdria ruminantium* (Cowdry, 1925) in Nigeria. Ph.D. thesis, Ahmadu Bello University (cited by Bath et al., 2005).

Jongejan, F., Uilenberg, G. and Franssen, F.F.J. 1988. Antigenic differences between stocks of *Cowdria ruminantium*. Research in Veterinary Sciences 44: 186–189.

LEAD. (The Livestock, Environment and Development) Initiative. 2006. "Livestock's long shadow: Environmental issues and options". Food and Agriculture Organization of the United Nations, Rome.

Lipp, E.K., Hau, A., Colwell, R.R. 2002. Effects of global climate on infectious disease: the cholera model. Clinical Microbiology Review 15:757-770.

Matheron, G., Barré, N., Camus, E. and Gogue, J. 1987. Genetic resistance of Guadeloupe native goats to heartwater. Onderstepoort Journal of Veterinary Research 54: 337–340.

Neitz, W.O. 1968. Heartwater, Bulletin De L'Office International Des Épizooties 70 (1968), pp. 329–336.

Oberem, P.T. and Bezuidenhout, J.D. 1987. Heartwater in hosts other than domestic ruminants, Onderstepoort Journal of Veterinary Research 54: 271–275.

Purse, B.V., Mellor, P.S., Rogers, D.J., Samuel, A.R., Mertens, P.P.C. and Baylis, M. 2005. Climate change and the recent emergence of bluetongue in Europe. Nature Reviews Microbiology 3: 171-182.

Singh, S.V. and Singh, Nem 2000. Effect of climate on Johne's disease incidence in goat herds. Indian Journal of Animal Sciences 70(5) : 492-493.

Trape, J.F., Godeluck, B., Diatta, G., Rogier, C., Legro,s F., Albergei, J., Pepin, Y. and Duplantier, J.M. 1996. The spread of tick-borne borreliosis in West Africa and its relationship to sub-Saharan drought. American Journal of Tropical Medicine and Hygiene 54(3), 289-293.

Uilenberg, G. 1983. Heartwater (*Cowdria ruminantium* infection): current status. Advances in Veterinary Sciences and Comparative Medicine 27: 427–480.

Suggested web-sites for further reference:

1.http://www.physorg.com/news162486984.html

2.http://www.sciencedaily.com /releases/2007/11/071106140029.htm

3.http://www.ars.usda.gov/is/np/ha/han39.htm

4.http://en.wikipedia.org/wiki/Global_warming

5.http://www.who.int/features/factfiles/climate_change/facts/en/index9.html

http://www.eurekalert.org/pub_releases/2007-11/asot-nth110607.php

❑❑❑

32

Animal Borne Diseases: Human Health and Environmental Concern

B.N.Tripathi*, S.K.Dixit and G.G.Sonawane
Division of Animal Health, Central Sheep and Wool Research Institute
Avikanagar-304501 (Rajasthan)

Introduction

Animal-borne diseases (zoonoses) have become one of the biggest threats to human health and are responsible for increase in environmental load of infectious microbes. Infection from animals may be transmitted to humans either directly or from their products or from contaminated environment. The infectious diseases or their agents naturally transmissible between animals and human beings are collectively referred to as "zoonoses" - meaning the animal (Greek-'*zoon*') diseases, (Greek-'noses') transmissible to man. This link between human and animal populations, and with the surrounding environment, is particularly close in the developing regions, where animals provide transportation, draught power, fuel and clothing as well as proteins (meat, eggs and milk). Many of these zoonoses are associated with the handling of diseased domestic and wild animals from their natural habitat or farms to markets and slaughter slabs, and slaughterhouses.

Many factors lead to the emergence of zoonotic diseases such as environmental changes, human and animal demography, pathogen changes and changes in farming practice. India has a strong population of over 485 million livestock with first rank in cattle and buffalo, and second and third in goat and sheep population, respectively. Due to increased pressure of human population, change in the climate and the environment, many new infections and re-emerging infections mostly of animal origin, pose challenge to medical and veterinary fraternity equally. In search of safe food of animal origin, organic livestock farming has been started in several countries including India, which may also lead to problems of animal and human health. Helminthes infestation is one of the major problems associated with organic sheep and cattle farms. It has been estimated that out of over 1400 infectious diseases that affect human beings, more than half are animal-borne. Thus, a large number of animal-borne infections affect human health and contaminate environment, but in the present paper only some of the important infections particularly of small ruminant origin such as salmonellosis, brucellosis, anthrax, listeriosis, leptospirosis, campylobacteriosis, Orf, Rift Valley fever, cryptosporidiosis, toxoplasmosis, Q-fever, etc will be briefly described. Control of animal-borne (zoonotic) infection will involve the control of infection at the animal level (reservoir host), environmental level, or at the human population (host) level.

Classification of animal-borne diseases

Economic losses due to reduced or lost productivity and cost on health management of animals and mankind are some of the globally known factors but owing to inadequate diagnostic facilities, lack of proper medical care, low socioeconomic condition, abundance of vectors, and more importantly lack of coordination between physicians, veterinarians and epidemiologists led to increased incidence of zoonotic diseases. Animal-borne diseases have assumed great public health significance particularly in India. Diversified agricultural practices, fascinating or forced movement of human and animal population, reduced trade boundaries with animal and animal products and developing tourism have often helped in propagation of various diseases.

Animal borne diseases may be classified as per etiological agents viz., bacterial, viral, rickettsial, chlamydial, mycotic and parasitic zoonoses, etc.

- Bacteria: Salmonellosis, campylobacteriosis, anthrax, brucellosis, *E. coli* infection, leptospirosis, plague, shigellosis and tularemia.
- Parasites: Cysticercosis/Taeniasis, echinococcosis/hydatidosis, toxoplasmosis, cryptosporiodosis and trematodosis.

- Rickettsial diseases: Q-fever
- Viruses: Rabies, avian influenza, Japanese encephalitis, kyasanur forest disease, foot and mouth disease, Ebola and Rift Valley fever.
- Unconventional agents: Bovine spongiform encephalopathy.

The zoonotic diseases may again be classified into following 3 types on the basis reservoir hosts.

- *Anthropozoonosis:* Infectious agent is transmitted from lower vertebrate animals to man as in case of rabies.
- *Zooanthroponosis:* The infection is transmitted from man to lower vertebrate animals, e.g. human tuberculosis.
- *Amphixenosis:* Infectious agent is maintained in both man and lower vertebrate animals and may be transmitted in either direction.

Depending on the transmission cycle, animal borne infection (zoonotic infections), can be classified as:

- *Direct zoonoses:* One infected vertebrate host may transmit the infection to susceptible host, e.g. rabies.
- *Cyclozoonoses:* More than one vertebrate hosts are required to transmit the infection, e.g. taeniasis and echinococcosis, etc.
- *Metazoonoses:* Invertebrate host is involved for biological transmission of infectious agent, e.g. Plague, Japanese encephalitis, etc.
- *Saprozoonoses:* This requires a non-animal site like soil, plant material, etc., e.g. mycotic infections.

Incidence and significance of animal-borne infection

Zoonotic pathogens originate in live animals and can spread throughout the food chain causing infection in humans (WHO, 2004, 2006). That is why, the food-borne diseases are widespread and growing public health problem, both in developed and in developing countries. It has been estimated that out of over 1400 infectious diseases that affect human beings, 58% are animal-borne; and out of 177 emerging or re-emerging infections, about 73% (130) originate from animals (Woolhouse and Gowtage-Sequeria, 2005). Further, it has been emphasized that 64% (14/22) of the major etiological agents for infectious diseases identified during two decades (1973 to 1994 were animal-borne or zoonotic in nature. All major zoonotic diseases, emerging, re-emerging or endemic, in addition to being direct public health problems by affecting the health and well-being of millions of people, also prevent the efficient production of food, particularly of much-needed proteins, and create obstacles to international trade in animals and animal products. These diseases, therefore, are an impediment to overall socio-economic development (Rahman and Malik, 2008).

Poor socio-economic conditions

In India, people engaged with animal husbandry such as farmers, livestock owners, animal handlers, veterinary extension workers and veterinarians have been found to commonly contact over 40 animal-borne diseases, whereas those engaged in production and processing of livestock products such as abattoir, dairy, pig and poultry enterprises suffer frequently with a number of zoonotic diseases including anthrax, brucellosis, tuberculosis, leptospirosis, salmonellosis, campylobacteriosis, listeriosis, verotoxic *Escherichia coli*, clostridial infections, plague, rabies, Japanese encephalitis and Kyasanur forest disease (KFD). While some of these zoonotic pathogens such as *Brucella, Listeria, Campylobacter, Leptospira, Coxiella burnetii* and *Chlamydia* spp. are potentially hazardous to human health, they are economically important from reproduction standpoint being associated with abortion, repeat breeding and infertility in animals (Malik , 2008a,b).

Emergence of zoonotic diseases

During last three decades, rotaviruses emerged as a major cause of neonatal diarrhoea, while there is an impending threat from the deadly *Ebola* virus, the cause of viral haemorrhagic fever in Africa and; *sin nombre* virus (Hantaan virus), the cause of acute respiratory distress syndrome or haemorrhagic pulmonary syndrome with renal syndrome in adult humans in the United States (Hinman, 1998). Lately, four new potent viral zoonotic agents including Hendra and Nipah as encephalitic agents, and; severe acute respiratory syndrome (SARS) and highly pathogenic avian influenza (HPAI) virus as potent pneumonic agents have been identified.

Animal's food-borne infections

In recent years, public concern on health matters associated with food has increased as a consequence of, *inter alia*, the outbreak of bovine spongiform encephalopathy (BSE) in the UK. Also of great concern are the world-wide epidemics of *Salmonella* serotype Enteritidis food poisoning (poultry meat and eggs), and the more localized outbreaks of illness associated with *Listeria monocytogenes* (dairy products, paté and salad crops) and *Escherichia coli* O157:H7 (ground or minced beef). The appearance of problems such as BSE and Enteritidis food poisoning has resulted in the enacting of specific legislation in several countries, while the general heightening of interest worldwide has prompted health professionals and the feed industry in many countries to scrutinize the control of potential pathogens and to formulate better procedures for purchasing and handling animal feed ingredients and the subsequent manufacture of compounded or formula feeds.

Several important infections of animal origin are transmitted to humans through food producing animals (e.g., cattle, sheep, goats, pigs, chickens and turkeys). These food are major sources of many of zoonotic organisms including *Salmonella, Campylobacter,* non-Typhi serotypes of *Salmonella* Enteritidis, *Listeria monocytogenes,* Shiga toxin–producing strains of *Escherichia coli,* and *Yersinia enterocolitica, Clostridium* spp., *Brucella* spp., *Staphylococcus aureus, Vibrio* spp., as well as foodborne viruses namely Norwalk and rotaviruses (Alice et al., 2002). These microbes can contaminate animal/poultry carcasses at slaughter or cross-contaminate other food items and are responsible for human illness. Food items such as eggs, meat and milk are rejected on account of contamination by *Salmonella,* and hence a great economic loss is also accrued, besides causing human illness.

The other important food-borne zoonotic pathogen *Shigella* spp. causes shigellosis (bacillary dysentery) due to faecal contamination of food. *Mycobacterium* spp. and *Coxiella burnetii* may be transmitted through ingestion of contaminated raw milk and milk products. The cases of food-borne brucellosis are mainly associated with *Brucella melitensis,* and also by *B. abortus* that are excreted in raw milk of goat, cattle, and sheep.

Animal-borne infection through organic farming

Organic farming is the most productive way to low-input agriculture. Organic farming and organic food processing are innovative systems with regard to efficient and sustainable land use, food production and food marketing. Organic farming provides better conditions for residue free animal products, but it poses a potentially higher risk of infectious and parasitic diseases, compared with conventional (particularly indoor) livestock systems (Mader et al., 2002; Hovi et al., 2003)

A number of health problems have been noted in organic livestock (poultry and pig) production. Helminthes infestation is one of the major problems associated with organic sheep and cattle farms. An increase or re-emergence of certain zoonotic diseases like *Campylobacter and Toxoplasma* in organic livestock production has also been reported (Rodenburg et al., 2004; Dubey et al., 2004; Kijlstra et al., 2004). Claims that organic products are healthier as compared to conventional products are questionable and research on the prevalence of certain zoonotic infections, risk factors, farm management, post-slaughter decontamination and consumer perception/education is needed. Logically, risk for contracting paratuberculosis appears to be higher on organic farms, but actual serological incidences have been found comparable between cattle of organic herds and conventional herds.

Sheep and goat-borne diseases

As stated earlier, a large number of animal-borne infection are important from human health and environmental points of view, but in the present paper only some of the important infection particularly of small ruminant origin will be briefly described. Diseases that can spread from sheep and goats are- salmonellosis, brucellosis, anthrax, listeriosis, leptospirosis, campylobacteriosis, orf, Rift Valley fever, louping ill, cryptosporidiosis, toxoplasmosis, Q-fever, etc.

Salmonellosis

This disease is caused by a widely prevalent bacterium belonging genus- *Salmonella* having more than 2435 serovars identified so far. *Salmonella* infections are prevalent all over the world among various species of domestic as well as wild animals besides poultry, ducks, birds, amphibians, reptiles and rodents. Salmonellosis caused by non-typhoidal species is not only more prevalent but has also shown an increasing trend world over with majority of cases being caused by *S.* Enteritidis and *S.* Typhimurium. *S.* Enteritidis, in particular, has emerged as an important cause of gastroenteritis, food-borne infection and a significant health problem in many countries.

In India, human salmonellosis is endemic and one of the most important animal-borne infection. The prevalence of *Salmonella* infection will probably continue unabated in the future because of the ubiquitous distribution of the organism in animal reservoirs. While *Salmonella* is not as common in sheep as it is in poultry. *Salmonella* can infect humans in the same manner as cryptosporidia. *Salmonella* produces high fever and diarrhea in both sheep and humans. Shepherds can get infected by handling or treating infected sheep. Washing hands in warm soapy water or in disinfectant after treating sick animals will prevent infection.

Leptospirosis

It is caused by a spirochaete- *Leptospira interogans*. The disease is contracted from infected rat's urine/contaminated water resources. Population at high risk includes farm workers, rice field workers, sugarcane cutters, cattle rearers, fishermen, slaughter house and sewer workers. During last two decades, large numbers of human cases of leptospirosis have been reported from southern states particularly Tamil Nadu, Kerala and Andaman due to farming and inadequate rodent control. Economic impact is due to cost for medical treatment, decreased productivity, impact on trade animals, semen losses by reproductive failures and reduced milk yield.

Brucellosis

In livestock species (cattle, sheep, goats, swine, and camel), the most frequent clinical sign following infection with *Brucella* is abortion (premature or full term birth of dead or weak calves) usually in the second half of gestation with retention of placenta and metritis (Acha et al., 2003; Seleem et al., 2009). The principal strain that infects cattle is *B. abortus*, cattle can also become transiently infected by *B. suis* and more commonly by *B. melitensis*. The brucellae localize in the supra-mammary lymph nodes and mammary glands of 80% of the infected animals and thus continue to secrete the pathogen in milk throughout their lives (Hamdy and Amin, 2002).

The main etiologic agent of brucellosis in goats is *B. melitensis*. In certain countries like Brazil where there is no *B. melitensis*, goats can get infected with *B. abortus* (Lilenbaum et al., 2007). As in cattle, brucellosis in goats is characterized by late abortion, stillbirths, decreased fertility and low milk production (Lilenbaum et al., 2007). Sheep brucellosis can be divided into classical brucellosis and ram epididymitis. Ram epididymitis is caused by non-zoonotic agent *B. ovis*, while classical brucellosis is caused by *B. melitensis* and constitutes a major public health threat equal to goat brucellosis (Acha et al., 2003).

One of the best descriptions of human brucellosis before discovery of antibiotics was "the disease rarely kills anybody, but it often makes a patient wish he were dead" (TIME magazine 1943). *B. melitensis* is associated with acute infection, whereas the infections with other species are usually subacute and prolonged. Most common symptoms of brucellosis include undulant fever in which the temperature can vary from 37 ^{0}C in the morning to 40 ^{0}C in the afternoon; night sweats with peculiar odor, chills and weakness. Common symptoms also include malaise, insomnia, anorexia, headache, arthralgia, constipation, sexual impotence, nervousness and depression (Acha et al., 2003). Human brucellosis is also known for complications and involvement of internal organs and its symptoms can be very diverse depending on the site of infection and include encephalitis, meningitis, spondylitis, arthritis, endocarditis, orchitis, and prostatitis (Acha et al., 2003). Spontaneous abortions, mostly in the first and second trimesters of pregnancy, are seen in pregnant women infected with *Brucella* (Khan et al., 2001). Live animal vaccines *B. melitensis*

Rev. 1 and B. abortus strain 19 are known to cause mild disease in humans. The course of the disease with vaccine strains is usually shorter and more benign (Acha et al., 2003).

Five out of the nine known *Brucella* species can infect humans and the most pathogenic and invasive species for human is *B. melitensis*, followed in descending order *by B.suis, B. abortus* and *B. canis* (Acha et al., 2003; Barbuddhe et al., 2007a, c). *B. melitensis, B. suis* and *B. abortus* are considered as potential bio-weapons by the Centers for Disease Control and Prevention in the USA. This is due to the highly infectious nature of all three species, as they can be readily aerosolized. In places where brucellosis is endemic, humans can get infected via contact with infected animals or consumption of their products, mostly milk and milk products especially cheese made from unpasteurized milk of sheep and goats and rennet from infected lambs and kids. Some specific occupational groups including farm workers, veterinarians, ranchers, and meat-packing employees are considered at higher risk. *B. abortus* and *B. suis* infections usually affect occupational groups, while *B. melitensis* infections occur more frequently than the other *Brucella* species in the general population (Acha et al., 2003; De Massis et al., 2005). Consumption of sheep or goat milk containing B. melitensis is an important source of human brucellosis worldwide and has caused several outbreaks. Because person-to-person transmission rarely occurs, infected persons do not pose a threat to their surroundings; consequently, eradication of the disease from the natural animal reservoirs leads to a dramatic decrease in the incidence of human infection. For example, in countries including the United States, Denmark, and France, where national bovine brucellosis eradication program has been launched, cases of human brucellosis have declined drastically or almost disappeared.

The disease is a widely prevalent in India and considered economically very important. Of various *Brucella* species, *B. abortus* and *B. melitensis* are the main causes of occupational zoonosis in farmers, veterinarians and persons associated with meat industry (Barbuddhe et al., 2007a, c). It is common in organized herds and in areas with high rainfall and humidity. Moreover, there are losses due to abortion in the affected animal population, loss of progeny, reduced milk production. According to a report brucellosis causes physical incapacity and loss of 3 million man-days of labour annually in humans (Singh, 2008).

Anthrax

The disease, caused by *Bacillus anthracis*, is a rapid fatal infection primarily of herbivores, and often characterized by sudden death, exudation of tarry unclotted blood from the mouth, nares and anus. Pigs, equines, dogs and camels are moderately susceptible whereas carnivores and birds are generally highly resistant. Man is moderately resistant; however, in high risk industries (wool, hair, meat and bone meal, leather), it remains a major occupational zoonosis with fatal pneumonia or malignant pustule or ulcer formation on skin. No true reservoir has been identified for it. The pathogen present in the body fluid of infected host when comes in contact of atmospheric air, forms highly resistant spores. Under favourable conditions, the spores have been reported to remain viable for about 40-60 years in contaminated soil and about 200±50 years in the bones of dead hosts.

In spite of considerable under reporting, the incidence of human anthrax in the world has been estimated to be 20,000 to 1,00,000 cases per annum. Out of all cases, cutaneous form of anthrax accounts for 95-99% worldwide including India. Animal anthrax has been reported from most of the states of India, however, it is enzootic in Tamil Nadu, Karnataka & Andhra Pradesh (Malik, 2008c). Its incidence during 1981 to 1994 ranged from 1.5 to 9.4 per million of population among cattle, sheep, goats and buffaloes. The number of sheep and goats affected with anthrax in 1994 was three times higher than that of bovines. Although the disease has not been reported from northern zone of the country during 1984-95, the overall cases of anthrax among animals are on the rise during recent years. In endemic areas of India, it is a sporadic disease in cattle with 479 reported deaths in about 3 years span. A recent outbreak of anthrax in three districts of west Bengal has been reported to claim lives of 10 animals (Malik and Barbuddhe, 2009).

In India, over 200 human cases majority being cutaneous anthrax, have been documented from tri-junctional zone of south-west Andhra Pradesh, south-east Karnataka and north Tamil Nadu. Many sporadic cases were reported from Kashmir and Bihar (in 1970s); north Arcot district of Tamil Nadu and various regions in Karnataka (in 1980s and 1990s). Several cases of human anthrax have been reported from various parts of the country like Chittoor district of Andhra Pradesh (25-30 cases in 1989, at least 6 cases in 1990), Davengare, Karnataka (3 cases in 1991) and Vellore, Kerala (23 cases in 1994 and 1995).

Due to recent surge of human anthrax cases in West Bengal (2000, 2007, 2008), and Orissa (2003, 2005 and 2006), anthrax appears to be an emerging zoonosis in the country. The hike in human cases has been presumably linked to the vanishing population of vultures- the natural scavengers of anthrax infected carcasses, in the country. Another cause of concern is development of resistance in *Bacillus anthracis* to penicillin and other antibiotics. As anthrax in human beings is directly linked to the occurrence of the disease in animals, the key to control anthrax in man and animals lies in the mandatory notification of anthrax cases in man, domestic and wild animals (Malik, 2008c; Malik and Barbuddhe, 2009).

Listeriosis

The disease is prevalent all over the world as an important food-borne zoonosis caused by pathogenic strains belonging to the genus- *Listeria* with six species, out of which only *L. monocytogenes* is an opportunistic pathogen in human beings and animals, whereas, *L. ivanovii* affects only animals (mainly the ruminants) as a cause of abortion, barring occasional cases in man. The disease has a case fatality rate of 28-30 per cent, with more reports pouring in developed countries. In USA, listeriosis with an estimated economic loses of $ 300 million/ year has been responsible for about 1,700 cases of sporadic human listeriosis with 450 adult and 100 foetal deaths occurring annually. The disease is prevalent all over the world with more reports pouring in from developed countries (Malik and Barbuddhe, 2009).

In India, cases of human listeriosis (2) and spontaneous abortions in women (4) have been reported with seroprevalence of the disease varying from 2.77 to 7.0% (Malik et al., 2002, Kaur et al., 2007). The pathogen has also been recovered from repeat breeding, infertility and mastitis cases in animals (Shakuntala et al., 2006; Rawool et al., 2007). Several outbreaks of listeriosis among animals have also been reported from various states (Malik et al., 2002: Malik and Barbuddhe, 2009).

Campylobacteriosis

Campylobacter infection in humans is the number one cause of food-borne illness generally from consuming undercooked meat. Many species of mammals and fish can carry *Campylobacter* asymptomatically in their intestine. *Campylobacter* infection in pregnant sheep is one of the major causes of ovine abortions. Infected lambs and placenta contain high number of the organisms and shepherds can be infected if they are not careful in handling aborted feti and placenta.

Paratuberculosis

Mycobacterium avium subsp. Paratuberculosis (MAP) causes paratuberculosis, commonly known as Johne's disease, in cattle, sheep, goats and other ruminants (Tripathi et al., 2002). The organism has zoonotic potential, as it has been repeatedly isolated from intestinal biopsy tissue from a proportion of patients with Crohn's disease. Whether this indicates a causative role for *M.A. paratuberculosis* in Crohn's disease, or simply a complication in infection, is the subject of ongoing debate within the medical, veterinary, and scientific community. Milk has been suggested as a possible vehicle of transmission of this organism to humans. Detectable quantities of *M. a. paratuberculosis* have previously been reported in the milk of both clinically infected and sub-clinically infected ruminants with Johne's disease. Although there have been no published reports of the isolation of *M. a. paratuberculosis* from sheep or goats' milk, there is an equal possibility that contaminated milk from these animals could also enter the food chain. In a recent report from CIRG, Makhdoom, MAP antibody has been reported in human population in India.

Contagious ecthyma (Orf)

This viral disease causes lesions on the lips of naive sheep. It can infect humans through a break in the skin. Typically the area will be reddened and inflamed with painful swelling around the lesion. It is critical that if human infection is suspected from the sore mouth virus, it must be informed to the medical doctor. It is often recommended bringing information along to the medical doctor since some doctors have never heard of sore mouth, and some may only know it by the name Orf, contagious ecthyma or sheep parapoxvirus.

Rift Valley fever (RVF)

Although the disease, named after the Great Rift Valley in East Africa, was known in that area for decades, its cause was established only in 1930. It is mosquito-transmitted viral disease of domestic ruminants, assuming epidemic proportions under conditions that favour multiplication of the vector, especially high rainfall. In sheep the disease is characterized by high mortalities in new-born lambs, massive abortion storm in pregnant ewes, necrotic hepatitis and widespread haemorrhages. The disease has also been reported in wild ruminants, cattle and camels. It has been identified in most sub-Saharan countries and as far as north as Senegal and Egypt as well as Medagaskar.

The virus is a member of the family *Bunyaviridae*, genus *Phlebovirus*. Zoonotic implication of the virus is quite significant and it poses definite danger to humans, therefore strict precautions must be taken in outbreaks. The usual manifestations are the sudden onset of influenza-like symptoms after a short incubation of 2-6 days. Fever, often biphasic, may last several days. Ocular lesion can occur in 20% cases. Headache, photophobia, loss of visual acuity, nausea, vomiting muscle and joint pains are often experienced. In severe cases widespread haemorrhages are seen in the body.

In South Africa over a hundred thousand of sheep died and half of them aborted during 1950-51 and 1976-78 outbreaks. Many veterinarians and animal health workers handling these outbreaks suffered partial blindness due to retinal detachment and some died also. In Egypt, about two hundred thousand people were infected with RVF virus and about 600 died. The disease has already spread to East Africa, Saudi Arabia, Yemen and the Middle East. The possibility of the RVF virus infection extending to Asia and Europe cannot be ruled out. The OIE strongly supports vaccination, rather than culling out, as a control measure for RVF in livestock.

Rickettsial infection- Q fever

Q fever is a ubiquitous zoonosis caused by *Coxiella burnetii*, an obligate intracellular bacterium that affects pets, birds, domestic and wild animals, arthropods and humans (Maurin and Raoult, 1999). Q fever provokes abortion and stillbirths in sheep and goats, whereas in cattle metritis and infertility are more frequent. The causative agent is shed in urine, vaginal fluids, faeces, milk and, in high concentrations, in birth fluids and placentas of infected small ruminants. In humans, infection can be asymptomatic, but in acute disease it may also present with fever, pneumonia or hepatitis. If the infection persists, it can become a chronic disease with more severe clinical signs (Maurin and Raoult, 1999). The source of *C. burnetii* infection is often unknown, although cattle, sheep and goats are the most common reservoirs.

The main route of infection is inhalation of contaminated aerosols or dust containing *C. burnetii* shed by infected animals, mainly at parturition when infected females shed great numbers of bacteria through birth products (Astobiza et al., 2009). Moreover, after lambing, animals shed *C. burnetii* in urine, faeces and milk for several months (Berri et al., 2005; Arricau-Bouvery et al., 2003; Guatteo et al., 2007; Rodolakis et al., 2007), and aerosols generated from contaminated environments could explain some outbreaks of human Q fever. To identify animal shedders, biological samples, such as vaginal swabs, faeces and milk, can be tested by polymerase chain reaction (PCR). *C. burnetii* can survive in the environment for long periods (Maurin and Raoult, 1999) and so control of this zoonosis is a challenge for veterinary and public health authorities. In Netherlands, there were three consecutive outbreaks of Q fever in humans, which were associated with outbreaks of *C. burnetti* infection in small ruminant population (Brom and Velloma, 2009, Schimmer et al., 2009). The best option to prevent the disease is vaccination, which reduces shedding of *C. burnetii* (Arricau-Bouvery et al., 2005), thereby decreasing environmental contamination and, consequently, the risk of human infection.

In India, seroprevalences of Q fever have been reported in humans (2.7-26%), Cattle (14.98%), sheep (6.2-14.41%), buffaloes (14.5-15.22%), goats (14.26-17.5%), equines (20.1%), swine (14.67%), dog (16%)and poultry

(11.87%). Most of these reports have come from Punjab, Haryana, Rajasthan, UP, M.P. and Karnataka (Malik and Vaidya, 2005; Malik and Vaidya, 2005; Malik and Barbuddhe, 20099; Barbuddhe et al., 2007b; Vaidya et al., 2008).

Cryptosporidiosis

Cryptosporidium species can infect a wide variety of vertebrate hosts, and numerous genetically distinct species have been described, most of which are morphologically indistinguishable. In sheep, *Cryptosporidium* infections have been described worldwide and it has been generally assumed that most *Cryptosporidium* infections with oocysts of 4–6 mm diameter were due to *Cryptosporidium parvum*.

C. bovis does not seem to have any zoonotic potential. Although the cervine genotype has been occasionally found in man, it is not at present regarded as a public health risk. However, *C. parvum* is one of the two major causes of human cryptosporidiosis (Mueller-Doblies et al., 2008). In areas where other *Cryptosporidium* species account for more ovine infections than *C. parvum*, the role of sheep as a potential source of zoonotic *Cryptosporidium* species has to be reconsidered. In the UK, *C. parvum* is a predominant *Cryptosporidium* species in sheep, and therefore sheep represent a transmission source of *Cryptosporidium* infection to humans. The ability of cryptosporidia to cause disease is directly related to the immune system of the animal or person. Young or immuno-suppressed shepherds are a greatest risk. Human infection occurs by ingestion of the oocysts that are present in feces. Washing hands in warm soapy water is the easiest and best way to prevent infection with cryptosporidia.

Toxoplasmosis

Toxoplasma gondii infection is widely prevalent in humans and animals worldwide (Dubey, 2009). Young cats can shed the parasite in large numbers in their feces. Sheep become infected by eating feed or water contaminated with cat faeces. In sheep, *T. gondii* infection may cause early embryonic death and resorption, fetal death and mummification, abortion, stillbirth, and neonatal death. Severity of infection is associated with the stage of pregnancy at which the ewe becomes infected, the earlier in gestation, the more severe the consequences. Infected sheep meat is a source of *T. gondii* infection for humans and carnivorous animals. The foetus and placenta contain high numbers of *Toxoplasma* and should be handled with gloves. Following infection with *T. gondii*, sheep develop humoral and cell-mediated immune responses against the parasite that provides effective protection against disease in subsequent pregnancies. A commercial vaccine is available, comprising a live, incomplete strain of *T. gondii*. The vaccine is administered to sheep prior to mating to protect against lamb losses due to toxoplasmosis.

Humans become infected post-natally by ingesting tissue cysts from undercooked meat, consuming food or drink contaminated with oocysts, or by accidentally ingesting oocysts from the environment (Dubey, 2009). The ingestion of undercooked infected lamb is considered an important source of infection for humans. Eating uncooked lamb is a risk factor for *T. gondii* infection in pregnant women in Europe. In a retrospective study of 131 mothers in the USA who had given birth to children infected with *T. gondii*, 50% recalled having eaten uncooked meat (Boyer et al., 2005). Toxoplasmosis also causes heavy economic losses to sheep industry worldwide (Buxton et al., 2007).

Factors for spread and emergence of zoonoses

Many factors lead to the emergence of zoonotic diseases such as environmental changes, human and animal demography, pathogen changes and changes in farming practice. Social and cultural factors such as food habits and religious beliefs play a role too. It is important especially a country like India with substantial population living in rural areas, to have an extensive system of surveillance and monitoring for zoonotic infections in order to assess their prevalence and socio-economical implications, with an ultimate aim to identify, prioritize and effectively control the nationally and economically important zoonoses.

Managemental strategies to control animal-borne diseases

Multi-pronged strategy is required for controlling the animal-borne diseases at regional, national or international levels, as a number of factors influence their occurrence. Socio-economic pattern of the population at risk, nature and hazard potential of the infectious agent and available resources, technology, manpower, social participation and administrative support are the important deciding factors that need to be taken into account for an effective zoonotic disease control programme.

Baseline data on the population at risk, case specific or general morbidity and mortality pattern in animals and humans, characteristics of the infectious agents, vectors/vehicles involved in disease transmission, environmental and ecological predisposing factors aiding survival, propagation and spread of infectious agents and their vectors etc., form a foundation for developing a strong control strategy at regional as well as national level. An "Early warning

System" can be developed from these data, which will ultimately help in the formulation of an action plan to prevent the spread of infections in a particular geographical area.

The basic principle behind control of zoonotic infection lies in either eliminating/reducing the viability of the infectious agent or to prevent contact between the host species and infective agent. The zoonotic infections can best be controlled by interruption of their transmission cycle between animals, environment and humans. Control of animal-borne (zoonotic) infection will involve the control of infection at the animal level (reservoir host), environmental level, or at the human population (host) level. It is imperative to note that a concerted effort at all the three levels simultaneously would be the most effective long term strategy to control any zoonotic infection.

Control of infection at animal level (reservoir host)

The best approach to control animal-borne infection is to strive for infection free animal farms, which, however, may not be practically possible at least in the developing countries. A few developed countries (European countries) have been able to completely eradicate some of the diseases like rabies, foot and mouth disease etc. The management of zoonotic infections depends on the type and number of species of reservoir animals involved in the life cycle of infectious agents. On the basis of the proximity of the animal species to the human habitat and consequently the risk of transmission of infection, the animals can be broadly divided into four main groups: namely, wild animals, synanthropic animals, companion/pet animals and domestic animals of agricultural use.

Due to the variation in the natural habitats of all the above groups of animals, strategies for control of infectious diseases may vary from total isolation of the human population from them as in case of wild animals and synanthropic animals to controlled co-habitation with supportive disease prevention measures like vaccinations and livestock health programmes in case of the pet animals or agriculturally useful livestock. General principle of control measures can be taken up. These include: avoid feeding contaminated feed, fodder and water to the animals and stressful conditions that predispose them to infections, vaccination against infectious diseases, prompt diagnosis, treatment and segregation of the infected animals, culling of animals with intractable diseases, ensure proper disposal of the carcasses that would otherwise act as a source of infection, and strict quarantine measures to prevent entry of an infectious agent into a new region, state or country.

Control of infection at environment level

The environmental condition of a particular geographical area plays an important role in transmission of infectious zoonotic diseases. Extensive manipulation of the environment that hampers the survival or propagation of the infectious agent or its vector is usually not possible. Some important measures listed below, however, can be considered, which will ultimately aid in the control of animal borne infections.

a. Systematically constructed animal sheds should be away from human habitation as far as possible.
b. All hygienic and sanitary measures may be instituted at livestock product processing plants like abattoirs, milk processing plants, meat plants, etc.
c. A thorough ante-and post-mortem examination of meat animals can be instrumental in reducing the transmission of infections from diseased animals to meat handlers and the consumers.
d. Effective control measures for vectors such as mosquitoes, flies, fleas and synanthropic animals like rodents and foxes in the animal sheds/ farms and in the vicinity of meat and milk processing plants may be adopted.
e. Strict hygienic and sanitary measures including proper storage, collection and disposal of garbage may be instituted.
f. Hygienic processing, storage and retailing of the animal products right up to the consumer level.

Control of infection at human level

Human population is usually at the receiving end of the transmission chain of any zoonotic disease. As a consequence, any disease control strategy used to control zoonotic infection at this level will ensure that the infectious agent reaches *cul de sac* of its transmission chain. It is however important to note that effective control of animal-borne infection at this level is just a short-term remedy and complete prevention of zoonotic infections is possible only if this strategy is adequately supported by the disease control measures at the animal and environment level. Some of the managemental strategies employed to control zoonotic diseases at human level include prompt diagnosis and medical care of sick cases including isolation if necessary, immuno- and chemoprophylactic measures for the high risk groups, and public awareness about the significance of animal-borne infection.

Initiatives taken by ICAR

Since its inception in 1971 at Indian Veterinary Research Institute (IVRI), Izatnagar, UP, the Division of veterinary public health (VPH) has taken initiatives for collaborative research, human resource development and knowledge sharing. The Division developed a "Model surveillance system for zoonotic diseases in livestock, poultry, fish and wild life for a developing country" and submitted it to WHO Indian Headquarters, New Delhi in 2005.

Prevalences of important zoonotic pathogens namely *Listeria monocytogenes, Brucella* spp., *Campylobacter* spp., *Toxoplasma gondii, Coxiella burnetti,* Japanese encephalitis virus and rotaviruses have been studied in clinical samples from man and animals by isolation, serological and molecular methods at Veterinary Public Health Division of IVRI, Izatnagar. The ICAR has recently started "National Network Programme on Important Zoonotic Diseases" and "National Agricultural Innovative Project (NAIP) on Diagnosis and control of important and emerging diseases of public health importance". The IVRI is playing a leading role in dealing with animal-borne infection with regard to surveillance and monitoring, development of sensitive and specific diagnostic test, and by organizing brain storming session, short-term training courses and winter school as part of human resource development in the country. The National Institute of Communicable Diseases and ICMR, New Delhi have also been playing significant role in tackling with communicable diseases in India.

Conclusion

Animal-borne diseases, which are transmitted to human beings, are threat to the public health throughout the world. A concerted effort from a large group of veterinary and medical professionals and general population is the key to the success of control of these diseases. Information required to control most of these diseases is still inadequate. The need of the hour is to put in a cohesive effort by the related professional groups to evolve a common strategy to fight such diseases. The role of media including the print and electronic media is very important in combating the animal-borne diseases. They could help in spreading mass awareness among the common population regarding the hazard of these diseases and also educating them the various measures needed to adopt to control the spread of such infections. The farmers, milk and milk products industry, breeding companies, consumers and the politicians must work together and find a practical eradication effort that is suitable for each country.

Acknowledgements

Authors are thankful to Dr Ashok Tyagi Head, Division of Veterinary Public Health and Dr S.V.S.Malik and Dr D.K. Singh, principal scientists of the same division of the Indian Veterinary Research Institute, Izatnagar for provoding literature on animal-borne infection.

References

Acha, N.P., Szyfres, B., 2003. Zoonoses and Communicable Diseases Common to Man and Animals, third ed., vol. 1. Pan American Health Organization (PAHO), Washington, DC.

Alice, A., Bungay, C., Methusyla, J., Estacio and Calvin, S., Reyes, de los. 2002. The "Emerging" Foodborne Bacterial Zoonoses, Volume 131 (1): 55-67.

Arricau-Bouvery, N., Rodolakis, A., 2005. Is Q fever an emerging or re-emerging zoonosis? Veterinary Research 36, 327–349.

Arricau-Bouvery, N., Souriau, A., Lechopier, P., Rodolakis, A. 2003. Experimental

Coxiella burnetii infection in pregnant goats: excretion routes. Veterinary Research 34, 423–433.

Arricau-Bouvery, N., Souriau, A., Bodier, C., Dufour, P., Rousset, E., Rodolakis, A. 2005. Effect of vaccination with phase I and phase II Coxiella burnetii vaccines in pregnant goats. Vaccine 23, 4392–4402.

Astobiza, I., Barandika, J. F., Hurtado, A., Juste, R. A. and García-Pérez, A. L. 2009. Kinetics of *Coxiella burnetii* excretion in a commercial dairy sheep flock after treatment with tetracycline. The Veterinary Journal, doi:10.1016/j.tvjl.2009.01.017.

Barbuddhe, S.B., Kalorey, D.R., Malik, S.V.S., Sahare, A.M. and Kurkure, N.V. 2007a. Food safety and Quality Enhancement Datasheet on *Brucella abortus*. www.cabicompendium.org/ahpc, pp.11 .

Barbuddhe, S.B., Malik, S.V.S., Kalorey, D.R., Sahare, A.M., Rawool, D.B., Vaidya, V.M. and Kurkure, N.V. 2007b. Food safety and Quality Enhancement Datasheet on *Coxiella burnetii*. www.cabicompendium.org/ahpc, pp.27.

Barbuddhe, S.B., Sahare, A.M., Kalorey, D.R. and Malik, S.V.S. 2007c. Food safety and Quality Enhancement Datasheet on *Brucella melitensis*. www.cabicompendium.org/ahpc, pp.31.

Berri, M., Crochet, D., Santiago, S., Rodolakis, A. 2005. Spread of *Coxiella burnetii* in dairy cows. Veterinary Research 38, 849–860.

Boyer, K.M., Holfels, E., Roizen, N., Swisher, C., Mack, D., Remington, J., Withers, S., Meier, P., McLeod, R. 2005. The toxoplasmosis study group, 2005. Risk factors for *Toxoplasma gondii* infection in mothers of infants with congenital toxoplasmosis: implications for prenatal management and screening. American Journal Obstetrics and Gynecology 192, 564–571.

Brom, R. Van den, Vellema P. 2009. Q fever outbreaks in small ruminants and people in the Netherlands Small Ruminant Research 86: 74-79.

Buxton, D., Maley, S.W., Wright, S.E., Rodger, S., Bartley, P., Innes, E.A., 2007. *Toxoplasma gondii* and ovine toxoplasmosis: new aspects of an old story. Veterinary Parasitology 149, 25–28.

De Massis, F., Di Girolamo, A., Petrini, A., Pizzigallo, E., Giovannini, A., 2005. Correlation between animal and human brucellosis in Italy during the period 1997–2002. Clinical Microbiology Infection 11, 632–636.

Dubey JP, Salant H, Sreekumar C, Dahl E, Vianna MC, Shen SK, Kwok OC, Spira D, Hamburger J, Lehmann TV. (2004) High prevalence of *Toxoplasma gondii* in a commercial flock of chickens in Israel, and public health implications of free-range farming. Veterinary Parasitology. 121:317-22.

Dubey, J.P. (2009). Toxoplasmosis in sheep—The last 20 years, Veterinary Parasitology 163: 1-14

Guatteo, R., Beaudeau, F., Joly, A., Seegers, H., 2007. *Coxiella burnetii* shedding by dairy cows. Veterinary Research 38, 849–860.

Hamdy, M.E., Amin, A.S., 2002. Detection of *Brucella* species in the milk of infected cattle, sheep, goats and camels by PCR. Veterinary Journal 163, 299–305.

Hinman A.R. 1998. Global progress in infectious disease control. Vaccine 16: 1116-1121.

Hovi, M., Sundrum A, Thamsborg SM. 2003. Animal health and welfare in organic livestock production in Europe: current state and future challenges. Livestock Production Science 80: 41-53.

Kaur S.; Malik S.V.S.; Vaidya, V.M. and Barbuddhe, S.B. 2007. *Listeria monocytogenes* in spontaneous abortions in humans and its detection by multiplex PCR. Journal of Applied Microbiology 103(5):1889-1896.

Khan, M.Y., Mah, M.W., Memish, Z.A., 2001. Brucellosis in pregnant women. Clinical Infectious Diseases 32: 1172–1177.

Kijlstra A, B.G. Meerburg and Mul MF. (2004) Animal-friendly production systems may cause re-emergence of *Toxoplasma gondii*. NJAS 52:119-132.

Lilenbaum, W., de Souza, G.N., Ristow, P., Moreira, M.C., Fraguas, S., Cardoso Vda, S., Oelemann, W.M., 2007. A serological study on Brucella abortus, caprine arthritis-encephalitis virus and Leptospira in dairy goats in Rio de Janeiro. Braz. Veterinary Journal 173: 408–412.

Mäder, P., Fließbach A, Dubois D, Gunst L, Fried P and Niggli U. 2002. Soil fertility and biodiversity in organic farming. Science 296: 1694-1697.

Malik, S.V.S. 2008a. Global and national perspective of zoonotic diseases and their management. In: National Training Programme on "Recent Advance in Animal Disease Diagnosis and their Treatment", March 11-18, Joint Directorate of Extension Education, Indian Veterinary Research Institute, Izatnagar, UP, pp.15.

Malik, S.V.S. 2008b. Global and national perspective of zoonotic diseases: Impact, concerns and strategies. In: National Workshop on "Veterinary and Medical perspectives on Emerging and Important Zoonotic Diseases in India", March 29, Division of Vety. Public Health, Indian Veterinary Research Institute, Izatnagar, UP, pp10-17.

Malik, S.V.S. 2008c. Prevention and Control of Anthrax: Need for Intersectoral co-ordination. In: Meeting of Standing Committee on Zoonoses at Nirman Bhawan, April 11th, National Institute of Communicable Diseases, New Delhi, pp.4.

Malik, S.V.S. and Barbuddhe, S.B. 2009. Zoonotic and Foodborne Diseases: Global and national impact, concerns and control strategies. Winter school on "Molecular diagnostic techniques for zoonotic and foodborne diseases". 7th to 27th Feb., 2009, pp. 1-15.

Malik, S.V.S. and Vaidya, V.M. 2005. Q fever: A neglected zoonosis in India? In: III Annual Conference of Indian Association Veterinary Public Health Specialists and National Symposium on "New Approaches in Food Safety and Quality control with special reference to emerging foodborne diseases and intoxications., Feb 9-10, College of Veterinary Sciences, Punjab Agricultural University, Ludhiana, pp.44-54.

Malik, S.V.S. and Vaidya, V.M. 2008. Molecular and immunological approaches for the detection of important pathogens in foods of animal origin. In: Food Quality Assurance: A concerted approach, S.P. Singh and S.C. Tripathi (Eds.), Compendium of select lectures in National seminar on "Quality assurance and prevention of contaminants, adulterants and pollutants in livestock products" Feb.27-28, 2006, Department of Veterinary Public Health, College of Veterinary Science, G.P. Pant University of Agriculture and Technology, Pantnagar, Uttaranchal (India)., pp. 139-152.

Malik, S.V.S., Barbuddhe, S.B. and Chaudhari, S.P. (2002). Listeric infections in man and animals in Indian subcontinent: A Review. Tropical Animal Health and Production 34 (5): 359-381.

Maurin, M., Raoult, D. 1999. Q fever. Clinical Microbiology Reviews 12: 518–553.

Mueller-Doblies, D., Giles, M., Elwin, K., Smith, R. P., Clifton-Hadley, F. A. and Chalmers R. M. 2008. Distribution of Cryptosporidium species in sheep in the UK Veterinary Parasitology 154: 214–219 218

Rahman, H. and Malik, S.V.S. 2008. Zoonoses acquired from foods of animal origin, their prevention and control. In: Food Quality Assurance: A concerted approach, S.P. Singh and S.C. Tripathi (Eds.), Compendium of select lectures in National seminar on "Quality assurance and prevention of contaminants, adulterants and pollutants in livestock products" Feb.27-28, 2006, Department of Veterinary Public Health, College of Veterinary Science, G.P. Pant University of Agriculture and Technology, Pantnagar, Uttaranchal (India)., pp.59-68.

Rawool, D.B., Malik, S.V.S., Barbuddhe S.B., Shakuntala, I., and Aurora, R. 2007. A multiplex PCR for detection of virulence associated genes in *Listeria monocytogenes*. International Journal of Food Safety 9: 56-62.

Rodenburg TB, Van Der Hulst-Van Arkel MC and Kwakkel RP. (2004) Campylobacter and *Salmonella* infections on organic broiler farms. NJAS 52: 101-108.

Rodolakis, A., Berri, M., Héchard, C., Caudron, C., Souriau, A., Bodier, C.C., Blanchard, B., Camuset, P., Devillechaise, P., Natorp, J.C., Vadet, J.P., Arricau-Bouvery, N. 2007. Comparison of *Coxiella burnetii* shedding in milk of dairy bovine, caprine, and ovine herds. Journal of Dairy Science 90: 5352–5360.

Schimmer, B., Dijkstra, F., Vellema, P., Schneeberger, P.M., Hackert, V., ter Schegget, R., Wijkmans, C., van Duynhoven, Y., van der Hoek, W. 2009. Sustained intensive transmission of Q fever in the south of the Netherlands. European Surveillance 14: 19210.

Seleem, M.N Seleem, M. N. , Boyle, S. M. and Sriranganathan, N. 2009. Brucellosis: A re-emerging zoonosis. Vetereinar Microbiology doi:10.1016/j.vetmic.2009.06.021

Shakuntala, I., Malik, S.V.S., Barbuddhe S.B. and Rawool, D.B. 2006. Isolation of Isolation of *Listeria monocytogenes* from buffaloes with reproductive disorders and its confirmation by polymerase chain reaction. Veterinary Microbiology 117(2-4): 229-234.

Singh, D. K. 2008. Brucellosis in India: Diagnosis and Prophylaxis. In: Training-cum-Workshop on Diagnosis and Prophylaxis of Economically Important Diseases of Farm Animals and Poultry " under Niche Area Project of ICAR, Feb. 25-29, Division of Vety. Pathology, Indian Veterinary Research Institute, Izatnagar, UP, pp.46-53.

Tripathi, B. N., Munjal, S.K. and Paliwal, O.P. 2002. Tripathi, B.N, Munjal, S.K. and Paliwal, O.P. (2002) An overview of paratuberculosis (Johne's disease in animals. Indian Journal of Veterinary Pathology 26(1&2): 1-10.

Vaidya, V.M.; Malik, S.V.S.; Kaur, Simranpreet; Kumar, Satish and Barbuddhe, S.B. 2008. Comparison of PCR, Immunofluorescence Assay, and Pathogen Isolation for Diagnosis of Q Fever in Humans with Spontaneous Abortions. Journal of clinical Microbiology 46 (6): 2038–2044.

Woolhouse, M.E.J. and Gowtage-Sequeria, S. (2005). Host range and emerging and reemerging pathogens. Emerging Infectious Diseases 11(12): 1842-1847. www.cdc.gov/eid.

World Health Organization (2004). WHO/FAO/OIE Consultation Meeting on zoonotic diseases, Geneva. http://www.who.int/en/

World Health Organization (2006). Zoonoses and Veterinary Public Health. http://www.veterianary-public-health.de/home e/index e.htm.

❑❑❑

33

Mycobacterium Avium Subspecies Paratuberculosis: A Predominant Endemic Biotic Stress Affecting Growth, Development and Productivity in Domestic Ruminants

S. V. Singh, P.K. Singh, A. Kumar and A.V. Singh
Microbiology Laboratory, Animal Health Division, Central Institute for Research on Goats
Makhdoom, Farah, Mathura-281 122, Uttar Pradesh

Introduction

Stress is ubiquitous, part and parcel of life on earth. Literarily 'stress' is a "state of affair involving demand on physical or mental energy". A condition or circumstance (not always adverse), which can disturb normal physiological and psychological functioning of an individual. In medical terminology 'stress' is 'perturbation of the body's homeostasis'. Stress has different meanings when considered with respect to primates, animals and plants. In primates there are different kinds of stresses; eustress, hyperstress, hypostress, and distress. Some of the important causes of stress are physical, psychological and behavioral, and there are symptoms of anxiety and depression. Broadly stress is abiotic or biotic. Abiotic stress is the negative impact of non-living factors on living organisms in a specific environment. Non-living variables must influence environment beyond its normal range of variation to adversely affect population performance or individual physiology of the organism in a significant way. Abiotic stress factors or stressors are naturally occurring factors (intense sunlight or wind) and essentially unavoidable and affects animals. Abiotic stress is most harmful factor concerning growth and productivity of crops worldwide. Most stressful of all the abiotic stressors is heat and cold and many species are unable to regulate their internal body temperature. Temperature determines metabolic rates, heart rates, and other very important factors within the body of animals. Extreme temperature changes can easily distress animal body. High genetic diversity is beneficial in providing resiliency against harsh abiotic stressors. **Biotic stress** means living organisms, which can harm plants and animals, such as viruses, fungi and bacteria and harmful insects. Despite ubiquitous arrivals of new microorganisms few survive and only a small fraction become naturalized and exert no demonstrable impact in their new range. Some naturalized species do become invasive and successful invaders in many cases inflict enormous ecological damage. The biotic stress has been described only with respect to plants and is less investigated in animals.

Aim of production system research is to improve the performance, animal health and welfare, and product quality in 'low input' animal production systems and main issues are:

Abiotic stress factors: Extreme temperatures and imbalanced diets are known to result in significant reductions in productivity and product quality in extensive small ruminant production systems. Heat stress is increasingly recognized as a major problem and predicted changes in climate are expected to increase heat stress incidence, especially in Southern Europe. Cold stress is expected to remain an important issue in northern and north-eastern Europe and in mountainous/alpine regions. Abiotic stress and the related consequences on the disruption of feed intake are also known to increase the susceptibility of animals to intestinal parasites and mastitis. Intensification of animal production has usually focused on, (a) minimizing the impact of environmental stress by introduction of housing systems (especially for dairy sheep or goats), (b) supplementary concentrate feeding, and (c) the use of hormones to be independent of seasonal lambing pattern. However, these practices increase input costs and the use of unnecessary housing and hormones is discouraged/prohibited under organic farming standards.

Global cost of animal diseases caused by organisms transported to new ranges and presented with susceptible new hosts is currently incalculable. Identifying future invaders and taking effective steps to prevent their dispersal and establishment is a major challenge to ecology, agriculture, aquaculture, horticulture, animal husbandry and pet trades, conservation, and international commerce.

Changing national and international quarantine laws by adopting a "guilty until proven innocent" approach, instead of the current strategy of denying entry only to species already proven noxious or detrimental, would be a productive first step. The global consequences of failing to address the issue of invasions effectively would be severe, including wholesale loss of agricultural, forestry, fishery and animal resources in some regions and disruption of the ecological processes that supply natural services on which the animal/human enterprise depends. Given their current scale, biotic invasions have also taken their place along with human-driven atmospheric and oceanic change as major agents of global change, and if left unchecked, will influence these other forces in profound but still unpredictable ways.

Biotic stress factors

Parasites remain one of the most important animal health and welfare problems in both 'low input' meat and dairy animal production. In dairy systems pathogens causing mastitis also provoke significant economic losses. These problems are currently mainly controlled by regular anthelmintic and antibiotic treatment, a practice which may result in (a) anthelmintic and antibiotic resistance in parasite/pathogen populations (b) loss of consumer confidence in health and welfare practices in 'low input' systems and (c) consumer concerns about residues of antibiotics / anthelmintics in meat and dairy products.

An ecosystem consists of a number of micro-organisms which co-exist and come into regular contact with each other. Some of these pathogenic organisms constitute a biotic stress, which may profoundly influence the livestock production. There are various pathogens that have the potential for the vast economic losses and depressed livestock production. With the increasing human population livestock farming has become more intensive and it has been associated with raising animal stocking densities and increased risk of transmission of diseases. Mounting biotic stress has raised concern about an increased survival of zoonotic / pathogenic agents in animals, their wastes, in environment and their possible transmission to other animals or their contamination of the human food chain. Infectious animal diseases and zoonoses represent a major constraint to the maintenance and development of livestock and present a major threat to public health and livelihood of farmers especially in developing countries, and to national economies. During the past few years, world has witnessed emergence and re-emergence of several infectious animal diseases that have had a major impact on animal production and human health. These have severely affected the economy of developed as well as developing countries. Therefore, improving animal health and fertility can play a major role in achieving efficient and economically rewarding production. The same fact was realized and therefore, World Organization for Animal Health (OIE) has been constituted with the primary missions to prevent the spread of animal disease through international trade of animals and animal products. In present paper the potential of *Mycobacterium avium* subsp. *paratuberculosis* as a dominant biotic stress for livestock production and possible risk to human health has been highlighted.

Animal diseases as major biotic stress

The global population is expected to increase from 6.2 billion to 9 billion during the next 40 years. Developing countries are expected to account for 85 per cent of the increased food demand. Livestock diversity is critical for food security and rural development. However, this diversity is under threat. Livestock producers will have to cope with both abiotic stress (like gradual climatic changes, frequent extreme climatic events, droughts, floods etc.) and biotic stress or diseases (infectious pathogens/diseases). Infectious diseases adversely affect livestock production and animal welfare, and often have major impact on human health. For example, the costs of existing endemic diseases are estimated to be 17% of the turnover of livestock industries in the developed world and 35 to 50% in the developing world. Furthermore, epidemics, particularly in developed countries, incur further major costs and have profound impacts upon the rural economy and on public confidence in livestock production.

The direct causes of disease are: (1) bacteria, (2) viruses, (3) parasites, (4) fungi, (5) nutritional deficiencies, (6) chemical poisons, and (7) unknown causes. However, of these, infectious diseases are the greatest threats or biotic stressors to livestock health. The impact of biotic stress or diseases is generally easy to identify but may be difficult to quantify for many production and chronic disease. It is the chronic infections rather than acute which cause losses to animal production system in innumerable ways. Besides tuberculosis, brucellosis, parasitic infestations and host of other chronic infections, the best known example of chronic infection in domestic ruminants is Johne's disease (JD) or paratuberculosis that continues to be a persistent and growing challenge for every country to increase the livestock production. Johne's disease, caused by *Mycobacterium avium* subspecies *paratuberculosis* (MAP), has emerged as major infection plaguing the domestic livestock across the world and this fact has long been recognized by the developed countries, however developing and under developed countries are yet to awake to the challenge posed by this bacilli to both animals and human population. Therefore, it is one of the major production diseases and now considered as "Disease of New Millennium".

Mycobacterium avium subspecies *paratuberculosis* as predominant biotic stress to livestock production

JD is a chronic wasting disease of domestic, wild and exotic ruminants, including dairy and beef cattle, sheep, goats, buffaloes, blue bulls, bison, cervids, camelids that occurs worldwide. MAP is a slow-growing bacterium that causes thickening of the intestinal wall of cattle; the thickening reduces absorptive capability. JD in cattle and other species is characterized by chronic, granulomatous enteritis that causes intermittent but persistent diarrhoea, progressive weight loss, and eventually death of the animal. The disease is untreatable and slowly progressive (Stehman, 1990).

Clinical features of paratuberculosis

Paratuberculosis has a protracted incubation period and clinical disease is the terminal stage of this process. Onset of clinical disease is unpredictable, but may be precipitated by parturition, lactation or by stressful events. In all ruminants, clinical disease is characterized by a progressive weight loss that leads to emaciation, sub-mandibular oedema and poor coat quality (roughness, loss of pigmentation, wool-slip), despite maintaining good appetite. Decrease in milk yield has been reported in infected animals. A major feature of the illness in cattle is chronic, intractable diarrhoea, although in some animals this may be intermittent. In contrast to cattle, diarrhoea is not a common feature, it may be intermittent depending on concurrent parasitic infections and mostly there is weakness and weight loss without diarrhea, in small ruminants. This is probably due to their greater ability to reabsorb water in the large intestines and food habit, which generally includes leaves of trees and bushes, with less water contents. However in advanced cases the feces may become soft and unformed. The diarrhoea is usually thick, without blood, mucus, or epithelial debris, and may be intermittent. Several weeks after the onset of diarrhea, a soft swelling may occur under the jaw. This swelling is known as "bottle jaw" or intermandibular oedema. This symptom is due to protein loss from the bloodstream into the digestive tract. Paratuberculosis is progressive; affected animals become increasingly emaciated and usually die as the result of dehydration and severe cachexia. Decreased serum concentrations of calcium, total protein and albumin have been reported in animals with clinical paratuberculosis.

Pathogenesis

MAP is an intracellular parasite. Ingested bacteria enter the intestinal wall through the mucosa, specifically via M cells lining the dome areas of the Peyers patches. The bacteria are subsequently phagocytosed by subepithelial macrophages, where it can avoid initial degradation by phagosomes by producing superoxide dismutase that eliminates oxygen radicals. Thus, MAP is resistant to intracellular degradation and will slowly replicate and stimulate inflammatory and cellular responses. An increased resistance to infection is seen with age. Some animals are able to control the infection and only 10-15% of infected animals develop clinical JD (though sub-clinical infection will result in significant production losses and hence economic losses (Olsen et al., 2002). Furthermore, they can survive in macrophages by secreting protein kinase G out of the phagosome to help prevent phagosome-lysosome fusion. Infected macrophages are enveloped by immune cells to avoid dissemination of the bacteria, which results in tubercle or granuloma formation in the host. The exact immuno-pathological mechanisms for development of clinical disease are not known. Gross pathology is primarily seen in the intestine and mesenteric lymph nodes. The intestinal wall is thickened and oedematous and the mucosa demonstrates transverse folds. The ileum is the primarily affected region but lesions can occur throughout the intestinal tract. Mesenteric lymph nodes are swollen and oedematous. Occasionally other organs, particularly liver and hepatic lymph nodes show lesions. In severe disease, animals may be alopecic, cachectic, anaemic and demonstrate peripheral oedema and serous effusion into body cavities. Histological lesions are characterized by multifocal diffuse granulomatous inflammation of the intestine and mesenteric lymph nodes (MLN). In mild lesions there are a few scattered giant cells and a few macrophages in the villi. In severe lesions there are a large number of both cell types infiltrating all layers of the intestinal wall and the lumen of lymphatic vessels.

Economic losses in livestock production

Contagious diseases are a threat to animal health and productivity, both nationally and at the farm level. Therefore, implementation of bio-security measures within the country and at farms is necessity to prevent their introduction and spread.

Johne's disease has been a frustrating problem for dairy and meat producers for more than 100 years. MAP generally impulse a negative effect of improving herds' quality could cause the loss of years of strategic-breeding improvements of the genetic material. JD being sub-clinical disease, the prevalence data are either lacking or are imprecise; therefore it is difficult to assess the economic consequences of this disease for individual cows, herds, or the nation. MAP is responsible for causing negative energy balance in the body, disease is a protein loosing enteropathy and damages the body immune system since MAP grows within lymph nodes (primarily mesenteric lymph nodes), resulting in severe morbidity, mortality and production losses to animal industries and individual owners. Losses attributable to clinical paratuberculosis stress are thought to arise as a result of: reduced milk production; increased calving interval; reduced slaughter weights; and shorter life expectancy, lost potential breeding value, infertility and increased incidence of mastitis, etc. These economic losses (qualitative or quantitative) have not been estimated in developing countries like India and un-developed countries, neither at farm or farmers' level. In the absence of data on disease prevalence and economic losses due to diseases, no program on prioritization of animals diseases for control and eradication could be initiated either at regional or national level.

(i) Losses at world level

In cattle, economic losses attributed to disease have been estimated to be over 50 billion US$ world-wide. It has been reported demonstrated by studying annual cost for JD infected 50 cows herd is US$ 2472. International estimates have been $100 to $200 per cow ($10,000 to $20,000 per 100 cows) or £5,500 to £11,000 per 100 cows.

(ii) Losses studied in America

In the US, several estimates of economic losses have been made, including an estimate of $15.4 million annually in New England (Chiodini et al., 1984), $54 million in Wisconsin, $5.4 million in Pennsylvania (Whitlock et al., 1985), and from $200 - $250 million annually in US dairy herds (Ott et al., 1999). By comparison, economic losses in Australia were estimated to be the equivalent of US $2.1 million annually (Gill, 1989). Economic consequences at the herd level were estimated as part of the 1996 National Animal Health Monitoring System (NAHMS) survey of U.S. dairy herds. For JD test-positive herds with fewer than 10 percent of culled cows showing clinical signs consistent with JD, the adjusted annual value of production was $40 per cow lower than for JD test-negative herds that had not reported culled cows with clinical signs. For JD test-positive herds with 10% or more culled cows showing clinical signs, the economic impact was $227 per cow, and the majority of the loss was attributable to reduced milk production with additional losses from higher cow replacement costs and lower cull cow revenues (NAHMS, 1997). Benedictus et al. (1987) apportioned JD losses into decreased production (32%), veterinary and treatment costs (2%), reduced value at slaughter (20%), loss due to idle production facilities (3%), and unrealized future income based on age at culling and prior production (43%). Groenendaal and Galligan (1999) used simulation models to predict average losses of $35 per cow per year, increasing to $52 and $71 per cow per year after 10 and 20 years, respectively. Nordlund et al. (1996) reported an economic loss of US$ 100 per cow when compared to Johne's-negative herds (reduced milk production and increased cow replacement costs). For Johne's-positive herds that reported at least 10% of their culled cows as having clinical signs of JD, economic losses were over US$ 250 per cow. These high-prevalence herds experienced reduced milk production of over 700 kg per cow, culled more cows but had lower cull-cow revenues, and had greater cow mortality than Johne's-negative herds. The economic losses due to JD is beyond expectation because the above stated cost is still underestimated as MAP infection affects milk components, somatic cell score, reproductive performance etc.

There was no significant effect of MAP infection on somatic cell score except decrease of 303.9 kg/lactation milk, 11.46 kg/lactation fat, and 9.49 kg/lactation protein yield and a decrease of 2.85 months of productive life in US Holsteins cows. A higher pregnancy rate (1.39%) was associated with infection, although statistical significance of this effect was only marginal. Result may be a false-positive association or related to efficacy or type of immune response. Several studies have shown that MAP infection, and not just clinical JD, decreases milk yield and productive life. When evaluating the economic impact of infection, effects on fat and protein yields should also be included. Fecal culture positive cows were removed on average 124 days earlier from the herd than negative cows and produced approximately 11% less milk than negative cows. The variations in these estimates are partly the result of differences in prevalence, herd size, management practices, and the varying assumptions that underlie the calculations. In all estimates of the economic impact of JD, however, the losses are significant. These losses associated with JD led the dairy industry to request that economic analysis of JD be an objective for US Department of Agriculture (USDA) and National Animal Health Monitoring Systems' (NAHMS) 1996 national dairy survey known as Dairy '96.

(iii) Losses studied in Europe

The net loss to farmers of subclinical infection with MAP in their animals, was estimated in Europe in 1987 to be £209 per infected dairy cow. These losses were mainly due to decreased milk production and increased cow replacement costs. The study estimated the costs in terms of reduced productivity alone to be $200 to $250 million per annum, which would be a underestimate of the total costs due to this disease. In the UK, no reliable field data is available on economic losses due to MAP infection. Studies have estimated the mean loss to be £2,600 per 100 cow herd. While UK beef herd gave a mean figure of £1600 per 100-cow herd. The hypothesis that there would be a reduction in production and reproductive performance between paratuberculosis-positive and negative herds was rejected in a study from Ireland, which showed no significant effect of herd paratuberculosis sero-status on milk yield, fat, protein, SCCS and calving interval. Stott et al. (2005) found that the financial effect of paratuberculosis is considerably lower than for other major endemic diseases of dairy cows. Based on a survey in 2006, clinical paratuberculosis in ruminants was declared a notifiable disease in Austria. Kudahl and Nielsen (2009) evaluated the effect of MAP infection on slaughter weight and slaughter value of dairy cow herds participating in the Danish MAP control program. Compared with presumably unaffected cows with at least 2 ELISA negative tests, slaughter weight and value were reduced by 10 and 17%, respectively, in cows with positive ELISA at slaughter. If the cow was also positive in fecal culture, slaughter weight and value were reduced up to 15 and 31%, respectively. The slaughter weight and value were reduced an additional 20 and 31%, respectively, for cases with recorded enteritis or edema. Thereby, summarized weight losses of up to 31% and slaughter value losses up to 48% occurred. These losses could be predicted by repeated milk ELISA tests with or without confirmation with fecal culture. Dieguez et al. (2008), in a study in Spanish dairy herds, indicated that the following management practices constituted major risk factors for association with status MAP infection: utilization of colostrum from cows with a previous positive MAP diagnosis, and housing replacement calves with adult cattle before they were six months old. Seropositivity to MAP was related to the herds' bulk tank somatic cell counts and incidence of clinical mastitis, but not to their reproductive performance.

(iv) Global existence

Surveys undertaken during the latter part of the 20th century show that paratuberculosis is spread worldwide, causing significant economic losses in the affected countries (Johnson-Ifearulundu & Kaneene, 1997; Kennedy & Benedictus, 2001). In these surveys, estimates of herd prevalence in Europe range from 7% in Austria to 55% in Denmark (Kennedy et al., 2001). In the United States, average herd prevalence in dairy herds was 22% in 1996, while it ranged from 20% to 40% depending on herd size (Wells & Wagner, 2000). The true prevalence is however difficult to assess, as methods to diagnose the disease have generally been lacking in sensitivity, and tests and sampling methods differ between countries. Local assays sometimes result in very high rates of infected herds, as 97.2% in Rio Grande de Sul (South Brazil) (Gomes et al., 2005) and 80% in Minnesota, US (Raizman and Wells, 2005). A few countries, including Sweden, have very low prevalence.

In India most of the studies were based on Johnin and faecal examination (Kulshreshtha et al., 1980, Singh et al., 1996). JD in India has been studied at limited scale using various types of clinical materials (feces, tissue, milk, and blood). Using serum ELISA, Singh et al., (2008a) reported that 28% bovine (cattle and buffalo) were positive in North India. Seroprevalence of JD in goat kid from farm and farmers herds was 47.9% in Agra and Mathura regions (Kumar et al., 2007). However, 30.9, 50.0 and 11.8% adult goats from South UP, west UP and Punjab were sero-positive, respectively (Singh et al., 2008). Limited studies have been carried out in buffalo and cattle. Prevalence of MAP in Mathura region was 20.8 and 28.3% in dairy by ELISA kit (develop using indigenous PPA from MAP 'Indian Bison Type' of goat origin) and fecal culture, respectively (Mishra et al., 2007). Using milk as a diagnostic test, 88.4 and 96.1 cattle from Ludhiana were positive in milk ELISA and culture (Singh et al., 2007a). Seroprevalence in buffalo was estimated to be 21.3% in Chennai (Sivakumar et al., 2003), 40.3 and 25.5% in south and west UP, respectively (Singh et al., 2008). However, using tissue culture 48.0% buffalo from Agra region were positive for MAP infection (Yadav et al., 2008). Pathologically, Sivakumar et al. (2005) reported that 4.9% buffalo from Bareilly region were MAP infected. In Hariana, Raut et al. (2003) using hypersensitivity reaction reported 8.5% of bulls infected by MAP.

(v) MAP resistance and survival tactics

High resistance of MAP to environmental stress is one of major factor that affect the disease control programs. Studies have shown that MAP can survive in the environment for longer periods of time. MAP is highly resistant to UV radiations, and requires UV dose greater than 15mW-s/cm^2 for complete disinfection compared to 2-6mW-s/cm^2 required for killing of most of other bacteria (http://www.johnes.org/). In soil MAP has been shown to persist for up to 55 weeks (Whittington et al., 2004), up to 48 weeks in dam water (Whittington et al., 2005), and for 841 days in lake water. MAP can survive freezing at temperature of -14^{0}C for a year or longer. MAP can survive in bovine feces, including slurry and deep litter for at least eleven months. Studies have shown that mycobacteria can resist the altered environmental conditions by infecting protozoa (Strahl et al., 2001). Whan (2003) showed that MAP can infect *Acanthamoeba polyphaga* and further demonstrated that *A. polyphaga*-internalized MAP were more resistant to chlorine levels commonly used for drinking water treatment (2μg/ml free chlorine) than free MAP. Studies of Mura et al. (2006) concluded that MAP has the potential for long-term persistence within environmental amoebae.

(vi) Transmission of MAP infection

a. *Postnatal infection:* Newborns are most susceptible group in a herd. Faecal contamination of teats, pasture, feed and water, and the presence of MAP in colostrum and milk expose neonatal animals to ingest large doses of MAP.

  - *Faeces:* Infected animals shed tremendous number of MAP (approaching 10^9 CFU per gram) in their feces (Merkal, 1973). MAP remains viable for long time in the environment. Thus fecal contamination of the environment is most common sources of infection for animals. Under field conditions the disease is transmitted principally by ingestion of feed and water contaminated by the feces (Yayo Ayele et al., 2001)
  - *Milk and colostrum*: Studies have suggested that as many as 35% of clinically infected cattle (Sweeney et al., 1992) and 11.6% of asymptomatic carriers (Taylor et al., 1981) shed MAP in their milk. Contaminated milk and colostrum expose the suckling animals to MAP early in their age.

b. *Prenatal infection:* Though faecal-oral route is widely known route of infection, animals may acquire infection *in utero* (Sweeney, 1996). Congenital infection by paratuberculosis was first reported by Alexejeff-Goleff (1929). MAP has been isolated from foetus, foetal membranes and the uterine mucosa (Doyle, 1958).

c. *Artificial insemination:* MAP has been detected in genitalia and semen of infected bulls. MAP also survives semen conservation process and thus may infect cow via semen collected from a shedder bull (Larsen et al., 1981). According to study carried out by Merkal et al., (1981) small number of MAP in the semen of a bull might be sufficient to establish hypersensitivity in a recipient cow. Such hypersensitivity could lead to abortions when such cattle are skin tested with johnin.

d. *Role of wildlife in transmission of MAP:* MAP has been isolated from wild ruminants and other free ranging animals (Yayo Ayele *et al.*, 2001). MAP contaminated feed, water and soil resources are major factors for the spread of disease to wild animals. Greig et al. (1999) demonstrated the inter-species transmission of MAP. Molecular typing had shown that similar MAP strains were infecting both wild animals and domestic livestock species (Pavlik et al., 1995, 1999).

Consequences on trade (International and domestic)

JD is spread most effectively through movement of infected animals that contaminate a new environment, thus setting the stage for widespread exposure of more animals. MAP has been recovered from semen and embryos from affected breeding stock. Consequently, JD has serious implications for domestic and international trade of live animals and germplasm. Identification of MAP in animal products also can affect trade, especially if a link between MAP and Crohn's disease is demonstrated conclusively.

International trade

International trade of animals has contributed to the global dissemination of JD. Infected animals of European origin are cited as the original source of JD in several countries. OIE considers JD a disease of major global importance and categorized as a List B transmissible disease, considered to be of socio-economic and/or public health importance within countries and significant in the international trade of animals and animal products (OIE, 2001). Current code recommendations are limited to live ruminants and address individual animal certifications and testing as follows:

Veterinary administrations of importing countries should require (for domesticated ruminants for breeding or rearing), the presentation of an international veterinary certificate attesting that the animals:

a. showed no clinical sign of paratuberculosis (JD) on the day of shipment;
b. were kept in a herd in which no clinical sign of paratuberculosis (JD) was officially reported during the 5 years prior to shipment;
c. were subjected to diagnostic tests for paratuberculosis (JD) with negative results during the 30 days prior to shipment.

Current OIE recommendations provide a limited protection against importation of MAP infected animals, because few affected animals show clinical signs, official reporting systems are not widely enforced, and no specific recommendations are provided for the choice of diagnostic tests or their interpretation.

Impacts

JD is likely to become more of a trade issue in the near future, both India and abroad. Implementation of various state JD control programs sets the stage for differing import requirements by individual states. International import restrictions also could increase as more countries embark on JD control and eradication programs. Australia has identified several of its states as JD-free zones, restricting the movement of animals into those areas (Kennedy and Allworth, 1999). The implementation of a national control and assurance program that incorporates internal movement control empowers Australia to require similar assurances of JD status from its global trading partners. Similar import requirements that go beyond the OIE international standard could be implemented within the legal context of the SPS by other countries that have JD control and eradication programs in place. If it is established that MAP can cause Crohn's disease, more restrictions on international movement of animals, animal products, and germplasm can be expected.

There are few restrictions on the interstate movement of JD exposed or MAP infected animals other than those that show clinical signs of disease and those organism test positive. Since it is difficult to effectively and economically screen animals for MAP, livestock is often bought and sold without consideration of MAP status. Most buyers who seek large numbers of cattle, sheep, or goats currently have no practical options for ensuring JD negative status for their purchases. Consequently, producers of rapidly expanding herds or flocks are at a very high risk of buying MAP infected animals. Current international standards for the safe movement of animals recommend JD testing, combined with clinical examination and herd history, although no specific guidance is provided for testing protocols or interpretation of results. Increased global concern about JD will encourage development of further trade barriers related specifically to JD and MAP. Export opportunities will be lost unless larger populations of JD free or low risk animals can be certified by government agencies.

Stress to human population

Transmission of MAP from animals to humans

(i) In food

It has long been known that infected animals secrete MAP in their milk. Fecal contamination of milk is another source of MAP. MAP is more thermotolerant than *M. bovis* and commercial pasteurization though reduces number of viable organisms, however, do not ensure destruction of all MAP bacilli (Gao et al., 2002). An Indian study also screened popular milk brands of North India regions and found that more than 70% brands were positive for viable MAP (Shankar et al., 2009). Naser et al. (2000) isolated viable MAP from breast milk of woman with CD, thereby increasing risk of exposure to newborns.

In many countries existing legislation still permits clinically diseased JD animals, in which MAP are widely present in liver, lymph nodes and other tissue, to be sent for slaughter and the meat and offal passed for human consumption (Hermon-Taylor and El-Zaatari, 2004). These animals contain huge numbers of MAP with a high risk of dissemination in the abattoir environment and surface contamination of other meat being processed. Vegetables are at risk where MAP-infected slurry is applied as a fertilizer (Hermon-Taylor and El-Zaatari, 2004).

(ii) In water supplies and aerosols

Information available for other zoonotic pathogens that can survive in the environment suggests that there is a high risk that MAP may transmitted to people in drinking-water or by aerosols (Hermon-Taylor et al., 2000). Contact time (CT) values for the effect of chlorine on MAP have been estimated to be up to 580-2300 times greater than those for *E. coli* (Whan et al., 2001). Water resources (lakes and rivers) may get contaminated by MAP run-off from heavily grazed pastures. If such MAP contaminated water is used for purification by treatment plant, is therefore unlikely to be destroyed by subsequent chlorination. These pathogens arriving at domestic outlets in high dilution may accumulate in biofilms present in household cold and hot water storage and delivery systems (Hermon-Taylor and El-Zaatari, 2004). If chlorination is insufficient to destruct MAP, we need to consider exploiting the susceptibility of MAP to UV irradiation and other processes like ozonization. Two published reports shows that in areas where heavily grazed pastures are disposed in water resources were associated with conspicuous clusters of CD. The first of these involved the village of Blockley, in Gloucestershire, England where CD incidence was increased 6.7-fold (Allan et al., 1986). The second such case was observed in town Mankato, Minnesota, USA (van Kruiningen and Freda, 2001).

(ii) MAP and Crohn's disease in Human

CD is one of the fastest growing diseases of the world, especially in western countries. The highest incidence rates of CD have been reported from US, UK and North Europe (Hendrickson *et al.,* 2002). Population based studies indicated that the incidence of the disease ranged between 3.1 to 14.6 cases per 100,000 people. Overall prevalence rate of CD was between 26-198.5 cases per year. The number of CD patients in United States was approximately one million and in United Kingdom, 13 per 100000 persons (Cobrin and Abreu, 2005). In India, the disease was not diagnosed till 1986. But in recent years, Crohn's disease has been frequently reported from different parts of the country especially in southern region (Pai and Khandge 2000).

Crohn's disease and ulcerative colitis, collectively known as inflammatory bowel disease (IBD), are complex disorders reflected by wide variations in clinical practice. Etiology of CD is still controversial and infectious cause for CD has been sought since the disease was first described in 1932 and number of micro-organism have been suggested as the cause of CD. But MAP has received greater attention as the causative agent of CD due to the clinical signs and pathological similarity. (Sechi et al., 2005, Naser et al., 2004). Early studies did not detect MAP in tissues from patients with CD by conventional staining and culture techniques. Failures in detection may be due unusual nature of cell wall deficient MAP in patients with CD and/or challenges in culturing MAP with its fastidious and slow growing characteristic. Problems in culture were overcome by use of MAP specific IS*900* insertion sequences for proxy diagnosis of MAP infection by PCR. But PCR fails to differentiate between live and dead MAP. Mishina et al. (1996) used RT-PCR amplification and confirmed the presence of MAP RNA in the test samples. Using *in-situ* hybridization by IS*900* specific probe, Sechi et al. (2001) confirmed the presence of MAP in biopsy samples of CD and provided evidence for role of MAP in the etiology of CD. MAP has been recently isolated from breast milk of lactating mothers (Naser et al., 2000) and from blood of CD patients indicating that MAP infection is systemic like paratuberculosis in animal (Naser et al., 2004).

The current position regarding the zoonotic potential of MAP is that this organism has not been unequivocably established as a cause of significant human disease. However, recent research publications suggest that there is evidence of some kind of an association, not necessarily causal, between MAP and at least some cases of Crohn's disease. If MAP is ever shown to have a role in Crohn's disease (causal or complicating infection) then there is sufficient evidence in the public domain indicating that cow milk is a potential vehicle of transmission of viable organisms from cattle to humans, even after pasteurization.

Risk management of paratuberculosis or Johne's disease

Risk management of JD in a dairy herd requires an assessment of the likelihood of JD occurring in the herd, the economic impact of JD on the herd and an evaluation of measures that can be taken to reduce this likelihood and impact. Likelihood of JD occurring in the herd is related to the regional herd-level prevalence of JD and herd management (e.g., introducing animals from other herds). Economic impact of JD includes production losses due to subclinical and clinical cases, losses due to increased replacement of animals and costs of control measures. Furthermore, a reduction of the price of milk from infected herds might result from consumer concerns about the zoonotic potential of JD. Measures that reduce the likelihood of JD occurring in a herd and its impact include preventive management measures (e.g. closed herd management and an effective separation of susceptible young stock from adult cattle), test-and-cull schemes for known infected herds and quality assurance schemes for test-negative herds. Keys to success of risk management of JD include realistic expectations of the results of JD control, quality assurance and control programs that are appreciated by farmers and incentives for farmers to participate in such programs.

Control Strategies

Controlling Johne's disease essentially helps control many other infectious diseases such as *Salmonella, Cryptosporidium* and several viral diseases affecting young calves. These diseases can spread from adults to kids through manure, the fecal-oral route of infection transmission. Overall, Johne's disease control practices yield healthier kids -less mortality and lower morbidity. Due to limitations in diagnosis of early infection and effective vaccine, there is no strategies that control the JD very effectively, however, incidence of the disease can be significantly minimized with available technology.

(i) Management practices

Control strategies usually depend on etiological agent, host range and environment. Knowledge of prevalence, dominant strains and husbandry practices play vital role in designing control and eradication strategies. The control program should basically aim to protect the uninfected farms and to control and prevent infection at the infected farm. Nature of MAP to cause slow progressive infection in animals has significant impact on the diagnosis and control of paratuberculosis. Largely used policy for prevention of MAP infection at farm level is identification of infected animals and their removal (test and cull policy). However, this policy has failed to control the paratuberculosis (Singh et al., 2007b). Experiences suggest that test and cull policy is expensive. The possible reasons for the failure of this policy is the lack of sensitive diagnostic tools for the detection of MAP infection in early stages and the ability of MAP to persist in environment for extended periods of time.

(ii) Vaccination

At present, vaccination is considered as the only affordable method to control the paratuberculosis in herds. The first vaccine against MAP was introduced in 1926 by Vallée and Rinjard (Vallée and Rinjard, 1926). Vaccines against paratuberculosis may contain live attenuated or killed MAP bacilli incorporated with an adjuvant (OIE, 2001). Vaccination has shown encouraging results in controlling paratuberculosis in several countries (Saxegaard and Fodstad, 1985; Perez et al., 1995) including India (Singh et al., 2007b). However, the fact that vaccination of animals against JD interferes with TB diagnosis, limits the widespread use of vaccination. Attempts are underway to design a marker vaccine capable of distinguishing between vaccinated and infected animals.

Conclusion

Infectious disease adversely affects as biotic stress to livestock production and animal welfare and has impacts upon both human health and public perception of livestock production. The epidemic of Johne's disease has now taken a dangerous form and the causative agent *M. a. paratuberculosis* is accused of not only threatening the global environment, but public health as well. MAP imposing the huge stress and visible losses attributed by MAP are not restricted to only livestock production and industries but continue to risk public safety. Direct losses occur by lowering of milk production, premature culling and reduced slaughter value, mortality, abortions or reductions in reproductive performance. Among these largest effect on cost was from milk yield. Financial losses associated with MAP result from reduced milk production, increased mastitis frequency, abortion, other reproductive disorders, weak calves, impaired calf health, birth of persistently infected (PI) animals, increased veterinary costs, cost of replacement animals etc, On dairy farms, economic losses occur through premature culling, reduced milk production, and body-weight losses in slaughter cattle. Though, the mystery for the etiological agent of Crohn's disease is still doubt-full but sufficient evidences for association of MAP with CD are still in hand which draws our attention that- Are we gambling with our lives? To decrease the MAP stress from environment it is very necessary to control immediately in animal population. Control of disease is not possible by the involvement of individual livestock owner, but the involvement of national government is also very important to determine the optimal policy against this disease to decrease the biotic pressure significantly.

References

Alexejeff-Goleff, N.A. 1929. Zur Frage der Pathogenese und Bazillenausscheidung bei Rinderparatuberkulose. Z. Infekt. Krank. Haus., *36*, 312–317.

Allan, R.N., Pease, P. and Ibbotson, J.P. 1986. Clustering of Crohn's Disease in a Cotswold village. The Quarterly Journal of Medicine 59: 473-478

Benedictus, G., Dijkhuizen, A. A. and Stelwagen, J. 1987. Economic losses due to paratuberculosis in dairy cattle. Veterinary Record 121:142–146.

Benedictus, G, Dijkhuizen, A. A. and Stelwagen, J, 1987. Economic losses due to paratuberculosis in dairy cattle. Veterinary Record, 121 (7): 142-14

Chiodini, R.J., Van Kruiningen, H.J. and Merkal, R.S. 1984. Ruminant paratuberculosis (Johne's disease): the current status and future prospects. Cornell Veterinarian 74: 218–262.

Cobrin, G.M. and Abreu, M.T. 2005. Defects in Mucosal Immunity Leading to Crohn's Disease. Immunology Review 206: 277–295.

Dieguez, F. J., Arnaiz, I., Sanjuán, M. L., Vilar, M. J. and Yus, E., 2008. Management practices associated with *Mycobacterium avium* subspecies *paratuberculosis* infection and the effects of the infection on dairy herds. Vet. Rec., 162:614-617.

Doyle T.M. 1958. Foetal infection in Johne's disease. Veterinary Record 70: 328.

Gao, L., Mutharia, S., Chen, K. and Rahn, Odumeru, J. 2002. Effect of pasteurization in survival of *Mycobacterium paratuberculosis* in milk, Journal of Dairy Science 85: 3189–3205.

Gill, I.J. 1989. The economic impact of Johne's disease in cattle in Australia. In Johne's disease, A.Milner and P. Wood, eds. East Melbourne: Commonwealth Scientific and Industrial Research Organization p. 41–45.

Gomes, M.J.P., Asanome, W. and Ribeiro, V.R. 2005. Prevalence of infection caused by *Mycobacterium avium* subsp. *paratuberculosis* (MAP) in dairy herds in Rio Grande do Sul - South Brazil. In *8th International Colloquium on Paratuberculosis*, Edited by S. Saxmose Nielsen. Copenhagen, Denmark: The Royal Veterinary and Agricultural University (KVL). Pp. 53

Greig, A., Stevenson, K., Henderson, D., Perez, V., Hughes, V. and Pavlik, I. 1999. Epidemiological study of paratuberculosis in wild rabbits in Scotland. Journal of Clinical Microbiology 37: 1746.

Groenendaal, H. and Galligan, D.T. 1999. Economical consequences of Johne's disease control programs. Center of Animal Health and Productivity. Technical Report. School of Veterinary Medicine, University of Pennsylvania.

Hendrickson, B., Gokhale, R. and Cho, J.H. 2002. Clinical aspects and pathophysiology of inflammatory bowel disease, Clinical Microbiology Review 15: 79–94.

Hermon-Taylor, J., Bull, T.J., Sherdian, J.M., Cheng, J., Stellakis, M.L. and Sumar, N. 2000. Causation of Crohn's disease by *Mycobacterium avium* subspecies *paratuberculosis*. Canadian Journal of Gastroenterology 14: 521–539.

Hermon-Taylor, J. and El-Zaatari, F. A. K. 2004. The *Mycobacterium avium* subsp. *paratuberculosis* problem and its relation to the causation of Crohn's disease. Chapter VI. Pathogenic mycobacteria in water: a guide to public health significance, Edited by By S. Pedley, Jamie Bartram, World Health Organization, 74-94.

http://www.johnes.org/

Johnson-Ifearulundu, Y. J. and Kaneene, J. B. 1997. Epidemiology and economic impact of subclinical Johne's disease: a review. Veterinary Bulletin 67:437–447.

Kennedy, D. J., Holmström, A., Plym Forshell, K., Vindel, E. and Suarez Fernandez, G. 2001. On-farm management of paratuberculosis (Johne's disease) in dairy herds. Bulletin of the International Dairy Federation 362: 18-31.

Kennedy, D.G. and Benedictus, G. 2001. Control of *Mycobacterium avium* subsp. *paratuberculosis* infection in agricultural species. Revue scientifique et technique (International Office of Epizootics) 20: 151-179.

Kennedy, D.J. and Allworth, M.B. 1999. Progress in national control assurance programme for bovine jouhne's disease in Australia. In E.J.B. Manning and M.T.Collins (eds.) proceedings of VIth International Colloquium on Paratuberculosis, International Association of Paratuberculosis. Madison, WI p. 19-26.

Kudahl, A. B. and Nielsen, S. S., 2009. Effect of paratuberculosis on slaughter weight and slaughter value of dairy cows. J. Dairy Sci., 92:4340-4346.

Kulshreshtha, R.C., Singh, J. and Chandirammani, N.K. 1980. A study on the prevelance of tuberculosis and Johne's diseases in cattle and buffaloes in Haryana state. Haryana Veterinarian 19: 139-141.

Kumar, P., Singh, S.V., Bhatiya, A.K., Sevilla, I., Singh, A.V., Whittington, R.J., Juste, R.A., Gupta, V.K., Singh, P.K., Sohal, J.S. and Vihan, V.S. 2007. Juvenile Capri-Paratuberculosis in India; Incidence and characterization of by six diagnostic tests. Small Ruminant Research 73: 45-53.

Larsen, A.B., Stalheim, O.H.V., Hughes, D.E., Appell, L.H., Richards, W.D. and Himes, E.M. 1981. *Mycobacterium paratuberculosis* in the semen and genital organs of a semendonor bull. American Journal of Veterinary Medical Association 179: 169-171.

Merkal, R.S. 1973. Laboratory diagnosis of bovine paratuberculosis. American Journal of Veterinary Medical Association 163: 1100-1102.

Merkal, R.S., Miller, J.M., Hintz, A.M. and Bryner, J.H. 1981. Intrauterine inoculation of *Mycobacterium paratuberculosis* into guinea pigs and cattle. American Journal of Veterinary Research 43: 676-678.

Mishina, D., Katsel, P., Brown, S.T. 1996. On the etiology of Crohn disease. Proceedings of the National Academy of Sciences of the United States of America 93: 9816–20.

Mishra, P., Singh, S.V., Bhatiya, A.K., Singh, P.K., Singh, A.V. and Sohal, J.S. 2007. Real time estimates of prevalence of Bovine Johne's Disease in dairy cattle herds in Mathura region of North India using fecal culture and indigenous ELISA kit and characterization of *Mycobacterium avium* subspecies *paratuberculosis* by IS*900* PCR. In: Neilsen, S. S. (Ed). Proceedings of Ninth International Colloquium on Paratuberculosis, Tsukuba, Japan, p. 220-223.

Mura, M., Bull, T.J., Evans, H., Sidi-Boumedine, K., McMinn, L., Rhodes, G., Pickup, R. and Hermon-Taylor, J. 2006. Replication and long-term persistence of bovine and human strains of *Mycobacterium avium* subsp. *paratuberculosis* within *Acanthamoeba polyphaga*. Applied Environmental Microbiology 72: 854-859.

NAHMS (National Animal Health Monitoring System). 1997a. Johne's Disease on U.S. Dairy Operations. USDA: APHIS: VS, CEAH, NAHMS: Fort Collins, CO.

Naser, S. A., Ghobrial, G., Romero, C. and Valentine, J. F. 2004. Culture of *Mycobacterium avium* subspecies *paratuberculosis* from the blood of patients with Crohn's disease. Lancet 364: 1039-1044.

Naser, S.A., Schwartz, D. and Shafran, I. 2000. Isolation of *Mycobacterium avium* subsp. *paratuberculosis* from breast milk of Crohn's disease patients, American Journal of . Gastroenterology 95: 1094–1095.

Nordlund, K.V., Goodger, W.J., Pelletier, J. and Collins, M.T. 1996. Associations between subclinical paratuberculosis and milk production milk components and somatic cell counts in dairy herds. Journal of American Veterinary Medical Association 208:1872–1876.

OIE (Office International des Epizooties). 2001. International Animal Health Code. Paris

Olsen, I., Siguroardottir, O.G. and Djonne, B. 2002. *Paratuberculosis* with special reference to cattle. A review. Veterinary Quarterly 24: 12-28.

Ott, S.L., Wells, S.J. and Wagner BA, 1999. Herd-level economic losses associated with Johne's disease on US dairy operations. Prev Vet Med, 40(3-4):179-92.

Pai, C.G. and Khandge, G.K. 2000. Is Crohn's disease rare in India? Indian Journal of Gastroenterology19:17-20.

Pavlik, I., Bejckova, L., Pavlas, M., Rozsypalova, Z. and Koskova, S. 1995. Characterization by restriction endonuclease analysis and DNA hybridization using IS*900* of bovine, ovine, caprine and human dependent strains of *Mycobacterium paratuberculosis* isolated in various localities. Veterinary Microbiology 45: 311-318.

Pavlik, I., Horvathova, A., Dvorska, L., Bartl, J., Svastova, P., Du Maine, R. and Rychlik, I. 1999. Standardization of restriction fragment length polymorphism analysis for *Mycobacterium avium* subspecies *paratuberculosis*. Journal of Clinical Microbiology 38: 155-167.

Perez, V., Garcia Marin, J.F., Bru, R., Moreno, B. and Badiola, J.J. 1995. Resultados obtenidos en la vacunacion de ovinos adultos frente a paratuberculosis. Veterinary medicine12: 196–201.

Raut, A., Manju, A., Kumar, B. and Sethi, R.K. 2003. Prevalence of paratuberculosis in breeding buffalo bulls at organized farms. Proceedings for 4th Asian Buffalo Congress on Buffalo for Food Security and Rural Employment. New Delhi, India. p.18

Saxegaard, F. and Fodstad, F.H. 1985. Control ofparatuberculosis (Johne's disease) in goats by vaccination. Veterinary Record 116:439.

Sechi LA, Scanu AM, Molicotti P, Cannas S, Mura M, and Dettori, G. 2005. Detection and isolation of *Mycobacterium avium* subspecies *paratuberculosis* from intestinal mucosal biopsies of patients with and without Crohn's disease in Sardinia. American Journal of Gastroenterology 100: 1529-1536.

Sechi, L.A., Mura, M. and Tanda, F. 2001. Identification of *Mycobacterium avium* subsp. *paratuberculosis* in biopsy specimens from patients with Crohn's disease identified by *in situ* hybridization. Journal of Clinical Microbiology 39: 4514–4517.

Shankar, H., Singh, S.V., Singh, P.K., Singh, A.V., Sohal, J.S. and Greenstein, R.J. 2009. Presence, characterization and genotype profiles of *Mycobacterium avium* subspecies *paratuberculosis* from un pasteurized individual and pooled milk, commercial pasteurized milk and products in India by culture, PCR, and PCR-REA methods. International Journal of Infectious Diseases Doi:10.1016/j.ijid.2009.03.031.

Singh, S. V., Singh, A. V., Singh, R., Sharma, S., Shukla, N., Misra, S., Singh, P. K., Sohal, J. S., Kumar, H., Patil, P. K., Misra, P. and Sandhu, K. S. 2008. Sero-prevalence of Johne's disease in buffaloes and cattle population of North India using indigenous ELISA kit based on native *Mycobacterium avium* subspecies *paratuberculosis* 'Bison type' genotype of goat origin. Comparative Immunology Microbiology and Infectious Diseases. 31: 419-433.

Singh, S.V., Singh, A.V., Singh, R., Sharma, S., Shukla, N., Misra, S., Singh, P.K., Sohal, J.S., Kumar, H., Patil, P.K., Misra, P. and Sandhu, K.S. 2008a. Sero-prevalence of Johne's disease in buffaloes and cattle population of North India using indigenous ELISA kit based on native *Mycobacterium avium* subspecies *paratuberculosis* 'Bison type' genotype of goat origin. Comparative Immunology Microbiology and Infectious Diseases 31: 419-433.

Singh, A. V., Singh, S. V., Makharia, G. K., Singh, P. K. and Sohal, J. S. 2008b. Presence and Characterization of Mycobacterium avium subspecies paratuberculosis from clinical and suspected cases of Crohn's disease and in healthy human population in India. International Journal of Infectious Diseases 12: 190-197.

Singh, N., Singh, S.V., Gupta, V.K., Sharma, V.D., Sharma, R.K. and Katoch, V.M. 1996. Isolation and identification of *Mycobacterium paratuberculosis* from naturally infected goatherds in India. Indian Journal of Veterinary Pathology 20: 104-108.

Singh, S.V., Singh, A.V., Singh, R., Sandhu, K.S., Singh, P.K., Sohal, J.S., Gupta, V.K. and Vihan, V.S. 2007a. Evaluation of highly sensitive indigenous milk ELISA kit with fecal culture, milk culture and fecal-PCR for the diagnosis of bovine Johne's disease (BJD). Comparative Immunology Microbiology and Infectious Disease 30: 175-186.

Singh, S.V., Singh, P.K., Singh, A.V., Sohal, J.S. and Gupta, V.K. 2007b. Comparative efficacy of an indigenous 'Inactivated vaccine' using highly pathogenic field strain of *Mycobacterium avium* subspecies *paratuberculosis* 'Bison type' with a commercial vaccine for the control of Capri- Paratuberculosis in India. Vaccine 25: 7102-7110.

Sivakumar, P., Tripathi, B.N. and Singh, N. 2003. Detection of *Mycobacterium avium* subsp. *paratuberculosis* in the intestinal and lymph node tissues of water buffaloes *(Bubalus bubalis)* by PCR and bacterial culture. Veterinary Microbiology 108: 263-270.

Sivakumar, P., Tripathi, B.N. and Singh, N. 2005. Detection of *Mycobacterium avium* subsp. *paratuberculosis* in intestinal and lymphnode tissue of water buffaloes (Bubalus bubalis) by PCR and bacterial culture. Veterinary Microbiology 108: 263-270.

Stehman, S.M. 1990. Johne's disease (paratuberculosis), 1990. In: Smith, B. (Ed.), Large Animal Internal Medicine, The C.V. Mosby Co., St. Louis, pp. 823–829

Stott, A.W., Jones, G.M. and Humphry, R.W. 2005. Financial incentive to control paratuberculosis on dairy farms in the United Kingdom. Veterinary Record 156: 825-31.

Strahl, E.D., Gillaspy, G.E. and Falkinham, J.O. 2001. Fluorescent acid-fast microscopy for measuring phagocytosis of *Mycobacterium avium*, *Mycobacterium intracellulare*, and *Mycobacterium scrofulaceum* by *Tetrahymena pyriformis* and their intracellular growth. Applied Environmental Microbiology 67: 4432–4439.

Sweeney, R.W., Whitlock, R.H., Hamir, A.N., Rosenberger, A.E. and Herr, S.A. 1992. Isolation of *Mycobacterium paratuberculosis* after oral inoculation in uninfected animals. American Journal of Veterinary Research 53: 1312–1314.

Sweeney, R.Y. 1996. Transmission of paratuberculosis. The Veterinary clinics of North America. Food animal practice 12: 305-312.

Taylor, T.K., Wilks, C.R. and McQueen, D.S. 1981. Isolation of *Mycobacterium paratuberculosis* from the milk of a cow with Johne's disease. Veterinary Record 109: 532-533.

USDA. 2001. State Control Programs.

Vallée, H. and Rinjard, P. 1926. Etudes sur l'enterite paratuberculeus des bovides. Rev Gen Med Vet 1926; 35: 1-9.

van Kruiningen, H.J. and Freda, B.J. 2001. A clustering of Crohn's disease in Mankato, Minnesota. Inflammatory Bowel Diseases 7: 27-33.

Wells, S.J. and Wagner, B.A. 2000. Herd-level risk factors for infection with Mycobacterium paratuberculosis in US dairies and association between familiarity of the herd manager with the disease or prior diagnosis of the disease in that herd and use of preventive measures. Journal of American Veterinary Medical Association 216: 1450–1457.

Whan, L. 2003. The incidence and persistence of *Mycobacterium avium* subspecies *paratuberculosis* in Northern Ireland water supplies. PhD thesis, Queen's University of Belfast, Belfast.

Whan, L.B., Grant, I.R., Ball, H.J., Scott, R. and Rowe, M.T. 2001. Bactericidal effect of chlorine on *Mycobacterium paratuberculosis* in drinking water. Letters in Applied Microbiology 33: 227–231.

Whitlock, R H., Hutchinson, L.T., Merkal, R., Glickman, L.T., Rossiter, C., Harmon, S., Spencer, P., Fetrow, J., Bruce, J., Benson, C.E. and Dick, J. 1985. Prevalence and economic consideration of Johne's disease in the northeastern US. Proceedings 89th Annual Meeting, US Animal Health Association, Milwaukee, WI, 27 October to 1 November, pp. 484-490.

Whittington, R. J., Marshall, D. J. , Nicholls, P. J., Marsh, I. B. and Reddacliff, L. A. 2004. Survival and dormancy of *Mycobacterium avium* subsp. *paratuberculosis* in the environment. Applied Environmental Microbiology 70:2989–3004.

Whittington, R.J., Marsh, I.B. and Reddacliff, L.A. 2005. Survival of *Mycobacterium avium* subsp. *paratuberculosis* in dam water and sediment. Applied Environmental Microbiology 71: 5304-5308.

Yadav, D., Singh, S.V., Singh, A.V., Sevilla, I., Juste, R.A., Singh, P.K. and Sohal, J.S. 2008. Pathogenic 'Bison type' *Mycobacterium avium* subspecies *paratuberculosis* genotype characterized from riverine Buffalo (*Bubalus bubalis*) in North India. Comparative Immunology Microbiology and Infectious Diseases 31:378-387.

Yayo Ayele, W., Machackova, M. and Pavlik, I. 2001. The transmission and impact of paratuberculosis infection in domestic and wild ruminants. Veterinary Medical Czech 46: 205–224.

❑❑❑

34

Transportation and Slaughter Stresses and their Effect on Meat Yield and Quality

N. Kondaiah* and S. Vaithiyanathan
National Research Centre on Meat, Hyderabad
Chengicherla, P.B.No.19, Uppal, Hyderabad-500 039, Andhra Pradesh

Small ruminants are one of the earliest domesticated animals in Asia and have widest ecological range to survive and thrive. They inhabit almost all climatic zones of the country. These animals are extensively reared and all the time they are on move looking for better grazing areas. These animals are reared mainly for meat, milk and skin. Meat has occupied a unique position in the human diet and regarded as an important ingredient in any menu. It is highly nutritious with excellent source of high quality protein and contains large amount of minerals and serves as a good source of essential vitamins. A number of factors including species, feeding, management, transport, stunning and welfare treatment of the animals before slaughter determine the quality of meat and meat products.

Breed/Genetics and stress

Generally it is evident that growth potential and resistance to stress are negatively correlated. Tropically adapted genotypes are resistant to the stress and so their growth potential is less than its counterpart in temperate region.

Goat is less susceptible than sheep to environment related stress. In a classical experiment, breed effect on meat quality after transport has been reported (Kadim et al., 2006). Batina goats from Oman were susceptible to transportation stress than Dhofari, and Jabal Akhdar goats. Meat from goats transported in a truck for 100 km had significantly higher ultimate pH, expressed juice, cooking loss percentage, shear force, but significantly lower sarcomere length, L^*, a^*, and b^* values.

Genetic basis of porcine stress syndrome

The porcine stress syndrome (PSS) gene is found to cause malignant hyperthermia (heat shock) when pigs are exposed to environmental stressors or to anaesthetic gas halothane. This gene is commonly referred as the halothane gene, because exposing pigs to the anesthetic halothane gas can trigger the PSS condition. Researchers established the presence of the PSS condition in 1968 when they observed that physically stressed; susceptible pigs would collapse in a shock-like state and die. Pigs carrying the PSS gene are more prone to producing pale, soft and exudative (PSE) pork, which is not only unattractive to consumers because of its unappealing grayish, soft and watery appearance, but is also less suitable for further processing because of its low water-holding capacity. The PSS condition is an inherited disorder in swine. Inheritance of the PSS gene is at a single locus and there are two alleles, one dominant (N) and one recessive (n). The disorder resulted from mutation (RYR1) for halothane gene encoding for a muscle specific isoform of the regulatory γ-subunit of adenosine monophosphate-activated protein kinase.

Feeding and stress

Nutritional factors are the most important in determining the growth potential and meat quality parameters. Technologies to increase feed efficiency and lean tissue deposition and to decrease fat deposition have been developed in an effort to improve profitability of animal production. But the increasing production efficiency and lean meat yield has led to poor quality meat. It is reported that even at conservative use of each of these technologies will result in a 5-10% (0.3–0.5 kg) increase in shear force with a similar reduction in perception of tenderness. However, there are some other metabolic factors and dietary additives that offer some potential to improve meat quality (for example immunocastration) and it is possible that these can be used on their own or in conjunction with somatotropin, approved â-agonists, anabolic implants and CLA to maintain or improve meat quality (Dunshea et al., 2005).

Another stress originating from feeding of animal with feeds containing anti-nutritional factors especially polyphenolic compounds on meat quality is the recent researchable area in the nutrition and meat science. Top feeds are rich in polyphenolics, which are supplemented to sheep after routine grazing, forms the main diet in goats. These polyphenolic compounds are implicated in reducing animal production performances through inhibition of protein digestion (Kumar and Vaithiyanathan, 1990). However, these compounds are also considered as antioxidants and when present in feed or food can act as radical scavengers and may involve in improving meat quality through inhibiting oxidative stress (Naveena et al., 2008; Vaithiyanathan et al., 2009). In an *in vitro* muscle model system it was found that lipid oxidation decreased significantly following addition of each of the natural antioxidants relative to the control and antioxidant potency followed the order: sesamol > ellagic acid > olive leaf extract > lutein (Hayes et al., 2009). *In vivo* system, meat quality parameters such as spoilage, TBARS and colour values from lambs of ewes fed with rosemary leaves scored better than control group (Nieto et al., 2010). Inclusion of quebracho tannins in sheep diets improves meat colour stability of fresh lamb during extended refrigerated storage (Luciano et al., 2009).

Management/Physiology and stress

During the period of pre-slaughter conditions and practices animals are exposed to a range of challenging stimuli, which dictates meat quality. As a consequence of pre-slaughter challenges, an animal may experience fear, dehydration and hunger, increased physical activity, fatigue and physical injury. Fear-eliciting stimuli activate neuro-endocrinal response in animal suffering from pre-slaughter stress phase. The two central integrated processes include the autonomic nervous system and hypothalamic pituitary-adrenal (HPA) axis. When these two systems are activated there will be a manifestation of release of glucocorticoids which results in significant changes in energy metabolism including lipolysis, glycogenolysis in muscle and gluconeogenesis (Ferguson and Warner, 2008). Stress produces number physiological changes, one of which is a reduction in muscle glycogen content. In general stress susceptible animals have unusually high temperatures, rapid glycolysis (pH drop) and early onset of rigor mortis in their muscles. If the pH drops very rapidly while the meat temperature is still high, muscle protein are denatured and the resulting exudates masks the myoglobin to give a pale, soft, exudative (PSE) appearance. The PSE condition is associated with lowered processing yield, increased cooking losses and reduced juiciness. The adverse economic effect of the PSE was estimated in 1972 between 230 and 320 million dollars per year in the United States. The normal rate of PSE incidence was reported to range from 10-30%, but in some isolated incidences up to 60%.

A dark, firm and dry muscle condition also can be produced in meat from animals with a degree of stress susceptibility, if they have survived a stress of sufficient duration to deplete their glycogen reserves. Muscle glycogen deficiently in these animals causes a slow rate and limited extent of glycolysis after death resulting in high pH meat. Major disadvantages of DFD meat are an unattractive dark, firm, dry appearance and a favourable pH for bacterial growth. These conditions cause monetary loss particularly in fresh meat trade. Severe shortening and early onset of rigor mortis may be induced by maintaining muscle at relatively high temperature (up to 50°C) which is described as heat rigor produced as a result of a rapid depletion of ATP stores. In the shortening range of 20-50 per cent, tenderness decreases as degree of shortening increases. Pre-slaughter residence and season are sources of stress for lambs and affect meat quality traits. Meat from lambs slaughtered in winter had some dark-cutting characteristics, with darker colour, higher ultimate pH, tougher meat and lower press juice.

Abattoir management may refuse to slaughter dirty animals, which may require costly and time-consuming transport to be cleaned with potentially adverse effect on meat quality. Cleaning may results in stress on meat animals and the associated effect on meat quality. Pre-slaughter treatment of a change from a warm air to a cold air environment is done for short duration, resulted in altered glycolysis rate and associated properties and improved meat quality.

Transport/handling and stress

It is generally accepted that loading at grazing field and off-loading at slaughterhouse are the most stressful parts of the transport. Stress associated with handling and transport can cause physiological changes, which may affect meat quality resulting in pale, soft exudative (PSE) meat in swine and toughened meat in swine and poultry (Gregory, 2003). Some commonly used physiological indicators of stress during transport are given in Table 1. Meat from highly stressed animals is more prone to putrefaction (Gregory, 2003). Cattle, which become agitated during handling and restraint, had tougher meat and dark cutting meat (Voisinet et al., 1997). In sheep multiple stresses like transport, shearing, mustering, restraint causes increased plasma cortisol concentration and the transport is only second to shearing stress in sheep (Knowles et al., 1995). The more stresses that a lamb has to go before slaughter, the more likely it is to produce high pH, which produce dark meat. The single most provocative of stresses in sheep is the swim washing (Bray et al., 1989). In addition, the transportation stress in sheep is muscle specific. Muscles such as triceps branchii, supraspinatus, semitendinosus and pectoralis produndus were prone to developing a high pH (Gregory, 2003). Dehydration during transportation is a common occurrence before the animals are slaughtered in hot climate. It has been reported animals lost 10% of their live weight due to dehydration while they are transported for 1420 km. But these animals recovered 40% of the lost weight when they had a chance to drink water. If they are not given drinking water the meat is likely to be drier, darker and tougher (Jones et al., 1990). Emotional stress during transport induces defecation and this adds to the hygiene problem during rainy season when diarrhoea is severe in cattle. This leads to faecal soiling of hind quarter and faecal soiling of other animals in the trucks when they are transported to slaughter house, other animals get contaminated. Means of transport also affect the infection by *Clostridium pefringens* type A in cattle of Brazil. Higher concentrations of bacteria were found in cattle while transported by rail in comparison to truck and the levels were higher in dry days compared with rainy days (Gregory, 2003).

Pre-slaughter fasting causes salmonella to proliferate in the rumen, and the longer the time from farm to slaughter; the greater is the chance that animal will carry salmonella in rumen (Gregory, 2003). The movement of animals from grazing area to slaughterhouse have some stress on the animals and depending on the severity of stress and health of the animal, the impact can vary from simple bruise to death. It is generally recognised that the most prevalent physical injury that occurs during pre-slaughter handling is bruising. Probably the most important effect on carcass resulting from transportation injuries is bruising and this occurs in all species but is particularly noticed in sheep and pigs (Sen and Naveena, 2003). At slaughter, excising of the bruised region on the carcass results in a net loss in carcass weight and yield. The death during transportation in sheep is a great concern as it leads to losses for traders. It is estimated that 0.02 to 0.03% of sheep death occurs on arrival at processing plant (Naidu et al., 1991).

Table 1. Commonly used physiological indicators of stress during transport

Stressor	Physiological variable
Measured in blood	
Food deprivation	↑ FFA, ↑ β-OHB, vglucose, ^urea
Dehydration	↑ Osmolality, ↑ total protein, ↑ albumin, ↑ PCV
Physical excretion	↑ CK, ?lactate
Fear/arousal	↑ Cortisol, ?PCV
Motion sickness	↑ Vasopressin
Other measures	
Fear/ arousal and physical exertion	↑ Hear rate, ↑ respiration rate
Hypothermia/hyperthermia	Body temperature, skin temperature

FFA=free fatty acids; β-OHB= β-hydroxybutyrate; PCV=packed cell volume; CK=creatine kinase (Knowles and Warris, 2005)

Animal welfare

Animal handling and transport have considerable influence on the welfare of meat animals. Improvements in welfare during handling and transport improve productivity and reduce losses associated with poor carcass quality. Handling and transportation of meat animals lead to stress, bruising and in some cases serious injury or death. Stress has deleterious effect on the colour, texture and keeping qualities of the meat and consumer acceptability, while bruising often requires expensive cuts of meat to be trimmed or discarded and sometimes condemn the whole carcasses. The techniques such as cooling devices in warm weather and avoidance of crowding, low noise and mixing of strange groups of animals as well as providing rest to animals minimize death loss and improve subsequent meat quality. Bureau of Indian Standards has developed standards for trucks carrying small ruminants (IS 14904:2001), which are given in Table 2. Government of India has enacted rules under the prevention of cruelty to animals act, 1960 for the well being of small ruminants when the animals are moved (Transport of Animals on Foot Rules, 2001) from one place to another are given in Table 3.

Table 2. Space allowance for sheep and goats during transport in a truck or rail

Animals	Weight in kg	Mean woollen sheep /goat dimensions in meter Width x length	Space required in m^2 Woollen	Space required in m^2 Shorn
Lambs	Up to 15	0.24 x 0.6	0.15	0.15
	16-20	0.25 x 0.7	0.18	0.16
Sheep/Goat	21-25	0.26 x 0.74	0.20	0.18
(Adult)	26-55	0.35 x 0.91	0.3 to 0.4	0.2 to 0.3
	More than 55		>0.40	>0.40

Table 3. Limits for movement of sheep and goat during transport on foot

Species (Animal)	Maximum distance covered/day/h	Temperatures range Min.-Max.	Maximum hours of walking/day (Travelling)	Period of rest (Interval)
Goats and Sheep	30 km/day 4 km/hr	12 to 30°C	8 hours	At every 2 hr for drinking and at every 4 hr for feeding
Kids and Lambs	16 km/day 2.5 km/hr	12 to 30°C	6 hours	At every 1½ hr for drinking and at every 3 hr for feeding

These figures may vary depending on the animals' breed, weight, size and fleece, presence or absence of horns as well as their physical conditions, the meteorological conditions and journey time. The space allowance should be increased by at least 10% during hot, humid conditions.

Stress due to animal handling at slaughterhouse

Proper and gentle handling of animals in well-designed slaughterhouse minimizes stress levels, improve efficiency and maintain good meat quality. Rough handling or poorly designed equipment is detrimental to both animal welfare and meat quality. Constant monitoring of animal handler is required to maintain high standards of animal welfare. Every extra handling procedure causes stress and bruises. Therefore floor, fence, crowd pens, ramps, restraint system must be designed in such a way so that stress on animal could be reduced.

Stunning vs Halal method of slaughtering on meat quality

Small ruminants are slaughtered by cutting jugular veins and carotid artery in halal method. The disadvantage of this method is that bleeding of slaughtered animal is not completed all the time and this produces inferior quality meat. While stunning of animal prior to slaughter is advocated in the present scenario of animal welfare and for producing good quality meat. Stunning of sheep either with electrical stunners or 80% CO_2 stunning produced quality meat (Vergara et al., 2009, Vergara and Gallego, 2000). Stunning with CO_2 resulted in more tender meat (lower SF value) than electrical stunning in sheep. Moreover, there was no blood splash in any of the carcass of the CO_2 stunned animals (Vergara et al., 2005).

Approaches to avoid stress in animals

Genetic selection

Selection of breeds/ strains not free from susceptible genes for meat quality.

Management and handling

Avoiding harsh weather, crowding, loud noise, mixing of strange group of animals and loading and unloading by trained personnel's.

Tranquilizers

Use of stresnil (azaperone) or promazine derivatives

Feed supplements

Increase level of tryptophan diet or supplementation of Vitamin E reduce incidence of PSE condition. Include feeds containing phenolic compounds to improve meat quality.

Handling at slaughter house

Unnecessary weighing of live animals, shearing etc shall be avoided

Humane stunning

Proper method of stunning technique shall be used.

Slaughtering method

PSE incidence reduced from 62% in carcass bled in suspended position to 25% in carcass bled in lying position.

Rapid chilling

Rapid chilling of carcass to reduce the adverse effect of stress on meat quality.

Financial incentives

The most powerful method for reducing losses during transport and handling is financial incentive to the truck driver and handlers for quality work.

Pre slaughter detection method

Non-destructive test for identification of stress susceptible animal can help in selection of animal for long distance transport. These include estimation of enzymes particularly CPK, aldolase, GOT, GPT, LDH, MDH and alkaline phosphatase.

References

Bray, A. J., Graathuis, A. E. and Chrustall, B. B. 1989. The cumulative effect of nutritional, shearing and pre slaughter washing stresses on the quality of lamb meat. Meat Science 25:59-67.

Dunshea, F. R., D'Souza, D. N., Pethick, D. W., Harper, G. S. and Warner, R.D. 2005. Effects of dietary factors and other metabolic modifiers on quality and nutritional value of meat Meat Science 71: 8-38.

Ferguson, D. M. and Warner, R. D. 2008. Have we underestimated the impact of pre-slaughter stress on meat quality in ruminants? Meat Science 80:12-19.

Gregory N G. 2003. Animal Welfare and Meat Science. USA, CABI Publishing.

Hayes, J. E., Stepanyan, V., Allen, P., O'Grady, M. N., O'Brien, N.M. and Kerry, J.P. 2009. The effect of lutein, sesamol, ellagic acid and olive leaf extract on lipid oxidation and oxymyoglobin oxidation in bovine and porcine muscle model systems. Meat Science 83: 201-208.

Jones, S. D.M., Schaefer, A. L., Robertson, W. M. and Vincent, B.C. 1990. The effects of withholding feed and water on carcass shrinkage and meat quality in beef cattle. Meat Science 28: 131-139.

Kadim, I. T., Mahgoub, O., Al-Kindi, A., Al-Marzooqi, W., Al-Saqri, N. M. 2006. Effects of transportation at high ambient temperatures on physiological responses, carcass and meat quality characteristics of three breeds of Omani goats Meat Science 73: 626-634.

Knowles, T.G., Brown, S.N., Warriss, P.D., Philips, A.J., Dolan, s.K., Hunt, P., Ford, J.E., Edwards, J.E. and Warking, P.E. 1995. Effects on sheep of transport by road for up to 24 hours. Veterinary Record 136: 431-438.

Kumar, R. and Vaithiyanathan, S. 1990. Occurrence, nutritional significance and effect on animal productivity of tannins in tree leaves. Animal Feed Science and Technology 30: 21-38.

Luciano, G., Monahan, F. J., Vasta, V., Biondi, L., Lanza, M. and Priolo, A. 2009. Dietary tannins improve lamb meat colour stability. Meat Science 81:120-125.

Naidu, A. S., Rao, K. S., Chandramouli, D. and Rao, K. S. 1991. Marketing of goats and sheep. In: Proceedings of the Workshop on Meat and Slaughterhouse by-products Handling System CLRI, Madras 15-17, July.

Naveena, B. M., Sen, A. R., Vaithiyanathan, S., Babji, Y., and Kondaiah, N. 2008. Comparative efficacy of pomegranate juice, pomegranate rind powder extract and BHT as antioxidants in cooked chicken patties. Meat Science, doi:10.1016/j. meatsci.2008. 06.005.

Nieto, G., Díaz, P., Bañón, S. and Garrido, M. C. 2010. Dietary administration of ewe diets with a distillate from rosemary leaves (*Rosmarinus officinalis L.*): Influence on lamb meat quality. Meat Science 84: 23-29.

Sen, A. S. and Naveena, B. M. 2003. Pre-slaughter stress and its effect on meat quality: A review. Livestock International. 2: 4-7.

Vaithiyanathan, S., Naveena, B. M., Muthukumar, M., Girish, P. S., Sen A. R., Babji, Y., and Ramakrishna, C. 2009. Effect of methyl gallate on physico-chemical qualities of spent hen meat patties. Journal of Food Science and Technology 46: 577-580.

Vergara, H. and Gallego, L. 2000. Effect of electrical stunning on meat quality of lamb. Meat Science 56: 345-349.

Vergara, H., Bórnez, R. and Linares, M.B. 2009. CO_2 stunning procedure on Manchego light lambs: Effect on meat quality. Meat Science 83: 517-522.

Vergara, H., Linares, M. B., Berruga, M. I., Gallego, L. 2005. Meat quality in suckling lambs: Effect of pre-slaughter handling. Meat Science 69: 473-478.

Voisinet, B.D., Grandin, T., O'Connor, S.F.O., Tatum, J.D. and Decsun, M.J. 1997. *Bos indicus*-cross feedlot cattle with excitable temperaments have tougher meat and a higher incidence of borderline dark cutter. Meat Science 46: 367-377.

□□□

35

Meat Production, Export Potential and SPS Measures

M.K. Agnihotri
Department of Animal Husbandry, Dairying and Fisheries
Ministry of Agriculture, Government of India, Krishi Bhawan, New Delhi- 110 114

Introduction

India, with 11 % of the world livestock population, occupies a significant place numerically in respect of livestock wealth. With 2.3% of the land area of the world, country is maintaining nearly 17% of world's human population and about 11% of the livestock. Country possesses about 57% of buffaloes, 14 %of cattle, 16 % of goat, 6 % of sheep and 1.5 % of world pig population. With such large population of livestock, on meat production front, it contributes meager 2.42 percent to the world total meat production of 269 million tones (FAO, 2007). In general, productivity of our livestock is very low, in comparison to the world average. The average carcass yield from sheep, goat and pigs is 12, 10, 35 kg as against the world average of 16, 12 and 79 kg, respectively.

Current status

Meat industry in India has great economic potential but received limited attention for its growth and development. It is envisaged to achieve 10%

growth rate in meat sector during 11th Five Year Plan period. As per FAO (2007) estimates, 12.45 million cattle, 10.86 million buffaloes, 19.54 million sheep, 54.30 million goats and 14.20 million pigs were slaughtered for meat production. Slaughterhouses have been under the control of municipal authorities /local bodies and no systematic efforts have been made to make meat production an economic activity. Barring some export-oriented abattoirs, it has been in the hands of those who have no knowledge of slaughterhouse hygiene, sanitation, clean environment, meat quality, food safety and animal rights. The hygienic conditions in most of the slaughterhouses are not very satisfactory and animal by-products are not properly handled and processed.

Production and supply of meat for local consumption is one of the most neglected and poorly organized sectors in the country. Meat is sold in open places attracting contamination from dirt, dust, flies, water etc. Though the consumption of meat and meat products is on rise, hygiene, safety and quality aspects have not changed much. With the introduction of National Food Safety and Standard Authority under the provision of the Food Safety and Standards Act 2006, production, packaging, transportation, supply, marketing and storage of meat and meat products under strict hygienic condition has become essential to safe guard human health.

Meat demand

Presently the animal protein supply per caput per day is only 10 g as against the world average of 29 g. The per capita consumption of meat in the country, as per FAO (2007) estimates is 13.70 g /day whereas the world average is 106.85 g. In USA, it is 337g, the highest followed by 331 g in Spain, 323 g in Australia. In China, it is about 148g/caput/day. This is due to not enough production of livestock products. The poor productivity in livestock is not only due to poor genetic makeup but also due to lack of adequate feeding and nutrition. Growing population and incomes, along with fast changing food preferences, are rapidly increasing demand for livestock products in the country while globalization is boosting trade in livestock inputs and their products. It is estimated that by 2020 country would require about 147million tones of milk and 14 million tones of meat (Dastagiri, 2004), which could be possible only through improving the productivity, rather than number of livestock.

Exports

There is a preference for meat exported from India because of certain inherent merits such as its lean character, relative freedom from toxic feed additive residues and near organic meat production. Currently India has been exporting meat to more than 50 countries. Buffalo meat is exported in frozen bone less and de-glanded form and is free from FMD virus due to its ageing for minimum of 24 h at 2°C to bring down the meat pH below 6.0. Meat is available at very competitive prices. The Indian buffalo and lamb meat has established itself in the markets' of South-East Asia, Middle East and African countries. Out of total meat production of 6.50 million tones, buffalo alone contributes about 1.50 million tones. With this much production of buffalo meat, India ranks first followed by Pakistan (0.68 million tones) and China (0.31 million tones). The world total buffalo meat production was 3.32 million tones in 2007.

India is the 5th largest producer of meat. The meat production by top five meat-producing countries is given in Table 1. The Country is 5th largest exporter of bovine (buffalo) meat in the world. The figures of top five bovine meat exporting countries are given in Table 2.

Table 1. Total meat production by top five meat producing countries

Name of the country	Quantity (in million tones)	% Of the world total meat production
China	70.46	26.19
USA	42.02	15.62
Brazil	18.89	6.94
Germany	7.41	2.75
India	6.50	2.42
World total	**269.00**	-

Source: FAO Statistics (2007)

Table 2. Total bovine meat export by top five countries

Name of the country	Quantity of bovine meat exported (in million tones)	% of total bovine meat export
Brazil	1.96	20.74
Australia	1.28	13.54
USA	0.60	6.34
Ireland	0.53	5.61
India	0.48	5.10
World total	**9.45**	-

Source: FAO Statistics (2007)

Buffalo meat is one of the major commodities, among livestock products, exported from the country. Among the animal products exported from India, meat and meat products account for more than 90% of the total exports volume. Remaining 10% are dairy products and honey. The export of meat and meat products, including poultry products, has gone up from Rs.2166 crore in 2004-05 to Rs.4170 crore in 2007-08, with an increase of almost 48%, which is quite significant. The country has made rapid strides in meat exports. In private sector, there are about 16 modern integrated abattoirs cum processing units where quality meat is produced adopting OIE guidelines and international quality standards.

Need for modernization

There are about 2638 registered slaughterhouses operating in the country. To regulate the illegal slaughter and improve hygiene and sanitation, modernization of existing slaughterhouses is needed at a larger scale. Environmental and animal right's issues, through modernization of slaughter, could be addressed more effectively. This will not only help in providing safe and wholesome meat to the meat eaters but also in building the images of meat industry worldwide.

To provide safe and wholesome meat to the consumers, in smaller towns, cities and the rural areas and provide pollution free environment, Department of Animal Husbandry, Dairying and Fisheries is implementing Centrally Sponsored scheme on 'Establishment / modernization of rural slaughterhouses. The proposed scheme will address those areas not specifically and fully covered by existing scheme of Ministry of Food Processing Industries (MFPI). Issue is of Public health importance with larger dimensions and the task is huge. Therefore, a multi-pronged approach is required to supplement the efforts of the States. Scheme is initially implemented in three states i.e. Andhra Pradesh, Uttar Pradesh and Meghalaya, on pilot basis through NABARD, with an approved outlay of Rs.48.50 crore.

Food safety, quality control and hygiene

In the interest of food safety and consumer protection, increasingly stringent hygiene measures are required at national and international trade levels. The key issues in this respect, which needs to be addressed, are meat food traceability, Good Hygienic Practices (GHP) and Hazard Analysis and Critical Control Point Schemes (HACCP). Extensive knowledge of hazards, other than that of microorganisms, is indispensable in modern meat processing. Thus, along with meat processing hygiene including causes for meat product spoilage and food borne illnesses, stress to control the entry of harmful residues in product chain is equally important. For the purpose of consumer protection and quality control of meat and products, simple test methods needs to be made available that can be carried out at the small enterprise level without sophisticated laboratory set-ups. To remain competitive in the world market meat has to be produced adopting OIE and Codex guidelines and quality standards. While the mandate of the Codex is to develop international standards, guidelines and recommendations on food safety for international trade, OIE (World Organization for Animal Health) has the mandate to develop international standards, guidelines and recommendations on animal health including zoonoses.

For producing hygienic meat to be internationally acceptable for exports, Codex Alimentarius General Principles of Meat Hygiene needs to be followed. The Department of Animal Husbandry Dairying and Fisheries and Ministry of Commerce and Industry through APEDA are regularly involved in various standards being formulated by the Codex Alimentarious Commission to ensure that India's interests are reflected in the decisions taken in the Codex Committee meetings. With technical inputs from FAO, WHO and OIE, Codex established its first code that helps to ensure the safety of food for human consumption through adherence to good animal feeding practices at the farm level and good manufacturing practices during all phases of animal feeding. Government of India with sole intention of preventing the occurrence of BSE in the country has issued a notification to ban the manufacture of ruminant feed using meat meal, bone meal, blood meal and any such product from animal origin. To safe guard human health from toxic effects of pesticides, heavy metals and other toxic undesirable elements through livestock products, maximum residue limits (MRL) have been specified in animal feed (Table 3). The abattoirs and meat plants engaged in export production in India are required to be registered with APEDA, compulsory vide DGFT notification 12/ (2004-2005) dated 21st December 2004. A committee consisting of officials of various Government departments periodically inspects the plants.

Sanitary and phyto-sanitary (SPS) measures

With the increase of international trade and travel, countries are becoming more and more exposed to the danger of introduction of known and unknown transmissible diseases, which have the potential for very serious and rapid spread, irrespective of national borders. They may have serious socio-economic or public health consequences and major importance in the international trade of animal and animal products. Therefore, to prevent the entry of any exotic disease through international trade and travel in to the country and to ensure the health and safety of the animal and human life, Government of India initiated a central sector scheme namely "Animal Quarantine & Certification Services" (AQCS) during the Fourth Five Year Plan (1969-70). The AQCS stations have the responsibility of preventing ingress of exotic diseases and thereby safeguarding the health of country's livestock population.

India as a member of the World Trade Organization (WTO), must ensure that its import policies and Procedures regarding Livestock & Livestock

Products are in line with its international obligations under the Agreement on the application of Sanitary measures. This agreement governs the imposition of measures that affects international trade for the protection of animal and human life and health. The major objective of AQCS is to prevent ingress of livestock and poultry diseases exotic to India and also to issue export certificate of live animals as per the international requirements in consultation with Export Inspection Council (EIC) in the areas not covered under EIC.

Table 3. MRL of pesticides, heavy metals and other undesirable substances permitted in compounded cattle feed

Particular	Maximum content
BHC	20 ppb
DDT	5 ppb
Endosulfan	10 ppb
Aldrin	1 ppb
Arsenic	2 ppm
Lead	5 ppm
Cadmium	2 ppm
Mercury	0.2 ppm
Fluorine	20 ppm
Castor seed husk	5 ppm
Free gossypol	2000 ppm

(i) Responsibilities of the importing country

The import requirements included in the international veterinary certificate should ensure that commodities introduced into the importing country comply with the national level of protection that it has chosen for animal and human health. Importing countries should restrict their requirement to those justified for such level of protection.

The International veterinary certificate should not include requirements for the exclusion of pathogens or animal diseases, which are present within the territory of the importing country and are not subject to any official control programme. The requirements applying to pathogens or disease subject to official control programmes in a country or zone should not provide a higher level of protection on imports than that provided for the same pathogens or disease by the measures applied within that country or zone.

(ii) Responsibilities of the exporting country

An exporting country should be prepared to supply the following information to importing countries on request:

a. Information on the animal health situation and national animal health information systems to determine whether that country is free or has free zones of specified diseases, including the regulations and procedures in force to maintain its free status.

b. Regular and prompt information on the occurrence of transmissible diseases, details of the country's ability to apply measures to control and prevent the diseases and information on the structure of the Veterinary Services and the authority which they exercise.

c. Technical information, particularly on biological tests and vaccines applied in all or part of the national territory and infrastructure facilities of referral diagnostic laboratories.

d. Veterinary administrations of exporting countries should have official procedures for authorization of certifying veterinary officers, defining their functions and duties as well as conditions covering possible suspension and termination of the appointment. In addition, it ensures that the relevant instructions and training are provided to certifying veterinary officers and also monitors the activities of the certifying veterinary officers to verify their integrity and impartiality.

e. The Head of the Veterinary Service of the exporting country is ultimately accountable for veterinary certification used in international trade.

f. As a member of WTO, it must ensure that its import policies and procedures are in line with its international obligations under the Agreement on the Application of Sanitary Measures.

Rules and regulations for export

a. Standards have been laid down for export of meat and meat products under Export (Quality Control and Inspection) Act, 1963. The export of Raw Meat (chilled and frozen) shall be allowed subject to the provision specified to the gazette notification on Raw Meat (chilled and frozen) under Export (Quality Control and Inspection) Act, 1963 in January, 1993. The notification lays down the Standards for abattoirs, meat processing plants and the products. Offal's too are subject to the same conditions of quality control and inspection.

b. All consignments of Raw Meat (Chilled and Frozen) and export of canned meat products need to accompany with a Pre-shipment Inspection Certificate for which the Govt. has designated three agencies (i) All State Directorate of Animal Husbandry (ii) Export Inspection Agency (iii) Directorate of Marketing and Inspection, Government of India, to carry out the inspection in accordance with either the standards prevalent in the exporting country or standards prescribed under the Meat Food Products Order, 1973 under Export (Quality Control and Inspection) Act, 1963 or orders made there under.

c. Export of meat and meat products will be allowed subject to the exporter furnishing a certificate to the customs at the time of export that the above items have been obtained/sourced from an abattoir/ meat processing plant registered with Agricultural and Processed Foods Products Export Development Authority (APEDA).

Export policy

The export of beef of cows, oxen and calf and offal's (includes heart, liver, tongue, kidneys and other organs) is prohibited and not permitted to be exported. Meat of buffalo (both male and female) and offal of buffalo except gonads and reproductive organs is free to export subject to the condition that exporter has to produce a certificate from the designated veterinary authority of the State, from which the meat or offal's emanate, to the effect that the meat or offal's are from buffaloes not used for breeding and milch purposes. The Quality control and inspection under (a) and (b) and (c) stipulated above under Rules & Regulations are required to be fulfilled. The meat and offal's of Indian sheep and goat is free for export subject to fulfilling the conditions (a) and (b) and (c) stipulated above. Tallow, fat and/or oils of any animal origin excluding fish oil are prohibited for export.

Major bottlenecks in meat production and export

i. Low productivity of livestock
ii. Livestock diseases
iii. Lack of proper infrastructure and hygiene
iv. Food safety and traceability
v. Least priority is given by the states due to controversies involved with the subject.

References

Dastagiri, M. B. 2004.Demand and supply projections for livestock products in India. Policy Paper (21), National Centre for Agricultural Economics and Policy Research (ICAR),New Delhi.pp.43.

FAOSTAT. 2007. www.fao.org.

Manual on Animal quarantine and certification service.2005.Ministry of Agriculture, Department of Animal Husbandry, Dairying and Fisheries, Krishi Bhavan, New Delhi, pp.257.

❑❑❑

36

Safety and Quality Assurance in Red Meat Processing and Marketing Chains

A.R. Sen and M. Muthukumar
National Research Centre on Meat, Chengicherla, P.B.No.19, Uppal
Hyderabad-500 039, Andhra Pradesh

Introduction

India is a rapidly growing and dynamic economy characterized by increasing incomes and changing consumer preferences. The consumers demand is not fulfilled with high nutritive value and sensory attributes, but also safety. Today food safety is an important global issue with international trade and public health implications. The change in the consumer needs and increased preference for minimally processed products further increased the concern for safety of the meat food products. The safety of meat has been at the forefront of societal concerns in recent years and indications exist that challenges to meat safety will continue in the future. Major meat safety issues and related challenges include the need to control traditional as well as "new," "emerging," or "evolving" pathogenic microorganisms, which may be of increased virulence and low infectious doses, or of resistance to antibiotics or food related stresses. Other issues and challenges include food additives and chemical residues, animal identification and traceability issues, implementation of HACCP at the production and processing level on the basis of food handler training and consumer education. These challenges become more important due to changes in animal production, product processing and distribution; increased international trade, higher numbers of consumers at-risk for infection and increased interest, awareness and scrutiny by consumers, news media, and consumer activist groups. This paper considers the application of quality and safety assurance, animal welfare, traceability, residues and their importance to produce safe meat in red meat production chain.

Importance of quality and safety assurance

Quality consists of those product features, which meet the needs of the consumers thereby, product satisfaction. Quality could be several inherent biological properties, attributes and could be negotiable. On the other hand, safety is an intellectual concept and not an inherent biological property of a substance. It refers to freedom from risk or danger and is not negotiable. There are divergent views on the importance of food safety but this may depend on the way the questionnaire put and perceived. The liberalization of the global trade, and the fact that the consumers in the industrialized countries are more and more demanding food to be not only economical, but also healthy, tasty, safe and sound in respect to animal welfare and the environment. In contrast to the quality oriented markets that are often subsidized and producers can always sell everything they produce and quality oriented markets are market driven. The majority of the real and perceived reasons for the increased concerns with the food safety and quality of meat apply to the pre harvest area of the food production chain.

Many countries in the world have implemented a consistent mandatory meat inspection, more and more stringent rules for post harvest safety improving the hygiene standard during slaughter, meat processing, storage and distribution of meat have led to a remarkable decline of meat related food borne illness. However, due to emerging pathogens and change in production and processing practices, new approaches to food safety and meat quality are becoming necessary. Secondly, modern agriculture is contributing to the increase of drug resistant pathogens in human. Lastly food safety issues can easily become non-tariff trade barriers and are increasingly used as marketing tools, nationally and internationally.

Quality attributes of meat

According to the International Organization of Standardization (ISO), quality is the "totality of features and characteristics of a product or service that bears on its ability to satisfy stated or implied needs aims at the satisfaction of clients' expectations". This is even more obvious in the successor definition published in ISO 9000:2000. The quality means 'achieving sustained customer satisfaction through meeting customer needs and expectations within an organizational environment committed to continued improvement of efficiency and effectiveness'. It is clear that the consumer's definition of food quality in relation to meat is now very wide and changing attitudes among consumers. The quality not only includes sensory characteristics such as meat tenderness, colour or flavour (Table 1) but also about the animal welfare, impact on environment and finally food safety.

Table 1. Consumers' perception of meat quality

Meat safety	Bird flu, swine flu, BSE, meat borne zoonotic diseases, residues
Animal welfare	Transport, handling, slaughter practices
Health	Fat, fatty acids
Taste	Tenderness, colour, flavour
Life style	Preparation time, convenience

Research shows that tenderness and flavour are rated by consumers as the most important elements of eating quality, while colour/freshness is the most important attribute at point of purchase. Related to the sensory aspects, pH and water holding capacity are important technological factors. All of the sensory traits except colour, are contributing factors to the palatability of meat and meat products. Quality characteristics of meat are influenced by various intrinsic and extrinsic factors such as muscle structure and its chemical composition ante mortem stress as well as postmortem handling and storage condition. Pre slaughter stress affects both the rate of onset of rigor mortis and the rate and the extent of the fall in muscle pH. Alterations in these parameters affect the appearance and eating quality of meat. The most common manifestation being pale, soft, exudative (PSE) pork and dark, firm and dry (DFD) beef. Because quality factors of meat are closely related to the sensory characteristics and consumer acceptability, designing ante mortem and post mortem strategies to optimize these quality attributes as well as elucidating the mechanism underlying changes in the quality of muscle foods during storage have been a challenge to the meat science researchers.

Colour is the first attribute of meat to be evaluated by the consumers and it is of utmost importance especially for fresh meat at the retail level. Surface discolouration may be considered unwholesomeness and therefore, discriminated against by the consumers. The content of myoglobin and hence the colour of meat depends on a number of ante mortem factors, such as animal species and age, the physiological function of the muscle, the nutritional status of the animal and the dietary regime. The colour change is influenced by the specific meat processing and storage conditions. Use of modified atmosphere packaging to retard microbial growth while maintaining the desirable appealing red oxymyoglobin colour is of great commercial interest.

Flavour of meat is usually perceived during consumption (except strong off flavor such as rancidity which may develop in mishandled meat samples and be easily detected without tasting), it cannot be manifested until the meat is actually cooked and consumed. In meat, flavor compounds include those naturally present in muscle and those generated during processing and through cooking. The influence of sex on meat flavor is well known. Boar odour is a problem associated with non-castrated male pigs. It is generally assumed that many flavor compounds from the diet can be absorbed and deposited in the adipose tissue of the animal. Muscles that are involved in locomotion are generally of high flavor intensity than muscles whose primary function is to support the carcass.

Tenderness of meat may be simply defined as the ease of teeth to cut meat fibres during mastication. Pre slaughter factors alone (breed, diet, growth path) explain less than one third in a quarter of the variability in mechanical strength or tenderness. In addition, the contribution of pre slaughter muscle characteristics to tenderness differs a lot between muscle types and production systems. For intact meat tenderness or toughness is determined by two groups of meat components: the connective tissue and the muscle fibres. Connective tissue is a fibrous structure composed primarily of collagen fibrils. The specific influence of both connective tissues depends on the thickness i.e. the amount of collagen present as well as the type of cross-linkings between collagen fibrils. Muscles in mature animals have higher contents of collagen cross-links than the same muscles from young animals. Another major contributor to toughness, muscle fibres also play a great role in regulating meat tenderness. Collagen experiences minimal chemical and biochemical changes and exhibits little structural alterations during ageing at refrigerated temperature. In contrast, the myofibril assembly undergoes pronounced changes during ageing like disruption of the structure and longitudinal fragmentation. Therefore, the enhanced meat tenderness during ageing has been attributed mostly to myofibrils and not to the collagen fibrils. Post mortem tenderization of meat through the ageing process has been a common industrial practice. There are a number of meat tenderization techniques like treatment of tough meat cuts with plant proteases to degrade both collagen and muscle fibres and subjecting meat to high pressure to disrupt myofibrils.

Juiciness refers to mouth feel of the moisture released from food during mastication. It is indicative of the moisture content in meat, which is critically affected by the water holding capacity as well as the hydration ability of meat. Myofibrillar proteins are believed to be largely responsible for water immobilization in meat. Juiciness is associated with higher levels of intra muscular (marbling) fat, but larger amounts of marbling are often found in meat that also has larger amounts of subcutaneous and intermuscular fat. But consuming large quantities of fat is undesirable from the viewpoint of health. Thus there is a potential dilemma that meat which is healthier for us to consume is likely to be less juicy and therefore have a poor eating quality than meat which is fatter and therefore less healthy.

Meat Food Safety issues

Major meat safety issues and related challenges include the need to control traditional as well as 'new', emerging or evolving pathogenic microorganism or of resistance to antibiotics or food related stressors. The cross contamination of other foods and water with enteric pathogens of animal origin, meat animal manure treatment and disposal issues are also concern for food safety. Other issues and challenges include food additives and chemical residues, animal identification and traceability issues, the safety and quality of organic and natural products. These challenges become more important due to changes in animal production, processing and distribution, increased international trade, changing consumers' needs and preferences. The potential for meat to become contaminated with chemical substances or microorganisms starts from the time it is harvested and continues right through until the time it is eaten. In general, the risks to food safety fall into two broad categories:

- Microbiological contamination (eg: bacteria, fungi, viruses or parasites). This category results in most cases in acute symptoms.
- Chemical contaminants, comprising environmental chemicals, veterinary drug residues, heavy metals or other residues unintentionally or accidentally introduced into the food supply during farming, processing, shipping or packing.

Microbiological contamination

The most serious meat safety issues resulting in immediate consumer health problems are associated with microbial and especially bacterial pathogens. The food borne illness caused by these pathogens have brought meat safety and associated issues at the forefront of societal concerns. The microbes on and in food animals are influenced by the surroundings. Microbes are ubiquitous and can enter the food chain at any point from the agriculture produce to the consumer's kitchen.

Bacteria

Bacterial pathogens such as *Escherichia coli* O157:H7, *Salmonella* and *Campylobacter* will continue affecting the safety of raw meat and poultry, while *Listeria monocytogenes* will be of concern in ready-to-eat processed products (Table 2). Research has indicated in recent years that there is continuous adaptation and development of resistance by pathogenic microorganisms to antibiotics and traditional food preservation barriers. Furthermore, there is evidence of existence of strains of pathogens with enhanced ability for survival in their hosts, low infective doses and increased virulence. These developments, which make pathogens more of a threat to human health, become more important when we also consider additional developments that may contribute to the problem. Despite major efforts and successes in the control of food borne pathogens, there is no reason to expect that their importance in meat safety will be eliminated in the near future.

Table 2. Important meat borne illness

Cause	Foods most often associated with the problem
Bacteria	
Bacillus cereus	Cooked meats and fish. Improper handling after cooking is a common feature of foods causing *B. cereus* associated foodborne illness
Clostridium perfringens	Reheated cooked meat and poultry, stews and soups.
Clostridium botulinum	Improperly canned (home preserved) fish, meat and poultry.
Escherichia coli (E.coli)	Undercooked meat
Campylobacter jejuni	Raw milk, poultry
Listeria monocytogenes	Raw meat, poultry, seafood, smoked meat and fish
Salmonella	Undercooked poultry, meat, shellfish and eggs
Staphylococcus aureus	Ham, poultry and eggs are the most common sources. Improper handling of food or poor hygiene lead to *S. aureus* spread into food.
Parasites	
Trichinella spiralis	Undercooked pork or game.
Toxoplasma gondii	Undercooked meat and poultry
Viruses	
Hepatitis A virus	Shellfish. Hepatitis A can be spread by contaminated food handlers inadvertently transferring the virus to the food they handle.
Prion	
Creutzfeldt-Jakob disease	Bovine Spongiform Encephalopathy infected cattle nervous tissues

Mycotoxins

Mycotoxins are toxins produced by certain fungi or moulds that grow on foods such as peanuts, tree nuts, corn, cereals, soybeans, animal feeds, dried fruits and spices. The toxins may be produced as crops grow or develop later during poor storage or handling. Mycotoxins can also enter the food chain via meat or other animal products such as eggs, milk and cheese as the result of livestock eating contaminated feed. The actual effects they have on health depend on the amount and type of the mycotoxins ingested. For instance continuous intake of aflatoxin is thought to be associated with liver cancer in people affected by Hepatitis B. Other mycotoxins have been linked to kidney and liver damage. Careful surveillance procedures and proper storage conditions of foods are important in helping to prevent the development of mycotoxicosis. In terms of protecting the consumer, National and International Organizations are constantly evaluating the risk that mycotoxins pose to humans.

Aflatoxin, ochratoxin, zearalenone and trichothecenes are some of the important mycoxins frequently encounted in feed and food materials. Aflatoxin, especially B1 constitute an important risk factor for hepatocellular carcinoma in exposed population. Ochratoxin A displays nephrotoxic, genotoxic, teratogenic, cancerogenic and immunosuppressive effects. Ergot alkaloids of various species of Claviceps infect millets and produce peripheral, vascular and CNS effects. Zearalenone and its derivatives are reported to show estrogenic effects in animals. In India, the problem is of greater magnitudes due to congenial climatic conditions, socio-economical backwardness and traditional and unscientific agronomic and storage practice. Through the infected animal feed animal products may get contaminated.

Creutzfeldt-Jakob disease (CJD)

Although no causal link has been formally established between ingestion of Bovine Spongiform Encephalopathy (BSE)-infected material and vCJD, only those who have eaten BSE-infected "specified risk material" (SRM) are thought to be at risk from vCJD. SRM refers to the parts of cattle that are most likely to be infected with the BSE agent and include the central nervous system including the brain, the spinal cord, the eye and part of the large intestine. The BSE agent has not been detected in muscle meat (beef) or milk and WHO and EU experts regard bovine milk and muscle meat to be safe.

Chemical contaminants

Pesticides

Of all the food contaminants, pesticides probably have received the most interest worldwide. Pesticides, which include insecticides, acaracides, herbicides and fungicides, are extensively used in crop production including production of feedstuffs for animals. Some insecticides are also used for control of flies in livestock production. These compounds may occur as residues in feedstuffs indigested by animals and thus have a potential to contaminate animal tissues. The chlorinated hydrocarbon groups of insecticides (DDT, lindane, heptachlor, aldrin, dieldrin and chlordane) are persistent and stable in the environment and when indigested by animals, they accumulate in fatty tissue rather than being broken down and secreted. Thus, low levels in feedstuff could be concentrated to significant levels in animal tissues. In the biological food chain, concentrations could ultimately reach lethal levels. The accumulation of organochlorine compounds in body fat due to their strong lipophilicity induce changes in biotransformation of endogenous and exogenous compounds resulting in variety of health problems, particularly endocrine dysfunction, birth defects, carcinomas, neurological disorders besides weakening the immune system Because of the concerns about the toxicity and general damage, caused by chlorinated hydrocarbon insecticides, the use of these compounds were severely restricted. Background levels in the environment have gradually decreased following the restrictions on use. Though their concentration has declined in farm products like food grains and vegetables, animal products are still the major sources of threat. Contamination of livestock products including meat was attributed from direct source of pesticides application to combat ectoparasites and indirectly through pesticide contaminated/residue bearing feed, effluents from pesticide manufactures, accidental spillage or throwing of empty containers of pesticides into the animal premises and pasture lands. The estimated daily intake of DDT by infants in India has been found to be at least 100 fold greater than the acceptable daily intake of FAO/WHO.

Antibiotics and antibacterial

These compounds are widely used therapeutically in treatment of infections. Injudicious use of veterinary drugs and not following properly the prescribed withdrawal period will result in the form of residues of animal products. Also added to livestock feeds at low levels as prophylactic drug to prevent the occurrence of infections and as feed additives to improve performance. The relative persistence of antibiotics in animal tissue varies widely depending on the compound and the method of administration.

The sulphanomides create the greatest residue problems especially in swine. Even accidental contamination of feeds with sulphanomides has resulted in significant residues in tissues. Amino glycoside antibiotics (neomycin, streptomycin) and tetracycline antibiotics are also rather persistent in animal tissues. The occurrence of residues depends on many factors like the formulation, dosage and the mode of administration, age of the animal, disease condition and husbandry practices even when pre-slaughter holding times are observed. The major concerns of antibiotics residues are allergic reactions and antibiotic resistance. As little as 10 micrograms of penicillin can cause an allergic response in sensitive individuals. This is equivalent to a residue level of 0.1 ppb in 100g of meat or milk.

Hormones and repartitioning agents

Both natural and synthetic anabolic agents have been administered to livestock to improve feed efficiency and increase the rate of weight gain. Other types of drugs have also been used to reduce the ratio of fat to lean. These include certain beta-agonists, such as clenbutarol, and some tranquilizers such as diazepam. All of these compounds can produce residues in animal tissues. Animal tissues contain low levels of naturally occurring anabolic steroids. Administration of these naturally occurring steroids to animals does not result in levels above those naturally present. Some synthetic anabolic agents such as diethylstilbestrol have been reported to responsible for development of breast in children and menstruation in infant girls. European Union banned the use of these hormones. EU believes that these compounds are responsible for cancer and increased level of estrogenic male infertility because of carcinogenic potential.

Estradiol stimulates cell division in hormonally sensitive tissues thereby increasing the possibility for accumulation of random errors during DNA duplication. This increased cell proliferation also has the effect of stimulating growth of mutant cells. However, the oral doses of estradiol have low bioavailability usually 12% or less. The United States Food and Drug administration has approved hormones estradiol, progesterone and testosterone, Zeranol and trenbolone acetate. However, the European Economic Community (EEC) has banned the use of anabolic agents and beta-agonists.

Environmental contaminants

Certain chemicals like polychlorinated biphenyls, dioxin, heavy metals and mycotoxins have been found to have a widespread potential for environmental contamination. The polychlorinated biphenyls were once used as electrical transformer in copy paper, and in many other uses. These compounds are chemically similar to the chlorinated hydrocarbon insecticides and behave in much the same manner in the environment. Like the chlorinated hydrocarbon insecticides, these compounds are concentrated biologically in fatty tissues of animals and may be concentrated to toxic levels. Although use of polychlorinated biphenyls has been phased out, residues remain in the environment, especially in stream and lake sentiments. Because of widespread environmental contamination, small amounts may sometime found in animal tissues. Fatty fish from contaminated bodies of water, fatty meats and dairy products can be a major source of human exposure.

Dioxins are a class of 210 different chlorine-containing compounds. Dioxins in food and the environment have been extensively studied over the past twenty years. They are highly resistant to breakdown in the environment. They are by-products in the production of certain herbicides and are also formed by combustion of organic matter. Low levels are widespread in the environment and they are also bioaccumulate in the fatty tissues. They persist in the environment and having half-life of 8.5 years. Pathways of entry into foods are atmospheric transport of emission and subsequent deposition on plants, soil and water. About 98 % of human exposure is through animal foods particularly meat, fish and dairy products, which are contaminated with soil that has accumulated dioxin from the environment. Dioxins have been found to be potent carcinogens in tests with rodents. Maximum permissible level for dioxins of 2 pg TEQ/g fat for dairy products and 1 pg TEQ/g fat for pork (European Commission).

Heavy metals are potential contaminants of animal tissues. For terrestrial animals, heavy metals may contaminate forage in the form of dust from industrial operations such as smelters, manufacturing operations using heavy metals, or contamination of trash containing metals. Crops grown on land treated with sewage sludge may contain elevated levels of heavy metals. In the past, crops grown near highways contained elevated levels of lead from road dust. This may no longer a problem since leaded gasoline was phased out. Because animals preferentially excrete indigested heavy metals, levels in animal tissues are lower than in diet and seldom if ever reach hazardous levels.

Traceability and meat safety

Animal identification and traceability with technologies such as electronic ear tags or retinal scanning, as well as food products recalls, are major issues of worldwide interest and may have major food safety implications. Implementation of effective systems can be very useful in tracking, containment and recalls of animals or their products when necessitated due to public health or other concerns. Success of animal identification efforts will depend on complete and mandatory implementation of effective systems. Intensified attention to food safety in general and to the incidence of pathogenic bacteria, particularly Salmonella, has contributed to and increased interest in the origin and treatment of the meat from stable to table.

The tracking and tracing are important in the contribution of quality assurance to food safety in the food industry. During food emergencies, they are used to locate defective or unsafe food, so that they can be removed quickly from retailer's shelves. Prompt recall reduces the potential negative economic impact and preserves consumers' trust in quality and their confidence in systems that are designed to protect them. The International Organization for standardization defines traceability as the "ability to trace the history, application or location of that which is under consideration". For a product "traceability can relate to the origin of materials and parts, the processing history and the distribution and location of the product after delivery". For livestock, traceability has emerged as a way to track animal movements and identify cohorts in case of a disease outbreak or food related problem and a way to track an animal's lineage to improve herd genetics. Traceability also has emerged as a marketing tool to assure consumers about the source of the meats they purchase. Slaughter plants and processors' have had two primary motives for establishing traceability for meat products, to manage their supply chain and assure quality control and food safety.

In view of Indian unorganized sector in livestock and huge animal population, it is virtually impossible to have any traceability of meat from the farmers to the consumers whether it is beef, lamb, pork or chicken. However, to meet the requirements of importing countries to this eventual risk analysis factor and keeping in view the stringent sanitary and phytosanitary (SPS) requirements of importing countries, meat-exporting companies are making huge efforts to have traceability of meat. (Farm to consumers) and ingredients of feed; an important component of their production and marketing. This will also ensure the transparency regarding the disease status of the animals.

Key areas of red meat production and marketing chain affecting quality and safety of meat and meat products

The quality of raw materials is crucial to ensure the safety and quality of the final product. Ultimately, the quality and safety of food depends on the efforts of everyone involved in the complex chain of agriculture production, processing, transport, food production and consumption. Therefore, a systematic approach is needed from farm to fork in order to produce consistent quality product and also avoid contamination of foodstuffs and to identify potential hazards. As the EU and the World Health Organisation (WHO) put it succinctly - food safety is a shared responsibility from farm to fork.

Importance of clean and healthy animal production

Farmers are the first people responsible for producing healthful food. They must know how to grow the food animals. Healthy and clean animals at slaughter minimizes the potential risk to human health, contributes to the production of safe meat, and improves the eating quality and shelf life of the meat and consumer confidence. Building design can influence cleanliness of livestock finished in housing. Poor ventilation, inadequate drainage and construction defects such as leaking roofs and guttering or floors with potholes can result in dirtier animals. Inappropriate sitting and design of feeders and drinkers can also lead to build up of contamination in these areas of the house. Straw bedding levels, frequency of bedding change and stocking density are vital.

The feeding system and composition of the feed in addition to the genotype have important role in determining the intramuscular fat level in animals. The fatty acid composition of meat lipid is strongly related to the fat composition of the feed used. Hence the feed formulation should be in such a way to produce acceptable level of intramuscular fat level in the meat. In general low levels of intramuscular fat associate with poor eating quality.

Maintenance of good animal welfare is also an important part of quality assurance programme. The five freedoms as defined by the Farm Animal welfare Council are the principle framework for evaluating animal welfare.

- Freedom from hunger and thirst
- Freedom from discomfort
- Freedom from pain, injury
- Freedom to express normal behaviour
- Freedom from fear and distress

Care and welfare of animals

The farmers as the first step in the meat supply chain have a monitoring role over the accommodation during transport with respect to animal welfare and hygiene (food safety). The transport process begins with assembly and includes loading, confinement with and without motion, unloading and penning in a new and unfamiliar environment. During transport, animals are exposed to environmental stresses including heat, cold, humidity, noise and motion. The transport and receiving stages must satisfy welfare legislation and quality assurance scheme requirements. The means of transport used must be designed, constructed, maintained and operated so as to avoid injury and suffering, and ensure the safety and welfare of the animals. This includes requirements for cleaning and disinfecting and the provision of anti-slip floors and adequate lighting. Moreover, handling of animals during journey to the abattoir has significant impact on the quality of the final product. Sufficient floor space and height must be provided for the animals appropriate to their height and the intended journey. High loading density results in low dressed carcass weight due to higher trimming of bruised tissue from the carcass. Bruising is an impact injury that can occur at any stage in the transportation chain and may be attributed to poor design of handling facilities, ignorant and abusive stockmanship and poor road driving techniques during transportation.

Restricting feed intake before slaughter significantly reduces microbial counts on the hides of animals. The effect of journey time to the abattoir was also has significant impact on the quality of the final product. A well-designed and maintained lorry along with an approved and experienced haulier may have masked some of the problems that could arise during cattle transportation. Anyone engaged in the handling and transport of animals must be trained or competent to do so in a way that does not, or is not likely to, cause unnecessary fear, injury or suffering. All necessary arrangements should be made in advance to minimise the length of the journey and meet the animals' needs during the journey.

Research has proven how seemingly unnoticeable levels of stress and exercise can have dramatic effects on meat quality. Today, the issue of animal welfare has stepped out of the arena of just ethics; it has become an essential requirement of meat quality. All meat animals will experience some level of stress prior to slaughter and this in turn, may have detrimental effects to meat quality. The magnitude of any negative effect is generally thought to be a function of the type, duration and intensity of the individual pre slaughter stressors and the susceptibility of the animal to them. There are a variety of environmental condition which can cause undesirable effect on meat quality such as pale, soft, exudative (PSE) meat and dark firm dry (DFD) meat (Table 3). The final quality of meat is greatly affected by the rate of pH decline in the meat after slaughter. If there was great lactic acids build up before slaughter, the pH of the meat declines too quickly after slaughter and PSE condition may develop. At the other extreme, if the animal is glycogen depleted before slaughter the pH may not drop quickly enough after slaughter because there is not enough lactic acid produced. In this case the meat will be very dry and dark in colour. This condition is known as DFD meat. Both these situation (PSE/DFD) can be avoided or restricted by good management on farm, transport and lairage. However, there is also a genetic cause for PSE meat. Pigs bearing the defective mutated version of ryanodine receptor (halothane) gene will develop PSE even under good management. Breeding organization can eliminate this gene from their stock by DNA testing.

Table 3. Some quality problems in meat

Cause	Quality problems
Genetic factors	
Stress susceptible pig breeds	PSE in pork
Callipyge lamb	Toughness
Production factors	
Emaciation	Dark cutting condition
Poor sanitation	Boar taint
Rough handling	Trauma, Bruising
Pre slaughter factors	
Excessive exercise	Dark cutting, PSE
Mixing of unfamiliar groups	Dark cutting condition
Slaughter factors	
Stunning	Blood splash
Post-slaughter factors	
Over stimulation	Excessive drip and toughness
Very fast cooling	Toughness

Role of processor in quality and safety of meat product

It is the food processing industry responsibility to meet consumer expectations that their products are safe, and meet all legal requirements. People, who process, pack and transport meat and meat products must make sure that meat is handled appropriately and kept at proper temperatures. Storage facilities must be kept clean.

Importance of proper slaughter and dressing

Animals should be held in lairages for approximately 24 hours before slaughter. Time in lairage allows animals to recover from the stress of transport. The lairages should have facilities for adequate watering, washing and disinfections of animals. Excessively dirty animals should be washed and allowed sufficient time to dry before slaughter. However, detaining the animals at lairages for a long period will encourage cross contamination with salmonella. Ante mortem inspection within 24 hours prior to slaughter is essential to detect and eliminate abnormalities including contamination.

Stunning must be done in a way that complies with the human slaughter act. The type of stunning method used can affect meat quality, either by inducing short term pre-slaughter stress or by affecting bleeding. The residual blood in the meat due to improper bleeding promotes spoilage, gamey flavour and discolouration of meat products. Blood splash (spots of blood in muscle) and speckle (pin point bleeding in fat) are other unsightly quality defects associated with poor stunning technique.

Removal of the soiled hide or fleece is the principal route by which contamination from the outside of an animal is transferred to the exposed muscle surfaces. If hides are contaminated with dung at the time of slaughter, there is a very real risk of the meat becoming contaminated with harmful bacteria, such as *E.coli O157, Campylobacter* and *Salmonella*. This can occur through knives during initial incisions through the skin; hands, arms and tools of slaughter men during separation of the skin from the underlying musculature; direct contact between contaminated fleece/hair and muscles; dust or aerosols created by the action of mechanical fleece/hide pullers; aerosols from uncontrolled drainage of water onto the floor and the use of high pressure hoses in the slaughter hall. Any pathogens on the coat around the neck incision area, which are transferred to the bloodstream, can be pumped to the internal tissues and may represent a human health risk.

Contamination with gastrointestinal pathogens can also occur during evisceration. Contamination of meat by faecal material or intestinal contents coming into contact with carcasses at the abattoir is an important risk factor contributing to the outbreak of foodborne illness. Care should be taken to avoid puncture of the viscera, and leakage from the oesophagus and anus prevented by tying or clamping the alimentary canal at either end. Spray washing prior to carcase inspection has been shown to spread faecal contamination to other areas of the carcass. Trimming of visibly contaminated areas on dressed carcasses cannot be wholly effective in eliminating faecal pathogens, since much of the microbiological contamination will be non-visible. Post mortem examination which involves, a systematic examination of dressed carcasses, their organs including blood immediately after slaughter by a meat inspector is essential to provide wholesome meat to the consumers.

Pressurized water spray after evisceration reduces the bacterial load of carcass surface. Hot water washing, chlorinated water and organic spray are some of the decontamination methods employed to reduce the spoilage and pathogenic organisms on meat surfaces. Carcasses of freshly slaughtered animals have surfaces that are warm and wet and thus provide a perfect substrate for the growth of pathogenic and spoilage organisms. Chilling immediately post-slaughter reduces the surface temperature to a value below the minimum growth temperature for many pathogens. Hygienic requirements demand that carcass sides be cooled as soon as possible after weighing for a period of 18 hours or more. Meat receives extensive handling during boning and cutting and fresh surfaces are exposed, making it more susceptible to contamination. The shelf life of chilled cuts is maximized by aggressive sanitation programme through out the harvest, chilling, cutting and packaging operation. The storage potential of the products can be enhanced by vacuum packing and modified atmospheric packing using different gases. Freezing preserves fresh meat for extended period of time. A numbers of quality problems suffered in the past by frozen meat have been attributed to poor packaging techniques. Packaging materials such as sarlyn are becoming available with low water permeability, adequate physical strength and soften on heating, can be tightly wrapped over sharp areas under vacuum without causing puncture.

For transportation of meat, depending on the type of trade and length of journey, meat should be transported in properly insulated and refrigerated vehicles. Transport of meat at chilled temperature lower than 7^0C is regarded as safe. Solid carbon dioxide is sometimes used, either as solid blocks or crushed and provides a temperature of 0-10°C.

Personnel hygiene and proper sanitation of equipments, knives, utensils and work surfaces are prerequisites to ensure microbiological quality and safety of processed meat and meat products. Proper and regular washing and disinfecting hands, wearing clean protective clothing, covering hair with head gear, avoiding jewels and watches, regular health check ups and illness reporting and prompt wound dressing are some of the important personnel hygienic aspects contain spread of microbial contamination.

Meat traders/Retail outlets

Handling of meat at retail shops plays a major role in maintaining safety of meat. In India meat is mostly marketed in the form of fresh, hot carcass meat through retail shops located in the residential areas. Frozen meat/meat products sale is limited to metro cities. Meat traders should be given adequate training for safe and hygienic handling of meat. The retail store should have basic infrastructure like refrigerator, freezer, proper flooring, water supply, lighting, drainage, cutting board, flies and dust proof enclosures to ensure hygienic condition.

Consumer's Role in Safety Practices

The consumer is the final element of the food chain. Food that has been perfectly safe at the point of purchase needs to be handled carefully to avoid contamination at home. The composition of our households has changed in ways that have led to changes in lifestyles, food preferences and food handling practices. The use of pre prepared foods has increased that need minimal preparation and offer convenience. Consumers are exposed to limited education related to proper meat handling practices. These consumers' preferences may lead to food safety risks, which become challenges to be addressed by those involved in assuring the safety of our food supply. To ensure that eating remains an enjoyable experience and is not spoiled by the risks of falling ill or the fear, a number of measures can be taken. Consumer should always check the "Use-By" date or "Best before" date marking on packaged meat before purchase and they should avoid products marked as "Keep refrigerated", "Keep chilled" or "Keep frozen" that have not been stored under adequate refrigeration. Meat foods that needs refrigeration, should be brought home quickly and place them in the refrigerator or freezer promptly. Periodical checking of the condition of frozen products is must. If thawed, they should not be refreezed repeatedly.

Cross contamination is the major cause of food poisoning outbreak at consumer level. Contact between raw and cooked products should be avoided. A knife used to cut raw meat may have bacteria on it, which can be transferred to other foods. Separate cutting boards and utensils should be used for raw and cooked foods. Always raw meats, poultry and fish should be stored near the bottom of the refrigerator and cooked foods on higher shelves. Frozen meat products should be thawed only in the refrigerator and should be cooked, immediately it has thawed. Meat should be cooked upto safe cooking temperatures and should be eaten immediately. Cooked foods should not be stored at room temperature longer than necessary and never for more than two hours. Promptly refrigerate leftovers in a shallow container. There is a need for intensive efforts to educate food handlers and consumers in food safety principles.

Strategies and approaches for Quality assurance and meat safety

In the meat industry, quality assurance are rapidly developing and are beginning to embrace all the aspects of quality that are important to consumers "from farm to fork". The potential for contamination of meat with microbial and chemical contaminants begin on the farm and thus a truly holistic meat safety programme involves risk mitigation strategies involving the live animal from its conception. Meat quality also is significantly influenced by the health and welfare of live animal and a good meat quality assurance programme addresses the events leading up to the point of slaughter as well as processing variables. Generally, three overall strategies may be distinguished depending on the manner and extent of the quality assurance measures taken: product testing, process control and system control. Application of valid sampling plans in the meat trade is neither economically nor ethically acceptable. Additionally, the financial implication of end product testing concept may be serious. Another problem arises when only time consuming and cumbersome testing methods are available, which is still the rule in microbiological testing. The process control is the second approach for safe guarding defined quality features. In order to prevent the quality criteria, preventive, supervisory and corrective measures are established in the course of the processes. To support process control, several quality management tools have been developed.

Effective quality control measures must be integrated to achieve and to maintain the intended product quality characteristics. System control measures apply to the whole production and marketing chain of a single product and therefore include all participating enterprises, processes and products. To drive the implementation of new technologies for improving eating quality, a system approach analogous to the HACCP approach in safety assurance is required. In some quality assurance schemes, proper handling of slaughter animals is a point of protocol for farmers, transport and slaughter house. For the farmer, pre slaughter feed withdrawal is included with respect to meat quality, safety and animal welfare. Monitoring can be done by measuring related parameters in the slaughter house and feedback of management information to the producer. A reliable system of traceability in the whole meat supply chain is an essential instrument for proper functioning of quality assurance. The principle of HACCP should be applied at the key stages of the meat supply chain (Farm, transport, slaughter and meat processing).

Quality Management Systems

It is a management system to direct and control an organization with regard to quality. Quality management systems are employed to provide confidence for customers that their quality requirements will be fulfilled. Traditionally, food safety quality control in meat production relied on inspection on slaughter lines and testing of end products. It is the responsibility of the food processing industry to meet consumer expectations that their products are safe, and meet all legal requirements.

The desired high quality of the final product is planned and obtained by conducting standard operating procedures (SOPs) that guarantee the desired quality of the products at every production steps. If an entire production chain is following a written description (handbook) of all SOPs along the entire product chain, the demands for good manufacturing practices (GMPs) are met. The management approach to long term success through customer satisfaction, based on the participation of all members of an organization in improving processes, products and services is called Total quality management (TQM).

Food processors rely on modern quality management systems to ensure the quality and safety of the products they produce. The three key systems in use are:

(i) Good Manufacturing Practices (GMP)

This entails the processing conditions and procedures hat have been proven to deliver consistent quality and safety based on long experience.

(ii) Hazard Analysis Critical Control Points (HACCP).

While traditional safety assurance programmes focused on identifying problems in the finished product, HACCP, a recent proactive technique, focuses on identifying potential problems and controlling them during the design and the production process itself. It is a quality management system that identifies, evaluates and controls hazards at all stages of process chain. Codex Alimentarious Committee on food hygiene recommended the use of seven steps or principles for HACCP:

- Conduct hazard analysis and identification
- Determine critical control points (CCPs)
- Establish critical limits
- Establish a system to monitor CCPs
- Establish corrective action
- Establish verification procedures
- Establish record keeping procedures.

It emphasizes prevention in the avoidance of food safety problems. Before developing an HACCP plan for a production procedure, the establishment of SOP's and GMP's is indispensable. Only the combination of these principles provides the possibility to have correctness and the high standard verified. Future food safety regulation and research activities should be based on the findings of proper risk assessments. The concept of risk analysis needs further development and adoption in order to lead to hazard control measures on the basis of performance process and product criteria. This approach will allow better international cooperation, collaboration and harmonization leading to improved control of food borne hazards. There is a need to conduct microbiological risk assessments in order to identify risk factors and to establish food safety objectives, before setting performance and process criteria for the industry to achieve through HACCP. Proper and effective implementation and management of food safety assurance process needs adequate and proper implementation of validated and verified HACCP plans. A complete SOP should address what is to be done, by whom, when, why and how and should also provide guidance as to what to do if a deviation or other problem develops.

CCPs in the red meat production chain

Animal Feeds → CCP2 Farm animals ← Contaminated Pastures

↓

Transportation

↓

Holding in Lairage

↓

Slaughtering (Stunning and sticking)

Cattle, sheep and goat

Skinning CCP2
↓
Evisceration CCP2
↓
Washing
↓
Chilling CCP1
↓
Cutting
↓
Packaging

Pig

Scalding CCP2
↓
Dehairing
↓
Singeing CCP2
↓
Evisceration CCP2
↓
Chilling CCP1
↓
Transportation
↓
Cutting/Boxing
↓
Packaging

CCP1 –Effective CCP; CCP2- Not absolute CCP

(iii) Quality Assurance Standards

Adherence to standards established by the International Standards Organisation (ISO 9000) ensures that food processing, catering and other food-related industries conform to prescribed and well-documented procedures. Independent experts regularly assess the effectiveness of these programmes.

Meat safety regulations and harmonizations

Food safety standards have been around for a long time but reasons for their development and the differences between countries and jurisdiction lead to ambivalence to them by industry and trading countries. There is an underlying assumption that these need to protect the public by reducing the contamination level of pathogens in raw meats if they are not completely eliminated. But there is little, apparent connection between public health goals and standards or guidelines except in a general way of reducing or limiting contamination. FAO and WHO have developed guidelines for food safety risk analysis covering chemicals, biological and other agents in food. The guidelines consist of risk analysis with its three components viz. risk assessment, risk management and risk communication. Risk assessment comprises hazard identification, hazard characterization, exposure assessment and risk characterization. The risk assessment of biological agents includes similar components as in chemical hazards. Codex is in the process of developing Guiding Principles for Food Safety Risk Analysis for use by national food safety authorities. It is important to harmonize national procedures with Codex standards and guidelines to facilitate international trade, apart from ensuring safety and quality of foods. The WTO Agreement also underlines that the safety of food in international trade should be based on risk analysis with the SPS Agreement covering measures to protect human health, animal health and plant health while ensuring under TBT Agreement that product standards and technical regulations do not create unnecessary obstacles to trade. These Agreements presume Codex standards as benchmark of safety and quality. The domestic institutional mechanism is gearing up towards the international food safety standards. The agreement on the application of sanitary and phytosanitary measures (SPS) relate to measures necessary to protect human, animal or plant life or health, WTO and Codex.

Indian scenario

Development of Infrastructure

India faces a major challenge in developing its infrastructure to the necessary levels of hygienic requirement. Currently, inadequate infrastructure viz., modern slaughter houses, comprehensive cold chain, adequate wagon tonnage, cold storage facilities, transport system and retail marketing acts as a hurdle in the production of wholesome meat.

Harmonization of Food Laws

Currently there are more than twenty laws relating to food at the state and national level. Moreover responsibilities are divided between a large number of different departments, including Food, Food processing the Agriculture, Industry, Health, animal husbandry, environment, etc. This diffusion of responsibility inevitable leads to substantial problems in terms of focus and implementation, and the interests of various departments frequently contradicting each other and even working against each other on certain occasions. There is obviously a strong need to simplify this administrative structure in order to have greater clarity and focus. The Government shall work in this direction to ensure avoidance of multiplicity of food laws and bring harmonization among various laws and the agencies implementing them.

It is important that the national Food Control System is such that the consumer is protected from unsafe food. So far, the Prevention of Food Adulteration Act prescribed food standards and also established an inspection system for marketed products. But it did not seek to identify and prevent sources of contaminants. With elongated food chain, rapidly changing technologies and greater consumer awareness, it has become necessary to modernize the Food Control System. The National Food Control System, therefore, should be effective and comprehensive with science-based food law and regulations and an institutional structure which is active and responds to the needs of food safety management. The Central, State and local authorities have complementary and interdependent roles in the implementation of the national food safety system with the ultimate objective of protecting the consumer. In particular the System must ensure that only safe and wholesome foods are marketed, empower authorities to detect sources of contamination and take necessary action to prevent contaminated foods from reaching the consumer and enforce compliance by farmers, manufacturers, distributors, importers, and other stakeholders.

In India, there are different agencies that dealing with the food safety of food products. The ministry of Food and Consumer affairs is the main Government agency dealing with product standards for consumption in the domestic market. The Bureau of Indian Standard (BIS) is the main standard setting body in India for all domestic market requirements. Notably BIS is the enquiry points of India under the WTO agreement on Technical Barriers to Trade. The domestic institutional and legal framework in India is evolving itself into a web of interlinkages. Be it the commercial interests or the health safety issues at the national level, a set of legal framework is already in place. Process control and management systems should be implemented on the basis of collaboration, cooperation and coordination among the various sectors involved including industry, scientific community, regulatory authorities and public health agencies.

Upgradation of Food Testing Facilities

In order to have better acceptability of processed foods in the global market, there is a need to upgrade food-testing facilities by creating latest infrastructure for estimation of quality at par with international standards. Recognition of quality control labs by the international testing organizations would also help in promoting our exports to the developed countries. Up-gradation of food testing laboratories at district level will be taken up in a phased manner. Efforts shall be made to provide closer link with R & D institutions/universities with processors and farmers.

Strengthening of Enforcement Agencies

The Central and State Government will be required to strengthen the enforcement agencies and restructure their operations to manageable and more efficient levels. The performance of enforcement agencies could be monitored on the basis of convictions to prosecution ratio so as to reduce frivolous prosecutions, which burden the judicial system and hamper the efficient functioning of the industry. To take major initiative in the direction the Government proposes that the prevention of Food Adulteration Act, 1954 will need to be updated to take care of the phenomenal changes in food technology, food habits and food composition to suit the needs of different classes of consumers. It should now be in conformity with international norms and standards. The State Government shall also work in close coordination with Central Ministries like food Processing, Health. Commerce, Science and Technology and their Agencies like APEDA, MPEDA, CFTRI, NRC on Meat and NDRI.

Food Safety Surveillance and Monitoring System

The object of food safety surveillance and monitoring system is to ensure that the food supplied in the market is safe. In the absence of an effective system, the consumer can be exposed to chemical and microbiological contaminants, causing a variety of food borne diseases caused by agents such as Mould, Yeast, *E.coli*, Coliform, Salmonella, *Staphylococus aureus, Vibrio cholera* etc. and chemical contaminants like pesticide residues, heavy metals, aflatoxins, etc. The effectiveness of the food safety system can be judged by the frequency and extent of such diseases. In the absence of requisite data it is not possible to assess the present state and size of the problem. Food contaminants monitoring program requires regular testing of identified food / commodities and contaminants along the food chain and on the basis of risk ranking. This must be accomplished under the responsibility of the Food Safety Authority.

Conclusions

Food safety is only ensured by the shared responsibility of everybody involved with food from the professional to the consumer. For optimization of the desired quality of meat and decreasing variability, collaboration is important between producers, slaughter house and feed suppliers in choosing appropriate combination of genotypes, feeding system strategy and composition. Animal production should meet environmental criteria for sustainable production, as well as criteria and standard food safety, animal welfare and meat quality. All along the food chain, various procedures and control mechanisms are implemented to assure that the food, which reaches the consumer's table, is fit for consumption, that the risks of contamination are minimized, so that the population as a whole is healthier from the benefits of safe and quality meat. However, zero risk within food does not exist and we have to be also aware that the best legislation and control systems cannot fully protect us against those with criminal intentions. The Indian Government recently has launched a comprehensive scheme for the modernization of abattoirs across the country in order to address quality standards, contamination and deterioration of produce and the amount of meat wasted. No one step in the system is the place where safety can be achieved totally. However, all the approaches must be integrated with aggressive technology and information transfer. The best way to practice food safety remains to be well informed about the basic principles of food production and safe food handling at home.

References

Desmarchelier, P., Fegan, N., Smale, N. and Small, A. 2007. Managing safety and quality through the red meat chain. Meat Science 77:28-35.

Felmer, R., Chavez, R., Catrileo, A. and Rojas, C. 2006. Current and emergent technologies for animal identification and their use in animal traceability. Archiv De Medic Veterin 38:197-206.

Ferguson, D.M. and Warner, R.D. 2008. Have we underestimated the impact of pre slaughter stress on meat quality in ruminants? Meat Science 80:12-19.

Huiskes, J.H., Eikelenboom, G. and Vander Fels, J.B. 2004. Farm level abattoir and processing plants. In: Encyclopedia of Meat Science. Jensen, W.K. (Ed), Elsevier Lltd., U.K. pp1111-1118.

Hui Y.H., Wai Kit Nip, Rogers R.R. and O.A. Young. 2001. Meat science and applications. Marcel Dekker, Inc., New York.

ICMSF (International Commission on Microbiological specifications for foods). 2002. Microorganisms in foods 7. In: Microbial testing in food safety management, Kluwer Academic/ Plenum Publishers, New York, pp.369.

ISO 9000. 2000. Quality management Systems-Fundamentals and Vocabulary. Geneva, ISO.

ISO 19011. 2002. Guidelines for quality and/or environmental systems auditing. Geneva, ISO.

Lindsay, L. 2000. Credible food safety assessment for the whole meat chain. Nutrition and Food Science 30:250-259.

Mousavi, A., Sarhadi, M., Lent, A. and Fawcett, S. 2002. Tracking and traceability in the meat processing industry. British Food Journal 104:7-19.

Sofos, N.J. 2008. Challenges to meat safety in the 21st century. Meat Science 78:3-13.

Todd, E.C.D.2003. Microbiological safety standards and public health goals to reduce food borne disease. Meat Science 66:33-43.

Wood, J.D., Holder, J.S. and Main, D.C.J. 1998. Quality assurance schemes. Meat Science 49: S191-S203.

❑❑❑

37

Present Status and Future Prospectus of Organic Farming in Small Ruminant Production

Vishnu Sharma and Sanjita Sharma
Research Centre for livestock Health & Production, SK Rajasthan Agricultural University
SFS Sector IV, Shipra Path, Mansarovar, Jaipur-302020, Rajasthan

Introduction

Organic term primarily and simply reflects something very close to nature, ethics and tradition in general and involves principles that generate produce of high quality that is coherent with environment in particular (Sharma and Sharma, 2006). According to the Codex Alimentarius Commission and all existing National Regulations, organic production is a holistic production management system that avoids use of synthetic fertilizers, pesticides and genetically modified organisms, minimizes pollution of air, soil and water, and optimizes the health and productivity of interdependent communities of plants, animals and people. Finally, organic production is not just about production but includes the entire food supply chain from production and handling through quality control and certification to marketing and trade.

Status of Organic Farming

Organic agriculture is no longer a phenomenon of developed countries but it is now commercially practiced in 120 countries with greatest share of global organic surface area (IFOAM, 2009) is in Oceania / Australia (37.46%), followed by Europe (24.14%) and Latin America (19.8%), Asia (8.9%), North America (6.8%) and Africa (2.7%). More over, it is widely known that a large part of global food production systems is non-certified organic agriculture, often at subsistence level.

Currently, India ranks 33rd in terms of total land under organic cultivation with certified organic area in India and Rajasthan in 2006-07 to be 413850.25 & 24868.23 ha. Uttarakhand state has identified organic practices as one of the important aspect of agricultural sector. The Government of India has implemented the National Programme for Organic Production (NPOP). The national programme involves the accreditation programme for certification bodies, norms for organic production, promotion of organic farming etc. The NPOP standards for production and accreditation system have been recognized by European Commission and Switzerland as equivalent to their country standards. Similarly, USDA has recognized NPOP conformity assessment procedures of accreditation as equivalent to that of US. With these recognitions, Indian organic products duly certified by the accredited certification bodies of India are accepted by the importing countries.

Organic Livestock Production

Organic animal husbandry has developed slower than organic crop production since organic movement has developed primarily from environmental concerns, with an early focus on soil fertility and human health. The situation for organic livestock farming has however changed radically during the past decade even though; organic livestock production faces major challenges with regard to harmonization and successful integration of organic animal husbandry into the whole organic production system (Hovi et al., 2003).

Livestock farming is an important part of organic farming systems both as a part of the concept and in practice, forming an integrated system with harmony between the land, the animals, and the people. Good animal health and welfare are important parts of an organic animal system whereas main aspects of criticism are the increasing use of chemical substances, especially mineral fertilizers and pesticides. The guidelines have been formulated and developed by the International Federation of Organic Agriculture Movements (IFOAM, 1996) and meanwhile have found application all over the world. Furthermore, the basic standards of IFOAM have been used as the baseline for developing the regulation. These standards are then elaborated into more detailed standards by national or local certification organizations.

Organic Livestock under NPOP

Government of India has launched the National Programme on Organic Production (NPOP) in the year 2000 which provides information on standards for organic production criteria and procedures. The standards and procedures have been formulated in harmony with International standards such as CODEX and IFOAM. A number of improvements have been made in the NPOP document keeping International requirements in mind. NPOP standards also take care of the organic livestock production. Salient features covering organic livestock production standards are as follows:

- Animal husbandry management should be governing by physiological and ethological needs of the farm animal so that animal is allowed to conduct basic behavioural needs.
- Flock size should not adversely affect behavioural pattern and sufficient free movement should be allowed.
- Land less animal husbandry system shall not be allowed.
- Herd/ flock animals shall not be kept individually.
- Animal product may be sold as organic only after the farm has been under conversion period for at least 12 months and standards have been met for appropriate time.
- Appropriate time for dairy and egg production is 30 days and for meat production organic standard should be followed for 12 months.
- All organic animals should be born and raised in organic holdings however when organic livestock is not available, the certification programme brought- in conventional animals.
- Breeds should be chosen which are adapted to local conditions.
- AI is allowed but embryo transfer technique is not allowed in organic standards.
- Hormonal heat treatment and induced birth not allowed.
- Mutilations not allowed except castration, tail docking of lambs and dehorning.
- The livestock should be fed 100 % organically grown feed of good quality.
- Agro-products from organic feed processed industry should be used.
- At least 50 % of the feed should come from the farm itself
- Synthetic appetizers, preservatives, colouring agent, urea, abattoir waste, droppings and dung, solvent extracted meal and genetically engineered organism or products shall not be included in feeding programme.

- Fodder preservatives as bacteria, fungi and bacteria may be used. Molasses are allowed in feed formulation.
- Management practices should be directed to the well being of animal for achieving maximum resistance to the disease and preventing future in infections
- Use of natural medicines and methods should be emphasized.
- Use of conventional medicines is allowed when no other justifiable alternative is available.
- Vaccination shall be used when diseases are known or expected to be a problem in the region and cannot be controlled by management practices. In such cases it needs to be clearly defined.
- Transport and stress should be minimized to slaughter animal and preferably stunning should be employed before being bled to death.

Research on small ruminant organic livestock

Vital issues related to small ruminant organic farming have not yet been fully evaluated though, identified and addressed by some workers during last decade. Organic sheep and goat farming is on the rise in Germany and the EU. Subjective records (on-farm surveys or expert opinions) are available and there is lack of objective based research studies. Author has attempted to review available research studies on small ruminant production, though many of them regards to general organic livestock farming, findings of those can be applied for small ruminants as general guideline for future research.

Organic sheep and goat farming is based on established and monitored production and processing guidelines. The process of conversion of small ruminant from conventional to organic seems apparently less complicated in terms of management procedures than in other livestock species and livestock production systems. The transition period from conventional to full organic certification is extremely variable depending on National regulation, type of production and the certification agency (from a minimum of 12 to a maximum of 48 months). During transition, producers experience many changes in management practices, with impacts on the entire production system (soil, crops and livestock management) and therefore tendency for a decrease in profitability can be expected in the transition period as it is accompanied by an increase in labour, infrastructure and machinery costs (Cobb et al., 1999). In a recent analysis report (Nykänen and Canali, 2006) on transitional research on organic food and farming in major European countries, Denmark had the largest fraction of animal husbandry research. Within this sub-subject area, most of the work has been done on dairy production and quite a small number of projects dealt with sheep and goat research. Most of the research in animal husbandry was done in production systems research. Health and welfare research has been done extensively but less research was carried out on feeding and growth. Since research on breeding and genetics was done only in few countries, this topic can be identified as a gap in organic animal husbandry research.

Nutrition

In small ruminant farming systems, especially when faced with marginal land with high climatic strains, feed availability represents one of the most limiting factor to an organic system. Organically grown feed cannot be synthetic hormones, antibiotics, pesticides, herbicides, chemical fertilizers, or other restricted materials. During transition period EU standards allows inclusion of maximum 10% conventional feeds per year for herbivores. Management of grazing lands should be in the manner that grasses; shrubs and top feeds must be certified and labeled organic. Additionally, anything fed (hay, grain, pellets, and milk replacer) to ewes, does, lambs, and kids must be certified organic. In organic production system, use of synthetic livestock feed additives should be avoided (Lampkin, 1990). Genetically modified feed and animal by-products are also prohibited. The primary nutritional benefit of organic diets stems from increased diversity more than individual food content *per se*. The nutritional adequacy of organic foods, as compared to food produced with high external inputs, includes generally higher vitamin C, less nitrates, higher zinc/phytate ratio, higher plant secondary metabolites and conjugated fatty acids in milk.

Health

Disease prevention in organic farming is based on the principles that an animal is allowed to exhibit natural behaviour, not subject to stress, fed optimal (organic) feed, consequently will have higher ability to cope with infections if necessary, alternative treatments instead of conventional drugs should be preferred. Animals which are treated with prohibited materials such as antibiotics, drenching and dipping for parasites, fly repellants etc., cannot be represented as organic. Vaccinations are acceptable on conditional basis. In an experiment it was concluded that isolates from organic herds were more susceptible than the isolates from conventional herds to most of the antibiotics tested (Linda and Ynte, 2002). Several authors found a decrease in the incidence of metabolic disorders and clinical mastitis on organic compared to conventional farms (Ebbesvik and Loes, 1994; Vaarst and Enevoldsen, 1994). However, manure application to forage crops needs strict monitoring for potassium contents as it tends to cause metabolic disorders in livestock (Sharma et al., 2005). Handling of endoparasites through grassland management is one important aspect of small ruminant organic production. The use of selected bioactive forages may have a positive influence on parasite disease control as well as on the quality and flavour of animal products. Consumption of forages high in condensed tannins, such as polyphenolic proanthocyanidins, has been demonstrated to be useful in reducing the level of parasitism in young ruminants, resulted in reduction of their fecal egg count and total worm burden (Niezen et al., 1996). Many times it is feared that organic farms face excessive veterinary costs, without good economic or welfare returns, particularly in sheep farms producing organic meat (Cabaret, 2003).

Quality of Product

It is commonly accepted that organic livestock farming systems is associated with improved food quality. Natural pasture based farming systems produce milk rich in fat and in micro-components, which are beneficial to human health (Morand-Fehr et al., 2007). Various recent studies have indicated positive interactions between organic animal production and poly-unsaturated fatty acids, particularly CLA and omega-3 fatty acids. The validation of products deriving from sheep and goat farming in the form of high quality products may help to maintain traditional low intensity farming in harmony with the needs of ecosystem (Boyazoglu and Morand-Fehr, 2001). Organic products from small ruminant livestock system are expected to be less contaminated by chemotherapeutic agents and by other chemical treatments. Similar conclusion drawn from a study (Shinde and Karim, 2009) regarding quality of sheep products stating that meat and milk produced by sheep in Jaipur region meets the norms of food safety with regards to levels of organochlorine pesticides residues.

Welfare, sustainability & environment

Organic animal standards may be used as the yardstick to measure animal welfare even in conventional non-organic forms of livestock production systems. Generally, except for parasite-related diseases, health and welfare in organic herds are better than in conventional herds. In a study conducted by Napolitano et al. (2002) observed that artificially reared lambs showed an altered behavioural pattern with increased suckling attempts and also displayed withdrawal behaviour in terms of reduced time of locomotion and increased latency time to the first movement. Author concluded that dam-rearing, which is compulsory in organic farming can improve carcass quality and affect animal behaviour, which, in turn, is a widely used welfare indicator. Equally important, proper handling, comfortable transport and humane slaughter assure better meat quality from small ruminants. Minimum space for organic sheep and goat keeping (m^2 / animal) is 1.5 per ewe / goat & 0.35 lamb / kid) for Indoor (stable) whereas for out door 2.5 per ewe / goat & 0.5 per lamb / kid is recommended by EU regulation. The concept of organic animal farming can fulfill the criteria for sustainability and to diminish environmental pollution of agricultural production (Sundrum, 2001). Greenhouse warming potential in organic systems is 29 to 37 percent lower, on per ha basis, because of omission of synthetic fertilizers and pesticides as well as less use of high energy feed. Methane emissions of organic rice and ruminants are equal to conventional systems but the increased longevity of organic livestock is favourable on methane emissions.

Future strategies

Relative to great opportunities and inherited favourable points in existing system of small ruminant production, very less attention has been diverted to develop the ideology where existing system can be transformed into organic one. Most of the time issues have been raised for only organic agriculture or at the most for cattle welfare, surprisingly, the issue has not being addressed properly in National bodies and policies. Practical approaches for organic farming should be based and developed from locally existing animal production systems which already have close resemblance to prescribed organic practices. A set of recommendations are required at various levels and prescribed as follow:

Government agencies

1. Organic livestock production should be placed on high priority while formulating various agricultural and livestock policies since it ensures sustainable ecosystem which is desired globally by different development actors.
2. The transition period may be challenging therefore proper subsidy arrangement should exist for farmers who are willing to convert their livestock to organic since transitional decline in productivity limits conversion initiation.
3. Existing standards for organic livestock needs revision since they are largely adopted from foreign countries where livestock production system, agro-climatic situation and socio-economic condition of farmers vary greatly than to our country.
4. Proper funds should be available for promotional research and awareness regarding organic livestock.
5. Organized marketing system for organic meat, milk, wool, yarn etc. so that farmer can get premium price for the product. Success of milk

cooperative societies can be translated in livestock organic cooperatives. Agencies like APEDA can play a big role regarding exploration of foreign market however strict certification measures needs to be implemented.

Scientific and extension agencies

1. An All India Net Work Programme on research and extension aspects of small ruminant organic production should be initiated by competent body encompassing various Regional centres.
2. Most of the standards for organic livestock are subjective and vague which needs to be objective and precise. For this, streamline research is required, evolving concrete recommendations, leaving minimum room for discretion of various inspection authorities.
3. Lack of scientific information from research in organic livestock production particularly for small ruminants is a great limitation. Issues related to organic lamb, organic milk with therapeutic attributes, organic and eco-friendly wool and yarn are few core aspects which are on high priority to address.
4. Looking to the diversified agro-climatic situation in India, regional models have to be evolved incorporating area specific suitable breed for easy conversion, identify abundant natural biomass and set of welfare practices taking into account socio-economic condition and awareness of the farmers of the region.
5. The biggest hurdle in adoption of organic principles is lack of awareness and sensitization among farmers, consumers and extension workers regarding short term and long term advantages of organic practices. Therefore, tailor-made training programmes are required for different sections of the society and mass campaign needs to initiate with regards to organic livestock and small ruminant organic products.

In conclusion, organic has become buzzword for marketing aspect however to make it realization requires a great will and efforts by various stakeholders. In contrast to developed countries where organic livestock intends primarily for welfare and ethics whereas economics has to play a big role in developing countries, require review of existing standards to be in line with local agro-climatic and socio-economic conditions.

References

Boyazoglu, J. and Morand-Fehr, P. 2001. Mediterranean dairy sheep and goat products and their quality. A critical review. Small Ruminant Research 40: 1–11.

Cabaret, J. 2003. Animal health problems in organic farming: subjective and objective assessments and farmers' actions. Livestock Production Science 80: 99-108.

Cobb, D., Feber, R., Hopkins, A., Stockdale, L., O'Riordan, T., Clements, B., Firbank, L., Gouldin, K., Jarvis, S. and Macdonald, D. 1999. Integrating the environmental and economic consequences of converting to organic agriculture: evidence from a case study. Land Use Policy 16: 207–221.

Ebbesvik, M. and Loes, A.K. 1994. Organic dairy production in Norway. In: Converting to Organic Agriculture. Scandinavian Association of Agricultural Scientists Report, (Eds., Granstedt, A., Koistinen), R., 93: 35–42.

Hovi, M., Sundrum, A. and Thamsborg, S. M. 2003. Animal health and welfare in organic livestock production in Europe: current state and future challenges. Livestock Production Science 80: 41-53.

IFOAM, 1996. International Federation of the Organic Agricultural Movement: Basic Standards for Organic Agriculture and Food Processing, 10th Edition.

IFOAM, 2009. The World of Organic Agriculture: Statistics and Emerging Trends.

Lampkin, N. 1990. In: Organic Farming, Farming Press Book, IPSWICH, UK.

Linda L. Tikofsky and Ynte H. 2002. Comparison of antibiotic susceptibility patterns for staphylococcus aureus in organic and conventional dairy herds. In: Organic farming research project report submitted to the Organic Farming Research Foundation: Cornell University.

Morand-Fehr, P., Fedele. V., Decandia, M. and Le Frileux, Y. 2007. Influence of farming and feeding systems on composition and quality of goat and sheep milk. Small Ruminant Research 68: 20-34.

Napolitano, F., Braghieri, A., Cifuni, G. F., Pacelli, C. and Girolami, A. 2002. Behaviour and meat production of organically farmed unweaned lambs. Small Ruminant Research 43: 179-184.

Nardone, A. 2000. Weather conditions and genetics of breeding systems in the Mediterranean area. Proceeding of XXXV International Symposium of Societa' Italiana per il Progresso della Zootecnia, Ragusa (I), 67-91.

Niezen, J.H., Charleston, W.A.G., Hodgson, J., Mackay, A.D. and Leathwick, D.M. 1996. Controlling internal parasites in grazing ruminants without recourse to anthelmintics: approaches, experiences and prospects. International Journal of Parasitology 8/ 9: 983–992.

Nykänen, A. and Canali, S. 2006. Coordination of European Transnational Research in Organic Food and Farming, Project No. ERAC-CT-2004-011716, Ministry of Agriculture and Forestry, Finland.

Sharma, S. and Sharma, V. 2006. Local biomass use and environment adaptation as pillars of organic animal production in dry regions of India. In: Proceedings 1st IFOAM International Conference on Animals in Organic Production University of Minnesota, St. Paul, MN, USA.

Sharma, V., Sharma, S., Sanwal, R. and Sharma, S. K. 2005. Organic forage and potassium management for prevention of clinical and sub clinical disorders in livestock. In: Proceedings of the National Seminar on Monsoon Herbages for Augmenting Animal Production, Bikaner, December, 17-18, pp 131-135.

Shinde, A. K and Karim, S. A. 2009. Screening of pesticide residues in meat and milk samples of sheep maintained in institute and field flocks. Indian Journal of Small Ruminant. 15: 92-94.

Sundrum, A. 2001. Organic livestock farming: A critical review. Livestock Production Science. 67: 207-215.

Vaarst, M. and Enevoldsen, C. 1994. Disease control and health in Danish organic dairy herds. In: Proceedings of the IV Zodiac Symposium, Biological Basis of Sustainable Animal Production. EAAP, Publication No. 67, pp. 211–217.

□□□

38

Small Ruminant Production and Sustainable Rural Livelihood

Shalander Kumar, K. Kareemulla and B. Venkateswarlu
Central Research Institute for Dry land Agriculture
Santoshnagar, Saidabad P.O., Hyderabad – 500059, Andhra Pradesh

Introduction

Small ruminant sector plays an important role in the rural economy at national level. More than 70 percent of the landless, marginal and small farmers of rural India rear them. The socio-economic value of small ruminant rearing as compared to other livestock species, for poor farmers is immense. The low input, high fecundity, easy marketing and unprejudiced social acceptance of their products are few of many advantages of this enterprise that provides assured higher income. Goat and sheep are also among the main meat-producing animals in India, meat (chevon/ mutton) of these species is readily preferred irrespective of caste, creed and religion. They produce a variety of products, mainly meat, milk, skin, wool and manure. The small ruminants are especially useful in the semi-arid and arid regions, where they sustain on sparse vegetation and extreme climatic conditions. Further, wherever irrigation facilities are poor, one can generally find large areas of waste and other common property land; on these lands the small ruminants survive. A major part of their fodder requirement is met from waste and other common property lands. It has been argued that these rural households have often developed highly efficient agricultural and livelihood systems that make the most rational and conservative use of the scarce resources available to them (Barbier, 1989). The rural poor who can not afford to maintain a cow or a buffalo find goat/ sheep as the best alternative source of supplementary income and milk. This is one reason why poor rural households maintain a few number of goats. Unlike a cow or buffalo, a few goats can be maintained easily and can be easily sold in the years of drought. Therefore this sector assumes critical importance in rain fed areas, high altitudes as well as in wasteland and fragile zones having low agricultural productivity.

In this backdrop, an attempt has been made to assess the status and role of small ruminants in terms of their contribution towards sustainability of rural livelihood. An analysis is based on the secondary data sourced from FAO website, National livestock census and other published sources. The study also uses primary data collected from southwestern semi-arid zone of Uttar Pradesh and eastern semi-arid zone of Rajasthan.

Growth and distribution

The small ruminants during the last few decades have become steadily important in the rural economy, particularly in the arid and semi-arid regions. In 1951, the total number of livestock in the country was 292.80 million. The sheep and goats constituted 29.47 per cent of the total livestock population. By 2003, the total livestock population had increased to 485 million. The number of sheep and goats, interestingly, had increased to 185.83 million, forming 38.32 per cent of the total livestock population (Table 1).

Table 1. Population growth rate of major livestock species in India

Species	Population (million)		Annual compound growth rate (%)				Current population* (million)
	1951	2003	1972-82	1982-92	1992-2003	1971-03	
Cattle	155.3 (53.04)	185.18 (38.18)	0.76	0.61	- 0.99	0.13	177.84
Buffalo	43.40 (14.82)	96.62 (19.92)	1.96	1.89	1.38	1.73	98.70
Sheep	39.10 (13.35)	61.47 (12.67)	2.01	0.40	1.93	1.43	64.27
Goat	47.20 (16.12)	124.36 (25.66)	3.50	1.93	0.78	2.04	125.46
Livestock	292.80	485.00	1.73	1.44	0.31	1.05	

Note: The figures in parentheses indicate percent to total livestock population
Source: Livestock Census, Govt. of India, * FAO (2007)

The goat population over the past few decades has increased steadily. The increase in goat population from 47.2 million in 1951-52 to 124.36 million in 2003 with mean increment of 1.51 million per annum and annual compound growth rate of 1.92 percent was observed. Its annual growth was 2.04 percent during 1971-2003. Combining the annual growth rate with mean slaughter rate of around 41 percent and mortality rate of about 15 percent, goat have shown the potential population growth of above 58 percent per year. This is the single most important factor that makes goat as most desired species of animal for meat production in the country.

The goat and sheep although are well adapted to a variety of agro-ecological regions, there is marked variation in their density among different states. Among the small ruminants, goats are more widely distributed (Rath, 1992). Among the major small ruminant keeping states, the density of goats per square km was highest in West Bengal (212) followed by Bihar, Tamilnadu and Rajasthan. The density of sheep was highest in Andhra Pradesh with 78 sheep per square km, followed by Tamilnadu, Karnataka and Rajasthan. A study on understanding the factors affecting the density of goats in different states conducted by Kumar and Pant (2003) demonstrates that average size of holding and percent net irrigated area were negatively associated with density of goats (Table 2), validating the general perception that goats are associated with marginal and small farmers and provide livelihood to the people in rain fed regions. The association between goat density and area under pasture/wasteland was positive and highly significant, which highlights the role of common property resources in small ruminant production system.

The annual compound growth rate of sheep and goat during 1992-2003 as depicted in table 3 for top 25 districts in the country shows that the population of sheep and goats has been increasing at a very fast rate in some of the districts. It may be mentioned that most of these fast growing top 25 districts, fall under rain fed regions. In case of sheep 15 and in case of goat 14 out of 25 top districts are the rain fed districts. In spite of general feed and fodder scarcity in the rain fed regions, these two species have well performed. It clearly indicates the higher utility and significance of small ruminants as means of livelihood security in the rain fed regions. The analysis of growth of small ruminant population further indicates that the districts with least or negative growth of goat and sheep population fall under irrigated regions.

Table 2. Linear estimates of determinants of goat density

Explanatory Variables	Regression Coefficient	t value
Percentage of people below poverty line in the state	-2.01	0.403
Average size of holding (ha.)	-64.84	1.275
Percentage of Pasture and cultivable waste and fallow land to the total	26.38*	3.446
Percent Net irrigated area	-11.35*	3.696
Bovine density per 100 ha.	0.92*	5.534
Constant term	-251.05	
Coefficient of determination (R^2)	0.82	

* Significant at one percent level P(< 0.01); Source: Kumar and Pant (2003)

Table 3. Districts with higher population growth of sheep and goats during 1992-2003 (compound Annual Growth Rate, CAGR)

State	Sheep District	CAGR, %	State	Goat District	CAGR, %
Uttar Pradesh	Kanpur Nagar	46.1	Tamil Nadu	The Nilgiris	39.3
Tamil Nadu	The Nilgiris	38.2	Uttar Pradesh	Kanpur Nagar	24.4
Assam	Goalpara	24.7	Gujarat	Gandhinagar	11.2
Kerala	Palakkad	21.2	Assam	Bongaigaon	9.7
Andhra Pradesh	Hyderabad	18.7	Andhra Pradesh	Cuddapah	6.7
Assam	Lakhimpur	17.4	Maharashtra	Yeotmal	6.4
Karnataka	Uttara Kannada	16.5	Karnataka	Bangalore	6.3
Andhra Pradesh	Nizamabad	15.0	Assam	Jorhat	6.3
Andhra Pradesh	Adilabad	14.9	Andhra Pradesh	Ananthapur	6.1
Andhra Pradesh	Medak	14.6	Andhra Pradesh	Kurnool	6.0
Assam	Hailakandi	14.2	Tamil Nadu	Ramanathapuram	5.7
Maharashtra	Sindhudurg	13.9	Andhra Pradesh	Guntur	5.6
Andhra Pradesh	West Godavari	13.3	Uttar Pradesh	Sonbhadra	5.6
Assam	Bongaigaon	13.1	Madhya Pradesh	Panna	5.5
Madhya Pradesh	Shajapur	12.9	West Bengal	Darjeeling	5.3
Assam	Nalbari	12.7	West Bengal	Jalpaiguri	5.1
Gujarat	Gandhinagar	12.5	Assam	Lakhimpur	4.8
Andhra Pradesh	Nalgonda	12.5	Assam	North Cachar Hills	4.8
Tamil Nadu	Thanjavur	12.4	Andhra Pradesh	Karimnagar	4.7
Andhra Pradesh	Krishna	11.8	Uttar Pradesh	Sant kabir nagar	4.6
Andhra Pradesh	Karimnagar	11.6	Andhra Pradesh	Krishna	4.6
Andhra Pradesh	Guntur	11.4	Assam	Dhubri	4.5
Andhra Pradesh	Ranga Reddy	10.9	Andhra Pradesh	Medak	4.5
Madhya Pradesh	Raisen	10.7	Madhya Pradesh	Jhabua	4.5
Assam	Barapeta	10.6	Orissa	Boudh	4.4

Contribution at national level

The small ruminants contribute significantly to the Indian economy by providing sustenance to rural resource poor especially in the arid and semi-arid regions. The contribution of goat and sheep to the national economy has been estimated and presented in Table 4.

Table 4. Contribution of small ruminants to the Indian Economy-2007 (at current price)

Items	Goats		Sheep	
	Quantity (000' tones)	Value (Rs.in Crore)	Quantity (000' tones)	Value (Rs.in Crore)
Meat[1]	543.0	8145.00	234.56	3518.40
Milk[2]	4000.0	5600.00	-	-
Pashmina[3]	0.043	12.04	-	-
Wool[4]	-	-	45.20	226.00
Offals[5]	325.8	1900.50	146.54	683.83
Manure[6]	17211.0	1376.88	8525.61	682.05
Blood[7]	54.3	27.15	23.45	9.77
Skin[8]	129.96	519.84	57.96	231.84
Increment in stock[9], 000 Nos.	940.00	80.30	970.00	82.10
Total	-	**17661.71**	-	**5433.99**

Note: The estimates are based on FAO (2007);[1] Estimated @ Rs. 130 / kg.; [2] Estimated @ Rs. 12 / kg; [3] Estimated @ Rs. 2500 / kg; [4] Estimated @ Rs. 50/ kg; [5] Since figures are not available, it is estimated as 35 % of live weight and valued @ Rs. 250 / animal slaughtered; [6] Since the information on manure produced is not available, the average yield of manure has been estimated @ 500 g/adult and 200 g/young/day and valued @ Rs. 600 /tonne. Ratio for adult and kids is 60:40; [7] Estimated @ 5 % of live weight and valued @ Rs. 5/goat slaughtered; [8] Estimated @ Rs. 40/kg; and [9] The incremental stock has been valued considering the period of last one decade. It is assumed that 50 % kids are born in February-March-April and 50 % in September – October. In the incremental stock the 50% kids has been valued at 8-9 month's age @ Rs. 1500/ animal and another 50% kids of 3-4 months age @ Rs. 600/ animal.

The goats and their products contribute Rs 17661.71 crores annually to the national economy, whereas the annual contribution of sheep was estimated to be Rs. 5433.99 crores. Thus the annual contribution per animal works out to Rs. 1407 for goat and Rs. 845 per sheep. The goat and sheep together contribute Rs. 23095.75 crores annually. Among different products, meat accounts for the largest share contributing about 50 percent of the total value of goat products and 65 percent of the total value of sheep products.

Small ruminant rearing as means of livelihood

Goats and sheep play a significant role in ensuring food and nutritional security for the families of millions of resource poor rural households. Being

Contd...

as an important means of income and employment generation for these households, goat and sheep rearing helps in alleviating poverty and regularize income distribution. The rearing of goat and sheep, which are mainly depend on common property resources (CPRs) for meeting their feed and fodder requirements, is a preferred option as self-employment by many rural resource-poor people. The CPRs comprise of barren and uncultivable lands, cultivable wastes, permanent pastures and other grazing land and land under miscellaneous trees, crops and other fallow land. In spite of their critical role in livelihood security of rural poor, the CPRs are declining continuously (Jodha, 1986). The erroneous stigmatization of goats and sheep as the major culprits for environmental degradation is unfortunate, because available evidence shows that when managed properly, especially in mixed species grazing, goats contribute to sustainable natural resource management (Rege and Agyemang, 1992 and Schwartz, 1983). The reality is that poverty and demographic pressures on the land drive environmental degradation through deforestation, overgrazing, overstocking and indiscriminate exploitation of fragile marginal ecosystems.

Cow and buffalo rearing, crop farming; agricultural wages, trade and services are the other components of small ruminant based farming system. Household's cash needs were met by selling goats, milk, manure, crop produce, wages and other sources. Family labour and common grazing resources were observed to be the critical and major inputs used in goat production system. The other major input was supplementary feed. The small ruminants are well integrated into the existing farming systems (Fig. 1). The landless people in the villages possess own labour as the only abundant factor which is free to them and they try to use it to its maximum for their survival and thus concentrate on animal husbandry (Pasha, 1991). In semi-arid regions with poor irrigation, opportunity of agricultural employment for landless rural people is not available through out the year. Moreover the large ruminant rearing is a less preferred option for the land less people as it demands relatively large investment and higher maintenance cost. Hence, these landless households are particularly depends on small ruminant rearing as source of income and nutrition.

The initial investment requirements for small units of goat/sheep are modest and there is quick pay-off due to fast multiplication. Studies in the past have shown that goat and sheep are economical in arid and semi-arid regions. It was reported that a goat in Andhra Pradesh provided an income of Rs 140 per annum (Sriramamurthy, 1977). Similarly at Jodhpur, Rajasthan, net income per goat was reported at Rs. 250 per year (Ghosh and Khan, 1980). Pasha (1991) reported a net income of Rs. 114 per small ruminant per

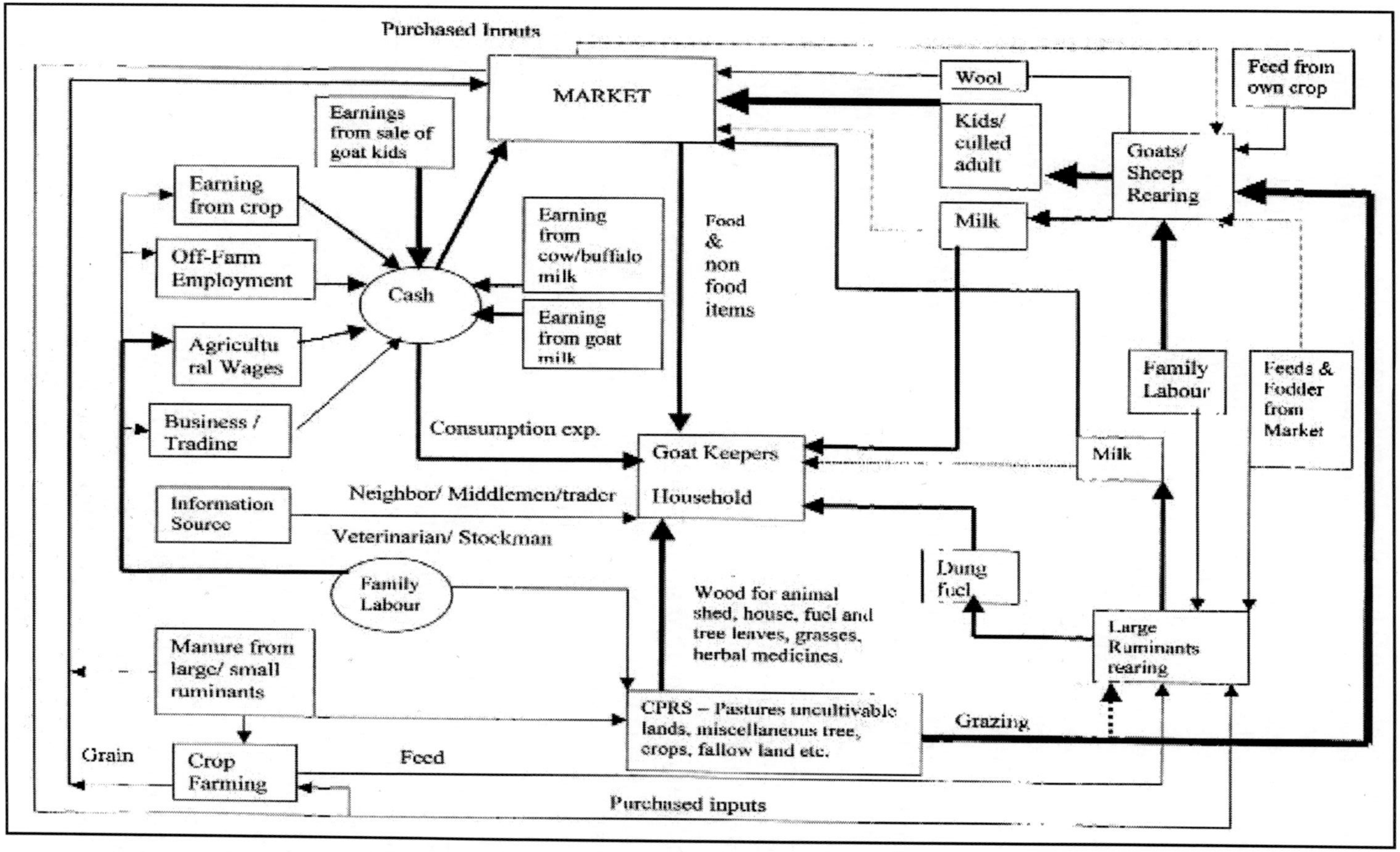

Figure 1: Resource Flows in the Farming System of Goat Keepers in Semi-arid Regions
Note: Thickness of connecting lines in the figure shows the intensity of the resource flow among different components of the production system

annum. Swain et al. (1982) found indigenous goats 2.5 times more economical than sheep on free range grazing under semi-arid region of Rajasthan. In a study of comparative economics of mutton production, it was found that the cost of rearing a lamb up to 6 months age was about Rs 114 and the total returns were Rs. 165 from sale of an indigenous lamb and Rs. 195 from cross bred lamb (Singh, 1981). The net returns from lamb fattening at Avikanagar were estimated at Rs 25 to Rs. 58 per lamb reared up to 6 months age under different feeding regimes (Singh and Singh, 1981). The cost of chevon production was estimated at Rs. 5.80 to Rs. 7.40 per kg under different feeding system (Sehgal and Singh, 1984). Shinde et al. (2003) have shown goat rearing was also profitable on organized farms. The income generated from goat rearing was estimated at Rs. 1.29 in first year and Rs. 1.36 in the second year per rupee of investment. Acharya and Singh (1992) also highlighted the crucial role of goats in livelihood security of resource poor rural households. Deoghare and Rekib (1996) found that the farmers could earn a net income of Rs. 331 per goat per annum and Rs. 74.00 per sheep per annum. In another study in Mathura district (Kumar and Deoghare, 2002), the actual cost of rearing a goat was Rs. 395 per annum and the net returns were Rs. 1126 per goat per year. All these studies indicate that it is quite remunerative to rear small ruminants with higher profitability in goats compared to sheep.

Cost and return from goat and sheep rearing in semi-arid regions

An analysis was done on the survey of 140 goat keeping households of southwestern semi-arid zone of Uttar Pradesh and another 140 goat keeping households of eastern semi-arid zone of Rajasthan. The selected households were classified into four categories based on the flock size of goat viz; category I (1-5 goats), category II (6-15 goats) category III (16-30 goats) and category IV (>30 goats). Small ruminant were the important source of livelihood security for these rural resource poor. In Uttar Pradesh only landless agricultural wage earners and marginal and small farmers were involved in goat/sheep rearing. However, in Rajasthan, where drought is frequent and crops are rain-fed, the farmers of the all categories adopted goat/sheep rearing. All the selected households had goats but sheep was not owned by every one of them. At the same time, the flock size of goat varied from 2 to 70 goats in different categories. In both the states, the total cost per animal per annum was negatively associated with the flock size. This was mainly attributed to higher expenditure on supplementary feed in small flock size categories and better utilization of labour in large categories. Imputed value of family labour was found to be major components of total expenditure, which accounted for 51 to 79 percent of the total cost of goat rearing in different categories. This shows that actual expenditure incurred by the family on rearing a goat or sheep was very low.

It ranged from Rs. 189 to Rs. 532 per goat and Rs. 163 to Rs. 204 per sheep per annum in Uttar Pradesh, and Rs. 191 to Rs. 319 per goat and Rs. 162 to Rs. 183 per sheep per annum in Rajasthan (Table 5).

Table 5. Costs of goat and sheep rearing (Rs. / annum)

Particulars	Category of small ruminant farmers							
	Uttar Pradesh				Rajasthan			
	I	II	III	IV	I	II	III	IV
Land holding size, ha.	0.30	0.19	0.25	0.0	1.12	2.39	3.38	0.51
A. GOAT								
Av. flock size (Doe)	2.43	11.09	20.68	36.00	3.47	10.72	22.56	45.59
Fixed cost	416	2032	3448	5629	630	2178	3974	6819
Total variable cost	5801	6934	10737	8344	4402	7966	13600	11447
Total cost (A+B)	6217	8966	14185	13973	5032	10144	17574	18266
Total cost excluding family labour	1293	3046	4730	6801	1077	3424	6328	8707
Cost/ goat excluding family labour	532	275	229	189	310	319	280	191
B. SHEEP								
Av. flock size (Ewe)	-	6.35	1.68	21.00	5.32	8.45	2.50	6.73
Fixed cost	-	997	239	2984	676	805	357	995
Total variable cost	-	3683	828	4625	6361	5864	1364	1578
Total cost (A+B)	-	4680	1067	7609	7037	6669	1721	2573
Total cost excluding family labour	-	1295	301	3433	974	1369	475	1162
Cost/sheep excluding family labour	-	204	179	163	183	162	190	173

The direct benefits from both goat and sheep rearing were live animal sale, change in flock inventory and manure. Additionally goat provides milk, which was crucial for the family nutrition, and sheep provide wool for sale. Goat and sheep rearing turned out to be a very good source of income for the landless as well as the land owners. The family of the small ruminant keeper earned a net annual income of Rs. 1383 to Rs. 1788 per goat and Rs 364 to Rs 663 per sheep in different flock size categories in Uttar Pradesh. Similarly in Rajasthan, the net annual income accrued from a goat ranged from Rs. 1303 to Rs 1873 and that of a sheep was from Rs. 371 to Rs. 602 in different flock categories. The families owning large flock generated an average annual net income up to Rs. 59344 from goats and Rs. 8978 from sheep, respectively in semi-arid areas (Table 6).

Table 6. Family's income from goat and sheep rearing (Rs. / annum)

Particular	Category of goat farmers							
	Uttar Pradesh				Rajasthan			
	I	II	III	IV	I	II	III	IV
GOAT								
Gross returns	5638	20746	33337	57240	6183	23501	44148	68051
Family labour income	4345	17700	28607	50439	5106	20077	37820	59344
Family labor income/ goat	1788	1596	1383	1401	1471	1873	1676	1302
Income from goat/ man-day	35	120	121	281	52	120	135	248
SHEEP								
Gross returns		3607	1414	124111	3030	6456	1402	4675
Family labour income		2312	1113	8978	4007	213	319	2102
Family Labor Income/ sheep		364	663	428	387	602	371	522
Income from sheep/ man-day		27	58	86	14	38	30	100

Case of sheep rearing in Rajasthan

A recent study on socio-economics of sheep rearing in Rajasthan (Suresh et al., 2008) shows that contrary to the ownership pattern of goats, the sheep are reared in larger flocks. The flock size on an average was 24 sheep in small category and 43 in medium and 91 in large flock. Agriculture was the main occupation (51 per cent), followed by animal husbandry (48 per cent) for these sheep farmers. The average size of operational holding was 5 ha, varying from 2.58 ha in the small to 6.97 ha in the large category of sheep breeders. The popular belief among farmers is that sheep-rearing is the occupation of very poor households seems to be gradually changing in the rural areas. Nearly 64 per cent of the sheep farmers were from semi-medium, medium and large land holding categories and accounted for 70 per cent of the sheep. At the same time 36 per cent sheep farmers belonging to landless, marginal and small land size categories possessed only 30 per cent of the total sheep population.

The sheep flocks are generally raised on the common grazing lands. Though feeding of concentrate mixture and mineral supplements are known to have significant positive effect on various production traits of sheep, its adoption was very low due to various economic and institutional constraints. Some fodder trees and harvested crop lands were reported to be leased for sheep rearing for a fixed period.

Cost and returns in sheep farming

The economics of sheep farming accounting only paid up cost demonstrate that the cost in sheep-rearing was maximum on feed and fodder, followed by veterinary care, hired labour and interest on capital. The overall annual average variable cost was Rs 3520 per flock @ Rs. 65 per sheep (Table 7). The returns from the sale of live-animals, milk, wool and manure together give a return of Rs 28252 for a flock of 54. The return over variable cost (net return or profit) worked out to Rs 24732, giving per animal return of Rs 456 per annum. The animals (male lambs) of 6-8 month are sold, particularly during the peak demand season of the year. They are sold mainly to the village agents/ middlemen. The average mortality was 14 per cent and was largely due to foot and mouth disease, enterotoxaemia and pneumonia. The farmers were found to depend mostly on the government veterinary clinics for treatment of animals.

Table 7. Feature and cost and returns from sheep in semi-arid region of Rajasthan

Particulars		Small (upto 30)	Medium (31-60)	Large (>60)	Overall
No. of sheep farmers		29	42	36	107
Size of operational holding (ha)		2.58	4.98	6.97	5.00
Livestock No.:	Sheep	24	43.4	91.4	54.3
	Goat	6.7	4.8	8.9	6.7
	Cattle	1.4	2.3	3.8	2.6
	Buffalo	1.6	2.8	5.5	3.4
Cost and returns in sheep rearing					
Expenditure					
Fodder and feed (%)		62.50	58.57	52.69	56.08
Medicine (%)		26.30	32.03	27.18	28.52
Hired labour (%)		5.48	3.73	14.48	9.74
Interest (%)		5.63	5.67	5.66	5.65
Total variable cost (Rs)		2115	2735	5567	3520
Returns					
Animal sale (%)		77.35	82.31	81.69	81.36
Milk (%)		4.87	2.63	3.26	3.26
Wool (%)		11.00	8.10	8.46	8.65
Manure (%)		6.87	6.96	6.59	6.72
Total returns (Rs)		12395	21822	48528	28252
Return over variable cost (ROVC) (Rs)		10280	19087	42961	24732
ROVC per animal (Rs)		428	440	470	456

Conclusions and recommendations

It may be concluded that goat and sheep rearing play a very important role in providing income, nutrition and gainful employment to the resource poor rural households especially in arid and semi-arid rain fed regions. The potential for goats and sheep for attainment of food security, economic development and environmental sustainability is tremendous. The broad genetic variability of Indian goat and sheep breeds enables them to survive under stressful environmental conditions, including high disease incidence, poor nutrition and harsh temperatures. Environmental pressure also maintains a wide range of genotypes, each adapted to a specific set of circumstances. Under on-station management, indigenous sheep and goat breeds have shown good growth and reproductive performances, indicating their potential and ability to respond to improvements in management, particularly nutrition and disease control.

The contribution of small ruminant sector in National GDP is significant. Therefore goat and sheep husbandry should invariably be encouraged as a potential source of income and employment for the rural landless, and small and marginal farmers especially in the arid and semi-arid and other marginal areas having low agricultural productivity. The attractive return from goat rearing also makes a strong case for its promotion on commercial scale. However there is a need to put a system in place for better disease prevention and proper marketing of small ruminants and their products. The development of fodder resources (CPRs) and economic feeding systems and imparting practical skill on scientific small ruminant keeping is also equally important.

Implementing the following specific recommendations would contribute towards sustainable development of small ruminant production as a means of livelihood security of resource poor rural people:

- Scarcity of feed and fodder being the major constraint in the existing small ruminant production system, better management of common feed resources is crucially important for improved fodder supplies in rain fed areas. In fact, each watershed should essentially have a component to develop common and private fodder resources as part of it and its compliance by the project implementation agencies (PIAs) should be monitored. As most of the PIAs are not allocating resources for development of livestock and fodder component in spite of such guidelines under the watershed programme.
- Efficient utilization of available fodder resources: Chopping of coarse cereal Stover (sorghum / ragi, etc), which is not common in southern

India, needs to be promoted to reduce wastage (by at least 50%) and improve digestibility.

- The Panchayats may be given incentives to develop common grazing resources in the village commons through convergence of NREGS (National Rural Employment Guarantee Scheme).
- With the involvement of animal husbandry experts and other major stakeholders (farmers, local veterinarians, dairy cooperatives, etc.), the potential indigenous breeds of different species need to be identified at micro level (development block) considering the yield potential, resource situation and socio-economic factors and should be used for grading up programmes.
- For weeding out poor quality breeding males of small ruminants, Panchayat have to play an effective role. Once the breeds of animals is promoted at block and village level, the Panchayat should ask its members not to keep breeding males of non-descript breeds. The poor breeding males may be replaced as part of breed improvement programme.
- Production and mortality losses in small ruminants due to diseases and parasites are huge, hence there is need to run an awareness campaign through mass media (TV, Newspaper, etc.) focusing on importance of prevention programme for diseases and parasites in small ruminants.
- Deworming against parasites and vaccination against major diseases should be taken up as campaign at National level continuously at least for five years. The major diseases in large ruminants are; food and mouth disease (FMD, Hemorrhagic Septicemia (HS), Black Quarter (BQ), etc. and for small ruminants; Enterotoxaemia (ET), Blue tongue (BT), Peste Des Petits Ruminant (PPR), FMD, etc.
- Poor bargaining power, low awareness, high transaction cost, smaller surplus for sale, low income (distress sale) coupled with lack of infrastructure are the main reasons for lower price realization of the livestock produce of the smallholders.
- There is need to link the smallholder producers directly with the market (processors, marketers/retailers and consumers).
- Farmers should be encouraged and supported for collective action in livestock production and marketing.
- The insurance of livestock is the best safeguard for minimizing the risk especially for smallholder producers. Its importance is paramount in

case of small ruminants because of higher risk of loss of production and animals due to diseases and feed scarcity. Though the insurance companies have provision for insurance of animals throughout the country, only a very small share of small ruminants has been insured. The major reasons of poor coverage of animals under insurance are: high cost of premium (4.5-8.25% of the value of animal) besides low awareness among the farmers. Further the insurance companies many times do not entertain request for insurance by the farmers because of the small scale of business and higher transaction cost. Hence, there is need to increase the farmers' awareness and make mandatory provision for the companies to undertake livestock insurance of interested farmers. There should also be redressal mechanism for sorting grievances.

- Because of the constraints inherent to the situation, the level of technology adoption in small ruminants is very low. Besides specific package of practices suggested above, there is need to provide a basket of technological options so that livestock holders may choose as per their needs and resources conditions.
- Farmers must be trained and retrained to develop their management skills for proper feeding including fodder development and conservation, proper breeding skills, disease control and prevention, basic on-farm processing methods to add value to their goat farming, simple record-keeping and the exploitation of synergies between livestock and crops.
- The focus should be on development of integrated farming system with livestock and other most remunerative activities as its components.

The small ruminant rearing has a great promise as source of income and employment and livelihood security of resource poor rural people throughout the country in general and the rain fed areas in particular. However, there is a need for appropriate policy and institutions for transfer of need based technologies, linking smallholders with the market, value addition and safeguards mechanism in face of increased competition due to globalization and climate change.

References

Acharya, R.M. and Singh, N.P. 1992. The role of goats in conservation of ecology and livelihood security. Pre-conference Proceedings, V International Conference on Goats, pp. 81-99.

Barbier, Edward, B. 1989. Sustaining agriculture on marginal land: A policy framework. Environment, 31(9).

Deoghare, P.R. and Rekib, A. 1996. Economics of sheep and goat production. CLRI-APAU Workshop on Small Ruminant Production and Post Production Systems: Current Status and Development, CLRI, Chennai, 4-6 December.

FAO. 2007. FAOstat, In: http://www.fao.org

Ghosh, P. K. and Khan, M.S. 1980. The goat in desert environment. Research Bulletin No.12, CAZRI, Jodhpur.

Jodha, N.S. 1986 Common Property Resources and Rural Poor in Dry Regions of India, Economic and Political Weekly, 31:27(1986): 1169-81.

Kumar, Shalander and Deoghare, P.R. 2002. Goat rearing and rural poor: A case study in south western semi-arid zone of Uttar Pradesh. Annals of Arid Zone 41:79-84.

Kumar, Shalander and Pant, K.P. 2003. Development perspective of goat rearing in India: Status issues and strategies. Indian Journal of Agricultural Economics 58:752-767.

Pasha, A.S. 1991. Sustainability and viability of small and marginal farmers: Animal husbandry and common property resources. Economic and Political Weekly, 26(13):A27-A30.

Rath, N. 1992. Economics of sheep and goat in Maharastra. Indian Journal of Agricultural Economics 47:62-78.

Rege, J.E.O. and Agyemang, K., 1992. The role of indigenous cattle breeds in African livestock production systems. In: Proceedings of the 43rd Annual Meeting of European Association on Animal Production, Madrid, Spain, 14–19 September.

Schwartz, H.J., 1983. Improved utilization of arid rangelands through multiple species herds. In: Proceedings of the V World Conference on Animal Production, Vol. 2, pp. 625–626.

Sehgal, J.P. and Singh, N.P. 1984. Economics of rearing a doe and cost of chevon production. Livestock Advisor 12(9): 29-34.

Shinde, A.K., Bhatta, R., Sankhyan, S.K., Singh, N.P. and Verma, D.L. 2003. Economics of goat rearing in an organized farm. Indian Journal of Small Ruminants 9:32-34.

Singh, N. P. and Singh, R.N. 1981. Economics of fattening native lambs. Livestock Advisor, 6(9):7-10.

Singh, N.P. 1981. Economics of mutton production. Research Bulletin, CSWRI, Avikanagar. pp. 9.

Sriramamurthy, V. 1977. Annadata magazine. December 1977, pp.6-14.

Suresh, A., Gupta D.C. and Mann J. S. 2008. Returns and economic efficiency of sheep farming in semi-arid. Regions: A study in Rajasthan. Agricultural Economics Research Review, Vol. 21 July-December, pp 227-234.

Swain, N., Jain, P.M. and Acharya, R. M. 1982. Relative economics of sheep and goats. III International Conference on Goat Production and Disease. January 11-15, Tucson, Arizona, USA, pp 290.

❑❑❑

39

Impact of Climate Change on Socio-Economic Status of Small Ruminant Farmers

Smita Sirohi[1] and Suresh A.[2]

[1]Division of Dairy Economics, Statistics & Management, National Dairy Research Institute, Karnal-132 001, Haryana, [2]National Centre for Agricultural Economics and Policy Research P. B. No. 11305, Library Avenue, Pusa, New Delhi - 110012

Introduction

Small ruminants, viz. sheep and goat that account for 42% of the 4.55 billion of the world livestock population (FAOSTAT) are mostly reared by small-scale farmers. Besides contributing to livelihoods of small-holders by providing food, clothing and income, the small ruminants also play significant role in socio-cultural and religious aspects of everyday life. In particular they contribute to the empowerment of women and children who often have responsibility for the management, production and health-care of small ruminants. The rearing of sheep and goats, fits well into the smallholder farming systems since their grazing preferences enable them to feed on weeds, shrubs and other plants that other species of domestic animals tend to refuse. Also, due to their small size they require less space and are easier to work with than large ruminants. By and large, the small ruminants are cheaper to buy and maintain for the resource-poor farmers.

Unlike the intensive livestock systems prevalent for the cattle, pigs and poultry in the developed countries, the small ruminants are largely maintained under pastoral and agro-pastoral systems, particularly in the African and Asian countries that together account for 68% of world sheep population and over 93% of the world goat stock. The economic potential of livestock managed under pastoral, agro-pastoral and small-holder livestock production systems is constrained by a number of abiotic factors associated with poor availability and access to resources, inputs, technology and markets. Additionally, due to close interaction of such types of livestock production systems with the natural environment, climate change and variability poses formidable challenge to the livestock farmers.

The scientific evidence indicates an increase in global average surface temperature by about 0.6 °C during the twentieth century. The predictions of further increase in temperature between 1°C to 2.5°C by 2030, changes in rainfall pattern and increase in the incidence of extreme events (IPCC, 2007), would have far-reaching consequences for the health and livelihoods of billions of people, especially in the underdeveloped and developing countries. In the context livelihoods of livestock farmers, the impacts that climate change will bring about are expected to exacerbate the vulnerability of livestock systems and to reinforce existing factors that are simultaneously affecting livestock production systems.

In this backdrop, this Chapter examines the vulnerability of small ruminant production system in India to looming threat of climatic change with a purpose to identify appropriate options that can help small ruminant farmers to adapt to changing climate. Before proceeding with the discussion on the various dimensions of the climate change impact on the prospects of livestock farming and socio-economic aspects of the livestock farmers, the Chapter presents a brief profile of the small-ruminant farmers in India to delineate the target groups for whom the coping mechanism need to be put into place.

Small ruminant production system in India: An overview

Out of 485 million livestock (2003 census) in India, more than 1/3 is small ruminants. The proportion of goats in livestock population (25.6%) is nearly twice that of sheep (12.7%). In comparison to the production potential realized in other regions of the world, although the productivity of these animals is very low in the country (Table 1), nevertheless small ruminants make substantial contribution to the value of output from livestock products.

Table 1. Productivity of small ruminants (kg/animal) in selected regions: 2008

Regions	Goat			Sheep			
	Meat	Milk	Skins	Meat	Milk	Skins	Wool, greasy
World	12.3	84.8	2.4	15.6	46.3	3.6	5.4
Australia	25.0	-	7.5	21.1	-	4.5	4.1
New Zealand	10.7	-	2.0	17.7	-	4.1	5.4
North America	28.3	-	2.5	29.2	-	3.1	3.4
Central America	16.8	188.9	2.9	19.4	-	2.5	0.6
South America	11.1	32.3	2.2	13.6	25.9	4.0	2.4
Europe	10.7	248.7	1.9	14.7	112.4	3.6	18.3
Asia	12.4	85.5	2.6	15.5	38.5	3.8	6.2
Africa	12.0	56.0	2.1	13.8	30.1	2.3	8.0
India	10.0	132.4	1.8	12.0	-	1.8	-

Note: - indicates information is not available Source: FAOSTAT

The annual value of mutton production was Rs.9136 crores in 2006-07 (at 1999-00 prices) that was 37% of the value of meat output in India. The production of wool (in value terms) has more or less stagnated at around Rs.208 crores during 1999/00-2006/07, but that of mutton has increased about 36% during this period. Besides mutton and wool, the contribution of small ruminants to the national economy also comes through goat milk and by-products like skins and dung. The small ruminants are distributed in nearly all the climatic regions of the country stretching from cold desert of Ladakh in the north to the coastal state of Kerela in the south and from dry desert of Rajasthan in the west to humid climate of Bengal in the east. The states of West Bengal, Rajasthan, U.P., Maharashtra and Bihar account for 55% of the goat population in India, while 78% sheep are concentrated in Andhra Pradesh, Rajasthan, Karnataka, Tamil Nadu and J&K (Table 2).

Table 2. Top-five states in small ruminant population: 2003

State	% share in all-India goat stock	State	% share in all-India sheep stock
West Bengal	15.1	Andhra Pradesh	34.8
Rajasthan	13.5	Rajasthan	16.4
Uttar Pradesh	10.4	Karnataka	11.8
Maharashtra	8.6	Tamil Nadu	9.1
Bihar	7.6	Jammu & Kashmir	5.5

(Source: Govt. of India, 2003)

Both, sheep and goat are generally reared under low-input extensive system by the economically weaker sections, largely belonging to scheduled tribes, scheduled castes and other backward castes (Singh et al., 2008; Misra et al., 2006). Due to their poor resource position the small ruminant farmers have limited adaptive capacity and alternate sources of income and hence are highly vulnerable to potential consequences of changing climate.

Vulnerability of small ruminant production performance to climatic stress

The thermal environment has a strong influence on farm animals. The effective ambient temperature which combines the various weather parameters, such as air temperature, wind velocity, precipitation, humidity etc., influences the physiology of animals. Although small ruminants are more tolerant of climatic extremes than other farm animals, yet the empirical evidence based on experimental studies indicates adverse impact of heat and cold stress on the growth, production and reproduction performance of these animals. Exposure of sheep to thermal stress affects voluntary feed intake and maintenance requirement resulting in a decrease of body weight, average daily gain (ADG), growth rate and body total solids—which is reflected by impaired reproduction (Marai et al., 1997a,b,2000; Shelton, 2000; Abdel-Hafez, 2002).

Ames and Brink (1977) conducted growth and efficiency studies for shorn lambs exposed to a wide range (- 5 to 35°C) of ambient temperatures and concluded that very high temperature deviations from the critical temperature led to low average daily weight gain. The animals of temperate breed have high productivity traits compared to the indigenous breeds in tropical countries, but when the their dams are reared for generations in hot, semi-arid locations, the lamb birth weights of temperate sheep breeds show a linear decline (Singh and Karim, 1995). Such a decline was manifested from the 6th generation in Rambouillet and Merino lambs , while in Suffolk and Dorset Horn lambs the reduction was apparent from the 2nd and 3rd generations, respectively, suggesting that in the longer run due to their low climatic stress tolerance levels, without the suitable adaptive strategies, the induction of temperate breeds in the stock of small ruminants in India may not be viable to improve the socio-economic status of farmers rearing these animals. Studies on effect of thermal stress on the reproductive performance of fine wool crossbred sheep Bharat Merino, an exotic and native crossbreed developed for the tropical environment indicated that although thermal stress did not affect the fertilization rate of the ewes but it adversely affected the quality of the embryos. The incidence of embryonic abnormalities was higher in case the embryos produced from the ewes exposed to thermal stress as compared to those kept under the control environment (Naqvi et al., 2004).

Although in general, native sheep breeds in the hot semi-arid areas when exposed to elevated ambient temperatures or solar radiation during hot summer months are less affected in their physiological functions and production potential compared to non-adapted exotic sheep and crossbreds (Naqvi, 1987; Naqvi and Hooda, 1991; Maurya et al., 1998), yet, in the climate change induced thermal and nutritional stresses will significant adverse effect on the production/physiological performance of the native breeds as evidenced by the changes in the estrus interval, estrus duration and blood biochemical parameters of Malpura sheep (reared for mutton production) under stress conditions (CSWRI, 2009).

The warming up of the climate would also impact the quantity and quality of wool produced. A study by Jolly and Lyne (1970) indicated that an increase in sub-dermal temperature of 5°C from current levels resulted in increased wool growth, but if the temperature was further increased, wool growth declined and then ceased. However, as discussed in the subsequent section, most effects will arise indirectly through changes in feed and fodder availability rather than being direct effects of climate. In general, since, the quality of coarse wool is less vulnerable than finer wools to the impact of changing climatic conditions, in India, the small-ruminant farmers in the Himalayan region, that rearing pashmina goats are likely to suffer serious set-back due to a change in the environment suitable for the survival and production of these specialty fibers. Cashmere is the undercoat of the pashmina goat, with an average diameter of 15.5μ diameter and is used to make luxury goods. Price of the cashmere fiber is highest among domesticated animal fibers (Ganai and Sheikh, 2004). In India, the cashmere production is mainly concentrated in the Changthang (a sub division of Ladakh) and parts of Uttarkhand. The economic importance of the animals lies in their role in providing livelihood to the rearers in the hilly region and the export earning on account of the value added products (Wani et al., 2008). A change in the climate parameters of the region is bound to threaten the habitat of these animals and the quality of the fibres. This needs proper strategies for breeding, nutrition and shelter management towards which research and development has to bear greater role.

Impact on pastures and feed resources

Globally, the research depicts varying responses of climate change on pasture production and productivity. For instance, Pachauri and Reisinger (2007) predicted increase in the pasture production in New Zealand's western, southern and high altitude areas by 2030, though gain may decline thereafter. Increase in pasture dry matter in New Zealand was also projected by Baisden et al. (2008), but in the dry years, dry matter yield of pastures is anticipated to decline substantially. Using various assumptions regarding temperature and associated biophysical changes, the authors projected scenarios of reduction in the sheep and beef production in that country, ranging from a figure of -6 per cent to -46 per cent by the year 2030 compared to the long term average figure of 1972-2002, painting a dismal picture of impact of climate change on the production of major meat items.

In Australia, there are likely to be regional differences in the response of pasture production to climate change. Crimp et al. (1999) suggested that a lengthening of the growing season due to higher winter minimum temperatures in Queensland's grazing lands, where pasture growth is currently limited by winter minimum temperatures, could result in an increase in pasture growth if nutrients are not limiting. However, under warmer climates with higher concentrations of CO_2 the suitability of pasture for sheep could be limited in eastern Queensland by the expansion of black speargrass, in the north by the presence of tropical tall grass pastures, and in the west by variable and low pasture production (Hall et al., 1998). In contrast, for many southern farming regions little change in pasture production is anticipated, although in some areas a shortening of the winter growing season may reduce the amount of forage available. In the western Australia, growth of pasture and fodder crops could increase by 2030 under higher carbon dioxide concentrations. However, this increase may be offset by lower nutrient content and less rainfall.

The positive effect of CO_2 fertilization on pasture production that has been reported in the research studies (Reillya et al., 2007) may plateau as CO_2 concentrations rise above 500 to 600 ppm (Allen et al., 1996). Further, as the positive effect of CO_2 fertilisation tends to be smaller in C4 plant species, e.g. tropical grasses, (Wand et al., 1999; Campbell et al., 2000; Ghannoum et al., 2001), the gains to pasture lands in tropical countries like India would be limited. Further, research studies indicate that elevated CO_2 concentrations coupled with warming may exacerbate nutrient deficiencies in pastures which are already deficient in nitrogen (Scholes and Howden, 2003).Broadly, the impact of climate change on pastures and fodder crops is likely to vary between geographic and agro-ecological systems because of the expected differences in the nature of climate change between regions. Generally the mid- and high latitude areas could see substantial yield gains from climate change effects, but the yield losses are likely in tropical regions (Reilly and Schimmelpfennig, 1999; Gitay, et al., 2001).

Pastures are important sources of nutrition for the livestock farming in India, particularly small holders and for small ruminant farmers (Jodha, 1985; Jodha, 1986; Pasha, 1991, Chopra et al., 1990). Grazing in common forests and pasture was estimated to account for 31% of livestock feed in India (World Bank 1999), as the area under fodder crops in India has stagnated at about 8.5-9.0 million hectares during the past decade and accounts for only about 4.6% of the total cultivated area. Based on the field survey of Andhra Pradesh, Karnataka, Rajasthan, Gujarat and Maharashtra during the period of 1982-1985, Jodha (1985, 1986) opined that, between 84 and 100 per cent of rural poor households gathered various products of economic importance from CPRs, of which fodder for livestock was a major component. At the all-India level, the National Sample Survey Organization (NSSO) survey data, showed that of all the households, about 56 per cent possess livestock and among the livestock farmers, a large number of them used common lands/ pastures for grazing the livestock or collecting the fodder with wide ranging variation across agroclimatic regions (Menon and Vadivelu, 2006). The dependence on common property resources (CPR) for fodder is particularly high in the Western Himalayas (Table 3). Except for parts of Indo-Gangetic plains where fodder is cultivated by the farmers, in general about 1/3 of the people are dependent on CPR for the fodder requirement of livestock, particularly for the small ruminants. In the arid state of Rajasthan, sheep production is more or less extensive and depends mainly on pastures for the nutritional requirement. A study conducted in the state indicated that the common pastures constitute major sources of green fodder for 85-99 per cent of the farmers during all the seasons (Suresh et al., 2007). Nearly about three-fourth of all the labour spent on sheep production (about 581 mandays for an average flock of about 50) was for grazing the animals.

Table 3. Dependence on CPRs for livestock fodder in different agro-climatic zones

Zone	Number of people per 1,000 persons
Western Himalayas	741
Eastern Himalayas and Brahmaputra valley	346
Lower Gangetic plains	163
Middle Gangetic plains	374
Trans Gangetic plains	131
Upper Gangetic plains	221
Central plateau and plains	312
Eastern plateau and hills	342
Western plateau and hills	346
Southern plateau and hills	322
East Coast plains & hills	283
Western Coast and hills	461
Gujarat plateau and hills	356
Western Dry region	475
Islands	234
All	342

(Source: Haripriya ,2005)

According to the estimates of land-utilization in India, about 3.4% (10.43 million hectares) of the area reported for land utilization is under permanent pastures and other grazing lands (Table 4). The area under forests, miscellaneous tree crops and groves, barren, uncultivable and fallow land which accounts for about 42 % of the land area also serves as source of livestock feed for the resource poor farmers. Over the years, while the area under forests and fallow land has remained more or less constant, that of pastures and other grazing grounds have declined. Besides shrinkage in quantity due to demographic pressures, the CPRS for grazing are also subject to considerable degradation in quality. The ruminants that subsist on these resources are already subjected to heavy stress as a result of poor quality herbages on CPR lands, especially in the arid and semi-arid areas. The current stocking rate of

Table 4. Land use classification in India (million hectares)

Classification	1950-51	1960-61	1970-71	1980-81	1990-91	2000-01	2004-05
I. Geographic area	**328.73**	**328.73**	**328.73**	**328.73**	**328.73**	**328.73**	**328.73**
II. Reporting area for land utilization statistics (1 to 5)	**284.32**	**298.46**	**303.76**	**304.16**	**304.86**	**305.88**	**305.23**
1. Forests	40.48	54.05	63.92	67.47	67.81	69.62	69.67
	(14.2)	(18.1)	(21.0)	(22.2)	(22.2)	(22.8)	(22.8)
2. Not available for cultivation (a+b)	47.52	50.75	44.64	39.62	40.48	41.55	42.30
(a) Not agricultural uses	9.36	14.84	16.48	19.66	21.09	23.81	24.72
	(3.3)	(5.0)	(5.4)	(6.5)	(6.9)	(7.8)	(8.1)
(b) Barren & uncultivable land	38.16	35.91	28.16	19.96	19.39	17.74	17.58
	(13.4)	(12.0)	(9.3)	(6.6)	(6.4)	(5.8)	(5.8)
3. Other uncultivated land excluding fallow land (a+b+c)	49.45	37.64	35.06	32.32	30.22	27.71	27.00
(a) Permanent pastures and other grazing land	6.68	13.97	13.26	11.97	11.40	10.83	10.43
	(2.3)	(4.7)	(4.4)	(3.9)	(3.7)	(3.6)	(3.4)
(b) Miscellaneous tree crops and groves	19.83	4.46	4.30	3.61	3.82	3.32	3.38
	(7.0)	(1.5)	(1.4)	(1.2)	(1.3)	(1.1)	(1.1)
(c) Cultivable waste land	22.94	19.21	17.50	16.74	15.00	13.56	13.19
	(8.1)	(6.4)	(5.8)	(5.5)	(4.9)	(4.4)	(4.3)
4. Fallow land (a+b)	28.13	22.82	19.88	24.75	23.36	25.04	24.94
(a) Fallow land other than current fallow	17.45	11.18	8.76	9.92	9.66	10.19	10.72
	(6.1)	(3.7)	(2.9)	(3.3)	(3.2)	(3.3)	(3.5)
(b) Current fallow	10.68	11.64	11.12	14.83	13.70	14.84	14.22
	(3.8)	(3.9)	(3.7)	(4.9)	(4.5)	(4.9)	(4.7)
5. Net area sown	118.75	133.20	140.27	140.00	143.00	141.16	141.32
	(41.8)	(44.6)	(46.2)	(46.0)	(46.9)	(46.3)	(46.3)

Note : Figures in parentheses indicate percentage to reported area.
(Source : Agricultural Statistics at a Glance, 2007, Directorate of Economics and Statistics, Ministry of Agriculture, Govt. of India)

livestock is already much higher than the carrying capacity of pasture land. For example, in the semi-arid regions, the carrying capacity is one adult cattle unit (ACU) per ha, but the stocking rate is about 51 ACU per ha (Shankar and Gupta, 1992). The corresponding figure for the arid region is 0.2 to 0.5 and 1 to 4 respectively (Raheja, 1966).Climatic changes would further complement the causative factors of the reduction of pasture areas and its quality, affecting the livelihood generation capacity of the shepherds.

The impact of the climate can have mixed effects on grazing lands in India. The areas with semi-ever green, moist deciduous, deciduous and thorny forests of the Western Ghats may witness an expansion of pastures whereas the regions with dry deciduous and dry thorny forests of the north western part of India may witness intensification of desertification. In drier regions, the area under the usable grazing lands may decline and composition of the vegetation may change to more thorny and hardy plants of xerophytic adaptations. On the other hand, in sub-temperate locations, more forest land may be transformed to grazing lands. Ravindranath and Sukumar (1996) forecasted that as a result of the climatic change, there would be a general shift in the case of the forest type boundaries along the altitudinal and rainfall gradients. This may result in the species migrating from the lower to the higher elevations and drier forest type transformed into montane types. With temperature increase and reduction of the frost incidents, the montane region of Western Ghats featured by the presence of mixture of stunted evergreen forests and grassland would give way to dominance of grasslands. Generally, it can be believed that the plant species preferring relatively lower temperature will move up the altitude giving way to expansion of the pastures. This provides an opportunity for increase in the pasture areas, at the cost of shrinking areas under the forest in some locations. The potential beneficiaries of the changes would be the small ruminants, notably sheep, which depend dominantly on the pastures. However, the usefulness of the pasture for the livestock production depends on the quality of the pastures also which may deteriorate due to temperature increase at least in arid and semi-arid tropics.

In the Himalayan region, a sizeable area of the region is under alpine meadows (locally called 'buggyals') famous for precious medicinal plants, and their use for sheep and goats grazing. In this region, the warming induced stimulation of growth will increase with increase in elevation, which may result in higher yields of some crops if warming is not coupled with water and nutrient stress, but will not be favourable for alpine species, which require chilling for germination and fruiting. Many important forest species are likely to fail to regenerate if the synchrony between their seed ripening and commencement of monsoon rains is broken due to the climate change. Quercus leucotrichophora, a species with high ecological as well as socio-economic value and also used for livestock fodder, shows low acorn production at lower elevation compared to higher elevations and hence is likely to be negatively affected by warming (Maikhuri et al. 2003).

Moraines exposed as a result of glacial retreat due to warming will drive alpine species upward but colonization may be constrained by erosion and nutrient limitations Many species of the alpine grasslands are able to start their growth with the supply of snow melt water, well before the commencement of monsoon in June-end. Obviously, their growths and life cycles are to be disrupted because of the lack of snow- melt water once glaciers are gone. The species distribution and composition of alpine meadows and forests are going to change both because of increased temperatures and loss of snow (Singh, 2008) and potential pest attacks that may be induced by enhanced climate variability (See Box 1). The impact of the climate induced pasture decline would further aggravate the severe constraints on the extensive system of livestock farming.

Box 1: Locust swarms devastate grazing grounds in Changthang

At an altitude of more than 4,000 metres in the trans-Himalaya, cold and dry Changthang plateau that extends from Tibet to eastern Ladakh, has been home to Changpa nomads for centuries. Changpas have survived here with their flocks of sheep, goats, yaks and horses in a delicate balance with nature, forever careful of its scarce resource "pastures". Over centuries they have evolved an indigenous and effective rangeland management system that involves reserving certain pastures for winters when snow covers higher grazing areas and regulating communities' movement according to the pasture's condition. Today this system is under strain because of changes in grazing patterns over the years and more so because desert locust swarms have attacked the pastures for four consecutive years, completely devastating the summer pastures. In the wake of locust attacks a reddish grass has replaced normal pastures. Animals do not eat this grass because it burns their mouth. Also, the livestock population pressure on reduced pastures is putting stress on rangelands, as a result the growth of grass is stunted and some important leguminous plants are facing extinction. The proliferation of weeds such as artemisia, is declining the quality of the Changthang pastures, which have been a mix of grass and legumes. Acute feed and fodder scarcity has led to heavy mortality of lambs and kids causing heavy losses to the shepherds.

Source: Morup, 2008

Impact on incidence of livestock diseases

Weather has critical affect on the timing and intensity of disease outbreaks. Warm and moist conditions are conducive to the growth of insects. Also, the rates of insect biting and maturation of the microorganisms within them are temperature dependent and increase when the air warms. The warmer and wetter climate and weather extremities are expected to enhance the chance of vector born diseases of livestock. Changes in rainfall pattern can influence an expansion of vectors during wetter years. Also, increasing temperatures have supported the expansion of vector populations into cooler areas, either into higher altitude systems or into more temperate zones. For instance, the rapid northward spread of bluetongue disease from southern Europe has been linked to changing climate patterns. Until fairly recently considered an exotic disease, the bluetongue virus (BTV) has spread to northern European countries in endemic proportions with more than 50,000 reported cases during 2007 in the EU.

Poor nutritional plane during the weather extremities would be further conducive for disease development and spread. Foot and Mouth Disease (FMD), Sheep and goat pox, Peste des Petits Ruminants (PPR), enterotoxaemia and skin diseases are some of the important diseases of small ruminants that have high morbidity and mortality rates (Table 5). The economic losses to the small ruminant farmers due to disease incidence are high, for instance, model simulations of sheep and goat pox outbreak during kidding indicate annual losses of 33-39% for the farmers in Maharashtra (Garner et al., 2000). Since the changes in the climate acts as a preconditioning factor for diseases development process, one can expect mostly positive role of climate change on livestock morbidity and mortality. In case of disease incidence, often the adaptive mechanisms like migration are physically depreciating for the livestock and increase the chances of morbidity and mortality. For example, in Pali district more than 10% animals, mostly sheep and goat died due to foot and mouth disease during migration. Mortality of small ruminants during migration has also been reported due to skin diseases, pox and PPR (Narain and Kar, 2005).

Table 5. Morbidity and mortality rates (mean ± s.d) due to diseases in small ruminants

Disease	Morbidity (%)	Mortality (%)
Contagious ecthyma	30.6±18.4	3.6±9.5
Enterotoxaemia	32.0±16.8	4.8±9.3
FMD	34.9±18.8	3.7±9.3
Rinderpest/PPR	42.6±22.3	17.1±16.6
Sheep and Goat Pox	63.5±4.9	49.5±9.2

(Source: Garner et al., 2000)

Impact due to increase in occurrence of climate related disasters

The weather extremities like floods, droughts, heat waves and cyclones are more likely to occur as a result of the climate change and the impact of these extremities are expected to be far greater than that arising out of average increase in temperature or mean sea level (IPCC, 2007; OECD, 2009). The societies in the developing countries are more vulnerable to the climate extremes as they lack adaptive capacity. This would be evidenced by the impact severe drought of 2002-03 on the livelihood of people of western districts of Rajasthan when the rainfall departed from the normal year by -64 per cent. The crops were damaged almost totally in 11.7 million ha during *kharif*, the loss being estimated as Rs.44140 million. During the succeeding *rabi* season of 2002-03, only 4.07 million ha was sown as against the normal of 8.21 million ha. (Narain and Kar, 2005). This created severe reduction in the household food security. The income sources for purchasing food from open market also shrinked. The impact on the livestock farming was mainly in the form of the fodder deficit. Based on a survey conducted in the drought affected districts, Narian and Kar (2005) reported reduction of fodder availability to the tune of 40-50 per cent. The purchase of the feed and fodder cost the farmers much higher than that during normal times. For example the price of dry fodder shot up to Rs. 300-400/q as compared to Rs. 200/q during normal years. Similar price trends were observed in the case of other feed and fodder items as well.

The deficiency of fodder leads to reduction in livestock population also. The inter-census growth of livestock population in western districts of Rajasthan between 1997 and 2003 livestock census indicates 18 per cent reduction in the population of all livestock, which was partly due to the drought years during this period (Table 6). The reduction was to the extent of 30% in the case of the sheep, 26% in case of camel and 17% in the case of buffalo. Early sale of the livestock was one of the important adjustment mechanisms adopted by the farmers to cope up with the drought. Distress sale of animals at younger age was very common. Govt. of Rajasthan (2004) reported increase in the slaughter of sheep by 32 per cent during 2002-03 compared to the previous year. These changes had lead to significant fall in the income from both crop and livestock. For example, the income from the agriculture reduced by 79% in the case of Barmer district during the drought year 2002-03, as compared to the previous year (Narain and Kar, 2005). The aforesaid analysis clearly brings out the vulnerability of the rural population towards drought for rural poor, in general and small ruminant farmers, in particular. The mitigation mechanisms against drought are costly and get rendered ineffective by the existing socio-economic imperfections.

Table 6: Change (%) in livestock population in western Rajasthan during 1997-2003

District	Cattle	Buffalo	Sheep	Goat	Camel	Others
Barmer	-0.1	+40.7	-29.4	-21.8	-38.9	-20.9
Bikaner	+8.7	+24.1	-19.1	+6.9	+1.4	+33.2
Churu	-34.6	-6.0	-40.6	-28.7	-35.9	-12.7
Ganganagar	-29.3	-19.2	+16.1	+10.6	-62.6	-7.0
Hanumangarh	-16.6	-5.6	-25.6	-36.2	+61.9	+33.1
Jaisalmer	-21.5	+120.5	-26.3	-34.1	-14.1	-42.2
Jalor	-14.0	+12.8	-20.7	-3.37	-33.5	-20.8
Jhunjhunun	+0.7	+7.3	-27.1	-4.1	-18.4	-0.3
Jodhpur	-22.3	+3.6	-43.3	-20.1	-29.7	-15.0
Nagaur	-25.5	-3.9	-36.3	-0.5	-40.9	+6.5
Pali	-30.7	-8.9	-34.8	+4.3	-8.2	-10.2
Sikar	-8.4	+10.6	-22.5	+13.2	-26.6	+54.8
Total	-17.0	+1.5	-29.9	-12.2	-25.7	-7.0

(Source: Narain and Kar, 2005)

Potential climate change induced impacts on livelihoods of small ruminant farmers

The above discussion brings out the likely adverse impact of climate change on the production performance of the small ruminants both, directly, through resulting thermal stress and increased exposure to extreme event and indirectly, through the changes in availability of quality fodder and feed resources from pasture and grazing lands and higher susceptibility to livestock diseases. Obviously these direct and indirect effects of climate change on the small ruminant production system will have implications for the livelihood security of the farmers rearing these animals. This section sharpens the focus on climate change induced effect on the economy of the small ruminant farmers by highlighting the key aspects related to pastoral farming systems, nutritional security of households and input use in sheep-goat farming in the context of climate change.

Pastoral farming systems

Studying the impacts of climate on pastoralism is complicated by the fact that pastoralism is essentially but not solely a form of adaptation of human societies to hazards and hardships induced, and imposed on them, by climatic constraints. The wandering husbandry of domesticated animals as a response of rural societies to climatic variability or limitations for human subsistence is about as old as irrigated agriculture. The impacts of climate on pastoralism, as a managed ecosystem that evolved as an adaptation to climate, vary in important but often subtle ways by the type of pastoralism practiced and the various management techniques adopted. Pastoral types of animal production systems may take many forms, viz., nomad pastoralism (where the whole household moves with the herd or flock), transhumant pastoralism (where only the herder moves with the stock), and semi-pastoralism where cultivation, usually of cereals constitutes a significant segment of activity). There are intermediate forms where the whole family may move with the herd or with a part of it for shorter or longer periods.

India has 34 million pastoralists managing a livestock population of more than 50 million (Pangare and Cincotta, 1993), mostly under transhumance system. Transhumant stock rearing is very common throughout the Himalaya; various nomadic groups, such as Gujars, Bakarwals and Gaddis, keep sheep, goats and even buffaloes under such systems. This system also exists in some states situated in the plains, such as Rajasthan, Madhya Pradesh, Tamil Nadu, Gujarat and Uttar Pradesh. The scale of this enterprise is widespread and is practiced by a variety of farmers, including landless and marginal farmers, who have adopted this profession for earning a livelihood. Sale of wool and live animals for meat is their only source of income. The transhumant system is practiced in order to locate the best herbage resources from pastures and grasslands. There are also well recognized pastoral tribes, like Gaddi community of Himachal, who practice a complete transhumance, moving from one place to another on traditional migratory routes. The dates of migration have traditionally been fixed. Even grazing rights rest with the migratory graziers by traditional usage, though they do not hold proprietary rights over the land. At the onset of winter (October/November), the Gaddis from Bharmour and Lahaul migrate with their flocks of sheep and goat to Kangra valley and Pathankot, to avoid fodder scarcity. During early April, folks return to their respective villages so as to manure fields, during the early growing season. Thereafter, malundi or shepherds gather the village stock for summer grazing in trakar/pastures situated on dhars/high mountain peaks. As summer approaches the stock migrates to still higher altitudes. At the end of the growing season, (September/October), when winter returns, sheep and goats are brought back to the lower ranges from the high altitude areas, following traditional routes. The age old practice of manuring fields during October in the lower ranges is still practised. This grazing practice sustains the grazing pressure. It also enhances the nutrient recycling in these areas to a great extent. Fertilization of fields during the to and fro movement of livestock enhances crop productivity at low economic cost.

The small-ruminant farmers in the plains also migrate temporarily in response to the demand-supply gap of fodder (Umamaheswari et al., 2001; Rathore, 2004; Narain and Kar, 2005) but unlike their counterparts in the hill areas, the farmers may not be in the habit of regular migration, but undertake migration as a response to the situation, for a shorter period, starting from the initiation of the crisis and ending with the onset of monsoon. Suresh et al. (2009) reported that in Rajasthan, nearly 32 per cent of the small ruminant farmers undertake temporary migration of varying duration. The variation in the climate is a major causative factor for migration. The status of migration has close relation with the incidence and severity of drought years. An analysis of the data indicates that in 1996-97, nearly 23% of the total migration was temporary, but it increased gradually to reach 77% by 2002-03, which was a severe drought year (Table 7). The state received a mean annual rainfall of 76 cm in 1996-97, 51 cm in 1999-00 and 27 cm in 2002-03, which impacted the temporary migration. A regression analysis undertaken to analyse the impact of the rainfall on temporary migration indicated that the share of temporary migration on total migration declined by 1 per cent for every 1 cm increase in rainfall.

Climate change increases the frequency of the climatic extremities, and there exists high chances that the option of migration would be exercised more often in the future. The practice of migration limits the income generation from small ruminant farming. For example Suresh et al. (2007) reported that the net income from a migrant sheep flock was less than that from non-migrant flock (Table 8). Thus, migration could be observed only as an adaptive mechanism, rather than a preferred management strategy. The migrant families also face serious constraints, including theft of the animals, high morbidity and mortality during migration, resistance from the locals often attaining the level of violence, high degree of mental tension etc (Suresh et al., 2009).

It is worthwhile to consider that IPCC First Assessment Report identified the greatest single impact of climate to be human migration- with millions of people displaced by shoreline erosion, coastal flooding and agricultural disruption. It is most widely predicted that the number of climatic migrants would amount to nearly 200 million by 2050 (IOM, 2008). The chances of higher level of migration of the livestock would add to the pressure and severely limit the welfare of human community.

Table 7: Trend in migration of sheep in Rajasthan (lakhs)

Year	Temporary Migration	Permanent migration	Total migration	Temporary migration as percent of total migration
1996-97	4.63	15.71	20.34	22.8
1997-98	2.36	6.17	8.53	27.7
1998-99	3.31	15.35	18.66	17.7
1999-00	14.88	5.68	20.56	72.4
2000-01	6.47	8.43	14.9	43.4
2001-02	9.73	6.68	16.41	59.3
2002-03	20.01	6.1	26.11	76.6
2003-04	2.81	5.79	8.6	32.7
2004-05	4.43	21.07	25.5	17.4
2005-06	10.54	22.35	32.89	32.0
2006-07	2.39	15.75	18.14	13.2
Mean (lakh)	7.41	11.73	19.15	-
Coefficient of variation	78.17	54.97	38.09	-
Growth rate (%)	0.12	0.73	0.85	-

Source: Government of Rajasthan (2007).

Table 8: Cost and Return from migrant and non-migrant sheep flocks (Rs/ flock/year)

S. No.	Particulars	Migrant Flock		Non-Migrant flock		Overall	
		Rs.	%	Rs.	%	Rs.	%
	Number of animals per flock	79		48		54	
	Variable Cost (VC)						
1	Feed and Fodder	3318	49.92	1605	0.26	1974	56.08
2	Medicine	1747	26.28	800	30.04	1004	28.52
3	Hired Labour	1205	18.13	107	4.02	343	9.74
4	Interest on VC	376	5.67	151	5.67	199	5.67
5	Total Variable Cost	6646	100	2663	100	3520	100
	Returns						
	Sale of Live animals						
1	Sale of Milk	31636	77.93	20618	82.90	22987	81.36
2	Sale of Wool	2618	6.45	456	1.83	921	3.26
3	Manure	3577	8.81	2135	8.87	2445	8.65
4	Total Return	2763	6.81	1663	6.69	1899	6.72
5	Return over variable Cost	40595	100	24872	100	28252	100
6	Net return per animal	33948		22209		24732	
		430		463		458	

(Source: Suresh et al., 2007)

Food security of small ruminant farmer households

Livestock products play key role in providing food security to the producers, as component of their food basket and as a source of cash income to purchase other food products. Sheep and goat being important livelihood options for the rural folks, any deterioration in the production condition would have direct bearing on their food security.

The long-term trends in global hunger show that in 2003-05, the number of chronically hungry people was 848 million (Fig. 1), that was 6 million more than the number in 1990-92, which is the baseline period for monitoring the progress of the targets set under Millennium Development Goals (MDGs) and the World Food Summit (WFS).

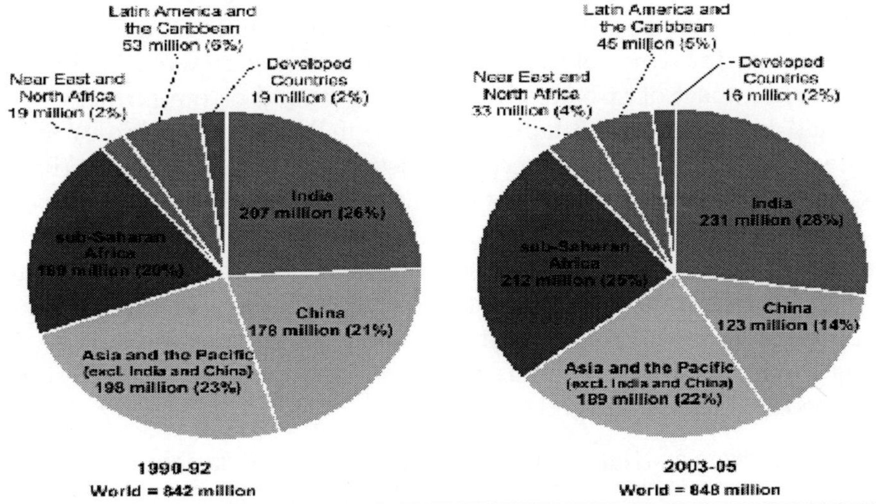

Fig. 1: Global Trends in Chronic Hunger
Source: FAO (2008)

The unprecedented surge in food prices during 2006-07 has aggravated world food insecurity, increasing the number of chronically hungry people by 75 million during 2003/05 to 2007 (FAO, 2008). Given the continued drastic price rises, it is very likely that the number of people suffering from chronic hunger would have increased further from 923 million in 2007 at the global level and over 258 million in India. About ¾ under-five children are iron deficient, ½ deficient in vitamin A and close to one in every two children are underweight in our country (Naidoo, 2009). The situation has close correlation with the economic status of the households and their livelihood security. In this situation, climate change induced deterioration of the small ruminant production would have detrimental effect on the food security of small ruminant producers and non-vegetarian consumers.

Likely increase in cost of production

The impact of climatic change on the livelihood of the livestock farmers is also likely to be transmitted through changes in opportunity cost, input and output prices. Traditionally, small ruminant population in India, particularly sheep have moved from the areas of high opportunity cost to the lower opportunity costs of sheep production (Roy, 2002). As more and more area was brought under irrigation in the Indo-gangetic plains of Bihar and Uttar Pradesh, the opportunity cost of sheep production increased and the concentration of sheep population declined in these agriculturally better endowed regions, while the same increased in the semi-arid and arid rainfed regions.

Climate change can also affect the opportunity cost of sheep farming, thereby affecting the population dynamics and economic returns. An analysis of economic performance of the sheep production system would help to assess the possible impact of climate change on livelihood of the farmers. A study conducted in Ajmer and Bikaner districts of Rajasthan (Table 9) indicated that the expenditure towards feeding constituted about 49 per cent (Rs. 7113/flock) of the total cost of sheep production that was about Rs.14447 per flock of 125 sheep (Suresh and Gupta., 2008). In the total cost of feeding, the expenditure share of fodder trees was highest (45%) followed by dry fodder (31%) and 5% of concentrate feed (Table 10). The price of the feed material ranged from Rs 5 to Rs. 8 a kg at Jaipur market during the survey period. During the brief period of the drought in March-September, 2009, the price of the feed and fodder surged to Rs.14 a kg.

Table 9: Expenditure and Net return from Sheep Farming in Rajasthan

Item	Ajmer	Bikaner	Overall
Total expenditure (Rs.)	**16079**	**12876**	**14477**
Percentage share in total expenditure			
Feed and fodder	49.9	48.2	49.1
Veterinary care	14.3	12.1	13.7
Labour	26.4	34.2	29.9
Miscellaneous	9.4	5.5	7.7
Gross Return (Rs.)	**51059**	**71118**	**61089**
Percentage share in total returns			
Wool	9.5	16.0	12.7
Animal sale	73.9	74.1	74.0
Manure	9.3	4.4	6.6
Milk	7.3	6.2	6.7
Net return (Rs.)	34980	58242	46612
Net return per sheep(Rs.)	287	451	372
Flock size	122	129	125

(Source: (Suresh and Gupta, 2008)

Table 10: Share of Feed Components in Feed Expenditure

Flock-size category	Total Feed Cost (Rs.)	*Percentage share in total feed expenditure*						
		Fodder tree	Harvested Field	Grains	Dry fodder	Concentrate Mixture	Gur	Oil
Small	4130	50.60	2.42	0	32.64	0	4.00	10.31
Medium	7456	44.93	1.03	1.50	32.55	8.88	1.28	9.87
Large	10736	42.61	7.98	2.66	27.29	1.99	0.96	12.27
Overall	7113	45.22	3.75	1.61	30.72	4.73	1.67	16.47

(Source: Suresh and Gupta, 2008)

In the context of climate change, with the shrinking of pastures in the arid and semi-arid regions and increasing desertification, stall feeding may acquire greater prominence. The resultant increase in demand for feed coupled with the supply side constraints (due to anticipated decline in agricultural production in the tropics as a result of climate change) would lead to a price surge of feed materials which would be reflected in the expenditure side of the sheep farming. In the long run, besides a sharp increase in the real cost of feed inputs, one can visualize increase in real labour cost of grazing due to long distance travel in search of fodder and increase in the expenditure towards veterinary treatment on account of higher occurrence of climate induced vector born diseases. The emerging situation may also lead to increased economic losses due to livestock mortality. In the areas which were not covered under intensive veterinary services, the mortality rates of sheep are already quite high ranging from 10-19 per cent (Suresh *et al.*, 2007, 2009), and are likely to be accentuated under climate change scenario if appropriate coping mechanisms are not put in place.

Climate change impact on livestock breeds

Much of the world's livestock diversity is bred and kept in dry lands – 90 % of breeds in the Near East region, 56 percent in Africa, 42 percent in Asia and 19 percent in Latin America. Due to harsh environments, many dry lands are predicted to be badly affected by climate change. One of the direct impacts of the climate change on the livestock will be the changes in the composition and diversity of the livestock population indigenous to particular regions. FAO (2007) reported that about 20 per cent of the classified livestock breeds are already at risk. If the breeds cannot be selected fast enough to adapt with the climatic changes, the risk of production losses and breed extinctions, possibly due to climatic stress, higher incidence of diseases, etc. will be increased. In several instances the farmers themselves undertake adaptive mechanisms that can suit the climate change but often there is a trade-off between ability to tolerate climatic stress and production potential of the animals. The change in the composition of sheep breeds observed in the semi-arid region of Rajasthan during recent times is a case in point. The Malpura tehsil of Tonk district of Rajasthan is known as the breeding tract of the Malpura breed of sheep. Earlier records and field level surveys indicate that almost 100 percent sheep farmers of this region possessed only this breed. During the past several years the Malpura region has been experiencing decline in rainfall that has compelled the sheep breeders to undertake short duration migration to mitigate fodder scarcity. The farmers have therefore developed and popularized Kheri breed, a cross of Malpura and Marwari breeds, as the former have better body weight while the later (Marwari) which are a basically native to northern districts of the state, are known for good walking capacity for long distances which is a desirable attribute for migration. Presently, about 86 per cent of the migrating breeders in the region owned Kheri breed, while that in the case of the non-migrant farmers this percentage is lower (Fig. 2). The development of the new breeds by the farmers can be viewed as a response towards declining rainfall in the region and increasing preparedness of the farmers to migrate (Suresh et al., 2009). However, the new breed has compromised on many of the yield parameters while acquiring the stress tolerance from Marwari breed.

In this context, conservation of the indigenous breeds, access to the conserved genetic resources, acknowledgement of ownership of genetic material with proper benefit sharing arrangement would be critical to technology development and evolving adaptive strategies to meet the growing challenge.

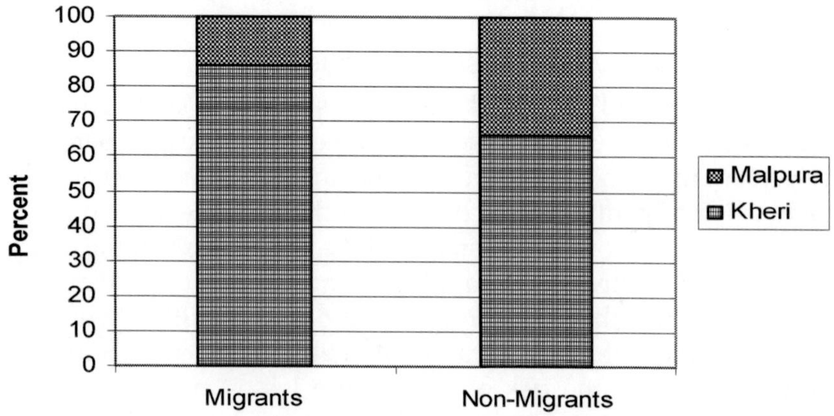

Fig. 2. Composition of sheep breeds in Malpura region of Rajasthan (Source: Suresh et al., 2009)

Summing up: Emerging R &D and policy imperatives

In the recent years, the issue of climate change is increasingly occupying the centre stage in R&D initiatives due to the pervasiveness of the impact of climate change on all spectrums of biophysical parameters of the nature and the possibility of containing the impact of this more or less anthropogenic malady through concerted human intervention. Though there is lot of uncertainly about the magnitude of climate change impact, the probability that it would affect various spheres of human economic activity is very high. Livestock farming is one such activity which is considered partly responsible for climate change through emission of green house gases (GHGs) and at the same time is modeled to be at the receiving end of the impact of climate change. The anticipated rise in temperature between 2.5°C and 5°C over the entire country together with increased precipitation and occurrence of extreme events resulting from climate change are likely to be detrimental to the socio-economic status of the small ruminant farmers by adversely affecting the productive and reproductive performance of their livestock, increasing incidence of livestock diseases, accentuating the feed and fodder shortages, entailing dislocation costs of migration, hampering food security, etc. However, from the macro perspective, a systematic research study is required to quantify the impact of climate change on small ruminant production system in India.

Adaptation research, particularly for developing and up-scaling strategies to cope with climate change is an important area that needs prime attention. Research efforts need to be intensified in this direction as *"......how the world deals with climate change today will have a direct bearing on the human development prospects of a large section of humanity"* (UNDP, 2007). While new knowledge about animal responses to adverse weather continues to be developed, there is a need for additional knowledge on managing livestock to reduce the impact of climatic changes. Management intervention is needed to ameliorate the constraints on production set by the climate, the physical environment and the health hazards in a region. Responding to the challenge of climate change requires formulation of a wide range of adaptation options for the smallholder livestock producers, encompassing human intervention for physical modification of the environment, improvement in nutritional management practices, improved animal health technology, genetic selection for stress tolerant high yielding livestock breeds, market responses that are potentially effective adaptation measures to climate change, such as insurance schemes, and income diversification opportunities, institutional and policy changes. The on-farm decisions need to involve selection, design and management of production facilities, while the collective impacts would guide regional or national policy and determine responses to potential large-scale changes. There is a general lack of developed models for adaptation assessment for livestock. The adaptation simulations should test wide possible combinations of farmer responses under different resource conditions and changes in regional, national and international agricultural policies relating to farm-level adaptation.

Adaptation would require substantial public and private investments. Assessing the investment requirements for coping with the challenges of climate change and prioritization of investment needs is a critical research agenda that has received little attention till date. Besides researching on suitable adaptation options and assessing the monetary investments for their implementation, another critical requirement is the development of collaborative learning processes to support the adaptation of animal production systems to better cope with the impacts of climate change. Without a comprehensive understanding of the context in which decisions about adaptation are made and of the capacity of decision makers to change, it is unlikely that adaptive capacity of various stakeholders would improve (Thorton et al., 2007). Farmers possess a wealth of indigenous knowledge for dealing with climate variability and risk that should be assessed for its efficacy and subsequently documented for wider dissemination. This exercise is to be done in conjunction with well-targeted capacity building efforts to help farmers deal with changes in their systems that go beyond what they have experienced in the past.

Another critical requirement is the development of collaborative learning processes to support the adaptation of livestock systems to better cope with the impacts of climate change. Research cannot hope to contribute to improving adaptive capacity without a comprehensive understanding of the context in which decisions about adaptation are made and of the capacity of decision makers to change (Thorton et al., 2007). Farmers possess a wealth of indigenous knowledge for dealing with climate variability and risk that should be assessed for its efficacy and subsequently documented for wider dissemination. This exercise is to be done in conjunction with well-targeted capacity building efforts to help farmers deal with changes in their systems that go beyond what they have experienced in the past.

Despite the vital importance of the livestock sector in providing livelihood to the millions of people in India, unfortunately, the sector has by-passed the attention of the planners for reducing its vulnerability to climate change. The policy support from the Government through appropriate institutional mechanisms suited for mitigating the climate change induced adversities is urgently required for livelihood security of the small ruminant farmers.

References

Agriculture, Zagazig University, Zagazig, Egypt.

Allen, L.H., Baker J.T. and Boote K.J. 1996. The CO_2 fertilization effect: higher carbohydrate production and retention as biomass and seed yield. In: F. Bazzaz and W. Sombroek, Editors, Global Climate Change and Agricultural Production, John Wiley & Sons, Chichester.

Ames,D.R.,and D.R.Brink.1977.Effect of temperature on lamb performance and protein efficiency ratio.J.Anita.Sci.44:136.

Baisden, T., Greenhalgh, S., Kerr, S., Newton, P., Renwick, J., Stroombergen, A. 2008. Costs and Benefits of Climate Change and Adaptation to Climate Change in New Zealand Agriculture: What do we know so far? as quoted in Research Paper No. 314, Lincoln University, Chiristchurch, New Zealand.

Campbell,D., D.M. Stafford Smith and GCTE Pastures and Rangelands Network members. 2000. A synthesis of recent global change research on pasture and rangeland production: reduced uncertainties and their management implications, Agriculture, Ecosystems and Environment 82, pp. 39–55.

Chopra, K., Kadekodi, G.K. and Murthy, M.N. 1990. Participatory Development: People and Common Property Resources. Sage Publications, New Delhi.

Crimp, S.J., McKeon, G., Hall, W.B., Howden, S., Stone, R.C., Jones, D.A., 1999. Climate change in Queensland's grazing lands: approaches and climatic trends. In: Elridge, D., Freudenberger, D. (Eds.), People and Rangelands: Building the Future. Proceedings VIth International Rangelands Congress, July 1999. Townsville, Australia, pp. 36–38.

CSWRI 2009. Annual report 2008-09.Central Sheep and Wool Research Institute, Avikanagar

FAO. 2008. Assessment of the World Food Security and Nutrition Situation. Thirty-fourth Session of the Committee on World Food Security, Rome, 14-17 October 2008.

FAO. 2007. The State of the World's Animal Genetic Resources for Food and Agriculture. (Eds) Rischkowsky, B. and Pilling, D. Rome.

FAOSTAT. Food and Agricultrual Commodity Production. http://faostat.fao.org

Ganai, T.A.S and Shiekh, F.D. 2005. Strategies for improving pashmina production in India. In: Risam, K.S., Das, G.K., Kumar, D and Kolte, A. (Eds.) Compendium of National Seminar on Angora rabbit wool and cashmere production and utilisation. Indian Society of Sheep and Goat Production and Utilisation, Avikanagar. 64-65.

Garner M.G, Sawarkar,S.D., Brett E.K., Edwards J.R , Kulkarni V.B., Boyle D.B. and Singh S.N.2000. The Extent and Impact of Sheep Pox and Goat Pox in the State of Maharashtra, India. Tropical Animal Health and Production 32: 205-223.

Ghannoum O., S. von Caemmerer and J.P. Conroy .2001. Plant water use efficiency of 17 Australian NAD-ME and NADP-ME C4 grasses at ambient and elevated CO2 partial pressure, Australian Journal of Plant Physiology 28: 1207–1217.

Gitay, H., Brown, S., Easterling, W. and Jallow, B. 2001. Ecosystems and their goods and services. In: McCarthy, J., Canziani, O., Leary, D. Dokken, K. White (Eds.),Climate Change 2001: Impacts, Adaptation, and Vulnerability, Cambridge University Press,Cambridge, UK.

Government of India. 2003. Livestock Census, Department of Animal Husbandry, Dairying and Fisheries, Ministry of Agriculture, New Delhi.

Government of Rajasthan, 2004. Prasasnik Prathivedan. 2003-2004, Department of Animal Husbandry, Jaipur

Hall, W.B., McKeon, G.M., Carter, J.O., Day, K.A., Howden, S.M. and Scanlan, J.C.1998. Climate change in Queenslands grazing lands: II. An assessment of the impact on animal production from native pastures, Rangeland Journal, 20,177–205

Haripriya, G. 2005. Can CPRs generate carbon credits without hurting the poor? Economic and Political Weekly, 40(10), 973-980.

IOM .2008. Migration and climate change, Migration research series No. 31, International Organisation for Migration. Geneva, Switzerland.

IPCC.1992 Global Climate Change & the Rising Challenge of the Sea, supporting document for the Intergovernmental Panel on Climate Change, World Meteorological Organization, and United Nations Environment Programme, Geneva.

IPCC. 2007). Contribution of Working Group I to the Fourth Assessment Report of the Intergovernmental Panel on Climate Change, Cambridge University Press, Cambridge, UK.

Jodha, N. S. 1995. Common property resources and the dynamics of rural poverty in India's dry regions. Unasylva 46: 23-29.

Jodha, N.S. 1985. Population growth and the decline of common property resource in Rajasthan, India. Population Development Review 11(2): 247-264.

Jodha, N.S. 1986. Rural common property resources and rural poor in dry regions of India. Economic and Political Weekly 21: 1169-1181.

Jolly, M. and Lyne, A.G. 1970. Response of skin and wool growth to local subdermal temperature changes in a sheep, Journal of Agricultural Science 75: 501–515

Maikhuri, R.K., Rao, K.S., Patnaik, S., Saxena, K.G. and Ramakrishnan, P.S. 2003. Assessment of vulnerability of forests, meadows and mountain ecosystems due to clmate change. ENVIS Bulletin Vol 11(2):1-10 , ENVIS Centre on Himalayan Ecology, Almora, Uttranchal.

Marai, I.F.M., Bahgat, L.B., Shalaby, T.H., Abdel-Hafez, M.A., 2000. Fattening performance, some behavioural traits and physiological reactions of male lambs fed concentrates mixture alone with or without natural clay, under hot summer of Egyptian Annals of Arid Zone 39 (4): 449–460.

Marai, I.F.M., Shalaby, T.H., Bahgat, L.B., Abdel-Hafez, M.A., 1997a. Fattening of lambs on concentrates mixture diet alone without roughages or with addition of natural clay under subtropical conditions of Egypt. Growth performance and behaviour. In: Proceedings of the International Conference on Animal Production & Health, Dokki, Cairo, Egypt.

Marai, I.F.M., Shalaby, T.H., Bahgat, L.B., Abdel-Hafez, M.A., 1997b. Fattening of lambs on concentrates mixture diet alone without roughages or with addition of natural clay under subtropical conditions of Egypt. Physiological reactions. In: Proceedings of the International Conference on Animal Production & Health, Dokki, Cairo, Egypt.

Maurya, V.P., Naqvi, S.M.K., Mittal, J.P., 1998. Reproductive behaviour of Malpura and Bharat Merino ewe lambs under semi-arid condition. Indian Journal of Animal Sciences 68: 533–535.

Menon, A and Vadivelu, G.A. 2006. Common property resources in different agro-climatic landscapes in India. Conservation and Society 4 : 132-154.

Misra, A.K., Subrahmanyam, K.V., Babu M Vijoy Sankar, Reddy, T.Y., Shivarudrappa, B and Ramakrishna Y. S. 2006. Improving the livelihood of landless and marginal farmers through sheep rearing in rainfed agro-ecosystem of India. Livestock Research for Rural Development 18: 5.

Morup, T. 2008. Pastures gone. Down to Earth. Vol. 17(10).

Naidoo, Jai. 2009. Food for thought at Copenhagen. The Hindu, New Delhi (ed) dated Dec. 7. 2009. Page no. 9.

Naqvi S.M.K.., Maurya, V.P., Gulyani, R., Joshi, A., Mittal, J.P.2004. The effect of thermal stress on superovulatory response and embryo production in Bharat Merino ewes. Small Ruminant Research 55:57–63

Naqvi, S.M.K., 1987. Physiological adaptation of sheep during energy crisis and thermal stress. PhD Thesis, Kurukshetra University, Kurukshetra, India.

Naqvi, S.M.K. and Hooda, O.K. 1991. Influence of thermal, nutritional and exercise stresses on some blood parameters of native and crossbred sheep. Indian Jornal of Animal Sciences 61: 660–662.

Narain, P. and Kar, A. (Ed.) 2005. Drought in Rajasthan: Impact, coping mechanism and management strategies. Central Arid Zone Research Institute, Jodhpur.

OECD. 2009. Policy guidance on integrating climate change adaptations into development co-operation. OECD, Paris.

Pachauri, R. K. and Reisinger, A. 2007. Climate Change 2007: Synthesis Report. Geneva, Switzerland: IPCC.

Pangare, G. and Cincotta, R. 1993. Pastoralists at the crossroads. Down to Earth, 2(23).

Pasha, S.A. 1991. Sustainability and viability of small and large rearers: Animal husbandry and common property resources. Economic and Political Weekly. 26(13): A27-A30.

Raheja, P.C. 1966. Rajasthan desert can bloom with forage, Indian farming. 15: 47

Rathore, J.S. 2004. Drought and household coping strategies: A case of Rajasthan. Indian Journal of Agricultural Economics, 59(4): 689-708.

Ravindranath, N.H. and Sukumar, R. Impact of climate change on forest cover in India Commonwealth Forestry Review. 75 (1)

Reilly, J., and D. Schimmelpfennig. 1999. Agricultural impact assessment, vulnerability, and the scope for adaptation, Climatic Change. 43(4): 745-788.

Reillya,J, Paltseva, S, Felzerb, B., Wanga, X., Kicklighterb, D., Melillob, J., Prinna, R., Sarofima, M., Sokolova, A., and Wanga, C. 2007. Global Economic Effects of Changes in Crops, Pasture, and Forests due to Changing Climate, Carbon Dioxide and Ozone.

Roy, Thirthankar. 2002. Changes in Wool Production and Usage in Colonial India. Gokhale Institute of Politics and Economics, Deccan Gymkhana, Pune.

Scholes, R., Howden, M., (2003). Rangeland Vulnerability and Adaptation in a Changing World: A Review. In: Allsopp, N., Palmer, A.R., Milton, S.J., Kirkman, K.P., Kerley, G.I.H., Hurt, C.R., Brown, C.J. (Eds.), Proceedings of the VIIth International Rangelands Congress. 26th July–1st August 2003. Durban, South Africa, pp. 1021–1029.

Shankar, V and J.N.Gupta. 1992. Restoration of degraded rangeland. In Restoration of degraded lands- Concepts and strategies (Ed. J.S.Singh). Sage publishers, Meerut, India.

Shelton, M., 2000. Reproductive performance of sheep exposed to hot environments. In: Malik, R.C., Razzaque, M.A., Al-Nasser, A.Y. (Eds.), Sheep Production in Hot and Arid Zones. Published by the Kuwait Institute for Scientific Research, pp. 155–162.

Singh, G., Karim, S.A., 1995. Changes in birth weight of temperate sheep breeds under tropical conditions. World Rev. Anim. Prod. 30 (3/4), 55–60.

Singh, M.K., Rai, B., Singh, P. Singh, P.K. and Singh, N.P. 2008. Goat production status in different agro-climatic regions of India: an overview. Indian Journal of Small Ruminants 14:48-70.

Singh, S.P. 2008. Climate change in relation to the Himalayas. www.climate-leaders.org/wp-content/uploads/slimatechange-spsingh.pdf.

Suresh, A. and Gupta, D.C. 2008. Final Project Report: Study on Production and Utilization of Wool and Wool Products in India, Central Sheep and Wool Research Institute, Avikanagar, Rajasthan, India.

Suresh, A., Gupta, D.C., Mann, J.S. and Singh, V.K. 2007. Sheep production in semi-arid zones- Management and economics, Research bulletin, Central Sheep and Wool Research Institute, Avikanagar, Rajasthan, India.

Suresh, A., Gupta, D.C. and Mann, J.S. 2009. Final report of the project "Impact Assessment and constraint analysis of adoption of improved technologies of sheep production", Central Sheep and Wool Research Institute, Avikanagar, Rajasthan

Thornton P., Herrero M., Ade Freeman, Mwai O., Ed Rege, Jones P., and McDermott J.2007. Vulnerability, Climate change and Livestock – Research Opportunities and Challenges for Poverty Alleviation. SAT eJournal, 4 (1). ejournal.icrisat.org

Umamaheswari, L., Krishnamoorthy, S. Nasurudeen, P. and Kolly, R.K. 2001. Pattern of droughts and survival strategies of farm household in a drought prone district in Tamil Nadu. Indian Journal of Agricultural Economics, 56: 683-695.

UNDP. 2007.Human Development Report 2007/2008. Fighting climate change. Human solidarity in a divided world. New York: UNDP

Wand S.J.E., G.F. Midgley, M.H. Jones and P.S. Curtis.1999. Responses of wild C_4 and C_3 grass (Poaceae) species to elevated atmospheric CO_2 concentration: a meta-analytic test of current theories and perceptions, Global Change Biology 5, pp. 723–741.

Wani, S.A., Wani, M.H., Shohaib Yusuf, Shaheen, F.A. and Showkat Ara. 2008. Pastoral nomadism in breeding tract of Changthangi pashmina goats. Indian Journal of Small Ruminants 14: 77-83.

World Bank .1999 India: Livestock Sector review: Enhancing growth and development. The World Bank and Allied Publishers, New Delhi.

❏❏❏

40

Production and Marketing of Small Ruminant Fibre and Meat in India — An Overview

Suresh. A . and D.C.Gupta
Central Sheep and Wool Research Institute, Avikanagar, via Jaipur 304 501,Rajasthan

Introduction

Besides acting as a major component in the food basket, small ruminants provides means of accessibility to the purchased food sources, thereby contributing significantly to the food security of the rural poor. This is mainly because of the overwhelming contribution of the small ruminants towards the income portfolio. It is reported that about 56 per cent of the rural population owns livestock, of which a major share is occupied by the sheep and goat (Menon and Vadivelu, 2006). As per the 2003 livestock census, India possesses 185 million small ruminants comprising of 61 million sheep and 124 million goats, thus accounting for nearly half of the total livestock. The smaller body size of the animals, lower feed requirement, low initial capital requirement, faster rate of reproduction, ready demand for their meat, ability to thrive on the sparse vegetation of the grassland, suitability to be a component of most of the livestock production systems and relative easiness for liquidation renders small ruminants the preferred one for the resource poor farmers of the country side. One significant aspect of the small ruminant sector is that it is one of the most equitably distributed productive assets in the rural household compared to other sources like land or even bovine stock (Pasha, 1991; Suresh and Gupta, 2008).

The major economic products of small ruminant origin are meat (mutton/ chevon), fibre (wool/ pashmina /hair), milk and manure. Among these, the meat and wool carries greater role in the national economy due to its role in directly providing livelihood as well as the ability to generate income through processing and value addition. In order to augment the small ruminant production, strengthening its production base is of paramount importance. This needs an assessment of the resource availability and prospects for technological intervention. Existence of a strong market is a pre-condition for augmenting technology adoption. In this paper we provide an overview of production and marketing of wool and meat (both mutton and chevon) highlighting various issues and prospects for their amelioration. Among the animal fibres, we concentrate on the sheep wool, as they contribute much to the value addition through manufacturing of carpets and other economic products compared to other small ruminant fibres.

Wool production and marketing in India

Wool based industries are some of the ancient industries in India (Roy, 2002). The woolen sector provides livelihood to more than 12 lakh persons employed directly in sheep production activities and 13 lakh persons employed in activities related to the woollen processing and value addition (GoI, 2006a). As on 2006, India was the seventh largest producer of raw wool with a production level of 45 million kg. This constituted 2.06 per cent of the world raw wool production (from 5.72 per cent of the world sheep population) (FAO, 2008). The wool produced in India is basically of carpet grade. About 80 per cent of the good quality Indian wool goes into the manufacturing of carpets. Nearly 95 per cent of the total carpets produced are exported and export of carpet alone earned foreign exchange worth US $ 928 million as on 2006-07 (RBI, 2007).The apparel grade wool constitutes only 5 per cent of the total wool production and originates from the north temperate region of India, mainly Jammu and Kashmir. Nearly 15 per cent of wool produced in India is very coarse and could not be used for carpet manufacturing. The carpet produced from India is highly preferred in the international markets. Traditionally India was an importer of apparel grade wool and net exporter of carpet grade wool. But, of late, the internal production of wool is not able to cater to the domestic demand for even the carpet grade wool. Therefore, wool of both apparel and carpet grade are imported to India, processed here and the final value added products are re-exported. This has contributed much to our foreign exchange earnings.

Trend in sheep population in India and its correspondence with the global sheep population

Since the wool and woolens are one of the major commodities in the global trade, it is worthwhile to examine the sheep population in India in the context of the global changes in the sheep population. Over a time span of about 15 years, the global sheep population was on gradual decline, from the level of 1207 million heads in 1990 to 1102 million heads in 2006. Such a slump in world sheep population occurred due to the dramatic decline in the traditional sheep producing countries like Australia, New Zealand and Eastern European countries, partly due to the low demand of wool for military purpose, persistent drought in major sheep growing counties like Australia and emergence of closer substitutes for the natural wool. However, noticeable increase in sheep population was observed in China, mainly due to the deliberate effort on the part of Chinese Government to increase the domestic wool and mutton production.

Though the growth rate of sheep in India also reduced compared to the earlier decades, the reduction in growth rate was not commensurate with that observed in traditional sheep producing countries, thanks to the fact that meat production is the major purpose of sheep farming in India. Moreover, unlike many other wool producing countries, the limiting factor for Indian woolen industry is not demand side constraints, but supply side one, and our wool is predominantly used for manufacturing carpets catering to export demand. On examining the population changes by using data for nearly two decades, it could be observed that the population of sheep increased from around 49 million in 1982 to 61 million in 2003 (Table 1). Sharma (2004) also noted that between 1953 and 2001 the sheep population in India grew at the rate of 0.88 per cent per year which was more than that observed in the case of total cattle and total bovines. But, a closer examination indicates that the rate of growth has declined considerably during the last inter-census period (1997 to 2003). It declined from the level of 2.51 per cent during 1992-97 to 1.21 per cent during 1997-03.

The growth rate varied significantly across states wherein Andhra Pradesh registered a growth rate of nearly 14 percent between 1997 and 2003 livestock census. Such a trend had been exhibited by the state since 1992 Census. During the last inter-census period, the population increased from 9.7 million heads to 21.4 million heads, thus becoming the state with the largest sheep population in India, relegating Rajasthan, the hitherto *numero uno* state to the second position. The reduction of sheep population in Rajasthan has serious implication on the carpet production as the wool produced in Rajasthan is highly suitable for carpet manufacturing. Of late, *Rajasthani* wool is used for mixing with the imported wool to impart the desirable bulk and resilience property to the carpets produced. Most of the sheep breeds of Andhra Pradesh are mutton type and the wool is generally not suitable for carpet manufacturing. Other than Andhra Pradesh, the only major state having significant positive growth rate was Jammu and Kashmir where the population increased at the rate of 1.23 per cent (from 3.1 million heads to 3.4 million heads). Most of the sheep breeds of the state belong to the category of Kashmiri merinos which are the crosses of the domestic breeds with exotic breeds like Rambuillet and Merinos.

Table 1. Population and growth rate of sheep in India

States	Decadal changes in Sheep population (million)			Inter census growth rates (per cent per annum)		
	1982	1992	2003	1987-92	1992-97	1997-03
(1)	(2)	(3)	(4)	(5)	(6)	(7)
Andhra Pradesh	7.52	7.79	21.38	2.53	4.58	13.99
Bihar	1.32	1.69	1.06	2.13	2.98	-9.68
Gujarat	2.36	2.03	2.06	5.40	1.25	-0.76
Haryana	0.76	1.04	0.63	3.22	4.39	-11.22
Himachal Pradesh	1.09	1.07	0.93	-0.66	0.07	-2.53
J&K	1.91	2.94	3.41	3.39	1.48	1.23
Karnataka	4.79	5.43	7.26	2.81	8.07	-1.62
Madhya Pradesh	0.96	0.83	0.55	0	0.19	-6.96
Maharashtra	2.67	3.08	3.10	1.39	1.82	-1.40
Oriss	1.99	1.84	1.62	-0.02	0.29	-2.32
Punjab	0.61	0.53	0.22	0.74	-3.72	-10.77
Rajasthan	13.43	12.50	10.05	4.70	2.75	-5.72
Tamil Nadu	5.54	5.85	5.59	-0.11	-1.68	0.67
Uttar Pradesh	2.31	2.40	1.44	1.96	-4.54	-4.59
West Bengal	1.36	1.49	1.52	0.38	-0.35	0.71
All India	48.75	50.78	61.47	2.13	2.51	1.21

(Source: GoI (2003) Livestock census, various issues and own estimation using data from livestock census)

Trend in wool production

Global Scenario

The global production of greasy wool was nearly 2.5 m tonnes in 1980-84 period, increased to around 2.8 m tonnes by a decade, but reduced to 2.2 m tonnes by 2005. But the trend in raw wool production varied across producer countries (Table 2). As on 2005, Australia topped in raw wool production with a production level of 521 million kg followed by China and New Zealand. At this production level Australia was 180 million kg short of its production level of 1980-84. The most drastic decline in wool production was noticed in the Eastern European Countries represented mostly by the countries covered by the erstwhile Soviet Union. The contraction of wool production was as high as 68 per cent since early 1980s (from 625 m kg in 1980-84 to 197 m kg in 2005). The reduction in the wool production was observed in almost all countries except a few, the notable one being China. China could improve its wool production mainly because of the deliberate effort to stimulate domestic wool production for import substitution. Moreover, the official efforts to upgrade the quality of China's wool production by crossing indigenous Chinese sheep breeds with the imported merino breeding stock of Australia helped in overcoming the quality shortcomings. Due to such efforts, sheep stock increased by around 18% since early 1997 to reach around 150 million heads by around 2001 (within a four year period). China accounted for only 7 per cent of total wool production in early 1980s, but it increased to around 18 per cent by 2005, and stands just behind Australia.

Table 2. Trend in global production of raw wool (m kg)

Country	1980-84	1990-94	2000	2003	2005
Australia	701	702	667	548	521
China	183	243	294	339	380
New Zealand	368	289	258	227	231
Argentina	167	125	63	68	80
Turkey	66	80	62	54	54
South Africa	110	86	48	42	46
India	33	41	48	49	45
United Kingdom	51	70	63	50	42
Uruguay	77	91	57	41	40
United States	49	39	24	21	20
Eastern Europe	625	535	190	195	197
All others	434	530	520	509	506
World Total	2524	2831	2295	2145	2164

(Data Source: FAO (2008) accessed on 27.06.2008)

Domestic scenario

Viewed from a time span of nearly two decades, India could improve the domestic production from 32 million kg (in 1980-81) to 45 million kg (in 2002-03) achieved mostly through the increase in population of sheep (Table

3). But in the last five years a decline of total greasy wool production is noticed. Bulk of the reduction in the total wool production occurred in Rajasthan. The state contributed nearly 13 million kg of wool in 1980-81, increased to 19 million kg by 2000-01 and then declined to 15 million kg by 2002-03. The recurrent drought in the state has contributed to the sudden fall of the sheep population and thereby wool production. Other major contributors might be the quantitative and qualitative decline of pastures, the major source of nutrition for sheep. Among the states, significant growth in production of wool had been noted only in Andhra Pradesh, Gujarat and Jammu and Kashmir.

Table 3. Trend in raw wool production in India (lakh kg)

States	1980-81	1990-91	2000-01	2001-02	2002-03
Andhra Pradesh	13.79	17	32.89	33.92	39.76
Arunachal Pradesh	0.48	0.58	0.592	0.59	0.13
Bihar	9.2	11.2	13.14	13.38	3.68
Gujarat	18.67	19	27.4	27.09	31.19
Haryana	9	14	23.28	24.03	11.35
Himachal Pradesh	11.85	14.3	15.82	15.96	16.02
Jammu & Kashmir	18.5	40	60.25	64.6	73.96
Karnataka	26.34	43.95	57.03	59.04	55.92
Madhya Pradesh	7.9	9.15	9.59	8.27	6.73
Maharashtra	12.17	14.4	16.28	16.43	16.38
Punjab	12.1	15.2	10.52	9.57	7.09
Rajasthan	132	165	194.11	200.6	153.94
Tamil Nadu	30	37.5	6.36	6.25	7.50
Uttar Pradesh	13.12	19.18	17.95	20.59	18.09
West Bengal	4.42	6.25	6.37	6.42	6.64
Total wool Production	319.54	426.71	491.582	506.74	448.81

(Source: Government of India (1996, 2006_b) and Wool Ways (various issues)

Wool Import

With the deepening of export demand for carpets, the domestic wool production could not cater to the internal requirements. Therefore, import of carpet grade wool from New Zealand started in 1970s. In 1991-92, the domestic production catered to the tune of around 61 per cent of the internal requirement, but it declined to 33 percent in 2005-06 (Table 4). During this period, domestic wool use grew at the rate of 4.59 per cent per annum, but the internal production declined at the rate of nearly 1.70 per cent and therefore, raw wool import increased at the rate of 6.63 per cent.

Table 4. Trend and instability of internal production and import of raw wool in India

Year	Indigenous production (m kg)	Import of raw wool (m kg)	Total wool use m kg	Internal production as a percentage of total wool use (per cent)
1991-92	41.60	26.66	68.26	60.94
1996-97	44.40	57.76	102.16	43.46
2001-02	49.50	72.74	117.68	42.06
2005-06	45.30	90.16	135.46	33.44
Growth rate (%)				
a. 1991-92 to 1995-96	0.84	9.94	4.89	-
b. 1996-97 to 2000-01	2.23	-0.82	0.56	-
c. 2001-02 to 2005-06	-2.97	5.87	2.50	-
d.1991-92 to 2005-06	-1.70	6.63	4.59	-

(Data Source: GoI, 2006c)

The import of wool (including waste) increased from around 68 million kg in 1997-98 to 93 million kg in 2004-05 accounting for total value of Rs. 678 crores to Rs. 909 crores in the respective periods (Table 5). As on 2004-05, the major sources of import were Australia, New Zealand and China. However, there was structural change in the sources of import over years. In 1997-98, Australia accounted for 38 per cent of total import in terms of quantity and 61 per cent in terms of value, followed by New Zealand accounting for 14 per cent in terms of both quantity and value. But as on 2004-05, the share of Australia came down to half of that in 1997-98 in terms of quantity 47 per cent in terms of value. The wool from Australia is almost exclusively used for apparel manufacturing. Though New Zealand hold the second position in terms of the total import value, its share in terms of quantity decreased to 11 per cent. During the period (1997-98 to 2004-05), the average unit price of wool reduced from around Rs. 100 / kg to Rs. 98/ kg. However, the price changes were not uniform across the importing countries. The import from Australia always fetched premium prices due to the finer wool. One notable change was the increase in the share of China in total import. In 1997-98, India imported around 0.13 million kg of wool at a value of Rs 1.35 crores from China. But as on 2004-05, the import was nearly 16.32 million kg of wool at a value of around 80 crores. Thus china accounted for 18 per cent of total import in quantity terms and 9 per cent in value terms.

Table 5. Growth and variability of import of wool

Country	Quantity (Tonnes)	Value (Rs. Lakh)	1997-98 % of total quantity imported	% of total value of import	Price (Rs/Kg)	Quantity (Tonnes)	Value (Rs. Lakh)	2004-05 % of total quantity imported	% of total value of import	Price (Rs/Kg)
Australia	25546	41133	37.59	60.65	161.02	17416	42589	18.73	46.84	244.54
New Zealand	9544	9739	14.04	14.36	102.05	10170	13060	10.94	14.36	128.42
Italy	3550	1678	5.22	2.47	47.27	5563	2830	5.98	3.11	50.87
Turkey	6349	2313	9.34	3.41	36.44	7248	3544	7.80	3.90	48.90
U K	4138	1380	6.09	2.03	33.35	5542	4121	5.96	4.53	74.36
Saudi Arab	1558	810	2.29	1.19	52.02	3807	1769	4.09	1.95	46.47
Argentina	861	1001	1.27	1.48	116.27	1491	1726	1.60	1.90	115.76
South Africa	1092	2239	1.61	3.30	204.94	1126	1179	1.21	1.30	104.71
Iran	2621	981	3.86	1.45	37.44	2899	1556	3.12	1.71	53.67
China P Rp	127	135	0.19	0.20	106.37	1632	7963	17.56	8.76	48.78
Greece	222	66	0.33	0.10	29.63	2694	941	2.90	1.03	34.93
Others	12357	6340	18.18	9.35	51.31	18698	9654	20.11	10.62	51.63
Grand Total	**67965**	**67816**	**100.00**	**100.00**	**99.78**	92977	90932	100.00	100.00	97.80

Value addition to the wool in India

The trend in the production of woollen items in India is given in Table 6. Among the woolens manufactured in India, the carpets- both handmade and machine made- assume great significance. As on 2006-07, the production of the hand knotted carpets was nearly 7.5 million sq. m whereas that of the machine made carpets was around 0.50 million sq. m.

Table 6. Production of woolens in India

Item	Unit	2000-01	2001-02	2002-03	2003-04	2004-05	2005-06	2006-07
Worsted Yarn	Mn (Kgs)	43.0	44.00	44.00	44.00	45.00	45.33	45.67
Woollen Yarn	Mn (Kgs)	33.00	33.00	34.00	34.00	34.00	34.34	34.68
Wool Tops	Mn (Kgs)	27.00	28.00	28.00	28.00	29.00	29.51	30.02
Fabric (Woollen/Worsted)	Mn (mtrs)	64.00	68.00	66.00	66.00	66.00	66.00	66.00
Shoddy Yarn	Mn (Kgs)	27.00	26.00	24.00	25.00	26.00	26.00	26.00
Blankets (Shoddy/Woollen)	Mn.(Pcs)	13.00	12.00	11.00	11.00	12.00	12.00	12.00
Shoddy Fabric	Mn (Mtrs)	18.00	18.00	17.00	17.50	18.00	18.00	18.00
RMG (Knitwear/woven wear and goods)	Mn (Kgs)	14.00	13.00	13.00	13.00	14.00	14.00	14.00
Hand knotted carpets	Mn. (Sq. mtrs)	07.50	07.50	08.00	08.00	8.00	08.17	08.34
Machine made carets	Mn. (Sq. mtrs)	0.500	0.50	0.50	0.50	0.50	0.50	00.50

(Source: GoI ,2006c)

Of the total production of handmade carpets and other floor coverings, more than 90 percent was accounted for by the woollen carpets, rest by silk and synthetics. The value of the total carpet production was increasing faster than the increase in physical production. In 1995-96, India produced carpets worth US$ 416 million whereas it increased to US$ 732.3 million by 2005-06 (Table 7). It may be remembered that the production of the hand made carpets has not shown any such kind of improvement as can be observed from Table 6. This clearly indicates that significant part of the improvement in the gain was on account of the improvement in the carpet prices, particularly from United States. The high price increase of the carpet can boost the prospects of the domestic carpet production. However, high demand for the Indian carpets in United States was mainly augmented by the economic boom. A reversal of the economic buoyancy would immediately transmit back to the production centres as the export demand of Indian carpet is highly price elastic, as happened in the recession that plagued the world economy during 2008-09.

Table 7. Trend in production of handmade carpets and other floor coverings (US$ Mn)

Year	Woollen	Silk	Synthetic	Total
1995-96	392.62	17.1	6.57	416.29
1996-97	430.89	19.42	5.06	455.37
1997-98	410.55	29.79	15.71	456.05
1998-99	436.98	33.09	23.31	493.38
1999-00	449.28	36.24	22.51	508.03
2000-01	466.49	37.72	23.78	528
2001-02	478.16	42.69	23.78	539.78
2002-03	496.62	43.97	18.85	559.44
2003-04	609.11	27.17	9.774	646.02
2004-05	566.37	41.59	13.54	621.5
2005-06	676.65	41.89	13.76	732.3

(Source: Carpet export promotion council, New Delhi)

The woollen industry in India is highly scattered in both rural and urban areas. They are mainly located in the states of Punjab, Haryana, Rajasthan, Uttar Pradesh, Maharashtra and Gujarat. Punjab accounts for about 40 per cent of the woollen units whereas Haryana accounts for 27 per cent and Rajasthan accounts for 10 per cent (GoI, 2006a). As on 2005-06, there were 718 woollen units in organized sector and a large number of units in the small scale sector. Ludhiana alone accounted for 225-240 units in the decentralized hosiery and shawl sectors. The installed capacity of the industry was about 6.04 lakh worsted spindles and 4.37 lakh non-worsted spindles. The production of the textile items depends to a great extent on the number of spindles available at various stages.

Between 1992 and 2005, the number of worsted spindle grew at the annual growth rate of 1.89 per cent and the non-worsted sector at the rate of 3.05 per cent (Table 8). In the case of power looms, there was near stagnation as the number of looms remained nearly 7200 for the period of 2000- 2005. This stagnation in the capacity expansion has lead to short supply of Indian carpets in the international markets as reflected from the high price increase of Indian carpets in the US and European markets. The import norm for carpet manufacturing was liberalized with a view to promote carpet manufacturing as well as enhancing private investment in this sector. But the benefits of such policy change were appropriated by the existing industries and have not resulted in significant influx of new private investment. Therefore, the liberalization of import policy needs to undertake measures to encourage private investment in the capacity expansion of carpet industry. Policy initiatives towards encouraging the private investment in the capacity expansion of the carpet industry call for immediate attention of the policy makers and the Government.

Table 8. Installed capacity and growth rate in woollen industry

Particulars	1992	1995	2000	2005	% Growth between 1992 and 2005
Worsted Spindles (lakh)	4.85	5.18	5.85	6.04	1.89
Non-worsted Spindles (lakh)	3.13	3.17	4.19	4.37	3.05
Power looms (No.)	7047	7063	7228	7228	0.20

(Data source: GoI, 2006c)

Wool production scenario at the field level

In order to have deeper understanding of the problems and prospects of wool production at the field level, results of a primary survey undertaken in Rajasthan, the major wool producing state in India during January 2008 is made use in the following sections. For this Ajmer and Bikaner districts were purposively selected as they were typical of semi-arid and arid regions of the state, respectively and had large sheep populations. A total of 60 farmers were surveyed comprising of 30 farmers from each district. The purpose of the survey was to examine the structural changes in the sheep production conditions in Rajasthan. Therefore, the survey schedule contained questions regarding the structural changes in the sheep production conditions in Rajasthan with regard to that existed 15 years back, possibility for improving sheep production in the state as perceived by farmers and the major constraints faced by the farmers in sheep production. Though the study was pertaining to sheep, the insight derived from the study can be applied to the small ruminant population in general, particularly of north western India.

Expenditure and returns in sheep farming

For better understanding of small ruminant production, we shall examine its economics in terms of the cost and returns (Table 9). The total expenditure was Rs. 14477 and the gross return was Rs.61089 giving rise to net return of Rs. 46612 for an average flock of 125. The net return per sheep for an average flock was Rs. 287 in Ajmer and Rs. 451 in Bikaner giving rise to an aggregate average of Rs. 372. The share of animal sale was nearly 74 per cent in the gross return, followed by wool (14%), milk (7%) and manure (7%). The difference in the net return was constituted mainly by the difference in the return obtained from live animal sale which constituted Rs. 37733 for an average flock in Ajmer, but gave rise to an average of Rs. 52698 in Bikaner district. Such a big difference was mainly due to the difference in the age of disposal of the animals about which we will be dealing in later part of this paper. One other factor that has contributed significantly towards the difference is the comparatively higher return for wool in Bikaner than in Ajmer. This aspect is discussed in detail in the following sessions.

Table 9. Expenditure and net return from sheep farming

Item	Ajmer	Bikaner	Overall
Expenditure			
Feed and fodder (%)	49.9	48.2	49.1
Veterinary care (%)	14.3	12.1	13.7
Labour (%)	26.4	34.2	29.9
Miscellaneous (Rs.)	9.4	5.5	7.7
Total expenditure (Rs.)	16079	12876	14477
Return			
Wool (%)	9.5	16.0	12.7
Animal sale (%)	73.9	74.1	74.0
Manure (%)	9.3	4.4	6.6
Milk (%)	7.3	6.2	6.7
Gross Return (Rs.)	51059	71118	61089
Net return (Rs.)	34980	58242	46612
Net return per sheep(Rs.)	287	451	372
Flock size	122	129	125

(Source: Field survey)

Contribution of wool and its marketing practices

In Rajasthan, sheep are mainly sheared 2-3 times a year. In semi-arid region the dominant shearing pattern was three times a year, where as that in the case of the arid region was two times. Shearing of the wool three times, though leads to slightly higher wool yield per animal, results in reduced fibre length. This renders the wool unsuitable for many of the carding and combing machines. Moreover, the wool from semi-arid regions suffers from the problems of presence of large amount of thorny material from the bushes. Manual removal of the thorns and other extraneous matter adds to the cost of processing of the fibre. These factors are major reasons for reduced prices of the raw wool produced in the semi-arid zones. Moreover, the wool from the arid regions is having better luster quality compared to that from the semi-arid regions. But a perusal of the cost data indicates that the reduction in the wool price is not commensurate with the cost escalation in the process of removing the extraneous matter. The average price of wool produced in Ajmer fetches something around Rs. 20-30. The wool yield from this would be to the tune of 50-55 per cent and one kg yarn fetches Rs. 90-135 depending on the quality. The material and labour cost involved in the process of conversion is not more that Rs. 5 per kg. It can be deduced that even after accounting for the increased cost involved in processing the wool, the extent of reduction of the price is higher than what is warranted for. These observations were also corroborated by Ray (1997).

Decline of wool prices in India and its impact on income

The demand for wool is derived demand, depending on the demand for the carpets, primarily in the export markets. Over years the export demand for carpet is on increase, notably to United States. As has been noted earlier, the proportionate increase in the value of the carpet exported is more than the proportionate increase in the physical volume of export, highlighting the fact that the unit value of Indian carpet was on increase. But the domestic price of wool did not show that trend. The price of wool had been declining both in absolute terms and in relative terms during the last decade. Fig. 1 compares the movement of price index of the wool with other commodities/ commodity groups for the period of 1996-97 to 2005-06 (at 1993-94 base).

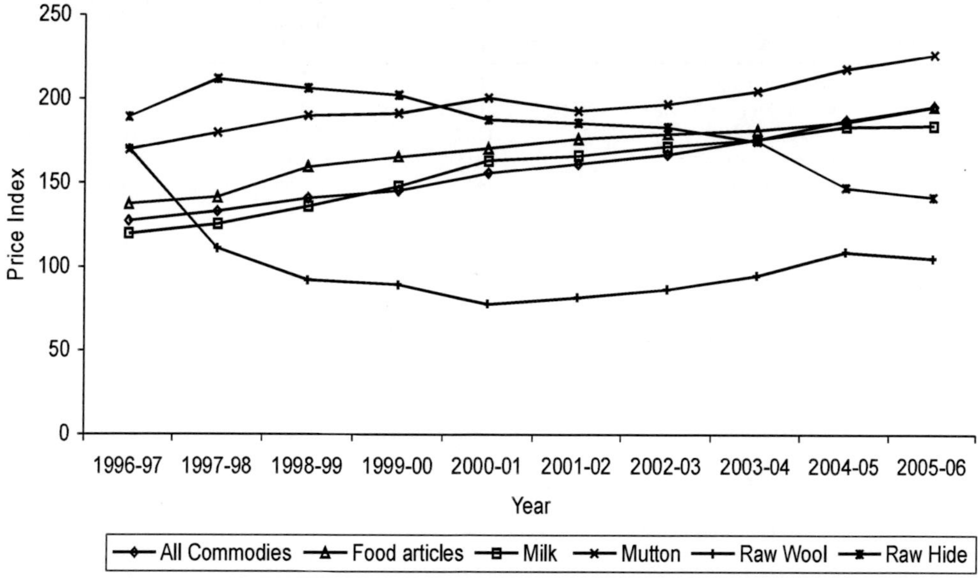

Fig 1: Index number of wool price *vis a vis* price of other important commodities

The price index of all these commodities except wool and hide increased at significant rate. The price growth rate was the highest in case of milk

(5.20 %), followed by all commodities (4.86 %) and food articles (3.72 %). The price of wool was declining at the rate of 2.64 per cent per annum. The price decline was associated with high degree of instability also. The instability was nearly 23 per cent compared to 1.22 per cent for all commodities.

The trend in the prices of wool showed considerable variation between various markets and this variation also contributed to the differing contribution of wool in the income realized by the farmers. An analysis undertaken to compare the mean and variability of the wool prices for various markets in India is indicated in Table 10. The prices were calculated for the period of 1994-2003. The highest mean price of wool was observed in Jammu market for the finer wool of 21-23 microns (Rs. 54 per kg). The wool which had the diameter of 32-34 microns and 34-36 microns also fetched high prices as this wool is used for manufacturing carpet. However, the prices were as low as Rs. 12 in case of the coarser wool from the breeds of Karnataka (in *Hubli* market). The coefficient of variation for the wool prices was also higher in case of the coarser wool compared to the finer wool.

Table 10. Mean and variability of wool prices across quality and markets in India (1994-2003)

Sl.No (1)	Quality/Market (2)	Mean (Rs./ kg) (3)	Standard deviation (Rs./ kg) (4)	Coefficient of variation (%) (5)
1	32-34 μ/ Bikaner	59.56	6.84	11.48
2	34-36 μ/Bikaner	51.56	4.98	9.66
3	36-40 μ/ Bikaner	42.13	9.01	21.40
4	34-36μ/Beaawer	50.00	11.45	22.90
5	36-40μ/Beawer	42.3	7.96	18.82
6	38-42 μ/Beawer	36.88	9.39	25.46
7	34-36μ/Panipat	52.67	8.09	15.37
8	36-40μ/Panipat	48	7.05	14.69
9	40-44μ/Panipat	40.67	8.73	21.47
10	32-34μ/Ludhiana	52.5	12.28	23.38
11	34-36μ/Ludhiana	46.5	11.84	25.47
12	36-40μLudhiana	44.12	11.69	26.50
13	21-23μ/Jammu	54.00	2.33	4.31
14	24-28μ/Jammu	40.56	7.32	18.04
15	32-34μ/Jammu	36.4	4.39	12.07
16	28-30μ/Shimla	42.88	11.85	27.64
17	40-44μ/Mirzapur	34.33	12.04	35.07
18	45-50μ/Mirzapur	27.38	10.74	39.24
19	34-38μ/Jamnanagasr	37.12	12.43	33.47
20	40-44μ/Jamnanagar	34.33	10.77	31.37
21	45-50μ/Hubli	14.67	3.57	24.35
22	50-60μ/Hubli	12.44	2.92	23.47

Note: The prices were calculated for a period of 1994- 2003; Mean values of the ranges were taken as the data points in calculating the parameter as the data contained only ranges. (Data source: Computed from Wool Ways, various issues)

These factors has lead to the realization of higher return from wool production in the Bikaner district compared to that in Ajmer district for an average flock size of 125 (Table 11). The average return from wool was to the tune of Rs. 4810 in case of Ajmer, whereas that was to the tune of Rs. 10667 in the case of the Bikaner, leading to the overall average of Rs. 7739 for an average flock.

Table 11. Gross returns from wool production distributed across flock category (Rs./ household)

District	Small	Medium	Large	Overall
Ajmer	1675	4168	10003	4810
Bikaner	4423	10405	20687	10667
Overall	2911	7766	14582	7739

Further analysis of the economics of the wool marketing indicated that on an average the expenditure incurred from shearing to sale in the market amounted to Rs. 1112, and the total net return amounted to Rs. 6627 per household. The expenditure towards shearing, transportation and market fee & marketing cost accounted for 56, 29 and 15 per cent respectively of total expenditure from shearing to sale.

Marketing channels of wool

Delineation of the marketing channels helps to identify the intervention points to improve the marketing efficiency of wool. Here we consider the number of intermediaries operating in the value chain while the wool passes from the producer to the yarn manufacturer. Details of the marketing channels prevalent in Ajmer district of Rajasthan is depicted below.

1. Farmer → Village level middleman → Commission Agents → Yarn manufacturers
2. Farmer → Commission Agent → Yarn Manufacturers
3. Farmer → Village level middleman → Yarn manufacturers
4. Farmer → Village level middleman → Big middlemen → Yarn manufacturer

The most widely prevalent marketing channel is farmers directly selling the wool to the market and the farmers selling the wool to the village middlemen who in turn selling the produce to the commission agents / trader in the market. The commission agents are many times purchasers of the produce also. The wool markets are traditional and are embedded in the non-market oriented relations. Trader loyalty is a common feature (Ray, 1999). The markets are highly vertically integrated that it is many times a family business and same family undertake various operations in the value chain starting from the job of commission agents in the market to carpet manufacturing. Due to this advantage they are able to influence the price formation of wool. Though many farmers sell the wool to the market through the village level middlemen who in turn sell it to the market, the incidence of the middlemen selling the wool directly to the yarn manufacturer is not uncommon. This is for avoiding the market charges and for tax advantages. The commission agents also reduce a portion of weight of wool on account of dust and other extraneous matters present in it. This may range from 5-10 per cent of the produce. Similarly a reduction is applied for coloured wools which are not generally demanded by the yarn manufacturers. The extent of reduction on these accounts depends on the bargaining power of the sellers also.

Production and marketing of small ruminant meat & meat products in India

Production performance of the small ruminant meat in India

As has been pointed out earlier, the major contribution of the small ruminants to the rural economy is its role as a source of the most preferred meat. The small ruminant meat products are highly preferred in the domestic market and the domestic production is not able to cater to the surging demand. The analysis reveals better growth performance of the meat sector in India comparable to even milk sector (Table 12).

Table 12. Production of meat in India

Meat	Production (millioin tones)			% annual growth	
	1980/82	1990/92	2001/03	1981-90	1991-2003
Large ruminants	0.52	0.72	1.13	4.0	5.5
Small ruminants	0.67	0.90	1.0	4.4	1.5
Poultry	0.29	0.56	0.95	6.5	4.7
Pork	0.08	0.14	0.34	6.9	8.8
Total meat	1.51	0.72	3.74	4.9	4.2
Milk	33.9	54.7	86.7	5.3	4.5

(Source: Birthal and Taneja, 2006)

The meat production in India increased from about 1.5 million tonnes in 1980/82 to 3.7 million tonnes in 2001/03. However, over years there were structural changes in composition of the meat production. In early 1980s small ruminants were the major suppliers (44%) of meat, followed by the large ruminants (35%) and poultry (19%). But by 2001/03, monogastrics, particularly poultry meat emerged as the most important meat with a share of about 35 per cent (Birthal and Thaneja, 2006). During this period, the growth rate of the meat production was above that of milk production, particularly during the 1980s. The drop in the growth rate of the meat production in 1990s was mainly due to the slower growth performance in the case of the small ruminant meat induced by deceleration in the population growth as well as the stagnation in the body weight of the small ruminants. To have a closer look at the small ruminant meat production, let us examine the growth performance of the major livestock population in India in terms of the population (Table 13).

Table 13. Population and growth rate of livestock in India

Livestock	Population (million)				Compound growth rate (%)		
	1982	1992	1997	2003	1982-92	1992-97	1997-2003
Cattle	192.5	204.6	198.9	185.2	0.6	-0.6	-1.2
Buffalo	69.8	84.2	89.9	97.9	1.9	1.3	1.4
Sheep	48.8	50.8	57.5	61.5	0.4	2.5	1.1
Goat	95.3	115.3	122.7	124.4	1.9	1.3	0.2
Pig	10	13	13.3	13.6	2.7	0.5	0.4
Poultry	207.7	307.1	347.6	489	4.0	2.5	5.9
Small ruminants	144.1	166.1	180.2	185.9	1.4	1.6	0.5
Bovines	262.3	288.8	288.8	283.1	1.0	0.0	-0.3

Though the population of all the major livestock exhibited significant positive trend over the time horizon of 1982 to 2003, the disaggregated analysis indicated that between 1997 and 2003 livestock censuses, the bovine population declined from 289 million to 283 million, and the small ruminant population registered marginal increase from 180 million to 186 million. Within small ruminants, growth rate for both sheep and goat were lower during 1997-2003 compared to that during 1992-97. This stagnation of the growth rate of the small ruminant population has affected the small ruminant meat production also. However, the lower growth rate in the case of small ruminants did not affect the total meat production due to the increased contribution from bovines and monogastrics. Since cattle slaughtering is legally banned in many states (except Kerala, West Bengal and north eastern states), the major contribution of bovine originates from buffaloes. The sudden increase in the buffalo meat production is mainly due to institutional interventions like contract farming, through which male buffalo calves could be made use for meat purpose through backward integration with high level of input supplies.

Consumption pattern and demand for the meat products in India

The consumption of the livestock products is on increase in India, triggered by sustained economic growth, population increase and changes in the taste and preference of the consumers. Between 1983 and 1999/2000, the per capita milk consumption nearly doubled from around 43 kg to 74 kg and meat consumption increased from 2.4 kg to 3.1 kg. The Increase in the meat consumption was driven by significant increase in the case of poultry and bovine meats. On the other hand, per capita consumption of the small ruminant meat has remained almost unchanged (Table 14) (Birthal and Taneja, 2006). This might be probably due to the slower growth rate of the small ruminant meat production in India, compared to the growth in other meat and meat products as well as the high price of the small ruminant meat compared to other livestock items.

Table 14. Per capita consumption of livestock products in India (kg/ annum)

Commodity	1983	1987-88	1993-94	1999-2000
Cereals	168.3	167.3	153.0	147.5
Pulses	11.5	11.8	9.8	12.5
Vegetables	47.6	52.4	61.5	76.1
Fresh fruits	3.2	11.7	19.3	18.1
Milk	43.0	54.4	58.6	73.5
Goat meat and mutton	1.1	1.1	1.0	1.0
Beef and buffalo meat	0.6	0.7	0.7	0.9
Poultry meat	0.3	0.4	0.4	0.7
Pig meat	0.2	0.2	0.3	0.2
Total meat	2.4	2.5	2.4	3.1
Eggs (NO.)	9.2	12.1	13.0	19.5
Fish	2.5	2.8	2.9	3.5

Source: Birthal and Taneja, 2006

Demand for meat and meat products

Based on econometric estimations various authors project sharp increase in the demand the meat products in India. For example, Kumar (1998) estimated that the demand for the meat by the year 2020 would be about 7.8 million tonnes, where as that by Dastagiri (2004) predicts a figure as high as 18 million tonnes. To cater to this emerging demand, the small ruminant production has to be increased substantially. Considering the surging export demand for the small ruminant meat from India, the opportunity for the small ruminant production in an organised industrialized manner is brighter. However, such a change needs enhanced awareness, capital investment and institutional support.

Marketing of live small ruminants

The small ruminant markets in India are generally unorganized and therefore, the primary producers are at the receiving end. One study conducted in Ajmer district of Rajasthan indicates that the small ruminant markets are unorganized, lacks basic amenities and are engulfed with oligopsonistic elements (Gupta et al., 2009). The traders/ commission agents are fewer in number and they form cartel, which successfully prevent the entry of new players into the business. Such observation has been made by Kumar and Singh (2007) also. The presence of the Government is near absent in the case of regulating the livestock markets. On an average about 4000 to 6000 animals are traded every operating day in Ajmer market generating large volume of business. However, these markets are not regulated and official recording of the data is altogether absent.

Marketing channels

Here we examine the marketing channels prevalent in semi-arid regions of Rajasthan as a case study. The most important marketing channel was the farmers selling the animal to the primary trade in the villages (who belongs to certain communities or castes) and he in tern bringing the animals to the terminal markets located at Ajmer or Jaipur, from where the butchers purchases it so as to reach the final consumer. The other major marketing channel includes a stage wherein the animals from the terminal markets are transported to mega markets located at Delhi or Mumbai from where the butchers purchase them. One another major marketing channel is the farmers themselves carrying the animals directly to the terminal market. The built in imperfection in the form of high level of oligopsonistic element (collusive oligopsony), entry preventing marketing rules, traditional system of price fixation, opaqueness of the price fixing mechanisms and absence of formal dispute settlement mechanisms acts as a major hindrance in the development of livestock marketing systems which puts the farmers at the disadvantage. Exploitation of the opportunities for vertical integration by innovative institutional mechanisms like contract farming and integrating various components of supply chain may be a solution to the problem (Ali, 2007b). Such an effort may take longer time frame in the context of the poor socio-economic development of small ruminant farmers. The evidences of the farmers venturing into organized commercial goat farming and realizing successes (Kumar, 2008) can set examples for further development of the sector.

Marketing of meat

Indian fresh meat industry is highly unorganised and most of the meat comes through traditional slaughter houses. There are about ten thousand slaughter houses in the country, of which nearly two third are unregistered. The consumer confidence on the fresh meat supplied from the slaughter houses is poor and calls for immediate attention of the local administration and the Government (Ali, 2007a). On the other hand, the organized slaughter houses maintain the world standard quality parameters for export purpose. Ensuring quality meat to the producers needs urgent intervention in the case of the slaughter procedures, maintaining the health register of the slaughtered animals and establishing cold storage facility.

Export of the small ruminant meat products from India

A study by Kumar et al. (2007) indicated that the export of the livestock products have increased sharply from around US $ 82 million in triennium ending in 1982 to US $ 674 million in TE 2006. During 1982, export of the bovine meat amounted to for US $ 3.65 million, accounting for only 4.45 per cent of the total value of export of the livestock products, but it increased to US$ 270 million by 2006, accounting for about two third of the total export of livestock products. During this period, the contribution of the small ruminants as percentage of total livestock product declined from about 12 per cent to 3 per cent. Within the small ruminant sector the export of goat meat was meagre, mainly due to high domestic demand for the goat meat. Similar to this, the export of the processed meat products also was not recording an encouraging trend. During 2004-05, the total quantity of the processed food products like homogenized meat preparations, meat extracts, meat juices, other poultry meat, preserved meats, sausages, canned meat etc. was to the tune of 1360 tonnes for a value of Rs. 945 lakhs, but as on 2007-08, the quantity decreased to 861 tonnes at revenue of Rs. 713 lakhs. However, this dismal performance is expected to pickup with the constitution of National Meat and Poultry Processing Board in 2008.

Processing and value addition of the small ruminant meat

Most of the meat consumed in India is sold as fresh and hardly one per cent of the total meat is processed or value added (Qureshi and Ranjhan, 2004). Pork and poultry meat are used for production of sausages, patties etc. for the elite market. Meat from the small ruminants is also used for production of the traditional kebabs. However, the meat industry have to diversify towards more value added products to serve the growing demand for the convenience items such as semi cooked, ready-to-eat, ready-to-cooked meat food products produced in the clean and hygienic environment. Only six percent of the total poultry meat is sold in processed form. Of this only about one percent undergoes processing into value added products (Ready-to-eat/ Ready-to-cook). Processing of large animals' meat is largely for the purpose of Exports. Total processing capacity in India is over one million tonnes per annum, of which 40-50% is utilized. Recognizing the importance to be accorded to the issues of production of hygienic, safe and wholesome meat products, Government of India has constituted the National Meat and Poultry Processing Board with a supervisory role in issues related with investment, financial assistance and entrepreneurship development in the meat processing sector. In order to encourage the processing of meat and meat products in the hygienic environment, the board promotes private investment in modernization of abattoirs under public private partnership mode under the aegis of the local bodies and grant in aid for construction of processing units. Government also encourages FDI in the case of the meat processing in India.

Food safety issues

Most of the export oriented meat processing plants in India follow strict traceability conditions and abide by various food safety orders enacted by the Government so as to align India's export quality in tune with the world standards. World class sanitary and phyto-sanitary measures prescribed by OIE, a referral institution of WTO and certification by HACCAP (Hazard Analysis and Critical Control Points), ISO 9002 are undertaken by the modern export oriented processing firms (Qureshi and Ranjhan, 2004). To ensure the quality parameters, the Government of India has enacted various laws viz. Prevention of Food Adulteration Act, Meat & Meat Products Order (MMPO), Cold Storage License, Packaged and Commodity Act, AGMARK (Agricultural Produce, Marking & Grading Act), Export clearances / Certificates / Registrations etc. However, one problem associated with the meat processing industry is the difficulties in getting the licenses from the multiplicity of agents, which restricts the growth of the industry. This situation needs to be looked into to augment investment in the meat processing sector.

Structural changes in the small ruminant production conditions

The increasing market opportunities for the small ruminant production and export can be exploited only if the underlying production condition of the small ruminants is favourable. The small ruminant production in India was considered as a low cost affair as they could be raised in the poor nutrition management regime depending on the vegetation available on the pasture land. Therefore, the supply of the small ruminant products was a function of the population of the animals, their reproduction rate, and quantity and quality of the vegetation available on the pasture land. As far as the arid and semi-arid regions of India are concerned- where most of the small ruminants are located- pasturelands supply fodder and grazing space for the livestock. In doing so, these pastures help in sustaining a number of livestock which would not have been permitted by individuals' owned land, especially for small farmers (Jodha, 1986). But that condition is gradually changing as there is high demand for the pastureland to be converted to competing uses like real estate and other agricultural uses. Decline of grazing lands affects the small ruminant production and rural livelihood adversely. Therefore, conservation of the pastures and improving its productivity bears key role in ensuring sustenance of the livelihood of the rural poor. The quantitative and qualitative deterioration of the pasturelands, changing socio-economic status of the breeders and the influence of the market can make changes in the production condition of the small ruminants, thereby affecting its supply. In this section an attempt has been made to delineate the changes in the production condition of the small ruminants in India. The insight into this has been obtained through the primary survey. Though the study has been undertaken to analyze the changes in the production condition of sheep, the results would be holding true in the case of the goat also since they share similar production systems.

Structural changes and its implication on the production parameters of sheep (small ruminants)

The farmers were asked to compare various parameters of sheep production currently observed with that existed 15 years back (based on their recall). This method was adopted as the data for the reference base year was not available. Even though, the method appears crude, it helps to provide a broader picture of the situation. About 75 and 87 per cent farmers reported reduction in wool productivity and body weight of the animal in the last 15 years. Nearly 87 per cent farmers also reported reduction of average age of disposal of lambs. The reduction was to the extent of 18 percent in the annual wool yield per adult sheep and that of body weight was to the extent of 20 percent at marketable age (at the age of six months) for male lambs (Table 15). The reduction in arrival of wool in markets of Rajasthan was reported by the State Government also (Government of Rajasthan, 2004).

Table 15. Change in the flock size, wool productivity and age of disposal of lambs

District	Wool productivity			Change in body weight			Change in age of sale		
	Earlier (g/sheep/year)	Currently (g/sheep/ year)	% Change	Earlier (kg/ sheep)	Currently (kg/sheep	% Change	Earlier (months)	Currently (months)	% change
Ajmer	1655	1367	-17.4	14.2	11.2	-21.1	9.7	4.7	-51.9
Bikaner	1605	1312	-18.3	13.4	10.8	-19.6	21.2	12.4	-41.4
Overall	1630	1339	-17.8	13.8	11.0	-20.3	15.5	8.6	-44.7

(Source: Field survey)

The age at which the male lambs were disposed for meat purpose decreased by 52 per cent in case of Ajmer district and 41 per cent in case of Bikaner district leading to considerable loss of animal wealth prematurely. Generally the male lambs are disposed after the age of 6 months, time by which they cross period of maximum growth rate. The average age of sale of male lambs in Ajmer was only 4.7 months and about 12 per cent of lambs were sold before crossing even three months of age (Fig. 2). This lead to significant reduction of the return from the live animal sale as can be observed from the Table 9. The difference in the age of sale of the lambs between the two districts is mainly due to the difference in the sheep rearing practices. The farmers in arid region are traditionally migratory and follow transhumance system whereas those in the semi-arid region are generally sedentary, and follow short distance-short duration migration. Therefore, the cost towards feed and fodder would be higher for the semi-arid system, pushing up the marginal costs. Decline of the pastures deteriorated the situation. Here, the important optimization strategy adopted by the farmers was to keep the flocks at a manageable level by disposing the male lambs at younger age. But this resulted in decline of net return as could be observed from the table. Early sale of male lambs is emerging as a major problem in small ruminant production (GoI, 2007) as it leads to early loss of precious livestock wealth and hampers the prospects of higher meat production.

Structural changes in the cost components of sheep production

Among various cost components, the most important one is the cost of feed and fodder as has been depicted in Table 9. Of the expenditure of Rs. 7113/year spent towards cost of feeding for an average flock of 125, the top feeds from fodder trees accounted for about 45 per cent. The expenditure on top feed was generally higher for small and marginal land holders as compared to the bigger holders both in absolute and in relative terms. The higher share of fodder trees on the feeding component is relatively a new phenomenon. This can be considered as the result of decline of the pastures that has lead to cost escalation, particularly for the landless and small farmers, affecting the sustainability of the production system. One other factor that might have contributed to the decline of the small ruminant production is the persistent drought witnessed in many parts of Rajasthan. During the drought period, the production parameters of the small ruminants declines and they happens to be the animal to be liquidated earlier compared to bovines.

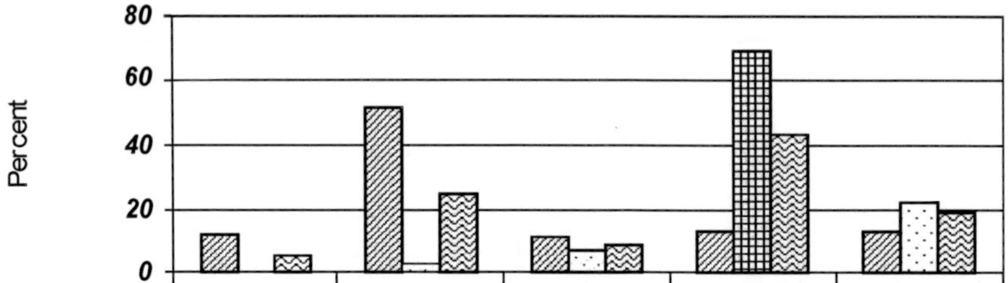

	0-3 months	4-6 months	7-9 months	10-12 months	>1 year
Ajmer	11.86	51.09	11.16	12.35	13.54
Bikaner	0	2.66	6.45	68.81	22.08
Overall	5.39	24.6	8.58	43.22	18.21

Age

Fig 2. Distribution of age of disposal of lambs

Conclusion and implications

The wool produced from India is largely suitable for production of carpets and the export demand for carpet, particularly from the United States and European countries is quite high. Similar to this, the demand for the small ruminant meat- mutton and chevon- is also on increase both from the domestic and export sectors. The export of the small ruminant meat products could not rise due to the high demand in the domestic sector itself. The woollen and meat products of small ruminant origin is price elastic and therefore, the domestic supply of these commodities has to be increased to have greater access to larger sections of the society. However, the population of small ruminants did not respond adequately to meet the growing demand. The population growth rate of the small ruminants is slowing down or is negative in many traditional small ruminant producing states. This slack in population coupled with stagnant productivity of wool and meat puts riders on the prospects of the ability of the country to meet the surging demand for these commodities. India, which was an exporter of carpet grade wool, now imports more than two-third of the internal requirement through imports.

This trend observed in the macro-economy corresponds well with the farm level observations. The structural changes in production conditions like decline of pastures, imperfections in the markets and unpreparedness to climatic extremities are acting as major constraints against the development of small ruminant sector. It needs deliberate institutional intervention in the form of conservation of the existing pasture land, increasing the productivity of the pastures, supply of elite germ plasm suitable for the local environment and provision for adequate veterinary care to augment the production of meat and fibres. In this endeavor the role of the market carries great role. The marketing system of the wool and meat are totally unorganized and are relying on the age-old practices and customs. The marketing channels are long, and the markets carry greater elements of oligopsony which could successfully prevent the new entrants in the business. The case of the meat marketing is worse compared to wool, wherein provisions for regulated markets are non-existent. This calls for immediate attention of the policy makers and administration. The failure of the market is reflected in the price formation also, particularly in the case of wool. The liberalization of import regulations of carpet grade wool has resulted in surge in import even from non-traditional wool exporters, which helped to increased the woollen production, affected the wool prices in the domestic market adversely to the farmers (Champavat, 1993). This development had adverse impact on the income of small ruminant origin to the farmers. Therefore, steps to ensure remunerative price for the wool produced by the farmers through support price schemes, or compulsory procurement of wool from the domestic market and market regulations to overcome the imperfection are necessary to boost the domestic wool supply. Moreover, effort to conserve the superior germplasm of the local breeds which could produce best quality carpet wool is also needed to insure our genetic wealth against its gradual loss.

On the long term, change in the organization of production is required to augment the supply of the small ruminant meat and fiber. This can be achieved by change in the system of production from the existing extensive grazing practices to more organized and intensive production practices. This can be achieved through better link to the market through innovative measure like contract farming or adapting landless intensive production techniques. Technological advances carries greater role in this endeavour. Such an attempt has to be supported by institutional support in the form of credit and market backings.

References

Ali, Jabir. 2007a. Livestock sector development and implications for rural poverty alleviation in India. Livestock Research for Rural Development 19(2): 55-63

Ali, Jabir. 2007b. Designing vertical coordination for Indian meat industry. In: S.Bhaskaran and S. Mohanty (Eds.), Marketing of Livestock and Livestock products in India. ICFAI University Press, Hyderabad.

Birthal, P.S. and Taneja, V.K. 2006, Livestock Sector in India: Opportunities and Challenges for Small Holders, In: Proceedings of International Workshop on Smallholder Livestock Production in India: Opportunities and Challenge, New Delhi, 31 January-1 Feb, New Delhi.

Champavat, P.S. 1993. Trend in Price of Raw Wool. Wool Ways April-June: 11-13.

Dastagiri, M.B. 2004. Demand and supply projection for livestock products in India. Policy Paper No. 21, National Centre for Agricultural Economics and Policy Research, New Delhi.

Government of India . 1996. Wool Statistics. Central Wool Development Board, Jodhpur.

Government of India. 2003. *Livestock Census*, Department of Animal Husbandry, Dairying and Fisheries, Ministry of Agriculture, New Delhi.

Government of India. 2006a. *Report of the Working Group on Textiles and Jute Industry for 11th Five Year Plan*, Ministry of Textiles, New Delhi.

Government of India .2006b. *Basic Animal Husbandry Statistics*, Department of Animal Husbandry, Dairying and Fisheries, Ministry of Agriculture, New Delhi.

Government of India .2006c. *Compendium of Textile Statistics*, Ministry of Textiles, New Delhi.

Government of India. 2007. *Approach Paper to 11TH Five Year Plan*. Task Force on Livestock Sector, Planning Commission, New Delhi.

Government of Rajasthan. 2004. *Prasasnik Prathivedan*: 2003-2004, Department of Animal Husbandry, Jaipur.

Food and Agricultural Organization (2008). FAOSTAT website accessed on 20.06.2008

Gupta, D.C., Suresh ,A. and Sethi, D. 2009. RPF II of the Research Project Marketing of Small Ruminants in India, Central Sheep and Wool Research Institute, Avikanagar, Rajasthan, India.

Jodha, N.S. 1985. Population growth and the decline of common property resource in Rajasthan, India. Population Development Review 11(2): 247-264.

Jodha, N.S. 1986. Rural common property resources and rural poor in dry regions of India. Economic and Political Weekly 21: 1169-1181.

Kumar, Anjani, Staal, S.J., Singh, N.P and Singh, D.K. 2007. Livestock sector trade of India: Surging momentum in the new liberalized regime. Indian Journal of Agricultural Economics **62**(3): 395-410.

Kumar, Praduman. 1998. *Food Demand and Supply Projections for India,* Agricultural Economics Policy Paper 98-01, Indian Agricultural Research Institute, New Delhi.

Kumar, Shalander and Singh, N.P. 2007. In: S.Bhaskaran and S. Mohanty (Eds.), Marketing of Livestock and Livestock products in India. ICFAI University Press, Hyderabad.

Kumar, Shalander. 2008. Final report of the project Commercial goat farming in India. Central Institute of Research on Goats,Farah, Mathura, India.

Menon, A and Vadivelu, G.A. 2006. Common property resources in different agro-climatic landscapes in India. Conservation and Society 4 (1): 132-154.

Pasha, S.A. 1991. Sustainability and viability of small and large rearers: Animal husbandry and common property resources. Economic and Political Weekly 26(13): A27-A30.

Qureshi, Sirajuddin and Ranjhan, S.K. 2004. Indian meat industry. Asian Buffalo Magazine 1(1):19-28.

Ray, Sunil.1997. Natural Resources, Organizations & Technology Linkages, Rawat Publications, Jaipur.

Ray, Sunil. 1999. Declining Production Conditions of Raw Wool: Analysis of Emerging Conflicts in Sheep Husbandry in Rajasthan. Economic and Political Weekly May 15: 1209-1214.

Reserve Bank of India. 2007. Handbook of Statistics on Indian Economy, Mumbai.

Roy, Thirthankar. 2002. Changes in Wool Production and Usage in Colonial India. Gokhale Institute of Politics and Economics, Deccan Gymkhana, Pune.

Sharma,V.P. 2004. Livestock Economy of India: Current Status, Emerging Issues and Long-term Prospects. Indian Journal of Agricultural Economics 59 (3): 512-554.

Suresh, A. and Gupta, D.C. 2008. Final Project Report, Study on Production and Utilisation of Wool and Wool Products in India. Central Sheep and Wool Research Institute, Avikanagar, Rajasthan, India.

❑❑❑

41

Wool and Chemical Processing in Carpet Perspective

K. K. Goswami and R. K. Malik
Indian Institute of Carpet Technology, Bhadohi- 221 401, Uttar Pradesh

Introduction

Carpet is a *'Woven'* or *'Knotted'* or *'Tufted'* or *'Knitted'* or *'Braided'* or *'Non woven'* felted thick and heavy textile; used primarily for floor covering but also for table and wall coverings. The product has hardly been technologically studied methodically by academicians or researchers. Carpet is a fabric of typical construction: woven, pile, cut or loop pile, machine made or handmade, knotted or tufted. The Indian Carpet Industry is an age-old Art and Craft (A&C) industry focused towards carpet manufacture. The intervention of Technology and Economy (T&E) has become a pre-requisite for carpet industry. The combination of these two engines (AC & TE) is possible effectively through institutional Research & Development programmes.

The product acquires subjective and objective properties to meet the anticipated requirements. In meeting anticipated requirements covering cost-effective aspects; various factors play their own role. The factors include: types of carpet (structure), materials, color, motif, design and chemical processing.

Observation revealed that handmade carpets in general are wool focused from material point of view. The types include: majorly hand knotted, hand tufted and rod aided hand knotting (Tibetan/ Indo-Nepali). Handmade carpet industry is important from socio-economic point in the international perspective in general, and in Indian context in particular. Inspite of the fact that India occupies the number one position globally in terms of *'value & volume'* (UVR); but it lies almost in the bottom position in term of 'unit value realization. There could be various reasons for very low UVR, but it is obvious that by better understanding of wool and chemical processing it could enhance UVR for the benefit of this sector. With this background the issues and prospects, related to wool and chemical processing of carpet, have been discussed.

Background

Introduction of Wool

Wool fibre and wool industry are very important in the overall textile industrial scenario. The importance lies on the facts of superiority in attributes and potential for diversified application. In spite of above facts, opportunities exist for further exploitation and necessity to combat the threats like improvement in availability of qualitative and quantitative graded wool especially in Indian perspective. The *'quality work life'* (QWL) of the farmers and shepherds also needs improvement.

Retrospective view on wool

Wool is a natural fibre for the benefit of human being. It is a green fibre in true sense due to sustainability and biodegradability. The advantage of environment friendliness; a sought after requirement, is present in wool besides many other inherent benefits. Thus, historically wool could earn a quality reputation for global value-chain members including consumers.

Performance is critical in textiles due to requirement of multi-capability of any fibre, which can easily be met by wool as evident from its 10000 years' legacy. Wool is well known for meeting, adopting and fulfilling complex requirements. The practical attributes of wool i.e. it is grown, not made; the typical physical cell-structure permitting natural breathing, unique property to absorb and release humidity ensures comfort. The fibre is naturally safe; besides high water and nitrogen content make it naturally flame retardant without the need for additional chemical treatments as otherwise needed for any other such fibres. The wool fibre has the capability to absorb unhealthy carbon particles in the atmosphere (a better environment provider). Wool is a *'dynamic versatile original smart fibre'* utilized in many sectors like apparel and fashion, activewear, flooring and interiors, aviation, architecture, manufacturing, medical use and protective apparel.

Wool has unique attributes which have been depicted pictorially below:

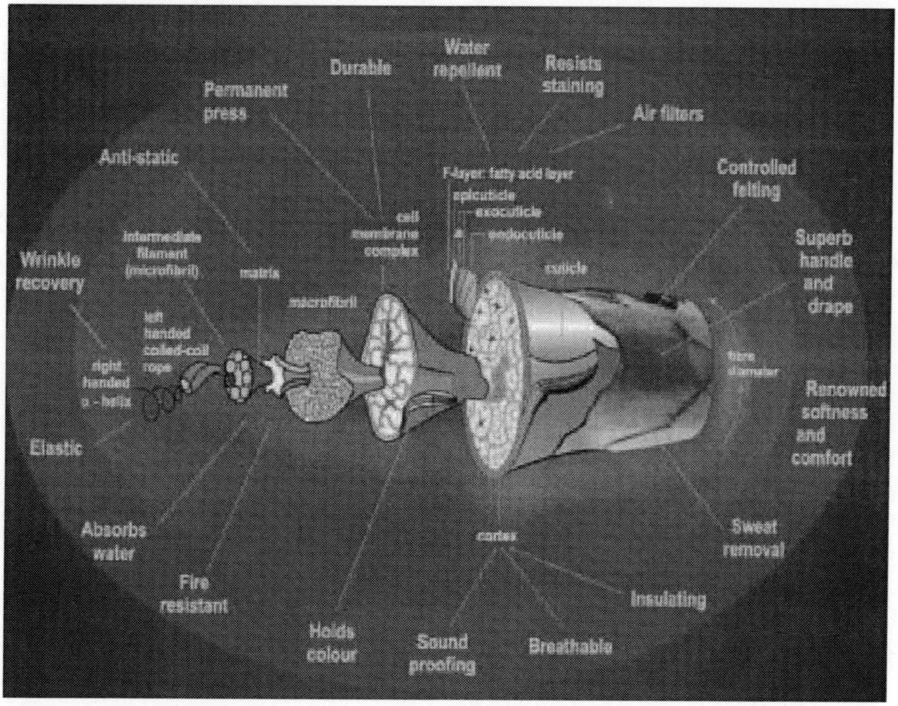

Wool in carpet perspective

Wool is an animal fibre forming the protective covering of the sheep. It is an organized structure growing from a root situated in the middle layer of the skin of the sheep.

(i) Morphological structure of wool fibre

The three main divisions of wool fibre cross section are summarized as:

Cuticle - the outer most layer composed of flat, plate like cells looking like scales.

Cortex – outer protective layer built with elongated cells lying parallel to the fibre axis.

Medulla – air filled cell wall or hollow channel along the length of fibre. Sometimes medulla is not found even in some coarser wool fibre.

(ii) Wool fibre grade used in carpet

The Wool Research Organization of New Zealand (WRONZ) organized a Seminar on 'Carpet Wool & Carpet Manufacturing' in 1978 with an objective to define the technical aspects of wool fibre required for carpet. It has been concluded that an ideal wool carpet should be composed of wool fibre having following properties.

Staple length: 50-125 mm for manufacturing yarn in woolen system and 75-170 mm for semi-worsted system.

Medullation: Higher Medullation caused flattening effect and less resistance to wear in carpet, but a small amount of medullation (2-5 %) in practice) improves certain functional properties (a) Good resiliency, (b) Improved appearance retention and (c) Bulkiness of pile yarn with better cover.

Fibre Diameter: 30-35 micron to provide good handle & bulkiness.

Crimp: Helical with high frequency for bulk & better resilience.

Kemps: Short, white hair like fibres (normally medullated) 4% by weight is considered to be the maximum limit.

Contaminants: Should be free from vegetable matter and other impurities.

Color: Color measurement of grey wool fibre is essential to avoid repeatability of dyeing. Colour is expressed as yellowness (Y-Z) units. For Australian the wool value for yellowness ranges from 7-18 units of (Y-Z).

(iii) Essential properties of carpet wool

Research work reveals that the ideal carpet wool is one that:

- Provide good coverage
- Inhibit deformation of pile and structure
- Inhibit shedding of pile
- Ensure less dropping on carding
- Inhibit matting and flattening of pile
- Have good luster
- Have good dyeability
- Resist to wear and abrasion
- Have good resistance and appearance retention property
- Resist to soiling
- Should be less prone to static generation
- Have good flame retardance properties

Comparison of wool fibre performance rating with other fibres (excluding the influence of carpet structure and finish)

S.N	Properties	Performance Highest			> lowest
1.	Resistance to abrasion	Nylon --	Pp --	Wool Acrylic	Viscose --
2.	Resilience and appearance retention	Wool --	Acrylic --	Nylon --	Pp Viscose
3.	Resistance to soiling	Wool Pp	Viscose --	Acrylic --	Nylon --
4.	Ease of cleaning	Acrylic Pp	Nylon --	Wool Viscose	-- --
5.	Absence of static	-- --	Wool Viscose	Acrylic Pp	Nylon --
6.	Flame retardance	Wool --	-- --	Nylon --	Acrylic Pp
7.	Ease of dyeing (therefore choice of colours)	Wool Nylon	Acrylic --	-- --	Pp Pp

Manufacturing of woolen carpet

India, being the premier *'Carpet producer (in quantity)'* country of the world, consumes about 85-90% of the total quantity of wool used in the non-approval sector. This amount of wool is mostly used in manufacturing carpet of hand knotted and tufted types.

(i) Raw material

Warp- Folded cotton yarn

Weft (pile) -Woolen yarn

(ii) Broad Classification of Handmade Carpet

Hand Knotted (Persian, Tibetan etc.)

Hand Tufted.

Washing/ chemical processing of woolen carpet

Experience data on washing/ chemical processing of carpet based on field survey is reproduced below. One can understand the prevailing washing conditions including use of chemicals and its dosage.

Step No.	Chemicals and Auxiliaries	Following Parameters			
		Reporter 1	Reporter 2	Reporter 3	Reporter 4
1.	Water (Normal Water)	Cold wash (temperature-20 to 30^{0}C for 10 Minutes)	Cold wash (temperature-20 to 30^{0}C for 10 Minutes)	Cold wash (temperature-20 to 30^{0}C for 10 Minutes)	Cold wash (temperature-20 to 30^{0}C for 10 Minutes)
2.	Sulphuric Acid + Bleaching powder	100gm/m^2 100gm/m^2 (Treated Temperature 20 to 30^{0}C for 30 Minutes)	100gm/m^2 100gm/m^2 (Treated Temperature 20 to 30^{0}C for 30 Minutes)	Bleaching powder – 2 to 4^{0}tw (temperature 20 to 30^{0}C for 30 Minutes)	100gm/m^2 100gm/m^2 (Treated Temperature 20 to 30^{0}C for 30 Minutes)
3.	Water (Normal Water)	Cold wash (temperature-20 to 30^{0}C for 10 Minutes)	Cold wash (temperature-20 to 30^{0}C for 10 Minutes)	Cold wash (temperature-20 to 30^{0}C for 10 Minutes)	Cold wash (temperature-20 to 30^{0}C for 10 Minutes)
4.	Caustic Soda	100gm/m^2 (Treated Temperature 20 to 30^{0}C for 30 Minutes)	100gm/m^2 (Treated Temperature 20 to 30^{0}C for 30 Minutes)	Caustic Soda – 2 to 4^{0}tw (temperature 20 to 30^{0}C for 30 Minutes)	100gm/m^2 (Treated Temperature 20 to 30^{0}C for 30 Minutes)
5.	Water (Normal Water)	Cold wash (temperature-20 to 30^{0}C for 10 Minutes)	Cold wash (temperature-20 to 30^{0}C for 10 Minutes)	Cold wash (temperature-20 to 30^{0}C for 10 Minutes)	Cold wash (temperature-20 to 30^{0}C for 10 Minutes)
6.	Sulphuric acid	50gm/m^2 (Treated for neutralization, Temperature 20 to 30^{0}C for 10 Minutes)	50gm/m^2 (Treated for neutralization, Temperature 20 to 30^{0}C for 10 Minutes)	Instead of sulphuric acid using acetic acid 50 to 100gm/m^2 (Treated for neutralization, Temperature 20 to 30^{0}C for 10 Minutes)	50gm/m^2 (Treated for neutralization, Temperature 20 to 30^{0}C for 10 Minutes)
7.	Water (Normal Water)	Cold wash (temperature-20 to 30^{0}C for 10 Minutes)	Cold wash (temperature-20 to 30^{0}C for 10 Minutes)	Cold wash (temperature-20 to 30^{0}C for 10 Minutes)	Cold wash (temperature-20 to 30^{0}C for 10 Minutes)
8.	Silicon softner (Like-Cirapon-PSLS, Ciba Soft)	25 to 50 gm/m^2 For softening they are using with acetic acid for 10 minutes temperature 20 to 30^{0}C	25 to 50 gm/m^2 For softening they are using with acetic acid for 10 minutes temperature 20 to 30^{0}C	25 to 50 gm/m^2 For softening they are using with acetic acid for 10 minutes temperature 20 to 30^{0}C	25 to 50 gm/m^2 For softening they are using with acetic acid for 10 minutes temperature 20 to 30^{0}C
9.	Hydro extraction	They are following manual procedure	They are using Hydro Extractor for 10 to 15 minutes	They are following manual procedure	They are following manual procedure
10.	Drying	Sun light / Dryer	Sun light / Dryer	Sun light/ Dryer	Sun light / Dryer

N.B: (i) Water proportion – 1: 50 and (ii) Step no. 2 and 4 are repeated according to the quality of carpet

Quality measurements on woolen carpet

Several testing procedures have been developed by WRNOZ, IWS etc. for evaluation of quality of woolen carpets. The different parameters for woolen carpet testing are summarized as below:

(i) Surface appearance

Pile fibre

- Assess whether the pile fibre is soft, harsh, kempy, hairy or lustrous.
- Assess by rubbing the pile surface whether the pile fibres are easily removed.
- Feel and smell the surface pile layer to detect the possible presence of excessive lubricants or additives from processing.

Texture and surface definition

- Observe the surface pile layer and assess whether the surface is evenly and cleanly finished and if the tufts are well defined.
- Observe whether untwisting of the yarns has occurred or is likely to occur. Semi-worsted yarns in particular are more likely to untwist than woolen yarns.

(ii) Design and colour combination

- Observe whether there are light or dark colours together or colours where cross staining in likely to occur.
- Observe whether there are large areas of pale colour, which are likely to be affected by soiling.
- Observe whether there are colours of similar hues, side by side, which are likely to become viewed as a single colour when flattened in use.
- Observe whether there are stripes resulted from yarn of different dye lots being used or from poor blending prior to carding and spinning.

Issues and Prospects

From the above background and field experience the issues and prospects that have emerged are mentioned as under:

Issues

Continuous thrust in research and development programmes can substantially push the potential of wool fibre further. Attempts are required to open all the doors in future that will safeguard the industry, which is a major worldwide employer providing multiple benefits to people in terms of products and remuneration. Despite the said potential of the wool fibre; consumers and planners (industry and government) continue to be unaware of the health and safety benefits that the wool can offer. As a result of subsequent low wool prices, wool farming is becoming less attractive not only globally but in the Indian context too. Therefore, wool industry needs support to combat such threats.

Authentic research and development work on the chemical processing aspect of the carpet is scanty. Chemical processing aspect of the carpet involves use of various chemicals as factors mentioned in the background. Besides unmentioned the other important factors that are involved are: mechanical part like throwing of liquor/ material liquor ratio, manual agitation and squeezing/ scrapping. The global concerns pertaining to climate change and conservation of energy related aspects have so far not been methodically and scientifically touched to contribute to the global sociology. The subjective and objective properties of the finished carpet neither can be predicted nor achieved to the desired extent due to prevailing unscientific approach.

Prospects

The facts of the wool industry are that it employs millions of people and has the potential to employ further. Wool it is natural, safe and healthy fibre and must be considered as strength as well as opportunity for further exploitation. The salient features includes: lower embodied energy, security of supply, lower transportation footprint, long-life, 100% biodegradable, low-carbon impact should become the subject of Research and Development programmes.

All necessary steps must be taken in the interest of global wool in general and Indian wool industry in particular so that involved farmers are attracted to produce quantitative, qualitative and well-graded fibre. This move itself can make the wool industry more export-oriented, less import-dependent and overall the industry can derive demographic dividend due to the availability of youths. Such youths can be provided with the *'Modular Employable Skill'* (MES) pertaining to the industry in such a manner that envisaged benefits can be obtained leading to demographic dividend not demographic disaster.

Better understanding of the chemical processing aspects of chemicals and its way of use in carpet processing aspect will lead to production of cost-effective carpet. The understanding is possible through methodical research in such a manner that desired anticipated requirement is met. Therefore, there is a scope for better understanding of the science & technology related to wool and chemical processing in carpet perspective and transfer of technology.

Conclusions

- For exploring the opportunities available in wool and chemical processing, institutions should develop knowledge bank using available publications
- The developmental activity should be backed by design of experiment identifying contributing factors and responses.
- The cost-effectiveness should be borne in mind and user should be in a position to evaluate the same in their perspective.

References

Choobineh, Alireza., Hosseini, Mostafa., Lahmi, Mohammadali., Sharifian, Saeed and Arash Hashemi Hosseini, A. H. 2004. Weaving posture analyzing system (WEPAS): Introduction and validation, International Journal of Industrial Ergonomics 34 (2): 139-147.

Bhattacharyya, S. 2000. Fiber properties and impact on carpet. In: Proceedings of the Skill cum Technological Upgradation Program IICT and SIDBI India, 28-31 August.

Bhattarcharyya, B. and Sahoo, L. The Indian Carpet Industry, 167.

Botkin, M. P., Field Ray, A., Johnson, C. LeRoy. 1988. Sheep and Wool: Science, Production and Management, Prentice Hall.

Edwards. C. 1975. The Persian carpet, Duckworth, pp 284.

First World Conference on Handmade Carpets, 2003. Carpet Export Promotion Council, 4-5 November, New Delhi, pp. 39-113.

Goswami, K. K. 2003. Handmade Carpet Industry - Intervention of Technology and Economy to Art and Craft, First World Conference, 4-5 November, CEPC, New Delhi, pp 75-77.

Goswami, K. K., Bhar, P. K. and Mishra, Anu. 2006, Natural Fibers: Vision 2020, 8-9 December, NISTI, New Delhi.

Goswami, K. K. 2009. Education: Training for Employability and Employment (TEE) in Textile Perspective. Seminar, Lucknow Management Association, Lucknow.

Goswami, K. K. Wool in carpet perspective. Seminar, Government College of Engineering and Textile Technology, Behrampore.

Goswami, K. K, Malik, R. K and Jana, D. 2005. Internal document, IICT Bhadohi India, pp. 17-20.

Goswami, K. K. 2006. Backing of hand tufted carpet: A new substitution technique, Indian Textile Journal (November) 27-29.

Goswami, K. K. 2009. Advances in Carpet Manufacture, Woodhead Publishing Limited, pp. 182-268.

Goswami, K. K. 2009. Advances in Carpet Manufacture, Woodhead Publishing Limited, pp. 138-172.

Goswami, K. K. and Bhar, P. K. 2008. Predicting and improving carpet pile stability, AATCC Review Vol. 8(10): 30 – 34.

Goswami, K. K. and Technical Team. 2006. Viscose in handmade carpets. Asian Textile Journal (May) 74-78

Goswami. K. K., Malik, R. K. and Jana, D. 2005. Natural colour for carpet wool and silk, Project Report IICT Bhadohi, pp. 55-57.

Gulrajni, M. L. and Gupta, D. 2003. Dyeing of natural dyes on carpet wool and silk. November, IIT, New Delhi, pp. 1-90.

Innovation, Vol. 7, July 2007, AATCC Review, 17.

IWTO Marketing Information. 2006. IWTO, Brussels, Belgium; Courtesy communication by Mrs G P Rane, Deputy Director, WRA India.

Khanna, J. K. 1986. Local Words Dictionary, Silver Jubilee Special, Bhadohi AICMA, February pp. 65-69.

Khosrow, S. 2003. First World Conference on Handmade Carpets, 4-5 November, CEPC, New Delhi, pp. 91- 94.

Kundell, L. 1983. Rug making, Vol 10, Carpet E World,pp 174 – 177.

Lewis, D. M .1992. Wool Dyeing. Society of Dyes and Colorists, pp 204-220.

NCEA News. 2007. Carpet Journal from Nepal, No. 11, January, pp.48-64.

Presentation to the World Bank's AFTPS Group. 2006. 29 November, OTF Group (www.ccca.org.af) Courtesy email, 12/113.

Shenai, V. A. 1983. Chemistry of Dyes and Principles of Dyeing, II Ed, Sevak Publications.

Simpson, W. S. and Crawshaw, G. H. 2002. Wool: Science and Technology. The Textile Institute, Wool Head Publishing Limited, pp 61-74.

Srivastava, S. and Goswami, K. K. 2007. The Innovation Journal: The Public Sector Innovation Journal, Article 5, Volume 12(2).

Wail, M., Van Riel, M. P., Snijders, C. J. and Van Wingerden, J. P. 1991. The effect on sitting posture of a desk with a 10° inclination for reading and writing, 34.5, 575-584, De Ergonomics.

Wattal, H. K. 1983. Art of carpet weaving, Vol 5 (63), Carpet E World, pp 63 – 66.

❑❑❑

42

Advances in Engineering of Carpet Yarn

S.M. Ishtiaque, Kushal Sen and Ajay Kumar
Department of Textile Technology, Indian Institute of Technology, Delhi-110016

Introduction

In the global fibre production, wool account for only 4-5% of the share. Even then it has held status of luxury fibre due its unique and aesthetic properties. The medium (24-30μ) and coarse grade wool (above 30μ) account for 48% of the global wool production and are used for furnishing fabrics, carpets, upholstery, blankets and other miscellaneous items. India produces about 50 million kg of raw wool of different grades and contributes to 2% in the global wool production. About 35.0 million kg of indigenous and nearly double the quantity of carpet grade imported wool is used by the Indian carpet industries for manufacturing high areal density, resilient and lustrous carpets which have great demand in export oriented markets.

The compressional behaviour of carpet pile termed as *'carpet resiliency'* is the ability of carpet pile fibres to resist the distorting effect of traffic and recovery after compression. In the process of pile yarn spinning for carpets, the different fibre components are mixed homogenously to obtain the desired lustrous, compressive, resilient and durable carpet characteristics. The homogeneous mixing distributes the component fibres uniformly in the yarn cross-section. In such yarns the bending rigidity of different fibre components is not fully exploited in the compressional behaviour of carpet pile.

Since, the position of the fibre in yarn geometry is very critical factor to assess the yarn stiffness. The position the different stiffness in fibres in layered yarn structure allows full exploitation of the fibre characteristics i.e. bending rigidity to improve the compressional behaviour of carpet. This may be achieved through formation of multi-layered yarn structure. It was observed that plying of yarn can improved the yarn characteristics relative to single yarn of the same linear density. The two roving feed siro yarn has further advantage of lower cost of production and better yarn quality than plied yarn. The double roving feed yarn was observed to be more compact and can withstand better compressional stresses. The bi-component core sheath yarn showed high yarn strength than the homogeneous blended single yarn (Sawhney et al., 1992). However, meagre information is available about core-sheath yarn formation by double roving feed spinning. Sarvaran (2008) attempted to produce such yarn through modified siro spinning method with long staple polyester in core covered by short staple cotton sheath for getting two layered yarn structure. In the present paper, brief account of different spinning systems used for carpet yarn formation are discussed in detail. Production of multilayered yarn (i.e. three layered yarn) on ring spinning system by siro spinning method with suitable modifications has also been presented.

Yarn formation

Woolen Spinning

Woolen spinning system is a highly versatile system. It is capable to spun yarn from any fibrous material or their blends. The yarn prepared on this system is coarser one, mainly utilized in carpets, hand knitting, upholstery, blankets, durries and other products of similar usage. The number of processes involved in carpet yarn formation is less compared to other systems of yarn manufacturing i.e. opening, blending, carding and spinning only. For manufacturing quality carpet yarns; batch blending and oiling are two important pre-carding processes to minimize cost, homogeneous blending of different fibre components (varying in fibre diameter and medullated fibre proportion), fibre breakage and static electricity in carding. Two sets of woolen cards usually perform the carding action. Besides the usual objectives of carding in other spinning system, woolen carding has to deliver the material suitable for direct spinning on ring frame by means of condenser fitted with finisher carding unit. The condenser performs the operations viz. splitting of carded web, condensing the web by rubbing and spooling of roving. The yarn fineness is mostly decided at the carding stage and only a marginal draft is imparted to the carded roving. The linear density of carpet yarn is about 1-6 Nm. The twisting and winding are the operations performed on ring frame in woolen yarn formation. A very low amount of twist is imparted to the yarn in range of 78-410 twists per meter as per the softness or hardness required in the final yarn.

Composite yarn spinning

The changing market trend and desired performance and functional end uses of the carpets compel the researcher to develop and impart these characteristics in the carpets. This can be achieved by surface modification through chemical means or modifying the yarn structure itself. The characteristics imparted by chemical means have the problem of functional durability due to washing or strength. Thus, it is better to impart these desired functional and performance properties to the possible extent by structural modifications of yarn. The process is started with homogeneous blending of different fibre component. It was found that the fibre blending was not completely fulfilling the expectation to the desired level. Plying the yarn of different characteristics can improve the desirable strength by filament yarns and comfort through the natural fibre yarns, but at the additional cost of plying. In continuation further efforts are made with Siro, modified Siro, and Dref spinning systems. In later systems, the prepared yarn has two components in core-sheath structure; one component forming the yarn core and other its sheath. The core component is for exploiting the fibre characteristics to the maximum possible extent in the functionality of end products.

SIRO Spun Yarn

CSIRO invented a new spinning system of two-strand spinning on conventional ring frame i.e. Sirospun. The method enables a special structure yarn to be made directly with the technological process, corresponding to the manufacture of normal single-ply yarn with the difference that the two rovings are spun simultaneously and then the two strands are twisted around each other in the single operation as usual in ring spinning machine. The system is mainly developed for woolen yarn spinning where bulk and slip resistance (plush sector) are important. The productivity of two-ply woolen yarn could be increased by 40% through this system and thus proportionally reducing the cost of production (Friederich et al., 1991). Being advantageous in two-strand spinning, Siro method is also incorporated in worsted and cotton yarn spinning systems. A resultant two ply yarn has either ZZ twist or SS twist whereas in contrast the conventional two ply yarn normally has S twist over Z twist in single ply. It is somewhat more smoother and have different abrasion properties can substantially reduce the hairiness problem with single ply yarns. In Siro yarn spinning, the yarn tension in the area of spinning triangle is relatively high which results to higher frictional contacts between fibres. Fibres are tightly placed in the yarn structure hence, yarn posses higher strength than the yarn of same linear density. The two-strand spinning method is not only cost-effective due to shortening of engineering process but also improves the yarn quality.

Two stand spinning on cotton system

The doubling of feed material at any stage of spinning process improves the evenness of delivered material viz. lap in card, drawn sliver in draw frame. Balasubramaniam and Trivedi (1973) investigated effect of roving size and doubling of short staple (cotton) strands at ring frame. They observed that the finer ingoing roving hank contributed to spinning performance. The doubling of feed strands improved the strength and mass irregularities in the final yarn for both the coarse and fine mixing, though the gain in yarn properties are marginal in case of fine mixings. The end breakage rate with double feed was found to increase for finer yarn count and higher spindle speed.

The two strand spaced polyester-cotton yarn had 14% higher strength than the similar blend yarn produced with the same rovings combined and drafted together in the spinning zone. The yarn structure changes the fibre slippage, hence the distribution of tensile strain between the component fibres in the yarn (Sawhney et al., 1988). The new distribution improved the load distribution in the component fibres inspite of their differences in stiffness. The compaction of the segregated fibre component in yarn cross-section improved the yarn strength. The higher packing density of siro yarn is one of the reasons for higher strength of siro yarn than ring yarn. The packing density increased up to an optimum strand spacing due to increase in the actual area of fibres in yarn cross-section inspite of increasing twist angle. On further increase of strand spacing, the twist angle dominated the effect of strand spacing. This resulted in reduction in the number of fibres in yarn of the same cross-section and thus caused decrease in the yarn packing density and finally the yarn strength (Ishtiaque et al., 1993).

Some other researchers have also reported that the yarn properties i.e. strength, elongation, mass irregularities abrasion resistance and hairiness of spaced strand yarn are better than zero spaced strands yarn and two ply yarn (Gupte and Chiplunkar, 1985; Sharma and Bhatnagar, 1989;

Subramaniam et al., 1989). The spaced strand yarn was more even in diameter and was tidy. The two strands are consolidated in the adjacent array and occupy half of the circle. The zero spaced single yarn on same spinning system though circular, but one strand is embraced on the other strand, while two strands in two-ply yarn are twisted in helix form and lie adjacently. The overall cross-sectional shape of two-ply yarn is oval. At constant linear density and twist level, the spaced strand yarn was better than the zero spaced single yarn for all yarn quality parameters (Sun and Cheng, 2000). It has been further investigated that, spaced strand siro yarn was stronger, less hairy and extensible. It also has higher abrasion resistance than two ply yarn of all yarn counts. Yarn evenness and imperfections, for coarser siro yarn is quite comparable to two ply yarn but finer yarns are less uniform and have more imperfections. Subramaniam and Natrajan (1990) measured the frictional properties (viz. yarn-to-yarn and yarn-to metal of two strand single, siro and two- ply yarns) by using the stick-slip method. They found that both the frictional properties of siro yarn were better than the single and two-ply yarn. The increase in strand spacing in siro yarn was also observed to increase the frictional properties that are postulated to increase the adhesion component of friction. Being smoother, yarn provides more area of contact because of better trapping of surface fibres in yarn periphery.

In two-strand spinning, the spinning geometry is affected by roving spacing, twist factor and spindle speed. The effect of the individual factor is difficult to estimate as they are interrelated to each other. Liu *et al.* (2007) studied the effect of strand spacing on siro yarn they reported that the increase in strand spacing results to increase in angle between the strands in the spinning zone which tends to increase in tension and torque on individual strands. Thus, increase in strand spacing results an increase in torque and ultimately twist in the strands at wider spaced strand. Plate (1983) and Chang and Sun (1998) also reported similar findings on roving spacing in two strands spinning. The effect of twist factor on spinning geometry was studied by Miao et al. (1993). They reported that with the increase in twist factor, the displacement of the convergent points toward nip of delivery roller and the angle between the strand is enlarged and cause shortening of strand. This results in increase in strand tension. The shortening of strand tends to increase the number of twists in the individual strand.

Since the twist in the two strands spinning above the convergence point is false twist; hence the individual strand rotates the torque of twist about its axis and move toward convergence point. A number of loose fibre ends on strands surface are striking to the surface of the neighbouring strand, which restrict them to rotate further. As the strand enters in the composite yarn structure, these protruding ends lie at a considerable angle to the mean fibre orientation and get trapped between the two strands in the resultant yarn and contributing to the quality of the final yarn. After development of two-strand spinning process, numerous experimental studies on cotton spinning system investigated the effect of spinning parameters, mainly the strand spacing, twist, drafting force and spindle speed on the resultant yarn quality.

Improvement in hairiness and abrasion resistance of siro yarn has been observed with increase in strand spacing (Chang and Sun, 1998; Liu et al., 2007; Plate, 1983) .The hairiness was improved to an optimum level of roving spacing and afterwards it was increased marginally. At wider strand spacing, the fibres in the strand spent more time in the convergence zone. This caused fibres to form more hairs and any other unfavourable conditions, such as less fibre cohesion, or a greater centrifugal force that further assisted in the formation of hairs. There also improvement in yarn hairiness at higher spindle speeds at lower twist levels and there was a critical-twist region i.e. TM ($tpc\times tex^{1/2}$) of 55 up to which the yarn hairiness was increased. On further increase in the twist level there was decrease in hairiness (Subramanium and Mohamed, 1991).

Plate (1983) found marginal increase in strength with increasing spinning parameters for woolen yarns. Whereas, Liu et al. (2007) in his theoretical analysis observed that there was increase in yarn strength due to increase in twist of strands in convergence point in two strand spinning method up to an optimum decrease of yarn strength for 12 mm strand spacing. Whereas for two strand spinning on cotton system, Chang and Sun (1998) observed that for optimum level of strand spacing or strand twist, the strength of resultant yarn was initially increased with strand spacing or strand twist. They observed that strand spacing of 9 mm and twist multiplier of (37-38 $tpc\times tex^{1/2}$) were optimum. Beyond this the strand emerging from front roller nip were found longer and tension on the strand was so great that the convergence point shifted sideways causing unequal stretching in the strand with adverse effect on the strength. Balasubramanian and Trivedi (1973) observed decrease in yarn strength with the increase in strand spacing contrary to finding of Plates (1983). Salohtra (1987) concluded that increase in yarn strength with strand spacing up to a certain level and longer fibre have higher optimum limit of strand spacing. Subramaniuam et al. (1989) reviewed and postulated that in two-strand spinning, the dominating factor between fibre slippage and strand twist depended on the fibre length. When the longer fibres are processed the twist factor is dominating whereas with short staples the fibre slippage is dominating at lower twist level. Below 55 TM increase in the strand spacing resulted in the decrease of the resultant yarn strength. The yarn strength and its CV% were found to deteriorate with increase in spindle speed. They also observed an increase in yarn even though suppressed by doubling of the strands after drafting in double roving feed and deduced that the irregularity wascaused due to lack of fibre control in the main drafting zone. The wavelength of irregularity in finer strand, introduced at the break-drafting zone, will become longer because drafting occurred in the main drafting zone.

Layered yarn

With respect to core sheath yarns, Isthiaque and Agarwal (2000) observed that apart from raw material properties, the geometrical arrangement of fibres within the yarn structure significantly influence the mechanical properties of the yarn. Similar results have also been reported by Balasubramanian (1992), Lord (1987) and Zhu et al. (1993). They also concluded that the strength of such yarn structure largely depends on the magnitude of the radial pressure exerted by the sheath on the core and on the frictional characteristics of both core and sheath fibres. Sawhney et al. (1992) observed that for core-sheath structure polyester cotton yarn on modified ring spinning system with polyester as core component was fully covered by sheath component cotton fibres. The yarn strength of that yarn is found to be greater than conventional blended yarn though yarn unevenness and imperfection is higher but with in acceptable limit. Where as with core sheath structure DREF-III yarn the core and sheath components have different stress-strain behaviour for applied stresses. The core component shows an initial very stiff rise and then a sudden drop in the stress value, due to more axially oriented fibres and low twist in the core. In core-sheath DREF-III yarn the core component individually shares a very small proportion of yarn tenacity. Sheath component is the major contributor and the interaction of core and sheath contributed significantly in the yarn tenacity (Das and Ishtiaque, 2004).

An attempt has been made by Sarvaran (2008) to produce three ply yarn structure through modified Siro spinning method, with long staple polyester in core, covered by short staple cotton sheath fibres. Multi strand spinning in modified ring spinning system and Dref core yarn spinning is able to improve the yarn characteristics. The present effort for different component yarn spinning is only up to core-sheath yarn structure, mainly exploiting the fibre strength and moisture characteristics for strength and comfort. The other fibre properties such as fibre diameter, bending rigidity, crimp etc. have distinct effect on yarn and the product there off i.e. carpet. Thus further efforts are required to produce multilayer yarn structure to improve the performance and functionality of the end products.

Approaches for multi-layer yarn formation

Materials

To position the different stiffness, fibres in layered yarn structure were used for fully exploiting the fibre characteristics i.e. bending rigidity of wool derived from three different native breeds. The selected wool samples were quite different in their fibre diameter, medullated fibre proportion and extent of medullation within the fibre. The stiffer Malpura wool was placed in the inner layer, medium stiffness Magra wool in the second layer and Chokla wool in the outer layer of the engineered yarn. The different fibres were analyzed for their fibre properties and fibre cross section are given in Table 1.

Table 1. Results of fibre physical characteristics

S. No.	Sheep Breed	Mean Fibre Diameter (μm)	Proportion of Medullation (%)	Fibre tenacity (g/tex)	Bending rigidity(B) x 10^{-2} (g.cm^2/fibre)	Mean length (mm)
1.	Malpura	48.3	90.5	15.81	3.17	57.59
2.	Magra	31.5	30.4	16.25	2.64	74.96
3.	Chokla	30.4	38.4	14.76	2.54	62.59

Different Methods of Yarn formation

The spinning of control and multilayer yarns was carried out on short staple ring frame LR G5/1 with 3-3 drafting system. In the process of producing multilayer yarns firstly two layer roving were prepared at Speed frame LF 1400 A. The two strand control with 10 mm of strand spacing and multilayer yarns were produced with modified siro spinning method with suitable guides and attachment, the methodology detailed below:

Formation of two layer roving at speed frame

The inner two layer of multilayer yarn structure was prepare during preparatory process of roving formation at speed frame by sandwiching the roving of inner most layer between the two sliver for the second layer. All the three strands are drafted collectively at the drafting system of the speed frame and the two layer roving was formed as shown in Fig. 1. The prepared roving is then spun into two-layer yarn on ring frame with normal process of yarn formation.

The two layer roving structure was prepared by means of a composite guide consist of two sliver and a roving guide position one over the other as shown in Fig.2. The guides were in a position such a manner that the roving guides were placed in between the sliver guides. The lower sliver guide and roving guide were adjoined at the exit for précised placement of roving for inner layer at the centre to the bottom sliver. However, the top sliver guide was off-set by 3 mm from the centre line of bottom sliver guide in the direction of roving twist for better covering of core fibres.

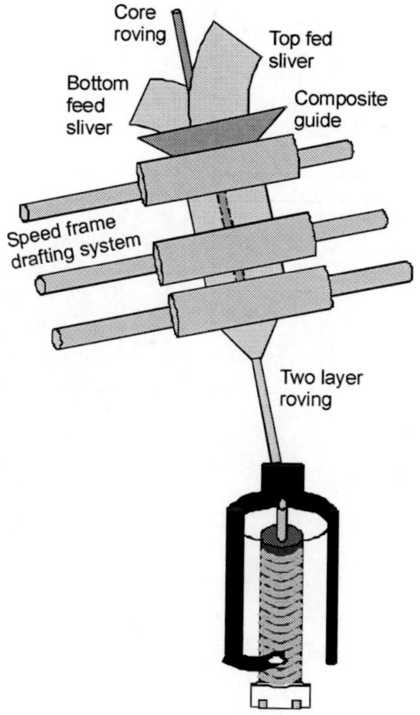

Fig. 1. Schematic diagram of two layer roving formation

Formation of multilayer yarn

Three different approaches were used to prepare the multilayer yarn on ring frame are follows:

(i) Two rovings on both side to form the third layer and two layered roving at middle to form the core and second layer of the Z-twisted resultant yarn.

(ii) Two rovings on both sides to form the third layer and two layered Z-twisted yarn at the middle from the front roller nip of the drafting rollers to form the core and sheath layer of the resultant multilayer yarn. To observe the effect of twist in the resultant yarn with two layered Z-twisted yarn in core. The multilayer yarn was produced with both Z & S twist to the sheath layer.

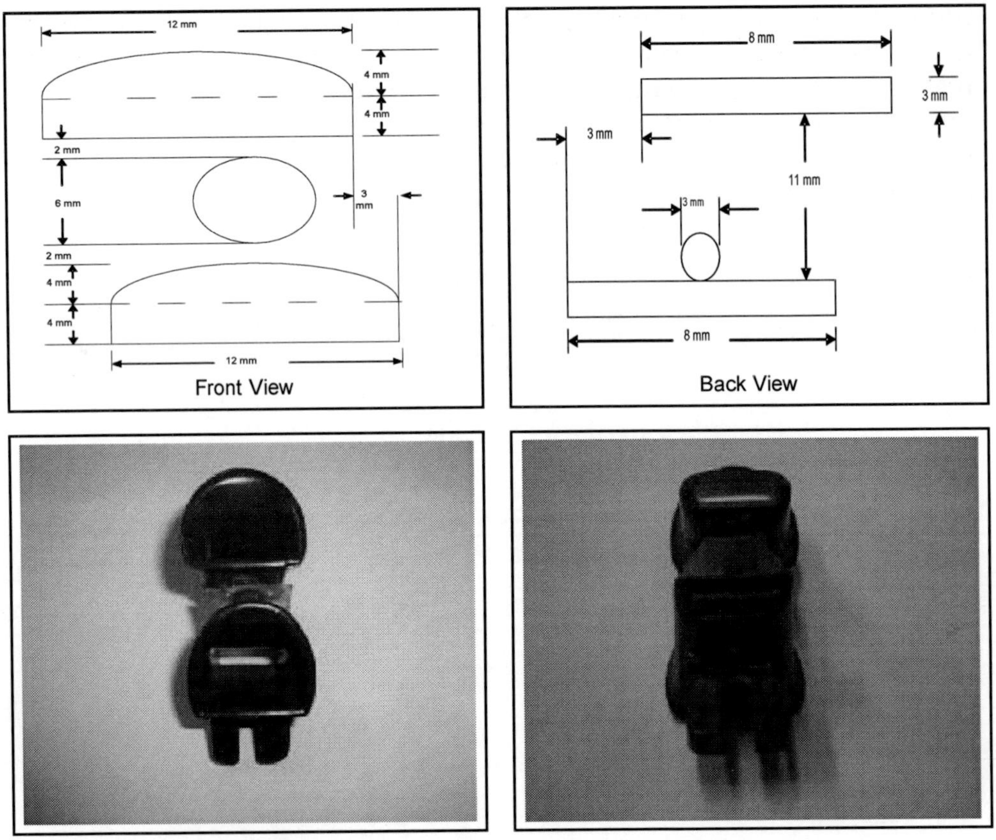

Fig. 2. Guide used in sandwiching the roving between slivers

Formation of multilayer yarn with multi (three) roving feed

The multilayer yarn with multi roving feed was prepared by placing the coarser two layered roving in between the two fine rovings for third layer at rear end of ring frame drafting system. The three strands are collectively drafted and spun to three-layer yarn structure as shown in Fig.3.

A composite guide was used to feed edge roving for final layer of yarn structure with the optimum roving spacing of 5mm from the coarser middle roving, which was comprised of three guides on horizontal plane to feed two fine rovings at both the ends and a coarse roving in the middle. The guides are of circular cross-section at the both ends. The dimensions and design of the guides are given in Fig. 4.

Formation of multilayer yarn with multi strand feed with two layer yarn in middle The multilayer yarn structure with two layer yarn and two fine rovings were produced by placing the two layer yarn at the front roller nip of the drafting system of ring frame and two fine rovings for the third layer at the rear of drafting system. The fine rovings were fed with edge guides of the composite roving guide used for multi roving yarn formation at roving spacing of 10 mm. Whereas the two layer yarn was fed precisely cantered between drafted strands for third layer formation through designed and fabricated attachment which comprised of yarn guide, yarn tensioning device and yarn package holder as shown in Fig.5. The front end of the attachment is a spring loaded disc type yarn-tensioning device, which provides the variable tension to in feed yarn. Two porcelain guides are used, first for guiding the yarn from package to tensioning device and second one for maintaining the position of the fed yarn at the middle of the spinning triangle.

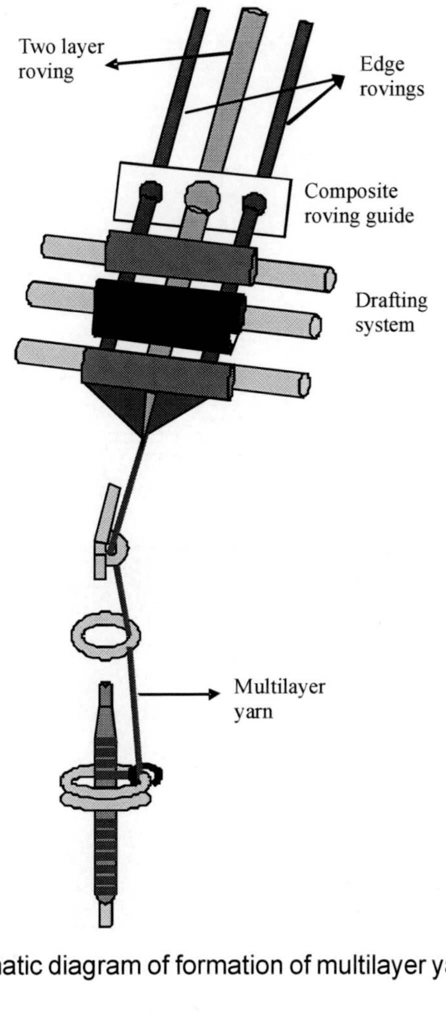

Fig. 3. Schematic diagram of formation of multilayer yarn DR(LRM)

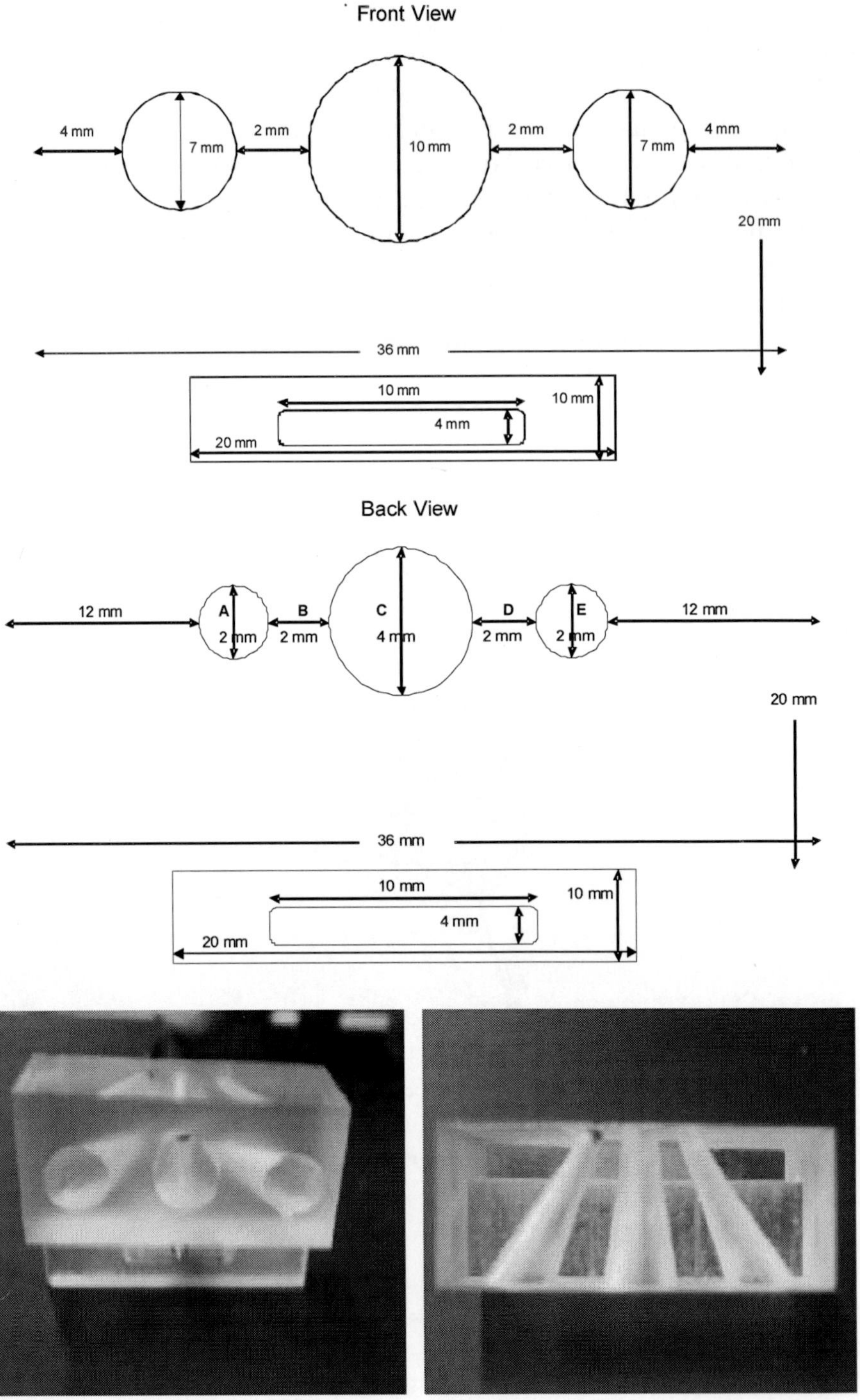

Fig. 4. Guide used in feeding three roving at rear end of ring frame

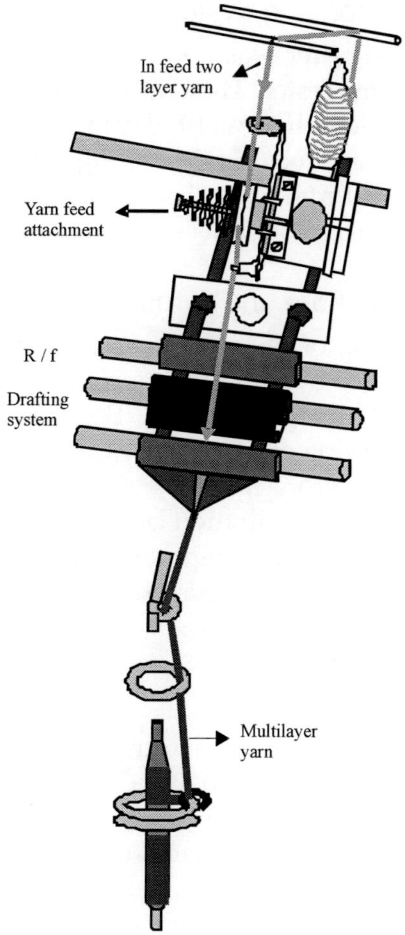

Fig. 5. Schematic diagram of formation of multilayer yarn DR(LYM)Z & DR(LYM)S

Evaluation of yarn

Yarn Irregularity

Uster eveness tester (UT-1) was used to measure the mass irregularities in the yarn. For different prepared yarns 1000-meter length per yarn were analysed at test speed of 50 m/min in range scale of 50 %.

Single yarn strength and elongation

The yarn strength and elongation were measured using Instron 4301 tensile tester. For different prepared yarns 30 tests per yarn were conducted at gauge length of 50 cm and rate of extension of specimen yarn is kept to 300 mm/min.

Yarn bending rigidity& bending hysteresis

The yarn bending rigidity was determined with Kawabata Evaluation System (KES-FB2), bending tester. The sample will be mounted on the system as paper windows, with length to width dimension of 10 ? 200 mm. On each paper window 10 yarns are fixed and bending rigidity of yarns is tested at maximum curvature of 50 mm/cm. The average yarn bending rigidity and hysteresis of the whole group of yarns can be obtained in terms of gf/cm^2.

Cross-section images of fibre and yarns

The radial distribution of fibres in layered yarn structure of engineered yarn produce was observed by different approaches. This was determined by means of Leica Q500 MC Image analyzer. Soft cross-section technique was used in cross-sectional cutting of yarn. The yarn sample first moulded in cork and the yarn cross-section from moulded yarn was cut through razor. The layered yarn structure and distribution of fibres in yarn was visualized on Leica microscope attached with computer and camera. It views the cross-section and displays it on computer screen.

Performance of different carpet yarns

Cross section of different fibres

In cross-sectional analysis only two morphological component of wool fibre viz. cortex and medulla were analysed. The fibres selected for different layers of engineered yarns are quit distinct in their morphological characteristics. The coarsest Malpura wool the experiment for the inner layer of the yarn observed to more intense keratinisation of cortical cells. The proportion of medullated fibre in the fleece ranged from 80-90 %. The extent of medullation is very high to the order of 50 - 90 % and extended to complete length of the fibres in most of the medullated fibres. Thus, the fleece belonged to coarser hairy type wool. Magra sheep wool selected for the second layer of engineered yarns was also found to be of intense keratinisation of the cortical cells but not to the extent as the Malpura wool. The proportion of medullated fibre was ranging from 30-50% and extent of medullation within the fibre was also to lower side ranging from 25- 50%. In the fleece most of the medullated fibres had unbroken thin central strands and interrupted medulla and thus, were categorized as hetro-typical fibres though some of the fibre also had hairy typical medullation. The above-mentioned Malpura and Magra wool fibres in the inner layers of the engineered yarn will better utilized the higher stiffness of these fibres because of higher diameter and medullated fibre proportion in yarn stiffness and improve the mechanical properties viz. compression and resilience of carpet pile. The third layer of engineered yarn was formed by medium to coarse type Chokla wool. Its cross-section analysis was found to lower proportion of medullated fibre in range of 15 - 40 % with less extent of medullation of the order of 5 – 25 %. The medulla is mostly of interrupted and fragmental type and belongs to category of hetro-typical medullation. This fibre will provide the desirable properties of lustre and durability to the carpet pile made from the said engineered yarns.

Yarn cross-sections

Different control yarns with single roving feed SRY and double roving feed DRY to observe the advantage of double roving over single roving yarn. The engineered yarns were prepared through modified siro method as described earlier, yarn DR(LRM) by placing two layer roving for core component of three layer resultant yarn and yarns DR(LYM) Z & DR (LYM) S by placing two layer yarn as core component having Z and S direction of twist in the resultant multilayer yarn respectively.

The results obtained for their unevenness (U %), imperfection breaking strength (g/tex), elongation at break, yarn bending rigidity and bending hysteresis (yarn recovery properties) of differently prepared yarns are given in Table-1. The cross-section images of different control and engineered yarns are shown in Fig. 6.

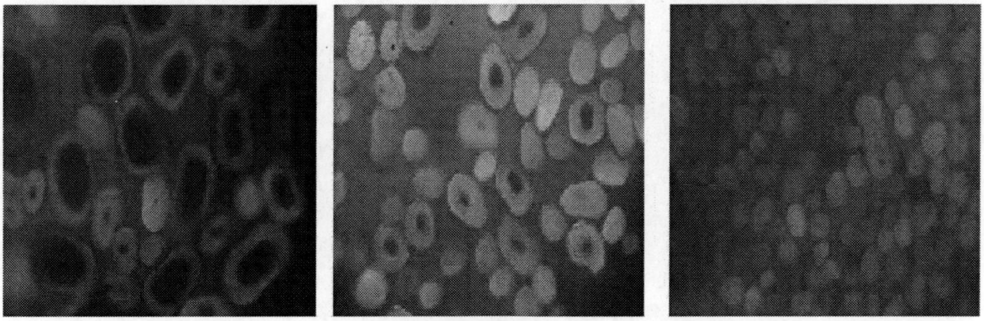

Malpura wool Magrawool Chokla wool

Fig. 6. Cross section images of different fibres used

It was observed that in control yarns being stiffer one the Malpura and Magra wool fibres are placed in to the outer periphery of the yarns. This is because of the migration of the stiffer fibres towards the outer surface of the yarn during yarn formation. In engineered yarn DR(LRM) had more uniform distribution of fibres in yarn cross-section, though the more stiffer Malpura wool fibres succeed in breaking the boundary open structure of third layer. Whereas in engineered yarn with Z twisted two layer yarn as core component, the Z-twisted resultant yarn DR(LYM)Z the core strand became more compact due to Z over Z twist, which is clearly observed by the placement of Malpura and Magra wool fibres in the inner layers of yarn and distinguished from third layer of sheath fibres of Chokla wool which was loosely packed over the core strand. The cross-section of yarn with S-twist in the resultant yarn DR(LYM)S and the reversal of twist direction on Z-twisted core strand caused partial unravelling of twist in the same. The yarn appeared somewhat of uniform fibre distribution similar to the yarn DR(LYM), but in sectorial distribution of fibres in yarn cross-section the more stiffer fibres were concentrated in some sections of yarn cross-section.

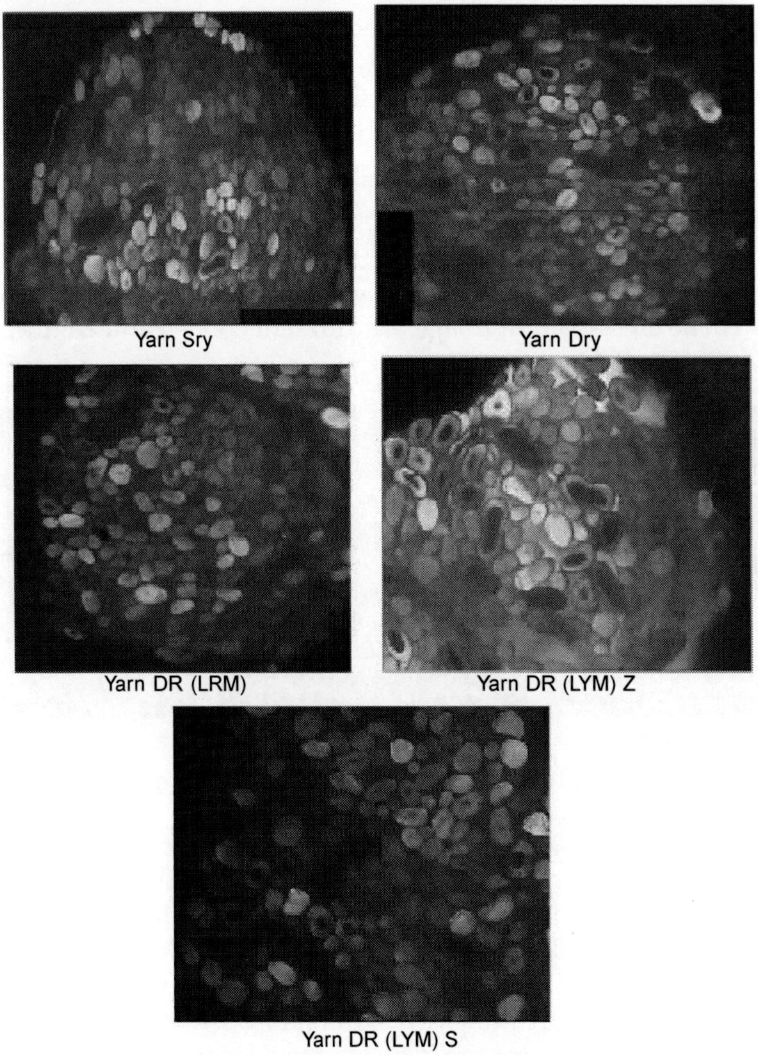

Fig. 7. Yarn cross- section images of different control and engineered yarns

Effect of yarn formation Method

From the uster results, it was observed that the uniformity (U %) of double roving feed control yarn and engineered yarns are better than the single roving yarn (SR). This is attributed to doubling of feed material and change in yarn structure due to fibre slippage because of change in distribution of tensile strain between the component fibres in the individual strand in double roving and engineered yarns prepared by siro and modified siro methods.

The breaking strength results were found highest for yarn DR among differently prepared control and engineered yarns. The higher strength values for the said yarn was attributed to more strand spacing of 10 mm compared to other yarns having 5 mm stand spacing in modified siro methods. This resulted in the increase of angle between the strand in the spinning zone causing higher tension and torque on individual strands. The resultant yarn had compact yarn structure and more uniform fibre distribution in yarn cross-section, so that the constituent fibres in the yarn uniformly shared the applied stresses. The breaking strength engineered yarns also had comparable strength values to the double roving control and were better than the single roving yarns because of the same reasons. Within engineered yarns, yarn DR(LYM)Z possessed lesser strength values, which may attributed to over twisting of the core strand and loose packing of Chokla wool fibres in third layer of the resultant yarn.

The yarn extension results were found to be higher for double roving and engineered yarns. This might be attributed to slippage effect between the strands in double roving yarn and between different layers in layered yarns prepared by modified siro methods. Among the engineered yarns, yarn DR(LYM)Z was observed to higher value for breaking extension. The contraction of the core strand due to over twist may be the reason for this higher extension value at breaking stress.

The bending rigidity of yarn, which may represent the resistance to distortion of pile, was found to improved to the tune of 4 - 25 % for double roving and engineered yarns. The engineered yarn DR(LRM) was observed to have highest value of bending rigidity (4.28×10^{-4} $g.cm^2/tex$) among all the prepared control / engineered yarns. This might be attributed to more compact yarn structure, which offers higher frictional resistance during bending stress. The engineered yarn prepared with two layer yarn as core component was found lesser value of bending rigidity compare to yarn have two layer roving as core component i.e. 25 % and 19 % for Z-twisted and S-twisted engineered yarns, respectively. The reason for which was the lesser coherence between the 2nd and the final layer and loose packing of fibres in third layer of Z-twisted resultant yarn. Open and uneven fibre packing in S-twisted resultant yarn may cause the fibre slippage during the application of bending stresses.

Table 2. Test results of differently prepared yarns

Yarn Sample	Yarn Uniformity (U%)	Breaking Strength (g/tex)	Breaking Strength CV%	Elongation at break (%)	Elongation at break CV%	Bending Rigidity (B) × 10^{-4} gf cm^2/ yarn/tex	Bending Recovery (2HB) × 10^{-4} gf cm^2/ yarn/tex
SRY	26.24	3.73	28.50	12.90	37.72	3.4697	4.5907
DRY	21.98	5.14	25.41	24.13	26.50	3.8585	6.5748
DR(LRM)	21.13	4.78	12.06	18.97	21.41	4.2859	5.0947
DR(LYM)Z	20.02	4.46	14.65	21.54	26.68	3.4294	4.8934
DR(LYM)S	21.19	4.95	11.71	16.80	18.24	3.5985	5.0776

The bending hysteresis value may represent the recovery characteristics of yarn; lower the value better will be the recovery properties. The higher values of bending hysteresis were observed for yarns prepared by siro / modified siro methods compared to single roving control yarn by normal spinning. This may be attributed to compact yarn structure of these yarns, which offers higher frictional resistance between the fibres, and resist the recovery of yarn to its original position. The highest value of bending hysteresis was observed 6.57×10^{-4} g.cm/tex with double roving yarn; the reason for which was more compact yarn structure due to wider strand spacing. The engineered yarns were observed to have lower value of bending hysteresis than double roving yarn due to lesser strand spacing and lesser friction resistance between fibres in different layers.

Conclusions

The double roving control and engineered yarns prepared by siro/ modified siro method of yarn formation produces compact yarn structure. This provides better uniformity, higher yarn strength and bending resistance, which may give better resistance to compression and lesser abrasion losses. But at the same it also exerts higher inter-fibre frictional resistance in the pile yarn at the time pile recovery after the removal of bending stresses during walk over the carpet. The application of suitable finishing agent will improve the recovery after bending of these yarns.

From the above attempt of yarn formation, it was possible to form multilayer yarn structure. The physical characteristics of fibres from different origin can be exploited further for improving the comfort properties of carpet, mainly compressibility and resiliency. The placement of coarser wool fibres of higher diameter and hairy typical medullation near the yarn axis improved the bending rigidity of the prepared yarn. In the course of stress during walking on the carpet made from such yarns most part of the applied energy is stored as potential energy in bent carpet pile. After the removal of compressional stresses, the pile returns back to its original shape with higher recovery properties than the normal carpet yarn. The higher resistance to compression and better recovery after compression of carpet from these engineered yarns resist better the distorting effect of traffic, as pile do not crush much and their surfaces are uniform and pleasing in appearance even under repeated traffic. Thus it provides higher durability, texture retention and comfort properties to the carpets. The formation of carpets from the prepared yarns is under process and their performance and comfort properties will be evaluated.

References

Balasubramanian, N. 1992. Friction spinning a critical review. Indian Journal of Fibre & Textile Research 17: 246-251.

Balasubramanian, N. and Trivedi, G. K. 1973. Effect of feeding conditions at ringframe upon yarn quality and spinning performance. Textile Research Journal 43: 1-9.

Cheng, K. P. S. and Sun, M. N. 1998. Effect of strand spacing and twist multiplier on cotton sirospun yarn. Textile Research Journal 68: 520-527.

Das, A. and Ishtiaque, S.M. 2004. contribution of core and sheath components to the tensile properties of DREF-III yarn. Textile Research Journal 74: 134-139.

Friederich, T., and bersbach, E. 1991. Siro-spinning method- appropriate way to manufacture two-ply yarn. Melliand Textilberichte 72(5): E 125-127.

Gupte, A. A. and Chiplunkar, C. R. 1985. Sirospun yarn on short staple machinery. Journal of Textile Association 46(5): 164-167.

Ishtiaque, S. M., Sharma, I. C. and Sharma, S. 1993. Structural mechanics of siro yarn by microtomy. Indian Journal of Fibre & Textile Research 18: 116-119.

Isthiaque, S. M. and Agarwal, D. 2000. The internal structure of sheath fibres in DREF-3 Yarn. Journal of Textile Institute 91: 546-562.

Liu, W.Y., Yu, Y.P., He, J.H. and Wang, S.Y. 2007. Effect of strand-spacing between roving and filament on sirofil yarn properties. Textile Research Journal 77: 200 -204.

Lord, P.R. 1987. Air-jet and Friction Spinning. Textile Horizon 7(10): 20-24.

Miao, M., Cai, Z., and Zhang, Y. 1993. Influence of machine variables on two-strand yarn spinning geometry. Textile Research Journal 63(2): 116-120.

Plate, D. E. A. 1983. An alternative approach to two-fold weaving yarns part V: The properties of two-strand yarns. Journal of Textile Institute 74(6): 320-328.

Salohtra, K. R. 1987. Some quality aspects of ply-spun yarns. Indian Journal of Fibre and Textile Research 12(4): 197-200.

Sarvaran D. 2008. A novel attempt to produce three ply yarns from the short staple ring frame using long staple core. IE(I) Journal-TX 89: 30-34.

Sawhney A. P. S., Robert, K. Q., Ruppenicker, G. F. and Kimmel, L. B. 1992. Improved method of producing a cotton / polyester staple-core yarn on a ring spinning frame. Textile Research Journal 62(1): P 21-25.

Sawhney, A. P. S., G. F. Ruppenicker, and L. B. Kimmel, H. L. Salaun and K. Q. Robert, 1988. New technique to produce a cotton/ polyester blend yarn with improved strength.' Textile Research Journal 58: 601-604.

Sharma, S. K., and Bhatnagar, S. 1989. Effect of siro spinning on the characteristics of cotton yarn. Journal of Textile Association 50: 25-27.

Subramaniam, V., and Natrajan, K. S. 1990. Frictional properties of siro spun yarn. Textile Research Journal 60(4): 234-239.

Subramaniam, V., Srinivasamoorthi, V. R. and Peer Mohamed, A. 1989. Effect of processing parameters on the properties of double-rove spun yarn produced on a short staple spinning system. Textile Research Journal 59(12): 762-767.

Subramanium, V. and Mohamed, P. 1991. A study of Double- rove Yarn Hairiness in the Short-staple- spinning Sector. Journal of Textile Institute 82: 333-339.

Sun, M. N. and Cheng, K. P. S. 2000. Structure and Properties of Cotton Sirospun Yarn. Textile Research Journal 70: 261-267.

Zhu, Y.R., Leaf, G.A.V. and Oxhenham, W. 1993. Fibre behaviour in the twisting zone of a friction-spinning process. Journal of Textile Institute 84(1): 57-67.

❑❑❑

43

Angora : The Majestic Fibre of Hills

Alka Goel* and Mansi Agrawal**
*Professor/National Fellow, **Ph. D Scholar
Depterment of Clothing and Textiles, College of Home Science, GBPUAT

Introduction

Besides the fiber obtained from the various types of sheep, large quantities of animal fibers not strictly classified as wool but known as specialty hair fibers are used in the manufacturing of clothing. These fibers are obtained from related species such as goats, camels, oxen, horses and fur-bearing animals (Bergen, 1954). The use of the hair covering of fur-bearing animals for textile purpose dates far into antiquity, and the early natives of western South America are known to have used the various breeds of the Chichilla family to make a soft warm fabric. During the early 1920s, rabbit hair and rabbit fur, as well as that of the hare and lately muskrat and other fur fibers were used in special fabrics both in France and the United States. The aim in these fabrics was to produce a furry, hairy appearance and a soft handle (Bachrach, 1954).

Shukla and Cheema (2002) also reported that the finest and most expensive fibers commercially known as specialty fiber are obtained from long lustrous hair growing animals like vicuna, kashmiri goat, camel, llama, alpaca, angora goat and angora rabbit. Gupta et al. (1990) termed fine fibers produced by goat, camel and rabbit as specialty hair. These fibers, being natural and very fine possess softness, warmth, pleasurable handle and provide comfort which enables such fibers to secure a firm place in the niche areas of luxury apparels and furnishing fabrics. These fibers are chemically protein fibers (Keratin) similar to wool. Specialty animal fibers have been occupying important position in world textiles particularly for producing luxurious apparels and clothing for elites. The animal species wise fiber types are illustrated below:

Goat Family	Camel Family	Rabbit Family
Angora goat (Mohair) Cashmere goat (Cashmere) Cashgora goat (Cashgora fiber) Common goat (Goat hair)	Camel dromedary (Coarse camel hair) Bactrian (Fine Camel hair) Guanaco (Guanaco hair) Llama (Llama hair) Alpaca (Alpaca hair) Vicuna (Vicuna hair)	Angora rabbit (Angora rabbit hair)

Global Scenario of Specialty Hair Fibers

Mcgregor (2007) has reported that luxury fibers or specialty animal fibers account for less that 0.05% of the textile market. The manufacturing of 100% rare animal fiber textiles requires specialized skills and equipment. These fibers are frequently used in blends to obtain softness attributes lacking in pure wool or manmade fibers.

According to Chattopadhyay et al. (2005), production wise in global scenario cashmere is the most important specialty hair with respect to contribution in production. Its percentage share is about 31.0% of total specialty hair production of the world. While the contribution of mohair, camel hair and angora rabbit hairs are 22.0%, 14.1% and 9.4% respectively.

Angora Rabbit Hair

Zoologically angora belongs to the order Lagomorpha, catalogued under family Laporidae, genus Lepus (Mauersberger, 1954). According to Bakre et al. (1994), angora rabbits are basically classified into four major breeds viz., German, French, Russian, and British. The fibers obtained from these breeds have good aesthetic value. German angora rabbit hair

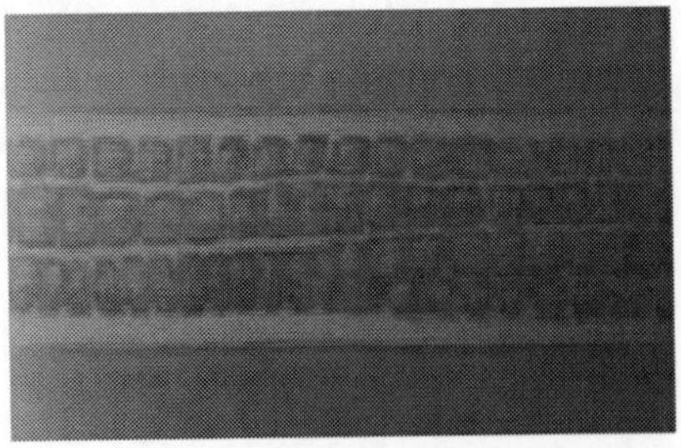

Microscopic appearance of guard hair

is supposed to be finest among all other rabbit breeds. The average number of fibers per square cm. ranges from 2,500 to 17,500.

According to Franck (2001), the angora rabbit produces three kinds of hair:

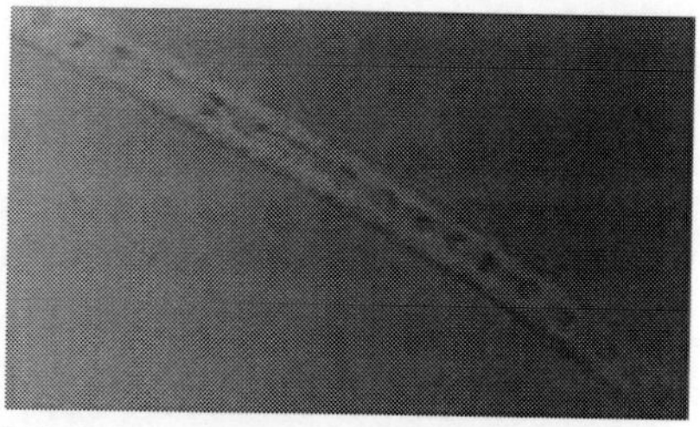
Microscopic appearance of fine hair

1. *Guide Hair*: 100-110 mm long; they guide and cover the growth of the other hair.
2. *Guard Hair*: 80 mm long. These have rough points that lock together, lie over the down and seal it off.
3. *Down*: 60 mm long. The diameter of 14 ìm makes down, one of the finest animal fibers used in textiles. The down fibers are very smooth with few cuticle scales. The angora rabbit produces hair of several colors but the strain bred for textile fibers is an albino strain that produces white fibers only. According to Mahajan (2004), salient angora wool production of different Breeds and their qualitative traits are:

Sl. No.	Breeds/Strain	Annual wool production (g)	Fiber length (cm)	Fiber Diameter (microns)	Guards hairs (%)
1.	Russian Angora	250-300	6-8	14-18	12-18
2.	British Angora	400-500	6-7	12-14	4-6
3.	German	700-800	6-8	10-12	4-6
4.	Crossbred Angora	400-500	5-7	12-14	5-7
5.	(Russian × British× German)	800-1000	7-9	12-18	10-12

Chattopadhyay et al. (2005) opined that angora rabbit hair, also called angora rabbit wool is a fine specialty fiber and possesses the characteristics of super whiteness, high bulk, and warmth. It is softer, finer and warmer than sheep's wool.

According to Singh et al. (2004), the angora breeds having very ancient history spreading back to Romans. In the textile industry 'Angora' refers solely to the hair produced by the angora rabbits which has tremendous potential for the preparation of value added products and has great demand in domestic as well as in international market. They are having white fur whose length can reach up to more than 6 cm in a dip of 75 days. Products like shawls, mufflers, tweeds, gent's chadders, blankets, caps, jackets, mats and several other decoration materials are prepared from this specialty fiber with less manpower.

Lebas et al. (2007) have reported that angora the hair of angora rabbit is one of the five keratinic textile fibers of animal origin of significant economic value. Wool from sheep is of course by far the main fiber at over 1.3 million tones per year. The four other: mohair, angora, cashmere and alpaca, each at outputs of 5000 to 30000 tones, exhibit original qualities of fineness, luster and feel for the production of high value added luxury items. Angora is often considered as one of the 'noble' fiber because of its pronounced non-circularity, and wide density distribution. In the matter of textiles, "angora" without any other qualification refers solely to the hair produced by Angora rabbits. Its international organization for standardization (1S0) symbol is WA: W for wool, reserved for noble textile hair, as opposed to H used for ordinary hair. The letter A is for the angora rabbit and distinguishes it from the symbol M use for mohair produced by the angora goat. The symbol for mohair is thus WM. The short hair of the ordinary rabbit is designated HK (K = Kaninchen which is 'rabbit' in German).

Misri (2004) have reported that wool is being used as a specialty animal fiber and utilized in the woolen industry mostly in fashion fabric and trade. Angora wool is very light, soft, fluffy and is slippery to handle but due to longer fiber length it can be spun easily as pure or blended yarn. Adult's rabbits produce 700 to 800 grams of wool per annum in 4 to 6 shearing and the qualitative attribute are:

Sl. No.	Item	Measurement
1	Staple length	6.0 cm
2	Fiber diameter	12.7 microns
3	Yield	95.5%
4	% guard hair	5 to 8
5	Guard hair diameter	48.5 cm

According to Bhasin (2004), angora is high quality wool often used to manufacture luxury garments and therapeutic clothing for people with arthritis and other joint disease. Prasanna et al. (2005) also reported that angora wool is believed to have medicinal values also for patients with arthritis apart from providing export quality valuable woolen garment for physical well-being.

Angora Wool Production in World

Sl. No.	Country	Angora wool production
1.	China	2000 tones
2.	Czechoslovakia	80 tones
3.	France	100 tones
4.	Germany	100 tones
5.	Denmark, Italy, Spain, Hungry, Poland, Belgium, Switzerland	100 tones
6.	Japan	40 tones
7.	Brazil, Korea	50 tones
8.	India	40 tones

In India rabbit rearing was initiated through a private venture in Kullu valley of Himachal Pradesh in 1960s. Systematic research in production and reproduction aspects was initiated by the Indian Council of Agriculture Research (ICAR) in 1970's with the import of angora varieties of rabbits from UK and then from USSR. The efforts were made to introduce commercial production of angora wool in other high altitude mountain area viz., Darjeeling, Otty, Sikkim etc. but such ventures are yet to make any significant commercial products (Gupta et al., 2002).

Morphological Structure of Angora Rabbit Hair

According to Birodkar (1987), the structure of fiber is determined by its chemical constitution and by its molecular arrangement, apart from conditions of growth or manufacture. The chemical and molecular factors determine the chemical and physical properties of the fiber. A microscopic view of the rabbit hair shows that the fiber has three physical sections, apical, medial, and basal. The cuticular scales have a varied pattern in the different sections of the guard hair. The cuticular scales vary in shape in the different regions of the hair. According to Mauersberger (1954), the medulla of both the guard hairs and the intermediary hairs is a series of a long column of cuticular air spaces, separated the solid connected medullary tissue. Each of the air vesicles, which are found in the medial and lower apical sections; may show a small amount of pigmentation along the bottom edges. The colour of this pigment in the white rabbit is extremely faint, whereas in the gray rabbit it is deep gray, almost black.

It is reported in the Encyclopedia of chemical technology (1980) that rabbit hair belongs to the family of protein called Keratin. Protein fibers are built up of proteins, which are high molecular substances, composed of many amino acids. These are the basic units and they combined to form polypeptide chains. A simple formula for wool protein is:

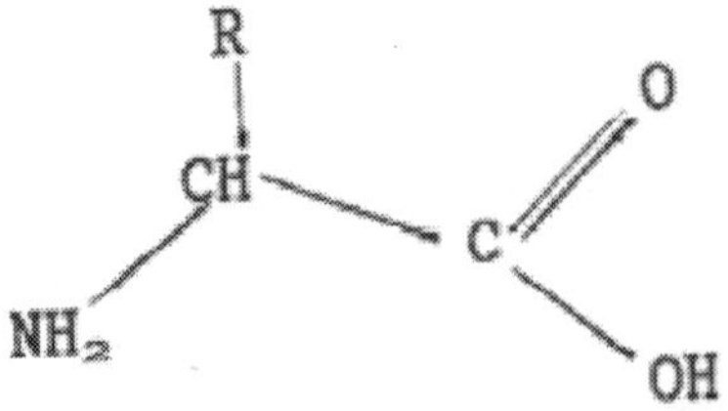

An amino acid contains a carboxylic group and an amino group. Whereas the carboxylic group confers upon its acidic properties, the amino group imparts basic properties. The protein of the rabbit hair, 'Keratin' is built up from sixteen different amino acids. One of which is cystine, contains sulfur. According to Hall (1975), the structural formula of keratin is $(C_{42}H_{157}O_{15}N_5S)_n$. This keratin molecule can exist in two physical form i.e. stretched one (â-keratin) and a folded as (á-keratin) and the transition from one to the other can be effected by stretching and release of strain of the wet fiber.

Physical and Chemical Properties of Angora Fibre

Table 1. Physical Properties of Fibers

Sl. No.	Properties	Angora 'A' grade fiber		Angora 'B' grade fiber		Angora Cross breed	
		Fine hair	Guard hair	Fine hair	Guard hair	Fine hair	Guard hair
1.	Length (cm)	6.3	7.4	5.3	6.4	4.2	5.9
2.	Tenacity g/denier	1.28	1.48	1.19	1.35	1.04	1.27
3.	Fiber fineness (denier)	3.94	9.12	3.96	9.26	3.99	9.34
4.	Elongation (%)	41.05	36.64	37.81	36.04	41.39	38.74
5.	Diameter (μ)	9.80	35.3	10.30	36.0	9.60	34.7
6.	Crimp No./ inch	2.4	1.76	2.60	1.60	2.50	1.40

Table 2. Chemical Composition of fibers

Sl. No.	Properties	Angora fibers 'A' grade	'B' grade	Crossbreed
1.	Ash Content	1.59	1.56	1.54
2.	Sulphur Content	3.96	4.32	3.46
3.	Nitrogen Content	16.86	16.81	16.72
4.	Moisture Content	7.10	7.22	7.43
5.	PH	7.6	7.2	7.5

Table 3. Chemical Reagents that Affects the Angora Fibers

Chemical Reagents	Observations	
	At room temperature (Appearance/Solubility)	On heating (Appearance/Solubility)
Dil. Sulphuric Acid (2%)	Unaffected/insoluble	Unaffected/insoluble
Con. Sulphuric Acid (98%)	Stained dark brown and swells	Changed into charred mass and dissolved completely within 2 minutes
Dil. Nitric Acid (2%)	Unaffected / unstained	Stained yellow and remains undissolved
Conc. Nitric Acid (72%)	Stained yellow, swells and shows slight disintegration	Dissolves completely within 2 minutes
Hydrochloric Acid (38%)	Stained in purple colour after 5 minutes	Remains undissolved and retains its purple colour
Sodium Hydroxide (80%)	Unstained/dissolved before heating	–

Table 4. Chemical reagents that do not affect the angora

Chemical Reagents	Observations	
	At room temperature (Appearance/Solubility)	On heating (Appearance/Solubility)
Ammonium Thiocynate	Unaffected	Unaffected
Cyclohexanone	Unaffected	Unaffected
Dimethyl formamide	Unaffected	Unaffected
Phenol	Unaffected	Unaffected
Formic Acid	Unaffected	Unaffected
Acetic Acid	Unaffected	Unaffected
Acetone	Unaffected	Unaffected
Benzene	Unaffected	Unaffected

Table 5. Effect of Colour Reaction

Sl. No.	Colour Reagent	*Colour obtained on different fibers*		
		'A' grade Angora	'B' grade Angora	Crossbreed Angora
1.	Zinc Chloride and Iodine	Light brown	Light brown	Light brown
2.	Malachite green	Light green	Light green	Light green
3.	Iodine reagent	Light orange	Light orange	Light orange
4.	Potassium permanganate	Light brown	Light brown	Light brown

Difference between Wool and Hair

- According to Potter and Corbman (1967), wool and hair fiber differ in its basic structure. Wool is distinguished from hair by overlapping scales, which gives wool fiber its felting properties. Rabbit hair is straight, lustrous and comparatively inelastic. It is smoother than wool. They have all the qualities of wool. In general they are even more expensive than wool.
- Mauersberger (1954) stated that rabbit hair has medulla with a complex structure, looking in a microscope it looks like ladder with regular rings. This discontinuous medulla is characteristics of fine fibers such as rabbit hair. According to Gupta (1992), the shape and size of medulla in rabbit hair is quite different from that found in wool. In this case ladder type medulla appears as a series of evenly spaced dark patches, these patches may be arranged in single longitudinal series (uniserial) or they may be multiserial.
- Singh (2004) stated that angora fiber differs from wool in several respects; angora is a medulated fiber, which makes it light and soft. Angora is a heterotype fleece and contains some coarse hair called bristle. These bristle prevent felting on the rabbit and imparts the characteristic fluffiness to the yarn. The down fiber is very fine, with an average fiber diameter of about 11 to 13 microns. However most of the commercial breeds have same average fiber diameter of the fleece.
- Rougeot (1986) have reported that angora fiber has a low density of about 1.15 to 1.18 gm/cm^3 compared to 1.33 gm/cm^3 for wool and 1.50 gm/cm^3 for cotton.

Draw Backs of Marketing of Angora Products

1. *Shedding of fibre*: a lot of researches have to be done to remove this problem of shedding of the fibre from the angora products.
2. *Seasonal marketing*: as our country is a tropical country and experience a tropical climate so the utilization of these products is only during winter seasons so during summer we face the problem for marketing of angora products.
3. *Traditional and conventional designing*: our angora products are far behind in terms of designing so motivation in the designing field is essential for the marketing of these products.
4. *Cost*: the cost of angora product is very high which is unable to satisfy the pocket of the buyer. Thus in the current price war where every single

rupee is crucial the customer want product at a lowest landed price with colour, style and fabric trend.

Main Reasons of Using Angora in Blend with Other Fibers

- *Economy and rare availability of angora*: Angora rabbit hair is costly and its production is limited. The addition of natural and man made fiber may bring down the cost assuring the availability of angora hair products to more people at reasonable price. According to Singh (2004), angora fiber is utilized by both the organized as well as the decentralized sector. The wool based processing and knitting industries are the major utilizers of the angora wool. However, it may be pointed out that the angora wool availability in the country is not sufficient to fulfill the demand of woolen industry and the supply also fluctuates considerably.
- *Ease of processing*: Processing difficulty of angora also favors its utilization as blends. According to Chattopadhyay et al.(2005), production of yarn exclusively of rabbit hair on cotton spinning system is not possible because of its smooth surface structure, absence of crimp and prominent medulla, all of which lead to lower inter fiber friction causing difficulty in twisting. Another processing difficulty faced is due to the generation of high level of static charge. This resulted in disturbance during carding, twisting operation or mechanical processing of pure angora. The problem can be overcome by the application of suitable anti-static agent or using other cellulosic fiber as blend, which is having good moisture absorbency thus can reduce static charge.
- *To avoid shedding of angora rabbit hair*: there is a serious drawback of shedding fibers from the fabric surface and after breakage, sticking to the surface of other underneath materials. This drawback present in angora fiber can be removed by the use of its combination with other natural and man made fiber, which can hold angora rabbit hair (due to more crimp) in the fabrics and improve the performance of fabric.
- *To produce fabric with better performance*: Blending helps to cover up drawback present in one fiber by combining it with another fiber. Therefore the angora can be use in blend with such fibers which can provide good strength, cohesiveness etc.
- *To obtain cross-dyed effect*: Fiber has a distinctive appearance luster or texture and they vary in their affinity to dye so that they can combine to give certain decorative textural, color effect arising from the difference (Roy, 1980). Angora is a protein fibre so it can be blended with other fibres like cellulosic fibres to obtain a cross dyed effect.

- *To add comfort properties in apparels*: While considering the disadvantages of angora from comfort point of view, one of the serious draw back is low moisture absorption of angora resulting in development of static charge and creates discomfort during wear. This problem can be overcome by blending of this fibre with cellulosic fiber having good moisture absorption properties.
- *To increase the availability of product in different seasons*: As our country is a tropical country and experience a tropical climate, so the utilization of angora products are possible only during winter seasons and during summer marketing of angora product face great problem. So by blending it with other cellulosic fibers marketability of angora can be extended for spring and autumn season also.

Use of Angora in Blend

Angora rabbit hair-Avivastra wool blends

Arora et al. (1983) reported the use of rabbit hair in blend with wool. According to him, the rabbit-wool blended shawls are superior to pure wool shawls with respect to softness, whiteness, warmth and feel. The blended shawls have comparatively higher strength and undergo less abrasion loss. Gupta (1992) reported that the rabbit hair wool blended yarn is more tenacious than pure wool yarn. Breaking elongation values of wool and rabbit hair blended yarns were high than pure wool yarn. The slightly lower rigidity of blended shawls was due to less stiffness in the rabbit hair fiber. The blended fabric could resist many number of abrasion cycles due to the higher number of fiber per yarn cross-section and higher strength of yarn and fabric.

Angora rabbit hair-Cotton blends

These blends were processed on the cotton khadi system, no difficulty was encountered, except in pure rabbit hair at drumming stage. It was due to lack of interfiber cohesion and light weight of rabbit hair, which hindered the formation of proper web and it's winding on the drum. With increase in the proportion of cotton in the blended yarn, tenacity increased and the percentage extension decreased. This is mainly due to higher breaking stress and lower braking strain of cotton fibers (Singh, 2004).

Angora rabbit hair-Polyester blends

Gupta (1992) reported that, the blended yarn (50 polyester: 50 rabbit hair) with fairly good tenacity of 14.9 g/tex and elongation value 10.2 % would be produced on commercial cotton system of machinery. The braking elongation value have shown reducing trend with increasing percentage of rabbit hair content. The pure 100% polyester and in blended form i.e. 20, 40, 60 and 80% with rabbit hair found to be with decreasing elongation at break value i.e., 12.6, 13.2, 11.8, 11.7 and 10.0% respectively.

Angora rabbit hair-Silk blends

According to Arora et al. (1983), rabbit hair blends with silk (50:50) exert less resistance to blending i.e., they are less stiff to figures and more papery to handle. Thus the rabbit hair/silk blended knit quantity appears to have superior consumer appeal with respect to luster, appearance, warmth and soft feel.

Angora rabbit hair-Acrylic blends

The rabbit hair acrylic blends were processed successfully on woolen processing systems. For the blends with acrylic, with 0, 20, 40, 60 and 80% rabbit hair, the elongation at break values were found to be 16.2, 18.9, 16.1, 14.2 and 10.4& respectively. Blended yarn showed increased value in yarn strength. 20% addition of rabbit hair in acrylic improved the yarn tenacity; further increase of rabbit hair proportion reversed the trend (Gupta, 1992).

Angora rabbit hair -Viscose rayon blend

Blending of angora wool with rayon brings about the favorable changes in the performance of resultant fabric. The blended cloths have comparatively higher strength and undergo less abrasion loss than the fabric woven from pure rabbit hair. The weight and stiffness of blended fabric also increases with an acceptable level (Gupta, 1996).

Angora rabbit hair- Rambouillet wool blend

In this study, blending of angora fibre with Rambouillet wool was done. Various physical and chemical properties of the fibres were examined and yarns were prepared by hand spinning method on various charkhas. Fabrics were prepared from the resultant yarns by both knitting and weaving technology, which were finally made into garments. Various designs suitable for weaving were prepared and then applied to the garments. The technology was then transferred through training, which was given to the rural women of different Self Help Groups.

Importance of Angora in Hill Areas

The hill economy is mainly based on agriculture and animal husbandry practices. The agro-climatic conditions and difficult terrain of the hills limit the production potential of both, land and the animal. It has been a known fact that under the shrinking pasture land and restrictions on grazing, the tradition of sheep rearing is declining while the demand of wool is still there. To meet the demand of wooly fibre, angora rabbit farming can play an important role. It can also contribute in improving the quality of yarns and apparels. Due to the multifarious activities associated with the rearing of this livestock and temperate zones of the country.

Advantages of angora rabbit farming in hills

a) *Suitable agro-climatic conditions*: angora farming is best suited for a temperature range of 10° to 25°C at a height of 3000 to 6000 feet above sea level. The agro-climatic and the topographical conditions of hilly regions are suitable for angora rearing.

b) *Efficient feed converter with simple food habits*: rabbit can be successfully reared on a variety of fodder-based rations. Rabbits can effectively utilize the kitchen waste and thus, effectively contribute in organic waste management.

c) Space requirement: as rabbit requires very less space hence a variety of housing systems can be easily set up in the fruit orchards, on the roof tops, and a s backyard units or on small scale and commercial lines.

d) Fast multiplication

e) Easy management practices

f) Employment opportunities: rabbit farming can provide a number of employment opportunities to unemployed youth, rural women, physically challenged people, small and marginal farmers and people involved in small scale and cottage industry. A number of subsidiary industries can be identified.

Transfer of technology to create entrepreneurial skill among rural/hill people for their livelihood security

Keeping in mind various advantages of rearing angora rabbit, training can be given to rural women regarding various basic techniques i.e., fibre blending, dyeing, spinning, etc. This will help them in establishing their own units, which can become a viable supplementary economical venture for the rural women of higher altitudes.

Conclusion

Angora rabbit hair, called as angora wool is produced in many parts of the world. In India, the angora rabbits are being produced in hilly areas like Himachal Pradesh, Jammu and Kashmir, Kumaun and Garhwal region of Uttaranchal etc. where the environmental conditions are most favorable for their production.

Rabbit hair comes under the category of specialty fibers not only because of its scarcity/limited production but also on account of special requirement of processing. The overall total production of rabbit hair is limited so it cannot fulfill the massive industrial demand of fibers as and when required. Therefore, the development potential for this fiber is lacking, as there is little scope for the textile mill owners to utilize it for bulk production. Angora rabbit hair has 4 -5 times less coherence than wool and it also generates high static electric charges. These problems cause frequent lapping during mechanical processing; the normal speed of machine cannot be maintained under normal dry climatic conditions, which makes spinning difficult.

In order to overcome these problems and to reduce the cost of the final product, blending is an ultimate and effective solution. More research and exploration is needed in this area.

Hence, to transfer this technology to the rural people training can be organized. Various basic techniques and skills are i.e. making yarn with spindle, hand knitting technique etc. Training may proved to be very beneficial to them and they would like to utilize the knowledge for income generation.

References

Arora, R.K.,Gupta, N.P., Patni, P.C. and Singh U.S. 1983. Performance of rabbit hair blend with cotton and wool in khadi system. Indian Journal of Textile Research. 8(4):127-129.

Bachrach, M. 1954. Textile fur fibers, animal brush fibers and down. In: Mathews' Textile Fibers: Their Physical, Microscopical and Chemical Properties,6thed. London, John Wiley and Sons. Inc., Chapman and Hall Limited.pp1283.

Bakre, P.S. and Kulkarni, P.R. 1994. Processing of angora fiber and its blends. The Indian Textile Journal. 104 (12): 86-87.

Bergen,W.V. 1954. Specialty hair fiber. In: Mathews' Textile Fibers: Their Physical, Microscopical and Chemical Properties.6thed. London, John Wiley and Sons. Inc., Chapman and Hall Limited.1283p.

Bhasin, V. 2004. Angora Rabbit Production in India: Scope and Challenges. National Seminar on Angora Rabbit Wool and Cashmere Production and Utilization held at Manali 25-26 Sept, 2004, pp46.

Birodkar, S. 1987. Structure and properties of textile fibers. The Indian Textile Journal. 98(1):68-74.

Chattopadhyay, S.K., Bhaskar, P., Ahmad, M., Gupta, N.P. and Pokharna, A.K. 2005. Properties of indigenous angora rabbit hair and cotton blended yarns spun using short staple cotton spinning system. Indian Journal of Fiber and Textile Research.30 (3):215-217.

Encyclopedia of chemical technology. 1980. 6th ed. New York, McGraw Hill company.5: 436.

Franck, R.R. 2001. Silk, Mohair, Cashmere and other luxury fibers. Cambridge, Woodhead Publishing Limited.247p.

Gupta, B. 1996. Blending of angora wool with viscose rayon, their physico-chemical properties and preparation of fashion apparel. *Thesis.* Master of Science in Clothing and Textiles. G.B. Pant University of Agriculture and Technology,Pantnagar.pp150.

Gupta, N.P. 1992. Wool and hair processing. The Indian Textile Journal. 103(2):166-174.

Gupta, N.P., Arora, R.K., Pokharna, A.K. and Patni, P.C. 1990. Mechanical processing of Indian wools and specialty hairs. The Indian Textile Journal. 100(7):138.

Gupta, N.P., Arora R.K., Shakyawar, D.B., Patni, P.C. and Pokharna, A.K. 2002. Angora rabbit wool a promising natural fiber. Central Sheep and Wool Research Institute, Avikanagar, pp48.

Hall, A.J. 1975. The standard handbook of textiles. 5[th]ed. London, Newness Butterworth. 94p.

Lebas, F.; Coudert, P.; De Rochambeau, H.; and Bault, R.G. 2007. *The Rabbit: Husbandry, Health and Production*, FAO (Food & Agriculture Organization), Animal Production and Health Division: Rome, Italy, 205 p., Retrieved March16, 2008 from, http:// www.fao.org/ docrep/ t1690E/t1690E00.htm

Mahajan, J.M. 2004. Practical problems in Angora farming and marketing of Angora and cashmere (Pashmena) specialty animal fiber. National Seminar on Angora Rabbit Wool and Cashmere Production and Utilization. Manali 25-26 Sept, 2004: proceedings. pp56.

Mauersberger, H.R. 1954. Mathews' Textile Fibers: Their Physical, Microscopical and Chemical Properties.6[th]ed. London, John Wiley and Sons. Inc., Chapman and Hall Limited. pp1283.

McGregor, B. 2007. Retieved December. 5, 2007, from http://www. dpi.vic.gov.an/ dpi/ nrenfa/fid./.

Misri, A.K. 2004. Angora Rabbit wool and Cashmere Production and Utilization. National Seminar on Angora Rabbit Wool and Cashmere Production and Utilization. Manali 25-26 Sept, pp 25-26.

Potter, D.M. and Corbman, P.B. 1967. Textile: Fiber to fabric.4th ed. New York. Mc Graw-Hill.495 p.

Prasanna, S.B. and Kumar, P. 2005. Rabbitery - An unexploited potential for rural upliftment. National Seminar on Entrepreneurship Development for Livelihood Security-Experiences, Prospects and Strategies for Rural India. Sovinier cum abstract. pp127.

Rougeot, J. 1986. Production of Rabbit skin and Angora wool. In Lekas, F.; Coudert, P.; Rouvier, R. and Rochambean, H. de (eds.). The rabbit Husbandry Health and Production. Series No. 2, Rome, FAO. pp 193-207.

Roy, A.S. 1980. Problems in blending of fiber. The Indian Textile Journal. 40(9):63-66.

Sharma and Goel, 2000

Shukla, L. and Cheema, R.S. 2002. Wool: The wonder fiber. *Textile Magazine*. 43(8):22-23.

Singh, U. 2004. Processing of Angora Rabbit wool. National Seminar on Angora Rabbit Wool and Cashmere Production and Utilization. September 25-26, 2004. Indian society for Sheep and Goat Production and Utilization. pp.57.

❑❑❑

44

Industrial Application of Wool Blended Non-Woven Felt

D. B. Shakyawar and N. P. Gupta
Division of Textile Manufacturing and Textile Chemistry
Central Sheep and Wool Research Institute, Avikanagar, via Jaipur- 304 501, Rajasthan

Introduction

Technical textiles are getting recognition world over due to their economic and strategic potential. In some of the developed countries, technical textiles products account for almost 50% of all the textile manufacturing activity and output. The economic scope and importance of technical textiles extend far beyond the textile industry itself and have an impact upon every sphere of human economic and social activities. Wool possesses a unique characteristic, which plays an important role to produce an irreversible structure by rubbing under specific conditions. The scaly structure of wool fibre due to directional frictional effect (DFE) helps in the formation of an irreversible structure. Longitudinally, the scale fit into one another like a stack of ice-cream cones or flowerpots. This leaves the rims projection, which on the wool fibre takes the form of imbrications or serrations caused by the free tips of scales. This irreversible structure is known as felt or non-woven product. Non-woven products have growing demand and versatile applications in the field of defense, railways, paper felts, filter abrasive clothes, clearing pads, polishing pads, tennis ball covers, washers, gaskets and many other items could be prepared out of wool fibre. The natural characteristics for fire retardancy and ability to felt make the wool fibres important in technical textiles despite the stiff competition from other fibres.

Wool as technical textiles

Pressed wool felt is made by utilizing the natural properties of wool to lock together when processed with water, steam, mechanical abrasion and drying. It is resilient and dimensionally stable and can be made to a wide range of thickness, textures and densities, depending on the intended use. Technical felt is pressed felt made to a specific formulation to carry out as particular engineering and technical function. Technical pressed felts are made to the highest standard containing between 50 to 100% wool (application dependant) with the balance normally being viscose. Technical felt has a wide range of applications in industrial and domestic surroundings, which includes sound and vibration absorbers, oil reservoirs and applicators, removal of unwanted liquids (wiping) and solids (filtration), removal of mists from gases, polishing, padding and packing, gaskets and spacers; air seals, garment stiffeners and medical uses such as corn plasters.

Flow Chart of Felt Manufacture

Sorting and Grading of wool

↓

Blending and Carding (For web preparation)

↓

Hardening (Combination of Heat, moisture and mechanical energy)

↓

Milling

↓

Special treatments (Dyeing and preservative proof etc.)

↓

Drying under tension

↓

Finishing processes
(Inspection, Pressing, Grinding).

Non-Woven or Pressed Felt Manufacture

In the manufacturing process of pressed felt, the web is used. Alternate layers of web are laid down at right angles to each other, so as to provide both lengthwise and crosswise strength, until a batt of required weight and thickness is obtained. The number of batts are placed on the hardener and steamed to provide the necessary heat and moisture. A top platen is then lowered and made to oscillate rapidly. Under the combined action of rubbing and pressing, the batts are compressed and some interlocking of fibres in adjacent layers occurs, yielding a sufficient product for the fulling operation. Fulling is carried out in hammer fulling mills. The hardened batt is moist with a fulling solution (usually high titer soaps for materials which are fulled rather lightly or sulfuric acid for very hard and dense felts). At intervals during the progress of the fulling process, the felts are pulled from the machine, straightened, and again folded into the machine. After fulling, which may last for several hours for dense products, the felt is washed, neutralized in acid fulled, and then dried. Depending on the final application of this versatile product, it may be impregnated with various sizing agents, elatedness or synthetic resins. Other treatments include water repellents and mildew proofing.

Industrial applications of felt

The felts used for industrial applications include washers, channels, rings, strips, filters, bulb and bait paddings, oil seeds and gaskets. Various kinds of other industrial applications are in automobile, packing, defence, jute industry, leather industry, railways, filter and glass industry. Mechanical filters find extensive application in various areas of personnel protection, most notably in industry where workers may be exposed to very fine dust or pollutants. CSIRO has developed an electostastically charged wool filter medium, which consumes little energy, is highly efficient and makes breathing easier. Woollen filters have a high dust holding capacity and durability. It is suitable for use in air conditioning system, personnel respirations and other industrial applications. Felt components of different nature are continuously being adopted by the modern industry for their various needs in wicking, fluid transfer, sound proofing, spacing, heat absorption and fluid reservoir conveyor belt for bakery industry. Some of important industrial applications are discussed below:

Polishing Felts

Polishing felt is generally a high wool content product available in sheet/ wheel and mounted cone format. This felt is used to polish or clean many surfaces ranging from ice skates to turbine blades and from diamond rings to spectacle frames. It is available in the higher densities from 0.50 gm/cm^3 to 0.80 gm/cm^3. It is supplied either in sheets or in custom-made wheels/discs in a variety of diameters and thicknesses up to 100 mm. Due to its capability of high compactness; liquid absorption and higher product life, 'Molded Felt Wheels' of various densities have technical edge over the traditional die-cut polishing wheels finding wide applications in the leather, glass, dental, crystal, metal and other industries. The *'Ring Briffs'* (wood/without wood), *'Knife Edge Wheels'*, *'Felt Buttons'* and *'Split Wheels'* are used in jewelry segments while 'Triangle Bobs' are popular with the floor polishing segment (Patni et al., 2006).

Sealants and wicks

Felts due to their properties of elasticity, absorption and release of the liquids serve as an excellent reservoir for the thickest viscous liquids. They have found large applications as sealants in railways, kilns and electric motors for non-stop continuous working life. Their low frictional capabilities have made them popular also in a large number of mechanical applications. Luminaries seals are also popular for grade protection.

Consumer products

Felt blocks have wide range of application in writing instruments, ink-pads, erasers, lining, underlay, door-mats, automobile carpets, die-cut part for lamp bases, furniture legs , base pad for ironing, dentistry, toys, educational kits, printer felts, dusters, boots and shoes. The application of custom-cut felts is also growing rapidly.

Shaped parts

Polishing heads fitted with metallic shank of various shapes (cones, cylinders and balls) are used for working on dies, metals and plastics.

Elite felts

Elite felts are a fantastic new high quality felts manufactured from 100% wool and are 5 mm thick. This material is extremely fashion oriented and appealing to many designers. These are currently used for making high class table wares, decorations, promotional items, key rings- hearts, stars and animal shapes.

Surgical felts

Surgical felts are 100% wool or a blend of wool/viscose fibres. These felts are required to meet appropriate national standards and are subjected to compression and recovery tests during the manufacturing process. The products are inspected carefully and any inclusions, which occur naturally in wool, are removed in order to provide the end user with a fault free product. The standard densities for surgical felts are 0.11gm/cm^3, 0.13gm/cm^3 and 0.16gm/cm^3 (Shakyawar et al., 2007).

Footsteps of mankind in future

Wool felt is a favoured material for advanced technological appliances in the field for space, defense, rocket and security press.

Indian Scenario of wool based technical felts

The hand made felts are generally used in handicraft and floor covering items while the machine made felts are used for industrial applications. The felts produced from machine are both soft and hard with the density varying from 0.12 to 0.35g/cm^3. The density can be controlled by mechanical pressure and felting time. The products are utilized as floor covering for protection against cold as well as for decorative purpose in drawing rooms. Such felts contain either embroidery or patchwork of coloured felt pieces over the felt sheet of single colour. The industrial application of wool based technical felts in the country is comparatively lesser than the developed countries. The Indian Standards cover a range of soft to extra hard type felts for different applications. The major applications of felts include filtration, sound absorption, thermal insulation, shock absorption, cushioning, padding, packing, surfacing and spacing. Sheep wool is mostly used for manufacturing of handmade felts. The use of wool in machine made paper maker felts are very limited due to the use of needle punching system with synthetic or resin coated multi filament.

Research and development work at CSWRI

The techniques were standardized for fibre selection, scouring, mixing, carding, hardening, felting and other chemical finishing treatment in developing apparel and technical felts. Inferior grade rabbit wool, which had little textile application for quality goods, was blended with short length crossbred sheep fine wool in various proportions. The blend optimization indicated that up to 40% inferior rabbit wool can be blended with wool for making superior quality lightweight and extra white hand made felts. Prior to felting, fibrous sheet was treated with fulling agent (soap solution), which served as lubricant during the operation and was subsequently removed during washing. Warm water was used for lighter felts and soap solution was used for soft-pressed felts. The felting time ranged from 5 to 10 minutes for lightweight felts and 10 to 15 minutes for soft pressed felts. The felts of less than 4 mm thickness were converted into value added products like jackets and women ruffles. These products had enhanced product quality and consumer acceptance with better luster, durability and thermal insulation value. Little embroidery work further enhanced the value addition and fetched much better price. These products have great demand and provide employment in the rural /unorganized sector.

Medium type felt of 4-6 mm thickness was utilized in manufacture of medical textiles. Medical field included injury preventive textiles, smart wound dressing and moisture absorption paddings. Felts of fine cross bred wool-rabbit hair blends, made as per ASTM - D2475 standards, were found suitable for orthopaedics surgical application as medical textiles. These felts possessed excellent softness, porosity or air- permeability and absorbency. The products provide the patients warmth, some impact resistance and protection against lateral shear and are also helpful to critically ill or old patients. Blended wool felts also have better healing effect without adverse effect on injury.

Non-woven felts, manufactured out of different blends of fine crossbred wool with viscose and cigarette filter fibres in the proportion of 50:50 with more than 6-mm thickness, were found suitable for technical applications such as polishing (metal and glass), automobile industry and civil engineering. These technical felts possessed good wear resistance, oil-absorption, capillary flow, thermal conductivity, coefficients of friction, compression resistance, energy absorption, etc. which are considered most important factors for technical felts.

Factors influencing feltability

When the wool fibre is rubbed against the scales it is somewhat higher than when rubbed in the reverse direction or with scales and the difference is more apparent when the fibre is wet. The '*Directional Frictional Effect*' (DFE) is the dominant factor in the felting process. The elastic property of the wool is also an important contributing factor in its ability to felt. The felting process is affected by a number of external factors but the two most fundamental requirements are that the wool should be wet and that it can be manipulated mechanically. Under the influence of intermittent forces of squeezing and twisting, the wet fibres migrate in a preferential '*root ward*' direction because of the DFE, and at the same time they tend to curd, loop, and entangle with each other. Because of the anchoring effects of the entangling, and the differential frictional properties this process proceeds irreversibly. The temperature, pH (i.e. soap solution, detergent and acid), abrasion time and pressure influence the feltability of wool. The effects of different parameters on felting process are discussed in detail.

Fineness and medullation

Fibre properties such as fineness and medullation influence the felting significantly (Gupta et al., 1987). They suggested that the relative felting property of a particular breed will depend on the distribution of fiber diameter as well as medullation. Chokla sheep wool (average fibre diameter of 26.5

microns and medullation 47%) is superior in felting properties than Malpura (average fibre diameter 41.4 microns and medullation percent 79%) because the aggregate scale effect in interlocking the fiber mass is predominant in Chokla due to lesser fibre diameter and high percent of pure fibres. It was thought that felting properties of wool should increase with their fineness. However, the study showed imperfect correlation between fineness and milling. The medullated fibre significantly influences the felt ability of the woollen felt and the properties of the felt.

Scales

The scales of wool fibre are flat, irregular and vary in size with their diameter, shape and breed. Studies on the scales structure of wool of various Indian sheep breeds indicate that the scales outline is closely related to the diameter of the fibre rather than breed. The size of these scales is the same for various types of wool but that the extent of overlapping creates an apparent difference. The amount of visible scale is an important means of differentiating wool from related fibres and also for distinguishing between different types of wool. The felting depends primarily on the scale structure of wool. The overlapping of the scales is such that the free ends project outward and towards the tip of the fiber, giving the edge its characteristic serrated appearance. On this account, the fibre can only move amongst its neighbour in the direction of its root (DFE) which is of importance in felting. The mechanism of felting shows that the scales on the fibre interlock with each other giving a compact structure. Therefore, the type and number of scales on the surface of the wool fibre, play a predominant role in making good quality felts besides other properties like elasticity and swelling. Merino wool, with well defined and projecting scales, felt much more rapidly than mohair with its less distinctive scales that adhere more closely to fibre.

Processing Parameters

pH

It was established that milling is most rapid at about pH 10 on the alkaline side of neutrality and that the maximum rate of milling is given by soap. On the acid side of neutrality, the rate shrinkage on milling starts to increase at pH 4 and continues to increase with decreasing pH. Shenai (1995) suggests that milling of wool in acid gives a better cloth without significant cloth damage and the synthetic surfactant used during this process promotes felting of wool as efficiently as soap. Felting power of wool depends mainly on the magnitude of the DFE in the milling medium, and the effect of pH on the felting power is due to influence of pH on the magnitude of DFE

Temperature

Effect of temperature was also studied by Umback (1985). He observed that the rate of milling with soap is most rapid at 46 to 49 °C increasing with rise in temperature and then falling.

Auxiliaries

Cationic detergents are strongly absorbed by the fibre surface through salt links, yielding a hydrophobic and essentially uncharged surface. The ionic detergents also influence the felting shrinkage of wool (Shenai, 1995).

Quality assurance for felts and Namdhas

The quality is a reflection of customer's opinion on the value they see in the product compared to the other products. In other words, the quality is whatever the customer says because the customer is the final judge of the quality. Quality holds significant importance in the world trade. Therefore, quality assurance is a must for all the products whether they are hand made or machine made. In case of felt the quality assurance is equally important. The Specifications for these are available under the Bureau of Indian Standards, which is briefly depicted in Table 1.

Table 1. Grading of hand made felts 'Namdhas' *(As per IS: 4392-2003)*

Grade	Designation	Percentage	
		Wool	Cotton
1	All wool	100	00
2	Special	50	50
3	New Chaloo	30	70

The wool and cotton used in the manufacture of Namdhas should be clean, well carded and free from dust, foreign matter and other impurities. In case Namdhas are made of mixtures of wool and cotton, the bottom and top layers should be of wool and the inner layer of cotton. All the layers should be reasonably uniform and the bottom and top layers should be reasonably equal in thickness. Mill spun wool yarn should be used as embroidery yarn for Grades 1 and 2 while hand spun wool yarn for Grade 3 of Namdhas. As per IS: 1719-2000 the pressed wool felt has five varieties (Table 2).

Table 2. Varity of pressed wool felt

Variety	Grade of Wool	Finish
Extra hard	64s/70s	Milled
Hard	48s	Milled
Extra firm, firm, medium firm and medium	48s	Milled
Soft (for use in orthopedics	64s noils	Hardened
Soft (for use in packing)	48s	Hardened

Hardened felt is obtained by pressing a number of carded wool web to ensure the requisite thickness and making some what hard under the influence of moisture, heat and pressure. Milled felt is obtained by further subjecting the hardened felt to milling to achieve the requisite thickness and compactness of texture. The physical requirements for general-purpose felts and the applications of different types of fėlts are summarized in Tables 3 and 4, respectively.

Table 3. Physical requirements for general-purpose felts

Variety	Density g/cm^3	Tensile strength (kp)	Splitting resistance (N/cm)
Extra hard	30.60	4100	75
Hard	40.46	3400	65
Extra firm	0.40	2900	55
Firm	0.34	2400	40
Medium firm	0.27	1500	26
Medium	0.23	1400	22
Soft	0.18	900	-
Extra soft	0.15	-	-

Table 4. Application of different types of felts

Variety	Recommended uses
Extra hard	For aircraft applications; extra hard density polishing wheels and buffs; hard washers and for such uses where felts possessing long riving properties are desired.
Hard	For uses where frictional wear is considerable (such as cases of precision instruments, as panels in saddles, hardness's and other saddler items); for living of inner side of shackles, doors of vehicles, polishing wheels for glass and ophthalmic lens; block cutters and print rolls, furniture polishing; soles of or shoes and boots; and artificial limbs

Medium hard	For pen industry; polishing wheels and buffs for lenses, mirrors, glass marbles and granite; fluid transfer rolls and furniture polishing
Soft	For padding in orthopedic departments in hospitals, vibration and shock mounting; beemper plugs; polishing wheels and buffs; fluid transfer rolls, oil and fluid wicks; grease and oil retaining washers

Future Scenario

The use of wool based technical textiles with new applications will have higher price realization. Lighter weight material and application of chemical finishes based on nano technology will enhance the performance of technical textiles. Wool and its noil/waste will find rapidly growing applications in paper felt as well as non-woven technical felts because of its inherent virtues. The quality enhancement of known products and development of new products through appropriate research and development is the need of the hour.

References

Gupta, N. P., Patni, P. C., Arora, R. K. and Singh, U. S. 1987. Influence of medullated fiber on mechanical processing and product performance. Indian Journal of Textile Research 12 (1): 46-52.

Indian Standard Specifications for Handmade Namdhas. 2003. IS: 4392, Bureau of Indian Standards, New Delhi.

Indian Standard Specifications for Pressed Wool Felts. 2000. IS: 1719, Bureau of Indian Standards, New Delhi.

Patni P. C., Shakyawar D. B. and Gupta N. P. 2006. Studies on animal fibre blended hand made felts: Part I Physical & mechanical properties. Indian Journal of Fibre and Textile Research 31: 553-558.

Shakyawar, D. B., Patni, P. C. and Gupta, N. P. 2007. Studies on animal fibre blended hand made felts: Part II Frictional, compressional and thermal properties. Indian Journal of Fibre and Textile Research 32: 301-305.

Shenai, V.A. 1995. Technology of Textile Finishinhg, Sevak Publications, Third Impression.

Umback, K. H. 1985. In: Proceedings of the 7th International Wool Textile Research Conference, Tokyo, Vol. III, pp. 178.

❑❑❑

45

Advances in Pashmina Wool Processing and Value Addition

Sarfaraz A Wani*, Asif H Sofi* and D B Shakyawar**
*Division of Livestock Products Technology
Faculty of Veterinary Sciences and Animal Husbandry
Sher-e-Kashmir University of Agricultural Sciences and Technology of Kashmir
Shuhama, Alastang Srinagar- 190006- India
** Senior Scientist, Textile Manufacture and Textile Chemistry Division
Central Sheep and Wool Research Institute, Avikanagar- 304501 (Rajasthan)

Introduction

Natural fibers are used extensively in textile markets in the return fashion on demanding natural and comfort feeling and healthy environmental awareness. These natural textile fibres come from three sources, viz: plant origin (bast, coir and jute fibres), mineral origin (Asbestos fibres) and animal origin (wool, silk, Pashmina etc). Among all these important natural textile fibres, wool occupies the predominant position because of its unique characteristics of providing comfort and warmth. Besides, rare fibres from goat, rabbit and camel family, possessing special qualities of fineness and lusture called Speciality or Luxurious fibres also contributes to a large extent. Ladakh in Jammu and Kashmir and Lahul Spiti valleys in Himachal Pradesh are the only areas in India that represents Trans-Himalayan high altitude cold arid desert with elevations ranging from 3500-4500m. MSL. Under this eco-fragile environment, livestock is the only alternative to provide livelihood to the nomadic tribal inhabiting the region. The region sustains some special livestock including two goat breeds (Changthangi and Chegu) that are famous for their softest, finest and warmest commercial natural animal fiber called "Pashmina". The processing of Pashmina is an important component of our cultural heritage. The utilization of this fiber for product development by Kashmiri artisans has made "Cashmere (Kashmir)" synonym of Pashmina.

Speciality Hair Fibres

The textile fibres obtained from certain animals of goat, rabbit and camel families, rarer than more commonly used fibres and are valued for some desirables properties as fine diameter, lusture and ability to impart pleasing hand (characteristics perceived by handling) to fabrics are known as Speciality hair fibres. The attribute and characteristics that give value to these fibers are their smooth and glossy surface, their scarcity, rarity, high price and their elegant and exclusive nature. These Speciality fibres are sometimes used alone but often in conjugation with sheep's wool to produce special effects such as additional beauty, texture, colour, softness, resilience, durability and lusture.

Pashmina wool

Pashmina, popularly known as "Cashmere" is an unique textile fibre well known for its fineness, warmth, softness, and having desirable handle and aesthetic value. Among various specialty fibres viz. Angora rabbit wool, Mohair, Vicuna, Camel wool, Alpaca etc. Pashmina is known as the king of specialty fibres. The Pashmina is a down fibre obtained from Cashmere goat. It is mixed with coarse outer coat known as guard hair. The down fibre is most valuable and the guard hair is very cheap as the same has very limited textile applications. The Pashmina fibre is mostly of two colours viz. white and brown, however, gray and fawn colours are also available. The quality of Pashmina depends on fineness colour, length, strength, fibre fineness distribution and coarse hair contents.

Pashmina, a prince of Speciality hair fibres is one of the finest natural fibre. It is the down fibre or undercoat derived from domestic goat known as *Capra hircus*, which is native to Asia. It is well known for its fineness, warmth, softness, desirable aesthetic value, elegance and timelessness in fashion. It is most luxurious fibre which is much softer than superfine merino of the same diameter with the result commands much higher price. It has occupied a unique position among the fibres of animal origin because of its warmth, lightness, handle and its better ability to absorb dyes and moisture. On equal weigh basis, it is having 3 times more insulating capacity as that of wool.

Cashmere is the down fibre derived from the hair of a form of domesticated goat *Capra hircus* indigenous to Asia. From which the subspecies of Capra hires the goat originally derived is impossible to originally to determine. At the present time it cannot be labelled either lanigor or igagrus. In fact, according to Dr. G.C. Goodman it is probably a descendant of the wild goat Capra hires blylhi found in Sind and Baluchistan. In Kashmir and Tibet, the Kashmiri and Cheghu breeds are good examples producing down fibre. Europeans, especially the French, were attracted by the exotic beauty of articles made from cashmere in Kashmir, India, that they wanted to grow the cashmere goat in France. The importation was made in 1812 of 40 pure bred cashmere goats of Tibet by M. Moorcraft from Bengal, India, to France. Some of these animals went to England. There were two importations of Cashmere goats into the United states. The first was made by Dr. Davis, who brought in one male and one female in 1849. The next importation was made in about 1858 under the Beware importation. The most beautiful shawls were hand-woven in the city of Srinagar, Kashmir, India and it is said that at one time, Kashmir had 16,000 looms in constant work for these shawls. Today this weaving is done only on a small scale in Kashmir but fine shawls can still be detained.

Production and Characteristics of Pashmina (Cashmere)

Chinese Cashmere

The Pashmina fibre production is very limited and the notable producing countries are China, Magnolia, Iran, Afghanistan, Russia, India, Australia and New Zealand. The annual production Pashmina is limited to 15 m kg. More than 70% of the Pashmina fibre is produced by China. The China is the major producer of Cashmere fibre and the annual production level is around 7.5 to 10 m kg greasy. The main portion of the Cashmere of China comes from the northwestern provinces, particularly from the provinces of Ningsia, Sui Yuan and Kansa. The natural colour of the down is white gray or tan with the gray and tan mixtures prevailing. The grade is based on the amount of down fibre present. The grades and colour of different Pashmina wool is presented in Table 1.

Table 1. Color and proportion of the fine and guard hair in Pashmina wool

Grade	Colour	Down (%)	Hair (%)
Unsorted	White/grey/brown	40-80	60-20
Sorted -1	White/light gray, dark gray, brown	78-82	22-18
Sorted -2	As above	48-60	52-40
Sorted-3	As above	20-40	80-60

Mangolia

It is the second largest Pashmina wool producing country in the world. The annual production level ranges in between 3 to 4 m kg greasy. The standard quality of raw cashmere has 50-60 percent down fibre and a superior quality of 70-80 down.

Iran

Iranian Cashmere is somewhat coarser than either Chinese or Mongolian. It is therefore less expensive. Unlike the Chinese or Mongolian, the Iranian Cashmere is shorn from the goat in the spring of the year in fleece form. The annual production is around 1 m kg. The sorting operation is highly specialized, women sorters doing only 1-1.5 kg per day. The colours of Iranian cashmeres are white, gray, dark brown, and black as well as bundles and fawns, which are not found in Chinese or Magnolia Cashmere.

Properties

Fineness

The fineness of fine (Pashmina) fibre is falling between 12-13 μm. The fineness distribution lies between 9-20 μm. The average fineness of guard hair is in the range between 50-65 μm, whereas, the average fineness of unsorted Pashmina i.e. mixture of fine and guard hair, lies between 16-20 μm with CV% of 70-90%, which shows wide dispersion in fineness thereby proving that elimination of guard hair is essential for proper spinnabity of these fibres. A demarcation could be seen between fine fibres and guard hair at 30-35 μm level with a few intermediate fibres between 17-36 μm. The fineness in tex, which express weight per unit length of fibre is about 0.3 for fine Pashmina wool, the tex value of guard hair falls in the range of 2.5- 3.0 tex, which is about 10 times of the fine fibres.

Fibre length

Pashmina under coat fibres has fibre length of 55-60 mm. The length of Indian Pashmina wool depends on its source of supply/origin/genotypes and grade. The mean fibre length varies from 25-93 mm, which needs to be combed for preparation of good quality of the yarn. In contrast to fibre length reported from goats of other countries, Indian Pashmina lacks in fibre length even when graded. There is scope to increase the fibre length through genetic means maintaining the fineness for better spinnability, uniformity and strongmen yarn.

Mechanical properties

Mechanical properties i.e. load elongation curve of fine Pashmina wool significantly differs with those of guard hair. The tenacity of guard hair is significantly higher than fine fibre. On wetting, the difference is much higher than dry state. The tenacity of Pashmina wool is in the range of 12-13 g/tex in dry state, however, it is about 10-11 g/tex in wet state. The extension at break of Pashmina wool is about 32-35 % in dry condition, which significantly increases in wet conditions and extended upto 60 %. From mechanical properties point of view, the Pashmina wool is suitable for blending with fine wool, acrylic, angora and silk fibres for production of good quality products i.e., shawls and sweaters.

Marketing of Pashmina

The marketing of Pashmina is generally done in Leh/Ladakh and other producing areas. The price of the fibre mainly depends on the fineness, length, colour and scouring yield. These fibres are used locally in small quantities and mainly brought to Shrinagar and Kullu valley for marketing utilization. The presence of guard hair adversely affects the price. The guard hair is generally separated manually which makes the Pashmina very costly.

Pashmina Wool Processing

Pashmina is utilized for the development of aesthetic products like Knitwear in Scotland, woven fabrics as blends in Italy and Switzerland. After spun into yarns, pure pashmina can be knitted into jumpers, hats, gloves, socks and other clothing or woven into fabrics than cut and assembled into garments such as outer coats, jackets, pants, pajamas, scarves, blankets and other items. However in India, majority of pashmina is utilized for preparation of shawls in Kashmir valley.

Dehairing

Dehairing is a process through which the outer coat (guard) hair is eliminated from the fine undercoat fibres. Pashmina wool is an admixture of fine, intermediary and very coarse fibres. The elimination of unwanted coarser guard hairs improves the spinnability and results in improvement in product quality in many aspects. Before spinning into yarn, the raw pashmina is dehaired. During dehairing process, the coarse hair is removed from fine fibre. This process is being carried out manually which is labour intensive. With change in technology, the dehairing technology has been developed. Presently, the dehairing is being carried out using machinery. The raw pashmina after scouring is passed through cotton carding machine running at very lower speed of flats and cylinder. The coarser fibres are get removed due to differential speed principle. Complete dehairing has been carried out after five passage of carding machine. The dehairing equipment available commercially is very costly and has very high production, which hardly suits the need of our country. In order to provide the facility for dehairing of Pashmina wool, there is a need to develop a dehairing and processing machines of capacity of 30-50 kg/day. Therefore, a research programme is to be carried out to design & develop suitable dehairing equipment for Pashmina wool mainly for cottage industry, which will not only improve the product quality but will also reduce production cost of the product by reducing wastage of the fibre during processing.

Spinning and shawl weaving

On account of small availability of this specialty fibre most of it is utilized locally with the help of specially designed equipment operated manually. The yarn is spun manually using Khadi spinning system. Generally, 2/32 to 2/64 Nm yarn is spun for high quality shawls knitwears and apparels. (Fig. 1)

Fig. 1. Pashmina spinning on Charkha

The yarn produced from hand spinning system is used in handloom sector for manufacturing shawls. Shawl of 200 gm quality is produced from pashmina yarn. The designs are introduced during weaving. One of the unique design generally used in pashmina shawl is known Kani shawal (Fig. 2). Special type of handloom is used with different colour combination.

Fig. 2. Weaving of Kani shawl

Some quantity of hand spun yarn is also used in knitting for manufacturing of Pullover & Sweaters. Apart from hand spinning, some quantity of pashmina wool is also processed on modified cotton and worsted spinning systems. In order to spin fine quality yarn from pashmina fibre, suitable additive is used which facilitate spinning of 100 Nm yarn. The additive is removed either before / after weaving. These technologies are presently under developmental stage which needs to be Pashmina is being processed in blends with wool, silk and other fibres. The pashmina product in pure form or in blends can be further upgraded with appropriate embroidery work and such products enjoy very high demand both in export and domestic markets.

Blending

Blending in a textile industry is a unique technique to mix two or more textile fibres of different origin but more or less with similar physical properties viz: fibre length and fineness to overcome the shortcomings present in the fibre of one origin. The blending of wool with other fibres especially speciality fibres have gained popularity all over the world. Generally, the blended products possess high durability; easy care properties; good handle and more importantly are cheaper than highly valued speciality hair fibre products.

Blending of fibres can help to prepare a fabric with improved or unique characteristics which could not be achieved in a fabric with single fibre. It can remove many technical and application deficiencies derived from single fibres more cheaply than developing a new fibre. It enables the production of fabrics and products with a diverse range of properties. In blended products, the wide range of fibre characteristics, give more opportunity to create blends of different types, composition and fabric structure.

Types of Blends

Intimate Blend: It is that type of blend where fibres are converted into blended yarn by spinning different origin fibres together.

Mixture Blend: This type of blend is also called Union blend. In this type, fabric is prepared by using different types of yarn during weaving or knitting e.g. wool yarn in weft direction and silk in warp direction.

Composite structure Blend: In this type of blend, the product is prepared by combining the different fabrics in composite structure utilizing properties of different fabrics in one single structure. e.g. sportswears having woolen fabric towards innerside giving sweat absorbing ability and polyester towards outside.

Quasi-Chemical Blending: This type of blending is important in synthetic polymer textile industry rather than in natural fibre industry. In this, the synthetic fibres are generated by extruding two or more polymers through spinneret to form a blended fibre of the polymers.

In addition to these, mixture yarns can be prepared by blending. Mixture yarn is that yarn which is being formed after spinning by twisting together two or more strands of spun yarn or continuous filament.

Pashmina Blends

Due to the limited availability of the raw material, high cost of production together with some technical problems due to their smoother, straighter, crimpless surface, for which more specialized techniques of processing are needed, these fibres/fabrics are costlier and hence find limited market. To overcome this, the addition of some natural fibres to pashmina will solve the problem of processing, add desired functional, wearing and aesthetic properties as well as bring down the cost and assuring the availability of this type of products to more people with better market.

Trails conducted on Pashmina, wool and other speciality hair fibre blends have indicated that up to 20% angora: pashmina (20:80) blend and up to 30% wool: pashmina (30:70) blend have revealed the desirable property. Beyond this the quality deteriorates as intimate blend. However as mixture blend, silk Pashmina (50:50) has shown highly acceptable properties. The physical and mechanical properties of Pashmina fibres and blended yarn are presented in table 2.

Table 2. Physical and mechanical properties of Pashmina fibre and blended yarn

Sample	Pashmina: wool (0:100)	Pashmina: wool (70:30)	Pashmina: wool (80:20)	Pashmina: wool (50:50)	Pashmina: Angora (80:20)
AFD± S.E (μ)	13.51±0.01	14.42±0.04	15.66±0.86	16.33±0.38	14.86 1.12
Actual count (Nm)	56.72	81.54	74.49	38.7	30.62
No. of fibres/ cross section	31.88	41.66	32.33	42.33	35.66
Actual count (tex)	15.9	15.7	11.5	26.1	11.9
Breaking strength (gm)	52.0	48.0	81.0	106.0	83.0
Tenacity (gm/ tex)	3.27	3.06	7.04	4.06	6.97
Elongation at break (%)	3.68	6.26	3.95	3.60	3.85

(Source: Wani, 2003)

The pure and blended pashmina yarn was used on Handlooms for development of shawls. The physical and mechanical quality of pure pashmina shawls and blended shawls in different proportions is presented in table 3.

Table 3. Physical and Mechanical characteristics of Pure and blended Pashmina shawls

Sample	Pashmina: wool (100)	Pashmina: wool (70:30)	Pashmina: wool (80:20)	Pashmina: wool (50:50)	Pashmina: Angora (80: 20)
AFD± S.E (μ)	13.51±0.01	15.66±0.86	14.42±0.14	16.33±0.38	14.86 1.12
Warp (Ends / cm)	18.4	27.8	28.8	34.0	33.0
Weft (Picks / cm)	13.6	13.7	18.4	18.4	18.3
Length (cm)	198	201	199	200	200
Width (cm)	98	96	97	97	98
Thickness (mm)	0.49	0.48	0.49	0.43	0.42
Weight (gm)	210	210	182	179	173
Shrinkage warp way (%)	0.13	0.67	0.61	0.93	-0.13
Shrinkage weft way (%)	-0.66	-0.93	-1.07	-0.94	-0.67
Air permeability ($m^3/m^2/min$)	65.7	74.6	92.8	81.8	80.8
Thermal conductivity ($w/m^o k$)	0.0142	0.0150	0.0119	0.0172	0.0114
Breaking Strength warp way	6.1	4.0	3.0	5.1	5.1
Breaking strength weft way	14.6	13.9	6.7	10.4	10.2

(Source: Wani et al., 2004)

Table 4. Properties of Silk: Pashmina (Warp: Weft) shawls in the 50:50 blend

Physical Parameters		Mechanical Parameters	
Warp (Ends / cm)	28.65±0.89	Breaking strength warp way	46.22
Weft (Picks / cm)	15.7± 0.62	Breaking strength weft way	10.36
Length (cm)	206±0.79	Elongation % at break wrap way	19.14
Width (cm)	104±0.22	Elongation % at break weft way	13.88
Thickness (mm)	0.4 ±0.02	Shrinkage % at break wrap way	1.8
Weight (gm)	200 ±0.20	Shrinkage % at break weft way	-(0.2)
		Air permeability($m^3/m^2/min$)	115.7
		Thermal conductivity ($W/m^o k$)	0.0182

(Source: Wani, 2003)

Shawls manufactured on handloom at Kullu using different blends were evaluated for comparative performance (Table 5 and 6).

Table 5. Comparative performance of Pashmina, rabbit hair and merino wool shawl

Blends	Thick ness (mm)		Threads /inch		Count (Nm)	Areal density g/m²	Density g/cm³	Bulk cm³/g
			Ends	Picks	Warp	Weft		
Angora wool	0.50	62	27	52/2	48	134	0.268	3.731
Pashmina wool	0.45	59	65	52/2	42	150	0.333	3.000
Merino wool	0.49	53	46	50/2	46/2	162	0.330	3.024

Table 6. Comparative performance of Pashmina, rabbit hair and merino wool shawl

Blends	Abrasion loss (%)	Frictional properties	Flexural Rigidity g.cm			Shrinkage (%)		
	F	μ	Warp	Weft	Average	Warp	Weft	
Angora wool	2.34	169.8	0.67	0.734	0.195	0.379	4.79	5.8
Pashmina wool	4.52	179.9	0.71	0.451	0.383	0.415	0.8	4.0
Merino wool	2.72	181.9	0.72	0.631	0.512	0.568	2.8	4.8

Conclusion

Processing of Pashmina is delicious which involve manual work. With developmental of technology and microprocessors, processing of pashmina on machine is being developed. These technologies will reduce processing cost significantly which will enhance use of Pashmina. Processing of Pashmina on cotton spinning and worsted spinning system damage the fibre during carding, which need to modification in the processing, so the fibre damage at carding stage could be minimized Moreover, optimum processing conditions are to be established for better quality of the yarn from Pashmina. During finishing the Pashmina products are given various harsh chemical treatments, which adversely affects the handle of the products. In order to improve the handle of the products the softening treatments using amino silicone softeners are one of the options, which may improve the handle of the product. Although lot of work has been done on Blending of textile fibres but still there is a need to develop different types of blend of specialty fibres for higher returns. Further, the methods of identification of blends need to be developed so that these could not be used as a means of adulteration in specialty hair fibres especially highly valued ones like Pashmina and Angora.

References

Arora, R.K.1988. Speciality hair blended products and their quality evaluation. Short course on specility hairs-their quality evaluation, processing and products. May 21 to 30, CSWRI, Avikanagar.

Pathak, V. 2003. Final Project Report of National Agricultural Technology Project subproject entitled "Processing of Different Hair Wool for Value Added Products".

Patni, P. G. 1988. Utilisation of rabbit hair fibre on cotton spinning system. Short course on specility hairs-their quality evaluation, processing and products. May 21 to 30, CSWRI, Avikanagar.

Pokharana, A. K 2003. Final Project Report of National Agricultural Technology Project subproject entitled "Processing of Different Hair Wool for Value Added Products".

Shakyawar, D. B. 1996. Angora rabbit hair-production, properties and processing. Special training course on wool and woolen product development and evaluation. 11 sep to 10th oct 1996. CSWRI Avikanagar.

Wani, A. Sarfaraz 2003. Final Project Report of National Agricultural Technology Project subproject entitled "Processing of Different Hair Wool for Value Added Products".

Wani, A. Sarfaraz, Ishrat Y., Mir Salahuddin and Malik A.H 2004. Processing and product development from Cashmere fibre. National Seminar on Angora Rabbit Wool and Cashmere Production and Utilization. September 25-26, pp174-179.

Wani, Ahmed Sarfaraz and Gupta, N. P.1989. Studies on Changthangi Pashmina, India Textile Journal Vol. C(2) :39.

❏❏❏

ABOUT THE EDITORS

Dr. S.A. Karim, Director, Central Sheep and Wool Research Institute, Avikanagar, completed his B.V.Sc. & A.H. and M.V.Sc. (Animal Nutrition) from Orissa Veterinary College Bhubneshwar in the year of 1974 and 1976, respectively. He was awarded University Gold Medal for securing first position in M.V.Sc.(AN). He completed his Ph.D. degree in Animal Nutrition from National Dairy Research Institute, Karnal in the year of 1991. He joined Agriculture Research Service(ARS) in 1978. He has more than 26 year of research experience in the filed of ruminant nutrition with specialization in nutrition-environment interaction, growth maximization of lambs, range managed small ruminants' nutrition and carcass evaluation. He has published 140 research papers, 45 invited papers, 15 popular articles and 200 contributory papers. He has guided several Ph.D. students. He is a member of several important academic bodies and as Board of Studies, Academic council, Research Advisory committee.

Dr. Anil Joshi, joined Industrial Toxicology Research Centre (ITRC), Lucknow in 1979 as a CSIR Research Fellow and was awarded Ph.D. in 1984 in Biochemistry from Lucknow University for his work done at ITRC. He did his Post Doctoral Research work in ITRC from 1984 to 1986. He joined Central Sheep and Wool Research Institute, Avikanagar as Scientist S-1 (Animal Biochemistry) in 1986 and is Principal Scientist since July 2006. His significant research achievements include development of protocols for ram semen freezing, validation of computer-aided semen analysis for ram semen evaluation during various stages of freezing, freezing of ovine embryos and was associated in development of laparoscope aided and transcervical artificial insemination techniques for using frozen ram semen. His group is credited to report for the first time research findings on the work done on prolific sheep and ram lambs of which 2 were published in "The Veterinary Record" and 1 each in "Animal Reproduction Science" and "Tropical Animal Health and Production". He is twice recipient of ICAR Team Award for Outstanding Research for the Biennium 1997-98 and 2003-04 and also got ISCA, NAAS, ISSRF and ISSGPU awards for best paper presentation. He has published 81 papers in referred National and International and has contributed several papers in International and National Seminars. He is the Life Member of 7 Scientific Societies and the current Editor of the Indian Journal of Small Ruminants.

Dr. S.K. Sankhyan did his B.Sc. (Ag.)from University of Rajasthan in 1986, M.Sc. and Ph.D in Animal Nutrition from Himachal Pradesh Krishi Vishva Vidhyalaya, Palampur in 1988 and 1991 respectively. He was awarded University merit fellowship during M.Sc. and Ph.D. programme. He joined Agricultural Research Services as Scientist in 1991 at Central Sheep and Wool Research Institute, Avikanagar and presently working as Principal Scientist and I/C Head Animal Nutrition. He has 18 year of research experience and pursued the research in the area of nutrition of sheep and goats on pasture and mineral nutrition of field animals for the last fifteen years. He is presently conducting research in AICRP on "Improvement of feed resources and its utilization in raising animal production". He has published 3 Books, 58 research papers in National and International

Journals, 12 lead/invited papers and presented 54 abstract papers in National Seminar. He is life member of five National Societies of Animal Science.

Dr. A.K. Shinde did his M.V.Sc. (AH) and Ph.D. in Livestock Production and Management form College of Veterinary Science and Animal Husbandry, Jawaharlal Nehru Krishi Vishwa Vidhyalaya. Jabalpur in 1983 and 1996. He has started his academic career as Veterinary officer in Madhya Pradesh Dugdh Mahasangh, Ujjain. He joined Agricultural Research Services as Scientist in Indian Council of Agriculture Research in 1989 at Central Sheep and Wool Research Institute, Avikanagar and now holding the position of Pricipal Scientist. He pursued the research in the area of nutrition of sheep and goats on pasture and mineral nutrition of field animals for the last seventeen years. He has published 50 research papers in National and International Journals, two Books, four technical bulletins, presented 54 abstract papers and 10 invited papers in National and Internationals Seminars. He has also written a book on " Applied Animal Husbandry" in Hindi and contributed chapters in books published by Indian Publishers. He is life members of four National Societies of Animal Science. Recently he has received Dr Rajendra Prasad Award for technical book in Hindi from ICAR, New Delhi and Rajiv Gandhi Rashtriya Gyan Vigyan Molik Pustak Lekhan Puruskar Yojna from Ministry of Home Affair, New Delhi.

Dr. D.B. Shakyawar obtained his graduation degree in Textile Technology from Kanpur University. He has completed his M.Tech. and Ph.D. from IIT Delhi in Textile Engineering. He started his career as Lecturer at Government Polytechnic, Kanpur. Later he joined Agricultural Research Services in 1992 as Scientist. Presently he is working as Senior Scientist in Textile Manufacturing, Processing of angora and pashmina wool, manufacturing of shawl, non-woven felt and carpet, quality evaluation and application of computer in wool technology, are research area of his interest. He has published 50 research papers in various research journals. He was also awarded CSIR Senior Research Fellowship for his Ph.D. work. Presently he is Co-principal Investigator of National Agricultural Innovation Project on "Value Chain on enhancing productivity and profitability of Pashmina Fibre".

Dr. S.M.K. Naqvi is Principal Scientist and Head, Division of Physiology and Biochemistry at Central Sheep and Wool Research Institute, Avikangar.Dr. Naqvi had an illustrious academic carrier and obtained his Ph.D. in Animal Physiology from National Dairy Research Institute in 1988. He has more than 25 years of research experience and worked on different aspects of Adaptation Physiology , Reproduction and Embryo Biotechnology. He has been trained at CCMB, Hyderabad; BARC,Mumbai and also visited Ag-Research, New Zealand. He has carried out several internal and externally funded research programmes. He was first to report in the country in 1991, production of large number of sheep and goat embryos through IVM-IVF-IVC. The birth of first lamb in the country from frozen-thawed embryo was also achieved under his leadership in January,1998. He was also credited with the birth of first full term lamb following transfer of embryo produced through IVM-IVF-IVC in 1999. Dr Naqvi and his team have produced 240 elite lambs through ETT and cryoconserved 263 embryos of various sheep breeds. He is a recipient of several prestigious awards and honours during his academic and research career, of which most significant are from ICAR,ISCA and ASC. He was awarded twice "ICAR award for Outstanding Team Research", first as a Team Leader in the biennium 1997-98 for contribution in the field of Small Ruminant Production and secondly as an associate for contribution in the field of Genetic improvement of Sheep in the biennium 2003-04. He is also recipient of Dr D.N. Mullick Memorial Award (2006-07) given by the society of Animal Physiologist of India. Dr. Naqvi has 211 publications to his credit of which 95 research papers have been published in referred National and International journals.Dr Naqvi and his team have filed two patents through ICAR. Two records of their work were published in the Limca Book of Records (India).

Dr B.N.Tripathi, M.VSc., Ph.D., DICVP, is Principal Scientist and Head of the Division of Animal Health, Central Sheep and Wool Research Institute, Avikanagar. Before joining at CSWRI, Avikanagar, Dr Tripathi has served in various capacities at Division of Pathology, Indian Veterinary Research Institute, Izatnagar for about 19 years (post-doctoral). He has been the faculty member of the pathology discipline for over 15 years and guided 8 postgraduate students. He has published more than 80 research and review papers in national and international journals of repute. He has authored two books, one manual, edited two conference proceedings and has organized one national seminar. His major area of research has been the molecular pathogenesis and diagnosis of infectious diseases of ruminants with special interest on paratuberculosis. Dr Tripathi has visited a number of countries including UK, Denmark, France, Belgium, Austria and Japan for advanced trainings and for attending conferences. He has received a number of awards including best poster presentation award, best paper awards of IAVP, best Ph.D. thesis award for his student, Drs. Jain and Vegad outstanding pathologist award, International Wellcome Trust Fellowship (London), etc. He has been conferred with fellowships of Society for Immunology and Immunopathology (SIIP), National Academy of Veterinary Sciences (NAVS) and Indian Association of Veterinary Pathologists (IAVP). Dr Tripathi is the Chief Editor of Indian Journal of Veterinary Pathology and IAVP Newsletter, The Lesion from 2008.